PHARMACOTHEON

PHARMACOTHEON

Entheogenic drugs, their plant sources and history

JONATHAN OTT

NATURAL PRODUCTS CO.
KENNEWICK, WA
SECOND EDITION DENSIFIED
1996

Other books by Jonathan Ott:

HALLUCINOGENIC
PLANTS OF NORTH AMERICA
(Wingbow Press, Berkeley, 1976, 1979)

TEONANÁCATL: HALLUCINOGENIC
MUSHROOMS OF NORTH AMERICA
Co-edited with J. Bigwood
(Madrona Publishers, Seattle, 1978, 1985)

THE CACAHUATL EATER: RUMINATIONS
OF AN UNABASHED CHOCOLATE ADDICT
(Natural Products Co., Vashon, WA, 1985)

PERSEPHONE'S QUEST: ENTHEOGENS
AND THE ORIGINS OF RELIGION
Co-Authored with R.G. Wasson,
S. Kramrisch and C.A.P. Ruck
(Yale University Press, New Haven, 1986, 1992)

AYAHUASCA ANALOGUES: PANGÆAN ENTHEOGENS
(Natural Products Co., Kennewick, WA, 1994, 1995)

THE AGE OF ENTHEOGENS & THE ANGELS' DICTIONARY
(Natural Products Co., Kennewick, WA, 1995)

Forthcoming:
PHARMACOPHILIA OR, THE NATURAL PARADISES

Printed in the United States of America
Using recycled, acid-free paper
History: First edition of 5000 copies in July 1993

Design by Pablo Moya Rossi, typography by Jonathan Ott
Cover: *Pregnant by an Anaconda*, Pablo Amaringo, 1989
Photo: Luis Eduardo Luna; spine photo: Jeremy Bigwood

ISBN 0–9614234–8–X (limited Smythe-sewn hardcover)
ISBN 0–9614234–9–8 (sew-and-glue paperback)

Sales: Jonathan Ott Books / Post Office Box 1251 / Occidental, CA / USA 95465

TABLE OF CONTENTS

Dedicated to the Memory of

R. GORDON WASSON

Rediscoverer of *Teonanácatl*
and the entheogenic origins of religions

Pioneer in the study
of *Ololiuhqui* and *Ska Pastora*

First to recognize *Soma*
and the *Kykeon* as entheogens

Innovative scholar, brilliant writer,
revered teacher, kind and loyal friend

FOREWORD

Albert Hofmann

One of the most important criteria in the evaluation of a newly-published book is its actuality, that is, its bearing on the problems of the time. Measured by this criterion, *Pharmacotheon*, this new book by Jonathan Ott, is of the greatest actuality, since it is an important contribution to the worldwide discussions on one of the gravest and most complicated problems of the present time; namely, the drug problem.

Furthermore, in evaluating a new book, one must make comparisons to existing publications in the field in question. In this regard, *Pharmacotheon* is also a valuable new publication, in that this work distinguishes itself in two respects from the numerous drug books which have appeared in recent years.

It is the first comprehensive scientific compendium on the subject of entheogenic drugs, a particularly interesting sector of the drug world. The emphasis is on *comprehensive* and *scientific*, as this book deals in detail with all aspects of entheogenic drugs—their botany, chemistry, neuropharmacology, ethnology and history. Herein the scientific specialist will find access to all of the source publications in a voluminous bibliography, to which reference is made in the text.

Besides this comprehensive, scientific documentation of the objective facts on the subject of entheogenic drugs, the question of the meaning and importance of this particular class of psychotropic drugs for contemporary society is discussed in detail.

Moreover, it should be noted that all of the evaluations and analyses are subjective, inasmuch as they are always based on personal experiences, or on personal evaluation of the experiences of others.

Ott draws on a rich treasure of personal experiences with entheogenic drugs, which bestows competence and authority on his remarks with respect to their value and significance, and to his thesis on drug prohibition.

The juxtaposition of the objective, scientific aspects with the purely subjective, experiential side of the drug problem constitutes the unique character of *Pharmacotheon* and endows this book with singular value. It could only have been written by a person like Jonathan Ott, who combines the multifaceted talents of the creative writer with the specialized knowledge of the scientist—Ott studied organic chemistry.

Mystical experiences of nature and experiences with entheogenic drugs have decisively determined Jonathan Ott's world-view and path in life. He acknowledges how these drugs opened his eyes to the wonder of that deeper, all-encompassing reality, into which we are all born as a part of the creation. This is the reality which all of the great mystics and founders of religions described; it is in truth the kingdom of heaven destined for humankind. There is, however, a fundamental distinction; whether one knows of this reality only from the reports of others, or whether one has experienced it personally in beatific moments; spontaneously or with the aid of entheogenic drugs.

Ott characterizes the entheogens as one of the tools which can help us to overcome the materialistic world-view, to which we can ultimately attribute all of the great problems of our day—environmental contamination, spiritual, political and social abuses, wars. These medicaments, which have been bestowed upon humankind by Nature—the most important of the entheogens are of botanical derivation—should not be withheld from contemporary society. Thus Ott's passionate stance against drug prohibition.

Allow me here a remark on the conception of entheogens as a gift from the plant world.

While we know the function of most of the constituents of plants, we do not know the purpose of phytochemicals called alkaloids. We know not how the plant uses the alkaloids. Certain it is, that they are not essential to life. This we can conclude from the observation that for every particular species of plant that produces given alkaloids, there exist botanically identical varieties which contain no alkaloids. If the entheogenic constituents have no purpose in the life of the plant, this begs the question: why then does the plant produce them? Especially for humankind? The answer to this question, which pertains to the mystery of the entheogens, is a matter of belief.

Jonathan Ott lives in México on a ranch in the mountains of the state of Veracruz. His ranch bears the name "Ololiuhqui." This name has its special significance. That is, *Ololiuhqui* is the Aztec name for one of the ancient Mexican magic drugs, the seeds of plants from the morning glory family (Convolvulaceae).

Ololiuhqui has a connection to my friendship with Jonathan. My chemical investigations of *Ololiuhqui* seeds led to the unexpected discovery that the entheogenic principles of *Ololiuhqui* are alkaloids, especially lysergic acid amide, which exhibits a very close relationship to lysergic acid diethylamide (=LSD). It follows therefrom that LSD, which hitherto had been considered to be a synthetic product of the laboratory, actually belongs to the group of sacred Mexican drugs. I had the fortune to obtain the services of Jonathan Ott for the English translation of my LSD book, *LSD: My Problem Child.* In the course of this work, I came to know of his comprehensive knowledge on the subject of plant drugs, as well as his mastery of the art of writing.

We are already indebted to Jonathan Ott for three valuable books: *Hallucinogenic Plants of North America*; *Teonanácatl: Hallucinogenic Mushrooms of North America*; and the delightful chocolate book *The Cacahuatl Eater: Ruminations of an Unabashed Chocolate Addict.*

I wish for Jonathan that this new, far-reaching publication *Pharmacotheon* will likewise find its deserved attention in specialist circles, as well as among interested laypersons.

Albert Hofmann
Burg i.L., Switzerland
November 1992

A NOTE ON THE TEXT

As is immediately obvious from my title, I use the neologism *entheogen(ic)* throughout this book, a new word proposed by a group of scholars including Dr. R. Gordon Wasson, Prof. Carl A.P. Ruck and me. As we know from personal experience that shamanic inebriants do not provoke "hallucinations" or "psychosis," and feel it incongruous to refer to traditional shamanic use of *psychedelic* plants (that word, pejorative for many, referring invariably to sixties' western drug use), we coined this new term in 1979 (Ott 1996A; Ruck *et al.* 1979; Wasson *et al.* 1980B). I outline thoroughly the histories of words for sacred plant drugs in Chapter 1, Note 1. I am happy to say, seventeen years after launching the neologism on its literary career, that the word has been accepted by the majority of experts in this field, and has appeared in print in at least eight languages. The term is not meant to specify a pharmacological class of drugs (some, for example, conceive of *psychedelic* as implying indole and phenethylamine drugs with an LSD- or mescaline-like effect); rather, it designates drugs which provoke ecstasy and have traditionally been used as shamanic or religious inebriants, as well as their active principles and artificial congeners.

Similarly, I eschew use of the word *intoxicant* in favor of the more appropriate supposed synonym *inebriant.* This is not splitting hairs—*intoxicant* (from Latin *toxicum*, poison) is a pejorative word and suggests to the uninformed the unholy ludible drunkenness from ethyl alcohol (ethanol)—our western society's traditional inebriant. A close look at the dictionary will show that *inebriant* suffers not this stigma and the *Oxford English Dictionary* (Compact Edition, p. 1423) reveals that, while this word likewise has come to imply alcohol in the West, the first use for *inebriation* (in 1526) is apposite: "this inebriacyon or heuenly dronkennesse of the spiryte." In Chapter 4, Note 1, I summarize the history of another pejorative word for these sacred drugs, *narcotic*, and in Chapter 4, Note 2, I comment that "sacred intoxicant" is an oxymoron. We must recall that the great majority of people in the world have not partaken of entheogens, that the uninformed tend to categorize unknown inebriants together with alcohol, and we must be very careful not to prejudice these sacred inebriants by obtusely using terminology that relates invariably to alcoholic states when we speak of them.

By the same token, I have discarded the use of the word *recreational* in reference to non-medical or extra-scientific use of drugs. I myself have been guilty of misusing this flippant term, which tends to prejudice and to cheapen contemporary use of entheogenic drugs. Since I know that many modern users of entheogenic drugs have the profoundest respect for what they may regard to be their "plant teachers" (Luna 1984B) and thus use them seriously, in a type of vision quest (Drury 1989; Pinkson 1989; Rätsch 1991), their use cannot be termed "recreational." On the other hand, I know that a good many users do employ the entheogens casually, in a less-than-spiritual manner. Accordingly, I have settled on the use of the obsolete and neutral word *ludibund* or its variant *ludible* in general reference to modern extra-medical use of entheogenic drugs. The word, which derives from the Latin *ludere*, "to play," means literally "playful, full of play" (*Oxford English Dictionary*, Compact Edition, p. 1675), and would translate into Spanish as *lúdico/a*, the term Antonio Escohotado employed in his excellent *Historia General de Las Drogas* (Escohotado 1989A). Thus I speak of *ludibund drugs* or *ludible drug use*, so as not casually to dismiss modern use as "recreational" like video games or pinball machines.

Some will take issue with my use of the word *Indian* instead of the "politically correct" *Native American*. But I, too, am a "native American" and I indeed have a small percentage of Indian blood, but none would call me an *Indian*. This term supposedly derives from Cristobal Colón's mistaken impression that he had landed in India when he "discovered" the Americas. But there is an alternate explanation for the word. It has been pointed out that in Colón's day the commonest name for what we now call India was *Hindustan*, and Hispanic speakers today persist in calling people from India *Hindues*, not *Indios*. One prominent "Native American" spokesperson alleged that the word "Indians" (Spanish *indios*) means literally what it says in Spanish… *en dios*, "in god" referring to the fact that the inhabitants of the New World were found by Europeans to be living "in god," naturally, close to the land, like other animals, with little artifice of civilization. In this sense *Indian* is by no means an ignorant or pejorative term, and I use it in that spirit, out of respect and in the interests of precision. While on the subject of "politically correct" terminology, I have endeavored throughout to avoid the use of *mankind*, substituting instead the more cumbersome *humankind*, and in place of the awkward *he or she* I employ simply *(s)he*. Similarly, I speak of *preliterate* and not of *primitive* cultures.

I have also adopted the use of Ernst Jünger's fine term *psychonaut* (Jünger 1970) to refer to psychic voyagers who employ entheogenic drugs as their vehicle (although the term had been coined in German two decades earlier, an American researcher mistakenly claimed authorship of the neologism; Siegel 1989). We commonly refer to "trips" with drugs, and Jünger's word is precise and beautiful. I hope someday Jünger's seminal book *Annäherungen: Drogen und Rausch* ("Approaches: Drugs and Inebriation") will appear in an English translation, along with the rest of his work. It amazes me that this giant of contemporary German letters remains virtually unknown in the English-speaking world, although his work has been abundantly translated into Spanish, French and other languages.

For reasons I explained in detail in my book on chocolate (Ott 1985), I eschew the term "drug abuse." This politically *incorrect* term "connotes *any* use (whether moderate and controlled, or immoderate and excessive) of certain drugs proscribed by law or custom; whereas excessive, so-called 'abuse' of other legally-sanctioned drugs such as tobacco, coffee and (in the non-Moslem world) alcoholic beverages is blandly censured as mere bad habit or dietary indiscretion..." I examine this point closely in the Proemium. With the help of Dale Pendell, I have coined the words *matritheistic* and *patritheistic*, to refer to cultures revolving around worship of female and male deities respectively. I also refer to Our Lady Gaia [or *Gäa* in German, both pronounced "gay′–uh"], avoiding the more classic spelling Gæa, which would be pronounced "gee′–uh" [*Gea* or "hay′–ah" in Spanish]. For some reason, the orthography *Gaia* having been adopted, the mispronunciation "guy′–uh" has taken root in the United States, making the name for the most feminine of deities sound semi-masculine!

I use the word *shaman* throughout the text, from the Siberian Tungusic word *saman*, the name of the "medicine-man," once known by the pejorative term "witch-doctor." It has been suggested that, being an Asiatic word, *shaman* is inappropriate to describe New World practitioners, and Schultes and Raffauf (1992) recently chose to employ the Amazonian term *payé.* Like the word *shaman*, the Quichua equivalent *yachaj* and the Mazatec equivalent *cho-ta-ci-ne*, all mean approximately "one who knows," and I prefer to use the word *shaman*, which is widely understood by laypersons and accepted in scientific literature as a generic term to describe these traditional sages... those who know.

My friend and mentor Albert Hofmann has kindly written the foreword to *Pharmacotheon*, and I am happy that this new book first appeared on the 50th anniversary of his monumental discovery of the effects of LSD. I hope the publication of *Pharmacotheon* will mark the dawning of a new era of scientific tolerance and understanding of entheogenic drugs; that their untapped potential shall finally begin to be realized. May the shaman and the scientist now join hands and work together... may the psychonaut henceforth be accepted and cherished as a brave explorer of the great unknown, beyond yet somehow within, as vast and uncharted (and fraught with peril) as the trackless voids of interstellar space! With the aid of these wondrous *psychopharmaka*, may we concern ourselves ever more with the evanescent and eternally ephemeral beauty that is the here and now, that is quotidian consciousness—the only and all real wealth in this dimension of the universe!

ADDENDUM TO THE SECOND, DENSIFIED EDITION

In the three years since the publication of *Pharmacotheon*, the astonishing revival of interest in archaic religion, which I meanwhile dubbed the *Entheogenic Reformation* (Ott 1994A; Ott 1995B), has continued with undiminished force, accruing momentum. The resurgence in use of shamanic inebriants, which is the most visible manifestation of this astonishing historical atavism—this unprecedented "archaic revival" (McKenna 1991)—shows no signs of abating, and is most decidedly *not* some *newage* fad, however devoutly the forces of repression might wish it to be. Since this book was written, the "Reagan–Bush Dark Ages" drew to a dismal close. Even in the United States, which appropriated the dark mantle of the Pharmacratic Inquisition from its erstwhile bearers, the federal government has grudgingly opened the vault a crack, to limited renewed research of entheogens; and legislated full federal legal exemption of sacramental *péyotl* use (see Chapter 1) from its anti-drug laws! Without yet fully apprehending it, the imperialistic government on the Potomac has breached its drug-war frontlines, opening the floodgates to eventual legal use of sacramental entheogens by all its citizens. In the meantime, in Europe, joint and several movements toward drug decriminalization, legalization, "flexible enforcement" of existing laws, humane treatment of users, *etc.*, gather steam in various countries, threatening to leave the U.S. War on Drugs Juggernaut spinning its flat and treadless tires in the dust at the rear of the column. *Pharmacotheon*, with virtually no publicity and hampered by its weighty size, high price and information density, has established itself as a standard reference work in entheobotany, and I am pleased to offer this "densified" (if not physically expanded) and fully-updated second edition, with 130 new citations in the bibliography and many more additions. Withal, I might make bold to foretell by signs and portents, that the entheogenic genie is out of the bottle for good, never again to be confined nor obscured!

PROEMIUM

> The Prophets Isaiah and Ezekiel dined with me, and I asked them how they dared so roundly to assert that God spoke to them; and whether they did not think at the time that they would be misunderstood, & so be the cause of imposition.
> Isaiah answer'd: "I saw no God, nor heard any, in a finite organical perception; but my senses discover'd the infinite in every thing..."
>
> **William Blake**
> *The Marriage of Heaven and Hell* (1793)

My senses discovered the infinite in everything one summer night in Pennsylvania a quarter century ago, and sometime later in Hawai'i, as the lustral beams of moonlight danced over a tropical sea; then later still, high in the remotest mountains of Oaxaca, when mighty Tláloc's lightning bolts raged in the heavens and crashed into Mother Earth in the valley far below; and in the towering Ecuadorian forests of Sacha Runa, to the soothing melody of a shaman's whistled *icaro*, and the dry rustling rhythm of his leafy fan. For I have been privileged to be initiated into the sacred realm of the entheogens, sacramental plant teachers of countless generations of the family of humankind; have been vouchsafed a fleeting glimpse beneath Our Lady Gaia's skirts; have imbibed the *amrta* of Indra, the *ambrosia* of the Olympian gods, Demeter's potion; have for brief blessed instants gazed into Lord Shiva's blazing third eye. Having been graced by these and other holy visions, my life has been transformed and enriched beyond measure... I have become an initiate to the sacred Mysteries of antiquity, what the ancient Greeks called an *epoptes*, one who has seen the holy.

This book is about these wondrous entheogens, these strange plant sacraments and their contained active principles. The term *entheogen* was first suggested by classical scholars Carl A.P. Ruck and Danny Staples, pioneering entheogen researcher R. Gordon Wasson, ethnobotanist Jeremy Bigwood and me. The neologism derives from an obsolete Greek word meaning "realizing the divine within," the term used by the ancient Greeks to describe states of poetic or prophetic inspiration, to describe the entheogenic state which can be induced by sacred plant-drugs. This term replaces the pejorative words *psychotomimetic* and *hallucinogenic*, with their connotations of psychosis and hallucination, and the orthographically incorrect *psychedelic* (the correct spelling being *psychodelic*, as the word is commonly rendered in languages other than English), which has become so invested with connotations of sixties' popular culture ("psychedelic" art, music, *etc.*) as to make it incongruous to speak of ancient shamanic use of a *psychedelic* plant. I have summarized the logic behind the use of *entheogen(ic)* in Chapter 1, Note 1, and the interested reader is referred to the original paper proposing the word (Ott 1996A; Ruck *et al.* 1979; Wasson *et al.* 1980B).

My readers would be justified in asking "why yet another book on these drugs?" for over the years there have been many good books on the topic. I might mention in particular the excellent scientific book *The Botany and Chemistry of Hallucinogens* by American ethnobotanist Richard Evans Schultes and Swiss chemist Albert Hofmann, as well as their more popular, and more lavishly illustrated, *Plants of the Gods* (Schultes & Hofmann 1979; Schultes & Hofmann 1980). I will have occasion in the text following to refer to these and other valuable books on the subject. My goal in writing the present book was two-fold: first, to write a reference book for the specialist, citing the most important sources in the historical, anthropological, botanical, chemical and pharmacological literature, meanwhile placing this subject in the broader context of general ethnobotany. Thus I have updated and greatly enlarged the best extant bibliography to the subject, that of *The Botany and Chemistry of Hallucinogens*. The present bibliography is triple the size of that of Schultes and Hofmann, and even so, does not pretend to be exhaustive. My second goal in the writing of this book has been to detail the complex history of entheogenic drugs, and to trace in particular the story of how these drugs came to be available to non-traditional users in the twentieth century. In contrast to the authors of many other treatises on this subject, I consider the ethnobotany of entheogenic plants and their active agents in contemporary western culture to be every bit as important as their traditional ethnobotany, if not more so. As Gordon Wasson opined:

> Perhaps with all our modern knowledge we do not need the divine mushrooms any more. Or do we need them more than ever? Some are shocked that the key even to religion might be reduced to a mere drug. On the other hand, the drug is as mysterious as it ever was... (Wasson 1961)

Only recently have some academic anthropologists begun to consider contemporary drug subcultures to be worthy of formal study (Adler 1985; Holden 1989A).

I will neither promote nor inveigh against contemporary non-traditional use of entheogenic drugs. True, some of the drugs discussed in this book are illegal, and there are those who will think it irresponsible to discuss this subject without denouncing their illicit use (see comments in Lenson 1995). On the other hand, the bulk of the compounds studied in this book are legal, and there is no question that there are presently in the United States alone at least 2 million users of entheogenic drugs, mainly LSD (Goldstein & Kalant 1990; Henderson & Glass 1994), and it is to these *psychonauts* (Jünger 1970), as well as to interested scientists, that this book is directed. There is no need to encourage would-be users to try the entheogens—the drugs already have their devotees, and in any case the current supply is probably insufficient to meet the demand of established users (Blanco 1993).

In this exordium, however, I will denounce *in no uncertain terms* the futile, counterproductive and ill-advised proscription of entheogenic drugs by the governments of the United States and other countries. As Baruch Spinoza so presciently put it:

> All laws which can be violated without doing any one any injury are laughed at. Nay, so far are they from doing anything to control the desires and passions of men that, on the contrary, they direct and incite men's thoughts the more toward those very objects; for we always strive toward what is forbidden and desire the things we are not allowed to have. And men of leisure are never deficient in the ingenuity needed to enable them to outwit laws framed to regulate things which cannot be entirely forbidden... He who tries to determine everything by law will foment crime rather than lessen it.

It is self-evident that the millions of contemporary users of proscribed entheogenic drugs are laughing at the laws presuming to forbid them, and that they are far from deficient in the ingenuity needed to outwit those laws. It has ever been so with laws presuming to regulate the legitimate appetites of human beings; and there is no question that such laws represent an abuse of governmental power. As the great libertarian Edmund Atwill Wasson wrote in 1914, in a critique of the prohibition of alcohol in the United States (Wasson 1914):

> It is one thing to furnish the law, and another to furnish the

> force needed to ensure obedience. That is why we have so many dead-letter laws in this country,—we forget that a law is not self-enforcing.

In theory, law is the instrument of popular will in democratic countries, and in practice has been used as a weapon by majorities to repress and harass minorities, especially laws against drugs which are associated with those groups (Helmer 1975; Musto 1973). The prohibition of alcohol in the United States is an exceptional case of laws fomented by a fanatical and active minority resulting in the harassment and repression of the majority (Musto 1973; Wasson 1914). When a law is sufficiently unpopular, as was the Constitutional amendment prohibiting alcohol manufacturing and sale for ludibund purposes in the United States, the people in theory will rise to overturn it. Would that it were so with unjust laws, or unenforceable laws! When a government proves itself all-too-willing to attempt to "furnish the force needed to ensure obedience" to unenforceable and (arguably) unjust laws, then the very freedoms or "human rights" on which democratic rule is ostensibly founded are jeopardized (Shulgin 1991). This is the case with the contemporary "War on Drugs" and the unprecedented intrusions into personal liberty which it inexorably occasions. It is a case where the "cure" is far worse than the "disease"; in which the proposed "therapy" is toxic and will prove fatal if administered in sufficiently high dosage. While the use of the drugs this shock therapy addresses continues unabated or indeed increases, freedom and dignity are on the ropes, and in danger of going down for the count.

I will adumbrate four different lines of argument against the contemporary prohibition of entheogenic drugs and, by extension, prohibitions of other drugs—from alcohol, caffeine or nicotine (all of which have been illicit substances in the past) to cocaine, heroin or marijuana (all of which have been legal far longer than they have been controlled substances). These four lines of argument might be grouped under the following headings: 1) scientific; 2) practical or legal; 3) moral; and 4) economic. I will also pose the following question: "why is it that western society cannot cope with euphoria and ecstasy?" This question is at the heart of the prohibition of entheogens. Although they are disguised as "Public Health Laws," the strictures against the entheogens are first and foremost limitations on the practice of religion in a broad sense; or in a sense broader still, are attempts to enshrine in the law a certain perverse brand of what once was called "natural philosophy." I call it science, and the overzealous modern laws against entheogenic drugs are manifestly anti-scientific and indeed represent "crimes against nature."

A SCIENTIFIC PERSPECTIVE

Drug prohibition statutes are typically justified as "Public Health Laws," and conventional wisdom holds that in enacting and enforcing such measures, governments are exercising their paternalistic function of protecting the citizenry from dangers to the public health, much as they would in framing and enforcing laws regarding the disposal of sewage, vaccination of schoolchildren, or pollution of the air by motor vehicles and industrial processes. Regarded from this perspective, drug prohibition is seen as benign, indeed, beneficent, and this viewpoint has become so firmly rooted in the public consciousness as to make the concept accepted universally as a legitimate exercise; nay, as a solemn responsibility of capitalist and socialist governments alike (Szasz 1974; Szasz 1992). In the United States, only the Libertarian Party has consistently opposed drug prohibition as an abuse of governmental power. In some countries, violations of drug laws are called euphemistically *delitos contra la salud*, "crimes against [public] health."

Nevertheless, viewed from a dispassionate, strictly scientific perspective, this public-health justification for drug control simply won't hold water, and it can be argued rather that, by placing certain drugs outside of the established quality control regimen for pharmaceutical products, governments are *defaulting* on their responsibility to protect the public welfare. While some prospective drug users are dissuaded by laws prohibiting their chosen drugs, many, perhaps the majority, are not. During the experimental federal prohibition of alcohol in the United States from 1920–1933, some former alcohol users took the pledge and obeyed the law, whereas many, probably at least half, continued to use alcohol in spite of the laws (it is worth noting that alcohol *use*, like illicit drug use today, remained legal, and there were exceptions to the laws... sacramental wine was allowed to be manufactured and dispensed, and physicians suddenly discovered that prescription alcohol was a panacea, and it was prescribed liberally). Although it is impossible to establish firm numbers for present use of illicit drugs and the efficacy of the laws prohibiting them (Barnes 1988c), there is no question that many millions of users, more than 20–40 million in the United States or at least 10–20% of the adult population (Goldstein & Kalant 1990; Nadelmann 1989), are undeterred by the laws, and do use drugs illegally. During alcohol prohibition in the United States, many inveterate users were accidentally poisoned by methanol and other solvents—poisonings which would not have occurred had legal controls of alcohol purity and concentration been in place; poisonings which ceased to occur once ludibund use of alcohol and its sale for that purpose again became legal. Similarly, now there are annually some 3500 premature deaths *per* year in the United States due to this illicit drug use

(Goldstein & Kalant 1990), many of them so-called "overdose" deaths from injected drugs, principally opiates. Although these deaths are written off as "heroin overdose," the great majority are rather due to adulterants and contaminants in illicit drug products (Chein *et al.* 1964; Escohotado 1989A). After all, the typical samples contain only a few percent of heroin or one or another artificial succedaneum, and illicit products may also contain dust, mites and other minuscule arthropods, spores, virus particles and bacteria, which may either promote infection or sudden death from anaphylaxis or the toxicity of one or another adulterant. On the other hand, the injection, including self-administration, of sterile samples of pharmaceutical opiates of known potency is a common and safe procedure, and deaths as a consequence of such use are virtually unknown.

As for the presumed adverse ecological effects of illicit drug production, these are invariably consequences of the drug laws themselves. Official drug-eradication programs involving the spraying of 2,4-D, *Paraquat* and other herbicides have resulted in exposing smokers to toxic residues in marijuana, not to mention the massive ecological destruction, and its consequent deleterious effects on health of the exposed populace, occasioned by this anti-drug herbicide spraying. By fostering the spread of clandestine laboratories, often in pristine jungle environments, drug laws lead to uncontrolled and unmonitored environmental pollution from unregulated chemical facilities. Under a legal regimen, all presently illegal inebriating drugs would be manufactured in the open in existing facilities, whose liquid and gaseous effluents might effectively be observed. Not only are our health authorities defaulting on their reponsibilities with regard to regulating purity of pharmaceutical products, but our environmental authorities are guilty of defaulting on their responsibilities to protect the environment and public health.

There is no doubt that illicit injection of black-market samples of drugs has become a major vector of transmission of AIDS, hepatitis and other diseases. In the United States and Europe, around 25% of all AIDS cases, including the majority of cases in heterosexuals, children and infants, are a direct or indirect result of illicit intravenous drug administration (Nadelmann 1989). The barbarous practice of denying access to sterile syringes without a medical prescription prevails in the United States, and has even taken root in some other backward countries, whereas in the great majority of the world's countries, sterile syringes are sensibly made available at low prices in pharmacies, even supermarkets, over-the-counter. The U.S. House of Representatives recently voted to prohibit use of "federal" funds for independent state or municipal syringe-exchange programs designed to halt the drug-related spread of AIDS (Hamilton 1992). This cruel and misguided drug control measure *is directly responsible for at least 25% of the new cases of* AIDS *in the United States.* Far from protecting public health, drug prohibition is drastically expanding the AIDS epidemic and contributing to the deaths of thousands of individuals in the United States alone from "drug overdose"—individuals who are deprived of the protection of the Food and Drug Adminstration (FDA) and its counterparts in other countries. This is especially important when we reflect that not all black-market drugs are inebriants (Kreig 1967), not all illicit drug users are hedonists or thrill-seekers. Owing to the restrictive and monopolistic nature of the U.S. pharmaceutical industry, there are black markets in curative drugs which have not been approved for sale by the FDA but for which there is a demand. Recent examples of black-market medicines are the controversial cancer drug amygdalin or *Laetrile*, DiMethylsulfoxide (DMSO), a topical treatment for bruises and sprains (users have been forced to employ industrial-grade DMSO, as no pharmaceutical grade is available), and the AIDS drug *Retrovir*, AZidoThymidine (AZT)—thanks to reforms in the FDA this drug has been made more widely available, and it has all but disappeared from the black market. The AIDS drug *Dexulate* or dextran sulfate is another example of a medicine which American patients had to "bootleg" from other countries (Booth 1988B). There are even black-market drugs which don't fit either in the category of inebriants or chemotherapeutic agents—some products of the biotechnology industry are coming to be used illicitly by athletes. There now exists a black market in human Growth Hormone (hGH) and also in *Eprox* or human erythropoietin, now used surreptitiously by athletes to improve their performance (Spalding 1991). The size of the black market in steroids for athletes has been estimated at U.S. $100 million annually (Marshall 1988D) and is growing—athletic steroids are now being sold in health food stores! There are even athletic steroids which boost performance and are psychoactive—former East German scientists developed a psychoactive testosteroid nasal spray for illegal use by their Olympic athletes (Dickman 1991).

Other damage to the public health is occasioned by drug prohibition policies. Some presently illicit inebriating drugs have valuable therapeutic properties and thus potential to alleviate human suffering—they are not being systematically researched and developed as pharmaceutical products owing to the pall of disreputability cast over them by their legal mis-classification. As we will see in Chapter 2, the most famous entheogenic drug, LSD, was originally developed by Sandoz LTD. of Switzerland as a pharmaceutical agent, under the trade name *Delysid*. While the novel medicine showed considerable promise in psychotherapy (Delay *et al.* 1959B; Grinspoon & Bakalar 1979; Grof 1975; Heim 1961; Naranjo 1973A; Rätsch

1989), one of the most interesting and novel pharmaceutical applications which developed for the drug was as an analgesic and psychotherapeutic adjunct to true agonious therapy, treatment of patients with painful terminal cancer or other fatal diseases (*N.B.* this has been incorrectly called *agonic* therapy; misusing a geometric term meaning "without angles" as opposed to *polygonic* "with many angles"). LSD, DPT (see Chapter 3) and other entheogenic drugs proved to be valuable, long-lasting analgesic agents in some patients with severely painful, terminal conditions, drugs which did not benumb and cloud consciousness in the manner that potent opiate analgesics do (Kast 1963; Kast 1966; Kast 1970; Kast & Collins 1964; Pahnke *et al.* 1970A; Pahnke *et al.* 1970B). The novel drugs also proved their worth in "brief psychotherapy"—aiding dying patients to cope with their dire situation (Grof & Halifax 1977; Pahnke 1970; Pahnke 1971; Pahnke & Richards 1990; Richards 1975; Richards *et al.* 1977; Richards *et al.* 1979). Thanks to this demonstrated medicinal utility, the Swiss government has recently reclassified LSD as an experimental psychotherapeutic agent, making it at least temporarily available to physicians (Hofmann 1991; Rayl 1992). The entheogens have also shown promise in treatment of alcoholism (Mikuriya 1971; Mikuriya 1973; Rhead *et al.* 1977; see Grinspoon & Bakalar 1979 for a review of this controversial research). Despite this plethora of therapeutic benefits demonstrated by entheogenic drugs, their development as pharmaceutical agents was cut short by their legal proscription, and their illogical classification in Schedule I, as drugs with "no currently accepted medical use," all but eliminated any further research along these lines. Even much-maligned visionary drugs like the anesthetic phencyclidine (PCP or *Sernyl*) and its congener ketamine (*Ketalar* or "Vitamin K," employed by some as an entheogen; Moore & Altounian 1978; Turner 1994) have proven to have medicinal potential—as antagonists to *N*-methyl-D-aspartate receptor agonists in brain and potential protective agents against brain damage as a consequence of stroke and other neurological disorders (Barinaga 1990B; Olney *et al.* 1991). It has similarly been proposed to exploit the tendency of psilocybine to stimulate specific areas of the brain in the diagnosis of circulatory and other neurological problems (Gartz 1993), perhaps in combination with magnetic imaging technologies. Even heroin, considered to be deadly poison in the U.S., continues to be regarded as valuable medicine in other countries such as Great Britain. Known pharmaceutically as *Diamorphine*, heroin is considered to be more effective and safer than morphine in treating the pain of myocardial infarction (MacDonald *et al.* 1967). Since both heroin and LSD have legal, medicinal use in other scientifically advanced countries, their U.S. legal designation as Schedule I drugs (with "no currently accepted medical use") is patently false and prejudicial.

The illicit drug best known for its medicinal use is marijuana (see Appendix A; Grinspoon & Bakalar 1993; Paton *et al.* 1973; Roffman 1982; Zinberg 1979). This drug has many medicinally-valuable properties, but is best known as an anti-nausea medicine for patients receiving cancer or AIDS chemotherapy, and as a treatment for glaucoma—a drug to lower the excessive intraocular pressure of this disease, which might lead to blindness (Roffman 1982; Zinberg 1979). Both smoked marijuana and orally-ingested TetraHydroCannabinol (THC or *Marinol*, one of the active principles) have proven to be valuable adjuncts to cancer and AIDS chemotherapy and to glaucoma treatment. Nevertheless, the U.S. government, to avoid giving "mixed signals" in the matter of marijuana, recently stopped the distribution of government marijuana to new cancer, AIDS and glaucoma patients, although for the moment *Marinol* capsules will still be available (Blumenthal 1992). There is some evidence, however, that smoked marijuana may be more effective for some patients (Roffman 1982), and it would certainly be less expensive, especially were cultivation for this purpose permitted. In any case, the U.S. government *does* give mixed signals with regard to marijuana and THC—on the one hand the marijuana plant and its active principle are listed in Schedule I as having "no currently accepted medical use"; then the same government shows the error of this mis-classification by *itself* distributing marijuana and THC for medical use! Summing up the negative effects of drug prohibition on medical research in a recent article in *Science* magazine, Princeton University professor E.A. Nadelmann stated (Nadelmann 1989):

> Current drug laws and policies, however, greatly hamper the efforts of researchers to investigate these and other potential medical uses of illegal drugs; they make it virtually impossible for any of the illegal drugs, particularly those in Schedule I, to be legally provided to those who would benefit from them; and they contribute strongly to the widely-acknowledged undertreatment of pain by the medical profession in the United States.

These and other examples underscore the fact that a decidedly negative result of the prohibition of entheogenic drugs has been the curtailment of promising lines of clinical research, and the witholding from the public of potentially valuable medicaments. The laws are thus working *to the detriment of* public health, in dramatic contrast to their ostensible purpose of protecting public health. Meanwhile, the proscribed drugs are readily available to all comers on the street corner, and the user is deprived of the quality-control guarantees his tax dollars are paying the Food and

Drug Administration authorities (and their counterparts in other countries) to provide. Yes, "junkies" and "long-haired potheads" pay taxes too, and enjoy the same rights to protection as "nicotine fiends" and "short-haired gin freaks." We will leave until the next section a discussion of how the public health is being jeopardized by the criminalization of the black market in drugs. Just as serious as this direct deprivation of potentially valuable medicaments from the pharmacopœia is the curtailment of basic scientific research consequent to drug prohibition. Because of bureaucratic difficulties associated with research involving controlled substances (Strassman 1991), and due to stigmatization of the field in the eyes of personnel in granting agencies and the scientific colleagues of would-be researchers who "peer-review" their grant proposals or decide on awarding of tenure, *etc.*, basic research with entheogenic agents all but disappeared following their legal control in the 1960s. Indeed, investigating positive applications of illicit entheogenic drugs is considered to be the "kiss of death" to a conventional scientific career. Our scientific culture has decided it will "just say no" to information which can be derived from basic research on entheogenic substances (Horowitz 1991), information which could be vital to furthering our understanding of basic brain function. Scientists are thus forced for political reasons to discard a tool enabling them to approach the classic brain/mind problem of philosophy—the biochemistry of our consciousness itself! Since the illicit entheogen DMT is now known to be a neurotransmitter in mammalian brains (Christian *et al.* 1976; Christian *et al.* 1977; Corbett *et al.* 1978), research on this drug and related indole entheogens (many of which are already illegal) is a most promising line of inquiry for neurochemists studying information processing in the brain, and for biomedical researchers interested in developing therapeutic agents to modify pathological malfunctioning of the human nervous system. The laws are militating against this sort of research.

Nevertheless, such research will continue, perhaps in countries with fewer regulations or a more enlightened policy toward drugs. The passage in the United States of the "Controlled Substance Analogue Enforcement Act" of 1986 has been perceived as illegalizing research involving synthesis, with the intention of studying their effects in human beings, of any of the illicit entheogenic substances or their now illegal congeners (Repke 1992; 1993). It has become illegal in the United States even to attempt to synthesize and test completely novel compounds... the government essentially presuming to declare anything illegal unless specifically authorized! Talk about socialistic central planning and governmental control of industry! Pursuing this sort of draconian legal overregulation will ultimately doom the United States pharmaceutical industry to technological and economic inferiority, as the next generation of mind-drugs is developed elsewhere. After an American chemist working for a U.S. pharmaceutical company published (and before the enactment of the 1986 law) ethically flawless, legitimate research dealing with completely legal, novel analogues of DMT, research conducted on his own time, his company was subjected to a special invesigation by the U.S. Food and Drug Administration and he was threatened with dismissal! When pharmaceutical companies are restricted by excessive regulation, they simply invest elsewhere, where their research can be accomplished with a minimum of interference. A recent example was the decision of Swiss pharmaceutical multinational Ciba-Geigy to abandon plans to construct a new pharmaceutical production facility in the firm's home city of Basel, Switzerland. Because of the political power of anti-biotechnology activists in Switzerland, the firm decided to cancel construction plans for the $125 million facility in Basel, and instead is building the new factory across the border in Huningue, France (Aldhous 1992). Needless to say, jobs in Basel are threatened by this development.

Besides crippling neurochemical research and depriving the public of valuable medicaments, drug prohibition occasions other, tangential and collateral damage to the scientific enterprise. An important recent example has to do with the U.S. government's deployment of a line of "aerostats"—balloons outfitted with sophisticated radar equipment and tethered at around 10,000 feet altitude along the U.S./México border and the Florida coast. The purpose of these aerostats is to monitor non-commercial aviation traffic across the border in search of aircraft engaged in illicit drug smuggling (Marshall 1988B). These radar eye-in-the-sky balloons, however, interfere with radio astronomical research by observatories in Arizona and elsewhere. In particular, the aerostat radars, which are powerful radio transmitters, broadcast radio signals in the 1215–1350 MHz frequency range, and effectively blind the astronomical equipment to the red-shifted hydrogen spectra of distant galaxies (Stone 1991). Scientific research once again suffers because of the obsession of the U.S. government with drug enforcement—increasingly an anti-scientific endeavor. As an American citizen, it is profoundly embarrassing to me to contemplate the spectacle of an array of gigantic balloons strung along the border with México... just imagine, balloons... the country is coming to look ever more like some sort of immense used car lot, which the broken-down economy mismanaged by an anti-scientific government increasingly resembles as well!

PRACTICAL AND LEGAL CONSIDERATIONS

The fundamental problem with the concept of drug control is that most human beings, in all eras and cultures about which we know, have used and enjoyed drugs to modify their mood or state of mind. In the United States, for example, there are nearly 200 million people over the age of 12, of which 178 million are caffeine users (89%), 106 million are alcohol users (53%), 57 million are nicotine users (28%), along with approximately 12 million marijuana users (6%), some 3 million cocaine users (1.5%), 2 million heroin users (1%), and about a million users (0.5%) each of the entheogens and of non-ethanol solvents (according to the government's conservative data from a household survey; Goldstein & Kalant 1990). Not only are the numbers of illicit drug users greatly inferior to the numbers of users of legal psychoactive drugs (alcohol, nicotine, caffeine), but the scope of health problems associated with illicit *versus* licit drug use shows a similar disparity. Compared to the estimated three to four thousand deaths *per* year as a consequence of all illicit drug use combined, approximately 320,000 Americans die prematurely *each year* as a consequence of tobacco use, and they are accompanied to the graveyard by an additional 200,000 premature cadavers each year resulting from use of alcohol (Nadelmann 1989). Although there are approximately three times as many nicotine users in the United States as users of all illicit drugs combined, there are nearly 100 times as many deaths as a result; and although there are about five times as many alcohol users as illicit drug users, alcohol is responsible for some 50 times as many deaths. One might conclude that tobacco is some thirty times more dangerous than entheogens, marijuana, cocaine and heroin; and that alcohol is about ten times more dangerous... or one might claim that in time we will discover that additional premature deaths are in fact due to illicit drug use. Nevertheless, the disparity is striking, and it cannot be argued that illicit drugs are justifiably illegal because they are dangerous, as long as substances evidently much more dangerous are legal. Because something is dangerous does not justify illegalizing it, in any case. Whereas the comparatively benign psilocybine-containing mushrooms (see Chapter 5) are illegal, the deadly-poisonous amatoxin- and phallotoxin-containing *Amanita* and *Galerina* species are perfectly legal (Ott 1978B; Ott 1979B). Similarly, with regard to drug toxicity deaths, 70% are the result, not of illicit drugs, but of legal prescription drugs, of which it is said that 300 million doses *per* year are "abused" (Hollister *et al.* 1991).

I might also mention that, whereas both alcohol and nicotine are highly addictive substances (Byrne 1988; Schelling 1992), the entheogens show no pattern of habituation nor any withdrawal syndrome (Hofmann 1980). In a recent article arguing *for* drug control, on a 1–5 scale of "relative risk of addiction" (with 1 being the highest risk), addiction authorities A. Goldstein and H. Kalant rated nicotine a "2" along with heroin, with alcohol rating a "3" along with barbiturates and benzodiazepines or "sleeping pills" (Goldstein & Kalant 1990). Marijuana was given a "4," and the entheogens a "5," together with caffeine. In a rebuttal to letters in response to their article (Hollister *et al.* 1991), Goldstein and Kalant commented that the entheogens really *didn't even belong on a table of risks of addiction,* since these drugs are "aversive rather than reinforcing in animal models"—that is, that experimental animals will *avoid* them rather than become habituated to them! Although many people persist in ignoring the fact that nicotine is an addictive drug (a recent letter complained "to compare nicotine with crack would seem an assault on common sense"; Levin *et al.* 1992!), former U.S. Surgeon General C.E. Koop stated in no uncertain terms (Byrne 1988):

> The pharmacological and behavioral processes that determine tobacco addiction are similar to those that determine addiction to drugs such as heroin and cocaine... We should also give priority to the one addiction—tobacco addiction—that is killing more than 300,000 Americans each year.

In the former Soviet Union in 1990, tobacco shortages sparked widespread riots, forcing emergency importation of American cigarettes (Frankel *et al.* 1992B)! Long-suffering consumers would endure stoically chronic shortages of foods, clothing and energy, but not tobacco—this in the country in which the *real* Czar once ordered the execution of tobacco smokers (Szasz 1974)! As if to underscore the metabolic similarity between heroin addiction and nicotine addiction, the hypotensive drug *Clonidine* has been found to ameliorate or diminish both heroin and nicotine withdrawal symptoms (Glassman *et al.* 1984), and the former National Institute on Drug Abuse (NIDA) director W. Pollin avowed that tobacco addiction was "no different from heroin or cocaine" (Holden 1985). In magazine advertisements by Marion Merrell Dow, Inc., manufacturers of *Nicorette* chewing gum (containing nicotine polacrilex in 2 or 4 mg doses *per* piece), it is stated quite plainly: "your body's addiction to nicotine is a medical problem." Chewing the gum is said to "relieve the discomfort and anxiety that are nicotine withdrawal symptoms," and slowly reducing the daily dose of *Nicorette* will "enable your body to adjust and slowly overcome its addiction." The gum became famous when the former "Drug Czar" W.J. Bennett who, upon assuming his post had given up a two pack-*per*-day cigarette habit to set a good example (Marshall 1989), later admitted that he had relapsed, and was still hooked on nicotine gum. Just say no!

Not only is psychoactive drug use nearly universal among American adults, but virtually every culture that has been studied has been found to make use of one or another inebriating substance (Weil 1972). Moreover, there is increasing evidence for the use of medicinal and inebriating plants by non-human animals (Siegel 1989; Siegel & Jarvik 1975; Siegel *et al.* 1974; Sigstedt 1990; Williams 1989), of which the most famous example is the use of catnip (*Nepeta cataria*) as an inebriant by housecats, a use to which 'most any species of feline is susceptible, if given access to the drug (see Appendix B; Tucker & Tucker 1988). The American Association for the Advancement of Science recently held sessions on "zoopharmacognosy" at its annual meeting (Gibbons 1992). Clearly, use of inebriants is a normal, ordinary, animal activity, virtually universal among members of our species, and any legal attempts to prohibit one psychoactive substance in favor of another (which, after all, involve questions of taste, tradition and prejudice rather than any scientific criterion) is automatically destined for trouble. Laws simply will not deter many millions of people from using the drugs of their choice, but they can distort and pervert the legal system and wreak all sorts of havoc in the attempt.

An avowed purpose of drug control measures in the United States is to increase the street prices of illicit drugs. In this sense, the costs imposed on traffickers by the necessity of escaping detection and by the loss of occasional shipments or the arrests of personnel constitute a sort of "business tax" which is passed on to the consumer. The governmental expenditures on drug enforcement can be seen as a subsidy of the illicit drug dealers. As Professor Nadelmann put it (Nadelmann 1989):

> The greatest beneficiaries of the drug laws are organized and unorganized drug traffickers. The criminalization of the drug market effectively imposes a de facto value-added tax that is enforced and occasionally augmented by the law enforcement establishment and collected by the drug traffickers. More than half of all organized crime revenues are believed to derive from the illicit drug business; estimates of the dollar value range between $10 and $50 billion [U.S. $10–50,000 million!] per year... If the marijuana, cocaine, and heroin markets were legal, state and federal governments would collect billions of dollars annually in tax revenues. Instead, they spend billions in what amounts to a subsidy of organized criminals.

We will return below to the economic consequences of the drug laws. Here the important point to note is their lack of efficacy. In driving up the prices of illicit drugs, the laws enrich criminals and lead to petty theft and other crime to enable the users to pay the exorbitant prices which result. Besides arbitrarily classifying millions of users as criminals, and forcing the users into contact with the criminal element sometimes associated with drug trafficking, the drug laws *provoke* more crime—drugs which would otherwise be cheap become expensive as a consequence of official policy, and theft and related crimes increase proportionately. The public health is again degraded, as the citizen is placed in greater danger of muggings and burglaries, even of being an innocent victim of a shootout between rival drug gangs fighting over territory. A hard-boiled, medical analysis of drug laws in the *Journal of the American Medical Association* concluded (Edison 1978):

> The laws controlling narcotic and other psychoactive drugs... should be evaluated for effectiveness and safety in the same way we would evaluate surgical or pharmacologic treatment. As a treatment, the drug laws appear to be only marginally effective. Their side effects are so dangerous that the treatment is often more devastating than the disease. A judgment based strictly on the effectiveness and safety of the drug laws would require their immediate repeal or overhaul.

In a similar vein, Daniel E. Koshland Jr., then editor of the premier American scientific journal *Science*, a man with extensive career experience in the chemistry and pharmacology of opiate drugs, commented in an editorial entitled "The War? Program? Experiment? on Drugs" (Koshland 1989):

> The drug program recently unveiled by the Executive Branch... is at least a useful experiment, and should be labeled as such... A minimal requirement would seem to be ongoing analysis of the program's degree of success, to decide whether to continue in the same direction or to seek new directions if the program is not succeeding... The experiment will be acceptable only if accompanied by a scientific detachment that says, "The get-tough experiment is under way. If it fails, legalization is next."

Nevertheless, the government understandably shies away from studying the efficacy (or lack thereof) of its own efforts against drugs, and has repeatedly been accused of "flying blind" in the "War on Drugs" (Hamilton 1990; Marshall 1988A).

While the government experiments with the "get-tough" approach, scientific developments have compromised severely the forensic chemical basis for evidence in the ensuing drug-related prosecutions. The interesting discovery that the illicit entheogen DMT appears to be a mammalian neurotransmitter (Christian *et al.* 1976; Christian *et al.* 1977) and that the drug normally occurs in human cerebrospinal fluid (Corbett *et al.* 1978) raises important legal questions. Moreover, diazepam or *Valium* has been found to occur in rat brain and in trace amounts in wheat grains (Wildmann *et al.* 1987), and "diazepam-like" compounds have been found in bovine urine (Luk *et al.* 1983). Similarly, the controlled opiates morphine and codeine have been found to be normal components of human cerebrospinal fluid (Cardinale *et al.* 1987), and morphine has been found to be a trace constituent of cow and human milk, and to occur naturally in mammalian brain tissue. Trace amounts of morphine have similarly been detected in "various plants such as hay and lettuce" (Hazum *et al.* 1981). In ancient times, Pliny reported a lettuce variety called "poppy lettuce, from its abundance of juice with a soporific property" (Harlan 1986) and *lactucarium* or "lettuce opium" was introduced to the pharmacopœia in 1810 (Duncan 1810) and may still be purchased from companies advertising in "countercultural" drug magazines. Trace amounts of morphine in poppy seeds used in baked goods can show up in the urine of the diner. With the detection of morphine in urine being considered *prima facie* evidence of heroin use in methadone-clinic patients and in job applicants (Bigwood 1978; Potter & Orfali 1990), and with the drug laws flatly proclaiming that unauthorized possession or sale of "any material, compound, mixture or preparation which contains any quantity of" DMT, *Valium*, morphine and many other drugs, where does this leave the concept of drug control and forensic chemical evidence? If morphine occurs in hay and lettuce, in poppy-seed rolls, in every one of our bodies, even in mothers' milk… on what scientific basis can an unauthorized cultivator of opium poppies be punished, without also punishing lettuce and hay growers, or the proprietors and employees of supermarket chains and the corner Mom and Pop grocery for illicit trafficking in the morphine present in each and every quart of wholesome milk? On what basis… as citizens subjected willy-nilly to the unforseen and absurd consequences of the drug laws… we demand to know… *on what basis*?

The absurdities and incongruities into which we fall in the looking-glass world of the drug warriors by no means end there. A recent article in *Science* proclaimed that the U.S. National Institute on Drug Abuse (NIDA) "Aims to Fight Drugs with

Drugs," that "the agency is planning a massive search for medications to treat cocaine and other addictions," looking for "magic bullets for addiction" (Waldrop 1989)! The only "magic bullets" for addiction the authorities have found so far are the .38 caliber variety injected by police-special revolvers! Let's treat whiskey addicts with gin while we're at it... or heroin addicts with methadone... surely they can't be serious! Do they say this with tongue in cheek, or do they have something else in cheek... perhaps a goodly quid of leaves from the "stupid bush" which the CIA chemical warriors were searching for in the Caribbean in the fifties and seem to have found at home in Langley (Marks 1979)? We must recall that heroin was originally marketed as a "cure" for morphinism (Escohotado 1989A; Latimer & Goldberg 1981), and one of the "magic bullets" against addiction, bromocriptine or *Parlodel* (see Chapter 2, Note 9), is already suspected itself of being an addicting drug (Holden 1989B). The article goes on... fantasizing that this could be a "Manhattan Project for chemists"—so what does that mean, "nuke" your neighborhood junkie or hippie? Maybe that's not so far off the mark—a recent review of a book about the Manhattan Project by prominent physicist Freeman J. Dyson drew a specious analogy between LSD and nuclear weapons: "nuclear weapons and LSD are both highly addictive...Both have destroyed many lives and are likely to destroy many more..." (Dyson 1992). Nobody said Dyson was an expert on entheogenic drugs, but the scary fact is that *Science* published this absurd fancy, and this well-respected scientist was apparently serious. Of course, I realize NIDA has no intention of treating whiskey addicts with gin... more like treating whiskey addicts with methanol... forcing people off of one drug, the effects of which they happen to like, and substituting another drug which will do everything for them but provide the pleasure they originally sought in drugs! This is treatment... or assault?

Meanwhile, as thousands of people are being arrested for possession of cocaine, it has been found that another "material, compound, mixture or preparation which contains any quantity" of this illegal substance is the great bulk of American paper money! In an analysis of 135 American Federal Reserve Notes of varying denominations and from different parts of the country, all but four (97%) contained detectable quantities of cocaine. The average content was 7.3 mcg of cocaine *per* bill, and one banknote contained as much as 270 mcg of cocaine (Pool 1989). This means that virtually all Americans (save only the poorest, who might have only "spare change" in their pockets) are in possession of a Schedule II drug *all the time*, with the richest among us perhaps falling in the "possession with intent to sell" category based on the gross weight of a big bankroll of cocaine-containing greenbacks... or should we now call them "whitebacks"? But since the citizen carrying his hard-earned Federal Reserve Note is legally just a "bearer" of a monetary instrument which is the property of the Federal Reserve Bank, does this mean that it is the proverbial "higher ups" who are to be arrested... do I hear calls for an indictment against the Chairman of the Federal Reserve Bank and the Secretary of the Treasury for cocaine trafficking... or, since the "buck" ("cocabuck"?) ostensibly stops on the desk in the Oval Office, let's go right to the top of this sordid drug ring, to the President of the United States! Never mind the fact that the U.S. currency is printed on paper containing hemp (*i.e.* marijuana) fiber, or that Betsy Ross' first American flag was sewn of hempen cloth, or that the originals of the U.S. Constitution and Declaration of Independence are scrivened on hemp-fiber parchment (Herer 1990)!

Chemical detection technology has progressed to such a point that we are all in danger of being the "enemy" in the "War on Drugs"... or prospective casualties. Recently a military pilot, a commissioned officer in the United States Air Force, was ignominiously court-martialed for illicit drug use when amphetamine residues were detected in his urine. Thanks to a little scientific detective work, it was later proved that an over-the-counter anorexic (diet pill) he had been taking quite legally, a product which contained phenylpropanolamine as active agent, was contaminated in the manufacturing process with trace amounts of amphetamine, as were other lots of similar products tested. The court-martialed pilot was given back his commission and reinstated to active duty, but not restored to his prior flight crew status (Pool 1989). It is significant that a major legal challenge to government plans to screen all employees' urine for drug metabolites was mounted by U.S. Customs agents, the Grand Lodge of the Fraternal Order of Police and U.S. Department of Justice federal attorneys who commented: "they test; we sue" (Crawford 1988)! Note that these are the "frontline troops" in the "War on Drugs," and they don't wish "the people" to know what drug metabolites are in *their* urine! A company called Psychemedics is now fighting the "urinalysis lobby" for a piece of the $300 million *per* year U.S. drug-testing market—promoting a technology based on the detection of infinitesimal residues of drugs or drug metabolites in hair samples (Holden 1990c). There is some evidence that merely allowing your fingers to touch your hair after handling some of the Federal Reserve Chairman's cocaine-blighted bills could make you a candidate for a positive reading in a "hairanalysis" drug test... or taking a stroll through the park and inadvertently passing through some marijuana smoke exhaled by some brazen lawbreaker (it has been demonstrated that such "passive" exposure to *Cannabis* smoke can lead to false positive readings for marijuana use in blood and urine tests too; Morland *et al.* 1985). Urinalysis also involves the problem of "false positives" if detection thresholds are set low enough to detect most users (Schwartz *et al.* 1987). These ultra-sensitive analyses for drug metabolites in urine cannot tell whether morphine in the urine came from a shot of heroin or a few poppyseed rolls with dinner. Do you still think the troops fighting the "War on Drugs" are on your side… can you be certain you won't one day be considered to be the "enemy"? Perhaps the "skinheads" are on to something…

Let's face it, we're *all* on drugs, *all of the time*… I'm not talking about the industrial quantities of alcohol, caffeine, nicotine, marijuana, cocaine, heroin *etc.* consumed regularly by humankind, but about the DMT and morphine our bodies make for us and which we "consume" all of the time; or our very own sleeping pill, the endogenous ligand of the *Valium* receptor (which may be *Valium* itself); or the "anxiety peptide" which blocks that receptor (Marx 1985); or our endorphins and enkephalins (our own self-produced "ENDOgenous MORPHINES"; see Snyder & Matthysse 1975) which kill our pain; or "Substance P," our own pain-causing molecule (Skerrett 1990); or anandamide, the endogenous ligand of the THC (marijuana) receptor (Devane *et al.* 1992)… The life of the mind, of consciousness, is a constant, ever-changing pharmacological symphony, or to put it less romantically, a never-ending drug binge. The urge to ingest opiates or DMT or *Valium* is completely natural (Siegel 1989) and as "organic" as can be—we are only supplementing or complementing the drugs that make our brains work, and these drugs work for us precisely because they are identical to, or chemically similar to our own endogenous drugs. Researchers have found "commonalities" in "drug abuse" irrespective of gross pharmacological differences between various classes of drugs (Holden 1985) because on one level all psychoactive drugs are the same—they are all fitting into our own brains' own receptors for our own homemade, endogenous drugs.

The inequities and incongruities drug laws force on our legal system are many and weighty. Scientists presently are vociferously debating (and rightly so) the statistical and legal interpretations of forensic evidence based on DNA analysis, so-called "DNA-fingerprinting" in which the DNA of an individual left at the scene of a crime is amplified by PCR technology (Polymerase Chain Reaction, for which K. Mullis, then of Cetus Corp., won the 1993 Nobel Prize). A recent article in *Science* (Chakraborty & Kidd 1991) questioned claimed statistical significance of "matches" between DNA "fingerprints" (in reality, autoradiograms of electrophoretic separations on polyacrylamide gel of fragments of digested DNA), and the editors of the journal felt compelled to take the unprecedented step of simultaneously publishing a rejoinder to this article (Lewontin & Hartl 1991) and a news article explaining why (Roberts 1991), all followed by an editorial (Koshland 1992) and a spate of letters and rebuttals (Wills *et al.* 1992). This is as it ought to be, for the technology promises to revolutionize the nature of evidence, both accusatory and exculpatory. The extreme care with which the scientific community is treating the establishment of standards for DNA fingerprinting, however, contrasts markedly with the standards prevailing in a modern American drug-violation prosecution. Entrapment of the defendant is the rule, and sometimes undercover group A of municipal drug police is working assiduously to entrap undercover group B of state or federal police, and there have even been shootouts between two different police units. This is protecting the public welfare? Eyewitness testimony purchased from avowed criminals (whether outright with cash, or with pardons or reduced sentences) is *de rigueur*. The luckless defendant may have been subjected to an illegal wiretap or search and seizure without warrant or probable cause, but since the police were "acting in good faith" (the police are *always* "acting in good faith," aren't they?) the evidence is admitted. Even more shocking and fraudulent is the established American practice of regarding one gram of 10% heroin to be one gram of heroin (when in reality only one-tenth gram of heroin is involved) in considering sentencing or the charge (simple possession is distinguished from "possession with intent to sell," which carries much stiffer penalties, by the quantity of the drug seized as evidence). This is especially absurd when doses of LSD are seized, which may contain only 25 or 50 mcg of the drug on a piece of paper or gelatin weighing tens or hundreds of milligrams (Shulgin & Shulgin 1991). Imagine the innocent farmer wending a weary way to the barn in a bucolic setting with a couple of tons of hay on the truck... hay which contains morphine (Hazum *et al.* 1981) in trace quantities... by this standard (s)he could be arrested for possession of a couple of tons of morphine, and go down in history as one of the all-time great *narcotraficantes.* How about an Untouchables-type raid on the pasteurization plant, to bust the nefarious pushers of tons and tons of "morphine"—milk containing traces of the drug, that is? My ludibrious tone masks genuine concern—as a citizen subject to the possibility of entrapment and wire tapping, to all sorts of chicanery, prestidigitation and fraud in the name of law enforcement, I demand to know... we *must* know... on what basis can "the people" prosecute ill-starred individuals in possession of "grams" or "kilograms" of illicit drugs, meanwhile allowing traffickers in "tons" of *Valium*, morphine, codeine, DMT or any number of other controlled drugs to go free? *On what basis*?

Entrapment, wiretaps, searches without warrant or probable cause, arbitrary enforcement due to the very ubiquity of controlled substances in our own bodies, on our money, in the milk we drink... these disreputable, slipshod and unethical enforcement techniques of questionable legality threaten our freedoms and human rights. However bizarre or patently illegal a police tactic may be, once it is accepted in a court of law, and then cited in another judgement, a body of precedent begins to accumulate, and what once was a heavy-handed excess by rogue elements of police operating outside of the law slowly becomes standard practice acceptable in any courtroom (Shulgin & Shulgin 1991). The use of extraordinary "emergency" measures instituted to deal with the "epidemic" of "drug abuse" and tolerated by judges who have swallowed the anti-drug propaganda hook, line and sinker, is changing the relationship of citizen to state to the detriment of individual freedom. Our civil rights guaranteed under the Bill of Rights to the U.S. Constitution, such as the right to privacy, freedom from unauthorized search and seizure practices, *such as the presumption of innocence* are steadily eroded and wear away as surely as Thomas Jefferson's face disappears from an aging nickel coin, and police-state tactics that once were "wartime" expedients justified by the "deadly menace" of drugs are suddenly being applied to any and all areas of law enforcement. Already we are seeing the same Gestapo-inspired police-state tactics applied to the enforcement of other laws (*Gestapo* was the German acronym for GEheime STAats POlizei, or "Secret State Police" under the NSDAP, National sozialistische Deutsche Arbeiters Partei, National Socialist German Worker's Party, or "Nazi" government of Adolf Hitler). Bizarre and illegal raids and seizures have been directed against so-called "computer hackers," the police assiduously taking advantage of the legal dispensations given to the "drug warriors" (Gans & Sirius 1990; Holden 1990B; Levy 1991; Sirius & Gleason 1990; Sterling 1992). As a recent article in *Mondo 2000* lamented:

> Acting on request from certain corporations, the FBI and the Secret Service—armed with vaguely worded warrants—have raided businesses and homes of private citizens and seized tremendous numbers of computers and related items, with very few corresponding arrests. The language of the warrants was vague because even in the rare case where the government knows what it is looking for, on the electronic frontier, it probably has no idea what it is looking *at.* (Gans & Sirius 1990; italics in the original)

After snooping illegally on communications through electronic bulletin boards, and because of government agents' profound ignorance regarding the terminology employed, a business called Steve Jackson Games, Inc. was raided by the Secret Service, three computers and data for a product in development (a non-computer game) seized, and the company was almost driven into bankruptcy (Holden 1990B; Levy 1991). No crimes had been committed, nor were any criminal charges ever brought against the company or its employees, who were not compensated for damage to equipment (when the computers were returned six months later, one was destroyed and another required a $200 repair) nor for financial losses exceeding $125,000. Owner Jackson was forced to lay off eight of his 17 employees to stay in business. The raid was conducted pursuant to a vaguely-worded warrant which was not explained to the owner of the business, and when his attorney asked to see the warrant, he was told the information was "sealed." Thanks to the excessive zeal of our drug-bust-crazed police, eight people lost their jobs, having committed no crimes—will some of these innocent victims turn to drug-dealing to support their families? In a related case in which the government brought charges against an alleged "computer criminal" for supposed complicity in stealing information from a telephone company, information alleged to be "highly proprietary" and worth $79,000, the prosecution ignominiously dropped the charges in mid-trial when the defense showed that the alleged stolen property was public information, readily found in public libraries and openly distributed by the company in question for $13 by calling a toll-free number (Levy 1991)... the grand larceny charge evaporating to petty theft before the astonished prosecutor's eyes! This case exposed this legal charade for what it was—not police fighting crime, but a war over "freedom of information," over control and ownership of information, and against the libertarian element favoring freedom of access, whether to information or to drugs (Clarke 1992; Ross 1991). But the U.S. government insists on having unfettered access to information—the U.S. National Security Agency (NSA), in collaboration with the U.S. State Department, is prohibiting the export of "RSA" data-encryption programs (for encoding computer or other digital data) which exceed a standard, in this case allowing only "algorithm keys" of 40 bits or less. This enables the NSA, with its state-of-the-art computers, to be able rapidly to "crack" any codes it wishes, whereas a 512 bit "key" is considered necessary for relative security, given the speed of today's supercomputers (French 1990). The FBI has proposed a bill and a "Digital Telephony Amendment" to the 1934 "Communications Act" which would require any new communications system (including computer networks) to be designed so as to allow facile wiretapping by the authorities; even 'though in 1990 U.S. judges approved only 872 legal wiretaps (Levy 1992). This is like requiring that condoms, parachutes or automobile airbags have holes in them! Of course, the way to make computer networks secure against "hackers" and spies (which the NSA is ostensibly looking for—domestic spying is supposedly beyond its reach) is *to allow effective encryption of data*, not to conduct Gestapo-like raids, nor to seize or destroy computers. As long as the government wishes to have access, such will be available to anyone with the ingenuity to discover the "back door" to any computer system. In the Steve Jackson Games case, one of the computers seized was at the time running an electronic bulletin board, a form of expression which the U.S. Constitution protects as surely as it protects printing presses and broadcast media. Federal Judge Sam Sparks agreed, and he subsequently awarded Jackson and associates $55,000 plus court costs in their suit against the Secret Service, ruling that the investigation had violated the "Electronic Communications Privacy Act." In his judgement in Austin, Texas, Sparks held that electronic bulletin boards qualify as publishing under the law, entitling operators like Steve Jackson Games, Inc. to the protection of the "Privacy Protection Act" which limits government access to files and records of journalists and publishers (Ortega 1993). Although freedom of information appears to have won this round, can anyone be deluded into supposing that the U.S. government will draw the line at "computer hacking" as it flexes its new police muscle? Is it likely U.S. law-enforcement officials will draw the line anywhere?

In a recent interview with an American journalist, the chief of Amsterdam's narcotics police commented that the idea of a "War on Drugs" reminded him of the Gestapo, the German police who "thought they could change society's behavior. The police are a very dangerous element in society if they are not limited. We know what war means... We fight war against our enemies, not with our own citizens" (Beers 1991). In the Netherlands drug laws similar to the American laws are on the books, but the Dutch government administers them in a fashion characterized as "harm reduction" or "flexible enforcement"—narcotics chief Zaal commented that illegal drug users are "patients, and we can't help them by putting them in jail" (Beers 1991). In the wartime United States, then-Los Angeles Police Chief Daryl Gates testified to the Senate Judiciary Committee that illicit drug users "ought to be taken out and shot" for "treason" (Beers 1991). In the "War on Drugs" only the users are shooting the drugs, the police are shooting at us; *people* are the enemy, *people* become casualties. It is a dangerous cat-and-mouse game, and although the police are ostensibly the cats catching and destroying the mice, nevertheless the mice in this case are leading the cats around by their noses, always a step ahead. This is an inevitable and predictable result of concentrating drug control efforts on the supply, rather than the demand.

The U.S. "War on Drugs" is a "supply-side" endeavor—71% of the funds in the fiscal year 1991 "National Drug Control Strategy" were destined for reduction of supply (29% for "interdiction and international control"; 42% for law enforcement); only 29% for "demand reduction" (Goldstein & Kalant 1990). Since more than 75% of the 750,000 yearly arrests for drug law violations in the U.S. are for simple possession, mainly of marijuana (Nadelmann 1989), it can be said that the bulk of the U.S. law enforcement effort is directed at punishing users, rather than reducing the supply. "Interdiction and international control" efforts have been, by and large, ineffectual. Despite the intensive efforts directed against the illicit production of cocaine in South America, and toward interception of the drug at U.S. borders, the wholesale price of cocaine dropped 80% during the 1980s, while the purity of the drug as retailed increased *fivefold*, according to the U.S. Drug Enforcement Administration's (DEA) figures (DEA 1989). Since the DEA reported in 1987 that the foreign export price of cocaine represented only 4% of the U.S. retail price, there is no reason to expect a reversal in this utter failure to reduce supply—the drug is so cheap to produce and so lucrative that traffickers can and do easily counteract any increased activity or expenditures by the authorities. Once again, the drug laws constitute a subsidy to the traffickers—a "value-added tax," and the foreign aid money put into crop substitution programs in Perú constitutes a direct subsidy to increased planting of *coca.* Since the interest rates are so high, farmers simply plant a small parcel in one of the accepted substitute crops, as a cover, then use the bulk of the funds to plant more *coca*—the only crop sufficiently remunerative to enable them to repay the loans (Morales 1989). Except for opium poppies, that is... (Morales 1989; Ott 1992A)

Heroin production is even more lucrative and even less influenced by enforcement activities—according to the DEA, the foreign export price of heroin is only a fraction of 1% of its U.S. retail price. As the international control efforts against heroin have been directed chiefly at the "Golden Triangle" area of Southeast Asia and Eastern Europe, traditional opium poppy growing regions, the traffickers have simply begun to introduce opium and heroin production in areas not traditionally known for this. Opium poppy cultivation has become so widespread in México, that that country has emerged as one of the leading heroin suppliers to the U.S. market. Moreover, opium poppies have become the natural and preferred substitute crop for *coca* in South America, and heroin production is being introduced in Bolivia, Colombia, Perú and even Guatemala. Enforcement activities have thus led the black market to its *own* crop-substitution scheme, and opium poppies are being substituted for *coca*, with the inevitable result that any reduction in the supply of cocaine will be more than compensated for by a substantial increase in the supply of heroin. This is progress... this is protecting the public health?

The U.S. authorities have been relatively more successful in reducing the smuggling of marijuana into the country, yet there is a plentiful supply of marijuana on the U.S. market. Not only is the drug cheap to produce (foreign export price 1% of

U.S. retail price, according to DEA figures), but the unintended ('though entirely predictable) results of the U.S. campaign against the drug have been the conversion of the U.S. into one of the world's leading producers of marijuana and the transformation of many former marijuana smugglers into cocaine and/or heroin smugglers (Adler 1985)—as costs of smuggling increase, smugglers will turn to loads with a higher value *per* unit of weight. Thus the exaggerated attention focused by the authorities on the smuggling of marijuana has led to vastly increased domestic production, obviating the necessity of sneaking the drug past beagle-eyed customs officials. The value of the U.S. marijuana crop in 1987 was estimated at $33.1 billion ($33,100 million; Siegel 1989). The market is still supplied, but in a manner much less visible to the authorities, immeasurably more decentralized and much less susceptible to control efforts. While this development may work against the country's international imbalance of trade, it hasn't made much of a dent in the supply, and has made future attempts to influence the supply infinitely more difficult. Furthermore, the necessity of indoor intensive cultivation to escape surveillance has led to the development of super-potent strains of *Cannabis* approaching 20% THC, nearly double the concentrations found in natural, outdoor strains previously considered to be the most potent. The price has gone up, yes, but producers have managed to continue to supply the market with a product superior to that formerly smuggled, are much less likely to be arrested, and are making much more money! Does anyone still doubt, as Professor Nadelmann claimed, that the producers and traffickers of illicit drugs are the chief beneficiaries of the laws (Nadelmann 1989)?

Another predictable response to "supply-side" enforcement efforts has been the introduction to the black market over the past 15 years of a series of completely artificial heroin analogues. The first of these so-called "designer drugs" (Kirsch 1986) to appear on the U.S. market were derivatives of *Meperidine* or *Demerol*, such as MPPP, which is about 25 times the potency of the parent compound and about three times the potency of morphine. The most famous of the "designer narcotics," however, are the compounds known as "China White"—derivatives of the medicinal narcotic *Fentanyl*, a compound some 100 times the potency of morphine. The best-known of these black-market derivatives is α-methyl-*Fentanyl*, roughly 3000 times the potency of morphine (Seymour & Smith 1987). According to the DEA, starting materials and equipment to make a kilogram of this drug cost about $2000, the product being worth as much as a billion dollars ($1000 million)! It is important to note that this compound was an invention of the black market, never described in chemical literature (Baum 1985; Shafer 1984; Shafer 1985). Once again, the "supply-side" enforcement directed to opium poppy cultivation and heroin production has stimulated domestic production of inexpensive succedanea thousands of times the potency of morphine. In a similar manner, exaggerated attention focused on illicit cocaine production and smuggling is fueling the growth of the U.S. amphetamine industry. Annual domestic production of methamphetamine is estimated to be worth $3 billion ($3,000 million; Cho 1990). Again, the U.S. trade deficit has been lowered, but comparatively large-scale and visible enterprises such as heroin and cocaine production are simply being replaced by practically invisible small-scale substitutes. Instead of the international networks of growers and harvesters, chemists and smugglers, now all that is required are solitary chemists within the countries of consumption. As drug policy experts A. Goldstein and H. Kalant stated in a recent article:

> Advances in pharmaceutical chemistry are such that highly potent psychoactive drugs of every kind can be synthesized readily in clandestine laboratories, so the illicit market would adjust quickly even to a complete sealing of our borders, were that possible. (Goldstein & Kalant 1990)

Misguided enforcement efforts have resulted in the creation of decentralized and small-scale drug production alternatives, practically invisible to the authorities. Production costs go down, profits skyrocket, and the chances of detection and arrest are reduced—the illicit drug manufacturers and retailers couldn't be happier.

It is simply too easy to outwit the drug laws. Well before the authorities realize what is going on, talented surreptitious chemists have invented new, yet more profitable, and legal succedanea for controlled drugs. When one of these "designer heroin" labs was busted, the chemist told police he was experimenting with "snow cone flavorings" (Shafer 1984). When the results came back from the forensics laboratory, the police found they had no case against the person. When α-methyl-*Fentanyl* was finally identified (the first structure proposed by the DEA chemists, 3-methyl-*Fentanyl*, later turned out to be erroneous; Ayres *et al.* 1981; Baum 1985) and the drug was scheduled, the ingenious chemists made *para*-fluoro-*Fentanyl*, still legal. Finally, Congress passed the "Controlled Substance Analogue Enforcement Act" establishing the novel principle that any chemical or pharmacological analogue of any illicit drug could be deemed to be illegal! This is a textbook case of an unconstitutionally-vague statute, and is the purest essence of arbitrary and selective law enforcement, crystallized in a form more potent than any *Fentanyl* derivative. Never mind that this absurd law makes virtually anything illegal which some police chief or district attorney doesn't like (Shulgin 1992), and is virtually illegalizing scientific research into mind drugs and making the whole field of chemistry suspect; the important thing is it simply will not work. Sure, it will enable charges to be brought against manufacturers of new analogues, on the rare occasions when such are detected and arrested, but the genie is out of the bottle. The laws have made illicit drug synthesis so profitable and it is such a simple endeavor, that no law will stop it, not even capital punishment. The laws even serve as textbooks for would-be black-market-drug chemists, who look through the schedules for ideas for new products (Shulgin & Shulgin 1991).

Having touched on the subject of Constitutional vagueness, it is important to stress that scientific research continues to reveal new plant (and animal) species containing illegal compounds. Since controlled substances such as DMT, morphine and codeine appear to be general mammalian neurotransmitters, dog and cat (or other mammal) owners are technically in unauthorized possession of illicit drugs *all the time.* As we will see in Chapter 5, there are at least 98 species of mushrooms now known to contain illegal psilocybine, and another 60 species can safely be assumed to contain these compounds. This book mentions some 250 plant species known to contain illicit drugs. Some, such as the forage grass *Phalaris arundinacea*, are common articles of commerce which can be purchased inexpensively by the truckload; some, like the psilocybian mushrooms, grow adventitiously all over the world. Since one would have to be expert in plant taxonomy and phytochemistry, and would have assiduously to study the latest research reports in order simply to know which plants are illegal, plants which might grow unbidden on one's property at any time, it can be said that the laws interpreted as proscribing these plants are "unconstitutionally vague"—it is not immediately obvious to the ordinary citizen, nor indeed to anyone, just what is illegalized by these laws. With the advent of the "Controlled Substance Analogue Enforcement Act" of 1986, all plant and animal species can be said to be illegal, at the whim of the government. Short of being an expert in several scientific fields and devoting considerable time and effort keeping abreast of the latest phytochemical and botanical research, some of which is published in German (Gartz 1986c), Spanish (Guzmán 1983), French (Heim & Hofmann 1958), Italian (Festi 1985; Fiussello & Ceruti-Scurti 1972; Samorini & Festi 1989), Czechoslovakian (Pouzar 1953), Norwegian (Kvambe & Edenberg 1979; Nordbø 1979) or other languages, there is no way for any citizen to be certain (s)he is not in illegal possession of a proscribed drug (see Boire 1995 on vagueness issue).

This is all a result of misguided, supply-side enforcement. As long as demand exists for illicit drugs, and as long as the laws guarantee, nay, subsidize the profitability of meeting this demand, people will line up for the chance to enter this business. As even informed opponents of drug legalization acknowledge, only by targeting the demand side can we make strides toward reducing the consumption of illicit drugs (Goldstein & Kalant 1990; Jarvik 1990). Empty propaganda accompanied by a "war" against users (recall that 75% of drug arrests in the U.S. are for simple possession) who are treated as vermin, as the vectors of transmission of a "plague" (Szasz 1974) only alienates them still further from authority. Only by treating people with respect and offering them unbiased information and viable alternatives (*N.B.* jail is neither an effective deterrent nor a viable alternative; Packer 1968; Skolnick 1968) can governmental authorities hope to dissuade users from this or that drug. There is evidence that information campaigns can influence drug use (Ellickson & Bell 1990; Ferrence 1990). Suasion, not coercion is the answer, and the voice doing the persuading must be morally impeccable. As Shakespeare's Hamlet lamented: "ay, there's the rub."

MORAL ASPECTS OF WAR

It is commonly stated that illegalizing drugs is the "moral" thing for a government to do, since drug use is thought by some to be immoral, even to degrade the moral fortitude of citizens. But the governments taking this "moral" stance mostly sanction and support the use of drugs like alcohol and nicotine, as do the vast majority of those citizens "morally" opposed to illicit drug use, the great bulk of whom are themselves drug users. As an American and a Canadian authority on drug addiction research stated in a recent article:

> The time is long overdue to recognize officially, publicize, and incorporate into common speech and legislation the fact that tobacco (nicotine) and alcohol are potentially hazardous addicting drugs. We need to expunge from the language the phrases "alcohol and drugs" and "tobacco and drugs." This is not mere semantic nitpicking; language influences the way we think. (Goldstein & Kalant 1990)

I had already made this same point five years before (Ott 1985), in a book on chocolate addiction which treated our provincial and prejudiced, unscientific attitudes toward drugs with ludibry. As Princeton Professor Nadelmann put it in his well-conceived "moral" arguments *for* the legalization of all drugs (Nadelmann 1989):

> "Moral" condemnation by the majority of Americans of some substances and not others is little more than a transient prejudice in favor of some drugs and against others.

I might add that this holds true for the "moral" condemnation in some Moslem countries of alcohol, and the corresponding prejudice in favor of *hashish* and opium (Gelpke 1966A)—this is a pangæan, not a peculiarly American tendency, although the drugs socially accepted vary from one society to the next, as of course do the drugs scorned. So firmly rooted is our tendency to ignore alcohol and tobacco when thinking about "drugs," that the American Society of Pharmacognosy (which should know better) announced its 1992, 33rd annual meeting featuring two symposia, one of which was about "Drugs of Abuse," under the sponsorship of Philip Morris USA—one of the country's leading tobacco companies and pushers of one of America's most-abused drugs, which annually kills 320,000 Americans!

As for the immoralities of drug prohibition, the most obvious of these involve the above-mentioned perversion of law enforcement the drug laws inevitably foster. Since the nebulous alleged victims of drug law violations (our children? our schools? the public health?) do not file charges with the police, in order to enforce the drug laws the police have to become criminals themselves (some would argue that in many cases, this is a seamless transformation). Thus our tax dollars are used to buy and sell drugs, as the police disguise their true employment and act as 'though they were everyday illicit drug merchants, hoping to get close to "Mr. Big." Then they will try to sell him some of their "dope," or buy from him some of his, then... surprise! Out come the guns and badges. Not only do the police immorally become liars and drug dealers, but this type of operation invites corruption, and there are innumerable instances of police freelancing on the side. Annually in the U.S. some 100 police officials are indicted in federal courts on corruption charges related to drugs (Nadelmann 1988). Should "Mr. Big" come up short of cash for the big buy, no problem... some other "undercover" agents will step in and provide financing. There have even been cases in which reluctant individuals were provided with government money to buy government drugs, and then arrested! This is law enforcement... or manufacturing *ersatz* crimes? Not content to be ludificatory dope dealers, the "moral" police become spies and snoops, "Peeping Toms" tapping 'phones, espying windows, hiring criminals to spy on their associates, cajoling people to inform on their spouses, children to inform on their parents, even sifting through garbage in search of "evidence." Not only do we have shootouts between rival "gangs" of police fighting over turf and mistaking each other for the "enemy," but there was recently a case of illegal computer hacking *by the police.* During confirmation hearings for former "Drug Czar" W.J. Bennett, Delaware Senator J. Biden, Chairman of the Senate Judiciary Committee, described a case in which personnel of an unnamed federal agency involved in the "War on Drugs" "surreptitiously lifted another's budget by altering a computerized file" (Marshall 1989)! No wonder Czar Bennett went back to his nicotine habit!

Another immorality of the "War on Drugs" involves questions of emphasis. Grossly exaggerated attention has been directed toward apprehending and convicting drug offenders, many of whom become subject to compulsory sentencing. Although the staggering number of annual drug arrests in the U.S. represents only about 2% of the true number of "offenders," trying and punishing those convicted is clogging our criminal justice system. In Washington, D.C., for example, 52% of the felony indictments were for drug-law violations in 1986. In New York the following year the number was 40% (Nadelmann 1989). Vital police resources which ought to be destined for arresting and processing violent criminals are being squandered on drug users and the occasional merchant. Worse than that is the fact that already convicted, violent criminals are being released from jail early, to make room for the compulsory-sentenced drug offenders (Marshall 1988c). When another "Drug Czar," R. Martínez, was governor of Florida between 1986 and 1990, Florida spent more money than any other state on drug enforcement, and had in place strict mandatory-sentencing laws mandating three-year-minimum sentences for using, buying or selling illicit drugs within 310 meters of schools, public parks or college campuses. During his tenure, the average sentence served by Florida murder convicts *decreased* 40% and the average robbery sentence served *declined* 42%. The overall average sentence for all Florida convicts *declined* 38%, to the point where the average Florida convict was serving 32.5% of his sentence before release... less than a third (Keil 1990). The bottom line is that some luckless student caught sucking on a joint after school serves three years (if not more), while the armed criminal who knocks off the convenience store gets three years and walks in one. A society that coddles murderers and armed robbers in order to "get tough" on potheads is not walking the moral high ground.

Another egregious case of the immorality of drug prohibition involves the infamous "Operation Just Cause." In the name of police activity and drug-law enforcement, the sovereign nation of Panamá was invaded by a large American military force, hundreds of innocent bystanders were killed, hundreds of millions of dollars of private property was destroyed, and a couple of dozen "police" were killed in the line of duty, mostly by their own troops. Is it any wonder former President Bush was practically tarred-and-feathered when he foolishly dared to set foot in Panamá in spring of 1992? The ostensible purpose of the invasion was to arrest Gen. Manuel Noriega and "Shanghai" him to the United States to stand trial. We've all seen Hollywood "shoot-'em-up" cop fantasies, but by what standard of "morality" does any "police" operation justify such massive carnage and monumental property destruction? Never mind that Gen. Noriega (who was later tried as a prisoner of war, not as an arrested criminal) was a longtime U.S. government employee in various covert operations involving immoral attempts to destroy one sovereign government and prop up another. It is a basic tenet of police work that the innocent must be protected. "Just Cause" indeed... "Just 'Cause Uncle Sam says so"! Later, the government went to all lengths to convict Noriega to "justify" the operation. It is significant that former heads of the U.S. DEA were subpoenaed to testify on Noriega's behalf, and drug convict Carlos Lederer, considered by U.S. officials to have been one of the world's major international drug traffickers, led the hit-parade of criminals arrayed against him. Lederer was offered pardon in exchange for his turncoat testimony against Noriega, and one key witness was paid to testify for the prosecution (Cohn & Reiss 1992). In what way can this questionable conviction and imprisonment of Noriega be said to justify killing innocent victims?

Is it "moral" to launch aerial herbicide spraying programs in South America against *coca* cultivation, indiscriminately destroying crops and forests; polluting watersheds and in general causing untold ecological havoc? It is noteworthy that the Eli Lilly Company, manufacturer of the herbicide *Tebuthiuron* which the U.S. government wished to spray in Perú, refused to sell the product for this purpose, citing "practical and policy considerations" (Sun 1988). The herbicide is so persistent in the environment that it is not approved in the U.S. for spraying on cropland, and the area in which the *coca* spraying was to be carried out is interspersed with plots of food crops. We will see in Chapter 2, Note 15, that in the 1950s the Eli Lilly Company went to bat for the U.S. government in illicit LSD synthesis, but not this time, and a State Department official told Congress that the department was exploring ways to compel Lilly to produce the herbicide for the government! So this is how "free trade" works... In the Upper Huallaga Valley of Perú, 1.5 million liters of *Paraquat* have already been sprayed (Brackelaire 1992), while massive spraying of *Paraquat*, 2,4-D and *Glyphosate* in Colombia have already provoked health problems in the indigenous population (Bourgetau 1992). A successful non-government crop substitution scheme in Colombia's Cauca Valley, involving the planting of mulberry bushes to allow the cultivation of silkworms (offering prospective legal incomes *even higher* than available from illicit *coca* cultivation; unlike government-sponsored substitute crops) has been frustrated by U.S.-backed spraying of *Glyphosate* directed against illicit *coca* and opium poppy crops in the region (Liounis 1992). Is it moral to tell poor Peruvian and Bolivian peasants that they must cease to grow their traditional and most lucrative crop, *coca*, which is perfectly legal in their countries, in favor of some substitute acceptable to bureaucrats in the U.S., which will yield them a much lower return, perhaps only a third of their already meager income (Morales 1989)? It is immoral and a fundamental violation of their human rights (Boldó i Climent 1986; Ott 1992A)! Furthermore, how does a rich, well-shod, well-fed city-slicker explain this drastic pay cut to a poor, possibly malnourished and barefoot Indian... that (s)he must cease to grow her or his traditional crop (Martin 1970; Mortimer 1901; Plowman 1979; Schultes 1981), the legal stimulant *coca*, and substitute instead coffee, another legal stimulant acceptable to the *gringos*? Moreover, inasmuch as *coca* is considered to be one of the most nutritious vegetables available in the Andes, and is an integral and nourishing part of native diets (Burchard 1975; Burchard 1979; Duke *et al.* 1975), and coffee, apart from a decent amount of the B-vitamin niacin, is virtually worthless as a food (Ott 1985), forcing this stimulant substitution in the "moral" struggle against some drugs will increase malnutrition and hardship for these poor Indians. Furthermore, there is a glut of coffee on world markets, and coffee prices continue to fall, with no relief in sight for beleaguered growers (Frankel *et al.* 1992A). Finally, although *coca* monoculture, like any monoculture, causes ecological damage, at least the plant is well adapted to the environment of the Andes and Amazonia, while the substitute crops require even more energy and agrichemicals than does *coca*, resulting in *yet greater* ecological damage (Brackelaire 1992).

Of course, the chorus goes, we must explain to them that cocaine is destroying the health of our children a continent away, although we do need *some* of their *coca* to flavor our *Coca-Cola* (which is our accepted caffeinated stimulant, that we give to our children as a matter of course; Ott 1985) and likewise to produce cocaine for the pharmaceutical industry. But how would we feel if an expeditionary force of morally outraged South Koreans descended on Virginia and nearby states and began to spray herbicides on the tobacco crop and adjacent food crops, and to insist that our farmers instead plant ginseng? What an absurd idea, and anyway, what has that to do with the subject? It happens that our government recently coerced the Korean government into accepting American tobacco in exchange for computers and stereos (yes, and ginseng, too)... help balance the payments, you see. And there are Koreans who are justifiably outraged morally, and claim that our tobacco and "Marlboro Man" propaganda for use of this pernicious addictive drug (Schelling 1992) is destroying the health of young Koreans! What if a renegade band of hell-raising Mexican police swaggered into the U.S. and kidnapped an American citizen, dragooning him to México to be tried and punished under Mexican laws? American police *have* done precisely that in México (and more than once!), despite protests from the Mexican president and ambassador, and the Mexican government has threatened to banish American police, who were acting illegally, from national territory. How can it be possible that the U.S. Supreme Court ruled that American police operating outside of American territory are not bound by constitutional limitations on their power? That came as a shock to the Mexican government, which knew all too well that the DEA myrmidons were not operating under Mexican law, and a formal diplomatic request for a policy statement ensued. How can it be possible that the U.S. Supreme Court ruled that kidnapping a Mexican citizen in México did not violate bilateral American/Mexican extradition treaties? This decision has made the U.S. justice system the laughing-stock of the world, and provoked a serious crisis in U.S./Mexican relations. The Mexican government reacted by suspending temporarily DEA activities in México and demanded renegotiation of bilateral extradition treaties (Anon. 1992A). Is it "moral" that American tax monies be used to finance in other countries police tactics like indiscriminate roadblocks and searches which are illegal in the U.S.? The only "moral" principle being followed here is that "might makes right"!

Pursuant to the Americanism "money talks," there is another flagrant immorality in drug prohibition. The "false profits" generated by illicit drug trade create all sorts of "false prophets" in the society. Try 'though the government may to convince America's poor that "crime doesn't pay" and "drugs equal slavery" (a bizarre and insulting message to African-Americans whose ancestors were brought to the Americas in chains of literal slavery with the sanction of the very government making the statement), children in America's ghettos see that the people who are upwardly mobile in dead-end neighborhoods, the people who have the cars, friends and fancy clothes are the drug dealers. Many of the successful members of predominantly poor minority groups are living in the suburbs and gentrified urban neighborhoods with Whitey, out of sight, and they cannot set much of a day-to-day example. But the happy-go-lucky drug dealer on the corner is doing obviously much better than the guy flipping burgers for minimum wage or sweeping up at the supermarket. The lure of the *true* free market in drugs, and the profit to be made brings out the entrepreneurial instinct in people who haven't fair and open access to the legitimate business world. By making drugs a lucrative business open to all, prohibition sets bad examples for youth and there's the rub—young ghetto children can see where the opportunity is, and in the ghetto, it's not at the 'burger joint... it is in drugs.

I have already had occasion to detail the anti-scientific nature of drug prohibition and its adverse impact on public health. I need not mention that laws contributing to the spread of AIDS and hepatitis, laws which keep valuable medicines from sick people whose suffering would be alleviated by them, laws which hamper medical research, laws which lead to deaths by poisoning from contaminated and adulterated drugs the government is responsible for overseeing, that laws like these are immoral. Moreover, if we study the history of these laws, we find them also to be grounded in racial prejudice and discrimination against minorities. As J. Helmer has thoroughly documented in his study *Drugs and Minority Oppression* (Helmer 1975), the first American anti-drug laws were a thinly-disguised attempt to cripple Chinese immigrants in their all-too-successful economic competition with Americans. The first American drug law was passed in San Francisco in 1875 and illegalized opium *smoking*, a Chinese pastime, although opium was commonly used orally and such use remained legal. A law was passed in 1887 prohibiting importation of smoking opium, which only the Chinese used, and Congress formally endorsed the true intent of this "drug" legislation when it passed the "Chinese Exclusion Act" in 1901, which prohibited importation of *Chinese*. Later a similar pattern was repeated with cocaine, which was seen as a drug of America's blacks. In countless lurid stories in the press, the message was driven home that "cocaine is often the direct incentive to the crime of rape by the negroes of the South" (Helmer 1975). Such racist and immoral charges exacerbated racial tensions and led to numerous lynchings. History again repeated itself in the thirties, as the spectre of marijuana, the "Assassin of Youth," a drug then associated with poor Mexican immigrants, was employed to discriminate against Mexicans, leading to the infamous "Marihuana [*sic*] Tax Act" of 1937 (Helmer 1975). Racial discrimination is immoral and drug legislation, when used flagrantly as a cover for official discrimination, is morally tainted thereby.

But this litany of immoralities of drug prohibition, which by no means exhausts the subject, is perhaps less significant than the glaring and fatal flaw in the supposititious "moral" campaign of the United States government against "drugs"—that it is a case of the filthy pot calling the tarnished kettle black. For the U.S. government, like many other governments in the world, is and has ever been earnestly engaged in the drug business. According to U.S. government figures, recent annual direct tax revenues to federal, state and municipal governments in the U.S. from alcohol sales (excluding real-estate and income taxes on the companies engaged in manufacture and sale of alcohol), amounted to $10.3 billion ($10,300 million; Anon. 1987). In other words, all levels of government in the U.S. are engaged in the drug trade, making at least $50 *per* year in alcohol income from every adult American, teetotalers included. Federal, state and municipal governments in the U.S. also profit from taxes on the tobacco feeding American's nicotine habits, and the U.S. federal government has in place crop supports *subsidizing* the cultivation of this most deadly of all drugs (recall that tobacco use causes 320,000 premature deaths *per* year, in the U.S. alone). Congressman H.A. Waxman from California rightly called the tobacco industry "a multi-billion dollar drug empire" (Byrne 1988). Thus all levels of government in the U.S. are earnestly and profitably engaged in the drug business, even monopolizing the sale of alcohol in many states and fixing the prices. The "moral" campaign against illicit drugs is thus exposed for the hypocritical exercise it is: for "moral" reasons we won't let you use this or that drug, but we'll be happy to profit from your use of alcohol and nicotine! Hell, we'll even help guarantee profits of our tobacco growers, and help them push their dope on unwilling customers overseas. This is no moral campaign, it is the basest hypocrisy. It has also been argued that agricultural subsidies in industrialized countries tend to drive Third World farmers to produce illicit drugs, which instead of competing against those subsidies... enjoy rather their own (De Rementeria 1992).

Furthermore, as outlined in Chapter 2 (especially Note 15) and Chapter 3 (particularly Note 2), the United States government itself is guilty of massively abusing LSD and other drugs. Since these entheogens are not habit-forming, and because tolerance develops so quickly to the drugs' effects that it is impossible to experience these with regular use (many days, perhaps even a week, have to elapse between doses or little or no effect is felt; and in animal experiments the entheogens serve as aversive, not habituating agents; Hollister *et al.* 1991), one cannot "abuse" the drugs oneself—"abuse" consists in giving the drugs to unwitting or unwilling subjects. In the decade of the 1950s, the "Cold War" raged, and the overzealous activities of the U.S. government during this time have been characterized as the "American Inquisition" (Kutler 1982). One fruit of this institutional paranoia was MKULTRA, an insidious domestic "research" and spying operation run by the U.S. Central Intelligence Agency (CIA), and similar "nonconventional chemical warfare" studies conducted at the U.S. Army's Edgewood Arsenal. In a program of research into interrogation drugs and illegal chemical-warfare agents, LSD and many other entheogenic drugs were given to at least 1500 American military personnel and countless civilians (Lee & Shlain 1985; Marks 1979). Some of the soldiers were coerced into "volunteering" for the tests, and some of the civilians were given the drug without their consent or knowledge. One such dosing of a civilian employee of the CIA, Frank Olson, led to depression and suicide. The government kept secret the circumstances of the death ("national security" of course), but when a "Freedom of Information Act" lawsuit forced public disclosure of the MKULTRA files, then-President Gerald Ford was forced publicly to apologize to Olson's family. Canadian citizens subjected to psychological torture (including repeated doses of LSD) as part of this "research" later sued the U.S. government and were paid compensation. One civilian subject of the Edgewood Arsenal tests was killed by a massive overdose of MDA, an Army doctor commenting: "we didn't know if it was dog piss or what it was we were giving him" (Lee & Shlain 1985; Shulgin & Shulgin 1991). The CIA employed prostitutes and surreptitiously filmed U.S. citizens unwittingly drugged by the prostitutes, as they disported in bed. Helpless "mental patients" in a New York institution were almost killed by murderous injections of bufotenine and DMT combined with electroshock and "insulin coma" (Turner & Merlis 1959). Over 800 drugs, including LSD and bufotenine, were tested on hapless prisoners in the federal government's Lexington, Kentucky "Addiction Research Center Hospital." In this publicly-funded institution (officially a penitentiary) which existed to "cure" drug addiction, prisoners were given injections of heroin and morphine as payment for cooperation in the "experiments" (Lee & Shlain 1985). When Sandoz LTD. of Switzerland, owner of the patents on *Delysid* (LSD tartrate), refused to cooperate with the U.S. government's desire to stockpile huge quantities of the drug for military purposes, that government ordered the Eli Lilly Company of Indiana to make the drug in violation of international patent accords. Yes, Eli Lilly Company and the CIA became the first illicit manufacturers of LSD, more than a decade before the drug was illegalized! It goes without saying that dosing people with experimental drugs without their consent or knowledge, especially helpless "mental patients" and prisoners, is highly unethical and immoral, not to mention the immorality of employing prostitutes with taxpayers' money to dope unwilling "Johns" while perverse CIA agents made stag films behind whorehouse mirrors! There is no doubt the MKULTRA "research" was instrumental in spreading the extra-scientific use of LSD all over the United States and in many other countries as well (Lee & Shlain 1985; Stevens 1987), while publications by phony CIA "front" research foundations (such as the Josiah Macy, Jr. Foundation) were fostering scientific, popular and clinical interest in the drug (Abramson 1956; Abramson 1960). This immoral "research" and consequent promotion of ludible use of LSD was conducted by the same government which later presumed to illegalize entheogenic drugs on the specious grounds of "morals," being ostensibly motivated by proper concern for the public health!

Not only is the U.S. government engaged in trafficking legal inebriating drugs, and guilty of abusing LSD and other drugs in secret experiments, but there is abundant evidence that at times the same government itself has been engaged in illicit-drug trafficking to raise money for covert military campaigns. Under the pretext of aiding the Hmong people of Laos, our "democratic allies" in the "fight against communism" in Vietnam, secret CIA "front" companies such as "Air America" were engaged in smuggling opium to Saigon from the "Golden Triangle" area of Southeast Asia (McCoy 1972). Since the major cash crop of the Hmong was opium poppies for illicit heroin production, the government secretly went into the opium-smuggling business to help our "allies" get their product to refineries in Saigon. In a gruesome twist, the Criminal Investigation Division of the United States Army discovered that cadavers of U.S. soldiers killed in Vietnam were being gutted and stuffed with as much as 23 kg of heroin each, then transported on government 'planes to Norton Air Force Base in California (Kwitny 1987). This pattern of smuggling activity again was repeated in the shameful "Iran-Contra" affair during the administration of Ronald Reagan. In violation of a Congressional ban on military assistance to the Contras, a CIA-organized and funded band of anti-Sandinista *contrarevolucionarios* (the Sandinistas ran the legally-elected government of Nicaragua at the time), the Reagan covert warriors organized secret shipments of weapons and ammunition to the Contras. Some pilots engaged in the illegal gun-running later testified that once the munitions were unloaded from the aircraft in Central America, cocaine or marijuana was loaded for the return trip. In testimony before a U.S. Senate committee, pilot M. Tolivern described transporting 15 tons of weapons from Homestead Air Force Base in Florida to Aguacate, Honduras in a DC-6, which he flew back to Homestead loaded with 25,360 pounds of marijuana (Labrouse *et al.* 1992). This cocaine and marijuana no doubt contributed greatly to the off-the-books financing of the sleazy operation. When protesters broke into a session of the Congressional investigation of the mess, demanding that the subject of cocaine smuggling be probed, leading to questions by one panel member, panel Chairman Senator D. Inouye of Hawai'i called a secret session on the grounds of "national security," away from the cameras and the hearing of the public. One protester was given three years in prison; the cocaine smugglers working for President Ronald Reagan were never brought to trial (McCoy & Block 1992; Marshall 1991; Scott & Marshall 1991). One of the most famous black-market LSD chemists of the sixties, R.H. Stark, credited with having made as many as 200 million doses of the drug, was later exposed as a U.S. CIA "contract agent" in a sensational Italian trial (Escohotado 1989A; Lee & Shlain 1985). Was this man free-lancing, or was the CIA purposefully distributing LSD among radicals and "hippies" in a harebrained sort of "unconventional chemical warfare" attack? After all, the CIA *had* pioneered underground LSD synthesis, and *had* fomented use of the drug in "research" sponsored by phony CIA "front" organizations!

I submit that a government like that of the United States of America, which is running a profitable, multi-billion dollar legal drug-pushing operation, which kills hundreds of innocent people in order to "arrest" one of its former operatives (employed during four presidential administrations over a 15-year period in covert military operations); a government which has secretly poisoned countless civilians including helpless mental patients and prisoners with LSD and other drugs and surreptitiously espied doped taxpayers cavorting in bed with government-paid prostitutes; a government which has driven one of its own employees to suicide by secretly doping his cocktail with LSD; a government which has not hesitated to smuggle narcotics and cocaine to raise dirty money for illegal military campaigns in violation of Congressional bans; that such a government has no "moral" basis whatever for prohibiting *any* drug. The actions of this government, not its words, show a callous disregard for public safety, and a willingness to stoop to anything to further its domestic or international political aims.

THE ECONOMIC SIDE OF THE COIN

According to a recent economic analysis of drug prohibition in the U.S., in 1987 American drug enforcement costs amounted to at least $10 billion ($10,000 million). Approximately half of this expenditure is by the federal government; half by state and local governments (Nadelmann 1989). As the U.S. military forces, never known for economizing, get more deeply involved in the "war," costs are bound to skyrocket —Michigan Senator C. Levin estimated military costs at $2 million *per* drug seizure; U.S. Navy costs at $360,000 *per* arrest (Marshall 1988B)! Already the country with the world's highest *per capita* prison population, the U.S. Sentencing Commission estimates that as a consequence largely of drug laws, the federal prison population will double or triple from the 50,000 current inmates to 100,000 or 150,000 in the next decade, half of whom will be incarcerated for drug-law violations (U.S. Sentencing Commission 1987). Drug-related convictions have already become the leading cause of incarceration in the State of New York and elsewhere. As Prof. Nadelmann commented (Nadelmann 1989):

> State and local governments spent a minimum of $2 billion last year to incarcerate drug offenders. The direct costs of building and maintaining enough prisons to house this growing population are rising at an astronomical rate. The costs, in terms of alternative social expenditures foregone and other types of criminals not imprisoned, are perhaps even more severe.

Not to mention the loss of tax revenues from employed drug offenders who lose their jobs and go to jail... forcibly transformed from taxpayers to expensive wards of the state! This massive misappropriation of taxpayers' money is enriching criminals, contributing to the spread of AIDS and hepatitis, hampering biomedical research, degrading the morals of our police personnel who succumb to corruption, contributing to lack of respect for authority, and abjectly failing in deterring the 20–40 million Americans who persist in using illicit drugs. If, instead of ceding control of the drug market to criminals who thereby become rich and powerful, the government were to legalize these drugs, the $10 billion loss could be converted to at least $10 billion in new taxes which could be used for drug education and treatment, along with the $10 billion saved by not criminalizing 10 or 15% of the U.S. population. Note that this policy change would represent at least a net $20 billion benefit for federal, state and local treasuries, and could help reduce the federal budget deficit.

Far more important than monetary savings, however, is the fact that the government could begin to exercise control over the market, instead of defaulting on its responsibilities and relinquishing control of the market to the criminal element. Let there be no mistake about it—government "Newspeak" aside, illegalizing drugs in no way "controls" the market. The government illegalizing drugs is turning its back on control, and leaving it to the black marketeers to control the market. The illicit merchants, not the government, determine purity and adulteration; the manufacturers, not the government, decide what products to sell and set their prices. History proves that, besides being more economical, legal regulation is far more effective in reducing consumption. While the U.S. government illegalized alcohol consumption on a federal level during the period 1920–1933, the government of Great Britain opted for legal regulation—increased taxation, restriction of hours of sale and prohibition of sale to minors. While the U.S. death rate from cirrhosis of the liver (a consequence almost exclusively of alcoholism) dropped 50% during Prohibition (suggesting a 50% decline in alcohol consumption), it increased again to pre-Prohibition levels by the 1960s. In Great Britain, meanwhile, with legal control of a legal alcohol market designed to reduce consumption, the death rate from cirrhosis of the liver likewise declined 50% during the U.S. Prohibition period, *then declined 50% again* (to 25% of its previous high) by 1940, before settling in 1963 at a rate 33% of the 1914 rate (Vance *et al.* 1989). Besides raising taxes and avoiding waste of government funds and police resources, the British government was able to achieve equivalent or greater reductions in alcoholism under legal control, than was the U.S. government, which abandoned control and fostered the rise of organized crime. Instead of wasting $10 billion a year on a "War on Drugs" which only exacerbates the problem and subsidizes crime syndicates, it is high time the U.S. government stopped abdicating its responsibility and began to attempt to control the use of drugs in American society.

WHY CAN'T WE COPE WITH ECSTASY AND EUPHORIA?

For the sake of freedom and dignity, for the sake of democracy, in the interests of shoring up the battered U.S. economy, it is time we called a truce in the "War on Drugs," an unconditional cease-fire. We can start by decriminalizing the entheogenic drugs, reclassifying them as prescription medicines as the Swiss government recently did, so that our physicians and clinical researchers may resume the fruitful exploration of the therapeutic potential of these unique pharmaceuticals, which was so wrongly suspended in the 1960s. These wondrous medicaments, molecular entities which constitute a sort of "crack" in the edifice of materialistic rationality (Hofmann 1980), may be just what the doctor ordered for hypermaterialistic humankind on the threshold of a new millennium... a new millennium which could be the start of a new Golden Age, or the continuation and dreadful culmination of a cataclysmic cultural and biological Holocaust.

The essence of the experience conferred by entheogenic drugs is ecstasy, in the original sense of that overused word—*ek-stasis*, the "withdrawal of the soul from the body" (*Oxford English Dictionary*, Compact Edition, p. 831), what R. Gordon Wasson called the "disembodied" state:

> There I was, poised in space, a disembodied eye, invisible, incorporeal, seeing but not seen. (Wasson 1957; see also Chapter 5, Note 3)

More specifically, it is an ineffable, spiritual state of grace, in which the universe is experienced more as energy than as matter (Ott 1977A); a spiritual, non-materialistic state of being (Hofmann 1988). It is the heart and essence of shamanism; the archetypal religious experience. In the archaic world, and in the preliterate cultures which have survived in isolation into our time, shamanism and ecstasy represent the epitome of culture, the pinnacle of human achievement (Calvin 1991). The shaman is the cynosure of her or his preliterate people, (s)he is the thaumaturge, the psychopompos, the archetypal psychonaut journeying to the Otherworld to intercede with the ancestors or gods on behalf of her or his fellows. In the Age of Entheogens (Ott 1995B; Wasson 1980), in the archaic world, which still lives on in Amazonia and elsewhere, "every thing that lives is Holy," as Blake expressed it (Kazin 1946), especially the living, breathing, planetary biosphere, of which we are an integral part, and holiest of all are the sacred entheogens, imbued with spirit-power. Modern western culture has no official place for the entheogens precisely because it has no place for ecstasy. Dedicated, as we are, to treating the universe as matter, not as energy or spirit (Blake wrote that "Energy is Eternal Delight"), it embarrasses us to be reminded that our planet is alive and that *every place* is a sacred place.

Even our western religions with their vestiges of entheogenic plant lore (the ever-present "Tree of Life" with its entheogenic fruit; Ott 1979B; Wasson *et al.* 1986) have forgotten their roots and now worship symbols, knowing not the experience to which the symbols refer. As Joseph Campbell paraphrased Jung: "religion is a defense against the experience of God" (Campbell 1988). It is as 'though people were worshipping the decorations and hardware on a door—the portal to the Otherworld (Schele & Freidel 1990)—having lost the key to open it; having forgotten even that it is a door, and its threshold is meant to be crossed; knowing not what awaits on the Other Side. In the Judeo-Christian heritage, a horrendous duality has been imposed: the Divine is the Other, apart from humankind, which is born in sin. Despite overwhelming scientific and experiential evidence to the contrary, human beings are conceived of as a special creation apart from other creatures, and we are enjoined to subdue the world, which is matter. This horrible superstition has led to the despoiling and ruin of our biosphere, and to the crippling neurosis and guilt of modern people (Hofmann 1980). I call this a superstition because when people have direct, personal access to entheogenic, religious experiences, they never conceive of humankind as a separate creation, apart from the rest of the universe. "Every thing that lives is Holy," *us* included, and the divine infuses all the creation of which *we* are an integral part. As this dualistic superstition took root in our ancestors' minds, their first task was to destroy all aspects of ecstatic, experiential religion from the archaic ("pagan") world. The destruction of the sanctuary at

Eleusis at the end of the fourth century of our era (Mylonas 1961) marked the final downfall of the ancient world in Europe, and for the next millennium the theocratic Catholic Church vigorously persecuted every vestige of ecstatic religion which survived, including all revival movements. By the time of the "discovery" of the New World, Europe had been mostly beaten into submission, the "witches" and "heretics" mostly burned, and ecstasy was virtually expunged from the memory of the survivors. For the Catholics, and then for the Protestants after them, to experience ecstasy, to have religious experiences, was the most heinous heresy, justifying torture and being burned alive. Is it any wonder that today we have no place for ecstasy (Fericgla 1994B; Ott 1995B)?

In the New World, however, the Age of Entheogens and ecstasy lived on, and although in 1620 the Inquisition in México formally declared the use of entheogenic plants like *péyotl* (see Chapter 1) to be a heresy and the Church vigorously extirpated this use and tortured and executed Indian shamans, ecstasy survives there even now. It bears witness to the integrity of the New World Indians that they braved torture and death to continue with their ecstatic religion—they must have been bitterly disappointed in the "placebo sacrament" of the Christian Eucharist, which is a placebo entheogen (Ott 1995B)—and it is largely as a result of the modern rediscovery of the shamanic cult of *teonanácatl* (see Chapter 5) by R. Gordon Wasson in México in 1955 that the modern use of entheogens, in many respects a revival of ecstatic religion, began. Even 'though myriad justifications for the modern laws against entheogens have been offered up, the problem modern societies have with these drugs is fundamentally the same problem the Inquisition had with them, the same problem the early Christians had with the Eleusinian Mysteries—religious rivalry. Since these drugs tend to open people's eyes and hearts to an experience of the holiness of the universe... yes, enable people to have personal religious experiences without the intercession of a priesthood or the preconditioning of a liturgy, some psychonauts or *epoptai* will perceive the emptiness and shallowness of the Judeo-Christian religious tradition; even begin to see through the secular governments which use religious symbols to manipulate people; begin to see that by so ruthlessly subduing the Earth we are killing the planet and destroying ourselves. A "counterculture" having ecstatic experiences in California is quite as subversive (Einhorn 1970) and threatens the power structures in Sacramento or Washington just as much as the rebellious Albigensians or Cathars, Bogomiles, Fraticelli "de opinione," Knights Templar and Waldensians threatened the power structure in Rome in mediæval times (Cohn 1975; Ott 1995B).

Since ecstasy was heretical, *euphory*, or euphoria (etymologically "bearing well") was suspect, and the same Protestant ethic which warned that sex should not be enjoyed nor indulged in except for breeding held any ludible use of drugs to be sinful. This approach has been aptly described as "pharmacological Calvinism" (Klerman 1972). There was even a time when *any* use of *any* drugs was considered to be sinful, when herbalists and midwives were burned at the stake beside the heretics, prayer being accepted as the only legitimate therapy (Ott 1985; Ott 1995B), when even laughter and smiles were the Devil's handicraft. While some might consider these ideas to be quaint, even antiquated, we must recall that the American government has recently denied syringes to drug users and contraceptives to students—saying: "teenagers should be encouraged to say 'no' to sex and illegal drugs" (Anon. 1990)—"just say no" being considered to be the best contraceptive and the way to stem the drug-related spread of AIDS! Although we have at least 106 million alcohol users in the United States (54% of the population over 12 years of age), alcohol as inebriant is still illegal in parts of the U.S., and Puritan ideas regarding the sinful nature of inebriation are still dominant and underlie contemporary prohibition of just about every inebriant *but* alcohol.

Indeed, euphoria has generally been considered a *negative* side-effect of drugs, and structure-activity-relationship studies have been conducted with an eye to eliminating this "undesirable" trait! In reference to well-funded studies on alkaloids of opium and their derivatives, W.C. White, Chairman of a Committee on Drug Addiction of the U.S. National Research Council noted:

> One of the chemical difficulties in this research has been to provide drugs which would prolong the pain control factor so as to reduce the need for repeated dosage and at the same time to eliminate the fraction responsible for euphoria... If this could be done, the same result might follow as occurred with cocaine... rapid decline in the use of cocaine as an addiction drug after the discovery of novocaine... (Small *et al.* 1938)

Perhaps it was a little early to declare victory in the "War on Cocaine," but White was correct in noting that, in the case of that drug, it was possible to separate the local-anesthetic "factor" of the cocaine molecule from the stimulating aspect, yielding more potent local anesthetics with limited stimulating or euphoric effects, although it has been claimed that "experienced cocaine users" could not distinguish equivalent intranasal quantities of lidocaine, one of the artificial local anesthetics, from cocaine (Van Dyke & Byck 1982) and that cocaine's euphoric allure and addictive power have been greatly exaggerated (Alexander 1990). In this case, however, the medicinal effect to be separated from the psychotropic "side-effect" is a local, peripheral effect. In the case of the opiate narcotic/analgesics, the medicinal effect of analgesia is as rooted in the brain as is the euphoric "side-effect," and it has been claimed that the drugs are addictive because they so effectively change peripheral sensations from painful to pleasureable; that is, that a non-addicting opiate is impossible, a contradiction in terms (Szasz 1974). Indeed, the non-addicting narcotic appears to be the philosophers' stone of pharmacology, and the world has seen a parade of "non-addicting" (at least in pharmaceutical company propaganda) opiate analgesics, starting with heroin in the nineteenth century, some of which have even been marketed as "cures" for addiction (Escohotado 1989A). Some laypersons conceive of *Methadone* as being a "cure" for heroin addiction, when in reality it is just another potent, addicting narcotic substituted for heroin in "narcotic maintenance" schemes.

Apart from the Puritan anti-pleasure ethic, inebriants like morphine, heroin and cocaine acquired a bad reputation as a consequence of widespread use in so-called "proprietary" or "patent medicines" (Young 1961). The terms derive from the fact that the U.S. government, in the days before the "Food and Drug Act" of 1906, issued patents to manufacturers of medicines, who were required to disclose the ingredients only to the Patent Office, not to the general public; the patents were on the names, they were actually trademarks (Musto 1973). Many of these products bore names like "consumption [tuberculosis] cure"; infant "colic syrup," "teething syrup," "anodyne" *etc.*; "one-night cough cure" and so forth. Typical products were "Adamson's Botanic Cough Balsam" and "Dr. Brutus Shiloh's Cure for Consumption," both of which contained heroin, as did "Dr. James' Soothing Syrup Cordial" (Drake 1970). While opiates are certainly effective antitussives, and good palliatives to alleviate suffering from any disease, they are useless as therapy for tuberculosis (other than soothing cough) and today we don't regard the use of drugs to tranquilize infants as appropriate. It has been stated that the proprietary medicinal manufacturers were immorally selling palliatives as tuberculosis cures, and indeed the morality of this is questionable. On the other hand, in those days antibiotics did not exist, and there was no effective alternative therapy for tuberculosis which people might have taken *in lieu* of the anodynes, which at least made them feel better and cough less (thus theoretically reducing contagion) while they wasted away and died. Indeed, until the advent of the twentieth century, opium and its derivatives were among the few effective medicines available to physicians, and they undisputably deaden pain and alleviate suffering. No reasonable person would advocate the use of palliatives *in lieu* of any effective therapy, now that we have chemotherapies and other treatments for a great number of the ailments which afflict us. On the other hand, what is wrong with more widespread use of palliatives *as an adjunct to* curative chemotherapy, pursuant to the truism that the better the patient feels, the sooner (s)he will be afoot again? As William Blake wrote in a letter dated 7 October 1803:

> Some say that Happiness is not Good for Mortals, & they ought to be answer'd that Sorrow is not fit for Immortals & is utterly useless to any one; a blight never does good to a tree, & if a blight kill not a tree but it still bear fruit, let none say that the fruit was in consequence of the blight.

I say, why not conduct structure-activity relationship studies on euphoriant drugs to determine which drugs are the most euphoric and pleasureable, with the fewest side-effects? This research should be conducted with the same diligence we apply to searching for the best chemotherapy for tuberculosis or any other disease. Why shouldn't patients have access to the most euphoric and pleasureable drugs to alleviate their suffering and make their therapy as pleasant as possible? As Aldous Huxley mentioned more than 60 years ago (Huxley 1931A):

> The way to prevent people from drinking too much alcohol, or becoming addicts to morphine or cocaine, is to give them an efficient but wholesome substitute for these delicious and (in the present imperfect world) necessary poisons. The man who invents such a substance will be counted among the greatest benefactors of suffering humanity.

Instead of pursuing the impossible goal of engineering the euphoria out of pain-killing drugs, we need instead to find the ideal stimulant, the perfect euphoriant (what Huxley called *Soma* in *Brave New World*), the optimal entheogen (Huxley's *moksha*-medicine of *Island*). Gottfried Benn proposed just this sort of research, which he aptly characterized as "provoked life," commenting: "potent brains are not strengthened by milk but by alkaloids" (Benn 1963).

In a perverse way, the first steps toward this sort of "psychopharmacological engineering" have already been taken, in military research on performance-enhancing stimulants, in Nazi and CIA interrogation studies, in American research on "non-conventional chemical warfare" and in recent work on steroids to enhance athletic training and performance. Although the first tests of the effects of stimulants on soldiers, utilizing cocaine, were reported in 1883 (Aschenbrandt 1883), it wasn't until the Second World War that stimulants, mainly amphetamines, came to be widely used by soldiers, and much of the comparative research on the military applications dates from the postwar period (Cuthbertson & Knox 1947; Weiss & Laties 1962). Similarly, while the Nazi physicians at the infamous Dachau concentration camp pioneered use of entheogens, in that case mescaline, as interrogation aids, it was American researchers participating in the MKULTRA project in the postwar era who really pursued this questionable sort of work. The use of steroids to enhance athletic performance is a recent development, and the former communist government of East Germany especially furthered this work with a secret crash program during the 1980s (Dickman 1991). As many as 1500 scientists, physicians and trainers were involved in the research, which had as one goal the development of highly potent steroid derivatives active in sufficiently low doses as to be undetectable in "antidoping" tests. One major success of the project was a psychotropic nasal spray containing a testosterone precursor which would not register on the tests. R. Hannemann, a champion swimmer, described the effects as "like a volcanic eruption," and said its use was mandatory for athletes who wished to compete on the East German team at the 1988 Olympics in Seoul. In a recent refinement, Chinese athletes competing in the 1992 Olympics at Barcelona (along with their former East German trainers), were reported to have used a training potion based on birds' nest and toad skin, which probably contained many active compounds, some of which are controlled drugs (see Chapter 3; Anon. 1992B). It is regrettable that such perverse (but effective) applications have characterized the infancy of psychopharmacological engineering—we must recall the disproportionate success of the East German and Chinese athletes in recent Olympic competitions. I will endeavor to suggest some more positive approaches.

Nobody disputes the widespread utility and need for opiates as pain killers in many branches of medicine. It is high time we abandoned any notion of the non-addicting narcotic, and instead concentrated on finding the drugs which patients like best. We are not interested in the results of crude pharmacological indices of analgesia in rodents, such as the "hotplate method" or "tail-flick method," but in the results of clinical research with human subjects—in this case, I think it would be not the least bit difficult to find volunteers for this type of investigation. Since there is a considerable body of empirical testing which has been conducted outside of the laboratory among narcotic *habitués*, surveys can indicate promising candidates. Heroin has long been regarded to be the favorite drug of narcotics users, and would be a good place to start looking for the optimum narcotic. The contemporary use of *Brompton's Cocktail* (an analgesic and stimulating mixture of heroin, cocaine and alcohol) in British hospices for terminal patients is an example of comfort-oriented therapy which ought to be followed in the United States. I think we will find that if non-terminal patients suffer less and thus feel better, their convalescence times will be reduced.

There is also a demonstrated extra-medical need for stimulants in our society. Examples are pilots and air-traffic controllers who must work all night and require constant wakefulness and vigilance, truck and bus drivers, emergency medical workers, police, customs agents and other officials, and of course, military personnel. By accident of history, caffeine in coffee, soft drinks and tea (and in stimulant tablets, such as *NoDoz*), and nicotine in tobacco products have come to be the accepted stimulants for use in the above-mentioned professions (Schivelbusch 1992). I must stress, however, that caffeine and nicotine have been anointed as society's acceptable stimulants *by default*, since some of the alternatives are controlled substances, and in spite of research showing them to be inferior and unhealthful. Quite a bit of research has been conducted comparing caffeine with amphetamines, and almost invariably, the amphetamines turn out to be superior to caffeine. Studies on reaction times under the influence of stimulants have found that in general caffeine has no effect on reaction times whereas amphetamines *decrease* reaction times (Adler *et al.* 1950; Lehmann & Csank 1957; Seashore & Ivy 1953; Weiss & Laties 1962). Amphetamines were also able to restore reaction times lengthened by fatigue in sleep-deprived subjects (Seashore & Ivy 1953). Marijuana (see Appendix A) on the other hand *lengthens* reaction time and impairs performance (Paton & Pertwee 1973B). With regard to steadiness of the hands, caffeine was found to *impair* steadiness (Adler *et al.* 1950; Hollingworth 1912; Hull 1935; Lehmann & Csank 1957), whereas amphetamines *improved* hand steadiness (Adler *et al.* 1950; Seashore & Ivy 1953; Thornton *et al.* 1939). In various coordination tests, amphetamines were in general far more effective than caffeine in improving performance (Weiss & Laties 1962). Summarizing these and other studies, B. Weiss and V.G. Laties of Johns Hopkins University concluded (see also Silverstone & Wells 1979; Smith & Beecher 1959):

> A very wide range of behavior (with the notable exception of intellectual tasks) can be enhanced by caffeine and the amphetamines—all the way from putting the shot to monitoring a clock face. Moreover, *the superiority of amphetamines over caffeine is*

> *unquestionable*... Both from the standpoint of physiological and psychological cost, amphetamines and caffeine are rather benign agents. Except for reports of insomnia, the subjective effects of the amphetamines in normal doses are usually favorable. Moreover, no one has ever presented convincing evidence that they impair judgment. Caffeine seems somewhat less benign. Hollingworth's subjects, after doses of about 240 mg and above, reported such symptoms as nervousness, feverishness, irritability, headache, and disturbed sleep. Caffeine also produces a significant increase in tremor. *At dose levels that clearly enhance performance, the amphetamines seem not only more effective than caffeine, but less costly in terms of side-effects.* [italics mine]

Little of this sort of research has been conducted on nicotine, but tobacco smoking, and the resulting increase in carbon monoxide in the blood, is known to degrade night vision (Federal Aviation Regulations 1991; Levin *et al.* 1992; McFarland 1953; McFarland *et al.* 1944). Although caffeine and amphetamine stimulants have not been shown to improve intellectual performance, and caffeine has in fact been shown to *degrade* academic performance in college students (Gilliland & Andress 1981), there is evidence that some drugs, like arecoline, the stimulating principle of *betel* nut (Sitaram *et al.* 1978) and *Hydergine*, an ergot alkaloid preparation (see Chapter 2, Note 9; Hindmarch *et al.* 1979) can improve human learning and intellectual performance. Research into so-called "smart drugs" represents a burgeoning new field of psychopharmacological engineering, which merits scientific support (Erlich 1992; Jude 1991; Morgenthaler 1990; Morgenthaler & Dean 1991).

I don't know about my readers, but I'd feel much safer if my pilot on an all-night intercontinental flight had taken 10 mg of methamphetamine before departing, or perhaps an appropriate dose of arecoline hydrobromide, instead of chain-smoking *Marlboros* and gulping execrable airline coffee all the way. It is significant that the U.S. National Aeronautics and Space Administration (NASA), which *has* conducted research on optimizing performance of astronauts, settled on a NASA-developed "prescription" containing amphetamines for the pilots of the space shuttle orbiter Columbia:

> On the maiden flight of the shuttle in April, rookie astronaut Robert Crippen avoided the queasies by dipping into the medical kit for a NASA-developed prescription of Dexedrine, a stimulant,

and scopolamine, a tranquilizer. (Rogers 1981; see Appendix A)

Never mind that scopolamine has been found to *impair* human serial learning (Sitaram *et al.* 1978)... Meanwhile, Soviet cosmonauts were deprived of vision-impairing cigarettes, as Valery Ryumin lamented in his log during a 175-day sojourn in orbit (Bluth 1981):

> I am dying for a cigarette. I haven't had one in three months. And if I hadn't been kept so busy, I don't know how I would take it. Would give all those strawberries and sugar of our entire stay in space for just one...

And some people still persist in denying that nicotine is an addicting drug (Levin *et al.* 1992)! In cases where public safety is at stake, we need a drug policy based on research, not on prejudice; based on science, not on default and accidents of history (it is worth noting that caffeine was originally considered for legal control along with cocaine, heroin and morphine by early reformers). The U.S. Federal Aviation Administration (FAA) is guilty of defaulting on its obligations to protect the safety of air travelers, by allowing the use by pilots of inferior stimulants which impair steadiness of pilots' hands and degrade their night vision.

Some might object... even 'though caffeine is demonstrably inferior to amphetamines for pilots, everyone knows that amphetamines are "addictive" and hence unsuitable for such use. Such people would be well advised to consult the pharmacological literature on caffeine, which has been thoroughly documented as an addictive drug capable of eliciting tolerance and withdrawal symptoms (Colton *et al.* 1968; Dreisbach & Pfeiffer 1943; Goldstein & Kaizer 1969; Goldstein *et al.* 1969; Ott 1985; White *et al.* 1980). The fact that more than 90% of the U.S. population above 12 years of age are regular caffeine users (along with a sizable portion of the under-twelve set habituated to *Coca-Cola* and other caffeinated "soft" drinks) is ample testimony to the addictive nature of the drug (Goldstein & Kalant 1990). The 73 million 132-pound-bags of coffee consumed annually in the world correspond to 175 annual doses of caffeine (at 100 mg/dose, assuming an average caffeine content of 2%) in the form of coffee for every man, woman and child in the world (Frankel *et al.* 1992A), not to mention massive additional use of caffeine in the form of tea, *mate, guayusa, yoco, guaraná, cola, etc.* (see Chapter 4, Note 1). But... can't "abuse" of amphetamines lead to "amphetamine psychosis" (Cho 1990; Davis & Schlemmer 1979; Griffith *et al.* 1970)? Yes, excessive amounts of amphetamines can lead to a characteristic psychosis, as can overuse of caffeine lead to a "caffeine psychosis" (McManamy & Schube 1936). Although "caffeine psychosis" was first described in a patient who had consumed excessive amounts of caffeine citrate tablets (such as *NoDoz*) originally prescribed by a physician, the psychosis has also been observed following consumption of large amounts of *cola* soft drinks (20–25 cans in a day; Shen & D'Souza 1979), the moderate consumption of which is also associated with insomnia and anxiety (Silver 1971). Caffeinism can lead to symptoms virtually "indistinguishable from those of anxiety neurosis" (Greden 1974) and cases of "caffeine-induced delirium" have been reported (Stillner *et al.* 1978). There have even been deaths attributed to coffee overdose in the form of naturopathic enema remedies (Eisele & Reay 1980). Obviously, one doesn't wish one's pilot drinking a case of *Coca-Cola* or popping a bottle of *NoDoz*, any more than one would wish to be on a 'plane flown by somebody who had ingested a quarter of a gram of methamphetamine. The goal of psychopharmacological engineering of stimulants would be to find the optimal doses of the compounds which promote vigilance and wakefulness with a minimum of side effects like hand tremors and insomnia. It is vital to public safety that such research be conducted, and if drug laws stand in the way, this is yet another example of their adverse impact on public health and on scientific research.

As for medicinal use of the entheogens, their widespread use on the black market has given us some guidelines, as have better than two decades of experimental clinical use before their illegalization (see Grinspoon & Bakalar 1979; Grob 1995 and Yensen & Dryer 1995). However, new compounds continue to be developed and tested (Kline *et al.* 1982; Lin & Glennon 1994; Repke & Ferguson 1982; Repke *et al.* 1977B; Repke *et al.* 1981; Repke *et al.* 1985; Shulgin & Shulgin 1991), and some entheogenic plants or extracts such as *ayahuasca* (see Chapter 4) have begun to be employed in modern psychotherapy (Krajick 1992), along with the "empathogen" MDMA (see Chapter 1; Adamson 1985; Adamson & Metzner 1988; Leverant 1986). Thus new studies are necessary to determine the best entheogens for the following uses: 1) general, outpatient psychotherapy for various afflictions (Masters & Houston 1970); 2) "brief" psychotherapy in agonious treatment (Kast 1970); 3) long-lasting analgesia in such agonious therapy; 4) marriage counseling; 5) group therapy (Blewett 1970); and 6) in the experimental induction of dissociative experiences in psychotherapists as part of their training. I think we will discover that a variety of different entheogens will prove useful in various treatment modalities. For example, vaporized, high-dose DMT would probably be the most effective drug for rapid induction of dissociative states in medical training (Bigwood & Ott 1977); LSD is probably the best drug in agonious therapy (Grof & Halifax 1977); and DET or CZ-74 or the plant-drug *Salvia divinorum* (see Chapters 3, 5 and Appendix A), owing to their short durations, might prove optimal for outpatient psychotherapy (Böszörményi *et al.* 1959; Leuner & Baer 1965). Preliminary experiments with psilocybine (see Chapter 5) suggested this drug could help cut the recidivism rate of paroled convicts (J. Clark 1970; Leary 1968). Instead of going broke building prisons for drug offenders, ought we not investigate drugs to keep people out of those we have?

Virtually all of the entheogens, or their natural prototypes, have proven their worth in the induction of ecstatic states in shamanism (Browman & Schwarz 1979; Halifax 1979; Halifax 1982; La Barre 1970; La Barre 1972; La Barre 1979A; La Barre 1980A; Ripinsky-Naxon 1993; Rosenbohm 1991A; Schultes 1970B; Wasson 1961) and in the catalysis of "religious experiences" (Barnard 1963, 1966; Clark 1969; W.H. Clark 1970; Félice 1936; Heard 1963; Leary 1964; Leary & Alpert 1963; Leary *et al.* 1964; Masters & Houston 1966; Metzner 1968; Paz 1967; Ricks 1963; Watts 1962; Watts 1963; Zaehner 1957; Zaehner 1972; Zinberg 1977). Well-known examples of the shamanic use of entheogens, which will all be documented thoroughly in this book, are: primordial Siberian shamanic use of the fly-agaric, *Amanita muscaria* (see Chapter 6); the Mexican shamanic use of *teonanácatl*, the psilocybian mushrooms (see Chapter 5); pan-Amazonian shamanic use of *ayahuasca* in South America (see Chapter 4); use of tryptamine-containing snuffs in the Andes, Caribbean and Amazonia (see Chapter 3); divinatory use of ergoline alkaloid-containing morning glory seeds in Mesoamerican shamanic healing (see Chapter 2) and the North American shamanic use of the *péyotl* cactus (see Chapter 1). The value of the entheogens to organized religions has been amply demonstrated by the 2000-year survival of the famous Eleusinian Mystery religion of the ancient world (an annual, mass initiation employing an entheogenic potion containing ergoline alkaloids; Wasson *et al.* 1978; see Chapter 2) and by the modern examples of the "Native American Church" and "The Peyote Way Church of God" using *péyotl* as a sacrament (La Barre 1938A; La Barre 1970; Mount 1987; Stewart 1987) and the Christian South American churches with *daime* / *hoasca* (*ayahuasca*) as a sacrament (Henman 1986; Liwszyc *et al.* 1992; Lowy 1987; MacRae 1992; Prance 1970). Perhaps using these historical and modern examples as models will aid us in designing institutions to foster religious experiences in contemporary human users (Hofmann 1989). There is definitely a place in the modern world both for these organized entheogen-based religions and the shamanic practice of small-scale cultic or individual use; whether for group communion or for solitary psychonautic "travels in the universe of the soul" (Gelpke 1981; Stolaroff 1994)—as well as for *contractual* entheogen use in various psychotherapy modes.

FROM THE PAST TO THE FUTURE

We have seen that prohibition of entheogens and other drugs is economically ruinous, largely ineffective and anti-scientific. Far from guaranteeing protection for public health, prohibition fosters the spread of AIDS and hepatitis while inhibiting biomedical research and depriving the public of vital new medicines. We have seen how anti-drug laws are grounded in racism and foster crime meanwhile subsidizing organized and unorganized drug merchants and manufacturers, and favoring the decentralized domestic production of the most potent drugs. There is no doubt that enforcing drug prohibition distorts jurisprudence owing to the lack of "victims" to file complaints with police and because of the arbitrary nature of enforcement given the ubiquity of controlled substances in our bodies, in our food, even on our money. The laws immorally corrupt our police, lead to coddling of violent criminals, set bad examples for our youth and deprive us of our freedoms as they lead to a dictatorial police-state. In the international arena, the laws lead to bad relations with other countries, military and paramilitary invasions and covert military operations, the loss of human life and rights in Third World countries, and massive ecological destruction in herbicide spraying campaigns and in uncontrolled contamination from clandestine laboratories. In short, the drug prohibition laws are impractical, ineffective, uneconomic, anti-scientific, unhealthy, immoral, unecological, undiplomatic and dictatorial.

Happily, there is a straightforward way out of the horrible mess the drug-prohibition laws have got us into—legalize the drugs! Some people consider the notion of drug legalization to be bizarre and radical, a drastic step. But inebriating drugs have been mostly legal throughout the millennia of human existence; the drastic step was taken in the second decade of this century in the United States when for the first time large-scale, comprehensive legal control of inebriating drugs was implemented. Some people claim that legalization represents a daring and risky experiment, but they are wrong. *Prohibition* is the daring and risky experiment, and although it would be prudent to gather more comprehensive data on the results of this experiment in social engineering (Koshland 1989), it is safe to say as we have reached the end of the eighth decade of federal control of inebriating drugs that the experiment has been a dismal and costly failure (Escohotado 1989A). Human and animal use of inebriants is as natural as any other aspect of social behavior; it is the attempt to control this normal animal drive that is bizarre and unnatural, as I stated at the outset, it is a crime against nature; against human and animal nature. Although we seem far from taking the sensible course which alone will begin to "solve" the drug "problem," at least legalization is becoming a legitimate option to be discussed (Evans & Berent 1992; Holden 1980A). An Anti-Prohibitionist League began publishing a periodical in 1990 (Henman 1990) and prohibition has been justly decried at the annual Drug Policy Conference as a violation of academic and religious freedom (Roberts 1990).

The drug laws are the monstrous result of institutionalizing paranoia—they are the work of paranoid "control junkies" who have no faith in others or in human nature... they would control the lives of others according to their own, more "responsible," more "scientific," more "moral" scheme. But like the dog in the fable who snaps at his reflection in the water and loses his bone, the reformers' zeal for more control has led to less... our societies have *lost* control over inebriating drug use by placing this outside of the law. Every salvo in the quixotic "War on Drugs" is a backfire, a shot in society's own foot... we are hacking and hewing at the branches of the problem, never seeing the roots, which are the very laws against drugs. The problems we attribute to the "scourge of drugs" are the results of the drug *laws*, not of drugs... the "overdose" deaths... shoot-outs between rival drug gangs... drug-related spread of AIDS and hepatitis... In the paranoid fantasies of the reformist zealots, the drug laws are all that stand between the current level of inebriant use and a vastly increased "epidemic" of heroin, cocaine, marijuana and LSD "abuse." As Sasha and Ann Shulgin put it in their excellent book *PIHKAL*, however (Shulgin & Shulgin 1991):

> Yes, it's possible that with the removal of drug laws a few timid Presbyterians will venture a snort of cocaine, but in the main, drug abuse [*sic*] will be no worse than it is now, and—after some initial experimentation—things will return to a natural balance. There is no "Middle America" sitting out there, ready to go Whoopie! with the repeal of the drug laws. The majority of the population will, however, benefit from the return of the criminal justice system's attention to theft, rape, and murder, the crimes against society for which we need prisons.

A recent nationwide survey in the U.S. found only 2% of respondents were "very likely" or "somewhat likely" to try cocaine were it legalized, while 4% declared themselves "very likely" to try legalized marijuana, and an additional 6% "somewhat likely" to try the drug (Nadelmann 1992). At the turn of the century, with a free market in all inebriating drugs, it is estimated that only 4% of the U.S. population was addicted to the heroin, morphine, cocaine and the other drugs openly sold in patent medicines (Zinberg 1963). No, the great majority of today's would-be heroin, cocaine, LSD and/or marijuana users are already using these drugs, for the laws not only fail to deter them but even attract a sizable number of people who use illegal drugs out of rebellion. And the fact of the matter is, we already have an "epidemic" of psychoactive drug use in this country, as evidenced by the 178 million caffeine users, 106 million alcohol users, 57 million tobacco users, 12 million marijuana users, not to mention at least 3 or 4 million regular users of psychoactive prescription drugs, such as *Valium* (Goldstein & Kalant 1990). Whether drugs are legal or illegal, the vast majority of users exercise control and responsibility, and a (generally small) minority of users come to be controlled by the drugs. This happens with alcohol as well as with heroin, with tobacco as well as with marijuana. Legalizing heroin and cocaine will not prevent some unfortunate people from excessive use such that their lives come to revolve around the drug, any more than the legal availability of alcohol prevents this addiction syndrome from occurring in some uncontrolled users. Making all drugs available legally will certainly change the numbers of people using individual drugs, but the total number of users will stay about the same, because *already more than 90% of our adult population is using drugs.* If amphetamines become legal, some people will surely begin to use them, as they have always been popular when legally available (in 1962, the FDA estimated annual domestic amphetamine production at 9000 million doses; Cohen & Goldsmith 1971), but we can be sure that prospective amphetamine users are presently using caffeine, and if these people use amphetamines, they will use less caffeine, or none at all. Since caffeine generally appears to have more severe side effects than do the amphetamines (Weiss & Laties 1962), this could represent a net gain in public health. Similarly, heroin and other potent opiates are generally incompatible with alcohol (Burroughs 1959). It is safe to assume that were more people using legal heroin, fewer would be using alcohol. Since alcohol is far more toxic than heroin (Brecher 1972; Weil 1972), this too could represent a net benefit for public health.

The unfortunate fact is that our society has blindly accepted as its orthodox inebriants two of the most toxic pleasure drugs known to science. As I have already mentioned, together these drugs kill more than a half million Americans each year. Alcohol is more than simply an addictive drug... it is a carcinogenic drug... it causes irreversible brain and liver damage... it is a teratogen (it causes birth defects if taken at the wrong time by pregnant women; Brown *et al.* 1979; Clarren & Smith 1978). In a ranking of general carcinogenic hazards, it was estimated that the lifetime cancer-causing liability of drinking just one 250 ml glass of wine daily (30 ml alcohol) was more than *5000 times greater* than the combined lifetime cancer risk represented by the U.S. average daily dietary consumption of PCBS (PolyChlorinated Biphenyls), DDE (the common metabolite of the famous pesticide DDT) and EDB (Ethylene DiBromide, an antifungal fumigant—U.S. average dietary consumption of these chemical residues = 2.8 mcg/day; Ames *et al.* 1987)! Compared to the lifetime cancer-causing potential of the nitrosamines found in a 100 g daily ration of cooked bacon, the daily glass of wine represents more than *500 times the risk*! The connection between alcohol and crime and accidental injury is striking—54% of all jail inmates convicted of violent crimes in 1983 had used alcohol just prior to commission; in 10% of all work-related injuries reported in 1986, alcohol was a "contributing factor"; in 40% of the 46,000 traffic deaths in 1983 and 40% of suicide attempts that year, alcohol was likewise a "contributing factor"—alcohol use is estimated to cost the U.S. economy $100 billion ($100,000 million) each year (Dept. of Health & Human Services 1986)! Tobacco is more than a highly-addictive drug... it is a potent carcinogen, whether smoked, chewed or taken as snuff or in enemas (Hoffmann *et al.* 1986; Ricer 1987), and its widespread use has transformed lung cancer from a medical curiosity to a common disease. We have already embraced a couple of the worst drugs known with open arms... but we are so used to them that it's no big deal... we forget even that they are drugs... we talk about "alcoholism and drug abuse" as 'though alcoholism were somehow different from "drug abuse." By the same token, were heroin legal and widely used, although it might cause some health problems in a few, we would think it was no big deal (Trebach 1982). And indeed, heroin is not much more than an addicting drug. It is *not* carcinogenic like tobacco and alcohol; it does *not* cause brain or liver damage as do those legal drugs; it is *not* teratogenic... about the only health problem associated with its habitual use (excluding infections associated with dirty syringes, infections which don't occur with normal medicinal use of heroin in Britain) is constipation (Brecher 1972; Weil 1972)! There is no question that the United States, as a nation, would have far lower medical costs, if we had 106 million users of legal, sterile, heroin and 2 million alcohol users, instead of 106 million alcohol users and 2 million users of contaminant-ridden, adulterated *ersatz* "heroin." Truly, we already have about the worst situation *vis-à-vis* drugs, with our national drugs being carcinogenic, hepatotoxic, neurotoxic and teratogenic, and with the government having surrendered all control of the use of most other drugs to the criminal element. Verily, we've nowhere to go, but up!

There have already been some limited modern experiments in relaxing the drug laws, and in general use levels stay about the same or go down. In the 11 American states that briefly "decriminalized" marijuana in the 1970s, the number of users stayed about the same (Johnston *et al.* 1981). In the Netherlands, legal tolerance of *Cannabis* use and its legal control has led to a significant *decline* in consumption: in 1976, 10% of 17–18 year old Dutch citizens used illegal *Cannabis*, whereas by 1985 this percentage had almost halved, to 6%, according to the official Dutch figures (Ministry of Welfare 1985). The Dutch government is succeeding, as it intended, in making *Cannabis* use boring... no rebellion there. American proponents of drug control hem and haw and try to explain away the Dutch success by claiming that the Dutch problem is easier to deal with, owing to the "homogeneous population" (Jarvik 1990), which is a polite way of saying that the Dutch aren't burdened with a large, intractable population of black and Hispanic dope fiends! In fact, the Netherlands *does* have a large and growing minority population (over 5%) and there are poor urban districts which resemble U.S. ghettos (Beers 1991).

The Prohibition experiment has failed miserably, and it is high time we went back to the natural order of things, and let society learn how to regulate and control drug use socially and medically, not legally and by force. The introduction of distilled alcohol to European society led to "epidemics" of uncontrolled use (Horowitz 1979; Wasson 1979B), but in time, without special intervention, Western societies began to make their peace with alcohol (a process which is continually evolving), developing rituals to help control alcohol addiction, such as social approval of alcohol use only after the day's work, and general condemnation of alcoholic, dependant behavior (Zinberg 1977; Zinberg 1984). Modern societies will never sanction nor approve irresponsible, addictive use of legal heroin, cocaine or marijuana; just as they do not sanction uncontrolled use of alcohol. The legal availability of tobacco and alcoholic beverages does not mean societies encourage their use, and there is evidence that anti-alcohol and anti-tobacco advertising campaigns conducted by the U.S. and other governments are effective in restricting use. Only by bringing all ludibund drug use into the open can we hope to develop social restraints favoring responsible use of the presently illicit drugs. We must treat all citizens as responsible adults, not promulgate the absurd and fallacious notion that certain drugs (like heroin and cocaine) destroy individual will and self-control—thereby giving immature and irresponsible individuals a ready-made excuse for illegal or immoral behavior—the idea that one's heroin habit made one rob friends and family, or steal an elderly woman's pocketbook (Escohotado 1989A)! We must give people choices based on a free market and unbiased information about the benefits and dangers of all drugs, not unrealistically expect to scare people away from certain drugs with silly propaganda. Treat citizens like irresponsible children and many will behave accordingly. It is time our governments exercised a true and appropriate control over the presently illicit drugs, by guaranteeing purity and dosages and a fair market price—it is up to society and to us as individuals to do the rest.

In the pages that follow I will discuss in great detail that most exciting, most mysterious class of drugs, the stock-in-trade of shamans and thaumaturges the world over—the cacti, mushrooms, grasses, trees, shrubs and lianas which we call entheogenic plants, and their contained active principles. Of all the groups of proscribed psychotropic drugs, it is the entheogens which have been treated most unfairly, for these are in no way "drugs of abuse." Animals shrink from them rather than become habituated to them, people use them infrequently and mostly treat them with awe and respect for their divine potency (Schultes 1972E). Far from being addicting drugs, they show promise in aiding addicts to overcome their habituation to drugs like alcohol and heroin (Hoffer 1970). The controversial psychotherapeutic research on treating alcoholics with LSD and DPT has been summarized (Grinspoon & Bakalar 1979) and the promising initial results certainly justify further experimentation. The organized religious use of *péyotl* by the "Native American Church" has been recognized by personnel of federal government alcoholism clinics to be of some value in treating alcoholism (Albaugh & Anderson 1974; Osmond 1970), and was said by physician Robert Bergman, Chief of the U.S. Public Health Service on the Navaho reservation, to have a greater success rate than other alcoholism treatments. Bergman also noted the marked safety of *péyotl*, estimating only one bad reaction *per* 70,000 ingestions, calling that rate "probably over-estimated" (Bergman 1971). The propensity of the entheogens to work against drug addiction led advocacy of their therapeutic use to be termed an "anti-drug" position (McKenna 1989A; T.K. McKenna 1992).

Although its legal status was confused by the federal classification of *péyotl* and mescaline as controlled substances, and by a plethora of state laws against both the plant and its entheogenic alkaloid, in general American courts would uphold the Constitutional protection of sacramental use of *péyotl* by members of the "Native American Church" (an example is the 1964 California State Supreme Court ruling in the Woody case exonerating three Navaho péyotlists). Twenty-three states had in some way exempted *péyotl* from controlled substances laws (Blackmun 1990). In general, anthropologists who have studied the "Native American Church" have supported the right of Indians to use *péyotl* sacramentally on grounds of freedom of religion. For example, W. La Barre, D.P. McAllester, J.S. Slotkin and O.C. Stewart signed a "statement on peyote" to that effect in *Science* magazine (La Barre *et al.* 1951). When in 1937 New Mexico Senator D. Chávez introduced a bill to prohibit interstate transportation of *péyotl*, a number of anthropologists and ethnobotanists, including F. Boas, W. La Barre and R.E. Schultes, submitted letters opposing the bill, which was defeated (Stewart 1987). Church membership is restricted to citizens of participating tribes (Mount 1987). Nevertheless, a New York Federal District Court found in 1979 that "the use of peyote for sacramental purposes... is not to be restricted solely to the Native American Church," effectively clearing the way for non-Indians to use *péyotl* religiously, and the Arizona "Peyote Way Church of God" was incorporated in Arizona in 1979, and filed a discrimination suit in Texas when Arizona church members were arrested there while harvesting *péyotl*. Drug possession charges against the church members were later dismissed (Mount 1987; Ott 1992C). A Caucasian member of the "Native American Church" was recently exonerated of drug charges by the New Mexico State Supreme Court, Chief Justice J.G. Burciaga stating his court was "compelled to halt this menacing attack on our constitutional freedoms" (Gorman 1992). The 1994 amendments to the "American Indian Religious Freedom Act" of 1978 legalized "bona fide" religious use of *péyotl* by Indian tribal members (Ott 1995B). The Canadian government has tolerated sacramental use of entheogenic mushrooms by a religious organization called "The Fane of the Psilocybe Mushroom" ("fane" in the sense of "temple," rather than "fairy" or "banner")—the organization was chartered at a time when the psilocybian mushrooms were in legal limbo in Canada, due to a favorable ruling in a court case.

It is interesting that some anthropologists who supported the (non-traditional) use of *péyotl* as a sacrament by North American Indians have denounced use by non-Indians. La Barre, for example, called British *péyotl* or mescaline users from Havelock Ellis to Aldous Huxley "ethnologically spurious, meretricious and foolish poseurs" and ridiculed Huxley's book on his religious experience with mescaline, *The Doors of Perception*, as a "rather absurd book" (La Barre 1975). I don't know how one can be "ethnologically spurious" other than by faking field work *à la* Castaneda, and La Barre is certainly entitled to his opinion, but the man who wrote *The Perennial Philosophy* (Huxley 1944) cannot fairly be called "meretricious"—somebody with a more sincere interest in spiritual matters would be difficult to find. La Barre went on to denounce the "Neo-American Church," which had adopted entheogens as sacraments, as a "wholly synthetic, disingenuous and bogus cult"! This is pure, unalloyed discrimination... racial and religious discrimination. As we will see in the pages that follow, sacramental use of entheogens is as much a part of Caucasian heritage as it is a part of New World Indian heritage. I have just as much right to ingest *péyotl* or entheogenic mushrooms as any Navaho or Mazatec or Huichol Indian—to say otherwise, as La Barre has done, would be to discriminate against me because of my racial background and to deny me the right to worship as I wish or see fit.

It is my sincere wish that this book contribute to an objective reappraisal of entheogenic drugs and their place in the modern world. I have dedicated it to my late teacher Gordon Wasson, who more than anyone catalyzed the contemporary revival of ecstatic, shamanic religion, and who wrote beautifully about the "bemushroomed" state. At the outset I reiterated Wasson's rhetorical question, whether, with all our modern knowledge, we needed the divine entheogens any longer. I would answer with Wasson, that precisely *because of* our modern knowledge *we need them more than ever.* Mother Earth, Our Lady Gaia, is suffering mightily the ecological consequences of all that modern knowledge and especially the Judeo-Christian heritage which treats us as a special creation enjoined to subdue and master the Earth. But to paraphrase one of the greatest Americans, Chief Seattle, the Earth does not belong to humankind, humankind belongs to the Earth. Any experience, pharmacological or otherwise, which makes us aware that "every thing that lives is Holy," that we are all sisters and brothers... black, white, two-legged or four-legged, legless or centipedal; that the universe of which we are an integral part is divine and sacred... any such experience can be of vital importance in helping us overcome our ecological plight, which is the inevitable consequence of treating the world as matter, not as divine energy... as objects to be bought and sold, not as "Eternal Delight." I firmly believe that contemporary spiritual use of entheogenic drugs is one of humankind's brightest hopes for overcoming the ecological crisis with which we threaten the biosphere and jeopardize our own survival, for *Homo sapiens* is close to the head of the list of endangered species. We need to recapture the *mysterium tremendum* of the *unio mystica,* the millennial awe our ancestors felt in the divine presence, in the sublime majesty of our marvelous universe, in the entheogenic "bemushroomed" state the sage Gordon Wasson described (1961):

> Elsewhere I once wrote that the bemushroomed person is poised in space, a disembodied eye, invisible, incorporeal, seeing but not seen. In truth, he is the five senses disembodied, all of them keyed to the height of sensitivity and awareness, all of them blending into one another most strangely, until the person, utterly passive, becomes a pure receptor, infinitely delicate, of sensations. As your body lies there in its sleeping bag, your soul is free, loses all sense of time, alert as it never was before, living an eternity in a night, seeing infinity in a grain of sand. What you have seen and heard is cut as with a burin in your memory, never to be effaced. At last you know what the ineffable is, and what ecstasy means. Ecstasy!

PART ONE
Beta-Phenethylamines

CHAPTER ONE

Mescaline, Péyotl, San Pedro, Artificial Phenethylamines

> If the doors of perception were cleansed every thing would appear to man as it is, infinite. For man has closed himself up, till he sees all things thro' narrow chinks of his cavern.
>
> **William Blake**
> *The Marriage of Heaven and Hell* (1793)

In 1954 the famous English writer Aldous Huxley introduced mescaline to popular attention, when he published *The Doors of Perception*, a chronicle of his personal experience with this strange and mysterious drug (Huxley 1954). In 1931, while working on his novel *Brave New World* (Huxley 1932), Huxley had read "with a passionate and growing interest" the English translation of Louis Lewin's 1924 treatise on psychoactive drugs, *Phantastica* (Lewin 1924). Huxley wrote two short essays that year, describing the need for "a new pleasure," a non-toxic, beneficent pharmacological means "to take occasional holidays from reality" and said "the man who invents such a substance will be counted among the greatest benefactors of suffering humanity" (Horowitz & Palmer 1977; Huxley 1931A; Huxley 1931B). Huxley gave literary creation to such a substance in *Brave New World,* and called it *Soma* after the ancient Aryan entheogen (see Chapter 6). His *Soma* was purely imaginary, with three effects, "euphoric, hallucinant, or sedative," in Huxley's own words, "an impossible combination" (Horowitz & Palmer 1977; Huxley 1956). On 6 May 1953, Canadian psychiatrist Humphry Osmond administered 400 mg of mescaline sulfate to Huxley, which cleansed his "doors of perception" and inspired his famous and controversial essay by that name. Huxley was to devote the last decade of his life to research on what he called "phanerothymes" or "psychodelics"[1]—entheogens—and in his final book, *Island* (Huxley 1962), the fanciful *Soma* of *Brave New World* gave way to the *moksha*-medicine,[2] a cultivated mushroom patterned after the Mexican *teonanácatl* which had recently been discovered by V.P. and R.G. Wasson (see Chapter 5; Huxley 1967). Among other uses, Huxley's *moksha*-medicine was employed by residents of Pala, the Asian tropical island of his final book's title, to ease the transition from life to death, a use first proposed by V.P. Wasson five years earlier (V.P. Wasson 1957). Huxley availed himself of the *moksha*-medicine for the great transition, taking two 100 mcg doses of LSD-25 (see Chapter 2) as he lay dying of cancer on 22 November 1963, the day of President John F. Kennedy's assassination (Horowitz & Palmer 1977; Huxley 1968).

Huxley (like Blake) was a visionary, and his essay on the effects of mescaline was destined to stimulate widespread interest in, and use of mescaline and other entheogenic drugs. By the late sixties, when the non-scientific use of entheogens had attained its maximum visibility, mescaline was, next to LSD, the best-known and most widely-used entheogenic substance... or was it? Although authentic mescaline was available as a research drug until 1965, there is no evidence that it was widely distributed to the general public. Legislation proscribing mescaline and allied entheogens, enacted between 1965 and 1968, combined with the high cost of manufacture, led to the virtual disappearance of mescaline from the market. What, then, of the millions of doses of "mescaline" or "organic mescaline" which were widely sold throughout the United States and other countries in the late sixties and early seventies... which are still being sold to this day? What of the hundreds of thousands, if not millions, of individuals who speak with reverence of their mescaline experiences, contrasting them with experiences with LSD, which is almost invariably considered to be inferior?

One thing is certain. Mescaline has been more widely misrepresented than any other entheogenic drug on the illicit market. It is highly unlikely that more than a few tens of thousands of people have ever ingested authentic mescaline in pure form. Everyone else has been "ripped off" as the saying goes. This chapter will explain in detail where mescaline comes from, what mescaline is and how it may be identified. Moreover, it will trace the etiology of this most persistent and pervasive drug hoax, an interesting study which promises to afford great insight into the influence of user expectation on the effects of an entheogenic drug. Along the way, the reader may peruse some interesting information, penetrating at once the *arcanum arcanorum* of New World Indian shamanic spirituality and the obscurity of modern science.

PRE-COLUMBIAN HORIZONS

Mescaline is the main active principle of *Lophophora williamsii*, a small, hemispherical, spineless cactus native to northern México and the southwestern United States

(Anderson 1969; Anderson 1980; Schultes & Hofmann 1980).[3] *Lophophora williamsii* grows in calcareous deserts, in river valleys, generally under vegetation (Anderson 1969; Anderson 1980; Coulter 1894). Its growth is exceedingly slow, and the plant may require up to 15 years to mature. At maturity the cactus may attain a diameter of 12 cm, rising some 3–6 cm above the surface of the ground. The plant has a long, tapering, carrot-like root which may be 30 cm or more in length at maturity. Often accessory heads will sprout from this root, and small, tight clusters of heads are common. The flowers are pink to whitish, solitary, appearing at the crown of the cactus, there surrounded by a mass of whitish hairs (Anderson 1969; Anderson 1980; Anderson 1995).

In 1560, Spanish Franciscan friar Bernardino de Sahagún first wrote about this plant (Estrada Lugo 1991; Sahagún 1950; Sahagún 1982):

> There is another herb... called *peiotl...* it is found in the north country. Those who eat or drink it see visions either frightful or laughable; this inebriation lasts two or three days and then ceases. It is a sort of delicacy of the Chichimecas, it sustains them and gives them courage to fight and not feel fear, nor hunger, nor thirst, and they say it protects them from any danger.

Peiotl or *péyotl* was the name of this cactus in the Náhuatl language, tongue of the Mexicas (or Aztecs, as they are today known; the Chichimecas were their forefathers). The word probably meant something like "furry thing" to the Aztecs, as it referred at once to a species of silky caterpillar and the cactus under discussion, which is crowned with tufts of silky hairs (La Barre 1938A). There is every indication that the Aztecs (who lived in the Valley of México, the site of the modern capital) and other indigenous groups who lived in northern México, revered this cactus and used it as an adjunct to their religious rites (Anderson 1980; Del Pozo 1967; Stewart 1987). R.G. Wasson has proposed that the name *péyotl* is the origin of a contemporary Mexicanism, *piule*, referring to entheogens in general, since the term is applied to various inebriants, including some species of entheogenic mushrooms (see Chapter 5) and entheogenic morning glory seeds (see Chapter 2; Wasson 1963). This etymology was proposed independently by B.P. Reko (Reko 1919).

Under Hernán Cortés, the Spaniards conquered México or the Aztec empire in 1521 (Prescott 1843). A bloody *auto-de-fe* in persecution of the native religions ensued, destined to convert the unfortunate Indians to the "holy Catholic faith."

For the Indians, apostasy alone gave them a chance at survival. There is no indication that any of the Spanish friars like Sahagún ever ingested *péyotl* or seriously studied its use (indeed, Sahagún's extravagant statement that the effects of *péyotl* lasted two or three days testifies to this fact). Rather, on 19 June 1620, the "Inquisitors against heresy, depravity and apostasy" formally decreed in México City that:

> The use of the Herb or Root called Peyote... is a superstitious action and reproved as opposed to the purity and sincerity of our Holy Catholic Faith, being so that this said herb, nor any other cannot possess the virtue and natural efficacy attributed to it for said effects, nor to cause the images, phantasms and representations on which are founded said divinations, and that in these one sees notoriously the suggestion and assistance of the devil, author of this abuse...

In a word, use of *péyotl* and other entheogenic plants was vigorously persecuted by the Spaniards (Del Pozo 1975). The document continues:

> We decree that henceforth no person, of whatever class and condition may use or use of this said herb, this Peyote, or of others for said effects, nor others similar, under no title or color, nor suffer that the indians nor other persons consume these, being warned that doing the contrary, besides incurring said censures and penalties, we will proceed against whoever is rebellious and disobedient, as against persons suspect in the holy Catholic faith.

It bears testimony to the sincerity and integrity of the Mexican Indians, that they continued in the face of this persecution to use *péyotl* and other entheogenic plants. This use has survived to the present.

In northern México, *péyotl* is still used as a ritual drug by the Tarahumara, Huichol, Cora and other indigenous groups (Benítez 1975; Benzi 1972); the most common name for *péyotl* in northern México is the Huichol (and Tarahumara) *híkuri* or *híkuli*, and variants thereof (Anderson 1980; Artaud 1976; Schultes & Hofmann 1980). These indigenous groups have been the object of anthropological scrutiny for the past century (Anderson 1980; Blosser 1992; Bye 1979A; Furst 1972; Furst 1976; Gerber 1975; La Barre 1938A; La Barre 1957; La Barre 1960; Labra 1991; Lumholtz 1894; Mooney 1896; Myerhoff 1970; Myerhoff 1974; Schaefer 1992B;

Schaefer 1993; Schultes 1937A; Schultes 1937B; Schultes 1938; Stewart 1987; Urbina 1903; Wasson 1963).

NORTH AMERICAN HEGIRA

Use of *péyotl* has not simply survived in modern México. Sometime around 1870, as a central feature of the pan-Indian movement, use of this entheogenic cactus began to spread, diffusing to the north, and *péyotl* was adopted as a ritual drug by North American indigenous groups. The probable route of diffusion, according to La Barre's classic study *The Peyote Cult*, was initially to the nomadic Mescalero Apache of the southwest, who learned of *péyotl* from native groups in northern México (Boyer *et al.* 1973; La Barre 1938A; La Barre 1979B; Marriott & Rachlin 1971; Troike 1962). From the Mescalero thence its use spread initially to the Kiowa-Comanche and ultimately to myriad Plains Indian tribes in the United States and Canada (Carlson & Jones 1940; Schonle 1925; Slotkin 1952; Slotkin 1956; Vestal & Schultes 1939). Some have theorized that *péyotl* use supplanted the use of a red bean, the seed of *Sophora secundiflora*, known as the "mescal bean" (Campbell 1958; Howard 1957; Schultes 1963; Schultes & Hofmann 1980). However, this assumption has been contested vigorously in a thorough monograph (Merrill 1977). *Péyotl* use was a key part of the Great Ghost Dance movement in the 1890s (McAllester 1949).

There is no question that use of *péyotl* came to the Plains Indians at the height of the persecution and destruction of Indian culture by whites. Predictably, *péyotl* use was stigmatized and used by some of the whites to attack the Indians' ways, in such bigoted articles as "Habit indulgence in certain Cactaceous plants among the Indians" (Blair 1921). In self-defense, and in an attempt to salvage something uniquely Indian from the onslaught of white acculturation, Indian *péyotl* users allied with anthropologists and civil libertarians to seek protection under the Constitutional guarantees of religious freedom. After a tough battle, one of the few the Indians were to win, Cheyenne, Kiowa, Ponca, Otoe and Comanche leaders succeeded in incorporating the "Native American Church" in Oklahoma in 1918, with *péyotl* use as a sacramental observance (La Barre 1938A; Roseman 1963; Stewart 1987). Soon the Church had spread to many other states, and to Canada in 1954 (Anderson 1980), and today there are no fewer than a quarter of a million members. It is interesting to note that *péyotl* use met with some resistance among older Indians, still clinging to their cultural heritage (Aberle 1966). Use of *péyotl* now includes members of many North American tribes, and this use is now legally sanctioned, in spite of federal and state legislation making *péyotl* a controlled substance (Anderson 1980; Boyd 1974; La Barre 1938A; Lame Deer & Erdoes 1972; Ott 1992C; Stewart 1987). As late as 1964, however, Indians were still being convicted of *péyotl*-related offenses (Bates 1964). At least twenty-three states had specifically exempted Indian *péyotl* users from controlled substances laws, while the state of New York extended such religious exemption also to non-Indians (Blackmun 1990; Mount 1987; Stewart 1987), until the 1994 amendments to the "American Indian Religious Freedom Act" legalized the "bona fide" religious use of *péyotl* by tribal members. A New York federal court ruled in 1979 that sacramental use of *péyotl* could not be restricted solely to Indians, and that same year the "Peyote Way Church of God" incorporated in the state of Arizona, open to all worshipers, regardless of race (Mount 1987).

CHEMISTRY OF *PÉYOTL*

In 1888 Louis Lewin published in Berlin the first chemical paper on *péyotl* (Lewin 1888). This caused a sensation, as entheogenic plants had hitherto been unknown to European scientists. Lewin reported the isolation of an alkaloid, which he named Anhalonin (today considered to have been likely a mixture of alkaloids); this was the first published report of alkaloids from the Cactaceae. Lewin had obtained dried *péyotl* from the U.S. pharmaceutical firm Parke, Davis and Co. during a trip to the U.S. in 1887 (Bruhn & Holmstedt 1974; Holmstedt & Liljestrand 1963). Other scientists became interested in *péyotl*, and phytochemical work on the plant culminated in 1895 and 1896, when German chemist Arthur Heffter isolated four pure alkaloids from the plant, one of which he named *Mezcalin*, the others being Anhalonin, Anhalonidin and Lophophorin (Heffter 1896; Heffter 1898)—he also described the isolation of Pellotin (or Peyotlin) from *Lophophora diffusa*. Heffter was unable to detect visionary activity of his isolated alkaloids in animal experiments, which led him to employ the "Heffter Technique" (Ott 1994A), testing the alkaloids on himself, in an heroic series of self-experiments, which he summarized as follows:

> Mezcalin hydrochloride, 0.15 g, produces a pattern of symptoms which differs in only a few respects from the one obtained with the drug [*péyotl*]. (Heffter 1898)

The conclusive experiment took place on 23 November 1897, and this became the world's first *Mezcalin* "trip" and the first entheogenic experiment with a purified compound. Subsequent work, principally by E. Späth, resulted in the identification of a number of the *péyotl* alkaloids. In 1919 Späth identified *Mezcalin* as 3,4,5-trimethoxy-β-phenethylamine, and confirmed this structure by then synthesizing the compound (Späth 1919). *Mezcalin* was the first entheogenic compound isolated in pure form from a plant (I am excluding here harmaline and harmine, discussed in Chapter 4, isolated in 1841 and 1847 respectively, on the grounds that these compounds by themselves are of scant visionary activity, and their isolation inspired no significant experimentation), and the first to be synthesized chemically.

Mezcalin (or mescaline, as this is now rendered[4]) derives its name from *mezcal*, owing to confusion on the part of European scientists as to the nomenclature of *péyotl*. Dried *péyotl* "buttons" had been erroneously known as *mescal buttons* in Europe. *Mezcal* originally comes from the Náhuatl *mexcalli*, the Aztec name for *Agave* species, from which *octli* or *pulque*, a fermented beer, is still made (Bahre & Bradbury 1980; La Barre 1938A; La Barre 1938B). After the conquest, the Spaniards began to distill *pulque*, and the resulting liquor came to be known as *mezcal*. As a name for the active principle of *péyotl*, *Mezcalin* or *mescaline* is a misnomer.[5] "Peyotine" (pellotine, which Heffter applied to another alkaloid of *péyotl*) would have been more appropriate or, since the cactus is called *híkuri* in northern México, the active principle might well have been designated *híkurine*.

Since the pioneering work of Heffter and Späth, chemical studies have continued on the *péyotl* cactus. More than 50 alkaloids have been isolated from or detected in this diminutive plant (Anderson 1980; McLaughlin 1973), the total alkaloid concentration being about 8% of dry weight (Bruhn *et al.* 1978). Most of these alkaloids exist as trace constituents, though some may modify the effects of mescaline or contribute to the complex of symptoms attending the ingestion of *péyotl* (Anderson 1980; Schultes 1972A). Small amounts of mescaline are also found in a related plant, *Lophophora diffusa*,[6] probably the ancestor of *L. williamsii* (Anderson 1980; Bruhn & Holmstedt 1974; Todd 1969). This species is today of minor importance, being known only from one area north of the Valley of México. Mescaline is extremely stable and has been detected in *péyotl* samples dating from the last century (Bruhn & Holmstedt 1974), as well as in samples more than a thousand years old from a Mexican burial (Bruhn *et al.* 1978).

Mescaline also occurs in significant amounts in *Trichocereus pachanoi*, sometimes wrongly called *Opuntia cylindrica* (Turner & Heyman 1960), the stately *San Pedro* cactus of South America (Agurell 1969A; Agurell 1969B; Crosby & McLaughlin 1973; Poisson 1960). This cactus seems to have been important for millennia as a ritual entheogen in Andean cultures (Cordy-Collins 1977, 1980; Cordy-Collins 1982;

Dobkin de Ríos 1975; Dobkin de Ríos 1977; Dobkin de Ríos & Cárdenas 1980; La Barre 1979B), being still used in shamanic rites in Perú and Ecuador (Bianchi 1991; Calderón *et al.* 1982; Davis 1983B; Dobkin 1968; Joralemon & Sharon 1993; Polia & Bianchi 1991; Sharon 1972; Sharon 1978). A "sacred snail" motif in Moche art has been suggested to represent a snail which purportedly feeds on *Trichocereus pachanoi*, thereby sequestering mescaline and itself becoming entheogenic (Bourget 1990). *Trichocereus pachanoi* reportedly forms the basis of the *cimora* entheogenic potion, said to contain other plants, including the cactus *Neoraimondia macrostibas*, entheogenic *Brugmansia* species (see Appendix A), *Pedilanthus tithymaloides* (used as an anthelmintic by Mixe Indians of Oaxaca, México; Heinrich *et al.* 1992), *Isotoma longiflora*, and a species of *Iresine* (Cruz-Sánchez 1948; Dobkin de Ríos 1977; Schultes & Hofmann 1980). There is some controversy regarding the identification of *cimora* (Davis 1983B). It has been claimed the potion contains no cacti at all, just the *Iresine* species (Friedberg 1959; Friedberg 1960). According to one recent study, *cimora* refers to entheogenic *Brugmansia* and *Datura* species, whereas *timora* is the name of the *Iresine* species (Davis 1983B). Mescaline has been found in 12 species of *Trichocereus* (see Table 1), the highest concentration in *T. peruvianus* (Agurell 1969B; Agurell *et al.* 1971; Crosby & McLaughlin 1973; Pardanani *et al.* 1977; Poisson 1960; Reti & Castrillon 1951). Trace amounts of mescaline occur in other Cactaceae, including *Stetsonia coryne*, *Pelecyphora aselliformis* and *Opuntia spinosor* (Kruger *et al.* 1977; Neal *et al.* 1972; Pardanani *et al.* 1978; Shulgin 1979B; Vanderveen *et al.* 1974). An unidentified *Opuntia*, which may contain mescaline or a relative, is used by Amazonian Sharanahua Indians as an additive to entheogenic *ayahuasca* potions (see Chapter 4; Schultes & Raffauf 1990).[7] Traces of mescaline were found in *Islaya minor*, *Opuntia acanthocarpa*, *O. basilaris*, *O. ficus-indica*, *O. echinocarpa*, *O. imbricata*, *Pereskia corrugata*, *P. tampicana*, *Pereskiopsis scandens*, *Polaskia chende*, *Pterocereus gaumeri*, *Stenocereus beneckei*, *S. eruca*, *S. stellatus*, and lastly *S. treleasei* (Doetsch *et al.* 1980; El-Moghazy *et al.* 1982; Ma *et al.* 1986; Meyer *et al.* 1980).

PROPERTIES OF MESCALINE

The effective oral dose of mescaline in human subjects is between 150 and 1500 milligrams, a large amount when compared to the psychoactive dose of LSD-25 (25–500 micrograms) and psilocybine (5–120 milligrams; Anderson 1980; Grof 1975; Hofmann 1968; Rouhier 1927). The highest dose we know to have been given to a human subject is 1500 mg (Fisher 1963) and the "maximum safe dose" has been pegged at 1000 mg (Brown 1968). Following oral ingestion, the effects of mescaline will begin in about 1–2 hours and last for 8–12 hours. Nausea and mild abdominal cramps are often reported as side-effects, usually during the initial stages of the inebriation. Slight increase in body temperature is a common side-effect of mescaline. Peak effects are similar to those of psilocybine and LSD, being characterized by visual and auditory alterations, synaesthesia and ego dissolution, and the drug may show "cross-tolerance"[8] with LSD (Aghajanian *et al.* 1970; Balestrieri 1957; Wolbach *et al.* 1962A). Since it contains many other pharmacologically-active alkaloids, some of which, like the sedative peyotline or pellotine occur in significant quantities, the effects of *péyotl* are different, as Heffter commented, from the effects of mescaline in pure form (Schultes 1972A; Shulgin 1973). The whole drug also has medicinal uses apart from entheogenic use in vision quests (Bye 1979B; Schultes 1938). *Péyotl* extracts have been demonstrated to have antibiotic activity, justifying the external use of *péyotl* infusions or fresh *péyotl* juice to treat wounds or for analgesia, and *péyotl* tea has been used in parturition to ease labor (Anderson 1980; Benítez 1973; Latorre & Latorre 1977; McCleary *et al.* 1960; Mount 1987). An antibiotic substance called peyocactin was isolated from *péyotl* (McCleary *et al.* 1960) and later shown to be identical to hordenine (Rao 1970). The ancient Aztecs used *péyotl* medicinally, together with *Datura* spp., *ololiuhqui* seeds and entheogenic mushrooms (see Appendix A; Chapters 2 and 5)—a sort of super-entheogen—in their treatment of an "aquatic fever" thought to have been malaria or a similar disease (Sahagún 1950). There is evidence for traditional ingestion of *péyotl* in the form of enemas, which may have had some therapeutic rationale (De Smet & Lipp 1987).

NUTMEG AND THE ARTIFICIAL PHENETHYLAMINES AND AMPHETAMINES

Nutmeg, *Myristica fragrans*, a drug used in southeast Asian ethnomedicine (Ponglux *et al.* 1987), has long been alleged to be psychoactive (Devereux 1992; Green 1959; Painter 1971; Panyatopoulos & Chisold 1970; Payne 1963; Purkinje 1829; Schulze 1976; Sherry *et al.* 1982; Shulgin 1963C; Truitt *et al.* 1961; Weil 1965; Weil 1967; Weil 1969; Weiss 1960; Williams & West 1968; X & Haley 1964), and both myristicin and elemicin (this latter, like mescaline, a 3,4,5-trimethoxybenzene derivative) have been cited as psychotropic principles of the essential oil of nutmeg (Shulgin 1963A; Shulgin 1966; Shulgin & Kerlinger 1964; Truitt 1967), which was used traditionally in Afghanistan as a stimulant (Younos *et al.* 1987). A recent article questioned the psychoactivity of nutmeg (Gils & Cox 1994). Safrole is also a constituent of nutmeg essential oil, and these and other volatile oils can be converted by amination to the artificial phenylisopropylamines or amphetamines (Shulgin *et al.* 1967). Safrole, eugenol and methyleugenol are the major psychoactive components of seeds of *Licaria puchury-major*, widely used in Brasil as a sedative and tranquilizer under the name *puchuri* or *pixuri* (Carlini *et al.* 1983). One colleague reported a "visionary experience" after ingesting 10 ml of Brasilian oil of sassafras, which contains safrole. A great number of artificial phenethylamines and phenylisopropylamines have been synthesized and tested, and this extensive field is beyond the scope of this book. Moreover, the recent publication of *PIHKAL—A Chemical Love Story* by pioneering phenethylamine chemist Alexander T. Shulgin and Ann Shulgin (Shulgin & Shulgin 1991) reviews thoroughly the chemistry and human pharmacology of 179 such compounds. Nevertheless, I would like briefly to mention several important compounds in this series, and refer the reader to *PIHKAL* for detailed information, as well as to various review articles (Jacob & Nichols 1982; Pierce & Peroutka 1988; Shulgin 1970; Shulgin 1971; Shulgin 1976A; Shulgin 1982; Shulgin *et al.* 1969).

TMA SERIES: The amination of elemicin results in 3,4,5-trimethoxyamphetamine or TMA, also known as EA-1319 (*PIHKAL* Compound No. 157; see Shulgin & Shulgin 1991). This was the first completely artificial phenethylamine found to be psychoactive in human subjects, being reported in 1955 (Peretz *et al.* 1955; Shulgin 1963B). Shulgin and colleagues have synthesized all six TMA isomers, of which the most active is TMA-2 (2,4,5-trimethoxyamphetamine; *PIHKAL* No. 158), with a dose range of 20–40 mg, compared to 100–150 mg for TMA itself (Shulgin 1976C; Shulgin & Shulgin 1991; Shulgin *et al.* 1961). The essential oil corresponding to TMA-2 is asarone (see Appendix A). TMA is a controlled substance as (by extrapolation) are the other TMA isomers. These compounds do not appear to have escaped widely the confines of the laboratory, although TMA (as EA-1319) was used in chemical warfare studies at the United States Army's Edgewood Arsenal, and has also been tested in psychiatric patients (Shulgin & Shulgin 1991).

MDA SERIES: The amination of safrole yields 3,4-methylenedioxyamphetamine or MDA (*PIHKAL* No. 100), first prepared in Germany before the First World War, and psychoactive in doses of 80–160 mg (Anon. 1914; Shulgin & Shulgin 1991; Turek *et al.* 1974). Gordon Alles first wrote about the peculiar effects of this compound, describing diaphanous smoke rings in the air following oral ingestion in two doses of a total of 126 mg MDA hydrochloride (Alles 1959). As EA-1298, MDA was tested by the U.S. Army in the 1950s, and one such test caused the death of a psychiatric "patient" following a 500 mg intravenous dose (Shulgin & Shulgin 1991). This drug has also been tested in psychotherapy by Naranjo, apparently showing considerable promise (Naranjo 1973A). MDA has found rather a widespread use outside of the laboratory (Bigwood 1977; Shulgin & Shulgin 1991; Weil 1976). At doses 3–5 times the human psychoactive dose (on a *per* weight basis), MDA has shown significant neurotoxicity in rats (Ricuarte *et al.* 1985), and there is the possibility of similar toxicity in human users. Some *N*-substituted analogues of MDA are known to be psychoactive (Braun *et al.* 1980A; Braun *et al.* 1980B). Amination of myristicin yields MMDA or 3-methoxy-4,5-methylenedioxyamphetamine (*PIHKAL* No. 132), psychoactive at doses from 100–250 mg (Shulgin 1964A; Shulgin 1976D; Shulgin & Shulgin 1991). Many other related compounds have been made and tested (Shulgin 1964B; Shulgin & Nichols 1978; Shulgin & Shulgin 1991). Today the best known of this series is MDMA, famed "Ecstasy," 3,4-methylenedioxy-*N*-methylamphetamine (*PIHKAL* No. 109), psychoactive in doses of 80–150 mg (Braun *et al.* 1980A; Braun *et al.* 1980B; Eisner 1989; Nichols *et al.* 1982; Saunders 1993; Shulgin 1986; Shulgin & Shulgin 1991) and, like MDA, prepared first in Germany prior to World War I (Anon. 1914). This compound has found widespread ludible use leading to its summary illegalization (Barnes 1988A; Barnes 1988B). Like MDA, MDMA has shown some neurotoxicity in experimental animals (McKenna & Peroutka 1990; McKenna *et al.* 1991; Schmidt 1987). It is considered to be valuable as an adjunct to psychotherapy (Adamson 1985; Adamson & Metzner 1988; Leverant 1986; Metzner 1988). MDMA use has become popular on U.S. college campuses; common too among "ravers"—participants in impromptu concert/parties and in British travelers' festivals which appeal to latter-day gypsies (Foote 1992). The "rave" phenomenon, and associated use of MDMA, commenced in Ibiza, spread throughout Europe, and later appeared in the United States (Ott, unpublished; Pendell 1992). Besides MDMA and MDA, MDE (*N*-ethyl-MDA; *PIHKAL* No. 106), MDPR (*N*-propyl-MDA; *PIHKAL* No. 118), MDIP (*N*-isopropyl-MDA; *PIHKAL* No. 108) and MDDM (*N,N*-dimethyl-MDA; *PIHKAL* No. 105) have appeared on the black market, along with *N*-ethyl-*N*-methyl-MDA and *N,N*-diethyl-MDA (Janesko & Dal Cason 1987). See: Shulgin & Sargent 1967.

DOM/DOB/DOI: The most potent of these artificial phenethylamines are the 2,5-dimethoxyamphetamines (Shulgin & Dyer 1975). The first to be made was 2,5-dimethoxy-4-methylamphetamine (*PIHKAL* No. 68) or DOM, which became infamous under a street name "STP" in 1967, when large doses (20 mg) were distributed as street drugs in San Francisco (Bigwood 1977). Normally active in 3–10 mg doses, the high-dose DOM caused long-lasting effects, many leading to panic reactions (Shick & Smith 1972; Shulgin & Shulgin 1991; Snyder *et al.* 1968; Snyder *et al.* 1970). Since it had rapidly acquired a bad reputation, DOM had a short career as a ludible drug. Shulgin thereafter synthesized DOB or 2,5-dimethoxy-4-bromoamphetamine (*PIHKAL* No. 62) which proved to be even more potent, with a range of psychoactivity between 1 and 3 mg, and it also produces extremely long-lasting effects (Shulgin 1981; Shulgin & Shulgin 1991; Shulgin *et al.* 1971). Human metabolism of DOB labeled with radioactive bromine has been observed with a whole-body scanner (Sargent *et al.* 1975). Like DOM, DOB is illegal, and the drug has appeared on the illicit market. There is a human death on record from a massive overdose of DOB, which was mistaken for MDA and snuffed (Shulgin & Shulgin 1991). Also active at doses between 1.5–3 mg is DOI or 2,5-dimethoxy-4-iodoamphetamine (*PIHKAL* No. 67), which produces effects lasting from 16–30 hours (Shulgin & Shulgin 1991). This interesting compound appears to bind to the same receptors in rat brains as does LSD (see Chapter 2) and DOB (McKenna & Saavedra 1987; McKenna *et al.* 1989). This finding may explain the fact that LSD (an ergoline alkaloid having an indole nucleus) and mescaline (like DOI and DOB, a phenethylamine alkaloid) show cross-tolerance (see Note 8), and may account for the similarity in peak effects of these two compounds. Recently the compound 2C-B or 2,5-dimethoxy-4-bromophenethylamine (*PIHKAL* No. 20; DOB minus the side-chain methyl group which converts a phenethylamine to a phenylisopropylamine or amphetamine) has been in vogue among entheogen *aficionados*, active in a dose range of 12–24 mg. Sometimes 2C-B is combined with MDMA, being taken as the MDMA or "Ecstasy" effects are ending (Shulgin & Shulgin 1991).

NON-INDIAN USE OF *PÉYOTL* AND MESCALINE

Péyotl (and later mescaline) was the first entheogen made available to westerners. As previously mentioned, mescaline was at once the first entheogenic compound isolated in pure form, and the first to be synthesized. S. Weir Mitchell and Havelock Ellis are generally credited with bringing the drug to popular attention, although its effects had been mentioned earlier by others (Briggs 1887; Prentiss & Morgan 1895). Mitchell ingested a liquid extract of *péyotl* one afternoon in 1896 (this was an infusion of about six dried cactus heads or "peyote buttons"). After finding himself "deliciously at languid ease" and noticing patterns like stained-glass with his eyes closed, he went into a dark room. There he experienced visions that were to lead him to commend *péyotl* to the world. He was later to describe (Mitchell 1896):

> Stars... delicate floating films of colour... Then an abrupt rush of countless points of white light swept across the field of view, as if the unseen millions of the Milky Way were to flow a sparkling river before the eye. [...] Then I began to see zigzag lines of very bright colours. [then] definite objects associated with colours. [...] All the colours I have ever beheld are dull as compared to these.

Mitchell sent a supply of dried *péyotl* to William James, author of *The Varieties of Religious Experience* (James 1902), and the man who described the consciousness-altering properties of nitrous oxide. James ate only one *péyotl* button, and was "violently sick for 24 hours." He never repeated the experiment, saying he would "take the visions on trust."

One year later, after reading Mitchell's paper, Havelock Ellis ingested a decoction of three *péyotl* buttons in London. His self-experiment was carried out in a room lit only by flickering firelight, as Ellis felt this would be conducive to visions such as the Indians might experience. His visions were profound, and he wrote vivid accounts of them for the *Contemporary Review* (Ellis 1898A) and the *Annual Report of the Smithsonian Institution* (Ellis 1898B). The former account included the first published description of entheogen-induced synaesthesia. Ellis introduced a number of his friends to *péyotl*, including poets who were later to write about their visions. He also published an important and pioneering paper on *péyotl* in the European medical literature (Ellis 1897).

Stimulated by the descriptions of Mitchell and Ellis, European scientists began studies of the psychological effects of *péyotl*, of extracted mescaline sulfate and, after 1919, of synthetic mescaline. Before the First World War, mescaline research on human subjects was underway at the Kräpelin Clinic in Munich, where researchers Knauer and Maloney injected subcutaneous doses of up to 200 mg mescaline into volunteers who experienced psychoptic effects within four hours (Klüver 1966; Knauer & Maloney 1913). Soon after the end of the war, the German scientist Kurt Beringer conducted approximately sixty mescaline sessions, using as subjects male and female physicians and medical students. The results of this research, in which doses as high as 600 mg were injected subcutaneously, were published in 1927 (Beringer 1927). Meanwhile in Paris, the French pharmacologist Alexandre Rouhier was studying the effects of a *péyotl* extract on a few volunteers. He published his pharmacological data in an interdisciplinary study of the plant entitled *La Plante qui fait les Yeux Émerveillés—Le Peyotl* (Rouhier 1927). Heinrich Klüver, an American psychologist, also carried out research into the nature of mescaline inebriation, and published a monograph entitled *Mescal* [*sic*]*: The "Divine" Plant and its Psychological Effects* (Klüver 1928). In 1933, a Swiss pharmacy began to advertise *Peyotyl* [*sic*] as a sort of adaptogen, to "restore the individual's balance and calm and promote full expansion of his faculties," leading the Swiss Federal Public Health Service to recommend this *Peyotyl* be made available only with a prescription (McGlothlin 1965). On the heels of the Europeans and Americans, Erich Guttmann gave mescaline to more than sixty subjects at London's Maudsley Hospital (Guttmann 1936; Guttmann & Maclay 1936; Taylor 1944). This research produced some of the best descriptions of mescaline inebriation. During World War II, German physicians at the infamous Dachau concentration camp studied the effects of mescaline as an interrogation aid on thirty prisoners (Lee & Shlain 1985).

Louis Lewin, perhaps the best known researcher of *péyotl*, published a book about psychoactive drugs in 1924. This was written in German, and bore the title *Phantastica: Die Betäubenden und Erregenden Genußmittel. Für Ärzte und Nichtärzte* (Lewin 1924; see Chapter 4, Note 1). There was a chapter on *péyotl*, classified with other drugs as *Phantastica*, the word Lewin coined for entheogens. The English version of this important work, published in London in 1931, as explained in the introduction to this chapter, caught the attention of Aldous Huxley, and fired his interest in *psychopharmaka*, eventually leading to his famous mescaline experience in May 1953, immortalized in his essay *The Doors of Perception* (Huxley 1954). This was an important stimulus to use of entheogens in the sixties, as were the publications on self-experiments with mescaline by French writer Henri Michaux (Michaux 1956; Michaux 1957; Michaux 1965). Sometime before Huxley's famous initiation to entheogens, the American novelist William Burroughs ingested *péyotl*. He reported on the effects, and mentioned that the drug was legal, in his first book, *Junk*, originally published as *Junkie: Confessions of an Unredeemed Drug Addict* under the pseudonym William Lee (Lee 1953). Burroughs commented that, after ingesting four "buttons," "everything I saw looked like a peyote plant," and, other than that curious visual alteration, "I didn't feel any different from ordinary except high like on benny [*Benzedrine*]" (Lee 1953). Burroughs' writing on drugs had considerable influence on the Beats, many of whom, like Allen Ginsberg, began to experiment with *péyotl*, and there were reports in the sixties of "trips" by non-Indians (James 1964; Mellen 1963; Osmond 1961; Roseman 1963). As a result, the existing legal mail-order market for *péyotl* buttons (Morgan 1983B) began to expand.

In response to spreading use of entheogenic drugs, especially LSD (see Chapter

2), in the sixties, many countries followed the lead of the United States and illegalized these drugs, in effect making them available, with bureaucratic difficulties, to scientists only. Both *péyotl* and mescaline were classified as controlled substances with "a high potential for abuse" and "no currently accepted medical use" (Anderson 1980). Simple possession of *péyotl* and mescaline became criminal offenses. Prior to this legislation, *péyotl* and mescaline were rather freely available, at least in the United States (Flattery & Pierce 1965; Weil 1963B; Weil 1972). There is, however, little evidence that mescaline in pure form was ever widely used by the general public. Rather, most sixties users were introduced to entheogenic drugs by taking LSD. Being inexpensive to manufacture (on a *per* dose basis), LSD continued to be available after federal and state legislation made it illegal. Mescaline, on the other hand, all but disappeared from the market. Today it is available to researchers as the hydrochloride, hemi-sulfate or sulfate salt, for $91.10 *per* gram (or $35–$55 for a decent dose) from Sigma Chemical Co. (1996), which sells such research compounds labeled "not for drug use." Researchers in the United States must, however, be licensed by the Drug Enforcement Administration (DEA) in order to buy mescaline, and must have on file with the National Institute on Drug Abuse (NIDA) a research protocol demonstrating their "legitimate" need for the drug. Laboratories using mescaline and other controlled substances are subject to inspection by DEA agents, must have their licenses on display, and must have provisions for safeguarding the drugs, to avoid "diversion" (a curious bureaucratic *double entendre*). Bureaucratic procedures for conducting this research have been reviewed by Strassman (1991).

Mescaline sulfate, probably synthetic, is today available in limited amounts on the illicit market, selling for about $250 a gram. The entire supply, however, seems to be taken up by the elite of the illicit drug trade, and this rare compound is not widely distributed. Note that at this price, an average 500 mg dose would cost at least $125! *Péyotl* "buttons" are considerably more economical. In 1966, the going rate was $15 for 1000 buttons. Owing to the increasing demand and limited supply, this price had jumped to $80 *per* thousand buttons by 1983; although "green" (fresh) *péyotl* could still be had for $15 *per* thousand buttons (Morgan 1983A). By 1987, the price had again jumped to $100 for a thousand buttons, the current price (Schaefer 1992A; Stewart 1987). These prices refer to the legitimate trade between professional *peyoteros* and the Native American Church. Even at the 1987 price, a five-button dose could be had wholesale for only 50¢ ($0.50)—a true bargain!

Drugs alleged to be mescaline have been widely sold on the illicit market since the sixties. Analysis of street drug samples sold as "mescaline" almost invariably shows these to be LSD or PCP (phencyclidine or *Sernyl*, a veterinary tranquilizer;

Marshman & Gibbons 1970; PharmChem 1973). Amphetamines have on occasion been detected in putative mescaline samples. The rare specimens found to contain mescaline have been crystals or white powder; capsules, *not* tablets.

Summarizing analyses of 640 putative mescaline samples in four different American laboratories, Brown and Malone reported only 18 mescaline samples (2.8%) and 8 *péyotl* samples (1.2%). The remainder were as follows: 376 LSD (58.8%); 130 LSD plus PCP (20.3%); 27 PCP (4.2%); along with 81 "other" (12.7%) including a few mixtures of LSD plus amphetamines; "STP" or DOM (see above); a few amphetamine samples, *etc.* (Brown & Malone 1973A). The alleged "mescaline" tablets or capsules typically weighed from 10–150 mg each, insufficient to provoke a very strong mescaline "trip" even had they been 100% mescaline! In similar analyses made in Munich, Germany, only 1 of 14 putative mescaline samples (7.1%) was found to be genuine (Brown & Malone 1973B). Of 61 purported mescaline preparations analyzed by PharmChem Laboratories in Palo Alto, California in 1973, 52 or 85% contained LSD alone or in combination, while only 4 samples (6.6%) actually contained mescaline (PharmChem 1973).

Virtually all American users of entheogenic drugs claim to have tried mescaline at some point in their careers. Clearly, the great majority have simply tried LSD or PCP under an assumed name. There can be no doubt about this conclusion—mescaline has always been in short supply, and numerous studies on street drug samples support this view. Moreover, a 400–600 mg dose of pure mescaline sulfate will fill two or three large "00" capsules, and most users report having ingested only one capsule or tablet. Yet "sophisticated" users, when confronted with these facts, will usually claim that they have certainly tried the real thing, that they know the difference between LSD and mescaline, being *connaisseurs*; that LSD has this or that attribute, whereas mescaline may be distinguished by various superior qualities.

To put it bluntly, this is hogwash. Not only have the great majority of entheogen users never tried authentic mescaline but, I submit, under proper experimental conditions, many would be unable to discern much difference between mescaline and LSD. In fact, peak effects of these compounds are remarkably similar, and these drugs (as well as psilocybine and psilocine; see Chapter 5) show cross-tolerance,[8] suggesting they produce their effects by similar neural mechanisms (Ludwig & Levine 1966; Wolbach *et al.* 1962A). There is some evidence they may all bind to the same neuroreceptor in brains of experimental animals (McKenna & Saavedra 1987; McKenna *et al.* 1989).

Why then, all this fanfare about mescaline, the philosophers' "stone" of psychedelia? If street "mescaline" were only LSD, why did users invariably believe it to be different, superior, "cleaner," more desirable than LSD? I must digress a bit to arrive at a satisfactory answer.

In the late fifties, a new tranquilizer known as *Thalidomide* was admitted for medical use in Germany and other countries. It became apparent that the drug was strongly teratogenic, that is, that it produced grave birth defects if taken at the wrong time by pregnant women. The tragic result was a generation of "*Thalidomide* babies" with hideous and crippling deformities. The drug was immediately taken off the market, and regulations concerning the introduction of new drugs were tightened considerably in many countries.

At this time, under the trade name *Delysid*, LSD-25 was being distributed as an experimental drug by Sandoz LTD. of Switzerland (see Chapter 2). Since the drug was thought to produce a "model psychosis," Sandoz felt it might ultimately be an effective psychotherapeutic agent, and indeed it showed considerable promise in early trials. When in 1967 a report in the *New England Journal of Medicine* alleged that LSD caused chromosome damage (Cohen *et al.* 1967), the scare was on. No matter that the report did not support this allegation, which in later controlled experiments proved to be false (Dishotsky *et al.* 1971; Tjio *et al.* 1969), nor show that LSD is teratogenic (it is not). The media and governments seized this allegation as a means of attacking LSD use, which was spreading rapidly. The media mounted a vigorous scare campaign against LSD, which continues to this day.

LSD users in the sixties were principally in their late teens or early twenties, and many had vivid memories of the well-publicized *Thalidomide* tragedy, which had been graphically and luridly chronicled by the press. Many people came to fear LSD as a result of the scare campaign. Popular interest in LSD had stimulated interest in other entheogenic drugs. One result was the reprinting of Huxley's and Klüver's hitherto obscure books on mescaline, and an increasing awareness that LSD was not the only entheogenic drug.

In 1968 Carlos Castaneda published *The Teachings of Don Juan: A Yaqui* [*sic*] *Way of Knowledge*, which referred to *péyotl* use, and must have stimulated interest in mescaline, since Castaneda imputed to Don Juan, supposedly a Mexican shaman, the belief that *Mescalito* was the spirit of *péyotl* (Castaneda 1968). This is certainly spurious. As I have shown, European scientists in the last century confused *péyotl* with *mezcal*, a word originally referring to a completely different plant, and mescaline as the active principle of *péyotl* is decidedly a misnomer. Are we to believe that a Mexican shaman is party to this confusion?[9]

Meanwhile, there was already a sizable black market LSD industry in place (Lee & Shlain 1985; Stevens 1987), and the wily drug dealers seized on "mescaline" as a means to offset any declining sales of LSD brought on by the big scare. They labeled LSD as "mescaline" or "organic mescaline" and foisted the specious preparations on the unsuspecting public. The term "organic mescaline" is significant—*organic* mescaline was preferred by the *connaisseur* to ordinary or (we must presume) *synthetic* mescaline! What is the meaning of the term "organic"? To the chemist, *organic* chemistry is the chemistry of carbon compounds, such diverse compounds as LSD, mescaline, *Thalidomide*, strychnine, DDT, TNT (and literally millions of others, whether made by a plant or by a chemist) are alike *organic* compounds. The meaning imputed to "organic mescaline" was that it was a natural compound, from a plant, in contrast to LSD, which was a creation of the chemist not found in nature (at least not yet).[10] Thus, I submit, was born the great mescaline hoax. Some users of entheogens came to fear LSD because of a scare campaign by governments and the press. LSD was, after all, an artificial compound, and an unknown quantity. It had not existed prior to 1938 and little was known about the long-term consequences of its use. Mescaline, on the other hand, was extracted from a plant which had been used by human beings for millennia (although most "psychedelic" users did not know this), was a natural compound—it was "organic" and therefore safe![11]

Thus was born a linguistic confusion which persists to this day. Debate still rages about the relative virtues of "natural" *versus* "synthetic" vitamins, "processed" *versus* "organic" foods.[12] Whether synthesized by a chemist or by a plant, any given vitamin samples of identical chemical structure have identical biological effects. The same is true for drugs. Mescaline made by the *péyotl* cactus is the same as mescaline made by a chemist. As a rule, however, synthetic natural products (whether drugs or vitamins) *are of superior purity* to their natural counterparts as these normally are available commercially.

I have seemingly touched on a modern example of the primal fear of the gods. Drugs and vitamins made by human beings are thought to be unnatural and dangerous, whereas identical drugs and vitamins made by plants are god-given and safe. To presume to make things formerly made only by the gods is to commit the sin of Prometheus, to steal fire from the gods!

I have explained why LSD came to be misrepresented as mescaline, but why did LSD users consider it to be a superior high, if in fact street "mescaline" were simply LSD under an assumed name, the wolf in sheep's clothing? It is now well known that user expectation or "set" is an important determining factor in the quality of entheogenic drug experiences (Grof 1975; Metzner *et al.* 1965; Weil 1972; Zinberg 1977). Users wished to believe that "mescaline" was different, so they could join the *cognoscenti* who alone were party to superior knowledge of a drug safer and more desirable than the suspect LSD. Drug sellers readily reinforced this tendency in the gullible users. An elaborate folklore grew to surround mescaline, in spite of the fact that hardly anyone had ever tried it! "Mescaline" was usually priced higher than LSD, which was at once conducive to expanded profit for the seller, and a heightened feeling on the part of the user that (s)he was a member of the elite. It is now widely known among users that "mescaline" sold on the street is and has ever been almost invariably misrepresented. Nonetheless, nearly everyone believes that (s)he has actually tried the real thing, that (s)he is a part of a yet smaller elite, and that it is everyone else who has been duped!

In the 1980s, as part of the widespread "nature tourism" or "ecotourism" movement (I first heard the term *ecoturismo*, in Spanish, from the lips of a Quijos Quichua *ayahuasquera* in Amazonian Ecuador!), there arose the phenomenon of Mexican "*péyotl* tours" to the land of the Huichol (Krajick 1992). Advertised in magazines like *Magical Blend Magazine* and *Shaman's Drum: A Journal of Experiential Shamanism*, such tours invited prospective clients to visit Huichol "places of power" and to study "advanced techniques of shamanic healing" with Huichol shamans. In the Fall 1986 issue of *Shaman's Drum* (which featured articles on the Huicholes), there were no fewer than three advertisements for "*péyotl* tours." To the credit of the magazine's publishers, there was also a letter to the editor by S. Valadez, wife of a Huichol artist whose work was depicted in the issue, decrying "Guided tour spirituality: Cosmic way or cosmic rip-off?"... Valadez warned:

> Westerners who participate in peyote pilgrimages with Huichol[e]s... are endangering the Huichol[e]s who escort them. The soldiers patrolling the peyote desert are not impressed by Americans who claim they come for enlightenment. The Mexicans think the outsiders come for dope, and accuse the Huichol[e]s of dealing drugs to the "gringo Hippies." (Valadez 1986)

I have seen a similar phenomenon surrounding entheogenic mushroom use in Oaxaca in the seventies (even María Sabina was sent to prison for "dealing drugs to the *gringo* hippies"; see Chapter 5; Estrada 1977), and I share Valadez's concerns, which also include cultural disruption and spreading of diseases by highly-mobile outsiders to isolated communities of unimmunized Indians. Finally, as outlined below, excessive and destructive harvesting is endangering the small, slow-growing species *Lophophora williamsii*, which has a restricted range. I personally think outsiders should stay home and take LSD or grow their own *San Pedro* (*Trichocereus pachanoi*; see Note 11 below).

USE OF MESCALINE AND MESCALINE-CONTAINING CACTI

This is the state of affairs today, with mescaline virtually unavailable on the illicit market. Should one encounter alleged mescaline, common sense will enable one to ascertain whether one is being offered the real thing. First, if the material is in the form of a tablet, forget it. If it is in a capsule, one should open this and carefully examine the material. Is it a white or colorless crystalline substance, and is it extremely bitter? It had better be a large capsule, since it takes at least 200 milligrams of pure mescaline to produce much of a psychoptic effect, and 500–600 mg is a more desirable dose. A "00" capsule will hold only about 200 mg of crystalline mescaline sulfate, so one should be wary if a single capsule is reputed to represent a strong dose. The purist may wish to determine the solubility and melting point of the reputed sample, although such analytical work may be improper unless a large quantity is involved (which is unlikely, owing to limited supply).

Mescaline-containing cacti are far more readily available than the pure drug. *Péyotl* is still widely used by the "Native American Church," and, at least in some tribes, non-Indians may seek membership in the church (Mount 1987). There is some trade in dried *péyotl* as a ludibund drug, although this would appear to be minor. Because *péyotl* has such a restricted range, and since the cactus requires more than a decade to mature, the supply is naturally limited. Because of the CITES ("Convention on International Trade in Endangered Species") treaty, it is illegal to traffic in *any* species of wild cactus, although sale of cultivated material is permitted. There is some concern that the *péyotl* cactus may become extinct, owing to the depredations of eager collectors, the legitimate collection by the Huichol and other Mexican indigenous groups, and the demands of the Native American Church and the modern, Arizona-based "Peyote Way Church of God" (Anderson 1995; Mount 1987). One rancher from south Texas, within the natural range of *péyotl*, said that in 1945 the plant was so abundant on his property that it was like "walking on a mattress." According to a professional *peyotero*, in 1972 he and five assistants were able to harvest 19,000 *péyotl* tops in 8 hours in a collecting area of Starr County, Texas, which three years later yielded the same crew only 200–300 tops in eight hours of collecting. There is evidence the range of the plant is shrinking southward due to agricultural and development activities (Morgan 1976; Morgan 1983A; Morgan 1983B). Destructive harvesting is also to blame for increasing scarcity of the plant. According to G.R. Morgan, "most Indians use improper tools for harvesting, especially long shovels, which tend to mutilate the plant" (Morgan 1983A).

A far more abundant plant source of mescaline is the Peruvian *San Pedro* cactus, *Trichocereus pachanoi*, or one of the other *Trichocereus* species which contains mescaline, particularly *T. peruvianus*, which contains the highest concentrations, approaching mescaline amounts found in the *péyotl* cactus (Pardanani *et al.* 1977). Mature specimens may grow nearly a meter at 12 cm diameter in a year. Slices of mature *T. peruvianus* as thin as 1–2 cm contain threshold-level doses of mescaline. *T. peruvianus*, like *T. pachanoi*, is a large, fast-growing, columnar cactus, and may be available through plant stores and cactus dealers. In 1987, however, a Berkeley, California cactus nursery was wantonly destroyed by narcotics agents and its growing stock confiscated or killed, on the basis of a search warrant referring to sales of *San Pedro* and other mescaline-containing cacti. Charges were later dropped, but the owner was never compensated for the damage, and was thus forced out of business (Coblentz 1991). The seeds of *Trichocereus* contain no mescaline and are thus legal, and are sold by mail-order. *San Pedro* is easily grown from seed. I suggest the "Native American Church" and "Peyote Way Church of God" establish *Trichocereus peruvianus* gardens in the United States, as a means of ensuring a continued renewable supply of sacramental cactus for their rites, and of removing the pressure of extinction from remaining wild stands of the *péyotl* cactus in Texas. Perhaps South American *San Pedro* shamans could be invited to assist in the syncretistic integration of *San Pedro* and *péyotl* mythologies.

The tops of the *péyotl* cactus alone are eaten, and may be harvested without killing the root of the plant (Morgan 1983A), which in any case contains only traces of mescaline. The tops are severed at about ground level, leaving the root in the ground, so it may sprout more "heads." These tops or "peyote buttons" (as the severed heads are known) are then dried, and will retain their activity indefinitely. As mentioned, mescaline has been detected in 1000-year-old *péyotl* found in an ancient burial in México (Bruhn *et al.* 1978).

At the crown of the *péyotl* plant there is a shallow depression in which the flower develops. This depression is filled with tufts of fine silky white hairs. Today's *péyotl* eater is wont to pluck these hairs from the dried buttons before ingesting them. Popular opinion has it that these hairs contain strychnine, which causes the nausea often associated with *péyotl* ingestion. It is difficult to explain how this widespread and pervasive drug myth originated. *No part of the* péyotl *plant contains strychnine*, nor is this compound found in any other species of cactus. Strychnine is an alkaloid from seeds of *Strychnos nux-vomica*, and is unrelated to the *péyotl* alkaloids. Some users claim that the hairs contain lophophorine (a *péyotl* alkaloid which produces strychnine-like effects), or another alkaloid of *péyotl*, and do indeed cause nausea. It has also been suggested that the hairs cause nausea by irritating the lining of the stomach. This is all smoke of opinion. Ingestion of a large dose of the hairs produced no noticeable effect (Bigwood 1978). Chemical analysis has shown that no alkaloids occur in these hairs (Shulgin 1977A), nor has nausea been demonstrated to occur following their ingestion. Mexican Huichol Indians consider the tufts of silky hairs to be the tails of the sacred deer, and carefully remove them to use as sacred offerings—they are never simply disposed of. This may be the origin of contemporary *péyotl* hair-removal rituals (Schaefer 1992A; Schaefer 1992B).

About 4–12 of these *péyotl* buttons are chewed and swallowed to produce inebriation. Some Indian users have been seen to ingest up to 50 buttons at a sitting. As mentioned above, the taste is dreadfully bitter, and many users have difficulty ingesting enough material to experience the psychoptic effects. Sometimes a tea is brewed with the chopped or ground *péyotl* buttons (an electric coffee mill will serve as a grinder). Since mescaline is soluble in hot water, it will be extracted into the tea. This is, however, an exceedingly bitter brew, guaranteed to delight neither the eye nor the palate. Chewing raw or dried *péyotl* or imbibing this bitter cup should be avoided assiduously by the squeamish or faint-hearted.

It is also difficult to ingest *San Pedro* or other *Trichocereus* species. Besides being bitter, *San Pedro* has a strange consistency of "sandy jelly." The bitterness is unavoidable, since one must ingest enough cactus flesh to contain at least a half a gram of mescaline, an intensely bitter substance, which is accompanied in the cactus by many other bitter alkaloids. However romantic it seems, this "organic" means of ingesting mescaline is in my opinion strictly for the masochists and penitents. Many novice users succumb to the fate of William James, *viz.* they become so sickened by the taste of the drug that they cannot stomach enough to know the delights of a visionary dose of mescaline.

Some *péyotl* users will grind the dried buttons and extract them by boiling the ground material in water, filtering off the residue, then concentrating the resultant mescaline-enriched extract into a gummy "mescaline tar" which is then stuffed into large capsules for ingestion (the laborious ritual of removing the silky hairs from the buttons is unnecessary, unless one wishes to make an offering as do the Huicholes). In the case of *San Pedro*, it is known that most of the mescaline is concentrated in the green skin of the cactus, which is carefully peeled away and dried at low temperatures, then reduced to a powder. Some users will place this powdered *San Pedro* skin in large capsules for ingestion (it is said that the skin of about a 30 cm long piece of *San Pedro* cactus represents a dose of *Trichocereus pachanoi*). In the case of *Trichocereus peruvianus*, the skin of only about a 3 cm section is said to represent a strong dose. Some users of mescaline-containing *Trichocereus* species prefer to make an infusion of the powdered cactus skin, and to drink this as a tea, despite its bitterness.

When one ingests either pure mescaline or "péyo-tea," *San Pedro* tea or "mescaline tar" in capsules, there is a chance of slight nausea (Shulgin 1979A). This is due to the fact that such a large amount of alkaloidal material must be ingested in order to experience psychoptic effects. To overcome this annoying syndrome, some users ingest a pill of *Dramamine* a half an hour before taking the mescaline preparation. On the other hand, some users clearly like the "purgative" aspect of visionary cacti, which they mistakenly interpret as a "cleansing"—in reality the body is rebelling against a large dose of toxic alkaloids and attempting to "cleanse" the system of the drug! The experienced user realizes that one to two hours will typically elapse before the inebriation commences, in some cases as much as three or four hours. Therefore, generally at least three or four hours are allowed to elapse before attempting to augment the dose, in cases where the effects are marginal.

NOTES

[1] In a 1956 letter to Huxley, Humphry Osmond had proposed the term *psychedelic* for mescaline and related drugs. Huxley (whose vision was quite poor) apparently misread the word as *psychodetic*, and in his 30 March 1956 letter to Osmond proposed *phanerothyme* as an alternative, thinking it meant "that which makes manifest." Osmond replied with the following ditty: "To fathom Hell or soar angelic,/Just take a pinch of psychedelic." Later, Osmond was to render the line as "To sink in Hell or soar angelic/You'll need a pinch of psychedelic." Huxley responded with: "To make this trivial world sublime,/Take a half a gramme of phanerothyme" (Horowitz & Palmer 1977). Huxley was obviously thinking of mescaline, judging by the dose. In Osmond's later alternate reading, "trivial" is replaced by "mundane." Osmond settled on *psychedelic*, but Huxley instead used the etymologically correct *psychodelic*, which Osmond rejected, because of the connotation of "psychotic." *Phanerothyme* was then all but forgotten (Bieberman 1968), which is just as well, for the word would mean "manifester of passion, temper or anger" (Ruck *et al.* 1979). These drugs had earlier been designated *hallucinogens* by D. Johnson (Johnson 1953), who borrowed the term from Osmond and Americans A. Hoffer and J. Smythies. Other names were *psychodysleptic* and *psychotomimetic* (or *psychosomimetic*, Shulgin 1963B), which more than *psychodelic* suffered from the association of the drugs with psychosis (the term "psycho" to describe a deranged criminal became current with the success of Alfred Hitchcock's film *Psycho*). *Psychedelic* enjoyed popular success, and was spread in the scientific world by the seminal *The Psychedelic Review* (founded by Osmond, R. Metzner and T. Leary in 1963, and of which 11 numbers were published, the last being Winter 1970/

71; with issue No. 5 in 1965, the name was changed simply to *Psychedelic Review*), and later by the *Journal of Psychedelic Drugs*, first published in Summer 1967. The *Journal of Psychedelic Drugs* is still in print, but in 1981 changed its name with Volume 13 to the more appropriate *Journal of Psychoactive Drugs*. Aaronson and Osmond published *Psychedelics: The Uses and Implications of Hallucinogenic Drugs* in 1970, lending further currency to both *psychedelic* and *hallucinogenic* (Aaronson & Osmond 1970). Apart from being an incorrect verbal formation, however, *psychedelic* suffered connotations of 1960s drug use and of political and artistic associations deriving therefrom (*psychedelic* art, music, *etc.*; Rätsch 1993) such that it became incongruous to speak of traditional shamans using *psychedelic* plants. In any case, the word is decidedly pejorative for many people unfamiliar with these drugs, and evokes unpleasant associations (see also Chapter 4, Note 1 for a discussion of the pejorative use of *narcotic* in association with entheogens). Moreover, the word cannot escape the *psycho* stigma—it is commonly translated into Spanish as *[p]sicodélico* (to avoid the orthographically-complex and etymologically anomalous *[p]siquedélico*) and writers in other languages similarly employ the correct root *psycho-*. In 1979, Carl A.P. Ruck, Jeremy Bigwood, Danny Staples, R. Gordon Wasson and I proposed *entheogen(ic)* as an etymologically and culturally appropriate, non-prejudicial term to describe shamanic inebriants and replace those terms discussed above (Ott 1996A; Ruck *et al.* 1979; Wasson *et al.* 1980B). *Entheogenic* (literally "becoming divine within") refers to the common perception of users of *entheogens*, which is anything but an hallucination, that the divine infuses all beings, including the *entheogenic* plant and its fortunate human user. It derives from ενθεοζ of the ancient Greeks, a root to describe just such states of inspiration and inebriation A popular book dismissed *entheogen* as "a clumsy word freighted with theological baggage" (T.K. McKenna 1992), the author having neglected to appreciate its non-theological sense, and being apparently unaware of the use of the word in ancient Greece. Incongruously, this word was dismissed for its purported "theological baggage" in a book entitled *Food of the Gods*! B.R. Ortíz de Montellano, an expert in Meso-American ethnomedicine, adopted the term *entheogen* enthusiastically (Ortíz de Montellano 1981), saying that it mirrored closely ancient Aztec notions of the actions of their sacred plants, as evidenced by the Náhuatl terms *itech quinehua* ("it takes possession of him") and *itech quiza* ("it comes out in him") to describe the entheogenic experience (Ortíz de Montellano 1990). Prior to his pioneering mushroom *velada* with the Mazatec shaman María Sabina in 1955 (see Chapter 5), ethnomycologist R. Gordon Wasson was told it would be inappropriate for his companion A. Richardson to take photographs "*mientras que la fuerza le agarrara*" ("while the force seized her"), reflecting similar ideas in contemporary México (Ott & Pollock 1976A). The fact that the paper proposing this neologism *entheogen(ic)* was published first in *Journal of Psychedelic Drugs*, and in the same issue (which I edited) I called for changing the name of the publication to *Journal of Entheogenic Drugs* (Ott 1979A) may have contributed to the editors' decision to change the name two years later. *Entheogen* has been used by many leading experts in the field, including J. Bigwood, M.D. Coe, J.L. Díaz, W. Doniger (O'Flaherty), W.A. Emboden, A. Escohotado, J. Fericgla, P.T. Furst, J. Gartz, G. Guzmán, J. Halifax, A. Hofmann, F.J. Lipp, B. Lowy, D.J. McKenna, E. MacRae, B.R. Ortíz de Montellano, C.A.P. Ruck, R.E. Schultes, R.G. Wasson and others; though some, such as W. La Barre and A.T. Shulgin have shunned it

(La Barre 1988). *Entheogen* has appeared widely in print—in English, German, French, Italian, Portuguese and Spanish (the 1979 paper proposing the word was translated into Spanish and published as an appendix to the Spanish edition of *The Road to Eleusis*; Wasson *et al.* 1980B), even in Catalán and Slovenian. With the present book, it appears for the sixth time in a book title, the first being *Persephone's Quest: Entheogens and the Origins of Religion* (Wasson *et al.* 1986). The recent translation (1992) of *La Búsqueda de Perséfone* into Spanish used *Enteógenos* in Spanish in the subtitle (*Los Enteógenos y los Orígenes de la Religión*), and the editors of Fondo de Cultura Económica seem intent on establishing the word in Spanish—in the *verso*-cover copy, animadversion is made to "the incorrectly named hallucinogenic mushrooms—strictly speaking, *entheogenic* mushrooms..." ("*los mal llamados hongos alucinógenos*—enteógenos, *en rigor*..."; italics in the original; Wasson *et al.* 1986). A new bilingual (German/English) scientific journal which debuted in 1991 avoided *psychedelic, hallucinogenic* and *entheogenic*, opting instead to refer in the title to *geistbewegende* ("mind-bearing") plants and culture (a mistranslation of Huxley's proposed *psychophoric*), although in an introductory editorial, M. Horowitz mentioned Gordon Wasson's preference for *entheogen(ic)* (Horowitz 1991). A newsletter debuted in September 1992, entitled *The Entheogen Review* (De Korne 1992); another in Winter 1993, *The Entheogen Law Reporter* (Boire 1994); a 1983 conference organized at the University of California Santa Barbara, was entitled: "Entheogens: The Spiritual Psychedelics [*sic*]."

2 Huxley's mushroom derived its name from the Sanskrit *moksha*, "liberation," a goal of Hinduism, liberation from the cycle of rebirths. There is a classical Indian dance, in the Odissi style from Orissa (which derived originally from rituals attending the worship of the pre-Vedic god Jagannath at the Jagannath Mandir in Puri, Orissa), called *Moksha* (Marglin 1985). Huxley prophetically described a cultivated mushroom. As we will see in Chapter 5, it was cultivation technology which was to foster the widespread use of the entheogenic *teonanácatl* mushroom in the 1970s.

3 *Péyotl* was originally described botanically as *Echinocactus williamsii* in 1845; then as *Anhalonium williamsii* in 1886; *Mammillaria williamsii* in 1891; and *Ariocarpus williamsii* in 1894; before being classified as *Lophophora williamsii* in 1894, the classification accepted today (Anderson 1980; Coulter 1894). *Echinocactus rapa* is a little-known synonym. In 1888, based on studies of rehydrated specimens of Briggs' "Muscale[*sic*] Buttons" sent to Parke, Davis and Co. in Detroit, some of which were given to Louis Lewin (see Note 5 below), Hennings proposed the binomial *Anhalonium lewinii*, which is the best-known synonym for *L. williamsii* (Hennings 1888). Lewin continued to use this designation throughout his life (Lewin 1924), and it still appears in some modern publications in Europe (Escohotado 1989A). In the last century, chemists thought there were two species of *péyotl*, *A. lewinii* and *A. williamsii*. Some of the *A. williamsii* specimens analyzed chemically turned out to be *péyotl's* related species *Lophophora diffusa*, which is chemically quite distinct (Bruhn & Holmstedt 1974). See Anderson (1969; 1980) for a full discussion of historical and contemporary *péyotl* systematics.

4 Today generally written mescaline, although psilocybin[e] and psilocin[e] are commonly

written without the suffix *e*. All of these drugs were first named in the German language without the suffix. There is a convention in English and French of adding the terminal *e* to alkaloid and other amine names; in Spanish, Italian and Portuguese a terminal *a* is added. For consistency, the suffix will be used throughout this text, even with psilocybine and psilocine. Strictly speaking, the correct orthography for the drug in English would be *mezcaline*. As for *péyotl*, it has been suggested that this Náhuatl term may derive from a root meaning "inebriant," supposing the modern Mexicanism *piule* (applied to several entheogens all over México) to be etymologically related. Blas Pablo Reko proposed *pi-yotli →pi-yautli* "little inebriant" as a derivation (Reko 1919)—and today *yahutli (yya-hutli* or *yauhtli*) is still applied to the psychotropic *Tagetes lucida* (see Appendix B). Wasson proposed the following etymological relationship between the two words: *péyotl/péyutl→peyúle→piule* (Wasson 1963). In modern México, *péyotl* is obsolete, and the hispanicized version *peyote* is pronounced *peh-yoh´-teh;* nevertheless, the probable pronunciation in Náhuatl would have been *pei´-yohtl*, which is how Sahagún spelled the word (*peiotl*), and I have adopted in this text the best orthographic approximation: *péyotl*.

5 It is a wonder Heffter didn't name the drug *muscalin*. He was under the misapprehension that *péyotl* was known as *muscale buttons* (Heffter 1896). An American physician, J.R. Briggs of Texas had published the first scientific paper on *péyotl* (Briggs 1887), calling the drug *muscale buttons*. Briggs sent two consignments (the second of 5 bushels) to Parke, Davis and Co. of Detroit, and some of these were given to Lewin in 1887, during his U.S. sojourn (Bruhn & Holmstedt 1974; Holmstedt & Liljestrand 1963). The name *muscale buttons* was used in Europe for some years. *Péyotl* was also called *mescal buttons*, reflecting confusion with the previously-mentioned *mescal bean*, the seed of *Sophora secundiflora* (see Appendix B). All of these terms—*mescal button, mescal bean, muscale button*—are misnomers. Etymologically *mescal* (*mezcal*) refers to species of *Agave*, called in Náhuatl *mexcalli* (La Barre 1938B). The confusion with the correctly-named alcoholic beverage *mezcal* in part derives from mistaking the effect of *péyotl* for an effect like that conferred by alcohol. Since there was nothing else in their experience with which to compare it, whites viewing Indians under the influence of *péyotl* equated the effects with alcoholic inebriation (as early Spanish chroniclers had done in the case of the entheogenic mushrooms of México, see Chapter 5; and as Siberian explorers did in the case of fly-agaric, see Chapter 6), leading to misleading terms such as *dry whiskey, whiskey root* and *white mule* (the last a name for "moonshine" or homemade whiskey; Bruhn & Holmstedt 1974; Schultes 1937B). This semantic problem surely heightened the confusion of *péyotl* with *mezcal*. In his pioneering 1887 article, Briggs described a self-experiment with a third of a "button," which produced effects quite different from those of *péyotl*. These effects Briggs likened to cocaine and opium, and he felt "2 buttons would kill a *white* man" (italics in the original; Briggs 1887), leading some to question whether the *muscale buttons* Briggs had tried were a different and more toxic species of cactus (Bruhn & Holmstedt 1974). Nevertheless, the material he later sent to Parke, Davis and Co. was surely *péyotl*.

6 *Lophophora diffusa* in general contains only trace amounts of mescaline, with the principal alkaloid being peyotline or pellotine (Bruhn & Holmstedt 1974; Schultes & Hofmann

1980). This led to some early confusion in chemical studies, and the tendency, later vindicated, to separate *péyotl* into two distinct species. What is now considered to be *L. diffusa* was earlier identified in some chemical studies as *Anhalonium williamsii*; whereas the true *A. williamsii* (now knows as *L. williamsii*) was sometimes incorrectly called *A. lewinii*. There are anatomical and ecological differences, apart from the chemical variations, distinguishing the two species of *Lophophora* (Anderson 1969; Anderson 1980; Bruhn & Holmstedt 1974).

7 There are a number of other cactus species associated with *péyotl* etymologically, chemically or ethnographically (Der Marderosian 1966). *Ariocarpus fissuratus* is known to the Tarahumara as *híkuli sunamí* or *peyote cimarrón* and is said by these Indians to produce psychoptic effects (Bye 1979A; Ott 1979B). A related species, *A. retusus*, is called a "false peyote" and alleged to produce unpleasant effects (Bruhn & Bruhn 1973; Furst 1971; Schultes & Hofmann 1980). *A. fissuratus* contains hordenine, *N*-methyltyramine and *N*-methyl-3,4-dimethoxyphenethylamine (Norquist & McLaughlin 1970), compounds also found in *A. retusus* and *A. scapharostrus* (Schultes & Hofmann 1980). β-Phenethylamines have also been found in *A. agavoides* (Bruhn & Bruhn 1973), *A. trigonus* and *A. kotschoubeyanus* (Schultes & Hofmann 1980). *Coryphantha compacta*, known in Tarahumara as *wíchuri* or *bakana*, is another "kind" of *péyotl* (Bye 1979A) which, together with *C. macromeris*, *C. palmerii*, *C. cornifera* var. *echinus*, *C. ramillosa* and *C. calipensis* has been found to contain phenethylamines, including macromerine, normacromerine and others (Hornemann *et al.* 1973; Sato *et al.* 1973; Schultes & Hofmann 1980). *C. macromeris* and *C. palmerii* have both been reportedly used as traditional entheogens (Schultes & Hofmann 1980). *Echinocereus triglochidiatus* and *E. salm-dyckianus* are other "kinds" of *híkuri* or *péyotl* known to the Tarahumara (Bye 1979A). Some phenethylamines are known from *E. merkeri* (Bruhn & Bruhn 1973), and there is a report of 5-methoxy-*N,N*-dimethyltryptamine from *E. triglochidiatus* (Bye 1979A; McLaughlin 1979), as well as of *N,N*-dimethylhistamine from the varieties *neomexicanus* and *paucispinus* of *E. triglochidiatus* (Ferrigni *et al.* 1982). The Tarahumara call *Epithelantha micromeris híkuli mulato* ("the dark-skinned *péyotl*"), and are also known to use as a *péyotl*, *Mammillaria craigii*, which they call *wíchuri* or *peyote de San Pedro* (Bye 1979A). Like *Ariocarpus fissuratus*, the related *M. heyderi* contains *N*-methyl-3,4-dimethoxyphenethylamine (Bruhn & Bruhn 1973). *M. grahamii* var. *oliviae* is also known to the Tarahumara as a *híkuri* or "peyote" (Bye 1979A). *Mammillaria longimamma* and *M. pectinifera* (also known as *Solisia pectinata*, see below) may be known as *peyotillo* or may be confused with *péyotl* (Anderson 1980), and *M. senilis* is another cactus species "considered sacred." The Tarahumara make entheogenic use of the sap of *Pachycereus pecten-aboriginum*, which has also been found to contain phenethylamines (Bruhn & Lindgren 1976; Bye 1979A) in a ritual potion called *cawé* or *chawé*. *Pelecyphora aselliformis* is another well-known "peyote" from northern México also known to contain phenethylamine alkaloids (Bruhn & Bruhn 1973), including traces of mescaline (Neal *et al.* 1972). Another "peyote" in the genus, *P. pseudopectinata*, has been reported to contain hordenine (Bruhn & Bruhn 1973). Similarly, hordenine has likewise been found in two other *peyotillos*, *Solisia pectinata* and *Turbinicarpus pseudomacrochele*, with the former also reported to contain *N*-methyltyramine (Bruhn & Bruhn 1973). *Astrophytum asterias*, *A.*

capricorne, and *A. myriostigma* are other *peyotillo* species, similar in appearance to *péyotl*. *Aztekium ritterii* and *Strombocactus disciformis* are *peyotillos* with a superficial resemblance to *péyotl* (Anderson 1980). *Obregonia denegrii* is another *peyotillo* known to contain phenethylamines. *Carnegiea gigantea* is reported to contain tetrahydroisoquinoline alkaloids, and is the basis of a ceremonial fermented potion (Bruhn & Lundström 1976; Bruhn *et al.* 1970; Díaz 1979). Two non-cactaceous plants are also associated by the Tarahumara with *péyotl*. The terrestrial bromeliad *Tillandsia mooreana* is known in Tarahumara as *wa-ráruwi*, a *péyotl* "companion," and the epiphytic orchid *Oncidium longifolium* (=*O. cebolleta*) is considered by the Tarahumara to be a replacement for *péyotl* (Bye 1975; Bye 1979A; see Appendix B). But little chemical information is available on either of these last two unusual "peyotes" (recently phenanthrene derivatives of unknown pharmacology were isolated from the orchid by Stermitz *et al.* 1983; and flavonoids of obscure pharmacology from a related bromeliad, *Tillandsia purpurea* by Arslanian *et al.* 1986), and in Amazonian Colombia and Ecuador, Kofán Indians use extracts of a related orchid, *Oncidium pusillum* as a topical antiseptic (Schultes & Raffauf 1990), whereas *T. purpurea* is depicted on Mochica pottery and has been suggested to be entheogenic (Cabieses 1986; Hoyle 1938). *Oncidium carthagenense* is reportedly used as a headache remedy by Huastec Mayans of México (Alcorn 1984). Another orchid, *Cypripedium calceolus*, has been reportedly used as a dream-inducing agent by North American Menominee Indians (Moerman 1986; Smith 1923). In this context, it is also important to mention the use by the Sharanahua Indians of Amazonian Perú, of two cacti, unidentified species of *Opuntia* and *Epiphyllum*, as additives to their entheogenic *ayahuasca* potions (see Chapter 4). Again, we have no chemical information on these intriguing South American cacti which, like *Tillandsia mooreana* and *Oncidium longifolium*, must be considered to be putative entheogenic plants. The name *peyote* is also applied in contemporary México to several species of Compositae used as medicinal plants, including: *Cacalia cordifolia* (*Peyotl Xochimilcensi*), *C. decomposita*, *Senecio calophyllus*, *S. cervariaefolius*, *S. grayanus*, *S. hartwegii*, *S. praecox* and *S. toluccanus* (Díaz 1976). While the relationship of these *Senecio* species to *péyotl* in México is obscure, *Senecio elatus* is used in South America as an additive to potions based on the mescaline-containing *Trichocereus* cacti (Polia & Bianchi 1992). Schultes has published a long list of plants known as "peyote" in México (Schultes 1937B), and we must bear in mind the Reko/Wasson theory that the modern general term for inebriating plants in México, *piule*, is related to *péyotl*, or both to a common root referring to sacred inebriation (see Note 4 above; Reko 1919; Wasson 1963).

[8] The term "cross-tolerance" means simply that were any subject rendered tolerant to the psychoptic effects of LSD, psilocybine or psilocine, such that these no longer affected him (taking these drugs 2 or 3 days in succession will do this), he would also be tolerant to the effects of mescaline.

[9] In two thorough books and an article (De Mille 1976; De Mille 1979; De Mille 1980) an American psychologist demonstrated that Castaneda invented Don Juan. He brought to bear various arguments to support this position, but failed to mention this obvious and telling mistake of Castaneda's. *Péyotl* expert Weston La Barre devoted five pages to Casta-

neda in an appendix to the fourth edition of his classic study *The Peyote Cult* (La Barre 1975). For La Barre, Castaneda's work was a "literary sensation" and he commented that "no professional anthropologist who read the first book [Castaneda 1968] was ever able to suppose it made any contribution to Yaqui ethnography." Writing of *A Separate Reality* (Castaneda 1971), La Barre concluded: "the writing is pretentious... the book is frustratingly and tiresomely dull, posturing pseudo-ethnography and, intellectually, kitsch." See Chapter 5 for further evidence of the fictitious nature of Castaneda's books. Currently, even Castaneda's own publisher offers the books for sale under the rubric of fiction.

[10] The correct terminology we must apply here separates organic compounds into two classes: 1) *natural* compounds, those which have been found in plant or animal tissues; and 2) *artificial* compounds, those which have not been discovered in plants or animals. *Artificial* compounds are invariably *synthetic* (laboratory-made) or *semi-synthetic* (laboratory-made, but using a closely-related *natural* product as a starting material—such compounds, of which LSD is an example, are often called *analogues* or *derivatives* of their *natural congeners*), but *natural* compounds may be (and frequently are) prepared by synthesis or semi-synthesis. Vanillin is an example of a *synthetic natural* compound. Vanillin may be obtained purely as a *natural* product, by isolation from vanilla beans, *Vanilla planifolia*, ("pure vanilla extract" is a crude, vanillin-enriched, extract of *Vanilla* beans) or it may be synthesized from *natural* compounds such as eugenol or guaiacol, or from lignin-rich wastes of the paper industry. Whether extracted or *semi-synthetic*, vanillin is a *natural* compound. LSD, also *semi-synthetic*, remains an *artificial* compound because it has not yet been found to occur in plants or animals. Some tend to condemn or eschew *artificial* compounds, as being unnatural and hence dangerous. The problem with such blanket condemnations is that *artificial* compounds sometimes, with further research, prove to be *natural* compounds (that is, although discovered first in the laboratory, by synthesis or semi-synthesis, the compound is later found to occur in plants and/or animals). There are innumerable examples of this, and within the field of entheogenic drugs, two important compounds immediately come to mind. Lysergic acid amide (or LA-111, its laboratory code-name) was first synthesized by Albert Hofmann of Sandoz laboratories in the 1940s (and even earlier obtained as a degradation product of natural ergot alkaloids in London; Smith & Timmis 1932), during the same series of experiments which led to the synthesis of LSD (see Chapter 2). LA-111 existed as an *artificial* compound for almost 30 years until in 1960 it was discovered to be a *natural* compound, the active principle of the Mexican entheogenic morning glories (see Chapter 2; Hofmann 1961; Hofmann 1963A; Hofmann 1964; Hofmann 1978A; Hofmann & Tscherter 1960). This compound was even bioassayed and found to be entheogenic in 1947 (Hofmann 1963A), 13 years before it was known to be a *natural* compound and active principle of a traditionally-used entheogenic plant! In the ergot alkaloid series, iso-lysergic acid amide and lysergol likewise were first discovered as *artificial* compounds in the laboratory and only much later found to be in fact *natural* compounds. The same is true for *N,N*-DiMethylTryptamine (DMT; see Chapter 3). This compound was first synthesized by R.H.F. Manske in 1931 (Manske 1931), and remained an *artificial* compound until 24 years later, when it was found to be a *natural* compound, being then isolated by M.S. Fish and colleagues from

Anadenanthera peregrina (Fish *et al.* 1955), one of the first entheogenic plants reported from the New World in 1496. Actually, DMT, under the name *nigerina*, was first isolated in 1946 from *Mimosa hostilis*, but its identity with DMT was not known until 1959 (see Chapter 3; Gonçalves de Lima 1946; Pachter *et al.* 1959). In the case of LSD, we cannot be certain it will not be found in plants or animals in the future, and any *artificial* compound can be considered to be so only provisionally. There is a vague line separating *natural* compounds and closely-related *semi-synthetic artificial derivatives*, in any case. The enzymes in psilocybian mushrooms (see Chapter 5) which catalyze the transformation of DMT into 4-hydroxy-DMT or psilocine (technically, indole-4-hydroxylases) can accept the artificial DET (see Chapter 3) as substrate *in lieu* of DMT, and catalyze the transformation of DET into 4-hydroxy-DET or CZ-74 (Gartz 1989C). Similarly, receptor sites in our brains can accept this 4-hydroxy-DET *in lieu* of 4-hydroxy-DMT (psilocine); or DET *in lieu* of DMT; giving us the psychoptic effect in every case. These same mushroomic enzymes can also act on LSD-like ergot alkaloids (see Chapter 2), effecting chemical changes in them (Brack *et al.* 1962; Hofmann 1964). It is therefore of little meaning to attempt to judge compounds on the basis of their being *natural* or *artificial. Synthetic natural* vanillin, identical to the vanillin found in *Vanilla* beans, when made from lignin-rich wastes of the paper industry, is an enlightened example of recycling—converting chemical byproducts, that might otherwise end up being dumped or need to be confined as "toxic waste," into a valuable flavoring agent. See also the following note.

[11] As explained in the previous note, it is of little meaning to approve some compounds on the basis of their being *natural*, and reject others because they are *artificial*—we cannot be certain which *artificial* compounds will later prove to be *natural.* Moreover, some of the most toxic compounds known are *natural* compounds, such as: aflatoxins and other mycotoxins, botulinum toxin, cholera toxin, the Coelenterate palytoxin, amatoxins and phallotoxins (cyclic peptide toxins from *Amanita phalloides* and other mushrooms), tetrodotoxin, mytilitoxin or *Gonyaulax* toxin, batrachotoxins, halitoxin, *etc.* The list of unusually potent *natural* toxins grows by the day. It has been estimated that the average American diet contains 1500 mg daily of natural pesticides present in virtually all plant foods, and only 0.09 mg daily of artificial pesticides—more than 10,000 times more *natural* than *artificial* toxins (Gold *et al.* 1992)! Clearly, we cannot by any means equate *natural* with *safe.* The publication in 1972 of Andrew Weil's *The Natural Mind: A New Way of Looking at Drugs and the Higher Consciousness* (Weil 1972) was surely a potent stimulus to the desire for "organic" entheogens and "mescaline" as opposed to LSD. This book might fairly be described as the gospel of the "natural is better" or the "organophile" movement. One cannot quibble with Weil's thesis that *coca* leaf, as a more dilute, less concentrated form of the drug, is inherently safer to use than the isolated, concentrated active principle, in this case cocaine. This is a special case, inasmuch as *coca* leaf is known to be a nutritious food (Duke *et al.* 1975) and not known to contain toxic elements, other than the unconfirmed report of nicotine in the leaf (Novák *et al.* 1984). It would be mistaken, however, to elevate this to a rule or general principle. In the case of drugs that are smoked, such as *Cannabis*, it would unquestionably be safer to smoke the pure active principle (THC), in the appropriate dose, than plant preparations whose combustion will generate tars and

other pyrolysis products which are mutagenic and carcinogenic. It would certainly be more healthful to smoke pure DMT (see Chapter 3) than enriched plant preparations which contain it, for the same reason. Chewing of *betel* (*Areca catechu*, a palm nut masticatory, one of the world's most widely-used stimulants) is unquestionably carcinogenic. While the main active principle, arecoline, is a suspected carcinogen, in many studies it shows no toxicity by itself, or very little. The whole *betel* quid as chewed, however, with lime and *betle* leaf (*Piper betle*), contains many very active carcinogens (Sen *et al.* 1989). Pure arecoline would surely be a more healthful form of the drug, and in 4 mg doses it has been shown significantly to enhance serial learning in human beings (Sitaram *et al.* 1978). On the other hand, natural antioxidants including vitamins α-tocopherol and β-carotene have been cited to explain the observed "chemopreventive" effect of a *betle* leaf extract against benzo[*a*]pyrene artificially-induced stomach tumors in mice (Bhide *et al.* 1991); an effect, however, not observed in tests involving complex *betel* quids, which often contain also carcinogenic tobacco (a modern innovation introduced to India around the Second World War; Shulgin 1992), in addition to spices such as cloves and cardamom seeds. Pure nicotine (such as *Nicorette* gum) likewise would surely be a safer stimulant than tobacco preparations, which are carcinogenic no matter how taken, owing to myriad carcinogens present with the nicotine in the smoke of burned tobacco, or the juice of chewing tobacco (Becker Popescu 1985). The list of traditional medicinal plants now known to contain toxic levels of pyrrolizidine alkaloids gets longer every year. De Smet recently cited 62 traditional medicinal plants in three families—Asteraceae, Boraginaceae and Leguminosae—now known to contain toxic levels of hepatotoxic pyrrolizidine alkaloids, and a total of 284 plant species in six families containing these dangerous compounds (De Smet 1991). The best known is comfrey (*Symphytum officinale*), which is now considered by all but the most ideologically pure organophiles to be too toxic for any use other than topical (Der Marderosian & Liberti 1988; Weil 1990). Owing to its content of hepatotoxic alkaloids such as symphytine and echimidine, the British organization responsible for the sale of comfrey in the United Kingdom stated "no human being or animal should eat, drink, or take comfrey in any form" (Der Marderosian & Liberti 1988). In South Africa, at least 260 recent deaths from renal and hepatic failure have been attributed to medicinal and other use of *Callilepsis laureola* in the family Asteraceae, the tuber of which contains the toxic glycoside, atractyloside (Bye & Dutton 1991). Again, *natural* in no way can be equated with *safe*. In the present case, LSD *versus* mescaline or pure mescaline *versus péyotl*, there is no question that the *artificial* LSD is a more healthful entheogen than mescaline; and likewise that mescaline is safer than whole *péyotl*. A typical dose of LSD, 100–250 micrograms, is roughly equivalent in entheogenic potency to 400–1000 milligrams of mescaline; that is, LSD is about 4000 times more potent than mescaline. This means the body of the user of both drugs must metabolize 1/4000th the amount of alkaloid in the case of the dose of LSD as opposed to the dose of mescaline—both foreign substances to the body. In general, it can be said that the LSD dose represents much less wear-and-tear on the body's detoxification mechanisms. There is also much less likelihood of toxic side-effects from LSD, since such a minuscule dose is involved. Similarly, ingesting *péyotl* involves the ingestion of some 50 alkaloids (Shulgin 1979A; plus peptides, carbohydrates, amino acids, nucleic acids, fats, unknown potentially toxic constituents, *etc.*). Dried *péyotl* cactus tops contain about 8% alkaloids, a considerable amount, of which about 30% is mescaline; 17% peyotline or pellotine; 14% anhalonidine; 8% each of anhalamine and hordenine; and 5% lophophorine (Lundström 1971). Expressed as percentages of the dried *péyotl* buttons, the contents are: 2.4–2.7% mescaline; 1.4–1.5% peyotline or pellotine; 1.2–1.3% anhalonidine; 0.6–0.7% each of anhalamine and hordenine; and 0.4% lophophorine (Bruhn & Holmstedt 1974; Lundström 1971). In order to ingest 400 mg of mescaline, one would have to ingest 16 grams of dried *péyotl* buttons, and would in the process ingest a total of 1.28 grams of alkaloids, including 240 mg of peyotline or pellotine, 200 mg of anhalonidine; 100 mg each of anhalamine and hordenine; and 65 mg of lophophorine (plus another 175 mg of a soup of more than 40 other alkaloids)! Peyotline or pellotine is a sedative effective in 50 mg doses in adults (Jolly 1896), so the *péyotl* dose would contain nearly 5 times the active dose in human beings; anhalonidine exerts a similar effect, but with one fourth the activity—this compound probably does not contribute to the effects of *péyotl* (Shulgin 1973). Hordenine is a stimulant, but Heffter found a 100 mg dose to be inactive (Bruhn & Bruhn 1973). Lophophorine is highly toxic and produces strychnine-like convulsions at 12 mg/kg doses, but evokes nausea in human beings at much lower doses (Anderson 1980). Heffter found a 20 mg dose of lophophorine to produce vasodilation and headache (Heffter 1898). The choice is thus clear. One might subject one's body to a tenth of a milligram of LSD, or 400 milligrams of mescaline (4000 times as much), or 400 milligrams of mescaline in the form of *péyotl*, along with 880 milligrams of other alkaloids (13,000 times as much alkaloid as the LSD dose), some of them toxic, some of unknown toxicity, along with innumerable other, unknown, possibly toxic constituents. Which would likely be the more healthful for the body? A recent book (McKenna 1991) revived Weil's "natural is better" *dictum* with regard to the entheogenic drugs, promoting the *natural* products psilocybine, mescaline and DMT at the expense of the *artificial* LSD.

[12] As Andrew Weil acknowledged in his recent book (Weil 1990), "there is no important difference between natural and synthetic vitamins." I would modify this to say that not only is there no important difference, but that in many cases, the so-called "natural" vitamins contain the same synthetic vitamins as their more honestly-labeled cousins. As pointed out in Note 10, all vitamins are *natural* compounds and may be so labeled, whether isolated from a plant or animal or prepared by synthesis or semi-synthesis. Dishonest manufacturers sometimes exploit the public confusion on this point by foisting overpriced so-called "natural" vitamins on the unsuspecting public. An example is "Rose Hips Vitamin C" or "Acerola Vitamin C." The buyer is led to believe that the Vitamin C in the product is isolated from rose hips (dried fruits of *Rosa* spp.) or acerola cherries (fruit of *Malpighia glabra*). The label will usually read "standardized to contain" so many milligrams of Vitamin C. This means the stated label content of, say, 250 mg Vitamin C represents that amount of *synthetic* Vitamin C in each tablet, together with an unknown amount of rose hip or acerola cherry powder, which is really only flavoring, 'though it may contribute a modicum of Vitamin C. Read the labels carefully. Does it say how much of the Vitamin C is from rose hips or acerola cherries? If not, write the manufacturer and demand to know how much of the Vitamin C in the product is from the rose hip or acerola

cherries. Some such products are more honestly labeled as "Natural Vitamin C with Rose Hips." There are some vitamins on the market which really are isolated from plants or animals—Vitamin A from fish liver oils is a prominent example. But one problem with such products is possible contamination with fat-soluble environmental pollutants found in the oceans. Some Vitamin E is truly extracted from vegetable oils; most is not. Read the labels carefully and don't be duped by wily manufacturers. Reflect also on the ecological problems associated with extracting vitamins from foods for supplements. If it is a by-product of other food processing, as in the case of Vitamin A from fish livers, fine, and such products are usually inexpensive. But if good food is being ground up and extracted so (comparatively) rich and well-fed people can have supplements isolated from *natural* sources, this doubtless represents considerable waste, as well as unnecessary environmental contamination occasioned by chemical manipulation of the extracted foodstuffs. Be wary of the claims of manufacturers and remember that advertising and public relations are designed ultimately to sell products, and should always be treated with scepticism. Manufacturers are not loathe to manipulate cynically the public and current fashions in diet, politics and opinion, in their inexorable pursuit of increased sales. I recently much enjoyed eating a *Cloud Nine* brand chocolate bar, the label of which stressed the fact that "natural oil of the Tahitian vanilla bean" was used *in lieu* of "artificial vanilla flavoring." This is fine, and I personally think the richer, more complex taste of *Vanilla* bean extract, in comparison with pure vanillin, its main, but not sole, flavoring element, justifies its use and higher cost. The warm glow conferred by this excellent dose of my favorite drug (Ott 1985) was heightened by reading the manufacturer's claim that "10% of our profits goes directly to benefit rainforest conservation in cocoa producing areas." I quickly reminded myself, however, that such areas, precisely because they are devoted to cacao production, are mostly devoid of rainforest, which has been cut down to make way for cacao trees! The desired runaway success of *Cloud Nine* chocolate bars could in fact lead to increased pressure on diminishing rainforest areas, more of which might be cleared to allow expanded cacao production to meet the increased demand! Also, how do I know the *Cloud Nine* company has ever showed any profit? Ten percent of nothing is zero. I'd much rather learn *how much money* the company donated in the most recent year, and how that donation is being used to overcome or offset the massive ecological destruction cacao production has historically wrought on tropical rainforest areas.

TABLE I
MESCALINE-CONTAINING CACTI

Gymnocalycium gibbosum	Der Marderosian 1966; Ducloux 1930[1]
Islaya minor	Doetsch *et al.* 1980[1]
Lophophora diffusa	Todd 1969; Bruhn & Holmstedt 1974[1]
L. williamsii (=*Anhalonium lewinii*)	Heffter 1896; Heffter 1898
Opuntia acanthocarpa	Ma *et al.* 1986[1]
O. basilaris	Ma *et al.* 1986[1]
O. echinocarpa	Ma *et al.* 1986[1]
O. ficus-indica	El-Moghazy *et al.* 1982[1]
O. imbricata	Meyer *et al.* 1980[1]
O. spinosior	Pardanani *et al.* 1978[1]
Pelecyphora aselliformis	Neal *et al.* 1972[1]
Pereskia corrugata	Doetsch *et al.* 1980[1]
P. tampicana	Doetsch *et al.* 1980[1]
Pereskiopsis scandens	Doetsch *et al.* 1980[1]
Polaskia chende	Ma *et al.* 1986[1]
Pterocereus gaumeri	Ma *et al.* 1986[1]
Stenocereus beneckei	Ma *et al.* 1986[1]
S. eruca	Ma *et al.* 1986[1]
S. stellatus	Ma *et al.* 1986[1]
S. treleasei	Ma *et al.* 1986[1]
Stetsonia coryne	Agurell *et al.* 1971[1]
Trichocereus bridgesii	Agurell 1969B
T. cuzcoensis	Agurell *et al.* 1971
T. fulvilanus	Agurell *et al.* 1971[1]
T. macrogonus	Agurell 1969B
T. pachanoi	Poisson 1960; Agurell 1969B; Crosby & McLaughlin 1973[2]
T. peruvianus	Pardanani *et al.* 1977
T. spachianus	Pummangura *et al.* 1982
T. strigosus	Nieto *et al.* 1982
T. taquimbalensis	Agurell *et al.* 1971
T. terscheckii	Reti & Castrillon 1951; Agurell 1969B
T. validus	Agurell *et al.* 1971
T. werdermannianus	Agurell 1969B

NOTES

[1] These cactus species have been found to contain traces of mescaline, together with other phenethylamine alkaloids, some of them toxic. They cannot presently be considered to be entheogenic species (see listings in Appendix B), although there is the possibility strains may yet be found greatly richer in entheogenic mescaline. In the case of *Lophophora diffusa*, *péyotl's* ancestor, human bioassays have been carried out, resulting mainly in "very disagreeable" experiences, although two intrepid psychonauts reported "pleasant effects" (Díaz 1979). The only mescalinic species with well-established ethnomedicinal uses as entheogens are *péyotl*, *Lophophora williamsii* (Anderson 1980; Benítez 1975; La Barre 1938; Myerhoff 1974; Rouhier 1927; Stewart 1987; Wasson 1963), and *San Pedro*, *Trichocereus pachanoi* and *T. peruvianus* (Calderón *et al.* 1982; Cordy-Collins 1982; Davis 1983B; Dobkin 1968; Dobkin de Ríos 1977; Dobkin de Ríos & Cárdenas 1980; Joralemon & Sharon 1993; Polia & Bianchi 1991; Polia & Bianchi 1992; Sharon 1972; Sharon 1978).

[2] The well-known mescalinic *San Pedro* cactus of South America, today identified as *Trichocereus pachanoi*, was once erroneously thought to be the species *Austrocylindropuntia cylindrica*, also known by the synonym *Opuntia cylindrica* (Gutiérrez-Noriega & Cruz-Sánchez 1947). Because of this confusion, *Opuntia cylindrica* was reported to contain mescaline (Turner & Heyman 1960); in all likelihood the material analyzed was actually *Trichocereus pachanoi*. When authentic *Opuntia cylindrica* was tested, it was found to be devoid of alkaloids (Agurell 1969B), although trace amounts of mescaline were subsequently found in 6 true species of *Opuntia* (El-Moghazy *et al.* 1982; Ma *et al.* 1986; Meyer *et al.* 1980; Pardanani *et al.* 1978), and an unidentified *Opuntia* species is used by the Sharanahua Indians of South America (under the name *tchai*) as an additive to entheogenic *ayahuasca* potions (see Chapter 4; Rivier & Lindgren 1972; Schultes & Raffauf 1990). Mescaline appears to be potentiated by the monoamine-oxidase-inhibiting alkaloids of *ayahuasca* (Ott 1994A), and this *Opuntia* species likely contains at least low concentrations of this cactus entheogen. *N*-Methyltyramine has been isolated from *Opuntia clavata* (Vanderveen *et al.* 1974), and methyltyramines are also known from *Trichocereus* species (Mata & McLaughlin 1976).

PART TWO

Indole Derivatives

CHAPTER TWO
LSD, Ololiuhqui, Kykeon: The Ergoline Complex

> I suddenly became strangely inebriated. The external world became changed as in a dream. Objects appeared to gain in relief; they assumed unusual dimensions; and colors became more glowing. Even self-perception and the sense of time were changed. When the eyes were closed, colored pictures flashed past in a quickly changing kaleidoscope. After a few hours, the not unpleasant inebriation, which had been experienced whilst I was fully conscious, disappeared. What had caused this condition?
>
> **Albert Hofmann**
> *Laboratory Notes* (1943)

On Friday, the sixteenth of April 1943, Albert Hofmann was abruptly overcome by the symptoms described above while working in his laboratory at the pharmaceutical firm Sandoz LTD. in Basel, Switzerland, just over the Rhine River from Nazi Germany. That day, Hofmann had recrystallized *d*-lysergic acid diethylamide tartrate (the tartaric acid salt of Lysergsäure-Diäthylamid, abbreviated LSD), a semi-synthetic compound prepared from lysergic acid that he had obtained by degradation of natural ergot alkaloids. Hofmann suspected a connection between the unusual inebriation and the LSD salt. Although he was accustomed to scrupulously clean working conditions and took pains to avoid contaminating himself with toxic ergot preparations, Hofmann speculated that some of the LSD-tartrate solution might have contacted his fingertips during recrystallization. Accordingly, he resolved to attempt a self-experiment with the tartaric acid salt of LSD.

That weekend, to rule out the possibility that he had become inebriated from breathing the solvent vapors, Hofmann went to his laboratory and intentionally inhaled vapors of the solvents with which he had been working, experiencing only slight dizziness (Hofmann 1977). The following Monday, 19 April, Hofmann prepared a 0.05% aqueous solution of LSD-tartrate, and ingested 0.5 cc of the solution, representing 0.25 mg of LSD-tartrate (equivalent to about 0.17 mg or 170 micrograms of LSD base—the quantity taken was listed incorrectly in a popular book; Stafford 1983). Within 40 minutes Hofmann experienced "slight dizziness, restlessness... visual distortions, desire to laugh..." and it was evident that LSD had indeed been the cause of his inebriation the previous Friday. He soon found himself barely able to speak intelligibly, and asked his laboratory assistant to escort him home on bicycle, as in wartime Switzerland few automobiles were available. He began to experence bizarre alterations of perception, hallucinations, synaesthesia and out-of-body sensations. Fearing that his life (or at least his sanity) was endangered, Hofmann's assistant summoned a physician, who was unable to find any abnormal symptoms, other than widely dilated pupils. After a few hours, and once he was assured by the attending physician that his life was not in danger, Hofmann's terrifying perceptions slowly gave way to more enjoyable visual and auditory phenomena, and by late that evening, the bizarre effects had subsided altogether (Escohotado 1989B; Hofmann 1980; Holmstedt & Liljestrand 1963).

Subsequent experiments showed that LSD was active in doses as low as 10–20 mcg (10–20 millionths of a gram), and that Hofmann had inadvertently ingested some 5–10 times the minimum effective dose of the drug. Hofmann had thought he was being conservative in taking 0.25 mg of LSD-tartrate, for he was judging by comparison to the known activity of ergotamine and ergonovine, two ergot alkaloids which had been isolated in the Sandoz laboratories, and which by that time had found widespread application in therapeutics. Besides being an order of magnitude more potent than any other known ergot derivative, Hofmann's LSD was approximately 4000 times the potency of mescaline (see Chapter 1) or harmine (see Chapter 4), the only other similar visionary substances known in 1943! It was, and remains, one of the most potent drugs known to science.

In 1947, Swiss psychiatrist W.A. Stoll (son of Hofmann's superior at Sandoz, Arthur Stoll) published the first descriptions of the effects of the novel entheogen (Stoll 1947). Details of the synthesis of LSD had been published four years earlier (Stoll & Hofmann 1943). By the advent of the fifties, Sandoz had begun to distribute the new drug, under the trade name *Delysid*, as an experimental preparation. Throughout the fifties and into the early sixties, *Delysid* was widely used in clinical psychiatry (Grof 1973) and in brain research. Literally thousands of experimental reports dealing with *Delysid* were published in the scientific literature, testifying to the importance of Hofmann's discovery. Besides proving to be a valuable tool in exploring the mechanisms of the brain, LSD has also shown great promise as a psychotherapeutic aid (Alhadeff 1962; Bender 1970; Delay *et al.* 1959B; Eds. 1963; Grof

1975; Grof 1980; Leuner & Holfeld 1962; Solomon 1964; Unger 1964; Yensen & Dryer 1995). After experiencing the LSD-like Mexican entheogenic mushrooms (see Chapter 5), physician V.P. Wasson predicted that their active principle would be valuable "in treating terminal illness accompanied by acute pain" (V.P. Wasson 1957). This proved to be an astute observation, as LSD has indeed shown value in treating terminal cancer patients, having both pain- and anxiety-relieving properties (Kast 1963; Kast & Collins 1964; Ocaña 1993; Pahnke 1971; Pahnke *et al.* 1970A).

LSD use was not to be confined to the research laboratory. By the late sixties, Hofmann's fungal entheogen was being used all over the world for the "not unpleasant inebriation" it provoked. LSD became illegal in most countries, and vigorous scare campaigns were mounted by the press and governments to dissuade users, painting a distorted picture of the dangers inherent in the use of this singularly potent and valuable drug. In this chapter I will trace the origins of LSD and related drugs, and document their rise as ludible drugs.

NATURAL HISTORY OF ERGOT

Our story begins with ergot, from which LSD and its psychoactive relatives are derived. Ergot is the sclerotium (the form the plant assumes to pass the winter) of the mushroom *Claviceps purpurea*,[1] which is parasitic on rye, wheat, barley and other cultivated grains, and which also infests wild grasses. After infection of the host grass with spores (technically ascospores), the mushroom forms purplish sclerotia, which project from the husk of the ripening grain. The sclerotia then fall to the ground, where they pass the winter. With the first spring rains, the sclerotia fruit, that is, they develop large numbers of tiny purple mushrooms that release ascospores, which are borne by the wind and which may contact immature ears of grain and again initiate infection (Bové 1970; Guggisberg 1954; Hofmann 1964). Some of the sclerotia, however, may be harvested with the grain and ground into flour, which they then contaminate with toxic alkaloids (Hofmann 1964).

During the Middle Ages, mass poisonings by ergot alkaloids occurred throughout Europe, whenever ergot-infested grain was consumed in large quantities (Barger 1931; Giacomoni 1985; Matossian 1989). A cool, wet growing and harvesting season was a prerequisite to the heavy infestation of the grain with ergot, and rye was especially susceptible (even with modern techniques of harvesting, small amounts of ergot are generally present in all harvested rye). The poor, who lived almost exclusively on bread, were particularly vulnerable to being poisoned by ergot alkaloids in their flour (Matossian 1989). Ergot poisoning, or ergotism, existed in two distinct types: the *convulsive* (characterized by epileptiform seizures) and *gangrenous* (characterized by gangrene of the extremities; Bauer 1973). The latter form was more prominent, and was called *ignis sacer* ("holy fire") or "St. Anthony's Fire" (*das Antoniusfeuer* in German; *feu de Saint Antoine* in French), because St. Anthony was the patron saint of a religious order dedicated to care of the numerous ergotism victims.[2] The convulsive form especially involved bizarre alterations of behavior, and has been blamed for strange outbreaks of "dance mania" or "St. Vitus' Dance" (Camporesi 1989; Heim 1957B). Not until the seventeenth century was the cause of ergotism understood to be poisoning by alkaloids from a fungus parasitizing grain, and since then, outbreaks of the disease have taken place only sporadically, the exception being the Soviet Union, which continued to suffer outbreaks of ergotism well into the present century (Barger 1931; Bauer 1973; Bové 1970; Hofmann 1978A; Matossian 1989).[3] Vitamin A deficiency is thought to be a contributing factor to the devlopment of convulsive, as opposed to gangrenous ergotism (Barger 1931), and of course the poor would have been more susceptible to such nutritional deficiency.

Ergot had also been used ethnomedicinally in Europe since antiquity, by "white witches" or midwives. It was employed as an ecbolic, or a drug to precipitate childbirth. Such use was first mentioned in writing in 1582, in an herbal by the German physician Adam Lonitzer or Lonicerus (Lonitzer 1582). In 1808, the use of ergot as a uterine-constricting agent was first reported in the scientific literature by the American physician John Stearns, who learned of it from an immigrant German midwife (Stearns 1808). By 1824 it was recognized that such use, which can cause uterine spasms and thereby imperil the life of the child, was too dangerous (Hosack 1824). Since 1824, ergot (and more recently ergot derivatives) has been used in obstetric medicine principally for the control of postpartum hemorrhage (bleeding after parturition; Hofmann 1964; Hofmann 1978A; Hofmann 1980).[4] In honor of Stearns' introduction of ergot into scientific medicine, the ElectroMyeloGram (EMG) traces showing the "oxytocic" or "uterotonic" effect of the ergot alkaloids remain known to this day as the "Stearns effect" (see Der Marderosian *et al.* 1964B, figure 1, which illustrates the Stearns effect on isolated rat uterus).

CHEMISTRY OF ERGOT

Chemical studies on ergot were begun in the nineteenth century, but the first breakthrough was not attained until 1918, when Arthur Stoll of the Sandoz laboratories isolated the first pure alkaloid with medicinally-valuable properties, which Stoll named ergotamine (Stoll 1965). Earlier, in 1907, English researchers Barger and Carr isolated an alkaloidal preparation which they called ergotoxine, because it showed principally the toxic properties of ergot. Hofmann showed 35 years later, however, that ergotoxine was actually a mixture of three ergot alkaloids (Hofmann 1964).[5] French pharmacist C. Tanret had isolated *ergotinine cristallisée* in 1875, which Hofmann later determined to be the alkaloid ergocristinine. Tanret had also isolated what he called *ergotinine amorphe*, from which Barger and Carr were able to isolate their ergotoxine mixture (Bové 1970; Hofmann 1964).

In 1935, the specifically uterotonic (uterine-constricting) and hemostatic (stopping bleeding) principle of ergot, which accounted for its use in medicine, was isolated independently in four different laboratories, including Sandoz. The new alkaloid was ultimately designated *ergonovine* (Hofmann 1978A).[6]

It was also in the late thirties that Albert Hofmann began work on ergot alkaloids. His first important project was the synthetic preparation of ergonovine, which he achieved using as starting materials natural lysergic acid (obtained from the ergotoxine mixture) and propanolamine. This was accomplished in 1937, and was the first synthesis of an ergot alkaloid. Besides proving the structure of ergonovine, Hofmann's synthesis was of considerable economic importance, as ergonovine was valuable in obstetrics, but occurred in low concentrations in ergot, and could now be prepared from other, less-valuable and toxic ergot alkaloids.[7] Using techniques he had developed in the synthesis of ergonovine, Hofmann began to prepare a series of derivatives of ergot alkaloids, attempting to find substances with improved or novel pharmacological properties.

The 25th compound Hofmann prepared in this series was *d*-lysergic acid diethylamide, first made on 16 November 1938 and given the code-name LSD-25 (Hofmann 1955; Hofmann 1970B; Hofmann 1979A; Hofmann 1979B; Hofmann 1980; Horowitz 1976). Hofmann had hoped that this compound might have analeptic properties (that is, that it would stimulate respiration and circulation), as it was structurally similar to a known analeptic, nicotinic acid diethylamide (*Coramin*). He submitted the new drug to the Sandoz pharmacologists, who discovered it was not valuable as an analeptic, and that it possessed only 70% of the uterotonic effect of ergonovine. Significantly, the pharmacologists noted that LSD-25 produced "restlessness" (*Unruhe*) in the experimental animals. Because it showed no significant properties in pharmacological screening, the pharmacologists lost interest, and the compound was shelved. Hofmann, however, "liked the structure" and had a "striking presentiment" that his LSD-25 would be of pharmacological interest and, even 'though it was contrary to company policy (when once a new compound was screened pharmacologically and judged to be of no interest, it was to be dropped from the research program), he decided to prepare a second batch of the drug five years later in 1943, which led to the serendipitous discovery of its psychoptic effects, as I discussed in the introduction to this chapter (Hofmann 1980).

In the same series of experiments which led to the synthsis of LSD-25, Hofmann prepared *d*-lysergic acid amide, or ergine (code-name LA-111), and its isomer, isoergine (Hofmann 1963A). After his discovery of the visionary effects of LSD-25, Hofmann began to test in self-experiments a series of derivatives and analogues of LSD, searching for compounds with specifically entheogenic properties.[8] In 1947 he tested ergine and isoergine in self-experiments, and found both to be psychoactive, especially ergine (Hofmann 1963A). This finding was confirmed independently in another laboratory nine years later (Solms 1956A; Solms 1956B). Although in 1947 these compounds were known only as artificial LSD congeners (Smith & Timmis 1932), in 1960 they were shown to be natural products, occurring in two different, widely disparate branches of the plant kingdom (Arcamone *et al.* 1960; Hofmann & Tscherter 1960). The significance of these experimental results will become evident after a necessary brief digression to discuss *ololiuhqui*, a Mexican ceremonial entheogen related chemically to ergot.[9]

NATURAL HISTORY AND CHEMISTRY OF *OLOLIUHQUI*

After the conquest of México in 1521, a number of sixteenth and seventeenth century Spanish writers, in reference to the religious practices of the Aztecs and other indigenous groups, described the ritual use of entheogenic seeds called *ololiuhqui*, "round things." The seeds were said to come from a plant called *coaxihuitl* or *coatl-xoxouhqui*, "snake plant" or "green snake," illustrated in the *Florentine Codex* of Sahagún, and unmistakably a member of the Convolvulaceae, the bindweed or morning glory family (Hernández 1651; Hofmann 1980; Sahagún 1950; Sahagún 1982; Schultes & Hofmann 1980; Taylor 1944; Taylor 1949; Wasson 1963). Sahagún had described use of the *ololiuhqui* seeds in rituals and in phytotherapy as a topical treatment for gout, in combination with entheogenic mushrooms (see Chapter 5), *Datura* spp. (see Appendix A) and other plants. To treat an "aquatic fever" thought to have been malaria or a similar disease, the Aztec physicians prescribed ingestion of a super-entheogen—a combination of the *ololiuhqui* seeds, *péyotl* (see Chapter 1), the entheogenic mushrooms and a *Datura* species (Sahagún 1950; Sahagún 1982)!

In 1897, Manuel Urbina identified *ololiuhqui* as the seed of *Ipomoea sidaefolia* (today known by the synonyms *Rivea corymbosa* and *Turbina corymbosa*; Urbina 1897), an identification later accepted by B.P. Reko (Reko 1919; Reko 1929). Some incorrectly maintained that the Aztec "snake plant" was not a morning glory, but a species of *Datura*, in the nightshade family, Solanaceae (Hartwich 1911; V.A. Reko 1936; Safford 1915).[10] Finally in 1938, Blas Pablo Reko and Richard Evans Schultes collected the first good botanical voucher specimens of *coaxihuitl* and *ololiuhqui*, and definitively identified the plant as *Turbina corymbosa* (Schultes 1941).

Reko had earlier sent *ololiuhqui* seeds to C.G. Santesson of Sweden, who reported they were psychoactive, but was unable to isolate the active principle (Santesson 1937A; Santesson 1937B; see also Chapter 5, Note 6). Santesson's work suggested the presence of an active gluco-alkaloid, and a quarter of a century later two groups (including that of W.B. Cook, who was working for the CIA under project MKULTRA; see Chapter 5, Note 8) independently isolated a glucoside, turbicoryn, from seeds of *T. corymbosa* (Cook & Kealand 1962; Pérezamador & Herrán 1960). Since this glucoside did not also occur in more potent seeds of *Ipomoea violacea* (see below), it is probably not important in the psychopharmacology of the morning glory seeds (Hofmann 1963A), 'though it showed hints of activity at oral doses of 30 mg (Hoffer & Osmond 1967). However, synthetic mixtures of corresponding ergoline alkaloids mirrored effects of the alkaloid extract of *ololiuhqui* seeds (Isbell & Gorodetzky 1966). In some reports of self-experiments with *ololiuhqui* seeds, doubts were cast on their visionary properties (Kinross-Wright 1959; Reko 1934). In 1955, Osmond conducted self-experiments establishing psychotropic activity of *T.corymbosa* seeds (Osmond 1955).[11] In the summer of 1959, R. Gordon Wasson (an American banker investigating the Mexican sacred mushroom cults; see Chapter 5) sent a small sample (21 g) of *ololiuhqui* seeds to Albert Hofmann of Sandoz, together with a somewhat larger sample (204 g) of a related seed, called by the Zapotecs of México *badungás* or *badoh negro*, "black *badoh*," as distinct from *badoh*, the true *ololiuhqui* (Hofmann 1963A; Wasson 1963). The second sample represented *Ipomoea violacea* seeds (synonyms: *I. rubro-caerulea*, *I. tricolor*), a morning glory commonly grown as an ornamental. Mazatec Indian use of *I. violacea* seeds was discovered by Blas Pablo Reko (1945); Zapotec use documented by T. MacDougall (MacDougall 1960). Wasson suggested that *I. violacea* represented the Aztec drug *tlitliltzin* ("sacred black ones"; Wasson 1963), and this species is known to the Mayans as *yaxce'lil* (Garza 1990). Both *I. violacea* and *T. corymbosa* are still used as shamanic inebriants in México, for example by the Mixe Indians of Oaxaca. *Ipomoea violacea* is commonly known in México as *quiebraplato* or "plate breaker," which term likely derives from the Mixe name *piH pu'ucte·sh* "broken plate flower" (Lipp 1990). The Mixe consider *I. violacea* to be more potent than *T. corymbosa* (which chemical studies have borne out) and make a cold water infusion of 26 seeds of the former, ground on a *metate* by a virgin (a practice Wasson observed among the Zapotec in 1963; just as the Mixtec served him juice of entheogenic mushrooms ground by a virgin in 1960, and as the Mazatecs served him juice of *Salvia divinorum* ground by a virgin in 1962; Wasson 1963). Before serving the infusion of the morning glory seeds, the Mixe, Zapotec and Mazatec Indians strain out the residual seed material with a cloth. A generic Mixe name for the morning glory seeds is *ma-sung-pahk*, "bones of the children" (Lipp 1991). The Zapotecs also call *Ipomoea violacea* seed *la'aja shnash* or "seed of the virgin," perhaps being the origin of the contemporary Mexican term *semillas de la virgen* for entheogenic morning glory seeds (Wasson 1963). Although it is widely assumed that the name *semillas de la virgen* refers to the Catholic virgin, it probably derives from the Zapotec term, which more likely refers to the virgin appointed to grind the seeds.

With the small initial samples of both seeds, Hofmann was able to establish the presence of indole alkaloids, which prompted him to ask Wasson to obtain larger quantities, to enable him to isolate the active principles. Early in 1960, Wasson sent Hofmann 12 kilograms of *Turbina corymbosa* seeds and 14 kilograms of *Ipomoea violacea* seeds (Hofmann 1963A). He had obtained the seeds with the assistance of the eminent anthropologist Robert Weitlaner, his daughter Irmgard, and Thomas MacDougall. Before the year 1960 was out, Hofmann and his assistants had isolated and characterized the active principles. The main active constituent of both species was discovered to be *d*-lysergic acid amide, or ergine (LA-111). Lesser amounts of isoergine, chanoclavine and elymoclavine were also found. Trace amounts of lysergol were isolated from *Turbina corymbosa* and trace amounts of ergonovine from *Ipomoea violacea* (Hofmann 1961; Hofmann 1963A; Hofmann & Tscherter 1960). It was later ascertained that some of the ergine and isoergine were present in the seeds in the form of *N*-(1-hydroxyethyl)amides, which readily hydrolyzed to ergine and isoergine (Hofmann 1971). Total alkaloid concentration was 0.012% in *Turbina corymbosa* and 0.06% in *Ipomoea violacea* (Hofmann 1963A). The alert reader will recall that ergonovine was the third pure alkaloid to be isolated from ergot. Ergine and isoergine had been prepared synthetically in the forties in the Sandoz laboratories, tested and found to be psychoactive in the same series of investigations that resulted in the synthesis and testing of LSD. Both were shown to occur also in ergot from the wild grass *Paspalum* (Arcamone *et al.* 1960). Chanoclavine and elymoclavine had earlier been isolated from ergot of *Pennisetum* and *Elymus* (Abe *et al.* 1955; Hofmann *et al.* 1957), whereas lysergol had existed only as an artificial derivative of ergot alkaloids (Hofmann 1963A). Elymoclavine and lysergol elicited "an excitation syndrome" in various animals (Yui & Takeo 1958; see Table 2, Note 13). Roquet and Favreau mistook ergine for "a glucoside with an amide function," harking back to Santesson's preliminary reports and the subsequent isolation of the glucoside turbicoryn from *T. corymbosa* (Pérezamador & Herrán 1960; Roquet & Favreau 1981).

Although there was some intitial scepticism concerning ergot alkaloids in morning glories (Hofmann 1980; Taber & Heacock 1962), Hofmann's finding was soon confirmed (Genest 1965; Taber *et al.* 1963A; Taber *et al.* 1963B), and these alkaloids have also been found to occur in numerous other species of morning glories (see Table 2; Der Marderosian 1967; Der Marderosian & Youngken 1966; Der Marderosian *et al.* 1964A; Der Marderosian *et al.* 1964B). Their highest concentration, 0.3%, was found in seeds of "baby Hawai'ian woodrose," *Argyreia nervosa* (Chao & Der Marderosian 1973A; Chao & Der Marderosian 1973B; Hylin & Watson 1965). These alkaloids are also found in leaves and stems of *Ipomoea violacea* and *Turbina corymbosa* (Genest & Sahasrabudhe 1966; Hofmann 1963A; Taber *et al.* 1963B; Weber 1976; Weber & Ma 1976). In Ecuador, *Ipomoea carnea*, known as *borrachero* ("inebriating one") or *matacabra* ("goat killer") has been used traditionally as an entheogen, and its seeds have been shown to contain ergot alkaloids (Lascano *et al.* 1967; Naranjo *et al.* 1964). Numerous species of *Argyreia* and *Ipomoea* are now known to contain entheogenic ergoline alkaloids (see Table 2; Chao & Der Marderosian 1973B; Gardiner *et al.* 1965; Genest & Sahasrabudhe 1966; Staba & Laursen 1966), as is the species *Stictocardia tiliaefolia* (Hofmann 1961). Furthermore, based on their ethnomedicinal use, it is likely that species of *Convolvulus* (Albert-Puleo 1979; Genest & Sahasrabudhe 1966), *Ipomoea crassicaulis* (Zamora-Martínez & Nieto de Pascual Pola 1992), *I. involucrata* (Akendengué 1992; MacFoy & Sama 1983), *I. littoralis* (Austin 1991), *I. medium* (Beaujard 1988) and *I. pes-caprae* (Dagar & Dagar 1991; Ponglux *et al.* 1987; Pongprayoon *et al.* 1991) contain entheogenic ergoline alkaloids.[12] The elymoclavine-rich *Securidaca longipedunculata* of the Polygalaceae is reportedly used as an entheogen by the Balanta people of Guinea Bissau (Costa *et al.* 1992).

EFFECTS OF LSD, ERGINE, ERGONOVINE, METHYLERGONOVINE AND METHYSERGIDE

LSD: LSD and *Delysid* (LSD-tartrate) produce profound visual and auditory alterations and synaesthesia. The effective oral dose in human beings ranges from 50–

500 micrograms, above which a saturation level may be reached in most users, such that further augmenting the dose will not intensify the effects (Grof 1975; Shulgin 1980B). The effects of LSD generally begin within 45–90 minutes, and last for eight hours or more (Cohen 1964). Other than dilated pupils, side-effects are negligible, as are after-effects. Pharmacological studies have shown that little of an injected dose of LSD actually reaches the brain of experimental animals, and that the tissue concentrations reach a maximum within 10–15 minutes of injection, and rapidly subside thereafter. The drug is almost completely eliminated from the body before the peak effects commence, suggesting that it acts as some sort of catalyst, inducing the neurochemical changes which subsequently result in the visionary experience. Only about 1–10% of an injected dose of LSD is excreted unaltered, the remainder being metabolized to a variety of degradation products (Hofmann 1968).

ERGINE: Ergine or LA-111 produces a mildly visionary effect, characterized by pronounced sedative side-effects. Hofmann first established its activity in 1947, 13 years before it was known to be one of the active principle of *ololiuhqui* (Hofmann 1961; Hofmann 1963A; Solms 1956A; Solms 1956B). He showed that the drug was active at doses of 500 micrograms to 1 milligram. No psychoptic effect was noticed by Hofmann after taking 2 milligrams of isoergine, although sedative symptoms similar to ergine inebriation were prominent. Hofmann's description of perceiving the "unreality and complete meaninglessness of the outside world" after taking 2 milligrams of isoergine (Hofmann 1963A), however, sounds like the paradoxical depressant effect experienced commonly with threshold doses of psilocybine and other entheogens, and it is possible that isoergine is visionary at higher doses.

ERGONOVINE and METHYLERGONOVINE: Ergonovine is, as already noted, the specifically uterotonic and hemostatic principle of ergot. It has been widely used in obstetrics to control postpartum hemorrhage, at doses of 100–250 micrograms of the hydrogen maleate salt (*Ergotrate*; *Syntometrine*). The drug was not known to be psychoactive until 1 April 1976, when Hofmann ingested 2 mg of ergonovine maleate (representing 1.5 mg ergonovine base). This was probably the highest dose ever utilized in a human subject, and within an hour Hofmann experienced colored hallucinations and other psychic effects, lasting for several hours (Hofmann 1978A). Jeremy Bigwood and I later verified Hofmann's findings as to visionary properties of ergonovine, taking doses of up to 10 mg (Bigwood *et al.* 1979), and P. Neely and I extended them to show psychoptic effects of methylergonovine hydrogen maleate (*Methergine*), a semi-synthetic derivative (Ott & Neely 1980) once mentioned in the medical literature to have psychotropic side-effects (Waser 1965). Ripinsky-Naxon and colleagues (1993) found 6 mg of ergonovine maleate mildly entheogenic. See Postscriptum on pp. 141–144 for a rationale for these psychonautic experiments.

METHYSERGIDE: Methysergide is a potent serotonine antagonist (see Chapter 3 Note 5) widely used in medicine for the treatment of migraine. The normal medicinal dose is 2 mg of the hydrogen maleate salt (*Sansert* or *Deseril*) taken 2–4 times daily. At higher doses, however, the drug shows psychoptic effects, particularly above 7.5 mg. The visionary threshold dose, said to be equivalent to 25 mcg of LSD, has been calculated to be 4.3 mg (Abramson & Rolo 1967). Doses of 8–12 mg given orally to so-called "schizophrenic" children produced effects similar to 100–150 mcg doses of LSD (Bender 1970). Methysergide bears quite a close structural relationship to the above-mentioned methylergonovine (*Methergine*).

LSD AND MORNING GLORY SEEDS AS LUDIBLE DRUGS

While LSD, under its trade name *Delysid*, was circulating widely among members of the medical and psychological professions during the fifties, it was inevitable that the curiosity of some researchers would get the better of them, and they would decide to try the wondrous "psychotogen" outside of the laboratory. In some cases, subjects of experimental *Delysid* therapy cultivated an interest in trying the drug on their own, in a non-clinical setting, away from the prying eyes of individuals in white coats. Thus was born the first extra-scientific, or ludible use of LSD.

In the early sixties, John Beresford, who had been involved in LSD research, and Michael Hollingshead began to "turn on" people outside of a laboratory context (Hollingshead 1974). Beresford had purchased a gram of *Delysid* from Sandoz and some of the material, diluted in sugar in a mayonnaise jar, ended up in the possession of Hollingshead, who initiated a number of individuals, including prominent musicians, to the world of entheogens. Perhaps the most significant "turn on" by Hollingshead was of Timothy Leary, a Harvard lecturer in psychology who had been conducting research with *Indocybin*, Sandoz's other pharmaceutical entheogen, better known as psilocybine (see Chapter 5). Leary's introduction to LSD took place in the fall of 1961, and the drug so impressed him that he temporarily lost interest in psilocybine, and turned his attention to its more potent cousin (Leary 1968). In 1963, Leary placed an order with Sandoz for the then-unprecedented quantities of 100 grams of LSD and 25 kilograms of psilocybine (equivalent to about one million and 2.5 million doses respectively; Hofmann 1980). By this time, Leary's work had already made the Harvard administration uneasy—they were uncomfortable with the fact that Leary and his colleagues Richard Alpert and Ralph Metzner had a penchant for ingesting the experimental drugs themselves, together with the research subjects, at times in a party-like session (Leary 1968; Weil 1963B). Many hard-line experimentalists scoffed at this approach, claiming that the experimenter could not maintain "scientific objectivity" (whatever that is) if (s)he personally ingested a mind-altering drug.[13]

A further problem with Leary's Harvard research project was the fact that entheogenic drugs were sometimes being administered without the supervision of a physician, a technical illegality. Moreover, one of Leary's associates created unfavorable publicity in Denmark, when he, Leary and Aldous Huxley attended a psychological conference in Copenhagen. Leary's colleague gave psilocybine to some journalists who were interviewing him, and made some rather sensational remarks (Wasson 1977).

Back in Cambridge, Massachusetts, many of the students who had participated in Leary's experiments began to cultivate a taste for entheogenic drugs, and a rudimentary black market for *péyotl*, mescaline, psilocybine and LSD came into being (Jones 1963; Kreig 1967; La Barre 1975; Lee & Shlain 1985; Stafford 1983; Stevens 1987; Weil 1963A; Weil 1963B). That interest was rampant is attested by the fact that the fourth issue of *The Harvard Review* (Summer of 1963) was devoted to entheogenic drugs, and featured articles by R. Gordon Wasson, Richard Evans Schultes and Leary (Weil 1963A). At first, this entheogenic drug scene revolved around the Beats, and several coffee shops in the Harvard Square area of Cambridge, notably the Club 47, began to proffer LSD-laced sugar cubes. At this time, extra-medical use of LSD was beginning also on the West Coast of the United States, and underground manufacture of the drug had commenced. B. Roseman is sometimes credited with being the first to manufacture LSD outside of the pharmaceutical industry (Horowitz 1985), a process he described openly in a hand-lettered book (Roseman 1966). Even 'though LSD was was at that time legal, Roseman was arrested and charged with smuggling and "selling an unlabeled drug without a license" (Roseman 1966).

It must be said that Leary and his Harvard colleagues sincerely tried to stimulate responsible use of entheogens. They realized that the naive psychonaut (Jünger 1970) needed a "guide" to accompany him on his psychic "trip," and that the drug could not simply be given to an unwitting subject. Leary, Metzner, Alpert and others also started a scholarly journal, *The Psychedelic Review* (originally planned as

The Psychodelic Review, the name was altered to avoid association with the word "psychotic"—on 20 February 1963, editor Ralph Metzner wrote to R. Gordon Wasson about an article in *The Psychodelic Review*) which for several years published first-rate articles on entheogens. By the time it ceased publication, with the eleventh number dated Winter 1970/71, it had unfortunately degenerated to an underground "comix" format, replete with advertising for "Dynamite Dope Books," and a corresponding erosion of editorial standards—the title of an article referred to "Cannibus" [*sic*] in treatment of alcoholism (Mikuriya 1971). The journal had also strayed from the scientific straight-and-narrow into politics, advocating the "fifth freedom," the right to consciousness expansion (Barrigar 1964) and the pharmaceutical production of religious experiences (Leary 1964). Leary and colleagues, meanwhile, sought to introduce members of the intelligentsia to the spiritual aspects of entheogens. As Leary wrote (Leary 1964):

> We have arranged transcendent experiences for over one thousand persons from all walks of life, including 69 full-time religious professionals, about half of whom profess the Christian or Jewish faith and about half of whom belong to Eastern religions. Included in this roster are two college deans, a divinity college president, three university chaplains, an executive of a religious foundation, a prominent religious editor, and several distinguished religious philosophers. At this point it is conservative to state that over 75 percent of these subjects report intense mystico-religious responses, and considerably more than half claim that they have had the deepest spiritual experience of their life [*sic*].

Leary and colleagues even produced a manual "based on the *Tibetan Book of the Dead*" to guide entheogen users to a religious experience (Leary *et al.* 1964).

Later on the West Coast, LSD "cults" began to receive media attention. The most famous, the Merry Pranksters (Perry 1990), began to foster large-scale, open use of LSD. This clique would hold concert-parties, with rock-and-roll groups such as the Grateful Dead, in which punch ("electric *Kool-Aid*") doped with LSD was freely served. "Psychedelic" posters would exhort prospective customers to attempt to "pass the acid test" (Wolfe 1969). This unguided use of LSD inevitably led to adverse reactions in some few subjects, and LSD began to get a bad name (although the great majority of "acid test" takers apparently passed with flying colors, so to speak). Such sensational "happenings" led inevitably to the popular linking of LSD with "crazy hippies," a pejorative association, which unfortunately stuck, cemented firmly in the popular consciousness by the tragic association of LSD with the maniacal and murderous Charles Manson gang.

As an offshoot of experimental LSD therapy with a few Hollywood luminaries, LSD came to be associated with glamorous movie stars and was even called "Hollywood's status-symbol drug" (Gaines 1963). One early LSD patient was actor Cary Grant. Grant apparently used LSD profitably in the course of psychotherapy (Hoge 1977), and when *Look* magazine published in September 1959 "The Curious Story Behind the New Cary Grant" there was an upsurge of interest in the new pharmacotheon. Two years later, in 1961, the famous nutritionist and writer Adelle Davis (writing under the pseudonym Jane Dunlap) described in glowing terms her experiences with LSD-25 in psychotherapy (Dunlap 1961). Davis had become interested in the substance after reading R.G. Wasson's 1957 *Life* magazine article about Mexican entheogenic mushrooms (see Chapter 5; R.G. Wasson 1957). The following year, the sensational account of how parapsychologist Thelma Moss (also using a pseudonym; see Newland 1962) was cured of frigidity through LSD psychotherapy (see Ling & Buckman 1963; Ling & Buckman 1964), was a powerful stimulus to interest in LSD among laypersons. Another popular 1961 book (Ebin 1961) presented well-written descriptions of the experiences of users of LSD, *péyotl*, entheogenic mushrooms and other drugs. Mention should also be made of R.S. De Ropp's seminal 1957 popular book *Drugs and the Mind* (De Ropp 1957) as well as the sequel *The Master Game* (De Ropp 1968) and other important books which stimulated interest in LSD and allied entheogens (Aaronson & Osmond 1970; Blum 1964; Braden 1967; Cohen 1964; Kreig 1964; Hoffer & Osmond 1967; Sankar 1975; Solomon 1964; Tart 1969).

In response to the attention-getting activities of Leary's group and the Merry Pranksters, a large demand for LSD arose. On 23 August 1965, Sandoz LTD. voluntarily ceased distribution of *Delysid*, *Indocybin*, psilocine "and their hallucinogenic congeners" in response to what was increasingly viewed by the management as unfavorable publicity (Cerletti 1965; Hofmann 1980). Soon after this action was taken, laws began to be passed, proscribing LSD and other entheogens, which came under the same legal regimen as marijuana, cocaine and heroin. The new demand for LSD stimulated and was stimulated by the growth of illicit production of LSD (Lee & Shlain 1985; Stevens 1987). While Roseman may have been the first to manufacture LSD for non-pharmaceutical distribution (Horowitz 1985), the most notorious of the new breed of entheogenic chemists was probably Augustus Stanley, widely known by his middle name, Owsley (Lee & Shlain 1985; Stafford 1983).

Owsley was intimately connected with the Merry Pranksters and the Grateful Dead. Another notorious underground LSD chemist was R.H. Stark, who became involved with the "Brotherhood of Eternal Love," an organization devoted to distribution of LSD with evangelical zeal. Stark is credited with having made 20 kilograms of LSD—some 80–200 million doses—and was apparently a CIA contract agent, according to testimony in a sensational Italian trial (Escohotado 1989A; Lee & Shlain 1985) In the early days of the LSD market, many of the available tablets or capsules contained considerable doses—in the range of 300 micrograms and above (Brown & Malone 1973A). It was not uncommon for one tablet or capsule of LSD to provide impressive effects for four persons. By the end of the sixties, this situation had changed radically. A study of black-market LSD preparations in New York in 1972 showed each dose unit to contain an average of 110 micrograms of LSD, and extensive analyses of San Francisco "street acid" the following year by PharmChem Labs (a pioneering "street drug" analysis service) showed an average of only 65 micrograms of LSD *per* unit with individual samples rarely exceeding 100 micrograms (Ratcliffe 1973). PharmChem analyses also showed considerable quantities of iso-LSD, an inactive and harmless degradation product, testifying to the instability of black-market preparations. By the 1990s, average LSD doses fluctuated around 50 mcg (Marnell 1993). Owing to the inexorable decline in the potency of LSD tablets and capsules, by the seventies it was not uncommon for users to ingest two or three doses apiece, and units that could be shared among several persons were only a memory of the sixties' psychedelic "good old days."

While on the subject of nostalgia for the rough-and-ready "Psychedelic Sixties," it has been suggested that black-market LSD has been, by and large, badly made, tended to be contaminated by synthetic byproducts, and was incapable of producing the same "psychedelic" effect as LSD of higher purity made by Sandoz or Spofa (a Czech pharmaceutical firm which began to manufacture the drug when Sandoz's patents expired in 1963), available in the early to mid-sixties (Eisner 1977). This argument is specious, and is a product more of nostalgia than reason. If the effects of LSD were perceived as being any different in the early days of the "Psychedelic Age," this can easily be explained by two factors. First, as I have documented, and as many long-time users realize, the potency of LSD tablets and capsules declined considerably after 1969. Before then, users tended to take higher doses. More importantly, the early users were experimenting in a vacuum—there was little expectation, the effects were largely unknown, and the experience was entirely novel. Familiarity with the drug experience caused it to lose some of its wonder. As psychiatrist Norman Zinberg explained it in stilted, Freudian terms (Zinberg 1977):

> Those people who used LSD early and had no significant cultural preparation, or social learning, experienced the symbolization in their thoughts as a breakthrough from the depths of the mind, which could be characterized as primary-process derivatives. When personality structural elements—that is, the ego—were prepared for the experience and, generally speaking, felt in control of it, the same ideation no longer represented a breakthrough in its meaning to the individual.

No, it was mostly illicit LSD which catalyzed the "Psychedelic Age," and as numerous chemical studies have shown, it was chemically identical to its pharmaceutical prototype, *Delysid*.[14]

Similarly, frequently-repeated reports that black-market LSD was often adulterated with strychnine are false. While Albert Hofmann in 1970 detected strychnine in a putative LSD sample, the ingestion of which proved fatal to one unfortunate experimenter (Hofmann 1980), subsequent analyses of hundreds of black-market LSD samples failed to detect strychnine (Brown & Malone 1973A). Nevertheless, many users considered some LSD samples to be contaminated with strychnine. As Brown and Malone commented of their analytical work:

> We have analyzed several samples thought to contain strychnine on the basis of toxic symptoms, but in each case only LSD was detected—however, the amount of LSD detected per 'hit' was excessive (ranging between 300 and 500 micrograms). None of the other groups doing street drug analyses has reported strychnine in any LSD-containing sample [the most common active adulterant being phencyclidine or PCP, also known as *Sernyl*]. The answer is that large doses of LSD mimic the symptoms of strychnine poisoning and large doses of LSD (over 200 micrograms) are frequently encountered on the street-drug market. (Brown & Malone 1973A)

Summarizing the analyses of 581 black-market LSD samples, Brown and Malone reported: 491 (84.5%) contained LSD while 31 (5.3%) contained LSD and PCP. There were 11 samples (1.9%) with PCP only, and 5 containing LSD plus amphetamine or methamphetamine. One sample was really STP or DOM (see Chapter 1), and 2 contained only amphetamines. In all, 527 of these 581 samples, or 90.7% actually contained LSD (Brown & Malone 1973A). While occasional samples of LSD have been found to be adulterated with amphetamines (1.2% in the above sample), this was never a common practice, despite street folklore to the contrary. The common misapprehension that LSD was adulterated with amphetamines derives from the fact that LSD is itself a potent stimulant, more than two orders of magnitude more potent than methamphetamine, with which is shares some effects in common. Furthermore, methamphetamine and other amphetamines have always been worth more *per dose* wholesale than LSD on the illicit market, and one cardinal rule of adulteration is that one does not use a more expensive substance as an adulterant!

After the first publications in 1960 concerning the existence of psychoactive LSD-like alkaloids in morning glory seeds, ludible use of *Ipomoea violacea* seeds began to appear in the United States (Der Marderosian *et al.* 1964B). A number of horticultural varieties of *I. violacea* seeds were (and continue to be) widely and openly sold to gardeners. As chemical studies established the existence of alkaloids in *Argyreia* species, and that *Argyreia nervosa* was the most potent species, horticultural sources of seeds of this species began to be mined by entheogen users. As the seeds gained in popularity, many suppliers found themselves unable to keep up with the suddenly increased demand (Shawcross 1983). When LSD became more widely available, use of the less-desirable morning glory seeds appeared to decline. The seeds are still sometimes used today, and have been openly sold by mail order in countercultural drug magazines. It would appear, however, that they are not cherished as the most desirable of the entheogenic drugs, owing to side-effects (Bailin 1975; Shawcross 1983). Some of these undesirable effects may be due, however, to the ingestion of whole ground seeds, rather than filtered, cold-water infusions of the ground seeds as the Mexican Indians take them (Wasson 1963). In some cases, in a perverse and misguided effort at dissuading would-be users, the seeds may have been deliberately poisoned by suppliers, with warnings printed on the seed packets!

The reaction of the "establishment" to the rise in use of LSD and other entheogens in the sixties was rapid and drastic. Leary's contract was terminated by Harvard for non-performance in 1963, and Alpert was also dismissed that same year. This isolated Leary and Alpert from their professional peers, and effectively discredited them (Weil 1963B). Cut off from "legitimate" research, Leary and Alpert were reduced to the role of proselytizers for LSD. Three years later, as LSD use became the rage, the United States government decided to make an example of Leary. On 26 March 1966, Leary was arrested in Laredo, Texas for possession of scraps of marijuana, and shortly thereafter, on 16 April, his residence and headquarters at an estate called Millbrook in New York was raided by one G. Gordon Liddy, later to become famous as a Watergate principal and "fall guy" (Stafford 1983). The Laredo arrest resulted in a conviction and a draconian 30-year prison sentence. The die was cast. States were racing to outlaw LSD, sweeping other entheogens like DMT, mescaline, psilocybine and psilocine along with it. California became the first state to outlaw entheogens, and federal prohibition was mandated.

Unfortunately for the government, these drastic actions were counterproductive. Leary's arrest generated considerable publicity for LSD and other entheogens (Leary 1966A). Given the existing climate of social dissent, the government's censure of entheogens gave them rather the aura of forbidden fruit to young people, many of whom became yet more eager to experiment with the drugs. The laws were a dismal failure at curbing drug use, and served to exacerbate social dissent by arbitrarily placing literally millions of citizens in the criminal category, citizens who had committed no crimes against life or property.

Having failed with force, the United States government opted for coercion and persuasion. When in 1967 a scientifically-flimsy report alleged that LSD caused chromosome damage in human lymphocytes or white blood cells (Cohen *et al.* 1967), the National Institutes of Health seized the opportunity to mount a vigorous propaganda campaign, as outlined in the first chapter (Weil 1972). Significantly, this federally-endowed research organization ordered no tests to verify the preliminary report, which was taken at face value since it was welcome news to the government. The then-docile information media fell hook, line and sinker for the great chromosome-damage scare, and LSD became the new scapegoat (Braden 1970). The media and the government played on fears generated in the public mind by the *Thalidomide* tragedy of the late fifties and early sixties, still a vivid and gruesome memory to LSD users and non-users alike (see Chapter 1).

No scientific report, however, had ever demonstrated that LSD was, like *Thalidomide*, a teratogen (a substance causing birth defects). When controlled studies were conducted with LSD and chromosomes, and when long-time LSD users were examined, it was found that there was no significant link between LSD use and chromosome damage (Bender & Sankar 1968; Dishotsky *et al.* 1971; Tjio *et al.* 1969). It was also found that viral infections as well as many drugs, including caffeine and aspirin, could cause chromosome breaks in lymphocytes *in vitro*. Although LSD use declined initially in the face of the big scare, the end result was the irreparable loss of the United States government's credibility *vis à vis* drugs (Weil 1972). The government attempted to foist a few other spurious scares on the public: the "flashback" scare, the LSD-produces-psychosis scare, *ad nauseam*. Given the U.S. government's lack of credibility on drug-related issues, it is not surprising that these scare tactics had only minimal, if any, efficacy at deterring the extra-medical use of LSD.

In fact, a climate of lies and deception grew to surround LSD in the media. When a prominent bureaucrat in the Pennsylvania state health apparatus told reporters of some youths who had blinded themselves by staring at the sun while under the influence of LSD, it made international headlines. At first it didn't occur to members of the press to ask for names or other details, and when someone finally dug a bit, the report turned out to be a complete fabrication—but that fact was not deemed especially newsworthy! At this time, all any murderer had to do was claim to have been under the influence of LSD when committing his crime, to escape full legal responsibility. It was, after all, "common knowledge" that LSD caused insanity, murder, self-mutilation, suicide, rape, *etc.*

In the meantime, during the onslaught of lies disseminated by the National Institutes of Health and the drug enforcement authorities, ostensibly motivated by concern for the public welfare, the U.S. Central Intelligence Agency (CIA) was engaged in an insidious research project called MKULTRA, dedicated to gathering intelligence on psychoactive drugs (Lee & Shlain 1985; Marks 1979). Among other horrors, it involved deliberate poisoning of unwitting subjects with LSD and other drugs. At least one such poisoning led to the suicide death of a government scientist. The CIA and U.S. Army contacted Albert Hofmann with requests for kilogram quantities of LSD, for use as a chemical warfare agent (Hofmann 1977) and, when Hofmann and Sandoz refused to cooperate, the CIA persuaded the Eli Lilly Company of Indiana to synthesize the drug, in violation of international patent accords. The MKULTRA chemical warriors, through their Mafia contacts, set up two brothels with one-way windows concealing agents and cameras, to observe unwitting subjects disporting themselves with the prostitutes in the agency's employ, who would "spike" their drinks with LSD and other drugs (just such a setup was fictionally depicted in the second James Bond movie *From Russia with Love*, based on the Ian Fleming novel, but in the fictional case, it was the government of the Soviet Union which ran the operation!). The CIA established phony academic fronts, to offer fake grants to academicians and appropriate the fruits of their research. When the CIA learned of the Wassons' Mexican mushroom research, they offered a grant through the fake "Geschickter Fund for Medical Research, Inc." and thus managed to place a "mole," chemist James Moore of the University of Delaware, on the Wassons' 1956 expedition to México (see Chapter 5, Note 8; Marks 1979; Ott 1978A; Singer 1982; Wasson 1982A). Thereby the CIA was able to get samples of psilocybian mushrooms, in hopes of isolating the active principle and making it part of a secret chemical arsenal. Surely it was a sad state of affairs, if a 60-year-old man of Wasson's stature (he was at the time a Vice-President of one of Wall Street's largest banks) could not conduct an important scientific expedition, financed out of his own pocket, without clandestine government intervention![15]

From the history of the U.S. government's actions regarding LSD and other entheogens, it is obvious that concern for the welfare of the public was not a factor in outlawing the drugs. Rather, the government perceived that entheogen use was associated with a dissident minority. By illegalizing entheogens, the dissidents became criminals by *fiat*. By exaggerating the dangers of LSD use in the press, a sense of urgency was instilled in the general populace, such that civil liberties of users (or suspected users—anyone, in short) could be grossly and repeatedly violated in the name of law enforcement. Of course, the thrust of the effort was directed against opposition to the government and its infamous war in Indochina, and against members of militant black groups like the Black Panther Party. The drugs themselves merely served as convenient scapegoats, as other drugs have in the past, and as do many drugs to this day (Szasz 1961; Szasz 1970; Szasz 1974; Szasz 1992).

The legal attack on LSD all but halted several promising lines of scientific and medical research. By being classified as a drug with a "high potential for abuse" (which is certainly true, as the CIA has amply demonstrated) with "no currently accepted medical use," (which is certainly not due to any lack of medicinal utility), LSD became unavailable to physicians for therapeutic use. Cancer patients and other patients suffering painful, terminal conditions, were thereby deprived of a promising pain- and anxiety-relieving agent. Unlike narcotics, LSD was able to suppress pain in a lasting way, without clouding consciousness (Kast 1963; Kast 1966; Kast & Collins 1964; Pahnke 1971; Pahnke *et al.* 1970A; Pahnke *et al.* 1970B). Psychiatrists and their patients were deprived of a medicament which showed far more promise at resolving fundamental psychological problems than anything currently in use (Janiger 1959); a potential curative agent in contrast to the aptly-named "chemical straightjackets" used to drug mental patients into submission. The science of brain chemistry was deprived of one of the most potent entheogenic substances ever discovered, a substance active in such infinitesimal amounts as to show promise in attacking the classic mind/body problem of philosophy, the chemistry of thought and consciousness itself. Meanwhile, the drug continued to be readily available on the black market to all comers; but users were effectively deprived of the protection of government agencies like the U.S. Food and Drug Administration, and were at risk of fraud and poisoning by adulterants, owing to unregulated activities of sometimes unscrupulous chemists and black-market businessmen.

One ray of hope is emerging on the horizon in the last decade of the twentieth century. The government of Switzerland recently has sanctioned provisionally the experimental use of LSD in psychotherapy, placing the drug under medical, and not police, control. This farsighted policy will enable LSD to prove its worth as a medinal aid to psychiatry, and effectively turns the clock back to the early sixties, when LSD was electrifying the psychiatric profession, opening up possibilities undreamed of before (Gartz 1992A; Hofmann 1991; Pletscher & Ladewig 1994; Rayl 1992).

CONTEMPORARY USE OF LSD AND MORNING GLORY SEEDS

Authentic LSD is commonly seen on the illicit drug market, and other drugs are seldom misrepresented as LSD. The exception is phencyclidine or PCP (*Sernyl*), which may be sold as LSD. It is far more common for LSD to be misrepresented as something else, sold usually as "mescaline" or "psilocybine" (see Chapters 1 and 5). So-called "blotter" or "windowpane" LSD is most likely to be genuine ("blotter acid" consists of bits of absorbent paper on which drops of LSD solution have been placed, it is also called "microdot acid," *etc.*; "windowpane" is a gelatinous material containing LSD, which is sliced into tiny, thin squares, also called "clear light," *etc.*). Authentic LSD is found on the black market all over the world, and a recent study estimated some 1.8 million users in the U.S. alone (Henderson & Glass 1994).

Caution with dosage is required of users of black-market LSD preparations. There is the possibility the user will feel nothing, or (s)he may have a massive effect (the former is the more likely). On the other hand, there is the chance of achieving just the desired level of intensity. Uncertainty results from vagaries of packaging doses of such a potent drug, sloppiness of illicit chemists or merchants, and the fact that LSD is not very stable, and has minimal keeping qualities in its illicit forms (especially "blotter acid," with maximal drug exposure to air and light). To be safe, experienced users ingest one dose-unit of a given sample, to ascertain potency. The dose may then be augmented (leaving an interval of a few days, to avoid problems of tolerance), if a more intense effect is desired. With this precaution, excessive dosage is still possibile, as doses might not be uniform, even within a given sample of apparently identical tablets, capsules, "blotters" or "windowpanes." I must emphasize that there is no danger of death or injury from overdose of LSD, which must have about the highest therapeutic index of any drug known (the ratio of fatal dose to effective dose is unknown since no human being has ever died from an overdose of LSD, but must be very high, as individuals have mistakenly ingested hundreds of doses at a sitting; this is a way of saying that the drug is not at all toxic). The danger here is of experiencing a more intense effect than one is prepared for. High doses of LSD (in excess of 250 micrograms) can lead to temporary loss of ego or identity, a consequence terrifying to some, but much sought-after by others.

There are only two species of entheogenic morning glory seeds commercially available in the horticultural trade, *Ipomoea violacea* and *Argyreia nervosa. Turbina corymbosa* grows wild along the coasts of the Gulf of México, but this subtropical species is not commonly grown as an ornamental. There are several cultivars of *Ipomoea violacea* available commercially, having intriguing names: "Heavenly Blue," "Pearly Gates" and "Flying Saucers." *Argyreia nervosa* is commonly grown for the use of its large and lovely seed capsules or "wood roses" in floral arrangements. One should not confuse "baby Hawai'ian woodrose," *Argyreia nervosa*, with "Hawai'ian woodrose," *Ipomoea tuberosa*, which is not entheogenic.

Argyreia nervosa seeds are about five times as potent as wild-type *Ipomoea violacea* seeds, and the cultivars of the latter species tend to be even less potent (Chao & Der Marderosian 1973A; Der Marderosian *et al.* 1964B; Hofmann 1963A). Some seed companies, such as J.L. Hudson and ...of the jungle, sell untreated seeds of ethnomedicinal strains of morning glories, which have been selected by shamans for visionary properties rather than the size and color of flowers. Experienced users of entheogenic morning glory seeds usually start with low doses, later working up to higher amounts if a more intense effect is desired. The wise user will begin with no more than 4 or 5 seeds of *Argyreia nervosa*, or no more than 20–25 seeds of *Ipomoea violacea.* Seeds of *Turbina corymbosa* are about one-fifth the potency of the seeds of *Ipomoea violacea.* In México, I have seen doses of the true *ololiuhqui* seeds, *Turbina corymbosa*, measured as the quantity of seeds which will fill a bottle cap, and Wasson also reported this volumetric dosage aid in the Sierra Mazateca (Wasson 1963). Osmond found 60–100 *Turbina corymbosa* seeds to be an active dose, 'though he chewed and ingested the whole seeds, rather than making a cold water infusion of ground seeds (Osmond 1955; see Note 11).

The seeds are not ingested whole—they are not active in this form (Kinross-Wright 1959; B.P. Reko 1934). They are ground to a fine powder, which is then steeped for several hours in cold water, after which the solid matter is filtered off and discarded. The liquid is then drunk neat or with juice for flavoring.

Abdominal cramps in both sexes are commonly reported as a side-effect of inebriation with morning glory seeds (Bailin 1975; Shawcross 1983). When this happens, users have been observed to lie down facing up, breathing deeply until the cramps subside, which generally happens quickly. The morning glory seeds and LSD are strongly uterotonic, that is, they tend to cause contraction of the uterus. As such, use of these drugs should assiduously be avoided by pregnant women who, for that matter, would do well to avoid using *all* nonessential drugs during pregnancy and parturition; including, and especially, alcohol, caffeine and nicotine.

POSTSCRIPTUM: THE SECRET OF THE ELEUSINIAN MYSTERIES REVEALED

In the most exciting recent development in the study of LSD and other ergoline entheogens, R. Gordon Wasson, Albert Hofmann and Carl A.P. Ruck have advanced a startling new theory concerning the Eleusinian Mysteries of ancient Greece. The theory was first presented on the morning of Friday, 28 October 1977, at the "Second International Conference on Hallucinogenic Mushrooms" held at Fort Worden, near Port Townsend, Washington (I organized this conference; see Chapter 5, Note 11). A full-dress presentation followed in May 1978, when these three distinguished scholars published *The Road to Eleusis: Unveiling the Secret of the Mysteries* (Ruck & Staples 1994; Wasson *et al.* 1978; Wasson *et al.* 1980B). That the reader may appreciate the significance and meaning of this theory, I will review the history of the ancient Mysteries of Eleusis.

The Eleusinian Mystery was an annual celebration of a fertility cult, over which the goddess Demeter presided. Anyone speaking Greek could be initiated into the cult, but usually only once in a lifetime. The "Greater Mystery" was celebrated in the autumn, in a sanctuary at Eleusis, bordering the Rarian Plain, near Athens. For nearly 2000 years the annual celebration was held, but never was the secret of the Mystery revealed. Initiates passed the night in the darkened *telesterion* or initiation hall, where they beheld a great vision which was "new, astonishing, inaccessible to rational cognition." Of the experience, they could only say that they had seen *ta hiera*, "the holy"—it was forbidden by law, under penalty of death, to say more, and the seeing or *epopteia* converted the initiates or *mystai* into *epoptai* (Wasson *et al.* 1978).

Most of our information about the Eleusinian Mystery comes from the so-called *Homeric Hymn to Demeter*, an anonymous seventh century B.C. poem. The poem describes the mythical founding of the Mystery by Demeter, who was grief-stricken over the abduction of her daughter Persephone (also called Kore) by the god Hades, lord of the underworld. Demeter caused all of the plants on the Earth to die, and Zeus, fearing humankind would also die and there would then be nobody to make sacrifices to the gods, interceded with Hades, and forced him to return Persephone to Demeter. Persephone, however, had eaten a pomegranate seed in the underworld, and was therefore condemned to return to Hades for part of each year. This always saddened Demeter, who would again cause the plants to die, to be reborn again in the glory of springtime, with the return of Persephone to the world of light. This lovely myth symbolized for the Greeks the natural mystery of the changing seasons, and the miracle of the springtime rebirth (after burial in the cold Earth) of the cultivated grain on which their civilization depended.

Demeter ordered the construction of the Eleusinian sanctuary and, refusing wine, directed the preparation of a special potion, the *kykeon* ("mixture"). The ingredients of the *kykeon* are spelled out in the *Homeric Hymn*: barley, water and *blechon* (or *glechon*, a mint, probably *Mentha pulegium*, a plant burned as an offering by some shamans to Pachamama in Perú; see Appendix B; Wassén 1967; Wassén 1979). From fragmentary ancient reports, including the remains of a fresco at Pompeii, it is known that initiates to the Mysteries drank Demeter's potion as a prelude to experiencing a soul-shattering vision (Hofmann 1981). The Eleusinian Mysteries were driven into extinction by the Christians in the fourth century of our era. The "secret" was not vouchsafed to us by the Christians, if in fact they themselves knew it, which is extremely doubtful (Mylonas 1961).

Much has been written concerning the Eleusinian Mysteries, but apparently it had never occurred to anyone before Wasson that the potion, the *kykeon*, might have had something to do with the vision! Classical scholar G.E. Mylonas, for example, wrote a detailed book on *Eleusis and the Eleusinian Mysteries*, and concluded that: "the act of drinking the *kykeon* was one of religious remembrance, of the observance of an act of the Goddess, and implied no sacramental mystic significance" (Mylonas 1961). Three years before Mylonas made this dubious pronouncement, Wasson had connected Plato's "ideas" and world of "archetypes" with entheogens (Wasson 1958; Wasson 1959A) and just the year before, he had tentatively suggested in a lecture subsequently published (Wasson 1961; Wasson 1972D): "I predict that the secret of the Mysteries will be found in the indoles, whether derived from mushrooms or from higher plants or, as in Mexico, from both." This idea was first suggested by Wasson in a lecture on 15 November 1956, shortly after his first experience of mushroomic ecstasy (see Chapter 5). A recent book (T.K. McKenna 1992) has wrongly credited Robert Graves with first proposing that the *kykeon* was entheogenic in 1964 (see Graves 1957; Graves 1962; for examples of his speculations regarding entheogenic mushrooms, inspired by his collaboration with the Wassons). A 1936 book published in French (Félice 1936) first explored the concept of *ivresses divines* ("divine inebriations," obtusely characterizing such as "inferior forms" of mysticism!) and mentioned the Eleusinian Mysteries, but advanced no specific theories on the nature of Demeter's potion. With this elegant and exciting proposal advanced by

Wasson, Hofmann and Ruck in 1977–1978, Wasson's perspicacious prediction has been placed on a strong and specific scientific footing.

It is the thesis of *The Road to Eleusis* that Demeter's potion, the *kykeon*, was entheogenic, and elicited the ineffable vision experienced each year by thousands of initiates. According to the theory, ergot growing on the barley added to the *kykeon* accounted for the potion's visionary properties. Hofmann argued that, by making an aqueous extract of ergot-infested barley, the ancient Greeks could have separated the water-soluble entheogenic ergot alkaloids (ergine, ergonovine, *etc.*) from any non-water-soluble toxic alkaloids of the ergotamine/ergotoxine group (Bigwood *et al.* 1979; Hofmann 1978B). Hofmann further suggested the Eleusinian priests may have employed ergot of the wild grass *Paspalum*, which produces only the entheogenic alkaloids, and none of the toxic peptide alkaloids. Hofmann pointed out that the psychotropic properties of ergot were known in antiquity, and that such folk knowledge of these properties lingers on in Europe, as evidenced by the names for ergot: *Tollkorn* ("mad grain") and *seigle ivre* ("inebriating rye"; Hofmann 1978A).[16]

This simple and elegant theory is buttressed by examination of the rich symbolism attending the cult. Eminent Greek scholar Ruck meticulously showed how the ergot theory fit the available evidence. One of the more telling pieces of evidence is the fact that Demeter was often called *Erysibe*, "ergot," and that purple, the color of ergot, was her special color. Furthermore, an ear of grain was the symbol of the Mystery. Ruck has adduced further evidence in support of the theory presented in the book. He has proposed that Socrates was executed for profaning the Mysteries and making the *kykeon* in Athens with his disciples, and that Aristophanes escaped legal problems by burying hints of this in *Birds* and *Clouds* (Ruck 1981). We know from Plutarch that Alcibiades was sentenced to death for the same crime—profaning the Mysteries in Athens. In an analysis of Euripides' *Bacchae*, Ruck discussed use of wines in ancient Greece as vehicles for ingestion of entheogens and other drugs, contrasting the "cultivated" (grain and civilization) with the "wild" (ergot, thought to represent degeneration of grain to its wild precursor; Ruck 1982; Ruck & Staples 1994). This fascinating study illuminates some linguistic curiosities of the Bible, in which "wine" (*yayin* in Hebrew) is repeatedly compared or contrasted with "strong drink" (*shekar* in Hebrew), evidently an entheogenic potion (Ruck 1982; Wasson 1914).[17] Finally, Ruck identified the Hyperboreans with the Aryans, proposing that their first-fruit offerings were none other than their miraculous *Soma*—probably some entheogenic mushroom (see Chapter 6; Ruck 1983). The *amrta*, the immortal *Soma* potion, is etymologically identical to Greek *ambrosia*, which we now know, thanks to Ruck, Hofmann and Wasson, to have been some entheogenic potion.

Hofmann has often described the "magic circle" of his research on entheogens: starting with his discovery of LSD, a derivative of ergot alkaloids, he was brought into contact with R. Gordon Wasson, who supplied him with the sacred mushrooms of México, leading to Hofmann's discovery of psilocybine and psilocine, and who then supplied him with *ololiuhqui*, another Mexican sacred drug, in which Hofmann found the same alkaloids he had begun working with two decades earlier (Hofmann 1966; Hofmann 1967). Now it would appear Hofmann's "magic circle" has undergone a second revolution, again leading back to ergot as a sacred drug of ancient Greek culture, which is unmistakably our own, Indo-European culture.

A recent book extrapolated this theory of an ergotized, entheogenic *kykeon* to *Soma* (*vide* Chapters 4 Note 2 and 6 Note 11), arguing this was also an aqueous infusion of some ergot-infested grain (Greene 1992), not *Amanita muscaria* as Wasson (1968) had proposed (he having already discarded ergot; Doniger O'Flaherty 1968; Riedlinger 1993). Oddly, the author made pharmacognostical arguments, outside his field of expertise, committing egregious blunders which undermined his already flimsy case, as I thoroughly detailed in a recent review (Ott 1994B).

Intrepid experimenters with ergot (a good quantity may be hand-picked from a sack of "organic" rye) desirous of imbibing Demeter's *kykeon*, must exercise *extreme* caution. They should never forget that *ergot has poisoned and killed countless human beings throughout history. The ergot sclerotia should not be eaten whole!* To make Demeter's potion (according to Hofmann's theory), the sclerotia are reduced to powder, which is then steeped in cold water. The residual powder is then filtered off and discarded. *Extreme caution with dosage is mandatory*, and the wise user would try only a minimal quantity at first. The cautious experimenter would then wait at least a few days before trying a slightly higher dose, if a more intense effect were desired. Ergot, like LSD and morning glory seeds, is a powerful uterotonic drug, and should assiduously be avoided by pregnant women who should, as already mentioned, avoid *all* unnecessary drugs, especially nicotine, caffeine and alcohol.

NOTES

[1] The word *mushroom* is ordinarily used to designate all fleshy agarics, but in some parts of Great Britain may refer to only one species, the cultivated agaric, *Agaricus*. Wasson has proposed that the word be used to describe "all the higher fungi, whether Basidiomycetes or Ascomycetes, with conspicuous fruiting bodies" (Wasson 1980). In this book it will be used to describe *all* fungi, including the so-called "lower" fungi like ergot, to replace the invented, semi-scientific word, *fungus*. Ergot, after all, though it is best known in its sclerotial phase, produces tiny mushrooms as fruit bodies. See also: Shelley 1994.

[2] St. Anthony was born in Egypt in 251 A.D. and died in the Egyptian desert in 356 A.D., aged 105 years. At the age of 20 he retired to the desert and solitude, and is considered to be the founder of Christian monastic life. He became famous in Egypt and pilgrimages were made to seek him out. He was reputed to have had visions as well as repeated bouts with "daemons" or "devils." Although he had beseeched his two disciples to keep secret his burial place, to avoid his remains becoming relics, the location of his grave was "divined" some 200 years after his death and remains purported to be his transported to Alexandria and buried there in St. John's Church. More than a century later the Saracens took these remains to Constantinople for reburial; whence in 1070 they were taken by Crusaders to Dauphiné, France. Because of his reputed visions, St. Anthony became associated with ergotism victims, who also had bizarre visions. Gaston, a rich man of Dauphiné, vowed to donate his fortune to St. Anthony were his son to be cured of ergotism. The son subsequently got better, and Gaston made good his promise, financing a hospital for ergotism victims in which he, his son, and a neighbor worked as nurses. The Antonite Order came to specialize in caring for ergotism victims throughout Europe. There are many artistic representations of St. Anthony. The most famous are Bosch's "Temptation of St. Anthony" (Prado, Madrid) in which the saint, with his ever-present T–shaped staff and accompanied by a pig, contemplates a "daemon" rising from the water before him; and Matthias Grünewald's 15th century Isenheim Altar paintings (Unterlinden Museum, Colmar), a multi-panel work, one panel of which depicts St. Anthony being attacked by "daemons," his hands cramped in ergotism-like seizures and clearly showing gangrene of his fingertips (Bauer 1973; Bové 1970; Huysmans 1976).

[3] The mass poisoning which took place in the French town of Pont-St. Esprit in 1951 has been widely presented in the lay and scientific press as an example of ergotism. While the poisoning was traced to bread, ergotism was not the cause of the syndrome, which was due to a toxic mercury compound used to disinfect grain to be planted as seed. Some sacks of grain treated with the fungicide were inadvertently ground into flour and baked into bread. Albert Hofmann arrived at this conclusion after visiting Pont-St. Esprit, and analyzing samples of the bread (which contained no ergot alkaloids) and autopsy samples of the four victims who succumbed (Hofmann 1980; Hofmann 1991). On the other hand, the Swedish toxicologist Bo Holmstedt insists the poisoning was in fact due to ergotism (Holmstedt 1978). An American writer published a sensationalized account of the poisoning, *The Day of St. Anthony's Fire* (Fuller 1968), evoking "the possibility that a strange, spontaneous form of LSD" might have been involved! Fuller was attempting to cash in on the great LSD scare—some few of the poisoning victims had jumped from buildings, and this, of course, was a "known" effect of LSD! To be sure, LSD is an artificial compound, and no strain of ergot has been found which "spontaneously" produces LSD. In 1976 an American psychologist proposed convulsive ergotism as the cause of the Salem Village, Massachusetts "witchcraft" hysteria in 1692, one of the few cases of witchcraft persecution in the American colonies (Caporael 1976). This theory was immediately rejected by two Canadian psychologists (Spanos 1983; Spanos & Gottlieb 1976), based on the following criticisms: 1) Vitamin A deficiency is believed to be a prerequisite for convulsive ergotism, and since it was close to Salem Town, a seaport presumably well

supplied with seafoods, a good source of Vitamin A, such deficiency could not have prevailed in Salem Village; 2) the "bewitchment" syndrome at Salem only affected individuals, not whole families, as would be expected in ergotism; 3) the symptoms were not the symptoms of convulsive ergotism; and 4) the "hysteria" later spread to other towns in Massachusetts and Connecticut, areas not purported to have been affected by ergotism. In the original paper, the author stated that lysergic acid amide (incorrectly called isoergine) occurs in ergot and, having "10 percent of the activity of D-LSD" could have caused the victims' hallucinations. The critics rightly pointed out that "subjects who have ingested LSD very rarely report... that they perceive formed persons or objects which they believe are actually out there," that is, that the drug doesn't produce true hallucinations (Siegel 1977; Siegel 1992; Siegel & West 1975). It appeared the critics had won the day, until 1982, when historian M.K. Matossian wrote an article defending the Salem/ergotism theory (Matossian 1982). Matossian later wrote a book, *Poisons of the Past* (Matossian 1989) and an article (Matossian 1992), both essentially reiterating her support. In the paper, Matossian incorrectly stated that "ergot is the source of lysergic acid diethylamide (LSD), which some mycologists believe can occur in a natural state" (Matossian 1982), whereas in the book, she stuck to the more tenable "ergot is the source of lysergic acid diethylamide (LSD), and it may include natural alkaloids that act like LSD" (Matossian 1989). Again, regardless of what "some mycologists believe," chemists have never found LSD to occur as a natural product. Matossian went on to propose ergot as a cause of witchcraft epidemics in early modern Europe, and as a cause of the "Great Fear" in France in the summer of 1789, which in part led to the vote of the National Constituent Assembly to abolish the *ancien régime*. She further proposed ergotism as a cause of the "Great Awakening" of religious revival in New England in 1741, and poisoning by tricothecene toxins from *Fusarium* molds as the cause of the epidemic of "throat distemper" in New England in 1735–1736 (Matossian 1989).

[4] *Balansia cyperi*, a mushroom parasitizing *piripiri*, *Cyperus prolixus* or *C. articulatus*, has recently been found to be used in ethnogynecology in Amazonia. *Balansia cyperi* belongs to the Clavicipitaceae, the family of *Claviceps* or ergot, and tops of *Cyperus* clearly infected with *B. cyperi* are used by Achuar Jívaro (*Jívaro* is considered to be pejorative; Shuar and Achuar are the proper names) women of Amazonian Perú to prepare an infusion used as an ecbolic (Lewis & Elvin-Lewis 1990). Cultures of *B. cyperi* from two Amazonian and one United States species of *Cyperus* have been shown to produce "several unidentified ergot alkaloids" (Plowman *et al.* 1990), and ergoline alkaloids are known from at least two other species of *Balansia* (Porter *et al.* 1979; see Appendix B). *Cyperus* species possibly infected with ergot-alkaloid-containing fungi are also used as a contraceptive in the Peruvian Amazon, as an abortifacient by Shipibo-Conibo Indians of eastern Perú, and against postpartum hemorrhage by the Kokama Indians of Perú. The Tucuna of Colombia also use this plant complex as an ecbolic (Plowman *et al.* 1990; Schultes & Raffauf 1990). African ethnogynecological use of a *Cyperus* species suggests similar infestation by an ergot-alkaloid-containing fungus (Veale *et al.* 1992). A plant from a related genus, *Scirpus*, has been reported as a possible entheogen in México. Tarahumara Indians, who call this plant *bakánoa*, are said to regard the tubers as a powerful visionary medicine (Bye

1975; Bye 1979A). Another member of the ergot family, *Ustilago maydis* or corn smut, has also been reported to have been used traditionally by the Ojibway or Ahnishinaubeg as an ecbolic, but paradoxically, the Ahnishinaubeg consider the corn smut to be an anti-coagulant, rather than a hemostatic (Keewaydinoquay 1978). This is unusual, since the uterotonic ergot alkaloids show also hemostatic properties, and Hofmann has tested strains of this species and found them to contain no ergot alkaloids (Hofmann 1977). The corn smut, under the name *cuitlacoche* is widely used in Mexican cuisine, and although used medicinally as a hemostatic (Díaz 1976), does not appear to be known as an ecbolic and has not been reported to be used in México against postpartum hemorrhage. Of course, like ergot, corn smut strains may show considerable chemical variation, and the Ahnishinaubeg may have had access to a strain containing ergot-type alkaloids. On the other hand, other uterotonic alkaloids such as ustilagine, ustilaginine and ustilagotoxine may account for this Ahnishinaubeg ethnogynecological use of *Ustilago maydis* (Heim 1978; Samorini 1992D). Another mushroom in the ergot family, *Cordyceps capitata*, was reported to have been ingested along with a known psilocybian mushroom (see Table 4) of México, *Psilocybe wassonii*, in curing rituals (Guzmán 1958; Heim 1957A). *Cordyceps capitata* (as well as *C. ophioglossoides*) is called *tlakatsitsíntli*, "little men" and is parasitic on a subterranean truffle, *Elaphomyces variegatus* (or *E. granulatus*), called *su mundo*, "its world." Divinatory use of *tlakatsítsin* in Veracruz state was attributed to the ancestors of informants (Reyes G. 1970), and this doubtless referred to *Cordyceps capitata*, although a recent book rather dubiously suggested *tlakatsítsin* represented *Psilocybe* [*Stropharia*] *cubensis* (see Chapter 5; Garza 1990). Curiously, a European species, *Elaphomyces cervinus*, is known traditionally in Germany as *Hexenspitzel*, "witches' point" (De Vries 1991A), and is reportedly used in traditional European ethnomedicine to treat "feeble conditions" (Singer 1958B). In México, these "little men" are taken with *siwatsitsíntli*, "little women," *Psilocybe wassonii*. The chemistry of *Cordyceps capitata* is not known precisely, and in Tenango del Valle, where the "little men" and "little women" are consumed, they are taken with edible species, such as *Clavaria truncata* and *Nevrophyllum floccosum*, called *kustik nanákatl* (Heim & Wasson 1958). Hofmann found *Cordyceps capitata* to be devoid of psilocybine and psilocine, but to contain traces (0.004%) of a "different indolic substance" (Heim & Wasson 1958, p. 260). This intriguing compound remains unidentified, and the chemistry of this mushroom needs further characterization. A related species, *Cordyceps sinensis*, parasitic on the larvae of a Himalayan moth, which the mushrooms consume and transform into sclerotia, is a highly-esteemed tonic in Chinese traditional medicine (Davis 1983A), also used in Nepal as an aphrodisiac (Bhattarai 1992). Cordycepin, a nucleoside derivative (3′-deoxyadenosine) has been isolated from this species and from *C. militaris*, and has some anti-tumor activity (Rich *et al.* 1965). *Cordyceps ophioglossoides* is also used in Chinese medicine, and immunostimulatory glucans have been isolated from this species (Yamada *et al.* 1984). There is no evidence, of course, that these anti-tumor, immunostimulatory compounds are entheogenic. As in the case with the *Cordyceps*/*Psilocybe* "little men" and "little women" ingestion in Tenango del Valle, male/female pairing is involved in consumption of "female" psilocybian *Psilocybe mexicana* together with the "male" *Dictyophora phalloidea* in the Chinantec region of Oaxaca, México (Heim & Wasson 1958). Again, the chemistry of *D. phalloidea* is obscure, but Wasson appended this intriguing footnote to his interdisciplinary study of Mexican entheogenic mushrooms, to wit: "Mr. Roger Heim, during his recent trip to Thailand (Nov. 1957), has assembled information on the use of *Dictyophora phalloidea* in sorcery in that country, and will publish an account elsewhere" (Heim & Wasson 1958, p. 99). Heim later described the use of *D. phalloidea* in Thailand for "criminal poisoning," but also mentioned its use in sorcery by the Tanala and Betsimisaraka of Madagascar (Heim 1978).

[5] The three ergotoxine alkaloids were named ergocristine, ergocornine, and ergokryptine; the last existing in two isomeric forms, *alpha-* and *beta-*ergokryptine. Hofmann then prepared the dihydro-derivatives of these alkaloids, which resulted in a successful product, *Hydergine*. Later, another derivative, 2-bromo-*alpha*-ergokryptine (CB-154), became a successful product, under the trade name *Parlodel* (Hofmann 1979B; see Note 9). Ergokryptine is sometimes spelled *ergocryptine* or *ergocriptine*.

[6] Since it was discovered simultaneously in four different laboratories, the compound at first received four different names: ergobasin(e) (Stoll & Burckhardt 1935); ergometrine (Dudley & Moir 1935); ergotocin(e) (Kharasch & Legault 1935) and ergostetrine (Thompson 1935). To avoid confusion, the International Pharmacopœia Commission proposed the name *ergonovine* (the "novel" ergot alkaloid) to replace all these synonyms. Nevertheless, in Great Britain and in some of the British Commonwealth countries, the drug is still widely known as ergometrine; and the naming of derivatives is sometimes confused. A publication may refer to ergonovine and its derivative, methylergometrine (instead of saying methylergonovine).

[7] Most of the chemical studies described herein were made on ergot of rye, *secale cornutum*. Until fairly recently, this was produced by parasitic cultivation; that is, it was grown by intentionally infecting rye fields with ascospores of ergot, then separating the ergot sclerotia from the ripe grain. L. Hecke of Austria pioneered this methodology in 1921. By the 1940s Sandoz LTD. was mechanically injecting ascospores of ergot onto rye fields in Switzerland. Parasitic cultivation, however, was laborious and subject to the vagaries of weather. American A. McCrae was the first to work out the basic biology of ergot in saprophytic culture (direct growth of ergot mycelium on culture media) in the 1930s. This set the stage for submerged or "liquid" culture of ergot, first achieved on a laboratory scale by Americans Tyler and Schwarting in 1952. The following year, Stoll, Brack, Hofmann and Kobel of Sandoz were awarded a patent for production of ergot alkaloids in saprophytic culture of *Claviceps purpurea*. The group of Arcamone in Italy perfected saprophytic culture of *Claviceps paspali*, obtaining up to 2 grams *per* liter of simple lysergic acid amides. Also using *Claviceps paspali*, Kobel, Schreier and Rutschmann of Sandoz developed a means for producing a precursor to lysergic acid in high quantities (Bové 1970). Thus today lysergic acid is produced in ton quantities in submerged cultures in industrial fermentation tanks, and the various pharmaceutical preparations of ergot alkaloids (see following note) are synthesized from lysergic acid. Although W.A. Jacobs and L.C. Craig had isolated lysergic acid and reported its structure in the 1930s (Jacobs & Craig 1934A; Jacobs & Craig 1934B), the stereochemistry was not worked out until 15 years later, when

Hofmann's group solved the riddle (Stoll *et al.* 1949). A "total synthesis" of lysergic acid was achieved in 1954 and reported two years later (Kornfeld *et al.* 1954; Kornfeld *et al.* 1956). A superior method for synthesizing lysergic acid amides was published three years later (Garbrecht 1959), improving on Curtius' synthesis, used by Hofmann in 1937 for the first semi-synthesis of an ergot alkaloid, ergonovine (see Note 6); later applied to synthesis of LSD and a host of other lysergic acid amides (Stoll & Hofmann 1943). Hofmann's group also further refined the synthesis of lysergic acid amides (Hofmann *et al.* 1961).

[8] Hofmann synthesized and tested psychonautically some derivatives and analogues of LSD (Hofmann 1980). The isomers of LSD, *l*-LSD, *d*-iso-LSD and *l*-iso-LSD were all found to be inactive in doses as high as 500 mcg (20 times the perceptible dose of *d*-LSD). Prominent among many LSD-derivatives are: ALD-52, *N*(1)-acetyl-LSD; MLD-41, *N*(1)-methyl-LSD; BOL-148 (2-bromo-LSD); LAE-32 (lysergic acid ethylamide); LSM-777 (lysergic acid morpholide); LME-54 (lysergic acid methylethylamide); LMP-55 (lysergic acid methylpropylamide) and LEP-57 (lysergic acid ethylpropylamide). Both ALD-52 and MLD-41, with substituents on the indole-ring nitrogen, are equivalent to LSD in potency (Rothlin 1957; Shulgin 1971), although the latter has also been described as having only one-third the potency of LSD (Abramson 1958; Metzner 1963). BOL-148, LSD with a bromine atom attached, was inactive in human beings up to 500 mcg (Abramson & Rolo 1967; Metzner 1963). LAE-32, lysergic acid monoethylamide, approaches LSD in potency, as does LSM-777 (Callieri & Ravetta 1957; Delay *et al.* 1959B; Giarman 1967; Gilberti & Gregoretti 1960; Shulgin 1971). LME-54, LMP-55 and LEP-57 were inactive or, in the case of 1 of 5 subjects given 100 mcg LMP-55, weakly-active, dosed up to 100 mcg (Abramson & Rolo 1967). Activity of LA-111 (lysergic acide amide) will be discussed below. In cross-tolerance tests (see Chapter 1, Note 8) it was found that MLD-41 and LEP-57 (despite the latter compound's inactivity) could elicit cross-tolerance to the effects of LSD and psilocybine, whereas LAE-32 produced mild cross-tolerance to LSD and none to psilocybine (Abramson & Rolo 1967). LSD was shown to produce cross-tolerance to psilocybine and *vice versa.* Hofmann has published details on a few compounds; most of his self-experiments remain unknown outside of Sandoz. EHLAD, *N*(6)-ethyl-LSD (with an ethyl-group *in lieu* of a methyl-, on the piperidine-ring nitrogen) appears to have double the potency of LSD (Jacob & Shulgin 1994); animal tests suggested ALLYLAD or *N*(6)-allyl-LSD, could be even more potent (Pfaff *et al.* 1994).

[9] In the course of his work on the ergot alkaloids, Hofmann prepared a series of medicinally and financially valuable medicaments (Hofmann 1979B). *Methergine*, or methylergonovine, proved to be a more specific uterine hemostatic than ergonovine, and today is an important lifesaving medicine for obstetric control of postpartum hemorrhage. *Dihydergot*, dihydroergotamine, has found widespread application in therapy of migraine headaches, as has *Deseril* or *Sansert* (1-methyl-lysergic acid butanolamide). The most successful product has been *Hydergine*, the dihydro-derivative of the three "ergotoxine" alkaloids (see Note 5), valuable in geriatric medicine as a cerebral vasodilator. It so improves oxygenation of the brain that it is widely used in Europe as an adjunct to surgery, to give surgeons more time in the case of cardiac arrest, to resuscitate the patient before brain damage from lack of oxygen supervenes. *Hydergine* has also shown valuable stimulant effects even in healthy

young adults, and has been shown to improve mental processing and performance in 9–12 mg daily doses (Hindmarch *et al.* 1979), making it one of the most sought-after "smart drugs" (Jude 1991; Morgenthaler 1990; Morgenthaler & Dean 1991). It has long been Sandoz LTD.'s most successful product, one of the 10 best-selling pharmaceutical products in the world, with annual sales in excess of $300 million. Finally, *Parlodel* or 2-bromo-*alpha*-ergokryptine (also known as CB-154) has found widespread use in the treatment of Parkinsonism. *Parlodel* has recently been used experimentally as a "cure" for cocainism, but in cocaine *habitués*, the drug may itself be habituating (Holden 1989B). While today the discovery, testing and development of a new medicament is a decade-long project for a large team of scientists, this remarkable output of six successful pharmaceuticals (if we include *Delysid*, the trade name of LSD) was accomplished virtually single-handedly by Hofmann, at least the chemical and chemical engineering aspects (Hofmann 1980). The development of *Deseril* and *Parlodel* as pharmaceutical products involved collaborative work with other Sandoz scientists. Hofmann's later research into the chemistry of the sacred mushrooms of México (see Chapter 5) was to lead to the development of yet another successful product, *Visken* (also known as *Pindolol* and, like psilocine, a 4-hydroxy-indole derivative), today widely used as a hypotensive agent. F. Troxler, Hofmann's assistant in the mushroom research, was the discoverer of this product (Troxler *et al.* 1959).

[10] While Urbina and Reko used the synonym *Ipomoea sidaefolia*, much of the modern literature on entheogens employs the synonym *Rivea corymbosa* (Schultes 1964). Blas Pablo Reko, who accepted Urbina's 1897 identification in 1919, and who was the first modern researcher to identify the *teonanácatl* entheogen as a mushroom (B.P. Reko 1919), and the first, together with R.E. Schultes, to collect botanical specimens of the mushrooms (Schultes 1939), is not to be confused with his cousin, Victor A. Reko. Victor is perhaps better known outside of México, for the 1936 publication of a book in German, *Magische Gifte* (Reko 1936). However, Victor was a journalist, not a scientist, and the information in his book was rather inaccurately copied from his cousin Blas Pablo, who complained of Victor: "nor has he any personal experience with the drugs described, most of which he has not seen and would not recognize if he saw them" (letter to H. Wassén, 31 January 1937; quoted in Holmstedt 1967). As Mexican expert J.L. Díaz commented of Victor: "at best his book is a minor piece of newspaper sensationalist account that merely lists some plants of interest. There is good evidence that Victor took notes in bars and other places from his cousin Blas Pablo (Schultes and Ing. Aguirre Benavides independently told me of these scenes) so that the reliable ethnobotanical information that he has came from Blas Pablo" (Díaz 1980). R. Gordon Wasson had rightly dismissed Victor as "a notorious *farceur*" (Wasson 1963). It was thus surprising when prominent American chemist V.E. Tyler published "The case for Victor A. Reko—An unrecognized pioneer writer on new-world hallucinogens" (Tyler 1979), falsely claiming that *Magische Gifte* represented the modern rediscovery of *teonanácatl* as a mushroom. Tyler was unaware that Blas Pablo had published this identification 17 years before the appearance of *Magische Gifte*, and two years before Victor first came to México. Tyler was also wrong in concluding that Victor participated in the clarification of the *ololiuhqui* problem, inasmuch as the drug had been correctly identified 39 years before the publication of *Magische Gifte*, an identification

seconded by Blas Pablo in 1919; and as Tyler himself admitted, Victor A. Reko inclined to the misidentification of *ololiuhqui* as seeds of *Datura* in his 1936 edition (Tyler 1979). Blas Pablo had even published a paper two years before the publication of *Magische Gifte*, describing his self-experiments with morning glory seeds (B.P. Reko 1934). Tyler summed up his argument by conjecturing that Blas Pablo's presumed loss of priority (for the modern recognition that *teonanácatl* was a mushroom) explained why he had criticized his cousin Victor when he wrote to Henry Wassén in 1937. Tyler then stated that the only alternate explanation for Blas Pablo's deprecation of his cousin Victor was that his book *Magische Gifte* might indeed have been a "superficial" tome with no scientific value (Tyler 1979). Since I have shown that there was no loss of priority on the part of Blas Pablo Reko, that this had been secured seventeen years before Victor A. Reko published his book, it would seem that Tyler will have to accept his self-avowed only alternate explanation for Blas Pablo's displeasure—that *Magische Gifte* was indeed, as Wasson, Díaz, Holmstedt and others have concluded, an inaccurate and unscientific book lacking in originality. A recent German article (Haseneier 1992) wrongly credited Victor A. Reko (together with Schultes, Wasson and Heim) with the contemporary scientific "rediscovery" of the Mexican entheogenic mushrooms, failing even to mention Blas Pablo Reko, the true pioneer in these studies. To redress the injustice done to Blas Pablo, I dedicated my first book to him (Ott 1976B; Ott 1979B), and recently translated his pioneering 1919 paper.

[11] Santesson reported that his ethanolic extracts of *ololiuhqui* produced a "semi-narcosis" (*Halbnarkose*) in frogs and mice, and his chemical tests indicated the possible presence of a gluco-alkaloid (Santesson 1937A; Santesson 1937B). A quarter of a century was to pass before Santesson's glucoside, later named turbicoryn, was isolated from *ololiuhqui* and identified (Cook & Kealand 1962; Pérezamador & Herrán 1960). However, Santesson was unsuccessful in isolating the active principles, which later turned out to be ergoline alkaloids, not the glucoside. In their recent book on entheogenic psychotherapy, Roquet and Favreau mix up turbicoryn and ergoline alkaloids, calling ergine a "glucoside with an amide function" (Roquet & Favreau 1981). In 1934, Blas Pablo Reko (see preceding note) became the first scientist to test *ololiuhqui* in a self-experiment (B.P. Reko 1934), finding the seeds inactive. Reko failed to grind the seeds to a powder for extraction, as the Indians do (MacDougall 1960; Wasson 1963). One Dr. Marsh of the U.S. Agricultural Service likewise found the seeds to be inactive, owing either to insufficient dosage or failure to grind the seeds prior to ingestion (Schultes 1941). The seeds are not active if taken whole. Another experiment, in which eight male volunteers took up to 125 *ololiuhqui* seeds, also found no effect from whole seeds (Kinross-Wright 1959). It was H. Osmond who first reported psychoptic effects of *ololiuhqui* seeds, after conducting a series of four experiments on himself, taking doses of 14–100 seeds (Osmond 1955). While Osmond's first two experiments with 14 and 26 seeds chewed and swallowed produced mild but noticeable symptoms, he concluded that the higher doses were necessary to elicit the drug's full effects. Chewing and swallowing 60 seeds produced a definite trip, and Osmond's final experiment ingesting the powder of 100 ground seeds produced a stronger effect with "heightened visual perception and an increase in hypnagogic phenomena... which is very pleasant" (Osmond 1955). There is some evidence for ingestion of (presumably ground)

ololiuhqui seeds in antiquity in the form of enemas (De Smet & Lipp 1987). In an interesting historical aside to Osmond's pioneering experiment, he had intended to entitle his paper "Ololiuqui: Flower-her-Mother," this subtitle being a literal translation of the Mazatec name *na-so-le-na* for the seeds of *Turbina corymbosa.* R.E. Schultes, who edited the paper, felt this would be confusing, since the title *Ololiuqui* was an Aztec word meaning "round things." Osmond changed the title, but fortunately mentioned his original choice in a footnote, "so that readers who enjoy a lovely word should not be deprived of its euphony." See also Chapter 5, Note 6.

[12] The *ololiuhqui* seeds have also been reported in use in contemporary México as an ecbolic, one of the principal medical indications for ergot (see Note 4). The uterotonic effect of extracts of *Ipomoea violacea* has been demonstrated experimentally (Der Marderosian *et al.* 1964B). The Chinantec Indians of Oaxaca, México, employ seeds of *Turbina corymbosa* as an ecbolic, under the name *m''oo quiá' sée* (Browner 1985; Ortíz de Montellano & Browner 1985). Among the Mayans, honey of stingless bees was used as a uterotonic to aid in expelling the placenta, and as an ecbolic. This likely involved *xtabentún* honey, a medicinal agent in Yucatán, honey made by stingless bees from flowers of *xtabentún* or *Turbina corymbosa* (Roys 1931; Schwarz 1948). In a chemical study of Costa Rican *Ipomoea carnea*, a morning glory used as an entheogen in Ecuador and known to contain ergot alkaloids (Lascano *et al.* 1967; Naranjo *et al.* 1964), the nectar from extrafloral nectaries was reported to be devoid of alkaloids (Keeler 1977). Many other *Ipomoea* species possess extrafloral nectaries, including *I. violacea* (Keeler & Kaul 1979), and like *I. carnea*, extrafloral nectars from *I. leptophylla* and *I. pandurata* were devoid of alkaloids (Beckmann & Stucky 1981; Keeler 1980). It is not yet known whether *xtabentún* floral nectar or honey contains ergot alkaloids, but use of *xtabentún* honey as a medicament would suggest that it does. Studies are underway to clarify this point. In the Old World, a paste of young leaves of *Ipomoea pes-caprae* is used as an ecbolic by the natives of the Nicobar Islands, India (Dagar & Dagar 1991), and the leaves are used as a rheumatism remedy in Samoa (Uhe 1974). Samoan *I. pes-caprae* was shown to be active in pharmacological screening (Cox *et al.* 1989). In the Cook Islands leaves of this morning glory are used to treat sprains (Whistler 1985) and an infusion of *I. pes-caprae* var. *brasiliensis* is used in Tonganese ethnomedicine (Singh *et al.* 1984). Extracts of the plant are used in Southeast Asia as an antidote to jellyfish venoms (Ponglux *et al.* 1987; Pongprayoon *et al.* 1991) and in Vanuatu the juice of "nearly wilted leaves" of this cosmopolitan beach morning glory is used as an antidote to "ciguatera" poisoning (Bourdy *et al.* 1992), a sort of food poisoning involving ingestion of fish that feed on algae which produce ciguatoxins (Lange 1987). Extracts of leaves of *Ipomoea crassicaulis* are used as an ecbolic in contemporary Mexican ethnogynecology (Zamora-Martínez & Nieto de Pascual Pola 1992). The seeds of scammony, *Convolvulus scammonia*, known to contain alkaloids, were used in the classical world as a uterotonic and abortifacient (Albert-Puleo 1979). Use of pulverized root of *Ipomoea leptophylla* by North American Pawnee Indians to treat nervousness and bad dreams (Gilmore 1919) may point to psychotropic ergoline alkaloids in this species, and the same can be said for *I. medium*, used as a pediatric anticonvulsant in Madagascar (Beaujard 1988). Since leaf juice of *I. involucrata* is used as a hemostatic in Sierra Leone, Africa

(MacFoy & Sama 1983), and since juice of whole plants is used by the Fang of Africa as a stimulant and "medico-magic" remedy (Akendengué 1992), the presence of ergoline alkaloids in this species is also likely. Finally, use of flowers of *I. littoralis* as a hemostatic and of leaves of this morning glory against postpartum pain (Austin 1991) underscores the probability that this species, too, contains uterotonic ergoline alkaloids.

[13] This point is still a topic of debate in the halls of academia. To the *cognoscenti*, it is obvious that self-experiments by the researcher are a necessary prerequisite to investigations on entheogens. The effects of entheogens are so much a product of set and setting that the naive researcher is in danger of projecting his own biases onto the experiences of the experimental subjects. As R. Gordon Wasson so eloquently put it: "two psychiatrists who have taken the mushroom and known the experience in its full dimensions have been criticized in professional circles as being no longer 'objective.' Thus it comes about that we are all divided into two classes: those who have taken the mushroom and are disqualified by our subjective experience, and those who have not taken the mushroom and are disqualified by their total ignorance of the subject!" (Wasson 1961). Moreover, it should be noted that the three most important entheogens—mescaline, LSD and psilocybine—were all discovered by psychonauts, chemists evaluating their own chemical preparations in self-experiments. Those chemists, like Louis Lewin, who attempted to isolate the entheogenic principles of *péyotl* (see Chapter 1), and like James Moore, who attempted to isolate the entheogenic principles of *teonanácatl* (see Chapter 5); by relying exclusively on animal experiments to determine activity of extracts, uniformly failed. It was Arthur Heffter, testing a series of *péyotl* extracts on himself, who discovered mescaline; and Albert Hofmann and colleagues, testing *teonánacatl* extracts on themselves, who discovered psilocybine and psilocine (Heffter 1898; Hofmann *et al.* 1958). On the basis of animal tests in 1938, Sandoz pharmacologists had concluded that LSD was of little pharmacological interest—it was Albert Hofmann's hunch five years later which led him again to make the drug, opening the way for his serendipitous discovery of its extraordinary, human-being-specific effects in his own body (Hofmann 1980). In spite of this, researchers have used many different animals, from spiders (Christiansen *et al.* 1962; Witt 1960) to housecats (Díaz 1975) to elephants (Cohen 1964), in vain, in this case immoral, pursuit of the elusive animal model of "hallucinosis." See also Chapter 4, Note 6.

[14] Many black-market LSD preparations actually contained *N*(1)-acetyl-LSD, or ALD-52. This compound readily hydrolyzes to acetic acid and LSD. Its effects are identical to LSD, and it is virtually equipotent. The most famous preparation of ALD-52, "Orange Sunshine" (containing up to 300 mcg ALD-52 per "barrel") appeared in 1969, and was widely sold for a few years. This was the prototype of the so-called "designer drug." See Note 8 above.

[15] LSD has been classified as a drug with a "high potential for abuse," and the story of the use of the drug by the United States CIA and by the U.S. Army, certainly shows how the drug may be abused. Using phony funding agencies, like the above-mentioned "Geschickter Fund for Medical Research, Inc.," the "Society for the Study of Human Ecology" (this, before most Americans would have known what *ecology* meant!) and the "Josiah Macy,

Jr. Foundation" the CIA began to employ academic scientists to test LSD and other drugs. One such scientist, L.J. West, injected 300 milligrams of LSD into an elephant, hoping to induce an elephant psychosis—instead, the hapless animal collapsed and was killed by the good doctor who administered a combination of drugs in an attempt to revive him. A Canadian psychiatrist, E. Cameron, used LSD in experimental "treatments" on unwilling "patients," nine of whom later sued the U.S. government for the trauma this occasioned. These unfortunate inmates of Cameron's Allain Memorial Institute were sedated for months at a time, then subjected to repeated electroshock and doses of LSD, followed by "psychic driving"—being exposed under prolonged sedation to tape-recorded messages. This was in violation of the Nürnberg Code of medical ethics (ironically, Cameron had been a member of the Nürnberg tribunal which judged Nazi war criminals and sent some physicians to the gallows; Annas & Grodin 1992; Lee & Shlain 1985), as were the CIA-sponsored drug experiments on prisoners in the Lexington, Kentucky narcotics "farm." The latter "experiments" were under the control of H.S. Isbell, who dosed individual prisoners (mostly black) with ever-increasing quantities of LSD for more than 75 successive days! In 1953, CIA officials authorized the purchase of 10 kilograms of LSD (about 100 million doses), which Sandoz was not able or willing to provide. In violation of patent laws, the CIA then ordered the Eli Lilly Company of Indiana to synthesize LSD. That year one of the CIA scientists involved in the drug testing program, F. Olson, who had been given LSD unknowingly in his cocktail at a CIA retreat at Deepcreek Lake, Maryland, became depressed and killed himself some weeks after being dosed surreptitiously. Although the CIA kept the true circumstances leading up to the suicide secret, they became public following release of documents resulting from a journalist's "Freedom of Information Act" lawsuit, and doleful then-President Gerald Ford was forced publicly to apologize to Olson's family. In 1955 "Operation Midnight Climax" commenced, setting up the CIA-financed brothels. The "safehouse experiments" continued for eight years, and when G.H. White, the man in charge of the operation, retired in 1966, he said: "I toiled wholeheartedly in the vineyards because it was fun, fun, fun. Where else could a red-blooded American boy lie, kill, cheat, steal, rape, and pillage with the sanction and blessing of the All-Highest?" Where else, indeed? Meanwhile, the United States Army (when its infamous Chemical Corps wasn't killing livestock with nerve-gas in Colorado) commenced testing of LSD as an "unconventional chemical warfare agent." Major General W. Creasy, chief officer of the Army Chemical Corps, was an enthusiastic supporter of the concept. The Army, too, had its little mishaps. In 1953, as part of experiments funded by the Army Chemical Corps, a tennis player named H. Blauer was killed with an intravenous injection of 500 mg of EA-1298 or MDA (see Chapter 1; Shulgin & Shulgin 1991). An Army researcher blithely commented: "we didn't know if it was dog piss or what it was we were giving him." The Army tested LSD on some 1500 military personnel, some of whom later claimed they were coerced by officers into "volunteering." General Creasy even wished to test LSD on a large scale, in a subway system or in surface spraying of a large city, bemoaning the fact that permission to do so "was denied on reasons that always seemed a little absurd to me." All of this unethical, illegal and scientifically unsound "research" (in many respects analogous to medical "research" by Nazi doctors in Dachau and other concentration camps), was justified on the grounds of "national security" and the presumption that similar work was going on in the Soviet Union and China; although internal CIA documents failed to substantiate this, and there is no evidence the so-called "iron curtain" governments of these two "enemies" were as obsessed with chemical mind control as were their "free world" counterparts (Lee & Shlain 1985; Marks 1979). See also: Chapter 3, Note 2; Chapter 4, Note 6 and Chapter 5, Note 8.

[16] There is fragmentary evidence of folk knowledge of the inebriating potential of ergots. *Darnel* or *tares*, *Lolium temulentum*, has been known since antiquity as an inebriant, and recent research shows it owes its inebriating potential to common infestation by ergot or other mushrooms (Dannhardt & Steindl 1985; Hofmann 1978A; Katz 1949). Darnel was mentioned as an ingredient in three different recipes for witches' psychotropic "flying ointments" (De Vries 1991A; Hansen 1978). In the Canary Islands darnel seeds are said to be used as a tranquilizer and are known as *borrachera* ("drunkenness"), suggesting use as an inebriant (Darias *et al.* 1986). Similarly, darnel or *cizaña* is also known in Spanish as *borrachuela*, betraying traditional knowledge of inebriating properties. A nineteenth century Scottish chemist commented that darnel "creeps occasionally into our fermented liquors and our bread" and that it had "long been known to possess narcotic and singularly intoxicating properties. When malted along with the barley [darnel seeds] impart their intoxicating quality to the beer, and render it unusually and even dangerously heady" (Johnston 1857). A similar phenomenon was reported in Britain where it was said of darnel: "when brewed with barley, it communicates a very intoxicating quality to the beer" (Johnson & Johnson 1861). In Perú, seeds of *cizaña* or *L. temulentum* are added to the fermented beverage *chicha* to enhance its potency (Soukup 1970). Writing of darnel, Duke recently reported "the Lebanese hint that there is a mystic cult 'in the mountains' which infuses the grass or soaks the seeds to extract the ergot which is then used to induce religious ecstasy" (Duke 1983). Tremorigenic compounds lolitrem B and peramine have been found in *L. perenne* strains toxic to livestock, and derive from the fungus *Acremonium loliae* (Gallagher *et al.* 1984; Rowan *et al.* 1986). *Acremonium*-infested "sleepy grass" or *Stipa robusta* (likewise toxic to livestock) was recently reported to contain high concentrations of lysergic acid amide or ergine (Anon. 1992C; Petroski *et al.* 1989). In India, kodo millet, *Paspalum scrobiculatum*, also commonly infested with ergot, is known to be poisonous after a rain, causing "delirium and violent tremors" (Aaronson 1988; De Wet *et al.* 1983). The "outer covering of dehusked grains" of kodo millet (which is where the ergot would be found) has been reportedly used as an entheogen by the Lodha of Midnapur District, West Bengal (Pal & Jain 1989). In 1959, Indian researchers isolated a "tranquillizing principle" from *Paspalum scrobiculatum* grain, which showed the properties of a water-soluble alkaloid and had pharmacological effects similar to lysergic acid amide or ergine (Bhide & Aimen 1959). In Samoa, *P. scrobiculatum* seeds are thought to be poisonous (Uhe 1974). In the Ecuadorian Amazon, infusions of *Paspalum conjugatum* are used by Shuar Indians as a headache remedy, suggesting infestation by ergot-alkaloid-containing *Claviceps paspali* (Russo 1992). Finally, a *Cyperus* species known to be infested by ergot-alkaloid-containing *Balansia cyperi* (see Note 4), has been reportedly used as an additive to entheogenic *ayahuasca* potions in Amazonia (Chaumeil 1982; Plowman *et al.* 1990). Another *ayahuasca* additive, the fern *Lomariopsis japurensis* (Pinkley 1969; Rivier

& Lindgren 1972; Schultes & Hofmann 1979), may likewise contain ergoline alkaloids. Both this species and *L. nigropalatea* are used in Amazonian ethnomedicine in contexts suggesting possible content of ergoline alkaloids. The former is used by Quijos Quichua Indians against postpartum hemorrhage (Marles *et al.* 1988) and by the Runa of Ecuador as an abortifacient (Kohn 1992); the latter employed by Makú Indians as a general hemostatic (Schultes & Raffauf 1990).

[17] Given the fact that contemporary western society is obsessed with ethyl alcohol or ethanol as inebriant, we tend to consider alcohol to have been the dominant inebriant throughout history. Dionysus, the ancient Greek god of inebriation, is widely associated with the vine and wines, and it is commonly assumed that inebriation with Greek wines was a form of alcoholic inebriation. Yet we now know that Greek wines were very powerful infusions of various inebriating plants which required dilution with water to render them safe to drink. Since the ancient Greeks lacked distillation technology (Forbes 1948), their wines were limited to 12–15% alcohol content (at which point in the fermentation the yeasts which produce the alcohol as waste product would die from alcohol poisoning). These wines required dilution because they contained high concentrations of alkaloids and other plant secondary compounds. In effect, their inebriating properties proceeded from the drugs infused in them, and their alcohol content served more as a preservative than as an inebriating active principle (Samorini 1995). Dionysus was the son of Persephone and Zeus, key figures in the *Homeric Hymn to Demeter* which underlay the Eleusinian potion, the entheogenic *kykeon* (see Postscriptum). Dionysus represents the "wild" in Ruck's scheme (Ruck 1982; Ruck & Staples 1994), and he has been associated, in my opinion correctly, with shamanism (Emboden 1977; Samorini 1995)—the preliterate, matritheistic, autochthonous strain onto which was grafted the "cultivated," or the patritheistic Indo-European "civilized" strain—represented mythologically as the marriage of Persephone and Zeus; or indeed of Zeus with the whole pantheon of Earth Mother goddesses who preceded him. In ancient Greek there was no word for alcohol. Dioscorides described a wine infused with mandrake (*Mandragora officinarum*; see Appendix A) and so soporific as to be useful as a surgical anesthetic (Rätsch 1994; Stillman 1922). As Carl Ruck described it: "we hear of some wines so strong that they could be diluted with twenty parts of water and that required at least eight parts water to be drunk safely, for, according to the report, the drinking of certain wines straight actually caused permanent brain damage and in some cases even death... we can also document the fact that different wines were capable of inducing different physical symptoms, ranging from slumber to insomnia and hallucinations" (Wasson *et al.* 1978). Homer described how clever Odysseus got Polyphemus (the Cyclops) drunk by giving him straight a wine meant to be diluted with twenty parts water, and wines of this potency still existed in Pliny's day. The addition by Helen of *nepenthes* (thought to have been opium) to Telemachus' wine to assuage his grief is a well-known episode in the *Odyssey*. Plutarch described a distinctly visionary wine drunk in a Dionysian festival called the *Anthesteria*, a drugged wine which, according to Ruck "was responsible for opening the graves and allowing the departed spirits to return to Athens for a banquet" (Wasson *et al.* 1978). According to Xenophon and Aristophanes, a wine's quality was called its "flower," and a wine "deficient in flower" lacked potency—

literally it didn't have enough of the flowers (and/or leaves) of the plants which accounted for its particular effects. The ancient Aztecs similarly used the word "flower" (*xóchitl* or *ihuinti*) as a metaphor for the entheogens, even calling entheogenic mushrooms *xochinanácatl*—literally, "flower-mushrooms" (see Chapter 5, Note 3; Wasson 1980). The Aztecs, too, fortified alcoholic *Agave* wine—*octli* or *pulque*—with sacred inebriants, preparing a ceremonial *teoctli* or "wondrous *pulque*" for captured warriors before they were led in glory to the sacrifice, and for their priestly executioners (Gonçalves de Lima 1956; see Chapter 6, Note 12). In the *Old Testament*, a repeated distinction is made between wine and "strong drink," both of which were inebriants. Collectively they are mentioned nearly 200 times, and some eleven Hebrew words for wine are used, of which the most common is *yayin* (which appears nearly 150 times) and secondarily *tirosh* (appearing 38 times). *Tirosh* evidently was the word for grape juice and new wine, and when fermentation was complete, the product was called *yayin*—both *tirosh* and *yayin* were inebriating (Wasson 1914). But the *Old Testament* also refers repeatedly to *shekar*, or "strong drink" which was not the same as *yayin* or *tirosh*, but which could also inebriate, as for example in 1 Samuel 1.14, when Eli said to Hannah "How long wilt thou be drunken? put away thy *yayin* from thee," to which she replied proudly: "I have drunk neither *yayin* nor *shekar*." Like the ancient Greeks, the ancient Israelites did not know distillation technology, but possessed an inebriant other than wine, which apparently was more potent. Was the Biblical *shekar*, "strong drink," not an inebriating draught analogous to the ancient Greek wines, some of which were entheogenic potions? Down through history there have been innumerable instances of the addition of psychoactive plants to wines and other alcoholic beverages. Two celebrated nineteenth century examples are *Vin Mariani*, a fine Bordeaux wine infused with cocaine-containing *coca* leaves (Mariani 1890) as well as the various *absinthe* liqueurs made by distilling alcohol, into which volatile thujone-containing *Artemisia absinthium* plants were infused (see Appendix A; Conrad 1988). A modern survival of this common practice is the use of soporific hops (*Humulus lupulus*) as an additive to contemporary beers, thereby combining the sedative effects of 2-methyl-3-butene-2-ol to those of alcohol (Tyler 1987). An in-depth study of the many psychotropic additives to alcoholic beverages remains a *desideratum* of psychopharmacognosy, and the German ethnopharmacognosist Christian Rätsch has now attacked the Braumeister's side of the problem, with his new book *Urbock: Bier Jenseits von Hopfen und Malz* [*Urbock: Beer Beyond Hops and Malt*] (Rätsch 1996). See also Rätsch's appendix on the entheogenic "mead of inspiration" in Ralph Metzner's recent book *The Well of Remembrance* (Metzner 1994), as well as the "Inebriantia" section in Dale Alexander Pendell's *Pharmako / Pœia: Plant Powers, Poisons, and Herbcraft* (Pendell 1995).

TABLE 2
ERGOLINE-ALKALOID-CONTAINING PLANTS*

	I. CLAVICIPITACEAE:
Acremonium coenophialum	Porter 1995
Acremonium sp.	Anon. 1992C; Petroski *et al.* 1989
Balansia claviceps	Porter *et al.* 1979[1]
B. cyperi	Plowman *et al.* 1990[1]
B. epichloë	Porter *et al.* 1979[1]
Claviceps paspali	Arcamone *et al.* 1960[2]
C. purpurea	Stoll & Burckhardt 1935
Cordyceps capitata	Heim & Wasson 1958[9][3]
C. ophioglossoides	Heim & Wasson 1958[9][3]
Epichloë typhina	Porter *et al.* 1981
Hypomyces aurantius	Yamatodani & Yamamoto 1983
	II. CONVOLVULACEAE:
Argyreia acuta	Chao & Der Marderosian 1973B
A. barnesii	Chao & Der Marderosian 1973B
A. cuneata	Chao & Der Marderosian 1973B
A. hainanensis	Chao & Der Marderosian 1973B
A. luzonensis	Chao & Der Marderosian 1973B
A. mollis	Chao & Der Marderosian 1973B
A. nervosa	Chao & Der Marderosian 1973A; Chao & Der Marderosian 1973B; Hylin & Watson 1965
A. obtusifolia	Chao & Der Marderosian 1973B
A. philippinensis	Chao & Der Marderosian 1973B
A. speciosa	Montgomery 1990[4]
A. splendens	Chao & Der Marderosian 1973B
A. wallichi	Chao & Der Marderosian 1973B
Convolvulus tricolor	Genest & Sahasrabudhe 1966[5]
Ipomoea amnicola	Amor-Prats & Harborne 1993
I. argillicola	Amor-Prats & Harborne 1993
I. argyrophylla	Stauffacher *et al.* 1965
I. asarifolia	Jirawongse *et al.* 1977
I. carnea	Lascano *et al.* 1967
I. coccinea	Gröger 1963[6]
I. crassicaulis[7]	
I. diamantinensis	Amor-Prats & Harborne 1993

Ipomoea involucrata[8]	
I. leptophylla	Chao & Der Marderosian 1973B[9]
I. littoralis[8]	
I. muelleri	Gardiner *et al.* 1965
I. nil	Genest & Sahasrabudhe 1966[10]
I. orizabensis	Amor-Prats & Harborne 1993
I. parasitica	Amor-Prats & Harborne 1993
I. pes-caprae[11]	
I. piurensis	Jenett-Siems *et al.* 1994
I. purpurea	Hylin & Watson 1965[12]
I. turbinata	Banerjee & Bhatnagar 1974
I. violacea (=*I. rubro-caerulea*)	Hofmann 1963A; Gröger *et al.* 1963; Der Marderosian *et al.* 1964A
Stictocardia tiliaefolia	Hofmann 1961
Turbina corymbosa (=*I. sidaefolia; Rivea corymbosa*)	Der Marderosian *et al.* 1964A; Hofmann 1963A; Hofmann & Tscherter 1960; Taber *et al.* 1963B
	III. POLYGALACEAE:
Securidaca longipedunculata[13]	Costa *et al.* 1992

NOTES

[1] Certain *Cyperus* species infected with *Balansia cyperi* are used in ethnogynecology by Achuar "Jívaro" Indians of Peruvian Amazonia (Lewis & Elvin-Lewis 1990). Cultures taken from two Amazonian and one U.S. strain of this fungus produced "several unidentified ergot alkaloids" (Plowman *et al.* 1990). Since these same *Cyperus* species are also used as additives to entheogenic *ayahuasca* potions (see Chapter 4; Schultes & Raffauf 1990), there is the likelihood that psychoactive ergot alkaloids are involved (see Chapter 2, Note 4).

[2] Lysergic acid amides have been isolated from ergots of *Paspalum* species, and (see Chapter 2, Note 7) *Claviceps paspali* has become the industrial source of lysergic acid (Bové 1970; Hofmann 1977). Ergot of *Paspalum scrobiculatum* or kodo millet is toxic after rains (Aaronson 1988; De Wet *et al.* 1983), and Indian researchers isolated a "tranquillizing principle" which showed the properties of lysergic acid amide (see Chapter 2, Note 16; Bhide & Aimen 1959). "Outer covering of dehusked grains" of kodo millet is used for psychoptic effects by Lodhas of West Bengal, India (Pal & Jain 1989). *Lolium temulentum*, *darnel* or *tares*, has an inebriating reputation (Duke 1983; Hofmann 1978A; Johnson & Johnson 1861; Johnston 1857). Known in Europe as *Taumellolch* ("delirium grass") and as *ivraie* ("inebriating"), psychotropic properties of this wild grass may derive from alkaloids produced by fungi commonly infesting it (Hofmann 1978A; Katz 1949). Loline and "two minor alkaloids" were isolated from caryopses of *L. temulentum*, perloline from stems (Dannhardt & Steindl 1985). Loline was found to be non-toxic up to doses of 200 mg/kg after

i.p. injection into mice. Since caryopses were all "invaded by a fungus," there is the possibility loline is a fungal alkaloid. Since loline was non-toxic, ergoline alkaloids remain the best candidates for producing well-known psychoptic effects of *L. temulentum*. Tremorigenic compounds lolitrem B and peramine were found in *Lolium perenne* strains toxic to livestock, deriving from fungus *Acremonium loliae* (Gallagher *et al.* 1984; Rowan *et al.* 1986).

[3] As described in Chapter 2, Note 4, *Cordyceps capitata* and *C. ophioglossoides* are ingested together with psilocybian mushrooms (see Chapter 5) in mushroom curing rituals in México (Guzmán 1958; Heim 1957A). Although Hofmann had found the former species to be devoid of psilocybine, it did contain "une substance indolique différente, à l'état de traces (0.004%)"; "a different indolic substance in trace amounts of 0.004%" (Heim & Wasson 1958). This compound remains unidentified and the similarly-used *C. ophioglossoides* (which is of considerable value in Chinese medicine) has evidently not been examined for potentially psychotropic indolic compounds.

[4] Bioassay of five seeds of this African species found it to be visionary (Montgomery 1990).

[5] Although preliminary screening of seeds of *Convolvulus tricolor* detected traces (0.001% of fresh weight) of alkaloids in one (from Denmark) out of seven strains tested (Genest & Sahasrabudhe 1966), the authors suspected that "possibly seed contamination by *I. violacea*" occurred, referring to *Ipomoea violacea*, a known psychoactive species used ritually in México. A subsequent report failed to detect indole alkaloids in a strain of this species from Hungary, nor in *C. siculus* nor *C. sepium* (Der Marderosian & Youngken 1966), and *C. tricolor* was tentatively listed in a recent paper on Italian psychotropic plants (Festi & Alliota 1990). However, *C. scammonia* has been known since antiquity as an abortifacient and headache remedy (with pharmacological properties common to psychoactive ergot alkaloids), and *C. arvensis* was described by Dioscorides as a "birth-quickener" (Albert-Puleo 1979). Dioscorides suggested that seeds of *C. sepium* might be psychoactive, mentioning that their ingestion "is related to cause many and troublesome dreams." Recently Bahraini ethnomedicinal use of *C. arvensis* roots and leaves as a topical hemostatic was reported (Abbas *et al.* 1992). There is thus reason to suppose that at least some *Convolvulus* species may contain psychoactive ergoline alkaloids.

[6] Although *Ipomoea coccinea* was reported to contain ergot alkaloids (Gröger 1963), a subsequent analysis of a single commercial strain of *I. coccinea* var. *hederifolia* failed to detect indole alkaloids (Der Marderosian & Youngken 1966). Furthermore, in the original report, only agroclavine and elymoclavine were detected in this species. These alkaloids are not known to be entheogenic (but see Note 13 below), and this species is probably not psychoactive. As *I. hederacea*, seeds of a single French strain were found to contain only a trace of elymoclavine (Genest & Sahasrabudhe 1966), and traces of a few other ergot alkaloids were found in seeds of wild *I. hederacea* in a recent study (Wilkinson *et al.* 1986).

[7] Although *Ipomoea crassicaulis* has not yet been shown chemically to contain psychotropic ergoline alkaloids, extracts of leaves of this species were recently reported to be used as an

ecbolic (to precipitate childbirth) in contemporary Mexican ethnogynecology (Zamora-Martínez & Nieto de Pascual Pola 1992). Similar use of entheogenic and uterotonic seeds of *Turbina corymbosa* has been reported from Oaxaca, México (Browner 1985; Ortíz de Montellano & Browner 1985). Since ergonovine and ergine both occur in *I. violacea*, and are at once entheogenic and uterotonic, it is possibile, even probable, that the uterotonic principle of *I. crassicaulis* is a psychoactive ergoline alkaloid.

[8] Although not reported to contain ergoline alkaloids, the use of leaf juice of *Ipomoea involucrata* as a hemostatic in Sierra Leone, West Africa, makes it likely this species contains potentially visionary ergoline alkaloids (MacFoy & Sama 1983). The Fang of Central Africa take juice of fresh whole plants of this species as a stimulant and "medico-magic" therapy for illnesses thought to be related to sorcery (Akendengué 1992). Similarly, *I. littoralis* flowers have reportedly been used as a hemostatic and its leaves for postpartum pain and as a pediatric anticonvulsant, likewise suggesting content of ergoline alkaloids (Austin 1991; Whistler 1992). The use of *I. medium* as a pediatric anticonvulsant in Madagascar also recommends study of this species for alkaloids (Beaujard 1988).

[9] *Ipomoea leptophylla* roots were burned by North American Indians to treat sufferers of nervousness and "bad dreams" with the smoke (Gilmore 1919). This potentially psychoactive use points to possible content of visionary ergoline alkaloids.

[10] Although preliminary screening of 14 strains of *Ipomoea nil* had detected trace amounts (0.001% of fresh weight) of total alkaloids in seeds of two strains from California (Genest & Sahasrabudhe 1966), in both cases the authors suspected there had been "possibly seed contamination by *I. violacea*," admixture of seeds of the well-known psychotropic species *Ipomoea violacea*. In a subsequent study, no indole alkaloids were detected in any of five American strains of *I. nil* tested (Der Marderosian & Youngken 1966; see also Der Marderosian *et al.* 1964A, where one of these strains was also mentioned). That same year, seeds of three Japanese strains of *I. nil* ("Matzukaze," "Yuki" and "Chiyo no okina") were found to contain traces (0.007–0.011% of fresh weight) of total alkaloids (Staba & Laursen 1966). This last-mentioned Japanese strain of *Ipomoea nil*, "Chiyo no okina" is evidently named for Kaga no Chiyo, well-known poetess, who wrote a famous and suggestive *haiku* poem to the morning glory, "Asagao ya!" (Bates 1964).

[11] As is the case with *Ipomoea crassicaulis*, a preparation of the leaves of *I. pes-caprae* (the common sandy beach plant) is used in contemporary ethnogynecology as an ecbolic (a drug to precipitate childbirth) by the natives of the Nicobar Islands, India (Dagar & Dagar 1991). Similarly, extracts of the plant are used as an antidote to jellyfish venoms in Southeast Asia (Ponglux *et al.* 1987; Pongprayoon *et al.* 1991) and as an antidote to ciguatera poisoning in Vanuatu (Bourdy *et al.* 1992). Since *I. violacea* contains both ergine and ergonovine (ergoline alkaloids at once visionary and uterotonic), it is possible that the reported properties of *I. pes-caprae* likewise derive from these psychoptic alkaloids.

[12] Although a preliminary report described substantial quantities of alkaloids (0.423–0.813

mg/g) in seeds of two cultivars of *Ipomoea purpurea*, the strains were identified as "Heavenly Blue" and "Pearly Gates," known horticultural names for strains of *Ipomoea violacea*, one of the psychoactive species used ritually in México (Hylin & Watson 1965). An earlier report (Taber *et al.* 1963A), which has been criticized for lack of taxonomic and chemical rigor (Der Marderosian *et al.* 1964A), likewise suggested that *I. purpurea* seeds contained alkaloids. In 1964, one American strain of *I. purpurea* ("Crimson Rambler") was found to be devoid of alkaloids (Der Marderosian *et al.* 1964A). In 1966, 13 strains of genuine *I. purpurea* (with trade names like "Crimson Rambler" and "Double Rose Marie") were all found to be devoid of alkaloids (Genest & Sahasrabudhe 1966). In another study, five strains (with colorful names like "Crimson Rambler," "Sunrise Serenade," "Rose Marie" and "Tinkerbell's Petticoat") of *I. purpurea* were likewise found to be devoid of alkaloids (Der Marderosian & Youngken 1966). A recent study found small traces of ergot alkaloids in *I. purpurea* seeds (Wilkinson *et al.* 1986). The evidence indicates that Hylin and Watson committed a nomenclatural error, in substituting the specific name *purpurea*, "purple-colored" for what they really meant, *violacea* or "violet-colored." We must consider *I. purpurea* to be a mistaken attribution to *I. violacea*, as three separate studies have failed to detect alkaloids in a total of 19 strains of *I. purpurea*, with only one report of small traces of alkaloids in seeds of this species. A recent paper on Italian psychotropic plants noted that self-experiments with seeds of this species failed to demonstrate psychoactive properties (Festi & Alliota 1990). Unfortunately, this confusion has been perpetuated in secondary literature. In a 1969 paper reprinted in 1990, the seeds of "Heavenly Blue" and "Pearly Gates" varieties of *I. violacea* were mistakenly referred to as *I. purpurea*, citing the Taber group's paper (Savage *et al.* 1990). Even more recently, a "radical history" of entheogens and human evolution mistakenly referred to *I. purpurea* in a discussion of the ritual use of *I. violacea* in México (T.K. McKenna 1992).

[13] *Tchúnfki* roots, traditional entheogens of the Balanta of Guinea Bissau, contained elymoclavine—evidently psychoptic—also known from Mexican entheogenic morning glories.

* This table reports the occurrence of known psychotropic ergoline alkaloids in fungal and flowering plant species. The natural ergot alkaloids known to be psychoptic are: 1) lysergic acid amide or ergine (LA-111), first ingested by Hofmann and active at doses of 0.5–1.0 mg (Hofmann 1963A; Solms 1956A; Solms 1956B); 2) lysergic acid *N*-1-hydroxyethylamide (which readily hydrolyzes *in vivo* to lysergic acid amide; Hofmann 1971) and 3) lysergic acid-L-2-propanolamide or ergonovine (also known by the synonyms ergobasin[e], ergometrine, ergotocin[e] and ergostetrine; see Chapter 2, Note 6), first found by Hofmann to be visionary at doses of 2.0 mg of the hydrogen maleate salt (Hofmann 1978A) and subsequently tested in doses as high as 10 mg (Bigwood *et al.* 1979). It is possible there are other psychoactive compounds in these plants (such as elymoclavine; see the preceding Note), and many also contain pharmacologically-active non-psychotropic alkaloids. A number of species, such as *Cuscuta monogyna* (Ikan *et al.* 1968), *Argyreia capitata*, *A. maingayi* and other species of *Argyreia* and *Ipomoea* (Chao & Der Marderosian 1973B) have been reported to contain a great variety of ergoline alkaloids, but none of these are as yet known psychoactive compounds, nor have any of these species been reported to be entheogenic.

CHAPTER THREE

DMT, Cohoba, Epéna: Short-Acting Tryptamines

These authors have found *N,N*-dimethyltryptamine, together with bufotenine, in snuff powder prepared by Haitian natives from *Piptadenia peregrina* seeds which the natives used in their religious ceremonies. The psychotropic effect was blamed on bufotenine, but it was unknown whether dimethyltryptamine was hallucinogenic or not. So I decided to synthesize it, and then tried it out on myself... It was not active orally... Then we started giving it intramuscularly, doses of one mg/kg, which give a very fast and very strong reaction... The perceptual distortions are primarily visual in nature, and with closed eyes you can see illusions and color patterns, primarily geometrical patterns, moving very fast, having sometimes very deep emotional content and connotation.

Stephen I. Szára
Discussion on the Psychoactive Action of Various Tryptamine Derivatives (1967)

In April of 1956, Stephen I. Szára and "friends who were courageous enough to volunteer" became the first individuals to experience the profound visionary effects of the hydrochloride salt of pure *N,N*-DiMethylTryptamine (DMT), which the group of Fish, Johnson and Horning had identified the previous year as a constituent of *cohoba*, an entheogenic snuff prepared from seeds of *Anadenanthera peregrina* (Fish *et al.* 1955; Szára 1956; Szára 1957; Szára 1961; Szára *et al.* 1967). DMT had been synthesized 25 years prior to Szára's work, by the British chemist Richard Manske (Manske 1931). The artificial compound DMT was not thought to be of particular pharmacological interest, until 24 years after its discovery it was determined to be a natural product and possible active principle of a well-known entheogenic snuff. The synthetic natural DMT produced in Szára's laboratory proved to be powerfully visionary and "so short acting, it is over before you realize it happens," with an unusually rapid onset, merely two to three minutes following intramuscular injection (Szára *et al.* 1967).

Early in 1961, the American writer and drug experimentalist William Burroughs began self-experiments with DMT, in doses of around 65 mg, "with results sometimes unpleasant but well under control and always interesting" until he inadvertently took an "overdose" of about 100 mg which precipitated a "horrible experience," following which Burroughs "sounded a word of urgent warning" to other experimenters (Burroughs 1964). In spite of Burroughs' warnings, Timothy Leary and Ralph Metzner, then of Harvard University (see Chapter 2), decided to try DMT with controlled set and appropriate setting (Leary 1968), and in the premier issue of *The Psychedelic Review*, in 1963, Metzner reported that DMT was "in doses of 1 mg/kg, similar to LSD or mescaline, but with a shorter duration of effect" (Metzner 1963). Although religious philosopher Alan Watts dismissed DMT as "amusing but relatively uninteresting" (Watts 1970), Leary called it "this wondrous alkaloid" and commented "in 25 minutes (about the duration of the average sermon) you are whirled through the energy dance, the cosmic process, at the highest psychedelic speed. The 25 minutes are sensed as lasting for a second and for a billion-year Kalpa" (Leary 1964).

It would seem Leary's enthusiasm was justified—although DMT was never widely distributed either before or after its illegalization in the late sixties, it has always had its faithful adherents among entheogen users. Small amounts of pure DMT have continually been available to the elite of the entheogenic drug "scene," and it remains much sought-after in the 1990s. Moreover, as a component of South American entheogenic *ayahuasca* potions, DMT has moved to center-stage as one of the entheogens of choice of the late eighties and early nineties. While the history of DMT as a pure compound is short, it occurs in several important entheogenic plants of immemorial use in South America and the Caribbean, whose mark on history commenced in the fifteenth century, with Columbus' second expedition. An examination of the natural history of DMT-containing snuffs will provide perspective against which to view modern use of this potent entheogenic agent.

COHOBA, *YOPO* AND *VILCA*—THE ENTHEOGENIC LEGUMES

During Columbus' second voyage to the Americas, 1493–1496, the Admiral himself commented on a mysterious "powder" which the "kings" of the Taíno Indians of the island of La Española (Hispaniola) would "snuff up," and that "with this powder they lose consciousness and become like drunken men" (Torres 1988; Wassén 1967). Columbus commissioned Friar Ramón Pané to study the customs of the Taíno, and Pané wrote of the practice of the *buhuitihu* or shaman who "takes a certain powder called *cohoba* snuffing it up his nose, which intoxicates them so that they do not know what they do..." (Wassén 1967). Pané also referred to the drug as *cogioba*, and in the later text of Peter Martyr the name is given as *kohobba*.[1] More than four centuries were to pass before *cohoba* was definitively identified by American ethnobotanist W.E. Safford as a preparation of the seeds of *Piptadenia peregrina*, today more correctly known as *Anadenanthera peregrina* (Reis Altschul 1972; Safford 1916). While some had earlier confused *cohoba* with tobacco, also used by the Taíno, Safford in part based his identification on the widespread use of *A. peregrina* snuff under the name *yopo* by various South American Indian groups of the Orinoco River basin. Archaeological remains in Argentina, Brasil, Chile, Colombia, Costa Rica, the Dominican Republic, Haiti, Perú and Puerto Rico testify to the broad range and antiquity of entheogenic snuff use in the Caribbean and South America (Cordy-Collins 1982; De Smet 1985B; Franch 1982; Furst 1974B; Pagan Perdomo 1978; Torres 1981; Torres 1987A; Torres 1987B; Torres 1992; Torres 1996; Torres *et al.* 1991; Wassén 1965; Wassén 1967; Wassén 1972; Wassén & Holmstedt 1963). There is evidence of the modern survival of *Anadenanthera* snuff use among the Mataco Indians of the Río Bermejo and the Río Pilcomayo areas of Argentina (Ott, unpublished; Repke 1992; Torres 1992) and it was recently reported that three species are used in inebriating snuffs by Paraguayan Indians: *Anadenanthera peregrina* (*curupáy*); *A. colubrina* var. *Cebil* (=*Piptadenia macrocarpa*; *curupáy-curú*) and *Piptadenia rigida* (*curupáy-rá*; Costantini 1975). As late as 1971, *A. peregrina* snuffs were being prepared in the Orinoco basin (Brewer-Carias & Steyermark 1976).

Yopo snuff use was first reported in 1801 by the explorer A. von Humboldt among the Maypure Indians of Orinoco, and he identified the source of the seeds used in the snuff as *Acacia niopo* (later called *Mimosa acacioides* by R. Schomburgk), incorrectly, however, ascribing the potency of the snuff to the "freshly calcined lime" mixed with the fermented, powdered seeds (Humboldt & Bonpland 1852–1853). Fifty years later, the great botanist Richard Spruce made the first in-depth report of the use of *yopo* by the Guahibo Indians of the Orinoco basin, notes that were not published until another 57 years had passed (Schultes 1983C; Spruce 1908). Spruce called the source plant *Piptadenia niopo*. In Perú and Bolivia, a snuff called *vilca* or *huilca* (known as *cebil* in northern Argentina) is derived from seeds of the closely related *Anadenanthera colubrina* (Reis Altschul 1972; Reis Altschul 1967), the use of which was reported among Inca shamans in the sixteenth century (Schultes & Hofmann 1980). There is also circumstantial evidence the Incas employed *vilca* as a clyster or enema, although it is not clear whether the purpose was inebriation or purgation (De Smet 1983). There is evidence the Mura and Omagua Indians (and perhaps other Amazonian indigenous groups) employed *A. peregrina* also an an enema, under the name *paricá*; although this is a sort of generic name for visionary snuffs in parts of Amazonia, and usually refers to preparations of another plant, *Virola* spp., about which more will be said below (De Smet 1983; De Smet 1985A; Furst & Coe 1977). Since *Anadenanthera* species are not found in western Amazonia, there is some doubt in the case of the Omagua Indians whether the *curupa* leaves they used in entheogenic snuffs and enemas were referable to this genus (De Smet 1983; Reis Altschul 1972; Torres *et al.* 1991).

CHEMISTRY OF *ANADENANTHERA* SNUFFS

In 1954 V.L. Stromberg isolated 5-Hydroxy-*N,N*-DiMethylTryptamine (5-OH-DMT, a positional isomer of psilocine) or bufotenine from the seeds of *Anadenanthera peregrina* (Stromberg 1954). The following year Fish and colleagues confirmed this finding, identifying also DMT and the *N*-oxides of both compounds in the seeds and pods (Fish & Horning 1956; Fish *et al.* 1955), which led to Szára's testing of DMT for psychoptic properties. Bufotenine was first isolated in 1920 by H. Handovsky as a *minor* component of *Bufo vulgaris* venom (Handovsky 1920), and the compound has since been found to be widely distributed in plants and animals (Stowe 1959). The year following the discovery of bufotenine in *Anadenanthera* seeds, Albert Hofmann and colleagues of the Sandoz Laboratories published an improved synthesis of this compound and related oxytryptamines (Stoll *et al.* 1955). Being quite stable, bufotenine has recently been detected in nineteenth century *Anadenanthera* seeds (De Smet & Rivier 1987), in Spruce's 1854 collection of the plant drug (Schultes *et al.* 1977B) and in 1200-year-old samples of an entheogenic snuff from Chile (Torres *et al.* 1991). In 1955, bufotenine was first tested on four prisoners at the Ohio State Penitentiary, with intravenous injections of up to 16 mg of bufotenine as the creatinine sulfate salt. The unfortunate subjects receiving the higher doses were reported to have faces "the color of an eggplant" diluted, and to have experienced minor visual phenomena of short duration, leading the experimenters to conclude that the drug was "hallucinogenic" (Fabing & Hawkins 1956). Similar effects were reported later in another study involving the intravenous injection of 12–16 mg bufotenine

(Bonhour *et al.* 1967). In 1955, as part of U.S. central Intelligence Agency (CIA) MKULTRA experiments (see Chapter 2, Note 15), H.S. Isbell administered *cohoba* snuff and bufotenine to prisoners in the Lexington, Kentucky federal narcotics "farm." The snuff proved to be inactive up to doses of 1 gram repeated at 30 minute intervals, as did doses of bufotenine creatinine sulfate as high as 40 mg sprayed into the nostrils, but subjects receiving 10–12.5 mg doses by intramuscular injection allegedly experienced "visual hallucinations... a play of colors, lights, and patterns" (Isbell in Turner & Merlis 1959). In experiments with 14 "schizophrenics" at a New York mental institution, Turner and Merlis found dramatic physical symptoms following intravenous administration of 10 mg bufotenine to one of their hapless "patients," and ceased experimenting with the drug when three other "patients" nearly died after relatively small doses of bufotenine (Turner & Merlis 1959). Incredibly, Turner and Merlis injected their helpless "patients" with bufotenine "as they were coming out of insulin coma or following EST" (Electroshock "Therapy"), as well as after pretreatment with reserpine and clorpromazine. In the latter two cases "each of these injections almost proved fatal in small amounts (between 2.5 and 5.0 mg)" with cessation of breathing and the characteristic cyanosis, described cavalierly as a "plum-colored" face. As might be expected, the "patients became frightened to an extreme degree," a very sensible reaction to attempts by their physicians (and jailers) to kill them! One wonders if this "paranoia" contributed to their continued incarceration and "treatment" for "schizophrenia"... Undaunted, Turner and Merlis went on to experiments with intramuscular injections of DMT in ten "patients." Although 5–20 mg of DMT intranasally was inactive, as was up to 350 mg orally, intramuscular injection of doses above 25 mg were quite active. One "patient" reportedly said after a 25 mg injection "you frighten me... what have you done to me?" Nevertheless, the dose was increased up to 50 mg in subsequent tests. Only when a female "patient" nearly died of cardiac arrest after a 40 mg injection ("extreme cyanosis quickly developed" and the poor woman was without pulse for 30 seconds, necessitating cardiac massage) did the good doctors cease their murderous experiments with DMT. This case has been mistakenly reported in the literature as bufotenine toxicity (Chilton *et al.* 1979), an error repeated in a recent paper (Davis & Weil 1992). This unfortunate "patient" said of her tormentors "I don't like them!"[2] These authors concluded that bufotenine was not "capable of producing the acute phase of *cohoba* intoxication." Nevertheless, recent bioassays rather suggest bufotenine is indeed the visionary principle of *cohoba* snuff (Ott, unpublished) and the United States government saw fit to classify bufotenine along with LSD, DMT, mescaline, psilocybine and psilocine as a drug with "high potential for abuse," even 'though it would appear no one has used the drug intentionally for "kicks"—its only users having been decidedly unwilling prisoners and mental "patients," apart from the occasional ill-starred monkey (Evarts *et al.* 1956), rodent (Gessner *et al.* 1960), cat (Evarts *et al.* 1955) or psychonaut (Ott, unpublished)!

Besides DMT, bufotenine and their *N*-oxides in the seeds, bark of *Anadenanthera peregrina* has been shown to contain 5-MethOxy-*N,N*-DiMethylTryptamine (5-MeO-DMT), 5-MethOxy-*N*-MonoMethylTryptamine (5-MeO-MMT) including *N*-MonoMethylTryptamine (MMT; known also in some reports as NMT), as well as trace amounts of the *beta*-carbolines 6-MethOxy-2-Methyl-1,2,3,4-TetraHydro-β-carboline (2-Me-6-MeO-THBC) and 6-MethOxy-1,2-DiMethyl-1,2,3,4-TetraHydro-β-carboline (6-MeO-DMTHC; Agurell *et al.* 1968A; Agurell *et al.* 1969; Legler & Tschesche 1963). Bufotenine was isolated from the seeds of *Anadenanthera colubrina* (=*Piptadenia colubrina*; Pachter *et al.* 1959) and bufotenine, DMT and the *N*-oxides of both compounds have likewise been found in *Anadenanthera colubrina* var. *Cebil* (=*Piptadenia macrocarpa*; Fish *et al.* 1955; Iacobucci & Rúveda 1964; Rendon & Willy 1985). 5-MeO-MMT was found in bark of this species, and seeds of *Piptadenia excelsa* contained DMT and bufotenine (Iacobucci & Rúveda 1964). Seeds of *Piptadenia paniculata* were found to contain traces of alkaloids (Fish *et al.* 1955); likewise *P. communis*, *P. contorta* and *P. leptostachya* (Fish in Reis Altschul 1964). Three species of *Piptadenia*—*P. rigida*, *P. paraguayensis* and *P. viridiflora*—were found to be devoid of tryptamines (Iacobucci & Rúveda 1964). The seeds of *Anadenanthera peregrina* var. *falcata* contained bufotenine (Giesbrecht 1960; Schultes & Hofmann 1980). As mentioned above, the highly-stable bufotenine has been detected in a nineteenth century collection of *Anadenanthera* seeds used by the Brasilian Maué Indians to prepare an entheogenic snuff (De Smet & Rivier 1987) and in Spruce's original 1854 collection (Schultes *et al.* 1977B). An examination of snuff preparations found DMT, bufotenine and 5-MeO-DMT in *yopo* snuff from Colombia, and the same compounds plus harmine (see Chapter 4) in a snuff prepared from *A. peregrina* by Piaroa Indians of the Orinoco basin (Holmstedt & Lindgren 1967). Recently, 1.0% bufotenine plus traces of harmine were found in a *yopo* snuff of the Piaroa Indians (De Smet 1985A; De Smet & Rivier 1985). The finding of harmine in these snuffs suggests the use of some *Banisteriopsis* species (see Chapter 4) as an admixture, since harmine is the principal alkaloid of these pan-Amazonian drug plants, found neither in *Anadenanthera* nor *Virola* (Schultes 1984). Another sample of *yopo* snuff from the Orinoco was found to contain bufotenine and 5-MeO-DMT (De Budowski *et al.* 1974). DMT, 5-MeO-DMT and bufotenine were all recently detected in two snuff samples from a 1200-year-old burial at San Pedro de Atacama in northern Chile (Torres *et al.* 1991). The samples were taken from bags attached to a mummy bundle, which also contained snuffing paraphernalia. Other burials in the same area and *stratum* yielded bags containing identifiable seeds of *Anadenanthera*. 5-MeO-MMT has been screened in animals and shows some activity (Marczynski 1959; Marczynski & Vetulani 1960), but its human pharmacology is still unknown. 5-MeO-DMT showed activity in preliminary screening (Benington *et al.* 1965; Gessner 1970; Gessner & Page 1962; Gessner *et al.* 1968), and was first tested by Shulgin, who found parenteral absorption of 5–10 milligrams to produce psychoptic effects, citing inhaling of 6–10 milligrams of free-base vapor. The drug wasn't tested orally (Shulgin 1970; Shulgin in De Smet 1983). Thus there are at least two known visionary compounds in *yopo* snuffs, along with bufotenine—which, while not exactly visionary *via* intravenous injection, nevertheless is psychoptic when vaporized or taken intranasally, and seems to be the main active agent of *yopo*, *cohoba*, and *vilca* (Ott, unpublished).

EPÉNA, PARICÁ, NYAKWANA—ENTHEOGENIC SNUFFS OF THE WAIKÁ

In 1909, German anthropologist T. Koch-Grünberg reported the existence of a "magical snuff" called *hakúdufha*, used by the Yekwana Indians of the Orinoco basin for "a strongly stimulating effect" (Koch-Grünberg 1909). He did not identify the source of the snuff, but said it was prepared from the bark of a tree, not from seeds. Almost thirty years later, Brasilian botanist A. Ducke reported the use of a snuff by Indians of the upper Río Negro, made from dried leaves of *Virola theiodora* or *V. cuspidata* and called *paricá* (Ducke 1938). Since *paricá* is a generic name for snuffs in Amazonia, and may refer to *Anadenanthera* preparations, some confusion resulted from these reports, until in 1954, Richard Evans Schultes definitively identified the snuffs called *yá-kee* and *yá-to* by the Puinave and Kuripako Indians of the Colombian Vaupés (also written Uaupés), as being prepared from a reddish resinous exudate of the inner bark of three species of *Virola*—*V. calophylla*, *V. calophylloidea* and *V. elongata*. Schultes sampled about a quarter of a dose of the *Virola* snuff, and noted its "narcotic [*sic*] strength" (Schultes 1954B). Further studies showed that the bulk of the use of *Virola* snuffs was centered around the Orinoco basin in Venezuela and the Río Negro basin of Brasil (whence came the early reports of Koch-Grünberg and Ducke), among groups like the Yanomamö, Pakidái, Surára, Parahuri, Karimé, Karauetari, Shirianá, Kirishaná and others—collectively known as the Waiká or Guaiká (Schultes & Hofmann 1980). The most common names for *Virola* snuffs are *epéna* and *nyakwana* (Chagnon 1968; Chagnon *et al.* 1971; Seitz

1967; Zerries 1960) and the Yekwana call *V. elongata* snuff *akurjua* (Boom & Moestl 1990). The *yá-kee* snuff of Colombia contains also ash of *Theobroma subincanum*, a wild relative of cacao. The Waiká Indians use chiefly *Virola theiodora* to prepare *epéna*, but are also known to use *V. calophylloidea*, *V. cuspidata* and *V. rufula* as the principal ingredient, to which often are added powder of dried leaves of *Justicia pectoralis* var. *stenophylla*, or sometimes ash of bark of *Elizabetha princeps* (Brewer-Carias & Steyermark 1976; Chagnon *et al.* 1971; Schultes 1990; Schultes & Holmstedt 1968). Sometimes powdered leaves of *J. pectoralis* var. *stenophylla* are employed alone as a (presumably visionary) snuff (McKenna *et al.* 1984B; Schultes & Raffauf 1992). Tobacco juice is often taken in conjunction with *Virola* snuff—Arecuna Indians, for example, ingest tobacco juice through both nose and mouth after taking *V. calophylloidea* snuff (Wilbert 1987).

The Witoto, Bora and Muiname Indians of the Colombian Amazon prepare edible pellets of resin from *Virola theiodora* (as well as *V. elongata*, *V. pavonis*, *V. surinamensis* and *V. loretensis*), which are coated with ashes of a variety of plants, including *Theobroma subincanum* and *Eschweilera itayensis* (Schultes 1969B; Schultes & Raffauf 1990; Schultes & Raffauf 1992; Schultes & Swain 1976; Schultes *et al.* 1977A).[3] The ashes of both *Theobroma subincanum* and *Eschweilera coriacea* may be used similarly as additives to Tucuna tobacco snuffs (Wilbert 1987), while *Sterculia* ash is thus employed in Surinam (Plotkin *et al.* 1980). The Colombian Makú Indians are said to drink the crude resin of *Virola elongata* for its visionary effects (Silverwood-Cope 1980), and there are hints that Venezuelan Indians may also smoke inner bark of *Virola sebifera* (Schultes 1970A). There is a report of smoking a *Virola* species in Brasil as a tobacco additive (McKenna *et al.* 1984B). The resin of *Virola elongata*, moreover, has been reportedly used as an arrow poison by Yanomamö and other Waiká groups (MacRae & Towers 1984A). An arrow poison prepared from a *Virola* species by Brasilian Yanoamá Indians was recently reported to contain about 12 mg of 5-MeO-DMT *per* dart (which would be active in an adult human being, if injected intramuscularly by the dart; Galeffi *et al.* 1983). One of these species, *Virola surinamensis*, was reported as an additive to entheogenic *ayahuasca* potions in Amazonian Perú (see Chapter 4; Luna 1984B). Sap of this plant is used by Venezuelan Warao Indians to treat buccal sores (Beloz 1992) and the plant has been found to contain neolignans of unknown pharmacology (Barata *et al.* 1978).

Details of the preparation of *epéna* snuffs vary from group to group, but generally the red resinous exudate of the inner bark is collected by scraping, then dried or boiled down to a crystalline amber-red resin, which is ground and sifted (sometimes with ashes or *Justicia* leaf powder added) for use (Schultes 1954B). Large quantities of the snuff are blown into one's own nostrils with V–shaped snuffing tubes, or blown from the mouth of one individual into the nostrils of another, using a blow-gun-like tube (see Schultes 1979B; Seitz 1967 for photographs of the preparation and use of *epéna* among the Waiká). Powder of *curía* or *Justicia caracasana* is used as an additive to *chimó*, a "lickable" tobacco preparation from Venezuela analogous to the Witoto and Bora *ambíl* (Kamen-Kaye 1971; Kamen-Kaye 1975; Wilbert 1987). As the name *curía* also refers to *J. pectoralis*, it is thought that this species is likewise used as a *chimó* additive. Like *Virola* snuffs, *ambíl* often contains ash of wild *Herrania* species (members of the cacao family, Sterculiaceae), as well as the caffeine-containing bark of *yoco* or *Paullinia yoco* and possibly other active plants (Kamen-Kaye 1971). The Tanala of Madagascar employ *Justicia gendarussa* in sorcery, which might suggest psychoactivity (Beaujard 1988), and the plant is used in Madagascar to treat malaria (Rasoanaivo *et al.* 1992).

CHEMISTRY OF ENTHEOGENIC *VIROLA* SNUFFS

Numerous species of *Virola* have been studied chemically, and the bark from which the snuffs are prepared contains predominantly 5-MeO-DMT and DMT as entheogenic principles (Agurell *et al.* 1969; Holmstedt 1965; Holmstedt *et al.* 1980; McKenna *et al.* 1984B), although tryptamine, plus *N*-MonoMethylTryptamine (MMT or NMT), 5-Methoxy-*N*-MonoMethylTryptamine (5-MeO-MMT), and 2-Methyl-1,2,3,4-TetraHydro-β-carboline (MTHC) have also been found in bark and bark exudates (Holmstedt *et al.* 1980). Bark of *V. sebifera*, reportedly smoked in Venezuela, has been shown to contain DMT, 5-MeO-DMT and MMT (Corothie & Nakano 1969; McKenna *et al.* 1984B). Tryptamines, principally DMT, have been found in leaves, roots and shoots of *Virola* species, with 5-MeO-DMT, MMT and 6-MeO-DMT being also prominent constituents of some species (Holmstedt *et al.* 1980). The usually small quantities of β-carbolines detected in *Virola* species (Agurell *et al.* 1968A; Agurell *et al.* 1969; Holmstedt *et al.* 1980) by Agurell's and Holmstedt's groups were not confirmed in analyses of bark and leaf samples of various *Virola* species in subsequent work (McKenna & Towers 1985; McKenna *et al.* 1984B). The following *Virola* species have been found to contain visionary tryptamines: *V. calophylla*, *V. calophylloidea*, *V. carinata*, *V. divergens*, *V. elongata*, *V. melinonii*, *V. multinervia*, *V. peruviana*, *V. pavonis*, *V. rufula*, *V. sebifera*, *V. theiodora* and *V. venosa* (Holmstedt *et al.* 1980; Lai *et al.* 1973; McKenna *et al.* 1984B).

Chemical analysis of four specimens of *epéna* found 5-MeO-DMT to be the main component in three preparations (made by the Tukano, Waiká and Araraibo Indians of Brasil and Venezuela), followed by DMT in all of the snuffs. The Tukano snuff contained also 5-MeO-MMT, and the Waiká snuff contained MMT. Neither monomethyltryptamine was found in the Araraibo snuff. A 1956 sample of *epéna* snuff, collected from the Surára Indians of Venezuela, was found to contain no tryptamines, only β-carbolines harmine and *d*-leptaflorine or TetraHydroHarmine (THH), plus traces of harmaline (Holmstedt & Lindgren 1967). Apparently this same Surára snuff was analyzed earlier, with the same result (Bernauer 1964). Although trace amounts of 6-methoxy-β-carbolines have been found in several *Virola* species (Agurell *et al.* 1968A; Holmstedt *et al.* 1980) and 6-methoxy-harman, 6-methoxy-harmalan and 6-methoxy-tetrahydroharman are the main alkaloids of *Virola cuspidata* (Cassady *et al.* 1971), harmine, *d*-leptaflorine (THH) and harmaline are not known from the genus *Virola*, and the presence of these compounds in the botanically-undocumented Surára *epéna* snuff sample suggests it was prepared from *Banisteriopsis caapi*, of which harmine, *d*-leptaflorine (THH) and harmaline are the principal alkaloids (see Chapter 4; McKenna *et al.* 1984A). An earlier paper reported the isolation of harmine, harmaline and *d*-leptaflorine (THH) from the stem of a liana—evidently a *Banisteriopsis* species—said to have been used to prepare *paricá* snuff by the Tukano and Tariana Indians of the Río Negro (Biocca *et al.* 1964). A Brasilian *epéna* snuff prepared from *Virola theiodora* was found to contain principally 5-MeO-DMT, with lesser amounts of DMT, MMT, 2-Methyl-TetraHydro-β-carboline (MTHC) as well as its 6-Methoxy derivative (2-Me-6-MeO-THBC; Agurell *et al.* 1969). A Brasilian *nyakwana* snuff prepared from the same species likewise contained principally 5-MeO-DMT, with lesser amounts of DMT, MMT, 5-MeO-MMT and 6-MeO-MTHC, a total of 11% alkaloids (Agurell *et al.* 1969). It would appear that in general 5-MeO-DMT and secondarily DMT are the principal entheogenic constituents of *epéna* and related snuffs. These compounds, together with the apparently inactive MMT, were recently found in several samples of Yanomamö snuffs from Venezuela (McKenna *et al.* 1984B).

The pharmacology of the oral *Virola* preparations used by the Witoto and other groups is not so clear, however. Seven samples of orally-active *Virola* pastes were analyzed by McKenna's group; six of which contained significant quantities of tryptamines, principally MMT, 5-MeO-DMT and DMT (McKenna *et al.* 1984B). Four of the seven pastes were bioassayed in self-experiments by McKenna, two of which were found to be devoid of activity. One of these was also devoid of tryptamines, while the other contained principally the probably inactive MMT. The other two samples, containing 5-MeO-DMT and DMT showed "some degree" of activity, and the most active was "characterized by considerable physiological distress rather than the perceptual and psychological disturbances usually typical of hallucinogens" (McKenna *et al.* 1984B). Significantly, the pastes did not contain any β-carbolines, the presumed presence of which was thought to explain the oral activity of the Witoto *Virola* pellets (Schultes & Hofmann 1980). Alternate biochemical mechanisms for the activity of these pastes have been proposed (Gottlieb 1979; McKenna & Towers 1985) and there is the probability that tryptamines are not the active agents. We will return to this point in Chapter 4. *Iryanthera macrophylla* and *I. ulei*, related myristicaceous plants, may also be used in elaborating edible entheogenic pastes (Schultes & Raffauf 1990), and *I. ulei* was shown to contain 5-MEO-DMT (Holmstedt *et al.* 1980). *Iryanthera longiflora* may also be used by the Bora and Witoto Indians in preparation of entheogenic pellets (Davis & Yost 1983B), but chemical analysis of this species, as well as *I. macrophylla*, *I. ulei*, *I. crassifolia*, *I. jurensis* and *I. paraensis* failed to detect tryptamines (McKenna *et al.* 1984B). One of three samples of a related myristicaceous plant, *Osteophloeum platyspermum*, was found to contain DMT, 5-MEO-DMT and 5-OH-DMT (the plant was incorrectly identified as *O. platyphyllum nomen nudum* in the paper; Holmstedt *et al.* 1980), but a subsequent analysis detected only *N*-methyltryptophan methyl ester (McKenna *et al.* 1984B). This species has various ethnomedicinal uses, and was recently reported to be used an an oral entheogen by Quijos Quichua Indians of Ecuador (Bennett & Alarcón 1994; Schultes & Raffauf 1990). Glycerides and neolignans of unknown pharmacology have lately been isolated from this plant (Fo *et al.* 1984).

Chemical analysis of *Justicia pectoralis* var. *stenophylla*, common additive to *Virola* snuffs in Amazonia (Schultes & Holmstedt 1968), showed no tryptamines or other alkaloids present, and extracts proved to be inactive in animal experiments (McKenna *et al.* 1984A; MacRae 1984; MacRae & Towers 1984B). The evidence would seem to indicate use of this aromatic snuff additive for flavoring purposes, although preliminary tests by Holmstedt had indicated the presence of DMT (Schultes & Holmstedt 1968), and sometimes it is the sole ingredient in snuff preparations (Schultes 1984; Schultes & Raffauf 1992). An infusion of *Justicia pectoralis* is used in the Caribbean against coughs and colds, and in poultices as a vulnerary (Seaforth 1991; Wong 1976), and a decoction of whole plants is used by Amazonian Indians to treat pulmonary problems (Schultes & Raffauf 1992). Two *Justicia* species are used by the Tamang of Nepal, *J. adhatoda* and *J. procumbens* (Manandhar 1991); *J. adhatoda* has been reported to contain quinazoline alkaloids such as those found also in *Peganum harmala* (see Chapter 4; Chowdhury & Bhattacharya 1985). *Justicia pectoralis*, as well as *J. procumbens*, the latter used in Chinese medicine, have been discovered to contain antitumor lignans (Fukamiya & Lee 1986; Joseph *et al.* 1989). As for the use of *Virola elongata* resin as a dart poison, its activity was shown to involve the *bis*-tetrahydrofuran lignans rather than the entheogenic tryptamines (MacRae & Towers 1984A), although 5-MeO-DMT, in potentially highly-psychoactive quantities (even in large animals like human beings) as high as 12 mg/dart, has been identified in a Brasilian Yanoamá dart poison made from an unidentified *Virola* species (Galeffi *et al.* 1983). This recalls the 17th century report by Carmelite monk A. Vázquez de Espinosa, regarding "palm darts" on which the Indians "ponen yerba, que no es mortal, sino solo embriaga por 24 horas a los heridos..." ("put herb, which is not fatal but merely inebriates the wounded for 24 hours..."; Vázquez de Espinosa 1948). Novel flavonoids of unknown pharmacology were recently reported to occur in *Virola calophylloidea* (Martínez V. & Cuca S. 1987).

VINHO DA JUREMA, *DORMILONA* AND *CHACRUNA*
MORE DMT—ENTHEOGENS

In the eighteenth and nineteenth centuries, there were a number of reports from northeastern Brasil of the use of an inebriating beverage called *vinho da jurema* (Gonçalves de Lima 1946), a use said to be extinct today (Schultes & Hofmann 1980) but evidently continuing underground (Da Mota 1987). In 1946, the botanical source of *vinho da jurema* was identified as the roots of *Mimosa hostilis* (an early, invalid name for the plant was *M. jurema*), with *M. nigra* and *M. verrucosa* being cited as variant types of the drug (Gonçalves de Lima 1946; Lowie 1946; Schultes 1979D). *Mimosa* belongs to the Leguminosae family as does *Anadenanthera*. That same year, Gonçalves de Lima isolated an alkaloid from roots of *M. hostilis*, which he named *nigerina*. Thirteen years later, the identity of nigerine with *N,N*-DiMethylTryptamine (DMT) was established (Pachter *et al.* 1959), making Gonçalves de Lima's isolation of nigerine the first discovery of DMT as a natural product, nine years ahead of the work of Fish *et al.* (1955) with *Anadenanthera* seeds. Thus *vinho da jurema* shares DMT as an active principle with *cohoba* and *epéna* snuffs. *Mimosa verrucosa* may also contain DMT (Smith 1977) and tryptamine along with MMT has been found in Panamanian *Mimosa somnians* (Gupta *et al.* 1979).

Recently, American ethnobotanist J. Bigwood has discovered a *Mimosa* species once smoked as a "marijuana substitute" by Nicaraguan soldiers of Agusto Sandino's rebel army, the EDSN. The plant is called *dormilona* ("sleepy one"), and has been collected in Chalatenango, El Salvador (Bigwood 1987). The dried leaves are also made into a tea, which produces the "strongest effects." Thus far, there has been no chemical work on this specimen. In Veracruz, México, the name *dormilona* refers to *Mimosa pudica*, the common "sensitive plant" which is currently cultivated in home gardens for use as a soporific (Lazos Chavero & Álvarez-Buylla Roces 1988), and elsewhere in México concoctions of the root are used to control menstruation (Zamora-Martínez & Nieto de Pascual Pola 1992). Among the Tzotziles and the Chinantecs, *Mimosa albida* roots are used in ethnogynecology (Browner 1985; Velázquez Díaz 1992). *Mimosa tenuiflora*, the well-known Mexican *tepescohuite*, was shown to contain DMT (Meckes-Lozoya *et al.* 1990) and is conspecific with *M. hostilis*. Garífuna blacks of Caribbean Guatemala use a decoction of *Mimosa pudica*, which they call *espina dormilona*, as a remedy for urinary infections (Girón *et al.* 1991). Under the name *duermidillo* ("little soporific"), *Mimosa pudica* has been reported in use among Mayans of Belize as a soporific (Arnason *et al.* 1980) and juice of the roots of this plant was used as a soporific by the Aztecs, who called it *pinahuihuitztli* (Garza 1990). Use of *M. pudica* as a hypnotic tranquilizer has been reported in traditional Vietnamese phytomedicine (Nguyen & Do 1991) and the plant is used as a pediatric anticonvulsant in Madagascar (Beaujard 1988). In India it is used as a treatment for epilepsy and as an aphrodisiac (Lal & Yadav 1983). In Amazonia, the Quichua Indians use *M. pudica* to stuff pillows for insomniacs (Schultes 1983A). In Panamá, *Mimosa pudica* has reported medicinal uses, "an infusion of ground stem is drunk for arthritis" (Joly *et al.* 1987) by the Guaymí Indians, who call the plant *muigin* or *guaring*. The Spanish name for the plant is *dormidera* ("soporific"), and it is sometimes known as *sleeping grass* in English. The name *dormidera* is also applied to *Mimosa somnians* in Panamá (Gupta *et al.* 1979). Some chemical work has been done on *M. pudica* (Joly *et al.* 1987; Wong 1976), but thus far it has not been examined for tryptamines. The psychoactive Salvadoran *Mimosa* species most likely contains DMT and/or related entheogenic tryptamines.

Another important category of DMT-containing plants are the additives to entheogenic *ayahuasca* or *yajé* beverages, which will be discussed in detail in Chapter 4. The leaf additives to *ayahuasca*, sometimes called *chacruna* and *chagropanga* in Ecuador and Perú, are principally referable to two species: *Diplopterys cabrerana* (widely known in the literature by the synonym *Banisteriopsis rusbyana*, this liana is in the same Malpighiaceae family as the *yajé* or *ayahuasca* plant, *Banisteriopsis caapi*, and is known as *oco-yajé* in Colombia and Ecuador); and *Psychotria viridis* (Der Marderosian *et al.* 1970; Schultes 1967; Schultes 1970C; Schultes & Hofmann 1980). *Diplopterys cabrerana* was shown to contain DMT in high concentrations (Agurell *et al.* 1968B; Der Marderosian *et al.* 1968; Poisson 1965) together with minor amounts of MMT, 5-MeO-DMT and also bufotenine, as well as trace amounts of β-carbolines. *Psychotria viridis* leaves were found also to contain DMT as main active principle and another unidentified *Psychotria* species used by the Peruvian Cashinahua Indians as an *ayahuasca* admixture under the name *nai kawa*, was reported to contain DMT in the leaves (Der Marderosian *et al.* 1970). Other *ayahuasca* admixture plants, unidentified species of *Psychotria* used by the Sharanahua and Culina Indians of Perú under the names *pishikawa* and *batsikawa* (or *matsi kawa* or *kawa kui*) probably contain DMT, as one Sharanahua and two Culina *ayahuasca* potions brewed with them were found to contain DMT as about one-third of their alkaloidal fractions (Rivier & Lindgren 1972). Recent analyses showed *P. viridis* leaves to contain DMT as the major alkaloid, while one specimen contained traces of 2-Methyl-TetraHydro-β-Carboline (MTHC). A sample of *Psychotria carthaginensis*, sometimes used in place of *P. viridis*, was found to be devoid of alkaloids. A single sample of *Diplopterys cabrerana* likewise contained DMT as major alkaloid, together with "an extremely trace amount" of bufotenine (McKenna *et al.* 1984A). Although it was found to be devoid of alkaloids in a chemical study (Holmstedt *et al.* 1980), *Virola surinamensis* was recently reported as an *ayahuasca* admixture (Luna 1984B), and must be considered to be a potential source of tryptamines. The significance of these results will become apparent in Chapter 4, discussing the ethnopharmacognosy of South American *ayahuasca* potions. Another plant in the same family (Rubiaceae) as *Psychotria*, *Pagamea macrophylla*, has been reportedly used by Barasana shamans of Colombia, who make a possibly entheogenic snuff from the powdered leaves (Schultes 1980; Schultes 1985C; Schultes & Raffauf 1992), and the moraceous *Maquira sclerophylla*, known as *rapé dos indios* ("Indian snuff"), was also the source of an obsolete Brasilian entheogenic snuff (see Appendix B; Schultes & Raffauf 1990). These plants may also contain entheogenic tryptamines. Recently, *M. sclerophylla* snuff was studied pharmacologically and was found to produce amphetamine-like stimulation of the central nervous system following intraperitoneal injection of extracts into rats. Presence of cardioactive glycosides was conjectured (De Carvalho & Lapa 1990) and proven in subsequent analyses (Shrestha *et al.* 1992). Curiously, Bye (1979; McLaughlin 1979) reported the detection of 5-MeO-DMT in *Echinocereus triglochidiatus*, a cactus used by the Tarahumara Indians of México as a less-powerful substitute for *péyotl* (see Chapter 1). The Tarahumara know this cactus by the same name as the *péyotl* plant, *híkuri* (Bye 1979A). Given the oral inactivity of 5-MeO-DMT in absence of MAO-inhibitors, there is a remote possiblity the Tarahumara combined this cactus in some sort of potion with a plant containing MAO-inhibitors. More detailed ethnopharmacognostical and chemical information is needed in confirmation.

THE RIDDLE OF THE TOAD AND OTHER SECRETS ENTHEOGENIC

As we have seen, one of the major tryptamine components of *cohoba* snuff and its *Anadenanthera* seed source, is the mysterious 5-hydroxy-DMT or bufotenine; also found in three species of non-entheogenic, non-toxic *Amanita* mushrooms (Chilton *et al.* 1979).[4] Being a positional isomer of the well-known entheogen psilocine (in which the hydroxyl group is moved from the 4- to the 5-position; see Appendix C), and the dimethyl derivative of serotonine or 5-hydroxytryptamine, an important neurotransmitter, bufotenine would be expected to have clear-cut visionary properties (Weidmann & Cerletti 1959).[5] The ethically-dubious experiments in American prisons and mental institutions cast doubt on this conclusion, however, and Turner and Merlis nearly killed three "patients" with relatively small 2.5–5.0 mg doses of the drug (Fabing & Hawkins 1956; Turner & Merlis 1959).

As previously mentioned, bufotenine gets its name from *Bufo vulgaris*, as it was first isolated as a *minor* constituent of venoms of that animal. Toad toxin preparations have a long history of medicinal use in China and southeast Asia, and are mentioned in seventeenth and eighteenth century European pharmacopœias (Chilton *et al.* 1979; Davis & Weil 1992; Verpoorte *et al.* 1979). It was recently reported that Chinese athletes competing at the 1992 Olympics in Barcelona made use of a potion containing toad skins as an adjunct to their training (Anon. 1992B). The toad is the first ingredient Shakespeare's "weird sisters" added to the cauldron in the opening scene of the fourth act of *Macbeth*.[6] Toad motifs are common in grave markers and other artifacts from Old Europe (Gimbutas 1958; Gimbutas 1974). There are some reports of Amazonian Indians preparing arrow poisons from toad venoms (Abel & Macht 1911), and frog/toad motifs in South American indigenous folklore have also been documented (Wassén 1934A; Wassén 1934B). The pantheon of South American Warao Indians includes a toad god (Wilbert 1983), and Amahuaca Indians of Perú are said to rub toad or frog venom into self-inflicted burns for psychoactive effects (Carneiro 1970). Toxic frog species of the genera *Dendrobates* and *Phyllobates* have been implicated in this curious practice. Toxic Colombian frogs of the genus *Phyllobates* contain batrachotoxins and are used in preparation of dart poisons (Myers *et al.* 1978)—similar toxins were recently found in skin and feathers of birds of the genus *Pitohui* (Dumbacher *et al.* 1992). Numerous peptides of pharmacological interest have been isolated from skin secretions of a poisonous frog, *Phyllomedusa bicolor*. Like the Amahuaca Indians, Matsés Indians rub the toxic skin secretions of this species into self-inflicted burns. After weathering drastic and life-threatening symptoms and prolonged sedation, Indians who have anointed themselves thus experience a heightening of the senses and enhanced strength. They call this "hunter magic," and an American anthropologist who dared to try this went from a heart-pounding state of panic in which he "was hoping and praying" for death, to a day-long stupor from which he awoke feeling "god-like" (Amato 1992). *Bufo marinus* has been reported as an ingredient of the Haitian *zombi* powder said to simulate death (Davis 1983C; Davis 1983D; Davis 1988A). Furst has outlined the prominent role of toads in Mesoamerican and Asian mythology (Furst 1976; see also Kennedy 1982), and V.P. and R.G. Wasson (see Chapters 5 and 6) devoted the bulk of their pioneering work *Mushrooms Russia and History* to "The Riddle of the Toad[stool] and other Secrets Mushroomic" (Wasson & Wasson 1957A; with apologies to the Wassons for the title of this section). Several of the famous Mayan "mushroom stones" depict toads, and the Wassons had described one such artifact as a "Mayan toadstool" (Mayer 1977A; Wasson 1980; Wasson & Wasson 1957A). The American Mayan scholar J.E.S. Thompson cited a seventeenth century report by Friar T. Gage, to the effect that Pokoman Mayans of Guatemala fortified an inebriating potion with toads (Gage 1946; Thompson 1970). The ancient Mayans were known to use ritual enemas and made special vessels for that purpose (De Smet 1985B; De Smet & Hellmuth 1986; Schele & Freidel 1990; Schele & Miller 1986), and it has been suggested that they administered inebriants including toad toxin by the means of clysters (De Smet 1983; Dobkin de Ríos 1974). The Darien gold pectorals from Colombia, said to represent entheogenic mushrooms (Emmerich 1965; Schultes & Bright 1979), often depict these in conjunction with toads or frogs.

An intriguing report by ethnobotanist and Náhuatl scholar T. Knab described "the closely guarded secret of but a few *curanderos* and '*brujos*'" in "a few isolated *rancherias* in southern Veracruz"—the preparation of a toad-venom inebriant from animals identified as *Bufo marinus*. The preparation of the potion involved making a paste of the parotoid glands of 10 toads, which was then mixed with lime and ash, roasted and fermented, finally reduced to "hardened dough." The intrepid Knab ingested a beverage (which his informant did not deign to share with him!) made of "several small chunks" of this dough boiled in water and reported (Knab 1974):

> The drink starts to take effect within a half hour; profuse sweating is noted along with a sudden increase in heart beat. The heart beat becomes continuously harder and stonger. A pronounced chill sets in with twitching of the facial and eye muscles. A pounding headache and delirium shortly follow the onset of twitching... This state usually lasts from three to five hours and wears off very slowly.

This disagreeable effect recalls some of the symptoms reported by Turner and Merlis following injections of pure bufotenine (Turner & Merlis 1959), although bufotenine can hardly be regarded as important in toxicity of any toad. Knab's finding may in part explain the prominence of toads in Mesoamerican iconography. Toad venoms contain cardiac steroids much more potent than digitalis (Deulofeu 1948; Chen & Jensen 1929), which could easily account for Knab's wretched experience.

While the entheogenic properties of bufotenine are unproven, and the injected drug has decidedly unpleasant effects, recent work has shown the occurrence of the unquestionably psychoptic 5-MeO-DMT together with bufotenine in the venom of a toad species from the deserts of northern México and the southwestern United States, *Bufo alvarius* (Daly & Witcop 1971; Erspamer *et al.* 1965; Erspamer *et al.* 1967). It will be recalled that 5-MeO-DMT is one of the key ingredients of entheogenic *Virola* and *Anadenanthera* snuffs. A booklet written pseudonymously by one A. Most (1984) describes the identification of *B. alvarius* and collection and use of its venom as an entheogenic agent. This has spawned modern ludible and ritual use of *Bufo alvarius* venom (Davis & Weil 1992), and the animal has been called "The Toad of Light"; its venom a sacrament of the "Church of the Toad of Light" (Blosser 1991; Montgomery 1990). Since the venom contains 5-MeO-DMT in high concentrations, only trace amounts of bufotenine, and evidently does not contain toxic quantities of the cardiac steroids found in venom of *Bufo vulgaris* (or these steroids are destroyed during combustion of the venom), it can simply be dried after collection from the toad, and the resulting yellowish flakes vaporized, giving a visionary experience somewhat similar to that of inhaling pure 5-MeO-DMT vapor. The effects of "smoking" "a small chip" of dried *Bufo alvarius* venom in two subjects have been reported (Davis & Weil 1992; Weil & Davis 1994). This "Toad of Light" was recently depicted in *Newsweek* magazine, and reference was made to "smoking" its venom (Krajick 1992). Some naive individuals, however, have begun *licking* toads, including *Bufo marinus*, resulting in severe poisonings and hospitalization (Pulling 1990), although there is evidence that "smoking" venom of this common species, too, may be psychoactive, despite absence of 5-MeO-DMT (see Appendix A).

THE GENIE IN THE FLASK
ENTHEOGENIC TRYPTAMINES FROM THE LABORATORY

In response to the discovery of the entheogenic properties of DMT, bufotenine and 5-MeO-DMT as active principles of South American snuffs, a number of artificial derivatives of these tryptamines were made and tested. The best known and most widely tested of the artificial tryptamines are T-9 or *N,N*-DiEthylTryptamine (DET) and *N,N*-DiPropylTryptamine (DPT). DET was first tested in Hungary and found to be active following intramuscular injection of the hydrochloride salt in the same dose range as DMT, around 1 mg/kg (Böszörményi *et al.* 1959; Szára 1957). In contrast to DMT, however, the effects of an intramuscular dose are not felt until after about fifteen minutes (*versus* two to three minutes for injected DMT). Whereas injected DMT lasts about thirty to forty-five minutes, injected DET lasts about two or three hours (Böszörményi *et al.* 1959; Faillace *et al.* 1967; Szára & Rockland 1961). A similar difference in time course obtains for vaporizing the drugs. The effect of inhaled vapor of free-base DMT commences virtually immediately and lasts only ten to fifteen minutes, whereas vaporized DET free-base requires a few minutes to be felt and lasts for about one to two hours. There are qualitative differences between the two compounds as well. While DMT has a dramatic, sledgehammer-like power, the effect of DET is more subtle, and the drug is less likely to provoke anxiety and panic states which may occur following DMT administration. This fact, combined with the idyllic one to three hour duration of effect, makes DET one of the most desirable of all entheogenic agents, particularly advantageous for users naive to entheogens. As the Böszörményi group commented: "we believe DET to be the best and least noxious psychotogenic agent known thus far, which seems to have an unquestionable therapeutic effect as well" (Böszörményi *et al.* 1959). DET is reportedly active orally at high doses (Shulgin 1976A).

DPT was first tested by Szára in animals (Szára 1962), and later found to have properties similar to DET in human subjects (Faillace *et al.* 1967; Szára 1970). This intriguing compound has been explored as a means to induce "peak experiences" (mystical or religious experiences; see Maslow 1962) in terminal cancer patients. In doses of 90–150 mg of DPT hydrochloride injected intramuscularly, with the patient carefully guided by trained therapists, and isolated from distractions by blindfolds and headphones playing classical music, peak experiences were indeed induced in some subjects (Grof & Halifax 1977; Richards 1975; Richards *et al.* 1977). Although "quite dramatic positive results" resulted from DPT psychotherapy in some cases, "this study did not bring evidence that DPT could successfully replace LSD in psychedelic therapy of cancer patients" (Grof & Halifax 1977), and most therapists concluded that LSD was more effective. Evidently, the duration of injected DPT is directly proportional to dose; lower doses (around 50 mg) having a duration of only about one to two hours, whereas doses above 100 mg show a longer duration (Richards 1975). DPT has also been used as an adjunct to treatment of alcoholism

(Faillace *et al.* 1970; Grof *et al.* 1973; Rhead *et al.* 1977). Like DET, this compound is reportedly active orally in high doses (Shulgin 1976A), and the free-base is reportedly entheogenic when its vapor is inhaled (Stafford 1983).

Other DMT homologues have been tested, including *N,N*-DiAllylTryptamine (DAT), *N,N*-DiIsopropylTryptamine (DIT) and *N,N*-DiButylTryptamine (DBT). DAT and DIT are both active (Barlow & Khan 1959; Szára 1957; Szára & Hearst 1962), the latter compound showing some oral activity (Shulgin 1976A). DBT is only slightly active at high doses (Szára 1961). *N,N*-DiHexylTryptamine (DHT) is not active (Szára 1961).[7] See Shulgin & Shulgin (1996) for review of tryptamine pharmacology.

EFFECTS OF SHORT-ACTING ENTHEOGENIC TRYPTAMINES

DMT: DMT is not active orally. Single doses of up to a gram orally have no effect (Shulgin 1976B; Turner & Merlis 1959). Similarly, rectal doses of up to 125 mg DMT in 15 ml water were "without any discernible effect" (De Smet 1983). The average intramuscular dose of the hydrochloride salt is 50–60 mg, producing psychoactive effects commencing in two to five minutes, peaking in fifteen minutes, with the experience lasting a total of 30–45 minutes. An effect of equal intensity is produced by 25–30 mg of DMT free-base vaporized, with the entire experience accelerated dramatically. Onset following vaporizing is almost immediate, attaining a peak in two to three minutes, with the entire effect lasting only ten to twenty minutes (Bigwood & Ott 1977). Intravenous DMT fumarate was "hallucinogenic" at 0.2–0.4 mg/kg, with peak effects at 1.5–2 minutes; lasting less than half an hour (Strassman & Qualls 1994; Strassman *et al.* 1994). Although DMT-containing plant snuffs are active, intranasal administration of 5–20 mg of pure DMT was inactive (Turner & Merlis 1959). Orally, in combination with MAO-inhibitors (see Chapter 4), DMT is active in the same dose range as by intramuscular injection (Ott 1993). DMT and LSD show cross-tolerance (Rosenberg *et al.* 1964). Four hours left between doses does not elicit tolerance (Brown 1968). The asymmetrical isopropyl analogue of DMT, *N*-Methyl-*N*-IsoPropylTryptamine (MIPT) is active orally at a 25 mg dose, but produces amphetamine-like stimulation rather than psychoptic effects (Repke *et al.* 1985).

DET: DET or T-9 is weakly active orally at high doses (Shulgin 1976A). Vaporized or injected it has the same range of potency as DMT. Intramuscular injection of 50–60 mg results in an effect which commences in fifteen minutes, reaches a peak shortly thereafter, lasting a total of two to three hours (Böszörményi *et al.* 1959; Faillace *et al.* 1967; Szára 1957; Szára 1970; Szára & Rockland 1961; Szára *et al.* 1966). As in the case of DMT, the inhalation of 25–30 mg of DET free-base vapor produces an effect roughly equivalent to intramuscular injection of twice that amount, and again, the experience is contracted. The effects of vaporized DET free-base commence in two to three minutes and last one to two hours. Any tolerance is quickly acquired and as rapidly dissipates. DET is visionary when taken orally in combination with MAO-inhibitors. 4-Hydroxy-DET (CZ-74) and 4-phosphoryloxy-DET (CY-19 or CEY-19), the diethyl homologues of psilocine and psilocybine respectively (*vide* Chapter 5), are both visionary, producing effects following oral ingestion virtually identical to effects of the parent compounds, but of shorter duration (Leuner & Baer 1965; Schultes & Hofmann 1980; Troxler *et al.* 1959). Psilocybian mushroom cultures are capable of hydroxylating indoles which have been fed to them (Chilton *et al.* 1979; Gartz 1985H), and both CZ-74 and CY-19 have been biosynthesized by *Psilocybe* [*Stropharia*] *cubensis* mycelial cultures when they are fed synthetic DET (Gartz 1989C).

DPT: DPT shows some oral activity (Shulgin 1976A) and injected is in the same range of potency as DMT and DET (Faillace *et al.* 1967; Szára 1970). Unlike these drugs, however, the duration of DPT effects are a function of dose, at least following intramuscular injection of the hydrochloride salt. Whereas lower doses (around 50 mg) may last about one to two hours; doses of 100 mg and above may last longer (Rhead *et al.* 1977; Richards 1975; Richards *et al.* 1977; Richards *et al.* 1979). Again, inhalation of the free-base vapor greatly accelerates the drug's effects (Stafford 1983).

5-MeO-DMT: Like DMT, this drug is evidently not active orally. Vaporized it is about four times the potency of DMT. Shulgin conducted experiments with nine subjects, finding that inhaling 6–10 mg of the free-base vapor of 5-MeO-DMT produced a psychoptic effect starting in less than 60 seconds, reaching a peak in two to three minutes and lasting about twenty minutes (Shulgin in De Smet 1983). Shulgin had earlier reported merely that 5–10 mg of 5-MeO-DMT was active "parenterally" (Shulgin 1970). Combined with MAO-inhibitors (see Chapter 4), 5-MeO-DMT is active orally at a 10 mg dose (Callaway 1992). 'Though Jeremy Bigwood and I once commented that 5-MeO-DMT had "little recreational value" (Bigwood & Ott 1977) and M.V. Smith compared the effects of this drug to having a large elephant sit on one's head (Smith 1976), nevertheless it has its adherents, and recently a modern ritual cult has grown up around the "Toad of Light," *Bufo alvarius*, whose toxin contains considerable 5-MeO-DMT. As mentioned above, adherents to "Church of the Toad of Light" collect and dry the venom of this toad for inhaling its vapor as a sacrament

(Davis & Weil 1992; Krajick 1992; Most 1984). The asymmetrical isopropyl analogue of 5-MeO-DMT, 5-Methoxy-*N*-Methyl-*N*-isoPropylTryptamine (5-MeO-MIPT) is psychoactive orally at a 5 mg dose, but like the DMT analogue MIPT, produces amphetamine-like stimulation and not visionary effects (Repke *et al.* 1985).

5-OH-DMT (BUFOTENINE): Bufotenine is not active orally at 100 mg doses (Holmstedt & Lindgren 1967; Wassén & Holmstedt 1963), nor following spraying of 40 mg into the nostrils (Turner & Merlis 1959). While intravenous administration of 16 mg was described as being "hallucinogenic" (Fabing & Hawkins 1956), and Isbell described "play of colors, lights, and patterns" after intramuscular injection of 10–12.5 mg, later experiments by Turner and Merlis failed to substantiate this. Doses as low as 10 mg injected intravenously showed dramatic toxicity, and three "patients" almost died following 2.5–5.0 mg intramuscular injections of bufotenine after premedication with reserpine and chlorpromazine (Turner & Merlis 1959). All of this work was carried out using as subjects prisoners (Fabing & Hawkins and Isbell) and involuntary "patients" in a mental institution (Turner & Merlis). Since the symptoms of cardiopulmonary distress described following administration of bufotenine can hardly be pleasureable, and few among us would wish to see our faces the livid color of an eggplant, it is doubtful anyone would intentionally inject this drug. Indeed, there are no reports of its use as a ludible drug, despite its legal misclassification as a substance with a "high potential for abuse" (it can certainly be argued that the experiments on prisoners constituted abuse), and there is no information on effects of vaporized bufotenine free-base. Nevertheless, recent bioassays with bufotenine-rich *Anadenanthera* seeds suggest the drug is powerfully visionary.

NON-SCIENTIFIC USE OF DMT AND OTHER ENTHEOGENIC TRYPTAMINES

For five or six years following Szára's historic test of the entheogenic properties of DMT, experimentation with this drug and its homologues (DET, DPT *etc.*) and derivatives (5-MeO-DMT, bufotenine) was strictly a laboratory phenomenon, and there was no evidence of extra-laboratory or ludible use. Indeed, the research on these drugs occurred within the context of theories postulating entheogenic drugs as endogenous "psychotogens"—molecules formed as a consequence of faulty metabolism in sick human brains, provoking the various manifestations of psychosis. The early terms *psychotomimetic* or *psychosomimetic*, like *psychotogen* refer directly to the genesis of psychosis or psychotic states. Szára's first report of the properties of DMT referred in the title to its "psychotic effect" (Szára 1956) and twice in the following two years Böszörményi described DMT "experiments with psychotics" (Böszörményi & Brunecker 1957; Böszörményi & Szára 1958). A 1957 report described the "psychopathology" of DMT (Arnold & Hofmann 1957), and Sai-Halász characterized DMT as "ein neues Psychoticum," "a new Psychoticum," inventing a sixth new category to go with Lewin's *Phantastica*, *Euphorica*, *Hypnotica*, *Inebriantia* and *Excitantia*, although Lewin would surely have categorized the entheogenic tryptamines as *Phantastica* (as he did *péyotl*, the fly-agaric and *yajé*) or as *Excitantia* (as he had categorized *paricá* or *Anadenanthera* snuff; Lewin 1924; Sai-Halász *et al.* 1958; also see Chapter 4, Note 1). In 1957 Szára had published his "comparison of the psychotic effect of tryptamine derivatives with the effects of mescaline and LSD-25," clearly labeling the effect of the tryptamines as "psychotic" while implying this fact differentiated this effect from the effects of mescaline and LSD (Szára 1957). 5-MeO-DMT was later designated a "possible endogenous psychotoxin" (Benington *et al.* 1965). This theoretical characterization by the scientists, combined with their penchant for using locked-up human guinea pigs (prisoners and mental "patients") to test their creations hardly commended the entheogenic tryptamines to laypersons. *Psychotica*, psychotomimetics, psychotoxins... who, in any case, would wish to be poisoned by toad toxins, by bizarre compounds which would turn one's face the color of a plum or an eggplant?

Inspired by the early reports of DMT effects from Szára and Böszörményi, Los Angeles psychiatrist Oscar Janiger, one of the pioneers of LSD-assisted psychotherapy in the United States, ordered a local laboratory to prepare him a batch of DMT. Janiger first tested the drug on himself by injection, which he was later to describe as "a dangerously stupid, idiotic thing to do" (Lee & Shlain 1985; Stevens 1987). Janiger was interested in the endogenous psychotogen theory, and thought that DMT was an ideal candidate for the elusive molecule. Janiger later introduced Alan Watts to injected DMT. Watts, despite his dismissal of DMT as "amusing but relatively uninteresting," was reportedly left speechless by his first taste of the drug (Stevens 1987). Janiger gave some of his DMT to Al Hubbard, a key figure in the early dissemination of entheogens outside of the laboratory. Hubbard distributed it among early experimenters with entheogens, and evidently the first reports were in keeping with Janiger's experience and belief that the substance was a "psychotogen"—"everyone who took DMT agreed that it was a hellish half-hour, with no redeeming qualities" (Stevens 1987). It seemed that early entheogen users, like the scientists, were concluding that DMT in fact had "psychotic effects" and was in fact nothing but a miserable "psychotoxin," nothing more than a wretched new "Psychoticum"!

Indeed, seemingly in support of the endogenous psychotoxin theory, DMT and its biological precursor tryptamine have been found in human cerebrospinal fluid (Christian *et al.* 1976), and receptors for these compounds have been identified in the brains of mammals (Christian *et al.* 1977). DMT has been found in trace amounts in blood and urine of "schizophrenic" patients and of "normal" subjects (Shulgin 1976B). However, it has been found that "normal" individuals have the same levels of these tryptamines in their cerebrospinal fluid as have "schizophrenics" (Corbett *et al.* 1978), which would militate against the endogenous psychotogen hypothesis. The finding of DMT in normal human body fluids opens up interesting legal questions. Since DMT is illegal, as is "any material, compound, mixture or preparation" containing DMT, it would seem we are all guilty of possession of a controlled substance. Possession, or possession with intent to sell, of other human beings is clearly proscribed by modern "controlled substances" legislation! The question of whether DMT can make human beings mad remains open, pending further research. Was Szára right... was DMT only for psychotics?

On the other hand, if one could get past the titles of his pioneering papers on the effects of DMT, Szára had described "moving, brilliantly colored oriental motifs" and "wonderful scenes" following injection of DMT, for he had courageously and ethically experimented first upon himself (with doses of 60–75 mg DMT, 60 mg DET, 350 mg mescaline and 100 mcg LSD; Szára 1957). The Böszörményi group in Budapest had praised DET, however grudgingly, calling it the "least noxious psychotogenic agent known thus far" (Böszörményi *et al.* 1959). Talk about meiosis, about damning with faint praise! LSD had also been stigmatized as a "psychotomimetic," and it turned out to have effects highly desirable to many non-scientists. By the advent of the sixties, it was becoming apparent that "set and setting," the psychological state of the experimenter and the *milieu* or environment in which the experiment took place, were of crucial importance in determining the nature and quality of the experience (Metzner *et al.* 1965; Zinberg 1974; Zinberg 1977). In discussing the effect of the short-acting tryptamines, Szára commented on "the tremendous importance of the set and setting in determining the kind of reaction which a person can get" (Szára *et al.* 1967).

When the group of Leary and Metzner at Harvard experimented with DMT, taking care to optimize set and setting, they found it to be an entheogen, not a psychotogen, and to provoke short, ecstatic experiences "similar to LSD or mescaline, but with a shorter duration of effect," as Metzner commented, mentioning also DET and DPT, in the premier issue of *The Psychedelic Review* (Metzner 1963). By the following year, Leary was calling it a "wondrous alkaloid" in the pages of the same journal (Leary 1964), discussing its potential for the production of "the religious experience." This was a far cry from "psychotic effects"! In the seventh and eighth numbers of *Psychedelic Review*, Leary and Metzner described their experiences with injected DMT (Leary 1966B; Leary 1966C), including proposals for an "experiential typewriter," a paper-tape punching data-processing device suitable for recording rapid-fire experiences like those produced by DMT, which never reached the prototype stage. Leary also extolled the entheogenic properties of DMT in his 1968 autobiography *High Priest* (Leary 1968). DMT was to become part of the entheogenic bill-of-fare at Millbrook, the New York estate where Leary and Alpert took refuge following their separation from Harvard University (Kleps 1977; Lee & Shlain 1985; Stevens 1987).

In 1966, in the course of a sensational interview published in *Playboy* magazine, the by-then "controversial ex-Harvard professor, prime partisan and prophet of LSD" Leary stated "in years to come, it will be possible to have a lunch-hour psychedelic session; in a limited way that can be done now with DMT, which has a very fast action, lasting perhaps a half hour" (Leary 1966A). This interview, in which Leary described LSD as "the most powerful aphrodisiac ever discovered by man" and claimed a woman could "inevitably have several hundred orgasms" making love under its influence, was one of the major stimuli to widespread ludible use of entheogens in the United States and other countries. In part because of Leary's mention in *Playboy* of the possibility of a "lunch-hour psychedelic session" with DMT, the drug came to be known popularly as the "businessman's trip" (Bigwood & Ott 1977), the entheogen which a businessman could use on his lunch-hour, returning clear-headed to the office world of finance and lucre!

It is unclear just how many businessmen availed themselves of Leary's proposition, however, and DMT was swept up in the wave of state and federal illegalization of LSD in the period 1966 through 1969 (Chayet 1967), and both DMT and DET were included, along with bufotenine, in Public Law 91–513, the "Comprehensive Drug Abuse Prevention and Control Act" of 1970. This federal legislation made these compounds illegal throughout the United States, and their classification in Schedule I, decreed at once that they had "a high potential for abuse" and "no currently accepted medical use." Indeed, a prominent proponent of the police approach to control of entheogens claimed in 1967 that DMT had the "greatest potential" of any entheogenic drug for "widespread abuse," being the most easily manufactured and being susceptible to use by smoking, sniffing, ingestion and injection—in the process showing the ignorance of facts regarding the quarry which has often characterized the pronouncements of those favoring police control of drugs (Louria 1967).

Indeed, this "expert" frankly admitted that his only interest, other than knowing if the drug could benefit his "wife and dog," was in determining if the drug represented a public health problem, affirming that this orientation caused him to regard the "worst aspects" of the drug. It was unclear from this tendentious and loosely-worded statement whether, by "wife and dog" Dr. Louria was referring to one or two individuals, and it is evident he had already decided entheogenic drugs were a grave public health problem and of no benefit to anyone (Louria 1967). As of this writing, 5-MEO-DMT, DPT and other short-acting entheogenic tryptamines remain legal in the United States, but subject to classification as illegal DMT analogues under the catch-all 1986 "Controlled Substance Analogue Enforcement Act."

As a result of the anti-drug laws, DMT, DET and bufotenine are currently legally available in the United States only to researchers with a license from the Drug Enforcement Administration (DEA) who have filed a protocol with the National Institute on Drug Abuse (NIDA) demonstrating experimental need for the compounds. The current value of reagent-grade DMT free-base is $102.00 *per* gram. DET free-base was less expensive, selling in 1993 for $85.70 *per* gram; with the strange bufotenine, as the monooxalate monohydrate salt, topping the list at $194.40 *per* gram (Sigma Chemical Co., 1996, which sells these compounds for research only, marked "not for drug use"; bufotenine monooxalate $250.00/g from RBI). The legal 5-MEO-DMT free-base can presently be purchased for $107.80 *per* gram ($320.00/g for the oxalate salt from RBI). The other short-acting entheogenic tryptamines like DPT, DIT, and DAT do not appear to be available presently on the fine biochemicals market. The possibly inactive MMT free-base is available for $173.90 *per* gram.

Following the reports of Leary and Metzner regarding the use of DMT and related compounds in a supportive environment, and despite the illicit status of these intriguing drugs, they began to appear on the "street-drug" market. There were some early publications describing DMT synthesis, notably the anonymous *The Turn on Book* of 1967 and *The Psychedelic Guide to Preparation of the Eucharist in a Few of its Many Guises* (Brown 1968). The latter detailed procedures for synthesis of DMT and DET using M.E. Speeter and W.C. Anthony's method, and included useful diagrams of apparatus for the synthesis, as well as an appendix on "Homebuilt Laboratory Equipment" (Brown 1968; Speeter & Anthony 1954). This booklet doubtless guided some underground chemists to successful syntheses of DMT and DET, and it included references to the primary chemical literature. In the final issue of *Psychedelic Review*, Number 11 dated Winter 1970/71, there was an advertisement for "Dynamite Dope Books," one of which was *Drug Manufacturing for Fun and Profit* by "Mary Jane Superweed," in the advertisement presented as a "D.M.T. Guide" for the bargain price of $1.00 (Superweed 1970). This booklet described "how to make D.M.T.—a powerful smokeable instant psychedelic high" and six years later was still being sold as *D.M.T. Guide* by Flash Books for $1.50—"make powerful, smokeable psychedelic D.M.T."—through adds in *High Times* magazine. Not to be outdone, "High Times and Golden State Press" began to offer, for $2.00, a booklet called *Basic Drug Manufacture,* with instructions for synthesis of DMT as well as LSD, MDA, STP and THC (see Chapters 1, 2 and Appendix A)! Other publications, notably *Psychedelic Chemistry* (Smith 1976), the first edition of which appeared in 1973, detailed methodology for synthesis of DMT and other short-acting tryptamines.[8] There have even been drug-synthesis articles in *Head* and *High Times* magazines.

DMT and, less commonly DET and DPT, have been sold on the illicit market principally as the free-bases. Being rather unstable, black-market DMT is seldom seen as white or colorless crystalline material, the usual appearance of the crystals being salmon-pink. DMT has a characteristic smell which some liken to the smell of burning plastic, which may be due to contamination by skatole (3-methyl-indole; originally found in feces, hence the name). Black-market DMT has sold for as little as $40 *per* gram in the past, and went for around $100 *per* gram in the early eighties. The price today may be as high as $250 *per* gram. There has never been a large supply of DMT on the illicit market. It is relatively easy to synthesize, but certain reagents needed for the synthesis, like lithium aluminum hydride, are watched closely by the DEA and are therefore difficult to obtain. Since lithium aluminum hydride ($LiAlH_4$) may also be used in the synthesis of other drugs like LSD, which is worth much more *per* gram (representing 10-20,000 doses in the case of LSD; only about 20–40 doses in the case of DMT), scarce reagents like this are more likely to be employed for the synthesis of drugs more valuable than DMT. Nevertheless, synthetic DMT has been available consistently in small amounts to small circles of the entheogenic drug "scene" with access to some friendly neighborhood chemist.

Demand for DMT has been low in the past, in part owing to an early unfavorable reputation. Because of its noxious smell of "burning plastic," a smell of course heightened when the substance was vaporized, DMT came to epitomize the "plastic," "synthetic," "chemical." In addition, owing to its extremely rapid onset and its at times overwhelming potency, DMT was rumored to cause brain damage, a rumor still making the rounds today, and for which there is absolutely no evidence. Even 'though DMT is a natural product, black-market supplies were clearly synthetic, and DMT was characterized alongside LSD as a "chemical" when members of the drug scene began to express a preference for so-called "organic" (that is, plant-derived; see Chapter 1, Notes 10 and 11) entheogens, which spawned the great "mescaline" hoax described in Chapter 1. Thus DMT was consigned to a permanent back seat in the entheogen black market—its supply limited by the scarcity of chemicals needed to make it; its demand limited by a bad reputation.

On the bright side, however, black-market DMT has generally been of high purity and has not been widely adulterated, although on occasion PCP (phencyclidine or *Sernyl*) has been sold as DMT. The still legal 5-MeO-DMT, which may be purchased in five-gram quantities from chemical supply firms, has on occasion been passed off as DMT on the black market (Bigwood & Ott 1977), but it may also be sold under its own name, for it has its partisans. DET, in even more limited quantities than DMT, has appeared on the illicit market, and it is likely that rare lots of DPT and other DMT homologues have been distributed in small elite circles of the illicit entheogen trade. It cannot be said, however, that DPT and other homologues have ever been widely sold on the black market, even 'though they remain provisionally legal, albeit technically prohibited under the "Controlled Substance Analogue Enforcement Act".

MODERN USE OF DMT AND ENTHEOGENIC RELATIVES

Vaporizing, rather than injection, is generally the preferred means of administration of DMT. Most of the black-market material appears in the form of the free-base, which is more suitable for vaporizing than injection, and this is more economical—only about half as much DMT is needed to produce a given level of effect. The usual dose range for inhaled free-base DMT is 20–40 mg (Bigwood & Ott 1977; Shulgin 1976B), and analytical balances are needed to weigh such a quantity precisely. Some users weigh out a reference sample, setting this aside as a visual aid in estimating doses. Such estimation and apportionment should not be done under the influence of the drug! While I use DMT as an example, the following information applies equally to DET, DPT, 5-MeO-DMT, or other short-acting tryptamines, bearing in mind that 5-MeO-DMT is some four times the potency of DMT.

There are two ways in which DMT vapor is commonly inhaled, and each has its partisans. Some will inhale a full dose of DMT in a single, long "toke"—this will result in the maximum "rush," that is, in the strongest, most rapid psychoptic effect. *Aficionados* will inhale one or two such lungsfull in rapid succession, which leads to the maximum visionary effects of the drug. Others prefer to inhale small amounts of DMT vapor repeatedly, resulting in a "rollercoaster" effect of changing "altitude." The disadvantage of this latter method is the rapid tolerance elicited by DMT. This is a wasteful technique, and one is unlikely to experience the maximum visionary effects of the drug this way. The former procedure is the more economical and takes maximum advantage of the drug's effect, but has the disadvantage of difficulty—the vapor is harsh and it is not so easy to take in and hold the 20–40 mg dose needed to experience psychoptic effects of DMT. The former way of vaporizing DMT has been recommended in two different popular publications on DMT (Bigwood & Ott 1977; Stafford 1983).

As is the case with any entheogenic substance, and particularly with the short-acting tryptamines which rocket the user immediately from everyday consciousness to the peak entheogenic state, set and setting is of crucial importance. DMT *should not be used casually*, like a sort of marijuana. One should not drive or operate machinery under the infiuence of DMT or other short-acting tryptamine entheogen. The psychological state of the user is crucial. DMT should never be used if one is tense, anxious, worried, tired, *etc.* Most users prefer to commence the experience sitting down or reclining (the alternative might be falling down!). The setting should be sheltered and peaceful, free of noise and intrusions. The consequences of failure to observe these rules are vividly described by psychologist J. Houston, who used DMT in a cluttered, filthy environment, in a state of mental and physical exhaustion (Masters & Houston 1966).

There are two common ways of inhaling DMT vapor: 1) the crystals alone in a glass pipe; or 2) combined with some plant material in an ordinary pipe or "joint." In the former case, a single dose of crystals is placed in the bottom of the glass bowl, and the underside of the bowl is heated carefully until the crystals melt. As soon as they begin to fume, the user inhales slowly and steadily, keeping the flame below the bowl and continuing the inhalation until all the material has vaporized, leaving only a dark-brown crystalline residue. Inhalation before the crystals melt can result in wasteful aspiration of some of the material without appreciable effect (Bigwood & Ott 1977; Gracie & Zarkov 1985A), while squandering some lung capacity rather needed for the DMT vapor.

A regular pipe with screen is sometimes employed, the user placing a small quantity of dried herb (preferably non-psychoactive) onto the screen, with the DMT crystals carefully sprinkled above the plant material. In this case, the flame is applied to the top of the pipe, attempting to combust the herb and vaporize the DMT simultaneously. Only enough herb to serve as carrier for the DMT is used—no more than can be inhaled in a single "toke" along with the DMT (Bigwood & Ott 1977).

Another method occasionally employed for vaporizing DMT is to dissolve the DMT in a suitable solvent (such as absolute ethanol) and infuse some dried herbal material with the solution, later evaporating the solvent prior to vaporizing in pipes or "joints." Parsley infused with DMT has sometimes been sold on the illicit market, and PCP-laced parsley (PCP=phencyclidine, *Sernyl*) has been misrepresented as DMT as well (Bigwood & Ott 1977). The DMT free-base is in this case dissolved in ethanol, about 20 ml ethanol to a gram of DMT is typical, shaking or stirring until all the material dissolves. This DMT solution is then decanted into a small, clean glass dish, such as a petri dish. Typically, one gram of DMT in 20 ml ethanol, is added to 9 grams of dried herb, to attain a product that is 10% DMT by weight after evaporation of the ethanol. Often commercially-available "herbal smoking mixtures" (containing herbs like mint, catnip, parsley, damiana, *etc.*) are employed, as these may be quite flavorful and may help disguise the unpleasant taste of DMT. The herb is usually first sifted rather fine, and sprinkled into the DMT solution, then stirred until the plant material soaks up all the DMT solution. The wet herb is then spread out to allow the solvent to evaporate at room temperature, or with gentle heating. The herb is ready for use when the solvent has evaporated and only the sticky herbal material remains, with no scent of alcohol. Every hundred milligrams of herb prepared this way is equivalent to 10 mg of DMT, and this method has the advantage of enabling accurate weighing of DMT doses with an OHAUS 2610 triple-beam balance or equivalent, rather than a much more expensive analytical balance with 1 mg sensitivity. A 300 mg dose of DMT-laced herb contains a good 30 mg dose of the drug, and can be smoked as is in a normal pipe. Some make "joints" of DMT-laced herb, and the contents may be weighed out. A one-gram joint containing 100 mg DMT is typical. This treatment is ideal for the second method of DMT use—repeated small inhalations, 'though it is decidedly uneconomical. As much as half the DMT will surely be wasted in the "sidestream" smoke/vapor.

DMT is usually inhaled by one person at a time. After apportioning a single dose of DMT (whether pure or with herbal matter), this is inhaled by the first user in a group. The person in charge of loading the pipe is generally the last to inhale, for the effects are often incapacitating. Casual passing of the pipe, as in *Cannabis* smoking rituals, is unsuitable—the doses will not be uniform, and by the time the pipe comes around for the second round, some tolerance to the effects may have developed (Bigwood & Ott 1977). Many users like to have a refreshing beverage at hand, to cool throats burned by the harsh DMT vapor.

After inhalation of a full dose of DMT is a single breath, the effects will be experienced in ten or fifteen seconds, usually even before exhalation of the vapor. The initial "rush" sensation is similar to the feeling of rapid acceleration and may be accompanied by vertigo. Users often describe high-pitched sounds, which may be perceived as being insect noises. The peak effect occurs within two to three minutes, during which most users are stunned and speechless. Arabesque or geometric colored patterns seen with eyes opened or closed, similar to those experienced with LSD, mescaline or psilocybine are commonly-reported effects of DMT. T. McKenna has vividly described presumed contact with fantastic "machine elves" reported by some DMT users (McKenna 1991). Paranoia and panic reactions are probably more frequent following DMT adminstration than with other entheogenic drugs—a consequence, doubtless, of the extreme rapidity with which the user is torn out of his everyday consciousness and thrust into a swirling, screaming, visionary state. This makes set and setting extremely important. Ten minutes after inhaling the user invariably feels a diminution in the effect, and by the time fifteen to twenty-five minutes have elapsed, the effect has dissipated completely (Bigwood & Ott 1977). Generally there are no after-effects, although mild headache is occasionally reported. Although it has been suggested that the experience may be repeated at four-hour intervals without noticeable tolerance (Brown 1968), vaporizing no more than once daily will result in optimum results. It would appear that intravenously injected DMT is at least as potent as the inhaled vapor of DMT free-base, perhaps even more potent (Strassman & Qualls 1994; Strassman *et al.* 1994). The pharmacodynamic and other differences between DMT and its entheogenic cousins like DET, DPT and 5-MeO-DMT have been summarized above. The distinct and intriguing effects of orally-ingested potions containing DMT (*ayahuasca*, *pharmahuasca*, *anahuasca*) will be discussed in Chapter 4 (Ott 1994A; Ott 1995B).

In conclusion, the words with which Jeremy Bigwood and I concluded our 1977 article on "DMT: The Fifteen Minute Trip" are apposite:

> It is unfortunate that such a unique and desirable drug as DMT is not freely available and widely used. We feel that anyone who likes entheogenic drugs would do well to try DMT, if given the chance. Not only are the effects enjoyable, but most users are astonished to learn that a drug can so rapidly produce such profound effects which have such short duration. DMT may be the quintessential "wonder" drug, for the initiate cannot help but wonder at its awe-inspiring potency.

NOTES

[1] The definitive historical studies of *cohoba* and other entheogenic snuffs are the works of S.H. Wassén (Wassén 1964; Wassén 1967; Wassén & Holmstedt 1963). The original Spanish text of the first description of the strange inebriating powder by Columbus has been lost, and this is known only from an Italian translation of son Ferdinand Columbus' *Historie* published by Alfonso Ulloa in Venice in 1571 (Wassén 1967). Similarly, Friar Ramón Pané's account is known only from the Italian translation of Ulloa, where the snuff is called both *cohoba* and *cogioba*. The 1511 edition from Sevilla of Peter Martyr's *P. Martyris Angli-mediolanensis opera Legatio babylonica Occeani decas Poemata Epigrammata* marked the first publication of information about *cohoba*, taken directly from Ramón Pané's lost manuscript (Peter Martyr himself never visited the New World). This Latin text gives the Latinized name of the snuff as *kohobba* (Wassén 1967).

[2] During World War II, physicians loyal to the German Nazi party conducted a series of gruesome "experiments" on prisoners at the infamous Dachau concentration camp and elsewhere. Prisoners were deliberately infected with deadly organisms, injected with gasoline, crushed to death in pressure chambers and immersed in ice-water to measure survival times, among other horrors. One less drastic series of experiments involved dosing thirty prisoners with mescaline to study its usefulness as an interrogation aid (Lee & Shlain 1985). Some of the German doctors were sentenced to death by the Nürnberg war-crimes tribunal, which promulgated a code of medical and scientific ethics to govern human experimentation (Annas & Grodin 1992). Among other stipulations, the Nürnberg code mandated *full voluntary consent* as a prerequisite for the use of human subjects in scientific experiments. As outlined in Chapter 2, Note 15, the United States Central Intelligence Agency (CIA) and its wartime precursor Office of Strategic Services (OSS), in emulation of their Nazi predecessors, began to experiment on human subjects with entheogenic and other drugs (Marks 1979). One center of this patently unethical research was the U.S. Public Health Service Addiction Research Center Hospital in Lexington, Kentucky. This "narcotics farm" (where only duplicity and hypocrisy were sown; only misery reaped) was established ostensibly to "cure" heroin addiction. Officially a penitentiary, the prisoners were called "patients." More than 800 drugs, including bufotenine and LSD, were sent to H.S. Isbell for testing on "patients" in the Lexington "hospital." Isbell obtained "voluntary consent" from the prisoners by offering payment in kind—heroin and morphine were administered as payment for cooperation in Isbell's experiments (Lee & Shlain 1985). This, note, in a publicly-funded institution whose ostensible purpose was to "cure" drug addiction! Ethically speaking, what is the difference between this "research" and that conducted by German doctors at Dachau? The same can be said for Fabing and Hawkins dosing Ohio State Penitentiary prisoners with bufotenine, and Turner and Merlis dosing helpless "mental patients" in a New York institution with DMT and bufotenine. If Americans could be exonerated of guilt for crimes on the basis of "mental illness" which made them not wholly responsible for their actions, then how could such individuals, who became "patients" at mental institutions instead of prisoners in penitentiaries, give informed consent to dubious and potentially dangerous experiments?

[3] Wild cacao species are intimately related to entheogenic drug preparations in South America. Besides the use of ash of *Theobroma subincanum* as an additive to *yá-kee* snuff and as a coating for edible pellets of *Virola* resin in Colombia, this ash is used as an additive to tobacco snuff by the Amazonian Tucuna Indians (Wilbert 1987). Furthermore, edible or "lickable" tobacco preparations, called *ambíl* by the Witoto, are often kept in a hollowed-out fruit of *Theobroma bicolor* or *T. glaucum*, which is said to transfer a sweet taste to the preparation (Schultes & Raffauf 1990; Wilbert 1987), and husks of wild *cacao colorado de monte*, probably *Herrania breviligulata*, are added to *ambíl* by the Siona, who also add caffeine-containing bark of *yoco* (*Paullinia yoco*; Kamen-Kaye 1971). The parallel close association between cacao, known as *cacáhuatl* in Náhuatl, and entheogenic mushrooms in pre-Columbian México, has been detailed in my book *The Cacahuatl Eater* (Ott 1985), and was similarly highlighted in a previous essay on the Oaxacan Mazatecs (Munn 1973).

[4] Bufotenine was isolated in 1953 from European *Amanita citrina*, called by the synonym *A. mappa* in the report, so the compound was designated *mappin(e)*, before its identity with bufotenine was established (Geerken 1988; Wieland & Motzel 1953). European *A. citrina* was also found to contain bufotenine-*N*-oxide, 5-MeO-DMT and DMT. Bufotenine, bufotenine-*N*-oxide, and 5-MeO-DMT were also found in European *A. porphyria* (Tyler & Gröger 1964B). Bufotenine was detected in American *A. tomentella*, *A. porphyria* and *A. citrina* (Beutler & Der Marderosian 1981; Catalfomo & Tyler 1961; Tyler 1961) and in European material (Stijve 1979). An early report described detection of bufotenine in European *A. muscaria* and *A. pantherina* (Wieland & Motzel 1953); subsequent work has failed to substantiate this (Brady & Tyler 1959; Talbot & Vining 1963). Bufotenine would not be of any significance in the toxicology of any *Amanita* species. The compound has been found to be inactive orally up to a 100 mg dose (Holmstedt & Lindgren 1967; Wassén & Holmstedt 1963), and the three *Amanita* species confirmed to contain bufotenine are not known to be toxic (Chilton 1978), although *A. citrina*, called *gelben Knollenblätterpilz* in German ("yellow dumpling mushroom") is sometimes confused with the unquestionably deadly-poisonous *Knollenblätterpilz*, *A. phalloides*, which contains the amatoxins and phallotoxins (Tyler *et al.* 1966). As we will see in Chapter 6, the entheogenic activity of *A. muscaria* and *A. pantherina* is due to isoxazole amino acids, not to the dubious content of bufotenine. The extremely low amounts of 5-MeO-DMT detected in *A. citrina* and *A. porphyria*, and of DMT detected in the former species could not be of any significance toxicologically, and these compounds are not psychoactive orally in any case. However, the β-carboline derivative 3-carboxy-tetrahydroharman (1-methyl-tetrahydrocarboline-3-carboxylic acid) has been isolated from *Amanita muscaria* (Matsumoto *et al.* 1969) and could occur in some other *Amanita* species, although a subsequent study failed to detect this compound in North American *A. muscaria* (Chilton & Ott 1976). Since similar β-carboline compounds in *ayahuasca*, *Banisteriopsis caapi* (see Chapter 4), have been found to be MonoAmine-Oxidase (MAO) inhibitors, and to render active orally DiMethylTryptamine (DMT) and related compounds in plant additives to *ayahuasca* (McKenna *et al.* 1984A; Ott 1993; Ott 1994A), there is at least the possibility of a similar mechanism operating in the case of tryptamine-containing *Amanita* species. More research is needed to determine the distribution of tryptamines and β-carbolines in *Amanita* species. Recently a novel class

of β-carbolines have been isolated from the mushroom *Cortinarius infractus* (Steglich *et al.* 1984), that was then suggested to be entheogenic, which is doubtful (Samorini 1993A).

[5] Serotonine, 5-Hydroxy-Tryptamine (5-HT), is an important neurotransmitter in vertebrate brains. That is, it functions to transmit nerve impulses from one neuron or nerve cell to another, by diffusing across the synapse, a minute gap where one neuron joins another. It is thought that their chemical similarity to serotonine, and demonstrated effects on serotonine neurotransmission in the brain, "explains" the consciousness-altering effects of indole entheogens like DMT, psilocine and LSD (Fabing 1956; Fabing 1957; Gessner *et al.* 1960; Ott 1979B). Serotonine itself occurs in plants which synthesize also bufotenine or psilocybine (Andary *et al.* 1978A; Andary *et al.* 1978B; Tyler 1958B; Tyler & Gröger 1964A; Tyler & Gröger 1964B), and it may be involved in the biosynthesis of these compounds (Chilton *et al.* 1979). Serotonine was likewise found in 12 mushroom species of the genera *Panaeolus*, *Panaeolina* and *Panaeolopsis*, only one of which also contained psilocybine and baeocystine (Stijve 1987; Stijve *et al.* 1984), and was recently reported in the psilocybian species *Panaeolus* [*Copelandia*] *cyanescens* (Stijve 1992). Serotonine, as well as some indole entheogens may be synthesized *in vivo* from the common amino acid tryptophan (2-amino-3-indolyl-propanoic acid), which has the indole ring all these compounds share (Brack *et al.* 1961). Since tryptophan is a ubiquitous dietary amino acid, found in most common foods, it normally circulates in the bloodstream of animals, and there is a nebulous structure called the "blood-brain barrier" which functions to control the entry of compounds like tryptophan to the brain, so varying blood levels cannot wreak havoc on brain serotonine metabolism. In general, other 5-hydroxy-indole compounds like bufotenine and 5-MeO-DMT, because of their too-close structural similarity to serotonine, are likewise excluded from the brain by the "blood-brain barrier," and therefore they do not show any oral psychoactivity, as tryptophan does not (although psychiatrist S.I. Stein reported "many adjustments of nervous system functioning can be secured through... correct manipulation" of L-tryptophan; Stein 1960). The 4-hydroxy-tryptamines, like psilocine, which is a positional isomer of bufotenine (the hydroxy or "OH-" group is shifted from the 5- to the 4-position of the indole ring; see Appendix C) do, however, show oral psychoactivity. Tryptophan, tryptamine, and any higher methylated homologues, as well as their hydroxy-derivatives, including bufotenine, would all likely be psychoactive if injected directly into the brain or cerebrospinal fluid. See also: Shulgin 1977B.

[6] The famous play based on eleventh century historical events, revolves around the usurper Macbeth's consultations with three witches. In the first scene of the fourth act, the witches are in a cavern brewing a potion in a cauldron, and the First Witch rhymes: "Round about the cauldron go;/In the poison'd entrails throw./Toad, that under cold stone/Days and nights hast thirty-one/Swelter'd venom sleeping got,/Boil thou first i' the charmed pot." To which the assembled trio chant the famous refrain: "Double, double toil and trouble;/ Fire burn and cauldron bubble." The next ingredients are "Fillet of a fenny snake,/In the cauldron boil and bake;/Eye of newt, and toe of frog,/Wool of bat, and tongue of dog,/ Adder's fork, and blind-worm's sting,/Lizard's leg, and howlet's wing,/For a charm of powerful trouble,/Like a hell-broth boil and bubble." followed once again by the refrain.

The remaining recipe is recited by the Third Witch: "Scale of dragon, tooth of wolf,/ Witches' mummy, maw and gulf/Of the ravin'd salt-sea shark,/Root of hemlock digg'd i' the dark,/Liver of blaspheming Jew,/Gall of goat, and slips of yew/Sliver'd in the moon's eclipse,/Nose of Turk, and Tartar's lips,/Finger of birth-strangled babe/Ditch-deliver'd by a drab,/Make the gruel thick and slab:/Add thereto a tiger's chaudron,/For the ingredients of our cauldron." The refrain once again follows, and the Second Witch concludes: "Cool it with a baboon's blood,/Then the charm is firm and good." In all, 23 ingredients are mentioned, of which nine are clearly fantastic or likely unavailable to eleventh century herbalists in the British Isles: 1) scale of dragon; 2) witches' mummy; 3) maw and gulf of the salt-sea shark; 4) liver of "blaspheming" Jew; 5) nose of Turk; 6) Tartar's lips; 7) finger of birth-strangled babe (it could be argued that midwives would have had access to this, and herbalists in general to mummified parts of bodies, be they of a witch or Jew, Turk or Tartar—in the Middle Ages it was a common practice to consume mummified human flesh medicinally and at times to maintain corpses handy for such preparations; the much-esteemed *aqua divina* was a distillate of ground human corpses; see Barber 1988; Camporesi 1989); 8) tiger's chaudron (the tiger's reddish color); and 9) baboon's blood. Of the remaining 14 ingredients, only five are plants (and three of these in animal disguises): 1) tongue of dog=*Cynoglossum officinale*, source of cynoglossine; 2) Adder's fork=adder's tongue fern, *Ophioglossum vulgatum*; 3) tooth of wolf=monkshood, *Aconitum napellus*, a well-known poisoner's herb; 4) root of hemlock=*Conium maculatum*, a deliriant plant used in "witches' ointments"; and 5) slips of yew=*Taxus baccata*, which contains cardiotoxic alkaloids and is a symbol of sadness (Hansen 1978; Hartzell 1991; *Oxford English Dictionary*, Compact Edition, p. 3859). Of the nine animal ingredients, with the exception of the bat, howlet (or owl, both nocturnal flying animals) and gall of goat (primal symbol of Satan), it is significant that the remaining five, perhaps six ingredients in the potion are reptiles or amphibians, and the toad is the first ingredient, honored with its own pair of couplets in Shakespeare's verse. Moreover, in the opening scene of the play, the witches disperse after hastily setting their next meeting time and place, with the Second Witch saying "Paddock calls," referring to a toad familiar (*Oxford English Dictionary*, Compact Edition, p. 2052); while the First Witch says "I come, Graymalkin!" in response to her feline familiar. The "fenny snake" could mean either a snake from the "fen" or bog, or a "moldy" snake. The newt, or ask (asker), is a salamander-like amphibian from the British Isles which does not seem to be venomous, but was readily classed with venomous reptiles and amphibians, as did Shelley "he had tamed every newt and snake and toad" (1818) and Laurence Sterne in his incomparable *Tristram Shandy* "a Newt, or an Asker, or some such detested reptile" (1761). The "blind worm" seemingly refers to a poisonous reptile or insect (Fletcher 1896), and as for the "toe of frog" and "lizard's leg," it is guilt by association. Wasson and Wasson have reviewed references to "The Venomous Toad" in history and literature in their pioneering *Mushrooms Russia and History* (Wasson & Wasson 1957A). Of course the ingredients of Shakespeare's potion reflect more on contemporary urban ideas regarding witchcraft in the seventeenth century, than actual knowledge of witchcraft as practiced in the eleventh century. Far from being the epitome of evil, as the Inquisition would have had it, Shakespeare's witches are rather presented as wise seers. Following the brewing of the toad-potion, the Second Witch has a presentiment of the approach of the dastard Macbeth... "By the pricking of my thumbs,/Something wicked this way comes."

[7] The best known of other psychoactive tryptamines is *alpha*-MethylTryptamine (AMT) or IT-290. This compound became famous following descriptions of its use by the Merry Pranksters (see Chapter 2) on their bus odyssey (Perry 1990; Wolfe 1969). In 20 mg oral doses, it produces a stimulating effect with some similarities to LSD and amphetamine, which lasts up to 24 hours (Hollister *et al.* 1960; Shulgin 1976A). Etryptamine, or *alpha*-ethyltryptamine is less potent with a shorter duration, from 6–12 hours following a 150 mg oral dose. Tryptamine hydrochloride is reported to produce DMT-like effects during the process of slow intravenous injection, and free base vapor produced mild transient effects when inhaled in 30 mg doses (Bigwood 1977). The DMT analogues with substituents in the 6-position of the indole ring may in some cases be more active, as is the case with 6-hydroxy-DMT as opposed to DMT (Szára & Axelrod 1959); and 10 mg of 6-hydroxy-DET was reportedly equivalent in entheogenic effect to 60 mg DET (Szára & Hearst 1962). It has even been proposed that DMT and DET are converted *in vivo* to their 6-hydroxylated analogues (Metzner 1963). In support of this theory it has been pointed out that 6-fluoro-DET, in which 6-hydroxylation *in vivo* is blocked, does not produce visionary effects, 'though it does produce the peripheral effects of DET (Faillace *et al.* 1967; Szára *et al.* 1967). However, this theory was later disproved in experiments (again in Isbell's MKULTRA series) on several unfortunate "former opiate addicts" serving prison terms for drug-law violations. In comparison of intramuscular doses of DMT, 6-hydroxy-DMT and placebo, while DMT provoked "markedly significant mental effects," 6-hydroxy-DMT effects were "not significantly different from those produced by a placebo" (Rosenberg *et al.* 1963). In subsequent animal tests, 6-hydroxy-5-MeO-DMT was found to be significantly less potent than 5-MeO-DMT, again militating against the 6-hydroxylation theory (Taborsky *et al.* 1966). In squirrel monkeys and rats, 6-hydroxy-DMT was found to be less potent than DMT (Uyeno 1969; Uyeno 1971). As mentioned above, MMT does not appear to be psychoactive, and McKenna's group found some oral *Virola* preparations containing principally MMT to be inactive (McKenna *et al.* 1984B). *N*-Propyl-MMT and *N*-hexyl-MMT are both considered to be inactive (Shulgin 1976A; Speeter & Anthony 1954). 5,6,7-Trimethoxy-DMT showed activity in rats, perhaps psychotropic (Nir *et al.* 1974), but 4,5,6-trimethoxy-DMT is inactive (Carlsson *et al.* 1963). See Chapter 5, Note 9. In 1994, *alpha*-ethyltryptamine, once sold in the acetate by Upjohn as antidepressant *Monase*, was placed on Schedule I by the DEA.

[8] To Nick Sand, one of the better-known underground LSD chemists, who was one of the members of the Millbrook commune of Leary and Alpert, goes the honor of being the first underground chemist on record to prepare DMT. According to Lee and Shlain, Sand "began his illicit career by making DMT, a short-acting super-psychedelic, in his bathtub in Brooklyn." (Lee & Shlain 1985) Shades of the "bathtub gin" of American alcohol prohibition days! Surely the mysterious R.W. Brown of Austin, Texas was an early pioneer in underground synthesis of DMT and DET (Brown 1968), and we must not overlook the contribution of John Mann, a.k.a. "Mary Jane Superweed," the author of the D.M.T. *Guide or Drug Manufacturing for Fun and Profit* (Superweed 1970). There are doubtless innumerable other anonymous pioneers in this black-market branch of entheogenic chemistry.

CHAPTER FOUR
Beta-Carbolines and Ayahuasca Potions

> When I have partaken of *ayahuasca*, my head has immediately begun to swim, then I have seemed to enter on an aerial voyage, wherein I thought I saw the most charming landscapes, great cities, lofty towers, beautiful parks, and other delightful things. Then all at once I found myself deserted in a forest and attacked by beasts of prey, against which I tried to defend myself. Lastly, I began to come around...
>
> **Manuel Villavicencio**
> *Geografía de la República del Ecuador* (1858)

In 1858, the Ecuadorian civil servant Manuel Villavicencio described the unusual effects of *ayahuasca* (Quechua for "the vine of the souls"), a potion prepared from a vine by the Angatero, Mazán and Záparo Indians of the basin of the Río Napo, mighty Ecuadorian tributary to the Amazon River (Villavicencio 1858). Scant six years earlier, the great British botanist Richard Spruce (Sledge & Schultes 1988) had discovered that the Tukanoan Indian tribes along the Río Vaupés, Brasilian and Colombian tributary to the vast Río Amazonas, employed an entheogenic potion known as *caapi*, prepared from a liana which he described and named *Banisteria caapi* (Schultes 1968). Spruce's Indian friends offered him the *caapi* beverage, about which he had previously heard under the name *yajé*, and Spruce imbibed a small amount, and observed the Indian *caapi* ritual (Reichel-Dolmatoff 1975). Spruce was fortunate in that he found specimens of the plant from which the *caapi* potion had been prepared in full flower near his hosts' homes, and he presciently collected material for chemical analysis (Schultes & Hofmann 1980; Schultes *et al.* 1969). Two years later, in 1854, while traveling in the Río Orinoco basin of Venezuela, Spruce met some itinerant Guahibo Indians near the Maipures Falls who were observed to "chew the dried stem" of *caapi* "as some people do tobacco." Finally, in the Ecuadorian foothills of the Andes in 1859, Spruce encountered Villavicencio's *ayahuasca* in use among the Záparo Indians and, 'though he evidently did not see the plant from which *ayahuasca* was derived, concluded from Villavicencio's account that *ayahuasca* was prepared from the same plant as *caapi*, *Banisteria caapi*, today known as *Banisteriopsis caapi*. Although Spruce's detailed notes weren't published for half a century (Spruce 1908), he did publish earlier an important paper on Amazonian "narcotics"[1] (Spruce 1873), and descriptions of his discovery of *caapi* first appeared in Britain shortly after his first specimens arrived at Kew Gardens (Anon. 1855).

Subsequent research confirmed Spruce's identification of *Banisteriopsis caapi* as a pan-Amazonian entheogenic plant (Schultes & Hofmann 1980), and chemical analyses in the twentieth century led to the isolation of *telepathine* (Fischer Cárdenas 1923; Perrot & Raymond-Hamet 1927A; Perrot & Raymond-Hamet 1927B), yajéine (Barriga Villalba 1925A; Barriga Villalba 1925B), and *banisterin(e)* (Lewin 1928; Lewin 1929) from *Banisteriopsis* specimens, all of which were subsequently shown to be the well-known alkaloid harmine (Chen & Chen 1939; Elger 1928; Wolfes & Rumpf 1928). Harmine had originally been isolated from seeds of *harmel* or Syrian rue, *Peganum harmala* in 1847 (Fritzsche 1847). Louis Lewin established euphoria-producing effects of injected harmine (Lewin 1928), and two related compounds, leptaflorine or TetraHydroHarmine (THH) and harmaline, the latter first isolated from *Peganum harmala* in 1841 (Göbel 1841) and both also found in *Banisteriopsis* more than a century later (Hochstein & Paradies 1957), were shown to be psychotropic in the 1960s (Naranjo 1967). In recent years, *ayahuasca* has emerged as one of the most sought-after entheogenic drugs among *aficionados* in the United States, and it is to the story of the harmine- and harmaline-containing entheogenic drugs that we now turn in this chapter.

SYRIAN RUE OR *PEGANUM HARMALA*: *HARMEL*... *HAOMA*?

The *Avesta*, an ancient Iranian religious text in part attributed to Zoroaster (or Zarathustra) was composed sometime during the first millennium B.C. Tradition has it Zoroaster lived during the fifth and sixth centuries of the pre-Christian era, but most of the text of the *Avesta* is considerably more recent, 'though grounded in traditions antedating the life of the prophet Zoroaster. Three chapters of the *Avesta*, *Yasna* 9, 10 and 11, collectively known as the *Hom Yasht*, refer repeatedly to a sacred inebriating plant known as *Haoma*, which is etymologically (and possibly botanically, at least originally) identical to the Aryan (the Iranians also descend from the Aryans) *Soma* of India (see Chapter 6, especially Note 11). The Avestan scholar J. Darmesteter considered the *Hom Yasht* to be a later interpolation to the text of the *Avesta*, probably dating from B.C. 140 to A.D. 50 (Wasson 1968), and some contemporary scholars consider the *Hom Yasht* to have been composed during the Hellenistic era, from the sixth to the fourth centuries B.C. (Flattery & Schwartz 1989).

The *Soma/Haoma* complex has long been a subject of scholarly disagreement inasmuch as, to quote W. Doniger, one of our leading Vedists: "the history of the search for Soma is, properly, the history of Vedic studies in general, as the Soma sacrifice was the focal point of the Vedic religion" (Doniger O'Flaherty 1968). Since the use of the original *Soma* plant (as opposed to the use of surrogates, or substitutes, recognized as such by Brahmans, used in its place in contemporary *Soma* sacrifices) does not survive in India, the identity of *Soma* "is as obscure today as two centuries ago" when the West discovered the Aryan *RgVeda*, our main source of information about *Soma*, which antedates the *Hom Yasht* by at least a millennium (Wasson 1968). The same holds true for the Iranian sacrament *Haoma*, whose use in "a cultural-religious matrix... seems to have altogether disintegrated with the Islamic conquest of Iran in the seventh century" of our era (Flattery & Schwartz 1989). The 1968 publication by R.G. Wasson and W. Doniger (O'Flaherty) of *Soma: Divine Mushroom of Immortality* summarized the history of the attempts to identify *Soma*, and proposed an entheogenic mushroom, *Amanita muscaria*, as the original Aryan *Soma* plant (Wasson 1968). Besides stimulating modern awareness of the *Soma* problem, Wasson's book established beyond reasonable doubt that *Soma* was an entheogenic plant, not an alcoholic beverage or non-psychoactive plant, as many had supposed (Brough 1971; Doniger O'Flaherty 1968). Wasson, who had learned as a young boy about the *Soma* problem from his father, realized this fact in the mid-1950s, shortly after his pioneering experience of the effects of entheogenic mushrooms in México in 1955 (see Chapter 6). As W. Doniger was later to comment: "the broader hypothesis—that *Soma* was an entheogen—is more significant than the narrower one—that it was a mushroom," although she personally inclined towards Wasson's identification (Doniger O'Flaherty 1982). Many consider the problem of the identity of *Soma/Haoma* to be insoluble, and of little importance, beyond the astute realization by Wasson that *Soma/Haoma* was an entheogenic plant. Of the many other non-fungal botanical candidates for *Soma/Haoma*, the best-known is *Peganum harmala*, first proposed in name by P.A. de Lagarde (Lagarde 1866).

Unlike *Amanita muscaria*, used today as an inebriant in Siberia (see Chapter 6), *Peganum harmala* has not been reported in the historical record to be used as a ritual inebriant (Flattery & Schwartz 1989; Schultes 1976; Schultes & Hofmann 1980). A recent sketchy report from Ladakh, India had mentioned the "narcotic" use of *Peganum harmala* seeds (Navchoo & Buth 1990). Known as *techepak*, the seeds were roasted and puverized, and then "taken as such or smoked with tobacco." The related harmine-containing *Tribulus terrestris* was said to be powdered and dissolved in milk and "reported to cause delirious conditions" (Navchoo & Buth 1990). An equally vague report alleged swallowing of *harmel* seeds in the Near East for "hallucination and sexual stimulation" (Abulafatih 1987; Hooper & Field 1937), and Bahraini "narcotic" use of *harmel* seeds was catalogued in a recent review (Abbas *et al.* 1992). Without giving details, a second-hand report by J.A. Gunn ascribed "soporific and intoxicant" properties to the seeds, saying further that in North Africa "the seeds may intoxicate like alcohol" (Gunn 1937). A more modern report alleged that "in India and Pakistan the seeds are employed as an anthelmintic and narcotic," ascribing both stimulatory and depressive effects on the central nervous system (Hassan 1967). The main economic value of the plant in historical times has been as the source of vegetable dyes extracted from the seeds, although it has traditional ethnomedical uses as well. In Morocco, *harmel* is used variously as an anthelmintic, antirheumatic and antidiarrheal (Bellakhdar *et al.* 1991) and the seeds are used for rheumatism and eye diseases in northern India (Shah 1982). Recently, antimicrobial activity was demonstrated for the *harmel* alkaloid harmine, with harmaline and harmol showing lower activity (Ahmad *et al.* 1992). In Yemen, *harmel* likewise is used medicinally, and the plant was cited in the 12th Century pharmacopoeia of Ibn El Beithar, in Algerian Abderrezzaq's 18th Century compendium, and in an anonymous 12th century medicinal text (Fleurentin *et al.* 1983). Although *harmel* has been described recently as an aphrodisiac (Flattery & Schwartz 1989), it is used traditionally by Bedouins as an emmenagogue and abortifacient, as well as for "narcotic" purposes (Bailey & Danin 1981), properties that have been documented in animal experiments (Shapira *et al.* 1989). In Ladakh, India, Muslims use *harmel* leaves as an incense called *dhup* (Bhattacharyya 1991).

Recently D.S. Flattery and M. Schwartz published *Haoma and Harmaline*, a book inspired by Wasson's *Soma: Divine Mushroom of Immortality*, and accepting its main thesis—that *Soma/Haoma* was an entheogenic plant. In this recent book, however, the authors argue against Wasson's theory that *Soma* was an entheogenic mushroom, proposing instead *Peganum harmala* as the original Aryan entheogen (Flattery & Schwartz 1989; see also Naranjo 1990). The plant known today as *Harmel* in German, *harmal* in Arabic, *spand* or *spend* in Persian, *hurmur* in Urdu, *harmul* in Hindi—*Peganum harmala*—is equated with *Haoma* of the *Avesta* and *Soma* of the *RgVeda* on the basis of four lines of argument (I use here Flattery's own categories in his summary): 1) geographical correspondence—that *harmel* occurs throughout the Indo-Iranian area in which the ancient entheogen held sway; 2) pharmacological correspondence—that the ethnographic literature on *Banisteriopsis caapi* or *ayahuasca* (which Flattery uses in place of similar literature on *harmel* which does not exist) shows a pharmacological equivalence between *Soma/Haoma* and *ayahuasca* (which is assumed to be equivalent to *harmel* in its properties); 3) evidence from Iranian folk religion—that the ancient attributes of *Haoma* as recorded in the *Avesta* match modern ideas regarding *harmel* in Iran; and 4) evidence from Zoroastrian rituals—that modern surrogates for *Haoma* are plants with some relationship to *harmel* in folklore and tradition.

I find the proposal of Flattery and Schwartz to be weak and unconvincing. As for their geographical argument, this would seem to be irrelevant. The *RgVeda* states repeatedly that *Soma* grew in the mountains, not in the Indus Valley where it was consumed in Vedic times (Wasson 1968). Similarly, the *Avesta* tells us again and again that *Haoma* grew in the mountains, which Flattery needs chooses to interpret as a device "to assert its lofty origins" (Flattery & Schwartz 1989). The Aryan migration to the south and west of the mountain home of *Soma/Haoma* has been cited as a reason for adopting substitutes for the original plant, leading to its eventual abandonment (Wasson 1968). Flattery's geographical argument rather shows the plausibility of *Peganum harmala* as a substitute in the plains for the original *Soma/Haoma*, remote from its mountain home, although, as Flattery points out, *harmel* also grows in the mountains. However, as Flattery concedes, *Peganum harmala* is not common in India (Flattery & Schwartz 1989). Flattery's four points of proposed pharmacological correspondence between *Soma/Haoma* and *Banisteriopsis* have no bearing on the largely unknown pharmacology of *harmel* as an inebriant, and in any case are general principles that could apply to virtually *any* entheogenic plant with a history of traditional use, such as Siberian *Amanita muscaria* and Mexican entheogenic mushrooms, morning glory seeds, and leaves of *Salvia divinorum* (see Chapters 2, 5 and 6, and Appendix A) all of which, like *Banisteriopsis* and other entheogens in South America, meet all four of Flattery's proposed points of correspondence. The evidence from Iranian folk religion is supportive of the Flattery/Schwartz thesis, but not incompatible with the Wasson/Doniger thesis, that *Soma* was an entheogenic mushroom, and the later *Haoma* one of many known surrogates (a conclusion also reached in a recent Italian paper; Festi & Alliota 1990). Finally, the evidence regarding substitutes used in Zoroastrian rituals is again supportive, but indirect, and counterbalanced by similar evidence from India, for mushrooms as a primary substitute for *Soma* (Kramrisch 1975; Wasson *et al.* 1986). The reader of the Flattery/Schwartz book finishes with an empty feeling... where is the evidence, from the authors' own experimentation (if necessary), that *Peganum harmala* is a visionary plant? Why do the authors base their arguments on alleged correspondence with *ayahuasca*, an unrelated potion from another continent, that owes its psychoptic effects primarily to additives containing DiMethylTryptamine (DMT) and other entheogenic compounds, and not to the *harmel*-type alkaloids?[2]

CHEMISTRY OF *PEGANUM HARMALA*

Chemical work on the pigments of *Peganum harmala* or Syrian rue seeds commenced in the 1830s. The German chemist H. Göbel isolated an alkaloid he named harmaline from seeds of *Peganum harmala* in 1841 (Göbel 1841). Six years later, fellow chemist J. Fritzsche isolated a related alkaloid, harmine, from the same seeds (Fritzsche 1847). More than fifty years later, a third, related alkaloid named harmalol was also isolated from Syrian rue seeds (Fischer 1901), and later research has established the presence of harmol, ruine, dihydroruine and TetraHydroHarmine (THH) or leptaflorine (Allen & Holmstedt 1980). Structures for harmine and harmaline were proposed by Perkin and Robinson in 1919 (Perkin & Robinson 1919A; Perkin & Robinson 1919B) and these were confirmed by these two scientists working with British chemist R.H.F. Manske (first to synthesize DMT in 1931; see Chapter 3), when they synthesized both compounds in 1927 (Manske *et al.* 1927). Späth (first to synthesize mescaline in 1919; see Chapter 1) and Lederer proposed more practical syntheses three years later (Späth & Lederer 1930A; Späth & Lederer 1930B). The "harmala alkaloids" were found to share a common tricyclic indole nucleus (the nucleus consists of three attached rings, technically it is pyrido[3,4-*b*]indole) known commonly as the β-carboline ring system. Harmine, for example, is 7-methoxy-1-methyl-β-carboline; harmaline is the 3,4-dihydro- derivative of harmine and *d*-leptaflorine is (+)-1,2,3,4-TetraHydroHarmine or THH (the racemic, or *d,l*- form of THH was first isolated from *Leptactinia densiflora* and thus named leptaflorine; later *d*-leptaflorine was isolated from *Banisteriopsis caapi*; see Hochstein & Paradies 1957). The simple β-carboline alkaloids have been found to be widely distributed in plants; having been reported in well over 100 species in more than 27 families representing more than 60 genera (Allen & Holmstedt 1980). Besides the β-carboline alkaloids, epigeal parts of *Peganum harmala* contain quinazoline alkaloids such as vasicine (peganine) and vasicinone, which have uterotonic effects (Bellakhdar *et al.* 1991; H.N. Khashimov 1971; Zutshi *et al.* 1980) possibly accounting for the use of *P. harmala* as an abortifacient, and use of the closely-related harmine-containing *Tribulus terrestris* is used as an emmenagogue in Thai ethnomedicine (Ponglux *et al.*

1987). Quinazoline alkaloids are also known from two *Justicia* species used in Nepalese ethnomedicine (Chowdhury & Bhattacharya 1985; Manandhar 1991) and the vasicine-containing *Adhatoda vasica* is now used in Thai ethnomedicine as an antiasthmatic (Ponglux *et al.* 1987) and in Indian ethnomedicine as an abortifacient (Nath *et al.* 1992). The antimicrobial flavonoids quercetin and kaempferol have been found in cultured cells of *P. harmala* (Harsh & Nag 1984), and a novel flavonoid, peganetin, was recently isolated from whole plants (Ahmed & Saleh 1987). Novel anthraquinones of unknown pharmacology are likewise found in *harmel* seeds (Pitre & Srivastava 1987).

The mature seeds of *Peganum harmala* show the highest concentration of the β-carboline alkaloids in this plant, the reported range being from 2–7%, while the roots contain from 1.4–3.2% (Kutlu & Amal 1967; al-Shamma & Abdul-Ghany 1977). Harmine is normally the major alkaloid, but the ratio of harmine to harmaline shows seasonal variation. In studies of Syrian rue roots, winter was found to be the season of highest alkaloid content, with 1.8% harmine content and 0.4% harmaline content; the same strains in the summer showed considerably lower alkaloid levels, with increased content of harmaline—0.8% harmaline and only 0.6% harmine (K. Khashimov *et al.* 1971; Safina *et al.* 1970). A similar seasonal disparity has been observed for alkaloidal content of the seeds, with the ratios of the two compounds reversed as to season: in winter about twice as much harmaline as harmine is observed; whereas in the summer the reverse obtains (Kamel *et al.* 1970). The general rule is that alkaloid content is highest in the winter, and that in the winter there is a flux of harmaline from the roots to the reproductive parts; and a reverse flux of harmine from reproductive parts to the roots. Geographical variation has also been reported, with Iraqi specimens containing nearly twice the alkaloid content of material from the Soviet Union (K. Khashimov *et al.* 1971; Safina *et al.* 1970; al-Shamma & Abdul-Ghany 1977). The harmane-alkaloidal chemistry of *Peganum harmala* has been reviewed by Flattery in *Haoma and Harmaline*, which in my opinion might more aptly have been named *Haoma and Harmine*, since harmine is the principal alkaloid of *harmel* seeds, and also of *ayahuasca* or *Banisteriopsis caapi* (Flattery & Schwartz 1989).[3]

The main economic value of the Syrian rue seeds in modern times has been as a source of dyes for fabrics (Porter 1962). A yellow pigment is obtained by aqueous infusion of the seeds (Dollfus & Schlumberger 1842); and an important red dye used in tinting the felt for Turkish fezes, was obtained from chemical treatment of the seeds (Göbel 1838). Studies of the dyes produced by the Syrian rue seeds led to the isolation of harmine and harmaline, and the red pigment, in particular, is thought to result from the oxidation of the β-carboline alkaloids (Schutzenberger 1867).

AYAHUASCA, *CAAPI*, *YAJÉ*—ENTHEOGENIC POTIONS OF AMAZONIA

As we saw in the introduction to this chapter, the first reports of *ayahuasca*, *caapi* and *yajé*, alike entheogenic potions prepared from extracts of *Banisteriopsis caapi*, were those of M. Villavicencio and R. Spruce, and placed the ritual use of *ayahuasca* from the east in the area of the Río Negro in Brasil, out of the Amazonian basin and north to the Orinoco basin of Venezuela and finally west to the foothills of the Andes in Amazonian Ecuador (Anon. 1855; Spruce 1873; Spruce 1908; Villavicencio 1858). In the 140 years following these pioneering reports of Villavicencio and Spruce, that range has been extended westerly, to the Pacific coastal areas of Colombia, Panamá and Ecuador, where the Emberá and Noanamá Indians use *Banisteriopsis* potions under the names *pildé* and *dapa* respectively (Reichel-Dolmatoff 1960). Moreover, the traditional use of *Banisteriopsis* potions has been reported as far south as Amazonian Perú and Bolivia (Andritzky 1988, 1989; Baer 1969; Baer & Snell 1974; Dobkin de Ríos 1970A; Dobkin de Ríos 1970B; Dobkin de Ríos 1972; Dobkin de Ríos 1973; Friedberg 1965; Kensinger 1973; Kusel 1965; Luna 1984A; Luna 1984B; Luna 1991; Ott 1994A; Rusby 1923; Siskind 1973; Weiss 1973; White 1922). Widespread *ayahuasca* use by Colombian Indians has been well studied by G. Reichel-Dolmatoff (Reichel-Dolmatoff 1944; Reichel-Dolmatoff 1969; Reichel-Dolmatoff 1970; Reichel-Dolmatoff 1972; Reichel-Dolmatoff 1975) and by others (Bristol 1966A; Brüzzi 1962; Calella 1935; Calella 1944A; Calella 1944B; Goldman 1963; Koch-Grünberg 1909; Koch-Grünberg 1923; Morton 1931; Ott 1994A; Uscátegui 1959; Uscátegui 1961). Modern studies of *ayahuasca* use in Ecuador have established common use by groups of Quichua, Waorani and Shuar (widely known as "Jívaro" in the literature; now considered to be a pejorative epithet) Indians (Davis & Yost 1983A; Harner 1973A; Harner 1973B; Harner 1973D; Marles *et al.* 1988; Naranjo 1975; Naranjo 1979; Naranjo 1983; Ott 1994A). Use of *caapi* potions in Amazonian Brasil has likewise been well studied (Ducke 1957; Lowie 1946; Prance 1970; Prance & Prance 1970; Prance *et al.* 1977). Early papers by Schultes contributed much to the resolution of problems concerning the botanical identity of *ayahuasca* lianas (Schultes 1957A; Schultes & Raffauf 1960), and his recent publications have done much to clarify the ethnobotanical study of *Banisteriopsis*-based visionary potions (Schultes 1986B; Schultes 1988; Schultes & Hofmann 1980; Schultes & Raffauf 1990). We now know the use of *ayahuasca* potions to have been common among South American

Indians of Amazonian Brasil, Venezuela, Colombia, Ecuador, Perú and Bolivia, extending to the Orinoco basin of Venezuela and the coastal regions of Colombia, Panamá and Ecuador. Luna has enumerated no fewer than 72 indigenous groups reported to have used entheogenic *ayahuasca* potions (Luna 1986B; Luna 1986C) along with 42 different indigenous names for the potions. Archaeological research has shown that the use of *ayahuasca* in Ecuador may date back as many as five millennia (Naranjo 1986), 'though it is probably considerably more recent.

While most of the *ayahuasca/caapi/yajé* potions are based on extracts of Spruce's *Banisteriopsis caapi*, other species of *Banisteriopsis* have also been implicated. The most important of these other species is *B. inebrians*, chiefly used in the Amazonian foothills of the Andes (Cuatrecasas 1965; Morton 1931; Schultes 1957A), and now, along with *B. quitensis*, considered rather to be a synonym for *B. caapi* (Gates 1982; Schultes & Raffauf 1990). Another species, *B. martiniana* var. *laevis* (=*B. martiniana* var. *subenervia*), has been reported also to be used in preparation of *yajé* potions (García Barriga 1975; Gates 1982; Schultes 1975). *Banisteriopsis muricata* (=*B. argentea*; *B. metallicolor*) is used in place of *B. caapi* as a basic ingredient for entheogenic potions by the Waorani of Ecuador, who call the plant *míi.* The Witoto call this species *sacha ayahuasca* ("wild *ayahuasca*"), and consider it weaker than *B. caapi* (Davis & Yost 1983A). Other species reported as basic ingredients of *ayahuasca* potions are: *B. longialata*, *B. lutea* and *Lophanthera lactescens* (Schultes 1986B). In the Orinoco basin of Venezuela, *B. lucida* or *cají* is used in fishing magic—a piece of the bark put in the mouth of a small fish which is then thrown back, is thought to attract more fish (Boom & Moestl 1990). A related species of Malpighiaceae, *Diplopterys cabrerana* (=*Banisteriopsis cabrerana*; Gates 1982), once classified as *Banisteriopsis rusbyana*, is now considered to be an additive to *Banisteriopsis*-based potions, and has been found to be chemically distinct from *B. caapi.* This will be discussed in detail below. Both Spruce (1908) and Koch-Grünberg (1909; 1923) referred to different "kinds" of *caapi* in the Vaupés, and Schultes discovered the Makú Indians on the Río Tikié of Brasil preparing a *caapi*-like potion from the bark of the malpighiaceous *Tetrapterys* (or *Tetrapteris*) *methystica* (=*T. styloptera*; Gates 1986), about which we have no chemical information (Schultes 1954A; Schultes 1957A; Schultes & Raffauf 1990). The Karapaná Indians of the Río Apaporis of Colombia also prepare *caapi* from *T. mucronata* (Reis Altschul 1972; Schultes & Raffauf 1990). There is a report of use of the malpighiaceous *Mascagnia psilophylla* var. *antifebrilis* (=*Banisteria antifebrilis*; Gates 1982; *Callaeum antifebrile*; Gates 1986) as a basis for *ayahuasca*, but this is "open to serious doubt" owing to a mixed collection containing also *Banisteriopsis* species (Schultes & Hofmann 1979; Schultes & Raffauf 1990). *Mascagnia psilophylla* has been described as an *ayahuasca* admixture plant (see below; Luna & Amaringo 1991). In Brasil, *B. argyrophylla* root decoction is used to treat kidney ailments (Schmeda-Hirschmann & De Arias 1990).

Some errors and confusions have crept into the literature on the *ayahuasca* complex. A missionary in 1890 confused the entheogenic *Brugmansia* species (see Appendix A), which may be used as additives to *ayahuasca*, with the basic ingredient, *Banisteriopsis caapi*, an error that was widely parroted in secondary literature. Further confusion arose between the *Banisteriopsis* species and the genus *Aristolochia* (Schultes 1957A). Another curious error arose from apparent misinterpretation of Spruce's field notes that, whereas *ayahuasca* and *caapi* were prepared from *Banisteriopsis* species, the closely-related *yajé* was made from the apocynaceous *Prestonia amazonica* (=*Haemadictyon amazonicum*; Schultes & Raffauf 1960). This error was amplified in the chemical literature, when it was reported that *N,N*-DiMethyl-Tryptamine (DMT; see Chapter 3 and below) was detected in "*Prestonia amazonicum*" [*sic*], misidentified as *yajé* and found as a *Banisteriopsis* admixture in the Río Napo area (Hochstein & Paradies 1957). We now know that the *ayahuasca* admixtures used in the Río Napo area for their DMT content are referable either to the above-mentioned *Diplopterys cabrerana* or to the rubiaceous *Psychotria viridis*, and the 1957 analysis of putative *Prestonia amazonica* doubtless represented one of these species (Schultes & Raffauf 1960; Schultes & Hofmann 1980).

The extensive literature on the *ayahuasca* complex has been reviewed by Reichel-Dolmatoff (1975) Schultes and Hofmann (1980), P. Naranjo (1983) and most recently by Luna (1986A), Luna and Amaringo (1991) and Ott (1994A). In general terms, aqueous infusions or decoctions are made from thick stems or stem shavings of wild or cultivated lianas of *Banisteriopsis caapi*. Generally the liana stems or pieces of stems (which may or may not be pounded prior to extraction) are cooked in water, strained, and the extract concentrated down. In some cases, for example in the Colombian Amazon, "the bark is simply kneaded in cold water" (Schultes & Raffauf 1992), and sometimes the *ayahuasca* is boiled briefly, and not concentrated (Rivier & Lindgren 1972). Often leaves or other parts of additional entheogenic plants are added to the potion prior to cooking (see below for discussion of the many psychoptic *ayahuasca* additives), although the brew may be made exclusively of *Banisteriopsis caapi*. In the case of the itinerant Guahibo Indians observed by Spruce in the Río Orinoco basin in 1854, stems of *caapi* were simply chewed "as some people do tobacco" (Spruce 1908). There is some evidence for the use of *Banisteriopsis* species in South American visionary snuffs (see Chapter 3, "Chemistry of Entheogenic *Virola* Snuffs"; Bernauer 1964; Holmstedt & Lindgren 1967; Schultes 1984), and unconfirmed reports of the use of *Banisteriopsis* preparations as an enema (De Smet 1983; De Smet 1985B; Emboden 1979; Furst 1976; Furst & Coe 1977). Schultes has recently found the Witoto Indians of Amazonian Colombia smoking dried leaves and "young bark" of *Banisteriopsis caapi*, in cigarettes wrapped in leaves of a *Heliconia* species (Schultes 1985B). Normally, however, the *ayahuasca* brew is ingested orally, usually in a shamanic or ethnomedicinal context; that is, as a visionary aid in the divination of the natural or shamanic causes of illness, sometimes as an aid in the cure. It has been conjectured that the purgative effects of these *ayahuasca* potions are of importance as a type of chemotherapy for parasitic worms (Rodríguez *et al.* 1982) and the *ayahuasca* constituent harmine has been shown to possess UV-mediated toxicity to yeast and bacteria (McKenna & Towers 1981). *Ayahuasca* sessions are important in the apprenticeship of shamans, who often must pass first an apprenticeship with tobacco (Alarcón 1990; Wilbert 1987). In the case of mestizo Peruvian shamans, the *ayahuasca* plant, like other visionary plants, is *itself* the teacher of the aspiring shaman who, among other things, learns supernatural melodies or *icaros* from the plant (Luna 1984A; Luna 1984B; Montgomery 1991). It has been suggested that the magical songs (Bellier 1986) and *icaros* which the shamans learn from *ayahuasca* (Luna 1984A; Luna 1984B) may represent transmogrified *ayahuasca* visions (Gebhart-Sayer 1986; Siskind 1973) and the *ayahuasca* images are a prominent component of Amazonian art (Reichel-Dolmatoff 1971; Reichel-Dolmatoff 1972; Reichel-Dolmatoff 1975; Reichel-Dolmatoff 1978). The visual art and magical melodies as much as the entheogenic effects of the potions are said to lead to an "aesthetic frame of mind" thought vital to the healing process (Gebhart-Sayer 1986). Shamans' body paint is thought to represent "healthy" versions of the patterns which the shamans can see on the skin of a patient; different illnesses lead to different distortions in the healthy designs, and *ayahuasca* can help the shamans to "repaint" the patients, restoring health (Luna 1992; 1993). Similar aesthetic/therapeutic ideas may have prevailed in ancient México (see Chapter 5, Note 3; Cáceres 1984; Ortíz de Montellano 1990). The visionary experience of *ayahuasca* is so important and fundamental to the world-view of the Amazonian Indians that the use of the potion by *curanderos* has largely survived the forces of acculturation, and mestizos consult the *ayahuasca* plant-teachers even in modern-day cities (Dobkin de Ríos 1970B; Dobkin de Ríos 1973; Dobkin de Ríos 1992; Dobkin de Ríos & Reátegui 1967; Henman 1986; Lamb 1974; Lamb 1985; Luna 1984B; Ott 1994A; Ramírez de Jara & Pinzón C. 1986). Moreover, the fame of *ayahuasca* has spread far beyond its aboriginal home, and cultivation and use of *ayahuasca* has been established in the United States and other countries, in part due to proselytizing by religious groups.

THE CHEMISTRY OF *BANISTERIOPSIS* SPECIES

The first successful chemical work on *Banisteriopsis* was the isolation by a Colombian chemist of a crystalline alkaloid he named *telepatina* or telepathine (Fischer Cárdenas 1923); although no voucher specimens are available for identification and Fischer Cárdenas thought he was working with a species of *Aristolochia*. One Zerda Bayón had proposed the name *telepathine* as early as 1905 for an extract of an *ayahuasca* potion (Deulofeu 1967). Perrot and Raymond-Hamet isolated pure telepathine from authentic *Banisteriopsis caapi* in 1927 (Perrot & Raymond-Hamet 1927A; Perrot and Raymond-Hamet 1927B). In 1925, Colombian chemist Barriga Villalba isolated an alkaloid he called *yajéina* or yajéine (as well as a second compound named *yajénina* or yajénine, about which insufficient information was published to enable us to identify it today; it was likely harmaline or *d*-leptaflorine [TetraHydroHarmine, THH], the most important secondary alkaloids of *B. caapi*) from material he erroneously believed to be *Haemadictyon amazonicum* (=*Prestonia amazonica*; Barriga Villalba 1925A; Barriga Villalba 1925B). Meanwhile, in Germany, famous pharmacognosist and chemist Louis Lewin (see Chapter 1) isolated an alkaloid he named *Banisterin(e)* from material he called *Banisteria caapi* (Lewin 1928; Lewin 1929). Finally, in 1928, two independent European groups isolated the well-known harmine from "South American lianas" (Elger 1928; Wolfes & Rumpf 1928). Elger compared his material isolated from *Banisteriopsis* with harmine from *Peganum harmala* and with synthetic harmine, concluding that all three crystalline samples were identical. The situation was fully clarified in 1939, when Chen and Chen determined that telepathine, yajéine and banisterine were all alike synonyms for harmine, which they had isolated from *Banisteriopsis caapi* collected by botanist L. Williams near Iquitos, Perú (Chen & Chen 1939; Williams 1931). These researchers were able to isolate harmine from stems, leaves and roots of this documented *B. caapi* sample.

The structure of harmine was known by this time (Fischer 1899; Perkin & Robinson 1919A; Perkin & Robinson 1919B), and the compound had been synthesized in 1927 (Manske *et al.* 1927; Späth & Lederer 1930A; Späth & Lederer 1930B). In 1957, Hochstein and Paradies isolated from Peruvian *B. caapi* harmine as well as harmaline and *d*-leptaflorine or tetrahydroharmine (Hochstein & Paradies 1957). These compounds were also found in an *ayahuasca* potion from Perú, and harmaline and *d*-leptaflorine (TetraHydroHarmine) were proposed to be psychotropic compounds in this *ayahuasca* potion. In 1969, the stable β-carboline alkaloid harmine was found in quantities similar to fresh material in Spruce's original type collection of *Banisteriopsis caapi* from 1852 (Schultes *et al.* 1969)! Rivier and Lindgren found the same three β-carbolines as major alkaloids of *Banisteriopsis caapi* (Rivier & Lindgren

1972), together with small amounts of harmol and traces of 6-methoxytryptamine, while more recent studies have found trace amounts of six other β-carbolines: harmine-*N*-oxide, harmic acid methyl ester, harmalinic acid, harmic acid, acetyl-norharmine and ketotetrahydro-norharmine, some of which may be artefacts of chemical manipulation (Hashimoto & Kawanishi 1975; Hashimoto & Kawanishi 1976). Recent quantitative analysis of dried stems of six different *B. caapi* cultivars from Perú found total alkaloidal concentrations (dry weight basis) from 1.7–12.46 mg/g, (0.17–1.25%) with all specimens but one containing harmine as the chief alkaloid, followed by harmaline and *d*-leptaflorine (TetraHydroHarmine), with traces of harmol and one specimen with traces of harmalol (McKenna *et al.* 1984A). Normally harmine represented at least half of the alkaloidal concentration; the exception being the weakest strain, which showed slightly more harmaline than harmine. The pyrrolidine alkaloids shihunine and dihydroshihunine, of obscure pharmacology, have also been found in *Banisteriopsis caapi* (Kawanishi *et al.* 1982).

Studies on *Banisteriopsis inebrians*, now considered to be a synonym for *B. caapi* (as is the case also for *B. quitensis*; Gates 1982), have led to the isolation of harmine from the stems (O'Connell & Lynn 1953); whereas subsequent analysis of Peruvian material detected harmine and traces of harmaline (Poisson 1965). An "Australian" species, *Banisteria chrysophylla* (=*Heteropterys chrysophylla*; Gates 1982), incorrectly cited as *Banisteriopsis crysophylla* [*sic*] (in Deulofeu 1967), has been reported to contain alkaloids (Webb 1949), and five β-carbolines, including harmine and harmaline, have been isolated from leaves and stems of *B. muricata* (=*B. argentea*; Gates 1982; Ghosal 1972; Ghosal & Mazumder 1971; Ghosal *et al.* 1971), together with *N,N*-DiMethylTryptamine (DMT) and DMT-*N*-oxide. This interesting finding awaits confirmation, and one might be justified in suspecting contamination with a DMT-rich admixture plant. Ghosal's group analyzed specimens grown in a botanical garden in Calcutta, India. Moreover, Gates' *Banisteriopsis muricata*, the most widespread species in the genus, includes as conspecific about a dozen taxa, among them *B. argentea.* Chemical analyses of collections backed by voucher specimens are needed to confirm the report of DMT in *B. muricata*, stem infusions of which are used against headaches and fever by the Guaymí Indians of Panamá (Joly *et al.* 1987). *Banisteriopsis lutea* has been reported to contain harmine (Raymond-Hamet 1941), as has a species in a related genus, *Cabi paraensis* (today known as *Callaeum antifebrile*; Gates 1986; and previously called *Mascagnia psilophylla* var. *antifebrile*; Mors & Zaltzman 1954; Ríos *et al.* 1965). *Banisteriopsis nitrosiodora* (=*B. lutea*; Gates 1982) from Argentina has been found to be "practically devoid of alkaloids" and it has also been said that several *Banisteriopsis* species reportedly added to *ayahuasca* beverages remain to be tested chemically (Deulofeu 1967). Harmine is now known from at least twelve species in seven plant families (Allen & Holmstedt 1980).[4]

CHACRUNA, *CHAGROPANGA* AND OTHER *AYAHUASCA* ADMIXTURES

One of the common denominators in South American ethnobotany of *ayahuasca* potions, is the fact that the brews often contain other psychoactive plants apart from *Banisteriopsis caapi* (Luna 1984A; Luna 1984B; McKenna *et al.* 1986; Pinkley 1969; Schultes 1972B), and may be used at the same time as other psychoactive plants, such as tobacco and *coca.* I will discuss six distinct categories of *ayahuasca* "admixture" plants or cohorts in this section (see Table 3 and Ott 1994A).

TOBACCO: One of the most common and widespread additives to *ayahuasca* is tobacco; specifically, the cultivated tobaccos, *Nicotiana tabacum* and *N. rustica* (see Appendix A; Luna & Amaringo 1991; Schultes & Hofmann 1979). For some reason, other common additives to *ayahuasca* potions have received much more attention in the scientific literature. Recently, J. Wilbert has reviewed the ethnobotanical literature on South American shamanic use of tobacco, including its prominence as *ayahuasca* admixture or cohort (Wilbert 1987). The following information was gleaned from Wilbert's excellent review. The Shuar "drink tobacco juice alternately with *ayahuasca*" while the Shipibo *ayahuasquero* "mixes tobacco with *Banisteriopsis caapi.*" Shamans of the Piro tribe "drink *ayahuasca* followed by tobacco juice," whereas the Cocama Indians drink tobacco juice "in combination with *ayahuasca* when inducting young shamans." The Campa Indians "lick *ambíl* [an edible tobacco preparation; see Appendix A]... after imbibing *ayahuasca*" and "ingest *ambíl* simultaneously with *ayahuasca* (*Banisteriopsis caapi*) and coca (*Erythroxylum*)." Similarly, of the Barasana it was said: "considerable amounts of tobacco rapé are taken alternately with *yagé* (*Banisteriopsis caapi*) and coca." The Aguaruna are said to make enemas or clysters of "tobacco syrup mixed with *ayahuasca*" (Schultes & Raffauf 1990). While the Tecuana blow tobacco smoke "over the practitioners and their paraphernalia prior to imbibing *ayahuasca*," the Omagua shamans "take tobacco in conjunction with *paricá* (*Virola*) and *ayahuasca.*" The Lamista shamans smoke large cigars of tobacco "while ingesting various kinds of hallucinogens, like *Banisteriopsis caapi*," whereas the shamans of the Machigenga "achieve ecstatic flight by drinking cold tobacco juice; but *ayahuasca* and... coca (*Erythroxylum*), are also taken on such occasions." Quijos Quichua *ayahuasqueros* blow tobacco smoke over the *ayahuasca* potion and the participants in a ceremony, then smoke tobacco constantly during the effects (Ott, unpublished). Tobacco is also smoked during *ayahuasca* sessions by the Siona and Secoya Indians of Ecuador (Vickers & Plowman 1984). Similarly, in México, tobacco use may frequently accompany use of *péyotl* among the Huicholes (Schaefer 1992A), and entheogenic mushroom use among the Mazatecs (Ott, unpublished).

There has been a dearth of comment on the pharmacological consequences of mixing nicotine with the β-carbolines, although β-carboline components of tobacco smoke have been proposed to explain the visionary effects of this drug (Janiger & Dobkin de Ríos 1976). In general, there is a lack of appreciation of the visionary potency of pure, unadulterated tobacco, in contrast to the weak, bastardized products of modern commerce. Clearly, research is needed on this important *ayahuasca* additive. The very ubiquity of tobacco as an American shamanic drug may have obscured this connection with *ayahuasca*. Indeed, tobacco is *the* shamanic drug, fundamental to the world-view of the American shaman (Wilbert 1991). As Wilbert commented of the Záparo Indians: the shamans "take *ayahuasca* (*Banisteriopsis caapi*) to see better but believe that their true power derives from tobacco." Among Quichua groups of Amazonian Ecuador, the aspiring shaman must imbibe considerable quantities of tobacco juice before graduating to an apprenticeship with *ayahuasca* (Alarcón 1990), and tobacco ingestion is a part of shamanic apprenticeship throughout Amazonia (Schultes & Raffauf 1992).

GUAYUSA: Owing in part to the soporific effects of *Banisteriopsis caapi* extracts, the Shuar (Furst 1976; Russo 1992), Runa (Kohn 1992) and Quijos Quichua (Ott, unpublished) of Ecuador add leaves of the holly *Ilex guayusa* (Patiño 1968; Shemluck 1979) to their *ayahuasca* potions (Schultes 1972D; Schultes & Raffauf 1990). Shuar and Quichua Indians have also been reported to employ infusions of the *guayusa* leaf as a treatment for headache (Russo 1992). In Ecuador, *guayusa* leaf tea is taken with *ayahuasca* to "kill the bitter taste," "to prevent hangover" and to "give strength to deal with *ayahuasca*" (Schultes & Raffauf 1990). Jesuit missions once grew *guayusa* commercially and there is a 17th century report mentioning use of *guayusa* as an additive to a potion containing also *Banisteriopsis*, *Brugmansia*, and *Nicotiana* species (Schultes 1979F). A relative of a well-known South American stimulant *mate* (also spelled *maté*; *Ilex paraguariensis*; also known as *I. paraguayensis* or *I. paraguensis*), and of the recondite North American *yaupon* (*Ilex vomitoria*), leaves of an Achuar *guayusa* strain were recently shown to contain 7.6% caffeine, making this the most potent caffeine-containing plant yet documented. Achuar users of this strain were seen to vomit ritually after their morning cup, supposedly to avoid excess stimulation

(Lewis *et al.* 1991). Similarly, the "black drink" *yaupon*, of *Ilex vomitoria* leaf, was reportedly used as an "hallucinogen" to "evoke ecstasies" among North American Cherokee Indians, who likewise used strong infusions of these leaves to induce vomiting for ceremonial purification (Hamel & Chiltoskey 1975). This North American species also contains caffeine (Power & Chestnut 1919), and the only other *Ilex* species known to contain caffeine is *I. ambigua* (Bohinc *et al.* 1977). The subjective effects of *guayusa/ayahuasca*, prepared for me by a Quijos Quichua *ayahuasquero*, however, were still quite soporific, with no visionary or psychoptic effects. Another caffeine-containing drug, *Paullinia yoco*, a relative of the famous stimulant *guaraná* (*Paullinia cupana* var. *sorbilis*; Schultes 1942; Schultes 1986A; Schultes & Raffauf 1992), was recently reported as an *ayahuasca* additive among the Siona (Langdon 1986). There has been no research on the interactions of caffeine with the β-carboline alkaloids. The Campa and Barasana Indians take *ayahuasca* with the leaves of *Erythroxylum coca* var. *ipadú*, evidently seeking the stimulation their cocaine content affords (Holmstedt *et al.* 1978; Schultes 1981; Wilbert 1987).

CHIRIGUAYUSA: Various Indian groups of Colombia and Ecuador, including the Kofán, Siona, Ingano, Runa and Shuar, are known to add the bark, leaves or roots of *Brunfelsia grandiflora*, *B. grandiflora* subsp. *schultesii* (known in Quechua as *chiriguayusa* or *chiric-sananho*) and leaves of *B. chiricaspi* to their *ayahuasca* brews (Kohn 1992; Langdon 1986; Plowman 1977; Schultes & Raffauf 1990; Schultes & Raffauf 1992). *Brunfelsia chiricaspi* is used alone as an entheogen by the Kofán, Mai Huna, Siona, Ingano and other groups of the Colombian and Ecuadorian Putumayo (see Appendix A; Bellier 1986; Plowman 1977; Schultes & Raffauf 1990; Schultes & Raffauf 1992), and is considered by the Kofán and Ingano Indians to be preferable to *chiriguayusa* (Schultes 1985A). *Brunfelsia grandiflora* var. *schultesii* is likewise used alone by the Kofán and by the Siona-Secoya as an entheogen (Schultes & Raffauf 1990). The pharmacology of this intriguing solanaceous genus is obscure (see Appendix A), and there has been no research on the interactions of *Brunfelsia* species with extracts of *Banisteriopsis caapi*. The well-known Brasilian ethnomedicine *manacá*, root of *Brunfelsia uniflora*, has also been reportedly used as a shamanic inebriant, and like the *Brunfelsia* species added to *ayahuasca*, contains the coumarin scopoletin (Mors & Ribeiro 1957; Plowman 1977; Schultes & Hofmann 1980).

HUANTO: Another important category of *ayahuasca* admixture plants are the solanaceous *Brugmansia* species, known as *huanto*, *huantuc* or *huanduj* in Ecuador (Chango *et al.* 1984; Kohn 1992; Reinberg 1921). The Sharanahua, Ingano and Siona

Indians of Amazonia add *Brugmansia suaveolens* leaves to their *ayahuasca* potions, while in Loreta, Perú, leaves of *B. insignis* are so used. Leaves, stems, seeds, and ashes of leaves of other species of *Brugmansia* may be likewise added to some *ayahuasca* (Langdon 1986; Schultes & Raffauf 1990; Schultes & Raffauf 1992). The Shuar Indians possibly use *Brugmansia* species in their *ayahuasca* brews (Lockwood 1979). Siona and Secoya Indians of Ecuador are reported to use *Brugmansia* x. *insignis* alone as an entheogen and as an additive to *ayahuasca* potions (Vickers & Plowman 1984). The *Brugmansia* species, known generally in Spanish as *floripondios*, are potent entheogens in their own right (see Appendix A; Bristol 1966B), but no research has been done on the interactions of their constituent tropane alkaloids with the β-carboline compounds of *Banisteriopsis caapi.* Use of *Datura* has been mentioned as an *ayahuasca* admixture (Reichel-Dolmatoff 1975), but this report doubtless referred to so-called "tree *Datura*" species, an obsolete name for *Brugmansia* species.

MISCELLANEOUS ADMIXTURES: Makuna Indians of Colombia add crushed leaves of *Malouetia tamaquarina* and/or of tobacco to *ayahuasca* (Schultes 1960; Schultes 1987A; Schultes & Hofmann 1980; Schultes & Raffauf 1990; Wilbert 1987). This apocynaceous species (in the same family as *eboka*, *Tabernanthe iboga*; see Appendix A) has been little studied chemically, but alkaloids are known from *M. becquaertiana*, and steroidal alkaloids occur in various species of *Malouetia*, including *M. tamaquarina* (Bisset 1992B; Schultes & Raffauf 1990). An unidentified *Tabernaemontana* species (see Appendix A) has been reported as an *ayahuasca* admixture (Schultes & Hofmann 1979), along with two little-known apocynaceous species, *Mandevilla scabra* and *Himatanthus sucuuba* (Luna 1984B; Luna & Amaringo 1991), the former used in ethnogynecology by Brasilian Kayapó Indians (Elisabetsky & Posey 1989). The Ingano Indians of Colombin Amazonia have been reported to add the amaranthaceous *Alternanthera lehmannii* to *ayahuasca* (a use also reported among the Siona Indians; Uscátegui 1959), another species of obscure chemistry (Schultes & Hofmann 1980; Schultes & Raffauf 1990). Another plant in the same family, an unidentified species of *Iresine*, has been described as an *ayahuasca* admixture (Schultes & Hofmann 1979); similarly, a species of *Iresine* has been reported as an admixture to the Andean entheogenic potion *cimora*, based on the entheogenic cactus *Trichocereus pachanoi* (see Chapter 1; Schultes & Hofmann 1980). McKenna and coworkers reported analysis of three "uncommon admixture plants" used in Peruvian *ayahuasca* potions—bark of *Abuta grandifolia* (a well-known menispermaceous dart-poison plant; Bisset 1992B; Schultes & Raffauf 1990; also used by various Ecuadorian groups as a headache remedy; Russo 1992), leaves of *Teliostachya lan-*

ceolata var. *crispa* (generally, branches are used as an *ayahuasca* admixture, whereas the leaves are sometimes made into a separate entheogenic infusion; Schultes 1972C; Schultes & Raffauf 1990), and leaves of *Cornutia odorata*—of which only the first was found to be positive for alkaloids (McKenna *et al.* 1984A). Of course, one can only conjecture regarding the interactions of these chemically-unknown plants with the *Banisteriopsis* alkaloids. The Sharanahua Indians add powdered rhizomes of a *Cyperus* species (which may be infested with ergoline-alkaloid-producing *Balansia cyperi* fungi (see Chapter 2, Note 4) to *ayahuasca* (Schultes & Raffauf 1990)—this may be *Cyperus prolixus* (McKenna *et al.* 1986). *Calathea veitchiana* has been reportedly used as an *ayahuasca* admixture in Perú (Schultes 1972C; Schultes & Hofmann 1979; Schultes & Raffauf 1990). Two species of ferns, *Lygodium venustum* (*Lygodium mexicanum* is used by Huastec Mayans of México for its psychological effects in cases of insanity; Alcorn 1984) and *Lomariopsis japurensis* (*L. japurensis* is used against postpartum hemorrhage by Quijos Quichua and as an abortifacient by the Runa of Ecuador, suggesting content of ergoline alkaloids; *L. nigropalatea* is used by the Makú Indians as a hemostatic, again suggesting vasoconstrictive ergolines; Kohn 1992; Marles *et al.* 1988; Schultes & Raffauf 1990) are reported to be *ayahuasca* admixtures (Schultes & Hofmann 1979), the former used by the Kulina and Sharanahua Indians to "make the drink stronger" (Schultes & Raffauf 1990). A plant in the mistletoe family, *Phrygilanthus eugenioides*, has been used by two Peruvian Indian groups, who either boil the leaves with *ayahuasca* or drink the juice of the plant with *ayahuasca* (Schultes & Hofmann 1979; Schultes & Raffauf 1990). The Sharanahua also would chew one or two leaves of a *Clusia* species during an *ayahuasca* session, and the leaves might also have been boiled with the *ayahuasca* (Schultes & Hofmann 1979; Schultes & Raffauf 1990). Another plant also in the Guttiferae family, *Tovomita* sp., is likewise reported as an *ayahuasca* additive in Perú (Luna 1984B). Other *ayahuasca* additives include the mint *Ocimum micranthum* (a decoction of which is used as an anthelmintic and analgesic by Garífuna blacks of Guatemala and as a pain-killer and a pediatric remedy in México; Alcorn 1984; Girón *et al.* 1991; Zamora-Martínez & Nieto de Pascual Pola 1992) and the cacti *Epiphyllum* sp. and *Opuntia* sp. (Schultes & Hofmann 1979). The Sharanahua add "only one leaf" of the *Epiphyllum* species to an *ayahuasca* brew, "or else drink the unboiled juice of the cactus with *ayahuasca*" (Schultes & Raffauf 1990). The same Indians were observed to brew *ayahuasca* with an *Opuntia* species, making "the effects very strong" (Schultes & Raffauf 1990). *Opuntia spinosior* and other *Opuntia* species are known to contain small amounts of mescaline and other alkaloids (see Chapter 1; Ma *et al.* 1986; Pardanani *et al.* 1978), and alkaloids are also known from

Opuntia clavata (Vanderveen *et al.* 1974). "Persistent rumors" associated *Gnetum nodiflorum* leaves with *ayahuasca* in the Colombian Vaupés (Schultes & Raffauf 1990), and it has been suggested that this confusion has resulted from mistaking swollen-noded forms of *Banisteriopsis caapi* for *Gnetum nodiflorum* (D.J. McKenna 1992). *Gnetum nodiflorum* is employed ethnomedicinally as an anti-inflammatory (Schultes 1985A). The *Psychotria* relative *Rudgea retifolia* may have been employed as an *ayahuasca* additive in Perú (Schultes & Raffauf 1990), and the rubiaceous *Calycophyllum spruceanum* is so used (Luna 1984A). Other Rubiaceae species used as *ayahuasca* additives are *Guettarda ferox* and *Uncaria guianensis* (McKenna *et al.* 1986), along with the fruits of *Sabicea amazonensis* (Hugh-Jones 1979; Schultes & Raffauf 1990; Schultes & Raffauf 1992). *Sabicea diversifolia* is used in ethnomedicine as a remedy against dysentery in Madagascar (Beaujard 1988). The leguminous *Bauhinia guianensis* was recently reported as a Peruvian *ayahuasca* admixture (Luna & Amaringo 1991) and as a Venezuelan gastrointestinal remedy (Boom & Moestl 1990), also used in ethnogynecology by the Brasilian Kayapó (Elisabetsky & Posey 1989). Other *ayahuasca* additive species in the family Leguminosae are: *Caesalpinia echinata*, *Calliandra angustifolia*, *Campsiandra laurifolia*, *Erythrina glauca*, *E. poeppigiana*, *Pithecellobium laetum* and *Sclerobium setiferum* (Luna 1984A; Luna 1984B; McKenna *et al.* 1986). The euphorbiaceous species *Hura crepitans* and *Alchornea castanaefolia* have likewise been reported as Peruvian additives to the potions (Luna 1984A; Luna 1984B); the latter is particularly interesting since a related species, *Alchornea floribunda* is known to be ingested along with *Tabernanthe iboga* in Africa (see Appendix A; Schultes & Hofmann 1980). *Hura crepitans* seeds are poisonous, and a decoction of the bark is used in Caribbean ethnomedicine as a purgative and emetic (Seaforth 1991). Another interesting report is of the use in *ayahuasca* of the Amazonian panacea *Maytenus ebenifolia* of the Celastraceae family, a plant known to contain pharmacologically-active phenoldienones (González *et al.* 1982), as well as the use of the myristicaceous *Virola surinamensis* as an *ayahuasca* admixture (Luna 1984A; see Chapter 3 for a discussion of entheogenic *Virola* preparations). Other reported additives to entheogenic *ayahuasca* potions are: *Montrichardia arborescens* (Araceae); *Mansoa alliacea*, *Tabebuia incana*, *T. heteropoda* and an unidentified *Tabebuia* species (Bignoniaceae); *Cavanillesia hylogeiton*, *C. umbellata*, *Ceiba pentandra* and possibly a *Quararibea* species (Bombacaceae); *Carludovica divergens* (Cyclanthaceae); *Couroupita guianensis* (Lecythidaceae); *Coussapoa tessmannii* (related to *C. villosa*, the fruit of which placed in a decayed tooth causes it to fall; Boom & Moestl 1990), *Ficus insipida*, *F. ruiziana* and an unspecified *Ficus* species (Moraceae); *Petiveria alliacea* (Phytolaccaceae—root infusions are used in the Caribbean area as ethnogynecological remedies and leaves are used in Haiti to prepare an antidote to the *zombi* powder; Davis 1983D; Seaforth 1991; Wong 1976; the Panamanian Guaymí use stem bark and leaf decoctions for ritual ceremonies; Joly *et al.* 1987; it is used in Santeria rites in Florida; Andoh 1986; in Brasil, the plant is called *fetiçeira* or "magical"; Schmeda-Hirschmann & De Arias 1990); *Triplaris surinamensis* (Polygonaceae) and *Scoparia dulcis* (Scrophulariaceae—used in the Caribbean area and by Mexican Mixe Indians as a gastrointestinal remedy; Heinrich *et al.* 1992; Seaforth 1991). Other little-known additive plants are listed in Table 3 (Luna 1984A; Luna 1984B). An unidentified *Piper* species has been mentioned as an *ayahuasca* additive (Schultes & Raffauf 1990)—might this represent the *woorara* dart-poison ingredient *P. bartlingianum* described by J.C.D. von Schreber from Surinam in the 18th century (Bisset 1992A), or possibly the Yanoamá tobacco substitute *holehole be*, *P. cryptodon* (Wilbert 1987)? Finally, in Colombia the name *ayahuasca* is also applied to the solanaceous *Juanulloa ochracea*, a medicinal plant never reported as an *ayahuasca* admixture (Schultes 1972C) but said by Indians of the upper Río Apoporis area to have "magical properties" (Schultes 1985A). The same holds true for the violet *Rinorea viridiflora*, known as *ayahuasca* by the Siona-Secoya Indians, suggesting use in the entheogenic potion (Schultes & Raffauf 1990). Two species of *Rinorea*, *R. bengalensis* and *R. macrophylla* are used ethnomedicinally in the Andaman Islands (Awasthi 1991). With less security, *Pontederia cordata* (also found in North America, where the Micmac Indians used it as a contraceptive; Moerman 1986) has likewise been suggested to have been used as an *ayahuasca* admixture (Schultes 1972C).

CHACRUNA and CHAGROPANGA: The best-known and most widely-studied category of *ayahuasca* admixture plants are those containing tryptamines, principally *N,N*-DiMethylTryptamine (McKenna & Towers 1984; McKenna *et al.* 1986; Ott 1994A). The most common are *chacruna* or *amirucapanga*, *Psychotria viridis*, and *chagropanga*, *chalipanga* or *oco-yajé*, *Diplopterys cabrerana* (previously known in the literature as *Banisteriopsis rusbyana*; Kohn 1992; Schultes & Raffauf 1990). In both cases, it is the leaves of these two species which often are added to *ayahuasca* brews, supposedly to "heighten and lengthen" their visionary effects (Schultes & Hofmann 1980). Of the many early reports of *ayahuasca* admixture plants, perhaps the most prominent species mentioned was *Banisteriopsis rusbyana*, another malpighiaceous liana today classified as *Diplopterys cabrerana* (Schultes & Hofmann 1980; Schultes & Raffauf 1990). Voucher specimens of this liana were collected in the Colombian Putumayo by Klug and Cuatrecasas, under the name *chagropanga*, *oco-yajé* or *yajé-úco*; and Schultes documented the use of leaves of this liana as an *ayahuasca* admixture by the

Mocoa Indians of Colombia, to enhance the visionary effects of their potions (Cuatrecasas 1965; Harner 1973B; Reichel-Dolmatoff 1972; Reichel-Dolmatoff 1975; Schultes 1957A). Siona and Secoya Indians of Ecuador also employ *D. cabrerana* leaves as an *ayahuasca* admixture (Vickers & Plowman 1984). Previously considered to be another species of *caapi*, the β-carboline-containing primary ingredient of the potion, chemical analysis of *Diplopterys cabrerana* leaves in 1965 showed no β-carbolines, but high concentrations of *N,N*-DiMethylTryptamine or DMT, discussed in detail in Chapter 3 (Poisson 1965). Subsequent research verified this finding (Der Marderosian *et al.* 1968) and trace amounts of *N*-Mono-MethylTryptamine (MMT), 5-Methoxy-*N,N*-DiMethylTryptamine (5-MeO-DMT) and 5-Hydroxy-*N,N*-DiMethylTryptamine (5-OH-DMT or bufotenine) were also found in leaves of *D. cabrerana* (Agurell *et al.* 1968B). Trace amounts of *N*-methyl-tetrahydro-β-carboline were also detected in *D. cabrerana* leaves (Agurell *et al.* 1968A). The pharmacognosy of these other tryptamines was also discussed in the preceding chapter. Recent analysis of a single specimen of *D. cabrerana* leaf used as an *ayahuasca* admixture in Perú (where such use is rather uncommon, being much more common to the north and east, in Amazonian Ecuador and Colombia) found 1.74 mg DMT *per* gram of dried leaves (0.17%) together with "extremely trace amounts" of 5-OH-DMT or bufotenine (McKenna *et al.* 1984A). The pharmacological consequences of the use of *D. cabrerana* leaves in *ayahuasca* will be discussed below. Schultes reported that a related species, *Diplopterys involuta* (=*Mezia includens*; Gates 1982), is known in Perú as *ayahuasca negro*, suggesting its use as an additive to *ayahuasca*, 'though there have been no reports of this, nor of the chemistry of this liana (Schultes 1983B). Ash of burned leaves of another species, *D. martiusii*, were formerly used by Kubeo Indians of the Colombian Vaupés as an additive to powdered *coca* leaves (*Erythroxylum coca* var. *ipadú*; Schultes & Raffauf 1990). *Mascagnia psilophylla* var. *antifebrilis* (=*Callaeum antifebrile*; *Cabi paraensis*), once reported as a variant type of *ayahuasca* (Schultes & Raffauf 1990) has recently been cited rather as another *ayahuasca* admixture plant (Luna & Amaringo 1991).

The most common *ayahuasca* admixture plant in use in Amazonian Perú, also used in Amazonian Ecuador and Brasil, is *Psychotria viridis*, in the Rubiaceae or coffee family (Schultes & Hofmann 1980). Known as *chacruna* in Perú, and *sami ruca* (Kohn 1992) or *amirucapanga* in Ecuador (Miller 1993), like *Diplopterys cabrerana*, the leaves of this shrub are added to *ayahuasca* to strengthen its visionary potency (Kensinger 1973; Prance 1970; Prance & Prance 1970; Prance *et al.* 1977; Schultes 1969B; Weiss 1973). As in the case with *D. cabrerana*, DMT was found to be the main active ingredient in *P. viridis* leaves (Der Marderosian *et al.* 1970). From

0.16–0.22% DMT was also found in leaves of the Cashinahua *ayahuasca* admixture *nai kawa*, an unidentified species of *Psychotria* (Der Marderosian *et al.* 1970). Subsequent analyses by Rivier and Lindgren confirmed these findings, and small amounts of MMT and the β-carboline 2-Methyl-TetraHydro-β-Carboline (MTHC) were also detected in *P. viridis* (Rivier & Lindgren 1972). Recent analyses of three samples of *P. viridis* leaves from Perú found DMT to be the major alkaloid, present at the level of 1.02–1.58 mg *per* gram of dried leaves (0.10–0.16%), or slightly lower levels than were found in *D. cabrerana* (McKenna *et al.* 1984A). No other alkaloids were detected, with the exception of a trace amount of MTHC in one specimen. Sometimes a related species, *Psychotria carthaginensis*, is used in place of *P. viridis* as an *ayahuasca* additive, and two uncharacterized species of *Psychotria* known as *batsikawa* and *pishikawa* are so used by the Peruvian Sharanahua (Rivier & Lindgren 1972; Schultes & Raffauf 1990). Cashinahua Indians reportedly used two unidentified *Psychotria* species, one of which, *matsi kawa*, was devoid of alkaloids, and doubtless corresponds to the Sharanahua *batsikawa*, said to be inferior (Der Marderosian *et al.* 1970). Although Rivier and Lindgren detected DMT (in higher quantities than they found in *P. viridis*, together with traces of MMT and MTHC) in a sample of *P. carthaginensis* (Rivier & Lindgren 1972), the McKenna group failed to replicate this finding with a single sample of *yagé-chacruna* from Tarapoto, Perú, which was "tentatively" (or with some reservations) identified as *P. carthaginensis* (McKenna *et al.* 1984A). *Psychotria psychotriaefolia* has also been reported as an *ayahuasca* additive in Colombia and Ecuador (Pinkley 1969; Schultes 1969A; Schultes 1969B) and has been found to contain DMT (Der Marderosian *et al.* 1970; Der Marderosian *et al.* 1969—oral paper cited in Prance 1970). Schultes recently characterized the report of *P. psychotriaefolia* as an herbarium error (Schultes 1986B) and in their paper reporting DMT in leaves of this species, the Der Marderosian group concluded that the plant was later correctly identified as *P. viridis* (Der Marderosian *et al.* 1970). Other species of *Psychotria* are used ethnomedicinally, for example the Polynesian species *Psychotria insularum* (Cox 1991; Whistler 1992), shown to be active in pharmacological screening (Cox *et al.* 1989). Another related Polynesian species *P. forsteriana* has been shown to contain polyindoline alkaloids of the psychotridine type also found in *P. beccaroides* and *P. oleoides* (Roth *et al.* 1985). These alkaloids have pharmacological activity (Beretz *et al.* 1985). The West Sumatran species *Psychotria expansa, P. hirta* and *P. rostrata* were all shown to contain alkaloids (Arbain *et al.* 1989). The African species *P. rufipilis* is also used ethnomedicinally, in Sierra Leone—a decoction of leaves is said to cause movement of the fetus for detection of pregnancy (MacFoy & Sama 1983). The careful reader will recall that in 1957

Hochstein & Paradies reported the detection of DMT in *Prestonia amazonica* (=*Haemadictyon amazonicum*) or "*yajé*," the leaves of which were supposedly mixed with extracts of *Banisteriopsis caapi* by Ecuadorian Indians of the Río Napo area (Hochstein & Paradies 1957). Since DMT is unknown from the Apocynaceae (although, as we have seen above, the apocynaceous *Malouetia tamaquarina* is used as *ayahuasca* additive by the Makuna Indians of Colombia, as are three other apocynaceous species; see Table 3), and since *Prestonia amazonica* is unknown from the Río Napo area, it has been generally assumed that this report was in error as to botanical identification, and that either *Psychotria viridis* or *Diplopterys cabrerana*, both common *ayahuasca* admixture plants in the Río Napo area and both known to contain DMT, represents the plant actually analyzed by Hochstein and Paradies (Schultes & Raffauf 1960; Schultes & Raffauf 1990). Their report, in any case, is important, in that for the first time it associated DMT with an *ayahuasca* admixture. This underscores the importance of botanical voucher specimens[5] in phytochemical research. Since Hochstein and Paradies did not deposit voucher specimens (they apparently saw only an aqueous extract of the leaves and not the source plant itself), we today have no way of determining precisely what species was analyzed by them, and there is the possibility, however remote, that it was in fact *Prestonia amazonica* or some yet-unknown psychoactive species of Apocynaceae or of another family.

All told, then, there have been nearly 100 different plant species from 38 plant families reported as *ayahuasca* admixtures, of which about a fourth are known to be entheogenic plants (including several species of unknown chemistry from genera containing known entheogenic admixture plants, *viz. Diplopterys* and *Psychotria*). Many of these are potent entheogens often used alone, without *ayahuasca*. The remaining species are, with respect to entheogenic constituents, simply unknown chemically (with the exception of three known stimulants, the caffeine-containing *Ilex guayusa* and *Paullinia yoco*, and the cocaine-containing *Erythroxylum coca* var. *ipadú*) and may in the future be found to be entheogenic plants. Many indigenous groups are known to have employed various *ayahuasca* additives, such as the Shuar, who have been reported to use four different entheogenic additives to *ayahuasca* brews: *Diplopterys cabrerana* (Fericgla 1994A; Harner 1973B); *Brunfelsia* sp. (Schultes & Hofmann 1980); tobacco, *Nicotiana* spp. and *maikoa* or *Brugmansia* spp. (Schultes & Raffauf 1990; Wilbert 1987). The Sharanahua Indians of eastern Perú have been reported to have used no fewer than nine *ayahuasca* admixtures, including the well-known entheogens *Psychotria viridis* and two yet-unidentified species of *Psychotria* (Schultes & Raffauf 1990; Siskind 1973) as well as *Brugmansia suaveolens* (Schultes

& Raffauf 1990); and five plants of obscure chemistry: the fern *Lygodium venustum*; two cacti, *Epiphyllum* sp. and *Opuntia* sp. (the latter cultivated by the Sharanahua who consider it to be entheogenic); and species of *Clusia* and *Cyperus* (Schultes & Raffauf 1990). Eleven *ayahuasca* admixtures—*Alternanthera* sp., *Brugmansia versicolor*, *Calathea* sp., *Calycophyllum spruceanum*, *Cyperus* sp., *Himatanthus sucuuba*, *Mansoa alliacea*, *Ocimum micranthum*, *Petiveria alliacea*, *Psychotria poeppigiana* and *Scoparia dulcis*—are garden plants in Amazonian Perú (Padoch & De Jong 1991).

There is no doubt that some of the admixture plants are used to enhance the entheogenic potency of the *ayahuasca* brews. Certain of the admixtures, *viz. Brugmansia* spp., *Nicotiana* spp., *Psychotria viridis* and *Diplopterys cabrerana* are without question of greater visionary potency than the *ayahuasca* plant itself, *Banisteriopsis caapi*. I had a series of three different *ayahuasca* potions prepared for me by Quijos Quichua *ayahuasqueros*. EXPERIMENT 1, which consisted of *Banisteriopsis caapi* with a small amount of *Ilex guayusa* leaves (which contain caffeine, see above), produced mainly a dreamy sedation with no visions or related visionary effects. EXPERIMENT 2, with a minute amount of leaves of *Psychotria viridis* (about two to three leaves *per* dose) was virtually the same, but with a slight hint of threshold-level entheogenic effects. EXPERIMENT 3, in which the potion contained about 50 leaves of *Psychotria viridis per* dose, was potently psychoptic, producing vivid visions and synaesthesia. From my limited experience, I was left with the distinct impression that *ayahuasca* was a potentiator facilitating the oral activity of the DMT-rich *Psychotria viridis* leaves, which are not by themselves orally active (see Chapter 3). Based on self-experiments designed to recreate *ayahuasca* potions outside of Amazonia, T.K. McKenna settled on the ratio of 500 g *Banisteriopsis caapi* stem to 85 g *Psychotria viridis* leaves (fresh weight basis) to yield a dose which "would leave no one standing" (McKenna 1993), concluding also that the DMT-rich *Psychotria* leaves were the key ingredients for *ayahuasca* visions. McKenna had earlier reported that the typical ratio for *ayahuasca* potions in the vicinity of Pucallpa, Perú, was 2.5 parts *Banisteriopsis caapi* to 1 part *Psychotria viridis* (McKenna 1989B). The widespread pan-Amazonian use of potent entheogenic plants in *ayahuasca* potions suggests that the *ayahuasca* extract is normally used as a base for the administration of entheogens, rather than as an entheogenic plant in its own right. In this respect, the situation would be analogous to the use of *cacáhuatl*, aqueous cacao-based potions (made from *Theobroma cacao*) in México as vehicles for the administration of psilocybian mushrooms and other entheogens (see Chapter 5, Note 13; Ott 1985). As was the case with some of the Mexican additives to cacao potions, some of the *ayahuasca* additives may be strictly medicinal and non-psychoactive. On the other hand, the *aya-*

huasca plant is clearly psychoactive (mainly sedative, in my experience, and we must recall that the two second-hand reports of psychoactivity of *Peganum harmala* seeds mentioned specifically soporific and alcohol-like effects; Gunn 1937; Hassan 1967). I would describe the effects of unalloyed *ayahuasca*, or of harmine- and harmaline-containing infusions of *Peganum harmala* seeds as *Valium*-like, and indeed the β-carboline alkaloids are known to interact with benzodiazepine receptors in mammalian brains (Skolnick *et al.* 1982) although they have higher affinities for serotonine receptors (McKenna *et al.* 1990). Some indigenous groups have been reported to use plain *ayahuasca*, such as the Guahibo Indians Spruce observed chewing stems of the liana. However, the ubiquitous tobacco was likely being used in some form at the same time by the Guahibo. While the pharmacological interactions of the *ayahuasca* alkaloids with nicotine, cocaine and scopolamine (psychoactive agents found in tobacco, *coca* and *Brugmansia* species respectively) are largely obscure, some research has been done on the human pharmacology of the harmala alkaloids, and of the interactions of these β-carbolines from *Banisteriopsis caapi* with the tryptamines from *Psychotria viridis* and *Diplopterys cabrerana*, and it is to this subject that we will now turn.

CHEMISTRY OF *AYAHUASCA* AND PHARMACOLOGY OF *BETA*-CARBOLINES

Although harmine and harmaline had been isolated from *Peganum harmala* in the 1840s, the context of the research was a study of pigments, not of drugs, and it did not occur to the researchers to conduct pharmacological studies on the novel compounds. Only after Louis Lewin isolated banisterin(e) from *Banisteriopsis caapi* (Lewin 1928), and his colleagues Wolfes and Rumpf of the E. Merck company determined that banisterin(e) (as well as the previously-isolated telepathine and yajéine) was identical to harmine (Wolfes & Rumpf 1928), was the door opened to pharmacological investigation of the active compounds of *ayahuasca*, although French pharmacologist A. Rouhier (famous for his work on *péyotl*, see Chapter 1) conducted some early work on pharmacology of yajéine in animals (Rouhier 1924; Rouhier 1926). In his preliminary experiments, Lewin reported that 25–75 mg doses of harmine injected subcutaneously produced euphoria in human subjects (Lewin 1928). That same year, German pharmacologist and mescaline researcher (see Chapter 1) Kurt Beringer published a paper on his own preliminary research with Lewin's harmine (Beringer 1928). Two years later, German physician L. Halpern studied the properties of harmine as a therapy for Parkinsonism, and conducted self-experimentation with up to 40 mg ingested orally and up to 30 mg injected subcutaneously (Halpern 1930A; Halpern 1930B). Halpern found herself excited into belligerence, even starting a fight with a man in the street! Although claiming her consciousness was "in no way influenced and in no way abnormal," Halpern described her consciousness as "packed in ether" and described lightness and a "fleeting sensation" which she likened to sensations of "levitation frequently reported to occur with the crude drug *ayahuasca*" (Halpern 1930B). Use of harmine in 20 mg doses 4–6 times daily as a therapy for Parkinsonism was pioneered by K. Beringer and K. Wilmanns (1929). A decade later, A.G. Beer studied the pharmacology of harmine in cats, determining that it showed stimulatory effects in the central nervous system (Beer 1939A; Beer 1939B). Two more decades passed before the group of S. Udenfriend showed that harmine, harmaline and other β-carbolines were powerful, reversible inhibitors of an enzyme called MonoAmine Oxidase (MAO; Udenfriend *et al.* 1958). The enzyme MAO is widely distributed in vertebrate and invertebrate tissues, and important in this context is its function as an inactivator of normal neurotransmitter substances in brain tissues, such as dopamine and serotonine (see Chapter 3, Note 5). The following year, the group of A. Pletscher proposed that the psychotropic activity of the harmala alkaloids was due to their activity as MAO-inhibitors (Pletscher *et al.* 1959).

In a discussion of "schizophrenigenesis," W.J. Turner and S. Merlis (infamous for their unethical experiments with bufotenine on inmates of a New York mental hospital; see Chapter 3, especially Note 2), working with A. Carl, expressed their doubts that harmine was psychoactive (Turner *et al.* 1955). Nevertheless, H.H. Pennes and P.H. Hoch reported that intravenous injection of 150–200 mg of harmine into hapless "mental patients" produced "visual hallucinations" in 5 of 11 subjects, although the drug was "not hallucinogenic by the oral or subcutaneous routes" (Pennes & Hoch 1957). Indeed, these authors administered as much as 960 mg of harmine orally in a single dose (nearly 12 mg/kg), finding little activity, and negative side-effects such as nausea, tremors and numbness occurred above the threshold of 300–400 mg. Five years later, S. Gershon and W.J. Lang administered harmine to dogs, finding it caused restlessness and "apparent hallucinations" at doses of 2 mg/kg (Gershon & Lang 1962). One wonders how these researchers were able to learn of the poor dogs' hallucinations... in what way these were apparent.[6]

Probably the most complete study of the human pharmacology of the β-carbolines was that of C. Naranjo (Naranjo 1967). Naranjo found harmaline hydrochloride "to be hallucinogenic at dosage levels above 1 mg/kg i.v. or 4 mg/kg by mouth." He further found harmine to be about half as active, with a threshold of 8 mg/kg, and leptaflorine (racemic TetraHydroHarmine; *d,l*-THH) to be weaker still, with a threshold level of 12 mg/kg. Only 6-methoxy-harmalan was found to be a bit more potent, with a threshold of 2.7 mg/kg (Naranjo 1967). Naranjo chose to concentrate on harmaline, since it was the most potent of the natural compounds. However, all of Naranjo's 30 subjects could readily distinguish the harmaline from mescaline, based on its producing nausea and uncomfortable physical symptoms absent from mescaline sessions. Furthermore, harmaline did not produce the characteristic effects of mescaline and LSD involving distortions and alterations in the perception of the environment: "with harmaline, the environment is essentially unchanged." Unlike mescaline and LSD effects, the perception of music and the sense of time was unaltered in harmaline inebriation. Rather, "the typical reaction to harmaline is a closed-eye contemplation of vivid imagery... which is in contrast to the ecstatic heavens or dreadful hells of other hallucinogens." Harmaline was more of a "pure hallucinogen" in that it seemed to lack the profound emotional and sensual content of mescaline or LSD "trips," and seemed to exert rather a peripheral effect on the eye than a fundamental alteration in perception somewhere in the brain. Indeed, the direct action of harmaline on the retina was confirmed by recording electroretinograms in cats. While harmaline seemed to stimulate part of the "midbrain," its effect on the cerebral cortex was "hard to interpret and seems more that of a depressant..." (Naranjo 1967). Recently De Smet conducted two self-experiments with 0.5 mg/kg harmine free base, the first intranasally and the second orally. De Smet commented: "on neither occasion was a notable psychoactive or somatic effect felt" (De Smet 1985A). This report contrasted with an earlier experiment in which doses of 0.5 mg/kg harmine HCL injected intravenously resulted in transient subjective effects (Slotkin *et al.* 1970), and we will recall that C. Naranjo found harmine to be four times more active injected intravenously than ingested orally (Naranjo 1967). Recently European investigator M. Maurer characterized harmine as a mild sedative in low doses, causing "unpleasant vegetative and neurological symptoms" at doses above 300 mg (Leuner & Schlichting 1989).

Naranjo's characterization of harmaline as a CNS depressant is in keeping with the two vague reports of the effects of the harmaline- and harmine-containing seeds of *Peganum harmala*, said to be soporific, narcotic, and alcohol-like (Gunn 1937; Hassan 1967), and with the finding that β-carbolines interact with benzodiazepine receptors (Skolnick *et al.* 1982). Moreover, harmala-alkaloid-containing *Passiflora* species are used ethnomedicinally as sedatives and tranquilizers (Joyal 1987; Monardes 1990; Oga *et al.* 1984; Speroni & Minghetti 1988). However, some of the first-hand reports of *ayahuasca* effects stress the powerfully emotive, perception-altering effects characteristic of LSD and mescaline, hardly that detached contemplation alluded to by Naranjo (Flores & Lewis 1978). The ecstatic heavens and dreadful hells are definitely part of the psychic territory of *ayahuasca*. As one Indian informant said: "it is a fearsome thing, I was very much afraid" (Kensinger 1973). Part of the discrepancy derives from the fact that Naranjo's results came from experiments with harmaline, not harmine, and harmaline "is essentially a trace component in *ayahuasca*..." (McKenna *et al.* 1984A). The major difference, however, doubtless results from the common practice of adding other entheogenic plants to the *ayahuasca* potion—Kensinger's Cashinahua Indian informants had imbibed *ayahuasca* fortified with *Psychotria viridis* leaves.

After the Udenfriend group showed that harmaline and related β-carbolines were MAO-inhibitors, both the groups of W.M. McIsaac and V. Estévez, and N.S. Buckholtz and W.O. Boggan confirmed and extended this observation (Buckholtz & Boggan 1977; McIsaac & Estévez 1966). Besides harmine and harmaline, these groups found leptaflorine (which is racemic TetraHydroHarmine; *d,l*-tetrahydroharmine), harmol, harmalol, tetrahydroharmol, harman (passiflorine), norharman, tetrahydro-norharman, tetrahydroharman, 6-methoxy-tetrahydroharman, 6-hydroxy-tetrahydroharman, 6-methoxy-tetrahydro-β-carboline, 6-Methoxy-harmalan (or 6-MeO-harmalan) and 6-Methoxy-harman (or 6-MeO-harman) all to be potent reversible inhibitors of MAO (it will be recalled from Chapter 3 that the last two compounds are the principal alkaloids of *Virola cuspidata*; see Cassady *et al.* 1971), and later 2-Methyl-6-Methoxy-TetraHydro-β-Carboline (2-Me-6-MeO-THBC) was added to the list (McKenna *et al.* 1984A). On finding DMT in an *ayahuasca* admixture plant, *Diplopterys cabrerana*, the groups of A. Der Marderosian and S. Agurell suggested that DMT was an entheogenic principle of these *ayahuasca* brews, and that this orally-inactive compound (see Chapter 3) was rendered orally-active by the MAO-inhibiting effects of the β-carbolines from *Banisteriopsis caapi* (Agurell *et al.* 1968B; Der Marderosian *et al.* 1968; Schultes 1972B), an idea earlier proposed by Holmstedt and Lindgren (1967) to explain the activity of entheogenic snuffs. A similar mechanism was later suggested for the orally-ingested pastes or pellets of *Virola* resin (see Chapter 3; Schultes 1969B; Schultes & Swain 1976; Schultes *et al.* 1977A). This theory would explain why the Indians added DMT-containing plants to *ayahuasca*, and account for the similarity of the *ayahuasca* brews containing DMT to entheogens like mescaline and LSD, with their beatific heavens and terrific hells.

Sixteen years were to pass, however, before this theory was put to the test. The Canadian group of D.J. McKenna measured the MAO-inhibition of two Peruvian *ayahuasca* samples in a rat liver preparation, and found both to be "extremely effective" as MAO-inhibitors, as was an "*ayahuasca* analogue," a mixture of harmine (69%), leptaflorine or THH (26%; presumably the racemate) and harmaline (4.6%) mimicking the proportions found in the Peruvian *ayahuasca* samples (McKenna *et al.* 1984A). Theoretically, then, the MAO-inhibition of a typical *ayahuasca* potion could render any contained DMT (or other tryptamines) orally-active. The question remained, however... did this happen? The only way to know for certain would be for human subjects to ingest known amounts of β-carbolines with DMT to gauge the effects. To my knowledge, the first such experiment was reported by American J. Bigwood who, after finding an oral dose of 100 mg of harmaline hydrochloride to be inactive, ingested a capsule containing 100 mg harmaline hydrochloride together with 100 mg DMT free-base. Bigwood reported the first effects in 15 minutes, leading to a peak after 45 minutes with "DMT-like hallucinations" that "gradually tapered off" and had disappeared 4 hours after ingestion. Bigwood concluded: "in short, the experience was very similar to, in both time course and effect, that of a DMT- and harmaline-containing *ayahuasca* brew that I had previously experimented with" (Bigwood 1978; cited in Stafford 1983). This would seem to clinch the argument, except for the fact that, as McKenna pointed out, harmaline is a trace constituent in *ayahuasca* and "probably does not contribute significantly to the MAO-inhibition which the drug elicits." Moreover, harmaline is "slightly stronger" as an MAO-inhibitor than is harmine (McKenna *et al.* 1984A). While it may be splitting hairs, there is the necessity of doing further experiments using amounts of DMT and β-carbolines (ideally, McKenna's mix of harmine, THH and harmaline in the proportions found in *ayahuasca* potions) commensurate with quantities found in typical *ayahuasca* brews, then comparing the effects of the DMT/β-carboline mixture with the effects of the *ayahuasca* they mimic (see Ott 1994A for details of such research).

Which brings us to the question of quantitative analyses of the alkaloids present in *ayahuasca* potions... thus far, there have been only four published studies with quantitative analyses of alkaloids in *ayahuasca* potions. A preliminary and incomplete study of a single sample of *ayahuasca* (which had been kept at least two years unrefrigerated prior to analysis) prepared by the Amazonian Cashinahua Indians will be discussed below (Der Marderosian *et al.* 1970). L. Rivier and J.-E. Lindgren obtained nine samples of *ayahuasca* as prepared by Sharanahua and Culina Indians of the upper Río Purús in Perú, and submitted these to a quantitative assay using the technique known as Gas Chromatograpy/Mass Spectrometry (GC/MS). They found that a typical, 200 ml dose of *ayahuasca* prepared with DMT-containing leaves of *Psychotria viridis*, contained a total of only 65 mg of alkaloids, of which nearly half, 30 mg, was harmine, with 25 mg of DMT and 10 mg *d*-leptaflorine or THH (Rivier &

Lindgren 1972). The 40 mg of β-carbolines in a dose is about an order of magnitude below the psychoactive dosage of these compounds following their oral ingestion. While 25 mg of DMT is active when vaporized, this quantity is below the threshold for injected DMT. Up to a gram of DMT has been ingested orally without any effect in the absence of MAO-inhibitors (see Chapter 3). One recently-reported analysis of a *daime* sample (*ayahuasca* prepared from *Banisteriopsis caapi* and *Psychotria viridis* by members of a Christian church in South America who use the potion as a sacrament; see below) found 26.5 mg DMT plus 74.5 mg harmine and 69.5 mg *d*-leptaflorine or THH in a 50 ml dose (Liwszyc *et al.* 1992). Only traces of harmaline were found. While the *daime* contained quantities of DMT similar to those found by Rivier and Lindgren in Río Purús *ayahuasca*, in contrast to the 40 mg β-carbolines *per* dose in the Río Purús samples, the *daime* contained 144 mg β-carbolines *per* dose, with approximately equal amounts of harmine and THH. Subsequent to the report of Rivier and Lindgren, the Canadian group of D.J. McKenna studied eight *ayahuasca* samples obtained from *ayahuasqueros* around Pucallpa, Iquitos and Tarapoto, Perú, all but one prepared using the *Psychotria viridis* admixture. Thin-layer chromatographic analysis of the eight samples found harmine, *d*-leptaflorine (THH), harmol and harmaline to be present in all samples, while harmalol was found in only one sample (McKenna *et al.* 1984A). DMT was found in all samples save the one which did not contain *Psychotria viridis*. That sample contained instead *P. carthaginensis*, and analysis of the source plant showed it to be devoid of alkaloids. Five undiluted *ayahuasca* samples from Pucallpa were submitted to quantitative analysis using High-Pressure Liquid Chromatography (HPLC). Averaging the five samples, McKenna's group found the *ayahuasca* to contain 7.3 mg of total alkaloids *per* milliliter (0.73%), with the following distribution: harmine 4.7 mg/ml; *d*-leptaflorine (THH) 1.6 mg/ml; harmaline 0.4 mg/ml; and DMT 0.6 mg/ml. This would break down to the following proportions: harmine 65%; *d*-leptaflorine (THH) 22%; harmaline 6% and DMT 8%. These researchers reported that a typical dose of Pucallpa *ayahuasca* rarely exceeded 75 ml, and was more commonly 55–60 ml. A 60 ml dose, then, would contain 437 mg of total alkaloids, including 280 mg harmine, 96 mg *d*-leptaflorine (THH), 25 mg harmaline, and 36 mg DMT (McKenna *et al.* 1984A). This corresponds to ten times the quantity of β-carbolines *per* dose, as compared to Rivier & Lindgren's report (401 mg : 40 mg), nearly three times the β-carboline content of the *daime* sample analyzed by Liwszyc's group (401 mg : 144 mg) and almost half again as much DMT as reported in the other studies (36 mg : 25 mg or 26.5 mg). The difference in part can be explained by the fact that in Pucallpa the extract was typically boiled for 10–15 hours and concentrated considerably before ingestion. In contrast, the Río Purús *ayahuasqueros* boiled the extract only one hour and did not concentrate it. This may explain the discrepancy in β-carboline levels, but why is the resulting DMT content so similar? Evidently, the Río Purús *ayahuasqueros* used relatively more *Psychotria viridis* or a more potent strain of this admixture. In addition, these results may suggest that, while DMT may efficiently be extracted in 1 hour, extraction of the β-carboline alkaloids might require substantially more boiling time.

A more provocative interpretation of the discrepancy in the results of these two studies is that the 40 mg of β-carbolines contained in the average Río Purús potion *is sufficient to render orally-active the 25 mg of* DMT *present.* The obvious corollary to this is the observation that the Río Purús *ayahuasqueros* were, in fact, *seeking the effect of the* DMT *in the potion, and extracted only enough of the β-carbolines to render the* DMT *orally-active.* It will be recalled that, in the first human experiment on record, Bigwood found 100 mg of harmaline itself to be inactive, but sufficient to render a corresponding amount of DMT orally-active in a subsequent experiment. Indeed, even the tenfold excess of β-carbolines in the Pucallpa potions would seem to be of little pharmacological consequence, apart from its role as an MAO-inhibitor. We must recall that Naranjo found the oral threshold level for harmine effects to be 8 mg/kg, and for leptaflorine (racemic THH) to be 12 mg/kg. The threshold for harmaline effects was lower, 4 mg/kg. Assuming an average body weight of 70 kg, a threshold dose would thus represent 560 mg of harmine, 840 mg of leptaflorine (racemic THH), or 280 mg of harmaline. Even with 401 mg of β-carbolines in a dose of *ayahuasca*, and assuming additive effects (since the MAO-inhibiting effects of the β-carbolines are additive; McKenna *et al.* 1984A), a simple calculation shows the likelihood that this quantity would still be sub-threshold. The 280 mg of harmine would represent exactly 50% of a threshold dose of that compound, while the 96 mg of *d*-leptaflorine (THH) corresponds to 11% of threshold (although Naranjo's results were based on racemic leptaflorine, it is unknown whether the *d*-leptaflorine present in *ayahuasca* is of greater activity) and the 25 mg of harmaline to only 9% of threshold. This adds up to a dose of β-carbolines representing, at best, only 70% of a threshold dose for psychoactive effects, and we must recall that Pennes and Hoch (1957) found oral harmine to be "not hallucinogenic" up to a 960 mg dose. Clearly, DMT is where the action would be in these three sets of *ayahuasca* samples submitted to quantitative analysis. Even 'though the β-carbolines may have weak psychotropic effects in their own right, there is no evidence that they are present in "hallucinogenic" amounts in the *ayahuasca* potions studied thus far, 'though of course they may contribute sedative effects. In a recent book, L.E. Luna and P.

Amaringo reached the same conclusion: "the alkaloid responsible for the psychoactivity of the brew was most probably dimethyltryptamine, the alkaloids in *Banisteriopsis caapi* not being a large enough dose to elicit hallucinations" (Luna & Amaringo 1991). McKenna, Luna and Towers had commented: "DMT... is probably responsible for the hallucinogenic effects of *ayahuasca*" (McKenna *et al.* 1986). In the case of DMT, we know it to be orally active at a 100 mg dose in the presence of 100 mg of harmaline. Based on the results of McKenna's group, plus those of Liwszyc's group and Rivier and Lindgren, we can postulate that DMT is also orally-active in the range of 25–36 mg, and as little as 40 mg of β-carbolines may suffice to render it so. The next experiment would be to ingest, say, 30 mg of DMT along with 40 mg of McKenna's "*ayahuasca* analogue" (which would be, in this case, 28 mg harmine, 10 mg *d*-leptaflorine and 2 mg harmaline), to verify whether this mixture is, indeed, active (see section "Use of Harmel, *Ayahuasca* and Analogues" below for the results of such *pharmahuasca* self-experiments; detailed more completely in Ott 1994A).

The above-mentioned preliminary report by the Der Marderosian group found 30 mg of DMT in a typical 8 ounce (240 ml) dose of *ayahuasca* prepared by Peruvian Cashinahua Indians, together with only 20 mg "of harmine or harmaline" (Der Marderosian *et al.* 1970). The drink, called *nixi pae* (steeped only 1 hour), was prepared from *Banisteriopsis caapi* stems and leaves, with buds of two unidentified *Psychotria* species called *nai kawa* and *matsi kawa*, of which the latter was devoid of alkaloids. The former (said to be possibly *P. carthaginensis*, *P. alba*, *P. marginata* or *P. horizontalis*) contained 0.16–0.22% DMT in the leaves. There are several problems with this study, which led me to discard it in my analysis of *ayahuasca* pharmacology. Not only is the botanical identity of the *Psychotria* admixture unknown, but the resulting potion was kept for "at least two years" unrefrigerated before analysis. Furthermore, the authors did not analyze the content of *d*-leptaflorine (THH), subsequently found to represent 20–50% of the β-carboline fraction of other *ayahuasca* samples studied (Liwszyc *et al.* 1992; McKenna *et al* 1984A; Rivier & Lindgren 1972). This may explain the unusually low content of β-carbolines reported, which would appear to be sub-threshold levels for pharmacological activity. Finally, although the authors reported about 50% more harmaline than harmine in the aged *nixi pae* sample, they later mentioned being able to isolate and crystallize DMT and *harmine* from the potion. It is likely that harmaline would have crystallized rather than harmine, had the former in fact been present in higher amounts (since both have similar solubilities and other chemical properties).

While it is true that there are reports of *ayahuasca* brews containing only *Banisteriopsis caapi*, we haven't any reports on quantitative analysis of a typical dose. It seems obvious that a "hallucinogenic" dose of a DMT-less *ayahuasca* would have to contain at least half again as much β-carbolines as found by McKenna's group, and perhaps twice the amount. As McKenna's group reported, for hallucinogenic activity of a DMT-less *ayahuasca*: "concentrations of β-carbolines considerably greater than those measured in our samples would be required..." (McKenna *et al.* 1984A). This theory of *ayahuasca* as DMT-activator would go a long way toward explaining the widespread use of psychotropic admixture plants in the potions. It would explain my three experiences in Ecuador, in which *ayahuasca* with *guayusa* leaves or with a small amount of *Psychotria viridis* leaves acted only as a mild sedative, whereas a full-blown psychoptic experience resulted when a substantial amount of the DMT-containing leaves were added. Moreover, the results of quantitative analyses of *ayahuasca* brews cast considerable doubts on Flattery's attempt to deduce the effects of the DMT-less *Peganum harmala* from reports of DMT-enriched *Banisteriopsis caapi* potions in Amazonia (Flattery & Schwartz 1989; see Note 3). Finally, it would fit in well with the obvious fact that the South American Indians *like* tryptamines—they have found and use these in other plant forms, such as *Anadenanthera* and *Virola* snuffs and potions prepared from the roots of *Mimosa* species (see Chapter 3). In this context, it is also worth noting that the artificial DMT homologue, DiEthylTryptamine (DET, see Chapter 3) has itself been shown in high doses to be an MAO-inhibitor like the β-carbolines (Satory *et al.* 1961), and a number of other tryptamines have been shown to be MAO-inhibitors (including DMT, 5-MeO-DMT, psilocybine and psilocine; McKenna *et al.* 1984B). Furthermore, the psychoactive nutmeg compound myristicin is known to be an MAO-inhibitor (see Chapter 1; Truitt *et al.* 1963). Several myristicaceous plants, including species of *Iryanthera* and *Virola*, some of which contain tryptamines, are used by the Witoto and Bora in preparation of orally-active entheogenic pastes (see Chapter 3). Since these pastes were not found to contain the β-carbolines (McKenna *et al.* 1984B), it might make sense to look for myristicin and allied compounds in the pastes as prospective MAO-inhibitors, although McKenna's group found the MAO-inhibition of such pastes to be explainable by the weak MAO-inhibitory activity of their constituent tryptamines (McKenna & Towers 1984; McKenna *et al.* 1984B).

MODERN INTEREST IN *AYAHUASCA* AND *HARMEL*

As the ancient *ayahuasca* potion slowly yielded its secrets to the probings of modern chemistry and pharmacology, the drug began to insinuate itself ever more into modern consciousness. The American writer W.S. Burroughs concluded his first, autobiographical, book *Junk* (originally published as *Junkie: Confessions of an Unredeemed Drug Addict*; Lee 1953) with a chapter on *péyotl* or peyote, "a new kick in the states." Burroughs ended the book discussing *ayahuasca*: "I read about a drug called *yage*, used by Indians in the headwaters of the Amazon. *Yage* is supposed to increase telepathic sensitivity... I decided to go down to Colombia and score for *yage*... Maybe I will find in *yage* what I was looking for in junk and weed and coke. *Yage* may be the final fix" (Lee 1953). Making good his word, during January of 1953, Burroughs went to Colombia in search of what he had wryly called his "final fix," and by April had found a "*brujo*" in the Putumayo region to prepare the potion for him, complete "with a double handful of leaves from another plant" which Burroughs identified as "*ololiqui*." Burroughs had an attack of "violent, sudden nausea" and "blue flashes" in front of his eyes. He also experimented with *ayahuasca* prepared "Vaupés method"—a cold-water infusion of the inner bark with no admixtures—and reported "the effect was similar to weed." He returned to Bogotá with a crate of vine stems and made some experiments on extracts of the vine, which had a soporific effect (Burroughs & Ginsberg 1963).

A decade later, Burroughs and American poet A. Ginsberg published *The Yage Letters*, consisting of Burroughs' letters to Ginsberg from Colombia in 1953, and Ginsberg's letter to Burroughs from Perú in 1960, describing his own *ayahuasca* experiences in Pucallpa, during which: "the whole fucking Cosmos broke loose around me, I think the strongest and worst I've ever had it..." (Burroughs & Ginsberg 1963). Despite the negative tone of the experiences inelegantly reported (Ginerg appended a drawing of a hideous being called "The Vomiter"), nevertheless this book made the hitherto obscure South American *ayahuasca* potion famous in the United States and elsewhere. The legal battle surrounding the American publication of Burroughs' second novel *The Naked Lunch* (Burroughs 1959; excerpts were published in the *Chicago Review* in 1958 and the number was suppressed, leading to the resignation of the editorial staff; there was later a state Supreme Court battle in Massachusetts over the book) had become a *cause célèbre*, catapulting Burroughs to fame and drawing attention to the slim volume on *ayahuasca*. References to the drug were also found throughout the widely-read *The Naked Lunch*, as well as in Burroughs' subsequent books *The Soft Machine, The Ticket that Exploded, Dead Fingers Talk, Nova Express* and *Exterminator!* (Burroughs 1959; Burroughs 1961; Burroughs 1962; Burroughs 1963; Burroughs 1964; Burroughs 1966) .

In his first book, Burroughs had mentioned casually that: "*yage* is supposed to increase telepathic sensitivity. A Columbian scientist isolated from *yage* a drug he called *telepathine*" (Lee 1953; referring to Fischer Cárdenas' isolation of *telepatina* or harmine in 1923). This comment of Burroughs' about a rather fanciful exercise in nomenclature was to inform modern consciousness on the properties of *yajé* or *ayahuasca*, contributing to what A. Weil called "a considerable mythology of *yagé*" (Weil 1980), to "extravagant and unfounded claims concerning the powers of the drink, especially in regard to its 'telepathic' properties," as Schultes and Hofmann commented (Schultes & Hofmann 1980). It is difficult to conjecture why telepathy came to be particularly associated with *ayahuasca*, for, as Weil pointed out, telepathy is often associated with entheogenic plants, such as *péyotl* in North America. In his comprehensive study of entheogen use by Colombian Indians, G. Reichel-Dolmatoff had commented:

> The idea that *yajé* has telepathic powers has, of course, fascinated the credulous. Zerda Bayón, who traveled among the Indians of the upper Putumayo River in 1935, declares that *yajé* produces visions in which the person develops telepathic faculties. García Barriga mentions this traveler and writes: "Savage Indians who have never left their forests and who, of course, can have no idea of civilized life, describe, in their particular language, and with more or less precision, the details of houses, castles, and cities peopled by multitudes." The fact is that even fairly isolated Indians know a great deal about "civilized" life, having been told of its marvels by missionaries, soldiers, rubber collectors, traders and travelers, and having seen pictures in calendars and illustrated journals. (García Barriga 1958; Reichel-Dolmatoff 1975; Zerda Bayón 1915).

C. Naranjo has reported that city dwellers given harmaline frequently report seeing felines and jungle imagery (Naranjo 1967; Naranjo 1973A; Naranjo 1973B; Naranjo 1987), suggesting that the spirit of the jungle could be present even in synthetic harmaline (or that suggestion or coaching was at work)! Of course, as McKenna and colleagues have pointed out, harmaline is not even of pharmacological significance in *ayahuasca* potions (McKenna *et al.* 1984A), and Shulgin and Shulgin recount an amusing anecdote in which C. Naranjo, apparently not knowing with whom he was speaking, asked R.E. Schultes what he thought of the jaguars in the *ayahuasca* visions. Naranjo was disappointed to learn that Schultes, who by then had had considerable personal experience of the effects of *ayahuasca*, had never seen the jaguars, "only wiggly lines" (Shulgin & Shulgin 1991). So firmly rooted is this *ayahuasca* association, that Weil recounted an anecdote in which a Haight-Ashbury pharmacopolist in 1967 alleged that Eskimos had been given *ayahuasca* experimentally, experiencing visions of huge house cats (Weil 1980)! I might mention that Weil, Schultes, Shulgin and Naranjo were in San Francisco in January 1967 to attend an extraordinary conference organized by the U.S. Government's National Institute of Mental Health to help coordinate the *Ethnopharmacologic Search for Psychoactive Drugs* (Schultes 1966), title of the published proceedings, which contained a section on *ayahuasca* (Efron *et al.* 1967).[7]

The 1971 publication of *Wizard of the Upper Amazon* greatly expanded modern awareness of the existence of *ayahuasca* potions from Amazonia, and firmly cemented in modern consciousness the association of the drug with paranormal psychic events (Córdova-Ríos & Lamb 1971). It is worth examining the history of this book in some detail. In 1963, F.B. Lamb had sent a 30-page manuscript for review to R.L. Carneiro, an ethnographic expert on the Amahuaca Indians, the subject of Lamb's manuscript. Carneiro had studied the use of *ayahuasca* by the Amahuaca (Carneiro 1964; Carneiro 1970). Briefly, the manuscript detailed the life of one M. Córdova-Ríos, supposedly kidnapped as a boy by some Amahuaca Indians, then groomed by their chief to be a shaman and leader, learning the secrets of *ayahuasca* and other medicines (there was even a movie made, detailing just such a story, *The Emerald Forest*). On reviewing this, Carneiro told Lamb: "I thought it was an imaginative piece of jungle fiction and gave him very specific reasons for my views" (Carneiro 1980). Some years later, Natural History Press sent Carneiro, one of the few experts on the Amahuaca, "an expanded version" of the same paper, and since it was "no truer than the shorter, I advised the Press to reject it, which they did." Nevertheless, Lamb eventually persuaded Atheneum to publish the book in 1971, and after a 1974 reprint edition (Lamb 1974), Carneiro finally broke silence and explained why he was convinced the book was "jungle fiction," and more appropriately entitled *Chimera of the Upper Amazon* (Carneiro 1980). Carneiro explained:

> While I cannot categorically state that Córdova's adventure never happened, I find it extremely difficult to believe... Nothing in *Wizard of the Upper Amazon* convinces or even suggests to me that Manuel Córdova was ever captured by the Amahuaca, that he ever lived among them, or that he was ever groomed to be their chief, let alone actually serving in that capacity. The story Córdova told Bruce Lamb consists of fragmentary ethnographic tidbits gleaned

> indiscriminately from many tribes and encased in a matrix of personal fantasy.

While conceding that Córdova knew "a good deal about Amazonian hunting methods in general," Carneiro pointed out he knew "little or nothing about Amahuaca hunting methods in particular," emphasizing numerous incongruities in Córdova's tale. Córdova's story of the Amahuaca chief Xumu grooming him to be his successor was to Carneiro completely unbelievable, inasmuch as the Amahuaca don't even have chiefs! Nor do they live or dress as Córdova claimed, and they do not make or use *ambíl*, the "lickable" tobacco juice preparation carefully described by Córdova, which is known only among the Bora, Siona and Witoto Indians (Schultes 1945; Wilbert 1987). Indeed, Córdova appeared to have drawn his information from the Bora and Witoto of Northwest Amazonia: "the area Córdova knows best and from whose tribes he draws most of the traits he falsely assigns to the Amahuaca" (Carneiro 1980). Evidently Córdova chose to attribute his "jungle fiction" to the Amahuaca precisely because "they were so little known and he thought he could say anything he wished about them and no one would ever be the wiser" (Carneiro 1980). But Carneiro knew better, having studied among the Amahuaca, and finally the time came "to lift the mask of respectability and reveal the imposture" (Carneiro 1980). By this time, Córdova was dead, after enjoying considerable renown in his last years. When someone expressed too much awe at one of his tales, Córdova was quoted as saying: "Don't believe everything I tell you. It could all be a lie" (*No crean todo lo que les digo. Puede ser todo mentira*; Carneiro 1980). Nevertheless, Lamb challenged Carneiro's opinion (although he himself had originally sought it), claiming it was still possible to extract "ethnography" from Córdova's story (Lamb 1981A; Lamb 1981B).

But the damage had been done. Lamb's book gained broader attention when A. Weil referred to it in his best-selling first book *The Natural Mind—A New Way of Looking at Drugs and the Higher Consciousness* (Weil 1972). Weil, who had no reason to suspect the veracity of the book by Córdova-Ríos and Lamb, since Carneiro's *exposé* had still not appeared, accepted it at face value, as an ethnographic account of the Amahuaca and as valid ethnopharmacognostical accounts of the use of *ayahuasca* and "lickable" tobacco preparations. Indeed, Weil cited one of Córdova's accounts of an *ayahuasca* session in support of "The Reality of Shared Consciousness," characterizing the presumed Amahuaca ingestion of *ayahuasca* as: "group vision sessions in which all participants see the same visions," in this case visions of jungle cats, other animals, enemy tribes, and village scenes (Weil 1972; Weil 1974).

Indeed, Weil became so enthusiastic about this "reality of shared consciousness" that he recommended the book to his publisher for a paperback reprint, to which he wrote a laudatory introduction (Lamb 1974; Weil 1974), and the book was later reprinted by North Atlantic Books, categorized as "Ethnomedicine," replete with Weil's introduction and sponsorship of a "Society for the Study of Native Arts and Sciences," a non-profit educational organization. Moreover, this Society and North Atlantic Books brought out a sequel, *Río Tigre and Beyond* (Lamb 1985).

I do not wish to suggest that "telepathy" or "group vision sessions" are impossibilities, only that Córdova's account, being manifestly fictitious, or at least suspect of considerable embellishment, is by no means admissible as evidence of this (will we next hear of the pharmacodynamics of cocaine based on the experiences of Sherlock Holmes?). Even were we to consider as veridical (which we now would have no reason to do) Córdova's account of group visions as cited by Weil, this could be accepted as evidence of the "reality of shared consciousness" only by someone who already believed in this phenomenon. After all, even were he being truthful, how on earth could Córdova have known he and his "Amahuaca" companions were seeing precisely the same vision? Some years after promoting Lamb's book, Weil himself went to Colombia, "the land of *yagé*" to see if a Colombian Kamsá shaman "measures up" against Lamb's "untouched Amahuaca Indians." As so often is the case when reality confronts fantasy, Weil was disappointed. When he finally sampled *ayahuasca* (containing *chagropanga*, *Diplopterys cabrerana*, as well as *Brugmansia* and an unknown fourth ingredient), he was "sorry to say there were no jungles or jaguars" in his visions, "nor any telepathic news bulletins of distant events" (Weil 1979; Weil 1980). We will see in the final chapter how, when put to the test, the entheogenic "mushroom telegraph" failed to make telepathic connection between México and Maine in 1955 (see Chapter 6, Note 9). But by this time all the world "knew" that *ayahuasca* was a "telepathic" drug, and when the paperback edition of Lamb's book was reprinted with Weil's introduction, there was no mention of Carneiro's debunking of Córdova's "jungle fiction," and scant mention of Weil's failure to observe anything like telepathy or "shared consciousness" when he actually tried the drug. The whole situation is reminiscent of the Castaneda/Don Juan hoax (see Chapter 1 Note 9 and Chapter 5), except that Castaneda's books are now (finally) being catalogued by libraries as, and issued by the publisher under the rubric of, *fiction*, whereas the third printing of Lamb's *Wizard of the Upper Amazon* bears in red letters on the back cover the legend "Ethnomedicine/South American Indians." Moreover, there are two "blurbs" on the back cover; one by P. Marshall referring to "pleasant and important *communal* visions" (italics in the original), along with

Weil's "group vision sessions in which all participants see the same visions simultaneously." Surely Marshall is correct, in a sense he did not intend, that "this book is far superior to anything Castaneda has attempted"—after all, Castaneda's books have been relegated to the pulp fiction shelf, whereas Lamb continues to promote tall tales under the *imprimatur* of "Ethnomedicine"![8]

In 1970, Ecuadorian researcher P. Naranjo published the first full-length book on *ayahuasca*, *Ayahuasca: Religión y Medicina*, written in Spanish (Naranjo 1970) and later published in a revised edition (Naranjo 1983). Unfortunately, this excellent study has not been translated, and has thus had little impact beyond specialists in ethnopharmacology. In 1972 three books appeared which drew further attention to *ayahuasca*: M. Dobkin de Ríos' *The Visionary Vine* (Dobkin de Ríos 1972), W. Emboden's *Narcotic Plants* (Emboden 1972B) and P.T. Furst's *Flesh of the Gods* (Furst 1972). The first, together with three papers by Dobkin de Ríos (Dobkin de Ríos 1970A; Dobkin de Ríos 1970B; Dobkin de Ríos 1973), concentrated on the use of *ayahuasca* by mestizo curanderos on the outskirts of the Amazonian city of Iquitos, Perú. Furst's book, an anthology, contained a chapter by G. Reichel-Dolmatoff (Reichel-Dolmatoff 1972) describing the history, use and effects of *ayahuasca*. This anthology was widely read, and Reichel-Dolmatoff's concise but excellent review served to increase greatly public awareness of the existence and properties of the Amazonian *amrta*.

In 1973, C. Naranjo published *The Healing Journey*, an account of his use of entheogens, including harmaline, in psychotherapy (Naranjo 1973A), followed by a paper (Naranjo 1973B) in another anthology, *Hallucinogens and Shamanism*, edited by M. Harner (Harner 1973A). It is unfortunate that Naranjo's 1973 paper was entitled "Psychological Aspects of the *Yagé* Experience in an Experimental Setting," since it did not deal with the experimental use of *yajé* at all. Rather, it involved the experimental psychotherapeutic use of harmaline which, being a trace constituent of *ayahuasca* brews (Liwszyc *et al.* 1992; McKenna *et al.* 1984A; Rivier & Lindgren 1972), can in no way be described as "*yagé*." Naranjo's results with harmaline have little or no bearing on *ayahuasca* pharmacology, even leaving aside the important question of tryptamine and other additives to the potions. Once and for all, *harmaline is not* ayahuasca, *nor is it of importance in* ayahuasca *pharmacology* (*pace* Flattery; see Note 3 cited above)! Nevertheless, Harner's anthology was widely read, and no fewer than seven of the ten chapters pertain to *ayahuasca* and β-carbolines (Harner 1973A), including editor Harner's summary of his work among the Shuar (Harner 1973B) and his literature studies of *ayahuasca* (Harner 1973D). This book must have extended greatly the renown of the Amazonian entheogen in the English-speaking world. Harner had already published *The Jívaro: People of the Sacred Waterfalls* (Harner 1972), which dealt at some length with the use of *ayahuasca* by the Shuar Indians. G. Reichel-Dolmatoff's important book *The Shaman and the Jaguar* (Reichel-Dolmatoff 1975) appeared in 1975, and stands as one of the most complete reviews of the use of *ayahuasca* and other entheogens in northwest Amazonia. Mention must also be made of P.T. Furst's *Hallucinogens and Culture* (Furst 1976), and two other books by Reichel-Dolmatoff, *Amazonian Cosmos: The Sexual and Religious Symbolism of the Tukano Indians* (Reichel-Dolmatoff 1971), and *Beyond the Milky Way: Hallucinatory Imagery of the Tukano Indians* (Reichel-Dolmatoff 1978), which likewise made mention of *ayahuasca.*

We have already had occasion to note the importance of A. Weil's *The Natural Mind* (Weil 1972), and his second book *The Marriage of the Sun and Moon: A Quest for Unity in Consciousness* (Weil 1980), with its chapter "In the Land of *Yagé.*" These books, together with Weil's article in *High Times* (Weil 1979), have probably had more popular impact than any other writings on *ayahuasca.* A 1965 paper in *Psychedelic Review* (Kusel 1965) must likewise be credited with spreading the fame of *ayahuasca* beyond the Amazonian home of its constituent plants. There was also a 1970 report on a modern experiment with "yage" (Stafford 1970) which, as pointed out by the editors of the volume in which it appeared (Aaronson & Osmond 1970) "was probably not yage, but harmine or harmaline." Moreover, since the author started the "trip" by taking LSD and later smoked marijuana, the report was of little scientific value, although it did augment further the renown of the Amazonian entheogen. In the same volume (Aaronson & Osmond 1970), there was a brief review of *ayahuasca* effects as reported by anthropologists (Linzer 1970). Other earlier mentions of *ayahuasca* in popular literature were found in N. Taylor's *Narcotics: Nature's Dangerous Gifts* (Taylor 1966; paperback reprint of the 1949 *Flight from Reality*), R.S. De Ropp's *Drugs and the Mind* (De Ropp 1957), and M. Kreig's *Green Medicine: The Search for Plants that Heal...* (Kreig 1964). *Ayahuasca* was also briefly mentioned in S. Cohen's popular *The Beyond Within: The LSD Story* (Cohen 1964). There was also a chapter on *ayahuasca* in L. Lewin's classic 1924 treatise *Phantastica,* an American (and the second English-language) edition of which appeared in 1965, based on the 1926 expanded and definitive edition (Lewin 1924).

I would be remiss were I to neglect to mention in this context the obscure (but recently reprinted) book *The Invisible Landscape: Mind, Hallucinogens and the I Ching* (McKenna & McKenna 1975). Co-authored by *ayahuasca* researcher D.J. McKenna and his brother T.K. McKenna, this strange volume included the description of a sort of *ayahuasca* brew in which psilocybian mushrooms (*Psilocybe* [*Stro-*

pharia] *cubensis*) were used as a source of tryptamines in a potion the authors prepared, which precipitated a long-lasting trip characterized by one eyewitness as a "psychotic" reaction (McKenna 1993). One result was T.K. McKenna's launching in the foreword to *Psilocybin: Magic Mushroom Grower's Guide* of what co-author J. Bigwood was to call the "spores from outer space theory" (see Chapter 5; Oss & Oeric 1976). T.K. McKenna himself conceded in that foreword that the opinions expressed about *Psilocybe* [*Stropharia*] *cubensis* in the book were not scientific, and a recent book described the "spores from outer space" theory as being "in the realm of fantasy" (Gartz 1993). A bewildered professor of chemistry, on reading *The Invisible Landscape*, thought it was an academic joke, but co-author D.J. McKenna assured me "it was written in dead earnest." Nevertheless, in a foreword to the 1993 reprint, he admitted he was now "less willing to insist on the veracity of these concepts," some of which he called the "musings of a scientifically untutored student."

With the advent of the 1980s, the Reagan Dark Ages supervened, and there was little further publication of information on entheogens. Just before the door slammed shut, Schultes and Hofmann published a lovely "coffee-table book" on entheogens, *Plants of the Gods: Origins of Hallucinogenic Use* (Schultes & Hofmann 1979), complete with a chapter on the "Vine of the Soul" and portraits of *Banisteriopsis caapi* plus some of the prominent admixture plants. A. Weil and W. Rosen's *Chocolate to Morphine: Understanding Mind-Active Drugs* (Weil & Rosen 1983), which briefly mentioned *ayahuasca*, was a welcome exception to the reign of terror of the "just say no" (to information) Reagan administration. The same can be said for M. Dobkin de Ríos' *Hallucinogens: Cross-Cultural Perspectives* (Dobkin de Ríos 1984), which included information regarding *ayahuasca*. In 1987, M. Taussig published *Shamanism, Colonialism and the Wild Man* (Taussig 1987), a critique of colonialism and anthropology, which dealt at length with the shamanic use of *ayahuasca*. As Reagan gave way to his *protégé* Bush, Schultes published a magnificent collection of photographs of *Where the Gods Reign: Plants and Peoples of the Colombian Amazon* (Schultes 1988). This splendid book depicted *Banisteriopsis caapi*, *Diplopterys cabrerana* and other Amazonian drug plants, as well as a special ceramic *caapi* pot and a Makuna shaman dressed for the ceremonial use of the entheogenic potion, and was followed by a sequel dealing directly with *ayahuasca* and *ayahuasqueros*, *Vine of the Soul: Medicine Men, their Plants and Rituals in the Colombian Amazon* (Schultes & Raffauf 1992). In 1990, Schultes and chemist R.F. Raffauf published *The Healing Forest: Medicinal and Toxic Plants of the Northwest Amazonia* (Schultes & Raffauf 1990), a superb and encyclopaedic treatment of 1500 Northwest Amazonian medicinal plants, with photographs and botanical drawings of *Banisteriopsis caapi*, numerous admixture plants, and innumerable unique photographs of the preparation of *ayahuasca* and other entheogenic drugs. We have already had occasion to mention the 1989 publication of *Haoma and Harmaline* (Flattery & Schwartz 1989) which drew further attention to the β-carboline alkaloids and *ayahuasca*. In 1991 L.E. Luna and P. Amaringo published *Ayahuasca Visions: The Religious Iconography of a Peruvian Shaman,* a book devoted entirely to *ayahuasca* and the paintings of Peruvian *ayahuasquero* and co-author P. Amaringo, also featured in a recent article (Luna 1991; Luna & Amaringo 1991). P. Matthiessen's novel *At Play in the Fields of the Lord* described an *ayahuasca* experience (Matthiessen 1967) and was the subject of a 1992 film by the Brasilian director H. Babenco. This author's 1994 *Ayahuasca Analogues: Pangæan Entheogens* reviewed *ayahuasca* pharmacognosy (Ott 1994A).

All of the above-mentioned publications played their parts in expanding modern consciousness regarding the history and properties of *ayahuasca*. Running in parallel with the expansion of modern awareness of the wondrous potion from Amazonia, was broadened interest in shamanism (Wolf 1991) and an awareness of the necessity for rainforest conservation. In part owing to insights gained from entheogens, members of the American and European "counterculture" became increasingly aware of the ecological plight of our planet, and especially the destruction of tropical rainforests and their constituent organisms, plant and animal, including small and fragile tribes of preliterate humankind continuing their subsistence economies in Amazonia and elsewhere. Not only were rainforest habitats disappearing in Amazonia, but with them, plants like *Banisteriopsis caapi*, endemic to the Amazon basin, and many of its admixtures plants, together with countless other economic and unused species of plants (for the connection between ethnopharmacognosy and conservation groups, see King 1991; King 1992). Innumerable animal species, such as the jaguars of *ayahuasca* visions, who make their home in the Amazonian rainforest, were likewise disappearing. Just as important was the extermination of tribes of Amazonian Indians who suddenly, after five centuries of co-existence with European invaders, found themselves in the way of "development." Even where the physical survival of the tribes is not in question, the destruction of their cultures, and all the pharmacognostical and other knowledge these encase within a matrix of memory and oral transmission, represents an unimaginable tragedy, one repeated again and again throughout our pathetic history, down through the ages to this very day and right next door to every one of us (Huxtable 1992). The written word which enables us to communicate through the wondrous medium we call a book, such as you hold in your hands this minute, spanning perhaps millennia of time in the case of our most cherished books, or maybe just a few months or years in the present case, is the enemy of traditional knowledge, however diligently we might attempt to enshrine this wisdom also in books. As Gordon Wasson put it (Wasson 1980):

> I think the unlettered herbalists possessed a body of knowledge, commanding an infinity of empirical subtleties, that has escaped our botanists and anthropologists. In the prehistory of all cultures including those still existing, the herbalists are a repository of knowledge acquired through centuries of intensive observation and experience which they pass on from generation to generation by word of mouth from master to apprentice... These practitioners were hardly the ones to quicken with excitement and curiosity when the talk of the alphabet was abroad in the land. On the other hand those who took to the new-fangled writing were the aggressive intellectual leaders and scribes, including sometimes priests for their own reasons and some of the aristocracy, all of them beings from a different world, and the hidden knowledge of the herbalists would hardly have come their way, their corpus of knowledge not lending itself easily to writing.

How remarkable that the Age of Entheogens (Ott 1995B) lives on even today, in the most remote outposts of human habitation, although it can not and will not survive the onslaught of literacy! Again read Wasson, describing his astonishing lifting of the veil in México in 1955:

> I arrived in the same decade with the highway, the airplane, the alphabet. The Old Order was in danger of passing with no one to record its passing. The Old Order does not mix with the New. The wisdom of the Sabia, genuine though it was, has nothing to give to the world of tomorrow. I think it was ever so with the arrival of the alphabet. Now the young generation is intent on the new learning, wants to forget the mushrooms that only yesterday evoked their awe, chooses the young doctor from the medical school in the city in preference to the wise-woman, and is not learning or forgetting the language of his [*sic*] ancestors... Whether these trends are good or bad is not the question: they are inevitable. (Wasson 1980)

While I agree wholeheartedly with Wasson's vision, I dispute one particular: the Old Wisdom *does* have something to give to the world of tomorrow, and that priceless gift is the knowledge of entheogenic plants and their use. Encoded in the genes of entheogenic plants are instructions for the biosynthesis of molecules which open up to us the wonder and mystery inherent in the universe and in ourselves, ancient wisdom so readily outshone by the brilliant beacons of our modern knowledge; nevertheless residing in every human heart and soul, awaiting a chemical or other key for its unfurling.

It is the case that the use of *ayahuasca* potions, more so than any other entheogenic drug we know, has survived the onslaught of literacy and acculturation, to make a place for itself in the New Order. While there has been a modern resurgence of use of ancient entheogens like *péyotl* and *teonanácatl* (see Chapters 1 and 5 for their stories), *ayahuasca* had found its niche in the modern world long before it was "rediscovered" by the entheogenic subculture. I am referring to the fact that mestizo *ayahuasqueros*, after abandoning their jungle homes for the city, had continued to practice shamanic healing in urban areas of Perú, such as in Iquitos (Dobkin de Ríos 1970A; Dobkin de Ríos 1970B; Dobkin de Ríos 1972; Dobkin de Ríos 1973; Dobkin de Ríos 1992), and in Lima (Córdova-Ríos & Lamb 1971; Lamb 1985) and in the Colombian capital city of Bogotá (Ramírez de Jara & Pinzón C. 1986), even as their Indian relatives continued, in ever decreasing measure, to commune with *Sacha Runa* (the "jungle man") and other "plant spirits" (Luna 1991), in ever-diminishing islands of primary rainforest throughout Amazonia (Whitten 1976; Whitten 1985). Furthermore, despite nearly three decades of legal persecution of the entheogens (Chayet 1967; Horowitz 1991; Ott 1995B), neither the U.S. government nor the bulk of its Latin American counterparts, has yet seen fit to illegalize harmine and harmaline, alkaloids found in *Banisteriopsis caapi* (Sigma Chemical Co. 1996 prices *per* gram for the synthetic free-bases: harmine $50.00; harmaline $16.30; and $38.50 and $70.40 *per* gram for the respective hydrochloride salts of harmol and harmalol; all compounds sold for research and labeled "not for drug use"). Thus, although an *ayahuasca* potion containing the proscribed DMT might technically be illegal, the *Banisteriopsis* plant, its constituent alkaloids, plain *ayahuasca* potions, or those containing innumerable other additives, remain legal. In spite of anti-cocaine hysteria in South America (Antonil 1978; Boldó i Climent 1986; Morales 1989), and general anti-drug propaganda everywhere, *ayahuasca* continues to be used openly, with no stigma attached to it whatever, in Perú, Ecuador, Brasil and elsewhere!

Emblematic of the cultural niche for *ayahuasca* in the New Order is the Brasilian religious cult of *Santo Daime*. The roots of this modern cult, which has expanded with the 1961 founding of another *ayahuasca* church, *União do Vegetal* (UDV), can be traced back to the early 1900s (Henman 1986), particularly the founding in 1930 of a cult in Rio Branco, Brasil by Raimundo Irineu Serra, known to his disciples as Mestre Irineu (MacRae 1992). These Christian *ayahuasca* churches enjoy some legal dispensation in Brasil owing to two favorable governmental decisions (Henman 1986; MacRae 1992).[9] In the UDV iconography, the *ayahuasca* potion represents a union between light (DMT-containing *Psychotria viridis*) and power (MAO-inhibitors in *Banisteriopsis caapi*; Henman 1986). In 1970, ethnobotanist G. Prance had reported that there were latter-day *ayahuasca* cults around the Brasilian city of Rio Branco, capital of Acre state, in the Brasilian Amazon, just north of Bolivia and east of Perú. Prance mentioned that "in Rio Branco, there are several highly secret groups that meet to drink the narcotic [*sic*]," *ayahuasca*, which had "become a part of the Acre culture" (Prance 1970). Prance reported a similar phenomenon in Tarauaca, northwest of Rio Branco, and east of Pucallpa, Perú. By 1980, Rio Branco users had organized an open *ayahuasca* cult based on a Christian church. The *ayahuasca* potion, called by cult members *Santo Daime*, was prepared from "a mixture of approximately equal parts of an aqueous extract of the bark of *Banisteriopsis caapi* and the leaves of a rubiaceous plant, *Psychotria viridis*." The cult has expanded in South America to "countries whose native population never used the potion" and a recent analysis of a *daime* potion showed it to contain DMT and β-carbolines (Liwszyc *et al.* 1992). The approximately 250 members of the Rio Branco *Santo Daime* church cultivated the source plants "for the production of impressive quantities of the hallucinogen, which they consume during such celebrations as Christmas, All Saints Day, and the New Year," and ingestion of the resulting potion was said to be "one of the most significant influences in their lives (their 'raison d'être')." Large quantities of the potion (hundreds of liters) are stored on the premises of the church, and "the drink is freely dispensed on the occasions mentioned, as well as at other unspecified intervals. The congregation carries out their religious devotions in a church… built and decorated by its members, and it is here that they partake of their potion, women and children not being excluded from their ceremonies" (Lowy 1987). In keeping with its long history of religious intolerance ("freedom of religion" being little more than a propaganda line… in reality the U.S. Constitution merely separates Church from the *federal* State, reserving to the 50 states the right to discriminate with respect to religion, which they have historically done with great vigor; see E.A. Wasson 1914; E.A. Wasson 1965), the United States government reacted to attempts to establish the Church of *Santo Daime* in the United States by seizing supplies of *ayahuasca* and effectively proscribing the Church in the

U.S.! Nevertheless, as is always the case, law-enforcement efforts seved as the most effective advertising for *ayahuasca* possible, and people uninterested in rainforest conservation or ethnobotany were made aware of the existence of *ayahuasca* anyway. Meanwhile, the *ayahuasca* churches of UDV and *Santo Daime* have established themselves in many countries outside of South America (Luna 1992), are presently thriving in the United States, Spain and in other European countries, and individual *ayahuasqueros* are operating in México City and doubtless other cities far from the aboriginal home of the jungle *ambrosia* (Ott 1995B).

Rainforest conservation, riding on the coattails of modern interest in *ayahuasca* (and *vice versa*), has been a vehicle for the dissemination of the use of *ayahuasca* in the United States and other countries (see, for example, the Fall 1989 issue of *Whole Earth Review*, devoted to "The Alien Intelligence of Plants," with a special section on "Plants as Teachers"). As the decade of the 1970s gave way to the 1980s, the phenomenon of "nature tourism" or "ecotourism" came into being, including a specialized offshoot of "*ayahuasca* tourism." As early as 1980 a California group was promoting a "Shamans and Healers of Ecuador" tour at the rather steep price of $1790 plus airfare. Throughout the eighties and into the nineties, many people were introduced to *ayahuasca*, as well as to the Amazonian rainforest area, through special *ayahuasca* tours, costing as much as $3500! One tour group advertised no fewer than four shamanic tours in *Magical Blend Magazine*; "The Shaman's Journey" and "The Way of the Warrior" in Perú; "Visions of Power" in México and "The Healer's Journey" in Brasil (Ott 1994A; Ott 1995B). *Ayahuasca* tours were recently mentioned in *Newsweek* magazine (Krajick 1992).

By the end of the 1980s, *ayahuasca*, together with some typical admixture plants, was being cultivated in diverse parts of the United States, in greenhouses where necessary, for the preparation of *ayahuasca* potions. There exists at least one *Banisteriopsis* farm in the United States, and pre-mixed cocktails of *ayahuasca* plus *chacruna* (*Psychotria viridis*) are available sporadically on a rudimentary black market, selling for as much as $800 *per* dose! Finally, there has come into being, mainly in California, a small network of entheogenic therapists and guides, offering controlled, safe, guided introductions to the entheogenic experience. *Ayahuasca* has become one of the most popular substances for use in this informal sort of "psychotherapy," generally made with traditional ingredients, although analogues of Syrian rue and *Mimosa* root also are used, and mescaline, ibogaine, the artificial anesthetic ketamine (*Ketalar* or *Vetalar*), MDMA and other drugs may likewise be available to the client. Journalist J. Stevens, in the epilogue to his American social history of entheogenic drugs, *Storming Heaven* (Stevens 1987), described his fleeting contacts with the modern California entheogen scene, although in 1987 *ayahuasca* was not yet a hot topic, and rated nary a mention in the book, outside of describing the experiences of Burroughs and Ginsberg some three decades earlier. *Ayahuasca* therapy is also being practiced in the eastern United States (Krajick 1992).

Americans, ever on the lookout for innovations, particularly in an open and unregulated field such as the underground drug market, have put considerable effort into the creation of temperate-zone analogues of *ayahuasca*, that is, combinations of temperate-zone plants which will supply a source of DMT and a source of β-carbolines that, when combined, will yield *anahuasca* (Ott 1995B), a visionary potion similar to the decidedly tropical *ayahuasca*. Dennis McKenna has proposed the name *ayahuasca borealis* for temperate-zone *ayahuasca* analogues (D.J. McKenna 1992). The seeds of *Peganum harmala*, legally and cheaply available (a half-pound, containing from 4.5–16 grams of β-carboline alkaloids, can be had for $20–40) as a source of vegetable dyes, are the most widely-used source of harmine and related MAO-inhibiting β-carbolines (see Note 4 below for a list of plants containing MAO-inhibitors; and Ott 1994A for a list of tryptamine-containing plants). Not only are the seeds an article of commerce, but the plant, introduced to the United States early in the twentieth century, now flourishes in the deserts of the southwest, and is naturalized even as far north as central Washington state. Many species of the family Gramineae (grasses) contain DMT and other tryptamines, and two easily-propagated species now being used experimentally in temperate-zone *ayahuasca* are "giant reed" or "Spanish reed," *Arundo donax*, and "Canary reed," *Phalaris arundinacea* (Anon. 1991; Audette *et al.* 1969; Audette *et al.* 1970; Culvenor *et al.* 1964; Festi & Samorini 1993; Ghosal *et al.* 1969; Marten 1973A; Marten 1973B; Wassel & Ammar 1984; Williams *et al.* 1971). These two grasses were depicted, along with *Peganum harmala*, in a recent photo-essay, "Iconae Plantarum Inebriantium–1" published in the first number of *Integration: Journal for Mind-Moving Plants and Culture* (De Vries 1991B). *Arundo donax* has various important ritual uses among Mexican Huichol Indians—it is used in Huichol backstrap looms, as a dance staff held by *péyotl* pilgrims, and to make the shafts of votive arrows used in ritual hunting of *péyotl* (Schaefer 1993). An Australian species, *Phalaris tuberosa*, is known to contain DMT, 5-MeO-DMT and bufotenine (Baxter & Slaytor 1972; Gallagher *et al.* 1964; Oram & Williams 1967), and together with *P. arundinacea*, contains also traces of β-carbolines (Frahn & O'Keefe 1971; Gander *et al.* 1976; Shannon & Leyshon 1971; Vijayanagar *et al.* 1975). Another Australian species, *P. aquatica* (which may be synonymous with *P. tuberosa*), has been shown to contain DMT and 5-MeO-DMT (Mulvena & Slaytor 1982); whereas the *yopo* and *epéna* snuff constituent (see Chapter 3) 5-

MeO-*N*-methyltryptamine, of unknown pharmacology, has been found in *Phalaris arundinacea* (Wilkinson 1958). *Phragmites australis* is still another grass species now known to contain DMT (Wassel *et al.* 1985). Leaves and branches of the rutaceous *Vepris ampody* were shown to contain over 0.2% DMT, making this one of the richer known sources of the compound (Kan-Fan *et al.* 1970) and two other rutaceous species, *Limonia acidissima* and *Zanthoxylum arborescens* (and possibly also *Casimiroa edulis*) likewise contain DMT (Abu Zarga 1986; Díaz 1976; Garza 1990; Grina *et al.* 1982; Velázquez Díaz 1992). Bark of the leguminous *Lespedeza bicolor* (relative of *L. capitata*, a Ponca and Omaha analgesic and rheumatism remedy; Kindscher 1992; Moerman 1986) is likewise used in this context and also contains tryptamines (Gotu *et al.* 1958), as is also the case for the root of the leguminous *Desmanthus illinoensis* (traditional Paiute eye and dermatological remedy; Moerman 1986) recently shown to contain substantial amounts of DMT and MMT (Thompson *et al.* 1987). Bark of *Acacia maidenii*, leaves of *A. phlebophylla* and of other *Acacia* species likewise have potential for use as sources of entheogenic tryptamines in temperate-zone *ayahuasca* analogues (Fitzgerald & Sioumis 1965; Rovelli & Vaughan 1967). DMT has also been found in *Acacia confusa*, *A. nubica*, *A. polyacantha*, *A. senegal* and *A. simplicifolia* (Arthur *et al.* 1967; Liu *et al.* 1977; Poupat *et al.* 1976; Wahba Khalil & Elkheir 1975). Like *Phalaris* species, some *Acacia* species may also contain β-carboline alkaloids (Repke *et al.* 1973). The following species contain entheogenic tryptamines DMT, DMT-*N*-oxide, and/or 5-MeO-DMT, and could be used in *ayahuasca* analogues: various *Anadenanthera* species (Reis Altschul 1972); a *Delosperma* species (Rivier & Pilet 1971); *Desmodium caudatum*, *D. gangeticum*, *D. gyrans*, *D. pulchellum* and *D. triflorum* (Banerjee & Ghosal 1969; Ghosal 1972; Ghosal *et al.* 1972; Ueno *et al.* 1978; with *D. lasiocarpum* and *D. paniculatum* also likely to be active; Bodner & Gereau 1988; Kindscher 1992; Moerman 1986; Speck 1941); *Dictyoloma incanescens* (Pachter *et al.* 1959); *Mimosa tenuiflora* [=*M. hostilis*], *M. verrucosa* and *M. scabrella* (De Moraes *et al.* 1990; Gonçalves de Lima 1946; Meckes-Lozoya *et al.* 1990; Pachter *et al.* 1959); *Testulea gabonensis* (Leboeuf *et al.* 1977), numerous *Virola* species (see Chapter 3; Holmstedt & Lindgren 1967) and *Mucuna pruriens* (Bhattacharya *et al.* 1971). The famous "Yanqui ingenuity" is thus overcoming ecological constraints, creating temperate-zone equivalents of the wondrous potion from the tropical rainforests of Amazonia! Given that there exist nearly 70 species containing known MAO-inhibiting β-carboline alkaloids (Allen & Holmstedt 1980; Ott 1993) and more than 60 species presently known to contain entheogenic tryptamines (Ott 1994A; Shulgin & Shulgin 1996; T.A. Smith 1977), there can be conjectured at least 4000 possible plant combinations which will yield an *ayahuasca*-like entheogenic potion!

USE OF *HARMEL*, *AYAHUASCA* AND ANAHUASCA

Since harmine and harmaline have not appeared on the underground entheogen market, despite their low cost and legal availability (the reason for this would appear to be the somewhat undesirable effects, as detailed by Naranjo 1967), I will concentrate in this section on plant drugs—*Peganum harmala, Banisteriopsis caapi*, and genuine *ayahuasca* potions as well as their temperate-zone analogues.

Because there is no ethnographic literature on the use of *Peganum harmala* seeds as an inebriant, it was necessary to conduct self-experiments to establish the active dose and nature of effects. In all experiments ground seeds were extracted twice by boiling 15 minutes in 30% lime juice in water, followed by filtration. This resulted in efficient extraction of the *harmel* alkaloids, and it was determined that 15 grams of seeds was a psychoactive dose. For EXPERIMENT 4, I ingested the combined extracts of 15 grams of seeds, and one hour after ingestion it was obvious the seeds were psychoactive, producing a mild sedation which progressed to a peak at 2 hours and was mostly gone at 4 hours. Tinnitus was prominent, with a mild numbing sensation in the body. The effect was not overly unpleasant, but hard on the body, and there were no visual effects, save a bit of visual "tailing." Speech and concentration were normal, heartbeat slowed, and on attempts to sleep, there was slight vertigo with eyes closed. A hangover persisted throughout the next day after fitful sleep. I had no desire to repeat the experience, which I would characterize as involving more a *Valium*-like sedation than visionary effect, and it was similar to EXPERIMENT 1 in Ecuador with *ayahuasca* brewed without tryptamine admixture, but with a small amount of caffeine-containing leaves of *Ilex guayusa*. According to literature reports, the dose of 15 g *harmel* seeds would have contained 300–1050 mg of a mixture of harmine, harmaline and *d*-leptaflorine (THH), plus lesser amounts of other alkaloids. Judging by Naranjo's reports of the activity of these alkaloids, the seeds must have contained levels closer to the upper limit, about a gram of alkaloids. An "underground" publication referred to experiments with smoking alkaloid-enriched extracts of *harmel* seeds, as well as of *Banisteriopsis caapi* stems and *Passiflora incarnata* whole plants (this article appeared roughly contemporaneously with Schultes' article on Witoto Indians smoking of *Banisteriopsis caapi* leaves and bark; Schultes 1985B). The authors commented: "the high is not particularly psychedelic or hallucinogenic... One feels calm. At higher doses, dizziness and nausea sets in with very little increase in the high. Closed eye imagery is at best hypnagogic... No one who has experienced DMT or high dose mushrooms would ever call them visions" (Gracie & Zarkov 1985B). These researchers found that, although *ayahuasca* doses analyzed by McKenna's group had been found to contain some 400 mg of β-carbolines, with smoking: "we only needed to consume sufficient plant material for dosages in the 50 mg range... increasing the dosage did not increase the high but only aggravated the [noxious] physical symptoms." The authors of this interesting report then experimented with smoking pure DMT ten minutes after feeling the "high" from smoking the β-carboline alkaloid-enriched plant extracts, finding a threefold enhancement in potency of smoked DMT (15 mg with premedication by β-carbolines "felt more like 35–45 mg or roughly tripled intensity"), a lengthened visionary period (6 minutes instead of 2–3 minutes), and enhanced, "almost overwhelming" auditory effects (Gracie & Zarkov 1985B). But we are really interested in the interactions of orally-ingested DMT with β-carbolines; the smoking experiment suggests an enhancement in potency of DMT, but that compound is normally active when smoked (see Chapter 3), but inactive by oral ingestion.

Since the only experiment on record was that of J. Bigwood (1978; mentioned also in Stafford 1983), involving 100 mg each of harmaline HCL and DMT free-base (substantial amounts of both), it was necessary to conduct self-experiments to establish minimum orally-active doses of tryptamine/β-carboline combinations. EXPERIMENT 5 involved an extract of 5 g of *harmel* seeds (same conditions as above—this would be expected to contain 100–350 mg β-carboline alkaloids) with 20 mg (0.25 mg/kg) DMT free-base (isolated and crystallized from *Desmanthus illinoensis*; melting point 45°C) dissolved in the hot, acidic extract. Initial effects were felt within 45 minutes, and developed slightly over the next half-hour, lasting about 3 hours. This represented a definite stimulation from the DMT, but only threshold-level for psychoptic effects... a feeling of aliveness and excitement in marked contrast to the sort of deadbeat feeling I had experienced with three times the dose of *harmel* but absent the DMT. I definitely wished to repeat the experiment with a higher dose of DMT, and it was somewhat like EXPERIMENT 2 in Ecuador with *ayahuasca* containing only a few leaves of DMT-rich *Psychotria viridis per* dose. The above-mentioned authors reported experiments with oral combinations of *harmel* seed extract with synthetic DMT, concluding that "5 gm of seeds with 20 mg of DMT seems to be the threshold dose," which is exactly what I observed (Gracie & Zarkov 1986). I next experimented with an extract of 4 g *harmel* seeds (80–280 mg β-carbolines) to which 30 mg (0.38 mg/kg) isolated DMT free-base was added. This EXPERIMENT 6 produced distinct visionary effects of DMT commencing 1:10 after ingestion and building to a peak in 5 minutes, with a 45 minute plateau (to 2:00 after ingestion), followed by another hour of distinct, 'though diminishing, DMT effects consisting of colored patterns with eyes opened and closed, exhilaration and stimulation alloyed with the sedative effect of the *harmel* seeds, which caused me to yawn repeatedly. The orally-active DMT was less potent than smoked DMT, perhaps half as potent. While 30 mg produced a distinct DMT effect reminiscent of EXPERIMENT 3, *ayahuasca* with a large dose of leaves of *Psychotria viridis*, it was by no means a saturation-level effect; that is, 40 mg would surely produce a stronger effect. Gracie and Zarkov (1986) reported that "our nominal dose would be 10 gm of seeds with 40 mg DMT" and they found 30 mg of DMT active, and reported "our personal preference is 7 gm of seeds with 30 mg of DMT." It can thus be concluded that the active oral dose range for DMT in *ayahuasca*-type potions is from 0.25–0.5 mg/kg (15–30 mg for a 60 kg person; 20–40 mg for an 80 kg person like me). It can also be supposed that the extract of 4 g of *harmel* seeds (with estimated content of 80–280 mg β-carbolines) is more than necessary to activate the DMT, since the analysis of the Río Purús *ayahuasca* by Rivier and Lindgren (1972) found 25 mg of DMT *per* dose (clearly active in 50–60 kg Indians) and only 40 mg of β-carbolines *per* dose, which would correspond to an extract of only 0.57–2.0 g of *harmel* seeds. Accordingly, since I found the effect of the *harmel* seeds to be disagreeable, and wished to establish the minimum dose of β-carbolines needed to render DMT orally active, I extracted harmine from *Peganum harmala* seeds, and purified it as the hydrochloride salt (melting point 262°C), for further experiments.

EXPERIMENT 7 involved oral ingestion of a capsule containing 30 mg DMT free-base together with 47 mg harmine HCL, equivalent to 40 mg harmine free-base or 0.5 mg/kg (since Rivier and Lindgren had found only 40 mg β-carbolines in a typical dose of *ayahuasca*). Although I felt a slight hint of activity, in general this amount of harmine was insufficient to produce the oral activity of DMT I had experienced when I took the same quantity (30 mg) with the combined extracts of 4 g *harmel* seeds (estimated to represent from 1–3.5 mg/kg β-carbolines). Since the Sharanahua and Culina Indians who prepared the *ayahuasca* for Rivier and Lindgren likely weighed on average about 60 kg, the 40 mg of β-carbolines in their typical dose would represent 0.67 mg/kg. For an 80 kg person like me, this would correspond to 54 mg of β-carbolines. Accordingly, for my next experiment I increased the quantity of harmine HCL to 63 mg (equivalent to 54 mg harmine free-base), keeping the quantity of DMT free-base at the known active level of 30 mg. Again, the compounds were combined and placed into a gelatin capsule for ingestion. This EXPERIMENT 8 led only to a threshold-level DMT effect; prompting me to increase the dose of harmine HCL to 70 mg (=60 mg harmine base; 0.75 mg/kg), combined again with 30 mg DMT free-base. The capsule containing these quantities was ingested for EXPERIMENT 9, and produced a mild but detectable DMT effect commencing at 30 minutes after ingestion and still distinct at 2:40 after ingestion.

The effect was still, however, considerably milder than my previous experiment with 30 mg DMT combined with extracts of 4 g *harmel* seeds, and I decided again to increase the dose.

Accordingly, in EXPERIMENT 10 I ingested a capsule containing 30 mg DMT free-base plus 94 mg harmine HCL (=80 mg base; 1.0 mg/kg). The effect was similar to that of the previous experiment. 'Though more intense, it still fell short of the stronger effect 30 mg DMT had given when accompanied by extracts of 4 g *harmel* seeds. I increased the dose again, to 117 mg harmine hydrochloride (=100 mg harmine base; 1.25 mg/kg) with the standard 30 mg DMT base. This EXPERIMENT 11 again led to a threshold effect of DMT, still falling short of the effect of 30 mg combined with extracts of 4 g of *harmel* seeds.

For EXPERIMENT 12, I increased the quantity of harmine hydrochloride to 141 mg (=120 mg base; 1.5 mg/kg), and ingested this along with 35 mg DMT free-base (0.44 mg/kg). By 45 minutes after ingestion, it was obvious the dose was psychoptic, and I experienced a distinct DMT effect building to a peak at 1:05 after ingestion and maintaining a plateau until 1:50, with the effects largely dissipated by 3 hours after ingestion. This experience was of comparable intensity to EXPERIMENT 6 involving ingestion of a similar amount of DMT (30 mg; 0.38 mg/kg) with extract of 4 g of *harmel* seeds, and we may conclude that 120 mg of harmine (1.5 mg/kg) will effect sufficient *in vivo* MAO-inhibition to render DMT active orally with a longer duration and about half the potency of inhaled DMT vapor. To confirm these results, I decided to make another experiment with the harmine/DMT combinations, slightly increasing the amounts of both compounds. Accordingly, I prepared a capsule containing 188 mg harmine hydrochloride (=160 mg harmine base; 2.0 mg/kg) and 40 mg DMT base (0.5 mg/kg).

This capsule was ingested in EXPERIMENT 13 and indeed provoked a proportionally stronger DMT effect with the first effects felt in 20 minutes, building to a peak by 1:30 after ingestion with a plateau until 2:40, and clearly diminishing effects at 3:00 after ingestion. By 4:00 after ingestion there were no effects, nor after-effects. All in all, the experience was quite pleasant and similar to EXPERIMENT 3 in Ecuador with about 50 leaves of DMT-containing *Psychotria viridis per* dose, 'though somewhat less potent. A control EXPERIMENT 14 with 141 mg harmine HCL (=120 mg base; 1.5 mg/kg) without DMT evoked no perceptible effects, proving definitively that the visionary effects of the "*ayahuasca* capsules" were a result of DMT rendered orally active by simultaneous ingestion of an MAO-inhibitor. This mechanism, originally proposed by Holmstedt and Lindgren (1967) and by two groups in 1968 (Agurell *et al.* 1968B; Der Marderosian *et al.* 1968), and sixteen years later shown to be viable in *in vitro* experiments (McKenna *et al.* 1984A), is thus confirmed in a single human subject (Ott 1992B; Ott 1993; Ott 1994A). Bigwood's experiment with 100 mg each of DMT (1.18 mg/kg) and harmaline HCL (=86 mg harmaline base; 1.00 mg/kg) led also to psychoptic effects (Bigwood 1978), and while the β-carboline dose there was somewhat lower than levels I found active, we must recall that McKenna's group found harmaline to be "slightly stronger" than harmine as an MAO-inhibitor (McKenna *et al.* 1984A). Furthermore, Bigwood's DMT dose was five times the threshold level, and perhaps higher doses of DMT can compensate for slight insufficiency of MAO-inhibitors. See Ott 1994A for continuation of these psychonautic bioassays.

Upon completing these bioassays, I received a communication from American neurochemist J.C. Callaway, who has been working on mammalian metabolism of tryptamines and β-carbolines (Callaway 1994). Callaway described a self-experiment he conducted independently *on the same day* as my EXPERIMENT 12 (which was the first to give me an unequivocal *ayahuasca*-like effect with pure compounds). Callaway ingested 10 mg of 5-MeO-DMT together with 70 mg harmaline expressed as free-base. Since 5-MeO-DMT is roughly 4 times the potency of DMT when inhaled as vapor (see Chapter 3), this would be equivalent to roughly 40 mg DMT, or about 0.67 mg/kg in Callaway's case; with the harmaline dose being about 1.16 mg/kg, similar to the level Bigwood had found active. Callaway felt the first effects in 18 minutes and distinct psychoactive effects at 45 minutes, building to a peak by 1:25, although there were no visual effects and slight nausea. By 1:58 effects were diminishing, although there were persistent effects which Callaway likened to oral harmaline at 300 mg dose (Callaway 1992). This independent experiment confirms Bigwood's finding that harmaline appears to be more active that harmine as an MAO-inhibitor in *ayahuasca*, which the biochemical data seem to bear out (McKenna *et al.* 1984A). It furthermore suggests that 5-MeO-DMT can substitute for DMT as active tryptamine in *ayahuasca*-type potions, and would appear to be several times the activity of DMT, mirroring relative potencies of both compounds when inhaled (Shulgin in De Smet 1983). Another European researcher, M. Markus, found 5-MeO-DMT to possess "hallucinatory effects" when combined with harmine, harmaline or 6-MeO-harmalan in "*ayahuasca* capsules" (Leuner & Schlichting 1989). When the first edition of this book went to press, I received a brief summary of another series of experiments with "*pharmahuasca*" (Ott 1994A; Ott 1996B) using harmaline HCL as MAO-inhibitor. An independent researcher found 100 mg harmaline HCL (86 mg free-base, roughly 1.3 mg/kg) to be a threshold-level dose, with 150 mg (128 mg free-base or about 2 mg/kg) more effective. Combined with 100 mg harmaline HCL, even 120 mg of DMT free-base (4–6 times threshold) was "very mild," suggesting an insufficiency of MAO-inhibition. On the other hand 150 mg harmaline HCL combined with 150 mg DET (roughly equipotent with DMT) was "definitely an overdosage." The evidence seems to indicate that some 1.5–2.0 mg/kg harmaline or harmine (expressed as the free-base) is the true threshold level for *ayahuasca* MAO-inhibition, with some 0.25–0.5 mg/kg DMT free-base representing the tryptamine threshold level.

Since DMT is orally active in doses of 0.25–0.5 mg/kg in presence of 1.5 mg/kg harmine, it can be said that the quantities of DMT and β-carbolines found by McKenna's group in a typical 60 ml dose of Pucallpa *ayahuasca* (36 mg DMT : 401 mg β-carbolines) are sufficient to evoke psychoptic effects (McKenna *et al.* 1984A), even in a large 80 kg adult. Similarly, the quantities found in a 50 ml dose of Brasilian *daime* (26.5 mg DMT : 144 mg β-carbolines) would also suffice to evoke visionary effects in an 80 kg adult (Liwszyc *et al.* 1992). Naturally, in more typical 60 kg South Americans, these *ayahuasca* doses would be well above threshold, and we must remember that children are also known to partake of *daime* in the *Santo Daime* churches (Prance 1970). On the other hand, the quantities of alkaloids reported by Rivier and Lindgren in Río Purús *ayahuasca* (25 mg DMT and 40 mg β-carbolines in a large 200 ml dose), while adequate for visionary effects with respect to their DMT content, would appear to be sub-threshold with respect to the low content of β-carbolines (Rivier & Lindgren 1972). There are some possible explanations for the discrepancy, not least of which is the obvious imprecision with which doses are measured in typical use. It is possible the Sharanahua and Culina Indians Rivier and Lindgren observed are genetically more susceptible to MAO-inhibitors than are Caucasians or Indian/Caucasian mestizos. The taking of multiple doses of *ayahuasca* in a single session has been widely observed and reported, and it may have been common for the Sharanahua and Culina to repeat the dose various times, in which case the relatively high amount of DMT would lead to powerful effects. Finally, it is common for shamans to take *ayahuasca* two or more days in succession, which might lead to a cumulative MAO-inhibitory effect, and the potion in general is said to be more effective if used repeatedly. In the case of the single Cashinahua *nixi pae* potion analyzed by Der Marderosian's group, the 30 mg DMT found in a typical 240 ml dose clearly represents psychoactive levels, while the 20 mg β-carbolines reported *per* dose is obviously insufficient. The age of the sample (kept 2 years *sans* refrigeration prior to analysis) and the failure of the authors to report content of *d*-leptaflorine (THH) may account for this anomalous finding (Der Marderosian *et al.* 1970). T.K. McKenna's reported optimum dose of *ayahuasca* based on 500 g fresh *Banisteriopsis caapi* and 85 g fresh *Psychotria viridis* would represent 425 mg to 3.12 g β-carbolines *per* dose (according to analyses of the same source cultivars by brother

D.J. McKenna and assuming 50% water in fresh material) together with 43–67 mg DMT *per* dose (again assuming 50% water in fresh material; McKenna *et al.* 1984A; McKenna 1993). These levels are obviously well above threshold with respect to β-carbolines, and are comfortably above threshold with respect to DMT, and my data would suggest that substantial reductions in *Banisteriopsis caapi* might be possible. Clearly, more research into *ayahuasca* pharmacology is needed, particularly into the chemically-obscure admixture plants, and the interactions of known additive-plant compounds like nicotine and tropane alkaloids with the MAO-inhibitors of *Banisteriopsis* species.

In order to investigate the human pharmacology of *ayahuasca* analogues, for EXPERIMENT 15, I prepared *ayahuasca borealis* by grinding and extracting 4 grams of *Peganum harmala* seeds together with 27.6 grams of *Desmanthus illinoensis* root, calculated to contain 50 mg DMT according to literature reports (Thompson *et al.* 1987). The ground material was thrice extracted with 100 ml of boiling 30% lime juice followed by filtrations. Ingestion of the resulting 250 ml potion (the color of unfiltered apple juice) led to slight sub-threshold excitation from the DMT present, evidently in quantities insufficient for a full-blown psychoptic effect. Accordingly, I prepared another potion for EXPERIMENT 16, consisting of the same quantity of *Peganum harmala* seeds, 4 g, together with 56.2 g *Desmanthus illinoensis* root. This potion produced distinct visionary effects of DMT commencing at 30 minutes (first signs detected at the 12 minute point), building to a peak by 1:05 with a 30 minute plateau. By 2:00 effects had noticeably diminished, and had all but disappeared by 3:00 after ingestion. The effects were mild but unmistakable, with tinnitus, euphoria and mild visual phenomena (see Ott 1994A for further *anahuasca* experiments).

Monoamine oxidase-inhibitors are widely used medicinally as anti-depressants, normally with chronic, long-term, daily administration. I decided to combine oral doses of DMT with the pharmaceutical MAO-inhibitor isocarboxazid (5-methyl-3-isoxazole carboxylic acid 2-benzylhydrazide), known under the trade-name *Marplan*. The compound is ordinarily administered in a dosage of 30 mg daily (as a single dose, or three 10 mg doses) and the anti-depressant effect (which results from an increase in neurotransmitters like serotonine in the brain; see Chapter 3, Note 5) follows a latency period of a few days to a few months and persists for several weeks after ceasing administration of the drug. Occasional euphoric reactions to the drug are considered to be an adverse side-effect. I administered 30 mg *Marplan* in three doses of 10 mg at 9:00 AM, 2:00 PM and 7:00 PM, and one hour after the third dose ingested 30 mg DMT free-base in a capsule. This EXPERIMENT 17 provoked mild DMT effects commencing 35 minutes after ingestion and building to a peak by 1:10, with a plateau to 1:40, diminishing over the next hour. Thus it is possible to provoke an *ayahuasca*-like effect using an artificial MAO-inhibitor used in medicine, which appears, furthermore, to be several times the potency of the natural MAO-inhibitors found in *Banisteriopsis caapi* and other plants (Ott 1993; Ott 1994A).

It is evident that *ayahuasca* is presently the entheogen *en vogue* among *aficionados* in the United States and other countries. One result has been a proliferation of "*ayahuasca* tourism" to Brasil, Perú, Ecuador and Bolivia (Ott 1994A; Ott 1995B). Unfortunately, while this interest has helped draw some attention to the ecological plight of Amazonia, and may funnel some small amounts of needed money to underdeveloped zones of Third World countries, it has also lead inexorably to additional ecological and cultural disruption of affected areas, brought disease to unimmunized Indians, and attracted the wrong kind of attention to *ayahuasca* (see Chapter 1 and Valadez 1986, for a discussion of similar problems associated with "*péyotl* tourism"). Again, those interested in *ayahuasca* would be wise to stay home and cultivate their own source plants for *ayahuasca* analogues. I hope the dissemination of the *anahuasca* or *ayahuasca*-analogue technology in the overdeveloped world will curtail *ayahuasca* tourism, which can only lead to further ecological and cultural destruction in Amazonia, and could possibly result even in the illegalization of *ayahuasca* by the authorities in Perú, Ecuador or elsewhere (Ott 1994A).

Since the publication of this book in August 1993, the *vogue* in *ayahuasca* has increased, thanks in some measure to additional publications, such as my *Ayahuasca Analogues: Pangæan Entheogens* (Ott 1994A). There was also a recent reprint of *Ayahuasca Visions* (Luna & Amaringo 1991); whereas interest in the Spanish-speaking world was stimulated by the 1994 publication of a translation of Catalán ethnographer J.M. Fericgla's *Els Jívaros, Caçadors de Somnis* (*The Jívaros, Hunters of Dreams*; Fericgla 1994A), and the Spanish translation of *Pharmacotheon* (Liebre de Marzo, Barcelona, 1996). Happily, the focus has increasingly shifted to *anahuasca*, and Italian researchers proudly concocted all-European analogues, and made extensive phytochemical analyses of *Phalaris* species and *Arundo donax*, both potential tryptamine sources (Festi & Samorini 1993). Problems with toxicity, perhaps a human version of the "*Phalaris* staggers" affecting livestock, have cooled enthusiasm for use of these grasses in *anahuasca*, while *Mimosa tenuiflora* has emerged as the leading source of *anahuasca* DMT. False statements about purported *potentiation* of DMT by β-carbolines (Turner 1994) have occasioned a potentially hazardous fixation on MAO-inhibitors as supposititious pan-potentiators of entheogens (Ott 1995A; Ott 1996B). Finally, renewed scientific interest in entheogens led to the first systematic human pharmacological studies of DMT (Strassman & Qualls 1994; Strassman *et al.* 1994).

NOTES

[1] When British botanist Richard Spruce first described his discoveries of Amazonian psychoactive drugs, he referred to them in his title as "remarkable narcotics" (Spruce 1873). Ernst Freiherr von Bibra had already published one of the first studies of psychoactive drugs, which he entitled *Die Narkotischen Genußmittel und der Mensch* ("Narcotic Dainties and Man" Bibra 1855). Mordecai Cubitt Cooke made the same association in his pioneering study of psychoactive drugs, *The Seven Sisters of Sleep. Popular History of the Seven Prevailing Narcotics of the World* (Cooke 1860), although both he and von Bibra included the stimulant *coca* in their studies. The word *narcotic* (and its cognates *narcótico* in Spanish and Portuguese, *Narkotikum* in German, *narcotique* in French) derive from the Greek word *ναρκωτικ–υν*, "to benumb, to stupefy." The earliest use in English was by Geoffrey Chaucer in a 1385 poem: "The narcotykis & opijs ben so stronge" and the following year in his incomparable *Tales of Caunterbury*, in the Knyghtes' Tale, describing a potion to facilitate a jailbreak: "For he hadde yeve his gailler drynke so/Of a clarree maad of a certeyn wyn,/With nercotikes and opie of Thebes fyn,/That al that nyght, thogh that men wolde him shake,/The gailler sleep, he myghte nat awake;" (Pratt 1966). These quotations, and others, support the definition: "a substance which when swallowed, inhaled, or injected into the system induces drowsiness, sleep, stupefaction, or insensibility, according to its strength or the amount taken" (*Oxford English Dictionary*, Compact Edition, p. 1895). No other meaning is given, and the adjective *narcotic* has the same meaning: "of substances or their qualities: Having the effect of inducing stupor, sleep, or insensibility," as have all other forms of the word, *viz. narcosis, narcotical, narcotism, etc. The Heritage Illustrated Dictionary of the English Language* gives the meaning of narcotic as: "any drug that dulls the senses, induces sleep, and with prolonged use becomes addictive," this gratuitous reference to "addictive" being a modern sense, clearly deriving from the association of the term with the opiate drugs (Kapoor 1995; Small & Lutz 1932; alkaloids of opium, the dried exudate of incised, unripe capsules of the poppy *Papaver somniferum*; specifically morphine and codeine, as well as their numerous semi-synthetic derivatives such as diacetyl-morphine [heroin, *Diamorphine*], oxycodone, oxymorphone, *etc.*; and artificial analogues, such as *Meperidine*, *Methadone*, *etc.*). Indeed, from the very first uses by Chaucer, *narcotic* was related specifically to opium and any other drugs with like effects, inducing "drowsiness, sleep, stupefaction or insensibility." This meaning is very clear, and there is no question the opiate drugs are correctly designated *narcotics*. Spruce's use of the term to describe entheogens like *ayahuasca*, however, is etymologically questionable. While *ayahuasca* prepared without additives may have some soporific effects, and while *Brugmansia* plant admixtures might indeed enhance the soporific qualities of such potions, *ayahuasca* prepared with *chacruna* and *chagropanga*, DMT-rich admixtures, is very definitely a stimulant, and incorrectly designated a *narcotic.* The same can be said for virtually all of the classic entheogenic drugs—mescaline, LSD, psilocybine, ibogaine—these compounds are most decidedly stimulants, sleep being quite out of the question when under their influence. Louis Lewin recognized this semantic problem when he published his 1924 treatise on psychoactive drugs, *Phantastica: Die Betäubenden und Erregenden Genußmittel* ("Phantastica: Stupefying and Stimulating Pleasure Drugs") using von Bibra's *Genußmittel*

(literally, "means of pleasure") but avoiding the use of the adjective *narcotic, narkotisch* (Lewin 1924). Indeed, Lewin introduced no fewer than five categories of psychoactive drugs: 1) *Euphorica* or *Seelenberuhigungsmittel* (euphoriants or "anodynes for the spirit") of which the opiates were the prototypes, but including, paradoxically, *coca* and cocaine (Escohotado 1990; Hastorf 1987; Holmstedt *et al.* 1978; Mariani 1890; Martin 1970; Mortimer 1901; Plowman 1979; Schultes 1981); 2) *Phantastica* or *Sinnestäuschungsmittel* (phantastica or "sensory illusion agents") with *péyotl, Cannabis indica, Amanita muscaria*, various nightshades—*Hyoscyamus* spp., *Datura* spp., and *Duboisia hopwoodii*—as well as *Banisteriopsis caapi*; 3) *Inebriantia* or *Berauschungsmittel* (inebriants or intoxicants) including alcohol, and other solvents such as chloroform, ether and benzene; 4) *Hypnotica* or *Schlafmittel* (hypnotics or "sleep agents") such as chloral hydrate, barbital, paraldehyde, sulfonmethane, bromal hydrate, and the Polynesian potion *kava* (*Piper methysticum*); and 5) *Excitantia* or *Erregungsmittel* (excitants or stimulants) including camphor, *betel* (*Areca catechu*), *kat* (*Catha edulis*, source of cathinone; Elmi 1983; Getahun & Krikorian 1973; Kennedy 1987; Krikorian & Getahun 1973; Nordal 1980; Szendrei 1980; Zegler *et al.* 1980; recently alleged to have been a sacred plant in ancient Egypt; Musès 1989), the caffeine-containing drugs coffee, tea, *cola* nuts (*Cola nitida*), *mate* (*Ilex paraguariensis*; to which Lewin would surely have added *Ilex guayusa* and *I. vomitoria* or *yaupon*), and *guaraná* (*Paullinia cupana* var. *sorbilis*; with which Lewin would have grouped *yoco* or *Paullinia yoco*; Erickson *et al.* 1984; Henman 1982; Patiño 1968; Schultes 1942; Schultes 1979F; Schultes 1986A; Schultes 1987B; Shemluck 1979), plus cacao, tobacco and *paricá* snuff (*Anadenanthera peregrina*). The corresponding modern categories would be: 1) narcotics; 2) entheogens; 3) intoxicants; 4) hypnotics; and 5) stimulants, to which Hofmann added a sixth of "neuroleptic sedatives" (which I dubbed *Neuroleptica*; Ott 1995B) such as chlorpromazine and meprobamate, with the natural prototype *Rauwolfia serpentina*, which contains reserpine (Hofmann 1970A; Woodson *et al.* 1957). I would remove *paricá* snuff from the stimulants and reclassify it as an entheogen, and transfer *coca* and cocaine from the narcotics to the stimulants, but otherwise would agree with Lewin's classification. Of course, Lewin's *Euphorica* (opiates), *Inebriantia* (intoxicant solvents) and *Hypnotica* could all be designated *narcotics*, but Lewin was correct to separate them into three classes (in modern terminology, narcotics, solvents and hypnotics), and he was quite right in insisting that the entheogens and stimulants belonged in different categories entirely. Indeed, how can potent antagonists to sleep like LSD, cocaine and amphetamine be designated *narcotics*? Yet some specialists in ethnopharmacognosy, notably the dean of the field Richard E. Schultes, have used the term *narcotic* to describe the entheogens like *ayahuasca* and other DMT-containing drugs, among other plants (see for example Schultes 1961; Schultes 1979D). Schultes explained his use of the term thus: "the term *narcotic*, coming from the Greek *ναρκουν*, to benumb, etymologically refers to a substance which, however stimulating it may be in one or more phases of its activity, terminates its effects with a depressive state on the central nervous system" (Schultes & Hofmann 1979). Botanist William Emboden uses the term *narcotic* in the title of his book *Narcotic Plants* to embrace "hallucinogens, stimulants, inebriants and hypnotics," admitting "the term 'narcotic' is obviously a misnomer" (Emboden 1972B); but explaining that "I will use the term narcotic as it has been used by the United States Public Health Service to include those plants that are psychoactive regardless of the manifestation of this activity" (Emboden 1979). This usage has also appeared in the title of two anthologies, *Sacred Narcotic Plants of the New World Indians* (Schleiffer 1974) and *Narcotic Plants of the Old World* (Schleiffer 1979). G. Reichel-Dolmatoff's interesting study *The Shaman and the Jaguar* (Reichel-Dolmatoff 1975) was subtitled *A Study of Narcotic Drugs among the Indians of Colombia.* I consider Schultes' and Emboden's reasoning quite unpersuasive, and respectfully disagree with their use of the word *narcotic.* I reserve the term for the opiate drugs, and have already explained my reasoning behind my use of the word *entheogen in lieu* of *psychedelic* or *psychotomimetic* (see Chapter 1, Note 1). *Psychoactive* and *psychotropic* are precise, etymologically-correct terms to embrace all classes of drugs with effects on consciousness, as opposed to other categories of drugs, such as antimicrobials, diuretics, *etc.* I might mention in closing that a further problem with *narcotic* is that it prejudices people against the entheogens—since the word has acquired the meaning of "addictive" and since its legal meaning is "an illicit substance"; whereas, fortunately, many entheogens remain quite legal, and they are decidedly *not* addictive. See Eliade (1951) for an example of the pejorative use of *narcotic* in reference to shamanic inebriants.

[2] I will outline some of the errors and incongruities in the Flattery-Schwartz theory which leave me unconvinced (see also Chapter 6, Note 11). I will present my comments on respective sections in the order in which they appear in the book. In §7, Flattery took issue with Wasson's theory regarding the existence of *Soma* urine: "none of the data presented by Wasson on the subject of urine drinking has any relevance for *soma*." But Flattery ignored and/or suppressed Wasson's commentary on the section from the *Mahabharata* in which the *amrta* is offered in urine to Uttanka by Indra posing as an outcaste. "Come Uttanka, and accept this water from me. I feel great pity for you, seeing you so overcome by thirst." The urine ("and Uttanka saw copious streams of water flowing from his lower parts") was offered to slake the thirst of Uttanka by Krsna, who had promised him a boon. Uttanka was revolted and outraged and refused the drink. Krsna appeared to Uttanka and explained: "for your sake I said to Indra, 'Give the *amrta* to Uttanka in the form of water.'" But Indra objected saying "a mortal should not become immortal; give some other boon to him" (translation by W. Doniger from Wasson 1968). There is no question that this *amrta* (cognate with Greek *ambrosia*) is the *Soma* potion, here clearly represented in the form of Indra's urine. It was this passage from the *Mahabharata* that suggested to Wasson that *Amanita muscaria* might be *Soma*—it shows the *Soma* potion *in the form of urine being offered as a drink which would make the imbiber immortal.* Flattery ignored this inconvenient fact for, as he said, "if evidence could be found that the urine of *soma* drinkers was itself drunk, this would strongly support Wasson's identification." Flattery then incorrectly stated, and contrary to Wendy Doniger's testimony (Doniger 1990; Doniger O'Flaherty 1982), that "Wasson's reason for suspecting that the urine of *soma* drinkers was consumed comes from an ostensible reference to this practice not in the Rg Veda but in an Iranian source..." handily diverting the argument away from the primary Indian literature where he is not at home and into Iranian literature. As Wendy Doniger noted, however, "it was only when I casually mentioned to RGW the *urine-drinking, Soma-drinking* episode in the *Mahabharata* that he thought of *Amanita muscaria* as a possible identity for Soma" (my

emphasis). Furthermore, given the reference in the *RgVeda*, that men would "piss the flowing *Soma*," and that Indra would "Drink *Soma*, as much as you wish./Pissing it out day by day" (Wasson 1972B), plus the passage in the *Mahabharata* in which *Soma* urine is offered by Indra to be drunk by a thirsty person, it is ludicrous to suppose, as did Flattery, that urine drinking in India derived from practices in twentieth-century Arkansas! Several prominent Vedists, including W. Doniger, F.B.J. Kuiper, L. Renou and K.F. Geldner have considered the existence of *Soma* urine to be incontrovertible and of importance in the identification of the plant (Doniger O'Flaherty 1982; Wasson 1972B). Since, as Flattery and Schwartz conceded, urine drinking is also a feature of present-day Zoroastrian ceremonies (or did this also derive from Arkansas?), where does this leave their theory for *Peganum harmala* as *Soma/Haoma*? Where is the evidence that drinkers of a potion based on *P. harmala* piss out the active principles, the harmane alkaloids? In §8 Note 5, Flattery seized as given truth F.B.J. Kuiper's opinion that Santal *putka* and Sanskrit *putika* are not etymologically related (see Chapter 6, Note 11), although Kramrisch had the opposite opinion (Kramrisch 1975). Flattery glossed over Kramrisch's contrary opinion, and he did not inform us that Professor Kuiper, his unimpeachable authority here, had tentatively *accepted* Wasson's identification of *Soma* as *Amanita muscaria* (Kuiper 1970). Similarly, 'though Schwartz leaned on details of some of his arguments, he failed to mention that I. Gershevitch, an Iranianist, also tentatively accepted Wasson's *Soma* : mushroom theory (Gershevitch 1974). This is especially significant, in that Gershevitch concluded from the Iranian literature that "if one knew nothing of Mr. Wasson's book and the controversy, one could still, by cool reasoning, have arrived at a hallucinogenic mushroom" (for the identity of *Haoma*; Gershevitch 1974). In §38–42, Flattery committed the crucial error in the book, saying that he would "regard the psychopharmacological data on *yagé* as chiefly reflecting the properties of the harmala alkaloids" and argue that *Peganum harmala* was *Soma/Haoma* because it contains the same alkaloids as *Banisteriopsis caapi*, and the ethnographic data on the latter plant paint a picture of a drug resembling *Soma/Haoma*! This is an extremely weak line of argument, to say the least. In §39, Flattery proceeded to quote Claudio Naranjo at length on the effects of *yagé* and harmaline. As we will see in the following footnote, however, and in the section "Chemistry of *Ayahuasca* and Pharmacology of *beta*-Carbolines," it has been well established that harmaline is a trace constituent in *ayahuasca* brews, and does not contribute significantly to *ayahuasca* pharmacology. I will let D.J. McKenna and colleagues, cited by Flattery, speak on this point: "harmaline... is essentially a trace component in *ayahuasca* and probably does not contribute significantly to the MAO inhibition which this drug elicits" (McKenna *et al.* 1984A). In §40 Flattery cited G. Reichel-Dolmatoff describing the Tukano Indian use of *yajé* and in §41 quoted M. Harner's description of Jívaro (Shuar) Indian use of *yajé*. What he left out is significant, however. In the second paragraph of the quote from Harner, there is a lacuna in Flattery's extract in which Harner mentioned the addition to the *yajé* of "the leaves of a similar vine" which we now know to have been *Diplopterys cabrerana*, and stated that the beverage contained, besides the harmala alkaloids, "quite possibly N,N-dimethyl-tryptamine (DMT)" (Harner 1973B). Similarly, the Tukano Indians described by Reichel-Dolmatoff don't take *ayahuasca* straight, but are known to use the same additive as the Shuar, DMT-rich *Diplopterys cabrerana*, and that the practice of these Indians is that "considerable amounts of tobacco rapé are taken alternately with *yagé* (*Banisteriopsis caapi*) and coca" (Wilbert 1987). The Shuar likewise "drink tobacco juice alternately with *ayahuasca*" (Wilbert 1987). In other words, both the Shuar and Tukano Indians, whose experiences were cited by Flattery as evidence for the psychopharmacology of the harmane alkaloids, commonly brew their *yajé* with DMT-rich plants, and take it along with tobacco juice and snuffs. As we will see in the section on "Pharmacology of β-Carbolines," the chemical studies cited by Flattery in §38 (McKenna *et al.* 1984A; Rivier & Lindgren 1972) found that Peruvian *ayahuasca* potions contained subthreshold doses of harmane alkaloids, and that their psychotropic properties were due to the DMT they contained, the harmane alkaloids serving only as MAO-inhibitors, to render the DMT active orally. We know nothing of the interaction of the tobacco nicotine with harmane alkaloids, but, being a potent entheogen in its own right, tobacco effects surely influenced the experiences of the Shuar and Tukano Indians cited by Flattery. Contrary to what Flattery states, it is not at all "justifiable to regard the psychopharmacological data on *yagé* as chiefly reflecting the properties of the harmala alkaloids." Rather, given the limited data at hand, it seems justifiable to regard the psychopharmacological data on *yajé* as chiefly reflecting the properties of DMT, nicotine and scopolamine, as well as other, unknown active compounds in chemically-obscure admixture plants. Flattery's strained equivalence between *Peganum harmala* and *yajé* won't hold up—the visionary effects of the latter are not due to the harmane alkaloids but to DMT, scopolamine, and other active principles (see section "*Chacruna*, *Chagropanga* and Other *Ayahuasca* Admixtures"); 'though Flattery thereby convinced one would-be *Soma* expert (Rudgley 1994). Making this specious equivalence between *harmel* and *yajé*, Flattery essentially backed himself into a corner and began to suggest use of plant admixtures to *Peganum harmala* and to *Soma/Haoma* (for which, I hasten to add, there is absolutely no evidence)! Toward the conclusion of his part of the book, in §155 Note 5, he began to grasp at straws, to look for Indian *chacruna* and *chagropanga*—potential DMT-rich additives to *Soma/Haoma*! He suggesed particularly *Desmodium gangeticum* in the Leguminosae family, noting it is known as *saumya* or as *amsúmat* "rich in *soma* juice." He then went out on another shaky limb claiming "it appears the only way *Desmodium* species could have been effectively consumed as psychoactive drugs in India would have been by ingesting them with extracts of *Peganum harmala*, the one local source of these alkaloids"! While he was correct in noting DMT is inactive orally, requiring mixture with some MAO-inhibiting compounds like harmane alkaloids to render it orally-active, he failed to note two crucial points. First, *Desmodium gangeticum*, like *D. gyrans* and *D. pulchellum*, *itself* contains β-carboline alkaloids, as Flattery should have known by consulting one of his references (Banerjee & Ghosal 1969; see also Ghosal 1972; Ghosal *et al.* 1972). *D. pulchellum* contains some six different β-carbolines, including harman and *N*-methyl-6-methoxy-tetrahydro-β-carboline, known MAO-inhibitors (Buckholtz & Boggan 1977; McKenna *et al.* 1984A). Second, not only *Desmodium* species, but many other Indian plants contain β-carbolines (Allen & Holmstedt 1980). "*Peganum harmala*, the one local source of these alkaloids"... hardly! See Ott 1994A for a list of plants containing MAO-inhibiting β-carboline alkaloids, and Allen & Holmstedt's paper for a list of β-carboline alkaloid-containing plants. Even Wasson's candidate for *Soma*, *Amanita muscaria*, has been reported to contain a β-carboline alkaloid (Matsumoto *et al.* 1969). In animal tests, moreover, Ghosal found *concen-*

trated extracts of *Desmodium pulchellum* "only feebly active" (Ghosal 1972). There exist many other flaws in Flattery's arguments to which I could point, but I will cease in the interest of brevity. I cannot conclude, however, without taking issue with Flattery's repeated misuse of the word *intoxicant*, as in: "sacred intoxicant." The word means literally "to stupefy, render unconscious or delirious, to madden or deprive of the ordinary uses of the senses or reason, with a drug or alcoholic liquor." It can also mean "to 'poison'; to corrupt morally or spiritually" (*Oxford English Dictionary*, Compact Edition, p. 1471). Is Flattery so insensitive to the uses of language that he would speak of a "sacred intoxicant"? This is an oxymoron. Might I suggest he speak instead of a "sacred *inebriant*"? The meaning given to *inebriation* in the *Oxford English Dictionary* (Compact Edition, p. 1423) is appropriate: "extravagant exhilaration, excitement or emotion" and the first use of the word (1526) was apposite: "this inebriacyon or heuenly dronkennesse of the spiryte." In a book dealing with entheogens, and in which the bulk of the argument turns on the meanings of words, there is no place for such insensitive use of the English language. After publishing the first edition of this book in 1993, I offered Flattery a chance to rebut these devastating criticisms in *Integration*. He has declined... does this mean he is conceding?

[3] There has been an unfortunate confusion in the literature between *yajé* and harmaline, and between harmaline and harmine. In 1973 C. Naranjo published a paper on "Psychological Aspects of the *Yagé* Experience in an Experimental Setting" (Naranjo 1973B). As mentioned in the section "Modern Interest in *Ayahuasca* and *Harmel*," this paper in reality had nothing to do with experimental use of *yajé*, it rather involved previously described (Naranjo 1967) experiments with harmaline, incorrectly stated by Naranjo to be "the active alkaloid of *yagé*" (Naranjo 1973B). As detailed in the section "Chemistry of *Ayahuasca* and Pharmacology of *beta*-Carbolines," however, harmaline is at best a trace constituent in the *ayahuasca* potions analyzed to date—McKenna's group found only 25 mg harmaline in a 60 ml dose of *ayahuasca* from Pucallpa, which contained 437 mg total alkaloids, of which the great bulk (376 mg) was harmine and *d*-leptaflorine (TetraHydroHarmine or THH) in roughly a 3:1 ratio (McKenna *et al.* 1984A). In an earlier analysis of Peruvian *ayahuasca* samples, a 200 ml dose contained on average only traces of harmaline, and 40 mg of the 60 mg total alkaloids again was harmine plus *d*-leptaflorine (THH) in roughly a 3:1 ratio (Rivier & Lindgren 1972). A recent analysis of a *daime* potion found only traces of harmaline, and 144 mg of the 170 mg total alkaloids in a 50 ml dose consisted of roughly equal amounts of harmine and *d*-leptaflorine or THH (Liwszyc *et al.* 1992). In the case of all three potions, the psychoptic ingredient was DMT, with the β-carboline alkaloids harmine and *d*-leptaflorine (THH) being present in doses far too low for psychoactive effects, as Naranjo's own studies showed (Naranjo 1967). Rather, the β-carbolines in these potions serve as MAO-inhibitors (see section on "Pharmacology of β-Carbolines") to render the DMT orally-active. Even in this respect, harmaline, being a trace constituent "probably does not contribute significantly to the MAO inhibition which the drug elicits" (McKenna *et al.* 1984A). Clearly, Naranjo's 1973 paper had nothing to do with the pharmacology of *yajé*, and should have been entitled "Psychological Aspects of the *Harmaline* Experience in an Experimental Setting." Besides this misrepresentation by Naranjo, there have been at least six publications which have confused harmaline with harmine, effect-

ively claiming incorrectly that harmaline was the principal alkaloid of *ayahuasca*, rather than harmine. In his excellent 1975 study *The Shaman and the Jaguar*, Reichel-Dolmatoff made a slip on page 40, seeming to suggest that harmine and harmaline were synonymous: "the principal psychotropic substance contained in *Banisteriopsis* seems to be harmine (harmaline)," although on the next page he qualified this, saying quite correctly "*Banisteriopsis caapi* was found to contain—besides harmine—two other beta-carboline derivatives: harmaline and *d*-tetrahydroharmine" (Reichel-Dolmatoff 1975). In his 1980 book *The Marriage of the Sun and Moon*, Andrew Weil mixed up harmaline and harmine: "when German scientists first isolated the main alkaloid from the plant (*Banisteriopsis caapi*), they called it telepathine. (It is now known, less interestingly, as harmaline.)" (Weil 1980). Of course, *Colombian* scientist Fischer Cárdenas' *telepatina* or telepathine, is now known as *harmine*, not harmaline, whose only known synonym is *harmidine* (Chen & Chen 1939). Again, in their 1983 book *Chocolate to Morphine*, Weil and Winifred Rosen stated of "*Yagé*": "the plant owes most of its activity to harmaline" (corrected to read "harmine" in a revised edition), whereas quantitative analyses of various *Banisteriopsis caapi* cultivars have found *harmine* to be the principal alkaloid (McKenna *et al.* 1984A; Rivier & Lindgren 1972). While McKenna's group did find one of six cultivars assayed to have slightly more harmaline than harmine, the average for the six was harmine, just over 50% of the β-carboline fraction; harmaline, 24.5% (McKenna *et al.* 1984A). Moreover, in the *ayahuasca* brews assayed, harmine represented 65% of the alkaloidal fraction, *d*-leptaflorine or TetraHydroHarmine (THH) 22%, DMT 8%, and harmaline only 6%, suggesting harmaline is rather inefficiently extracted into the brews, or that some of the harmaline present in the plant is oxidized to harmine during the at times lengthy cooking process (Fischer 1899). As mentioned above, analyses of several *ayahuasca* brews by Rivier and Lindgren (1972) detected only trace amounts of harmaline, as did a recent analysis of *daime* from a South American Christian church (Liwszyc *et al.* 1992). In any case, *harmine* is the chief alkaloid of *B. caapi*, not harmaline, and harmine and *d*-leptaflorine (THH) represent 87% of the alkaloidal fraction of typical DMT-containing *ayahuasca* potions, and more than 93% of the β-carboline component (McKenna *et al.* 1984A). Again, in Peter Stafford's *Psychedelics Encyclopedia*, there are made repeated confusions between harmine and harmaline (Stafford 1983). On page 333–4, Stafford wrote: "in what follows, *ayahuasca* refers to the psychedelic [*sic*] species of *Banisteriopsis*, *yagé* to the drink made from their outer bark and harmaline to the primary psychedelic [*sic*] compound in the bark." Again, harmine, not harmaline, in the "primary psychedelic [*sic*] compound in the bark." Then, on pages 335–6, Stafford explained: "in 1923, Fischer assayed *yagé*, isolating an alkaloid that he named *telepathine*. The same year, Barriga–Villalba and Albarracin isolated two alkaloids from this drink; they called these *yajeine* and *yajeinine* [*sic*]. In 1928, Lewin isolated *banisterine*. Shortly afterward, Wolfes, as well as Rumpf and Elger, asserted that all these alkaloids were identical: they were harmaline..." (Stafford 1983). Again, *telepathine*, *yajéine* and *banisterine* were determined by Elger (1928) and by the group of Wolfes and Rumpf (1928) to be *harmine*, and not harmaline. There are several trivial errors in this sentence as well: 1) *yajénine*, misspelled by Stafford, was apparently different from *yajéine*, and probably was not harmine but another alkaloid; 2) Barriga Villalba, no hyphen necessary, did his work two years after Fischer Cárdenas, and both were working with plant material (which Stafford said he would call *ayahuasca*; whereas here Stafford says the isolation was from *yagé*, by which he means the beverage); 3) Rumpf was working with Wolfes in Germany, whereas Elger worked alone; 'though Stafford's wording makes it sound as though Rumpf and Elger were a team and Wolfes independent. Stafford again trips up in the next sentence: "this conclusion was in doubt for some time, until Chen and Chen, working with clearly identified botanicals, demonstrated that all these substances were harmaline." Again, Stafford here means to say *harmine*. Fortunately, on arriving at his section on chemistry, Stafford gets the names right on his diagrams, but gives pride of place to harmaline at the head of the page, and the chapter is entitled "*Ayahuasca*, *Yagé* and Harmaline," giving undue emphasis to harmaline rather than the main component harmine. Stafford trips up one last time on page 355, saying "Lewin tried harmaline clinically on mental patients in the late 1920s." Once again, it was *harmine* with which Lewin experimented in the twenties (Lewin 1928; Lewin 1929). In their 1981 book on psychotherapeutic use of "hallucinogens," which is full of similar errors, especially with regard to phytochemistry and ethnopharmacognosy, Roquet and Favreau also confuse harmine and harmaline (Roquet & Favreau 1981). These authors list harmaline and *d*-1,2,3,4-tetrahydroharmaline [*sic*] as the active agents of *ayahuasca*—harmaline, of course, is only a trace constituent, and it is 3,4-dihydroharmine. In reality the active agents are harmine and *d*-1,2,3,4-tetrahydro*harmine*. Finally, as already mentioned, Flattery and Schwartz erred in naming their book *Haoma and Harmaline*, since again, *harmine* is the principal alkaloid of *Peganum harmala* and *Banisteriopsis caapi*, subjects of their book. In section §93, Note 27, we find: "the report of clinical studies by C. Caller Ibérico (1941) in which small doses of harmaline were found to have pronounced effects directly on sexual organs..." when in reality Ibérico experimented with *ayahuasca* "in small doses, equivalent to 5 mg. of banisterine or harmine" (Ibérico 1941). See Note 2 above for review of more serious errors in this book.

[4] The following species of plants have been found to contain harmine: *Amsonia tabernaemontana* (Apocynaceae); *Calycanthus occidentalis* (Calycanthaceae); *Kochia scoparia* (Chenopodiaceae); *Carex brevicollis* (Cyperaceae); *Banisteriopsis muricata* (=*B. argentea*), *B. caapi*, *B. inebrians* (=*B. caapi*), *B. lutea* (=*B. nitrosiodora*), *Cabi paraensis* (=*Callaeum antifebrile*, *Mascagnia psilophylla* var. *antifebrilis*; Malpighiaceae); *Passiflora incarnata* (Passifloraceae); *Peganum harmala*, *Tribulus terrestris*, and *Zygophyllum fabago* (Zygophyllaceae). Besides *Banisteriopsis* species and *Peganum harmala*, *Passiflora incarnata* is the only other known source of harmaline, and the rubiaceous *Leptactinia densiflora* is the only other currently-known source of TetraHydroHarmine (in racemic form), likewise called leptaflorine (Allen & Holmstedt 1980). Besides *Peganum harmala* and *Banisteriopsis* species, the following 62 plant species have been found to contain known MAO-inhibiting β-carbolines (Allen & Holmstedt 1980; Buckholtz & Boggan 1977; McIsaac & Estévez 1966; McKenna *et al.* 1984A): *Coriolus maximus* (Agaricaceae); *Amsonia tabernaemontana*, *Apocynum cannabinum*, *Ochrosia nakaiana* (Apocynaceae); *Calycanthus occidentalis* (Calycanthaceae); *Hammada leptoclada*, *Kochia scoparia* (Chenopodiaceae); *Guiera senegalensis* (Combretaceae); *Carex brevicollis* (Cyperaceae); *Elaeagnus angustifolia*, *E. hortensis*, *E. orientalis*, *E. spinosa*, *Hippophae rhamnoides*, *Shepherdia argentea*, *S. canadensis* (Elaeagnaceae); *Arundo donax*, *Festuca arundinacea*, *Lolium perenne* (Gramineae); *Acacia baileyana*, *A.*

complanata, Burkea africana, Desmodium pulchellum, Mucuna pruriens, Petalostylis labicheoides, Prosopis nigra (Leguminosae); *Strychnos usambarensis* (Loganiaceae); *Cabi paraensis* (=*Callaeum antifebrile*; Malpighiaceae); *Virola cuspidata* (Myristicaeae); *Passiflora actinea, P. alata, P. alba, P. bryonioides, P. caerulea, P. capsularis, P. decaisneana, P. edulis, P. eichleriana, P. foetida, P. incarnata, P. quadrangularis, P.* aff. *ruberosa, P. subpeltata, P. warmingii* (Passifloraceae); *Calligonum minimum* (Polygonaceae); *Leptactinia densiflora, Nauclea diderrichii, Ophiorrhiza japonica, Pauridiantha callicarpoides, P. dewevrei, P. lyalli, P. viridiflora, Simira klugii, S. rubra, Uncaria attenuata, U. canescens, U. orientalis* (Rubiaceae); *Chrysophyllum lacourtianum* (Sapotaceae); *Symplocos racemosa* (Symplocaceae); *Fagonia cretica, Tribulus terrestris* and *Zygophyllum fabago* (Zygophyllaceae). A mushroom recently found to contain the β-carbolines infractin, 6-hydroxy-infractin and infractipicrin, *Cortinarius infractus* (Steglich *et al.* 1984), has been alleged to be "hallucinogenic" (Azéma 1987; Giacomoni 1987), a dubious proposition in absence of human psychonautic bioassay or other pharmacological data (Samorini 1993A).

5 Botanical "voucher specimens" are pressed, dried and mounted samples of a collection of plants to be studied chemically (or otherwise), complete with a label giving as much information about the collection as possible—date, place, elevation, collector's name and collection number, comments on the geology and ecology of the collection site (*i.e.* soil type, climate zone, other common plants found nearby *etc.*) and particularly ethnobotanical information (local names and their meaning, economic uses, folklore associated with the plant, *etc.*)—which are then deposited in a recognized herbarium. Ideally, the voucher specimen will include reproductive parts of the plant (flowers, fruits, seeds) as well as representative leaf and stem material. Often the reproductive parts are necessary to be able to identify the plant. The voucher specimen is thus available for later inspection to verify or *vouch for* the identification of any plant which, after being analyzed chemically, is to be reported in the scientific literature to contain one or another compound (Bye 1986B; Schultes 1962; Schultes 1966). The editorial boards of most scientific journals reporting the results of phytochemical analyses or ethnobotanical studies now rightly insist that papers include references to voucher specimens for all species analyzed, in the event doubts arise in the future as to the identification of the plant material. In the case of Hochstein and Paradies' reporting of DMT in *Prestonia amazonica*, specialists today doubt the identification of the source material, since DMT is not known from the Apocynaceae family, nor is *P. amazonica* known from the area in which the collection supposedly was made. Since all of the collection was presumably ground up and analyzed, and no voucher specimen was deposited in an herbarium (indeed, the authors apparently saw only an aqueous extract of leaves and not the source plant), we today have no way of unravelling the mystery of this collection. For information on a basic field kit for botanical specimen collection, and photographs of pressed specimens, see the articles by Rob Montgomery and "Veriditas" in the Fall 1989 *Whole Earth Review* (Montgomery 1989; Veriditas 1989).

6 As pointed out in Chapter 2, Note 13, animal experiments are of little value in phytochemical studies of entheogens, having proven useless in attempts to isolate the active fractions of the *péyotl* cactus and the *teonanácatl* mushrooms. Only through the use of

human experimentation were scientists able to isolate the entheogenic principles of these plants. As emphasized in Chapter 2, Note 15, and in Chapter 3, Note 2, however, it is highly unethical to use as research subjects imprisoned human "guinea pigs." It doesn't make any difference whether they are called prisoners (having been convicted of a crime, and sentenced to a penal institution) or euphemistically designated "patients" in a "mental hospital" or "addiction research center hospital" (people who have not been convicted of any crime, and given an indefinite, perhaps life, sentence; some of them having been accused of a crime, but judged mentally incompetent to stand trial). Whether called prisoners, convicts, addicts or patients, all such individuals are incarcerated against their wills, and it is unethical to use them as research guinea pigs. The Nürnberg War Crimes Tribunal concluded as much in the process of sentencing German physicians to the gallows for experiments little different in kind from those conducted by men like Turner and Merlis (Annas & Grodin 1992). If animal experiments are worthless, and experiments on prisoners and mental "patients" are unethical... what about employing volunteers? Technically, this is acceptable, but it would still be unethical to convince another person to ingest something one would not oneself be willing to ingest, what one had not *already ingested oneself.* In short, in order to conduct this sort of research, one must be willing to be a psychonaut, to use oneself as primary research subject, later employing other volunteer human beings when basic safety and dosage have been established. The efficient and ethical procedures for conducting this research have been admirably well worked out and explained in Alexander Shulgin's and Ann Shulgin's wonderful book *PIHKAL—A Chemical Love Story* (Shulgin & Shulgin 1991), which details the synthesis and human testing of 179 novel compounds. See Ott 1995A for ethics of human *vs.* animal testing of entheogens.

7 On examining *Ethnopharmacologic Search for Psychoactive Drugs* (Efron *et al.* 1967), the proceedings of the 1967 conference organized during the administration of L.B. Johnson, I note with sadness the extent to which the government of the United States has degenerated in the intervening 25 years. In 1967, even in the midst of widespread social unrest and a spreading so-called "drug plague" involving the use of marijuana and LSD by students and other elements of society, the National Institute of Mental Health (NIMH), a division of the Public Health Service in the former Department of Health, Education and Welfare, organized and financed an important international symposium dealing primarily with entheogenic drugs. Thirty-two scientists from eight countries (Argentina, Chile, Germany, México, Sweden, Switzerland, the United States and the ex-Union of Soviet Socialist Republics) were invited to San Francisco by D.H. Efron of the "Psychopharmacology Research Branch" of the NIMH to present and discuss the latest research on psychoactive drugs (*vide*: Efron 1970). There were six sessions: 1) *Piper methysticum* (*kava*); 2) pharmacology of *kava*; 3) *Myristica fragrans* (nutmeg); 4) South American snuffs; 5) *ayahuasca, caapi, yagé*; and 6) *Amanita muscaria* (fly-agaric). There was open and frank discussion of the law (Freedman 1967), with conference co-organizer and co-editor of the proceedings Nathan S. Kline opining: "we probably should not, and in any case *can* not effectively, legislate against exploration of these other worlds" (italics in the original; Kline 1967). The three editors (Americans Efron and Kline and Swede Bo Holmstedt) compiled a superb volume of proceedings of the symposium, produced by the U.S. Govern-

ment Printing Office in a utilitarian, hardcover edition, which was sold at the bargain price of $4.00 *per* copy. The book was 468 pages in length, with 6 maps, 27 tables, 47 graphs, and 98 illustrations including rare photographs of indigenous use of South American snuffs, of antique snuff-related artifacts, chemical structures of active compounds, and photographs and botanical illustrations of many entheogenic plants, including *Anadenanthera peregrina*, *Banisteriopsis caapi*, *Brunfelsia latifolia*, *Brunfelsia maritima* (later identified as *B. grandiflora*; Plowman 1977), *Lophophora williamsii*, *Salvia divinorum*, *Tetrapterys methystica*, *Trichocereus pachanoi* and *Virola calophylloidea*. I consider the $4.00 price to be a bargain by comparing it with the 1964 edition of Weston La Barre's *The Peyote Cult* which came out at $7.50 (260 pages in length) and the 1967 edition of Hoffer and Osmond's *The Hallucinogens*, which cost $15.00 (626 pages long). This book was the most complete study of *kava* hitherto published, and one of the most thorough studies of South American snuffs in print. It summarized the state of knowledge in 1967 on chemistry and pharmacology of nutmeg-related compounds, of the β-carbolines of *ayahuasca* and of isoxazole compounds from *Amanita muscaria*. This book has a good index and all of the papers have bibliographies. In short, our government in 1967 produced a valuable and useful book on psychoactive drugs, and made it available at an artificially low price. I found it to be one of the books in my library most frequently consulted during the writing of this book, and its value is further attested by the fact that, although the Superintendent of Documents of the U.S. Government Printing Office had not seen fit to keep the book in print, a commercial reprint edition of the *uncopyrighted* book was brought out by Raven Press in 1979. And what has happened in the intervening 30 years? Federal and state governments now spend more than $10 billion *per* year on a quixotic "War on Drugs" (Nadelmann 1989). How curious that the phrase "War on Drugs" was borrowed *verbatim* from the title of a magazine published by one of right-wing extremist Lyndon La Rouche's cover organizations, once beyond the pale politically and now part of official policy (Berlet 1981; Crawford 1982)! Since waging war is one of the few activities which the United States government does more or less competently and with enthusiasm, we presently have "wars" on drugs, AIDS, poverty (invoking images of napalm attacks on the ghettos), cancer *etc.* and former President Carter called the energy/œcological crisis "the moral equivalent of war" in order to get the public's attention (then Carter failed to win reelection principally because he neglected to sate the public appetite for *real* wars!). In former President George Bush's fiscal 1991 budget for the "National Drug Control Strategy," 71% of the funds were for interdiction and law-enforcement efforts, only 29% for "demand reduction" (Goldstein & Kalant 1990). "Demand reduction" includes education and research activities. Unfortunately, U.S. government drug "education" consists mainly of anti-drug propaganda, and, especially since the election of Ronald Reagan to the presidency, "drugabuseology research" has consisted mainly of a search for scientific rationalizations to support the prohibition of marijuana, cocaine and the entheogens. For someone today in the federal bureaucracy to organize a symposium, such as the one D.H. Efron organized in 1967, would be the "kiss of death" for her or his career… for a contemporary researcher to question the drug laws in a U.S. government publication, as N.S. Kline did in 1967, would today be tantamount to self-destruction—to automatic disqualification from further governmental research support, besides guaranteeing that the study would neither be printed nor disseminated. Imagine government employees today trying to publish a book like *Ethnopharmacologic Search for Psychoactive Drugs*! In an era in which there was an immediate hue and cry by the conservative element of the body politic over a proposed sex survey as part of the "War on AIDS," and in which the government has immediately caved in and canceled research or publications which the conservatives found objectionable, it would be unthinkable for such a publication to appear. A book with illustrations of illegal drugs lacking the appropriate captions ("Dangerous and Addicting Narcotics") just won't pass muster... a book with photographs of Indians snuffing (and enjoying) *coca* and DMT-containing snuffs, then dancing naked around the *maloca* (communal dwelling)! A book with several photographs of adult males depicting *full frontal nudity*... one cannot contemplate such a thing in 1996 without the fiery, smoking spectacle of bureaucratic careers going down in flames!

[8] Furthermore, Lamb's choice of the word *wizard* in the title of *Wizard of the Upper Amazon* is inappropriate and unfelicitous. The original meaning of "philosopher, sage," perhaps intended by Lamb, has been lost, is obsolete, according to *The Heritage Illustrated Dictionary of the English Language* (1979, p. 1471). While the *Oxford English Dictionary* (Compact Edition, p. 3805) gives this as the first meaning, but it is accompanied by the legend "often contemptuous, obsolete." The *Oxford English Dictionary* gives as a third meaning "a witch-doctor or medicine man," but the second meaning is "masculine correlative of witch," like the first meaning in *The Heritage Illustrated Dictionary*—"a male witch." We cannot overlook the fact that the word, owing to the success of the film *The Wizard of Oz*, has acquired the modern sense of "charlatan, imposter." A typical image conjured by the word is the graybeard buffoon with a pointy hat depicted in *The Heritage Illustrated Dictionary*. In any case, this term, in Lamb's usage, is at best equivalent to "witch-doctor," evidently the intended meaning, as a pre-publication excerpt in *Fate* was entitled "Witch Doctor of the Upper Amazon" (Horowitz 1992). "Witch doctor" is a pejorative and denigrating epithet having no place in a supposedly anthropological work. Or did Lamb have in mind *The Wizard of Oz*?

[9] Details of the life of Mestre Raimundo Irineu Serra and the history of *Santo Daime* can be found in Edward MacRae's new book (published on the 100th anniversary of the birth of Mestre Irineu) *Guiado Pela Lua: Xamanismo e Uso Ritual da Ayahuasca no Culto do Santo Daime* (MacRae 1992). Mestre Irineu (1892–1971) came into contact with Cashinahua and other Indian groups who employed *ayahuasca* traditionally while he worked as a rubber tapper and later as an official of the Brasilian government agency demarcating the border with Bolivia and Perú. He also met Antonio and André Costa, two brothers who had been introduced to *ayahuasca* by Peruvian shaman Don Crescêncio Pizango, and who later founded the Círculo de Regeneração e Fé (CRF) early in the 1920s. It was evidently during Mestre Irineu's association with CRF that he was initiated into the use of *ayahuasca*, and the CRF is considered to be the precursor to *Santo Daime*. Mestre Irineu had a falling-out with the Costa brothers, and soon founded his own church, the Centro de Iluminação Cristã Luz Universal (CICLU), commonly known as "Alto Santo," in Rio Branco, Acre state, around 1940. As early as 1930, Mestre Irineu began to attract disciples to his eclectic

ayahuasca church, which adopted ever more elements of Christianity, in an effort to avoid persecution under an 1890 federal law which illegalized practice of medicine without a license, *curanderismo*, and "poisonous substances" (*i.e. ayahuasca* and other shamanic inebriants). Mestre Irineu became a famous *curandero* and around 1930 began to call *ayahuasca* "Daime" from invocations such as "Dá-me amor, luz, força" ("grant me love, light, power"). *Daime* was the solar, masculine aspect in his doctrine, while the lunar, feminine aspect was Nossa Senhora da Conceição or Rainha da Floresta. We know that at least as early as 1931, Mestre Irineu was leading public *ayahuasca* sessions and teaching his doctrine, and that his church was affiliated with the Rosicrucian Order and other Christian esoteric groups. The *Santo Daime* doctrine emphasizes a series of dualities—sun/moon; father/mother; God/Our Lady; man/woman; *cipó* or *mariri* or *jagube* (*Banisteriopsis caapi*)/*folha* or *rainha* or *chacrona* (*Psychotria viridis*). The most successful of Mestre Irineu's many disciples was Sebastião Mota de Melo or Padrinho Sebastião, who became a disciple at Alto Santo in 1965, after Mestre Irineu cured him of a liver ailment and in the process introduced him to *ayahuasca*. Mestre Irineu authorized Padrinho Sebastião to produce *daime* at the latter's ranch Colonia 5000 near Rio Branco, with the understanding that one-half of the production would go to Alto Santo. When Padrinho Sebastião split with Mestre Irineu over political differences, Colonia 5000 became an independent group, which began to incorporate use of *Cannabis* (known as *Santa María* or *maconha* in Brasil) and other entheogens into the *Daime* liturgy. This led in October 1981 to a raid on Colonia 5000 by federal police, who destroyed the *Cannabis* gardens. This provoked negative publicity, which ultimately led to the illegalization of *ayahuasca* in Brasil in 1985. Padrinho Sebastião's group dropped the use of *Cannabis* and moved deeper into the forest in January 1983, two days' journey by canoe from the nearest town. The new colony was called Céu do Mapiá, and was located on a tributary of the Río Purús, near traditional territory of Culina and Sharanahua Indians, whose *ayahuasca* was among the first to be studied chemically by Rivier and Lindgren in 1972. The cult grew and attracted outsiders—at first hippies in search of shamanic inebriants. In 1982 the first *Daime* church outside of Amazonia was founded in Rio de Janeiro, the Chamou-se centro Ecléctico Fluente Luz universal sebastião Mota de MElo (CEFLUSME), called Céu do Mar for short. The cult rapidly spread to other urban areas of Brasil. Meanwhile, an independent group called Centro Espírita Beneficente união DO vegetal (UDV), founded in 1961 in Rondônia state by José Gabriel da Costa, began to spread in urban areas of Brasil, becoming today the largest *ayahuasca* church, later moving its headquarters to Brasilia, the new Brasilian capital, in the 1970s. Other *ayahuasca*-using groups flourished, such as the Centro Espírita Culto de Oração Casa de Jesus Fonte de Luz (later called Centro Espírita Daniel Pereira de Matos; then Centro Espírita e Obra de Caridade Príncipe Espadarte Reino da Paz, or "a Barquinha"), centro Ecléctico de correntes da LUZ universal (CECLU) and Centro Espírita Fé, Luz, Amor e Caridade, all of Acre state and derivatives of Alto Santo. This rapid expansion frightened the Brasilian authorities, under pressure from the United States government and the United Nations to join the "War on Drugs." In 1985 the Brasilian DIvisão de MEDIcamentos do Ministério da Saúde (Dimed) and the CONselho Federal de ENtorpecentes (Confen) added *Banisteriopsis caapi* to the controlled substances list. The UDV petitioned Confen to annul the ban, which they did on 26 August 1987. A government commission appointed to study the issue found no evidence of social disruption after six decades of sacramental use of *daime* and *chá hoasca*, and noted that the ethical and laboral behavior of members of the *ayahuasca* churches was above reproach. The commission based its conclusions on two years of field work among UDV and *Santo Daime* groups in Amazonia (Colonia 5000, Alto Santo, Céu do Mapiá) and in urban areas (Céu do Mar and others). Members were interviewed, ritual use of *daime* and *hoasca* was observed, and commission members, to their credit, *themselves* tried the sacrament in a ritual setting. The official report concluded that *hoasca* was an "hallucinogen," was little suited to ludible use owing to side-effects and that its use was well controlled by the ritual context of self-discovery and spiritual development. The 1987 removal of *Banisteriopsis caapi* from the Brasilian controlled substances list effectively legalized its sacramental use in Brasil, and a meeting of disparate *Daime* church groups in May 1989 at Céu do Mapiá led to the organization of a central church, Centro Ecléctico de Fluente Luz Universal Raimundo Irineu Serra (CEFLURIS), with the late Padrinho Sebastião as head. Plantations of *Banisteriopsis caapi* and *Psychotria viridis* have been established in Amazonia to supply the urban groups with the sacrament. Unfortunately, in 1988 there was an anonymous denunciation of *Santo Daime* to Confen in Rio de Janeiro. The preposterous (and cowardly, given its anonymity) complaint alleged there were 10 million "fanatics" of the *ayahuasca* sects, the bulk of whom were "toxicomaniacs or ex-guerillas" (here the right-wing political motivation of the complaint becomes manifest), who were given to smoking *Cannabis* and ingesting LSD during the rites. Adepts were alleged to have been enslaved by the cults (an apparent attempt to play on fears kindled by the mass-suicides in Jonestown). Once again, Confen appointed a commission to study *ayahuasca* churches, which once again received a clean bill of health. Besides reaffirming the 1987 decree legalizing ritual use of *hoasca* in Brasil, the commission recommended permanent exemption of the potion from controlled substances laws, in spite of the fact that a review of the scientific literature had disclosed correctly that the potions contained DMT and harmine, both of which had already been officially proscribed in Brasil by Dimed. Commission member Isaac Karniol courageously and sensibly concluded that prohibition of sacramental use of *ayahuasca* would cause much more harm than any pharmacological action of the potion ever could. Six decades of sacramental use of the potion in Brasil had produced many positive effects, with no serious side-effects, and church members had learned adequately to regulate use without interference from the state, interference which could only provoke problems. Thanks to the legal status of *hoasca* in Brasil, attempts have been made to export the church to other countries. Although in the United States the church has not yet fared well, it appears to be establishing itself in Spain, Catalunya and other European countries. There has even been some door-to-door canvassing by *Santo Daime* members in Spain, attempting to solicit recruits to attend weekend retreats at which *ayahuasca* potions are served! The UDV has also established the church in other countries, even obtaining tax-exempt status in a few states in the U.S. With the 1994 federal legalization of the *péyotl*-using Native American Church, and various federal court rulings extending religious freedom in the matter of genuine sacraments to non-Indians (Ott 1995B), it would appear the door is open to establishment of the *ayahuasca* churches in the United States. However, the tenuous legal status of UDV in the U.S. has more to do with ignorance than tolerance by U.S. officials.

TABLE 3
AYAHUASCA ADDITIVE PLANTS*

ACANTHACEAE
Teliostachya lanceolata Nees var. *crispa* Nees[1] (Schultes 1972C)
AMARANTHACEAE
Alternanthera lehmannii Hieronymus[1] (García Barriga 1958; Schultes 1957A)
Iresine sp. (Schultes & Hofmann 1979)
APOCYNACEAE
Himatanthus sucuuba (Spruce ex Mueller-Argoviensis) Woodson (Luna 1984B)
Malouetia tamaquarina (Aublet) DC. (Pinkley 1969; Schultes 1957A; 1960)
Mandevilla scabra Schumann (Luna & Amaringo 1991)
Tabernaemontana sp. (Luna 1984A; Luna 1984B; Pinkley 1969; Schultes 1972C)
AQUIFOLIACEAE
Ilex guayusa Loesner[2] (Furst 1976; Schultes 1972D; Schultes & Raffauf 1990)
ARACEAE
Montrichardia arborescens Schott (Luna 1984A)
Spathiphyllum sp.[3] (Luz 1995)
BIGNONIACEAE
Mansoa alliacea (Lamarck) A. Gentry (Luna 1984B)
Tabebuia heteropoda (DC.) Sandwith (McKenna *et al.* 1986)
Tabebuia incana A. Gentry (Luna 1984A)
Tabebuia sp. (Luna 1984B)
Tynnanthus panurensis (Burman) Sandwith (Luna 1984B)
BOMBACACEAE
Cavanillesia hylogeiton Ulbrich (Luna & Amaringo 1991)
Cavanillesia umbellata Ruíz et Pavón (Luna & Amaringo 1991)
Ceiba pentandra (L.) Gaertner (Luna 1984B)
Chorisia insignis Humboldt, Bonpland et Kunth (Luna 1984B)
Chorisia speciosa Humboldt, Bonpland et Kunth (McKenna *et al.* 1986)
Quararibea "*ishpingo*" (Arévalo Valera 1986; Wassén 1979)
CACTACEAE
Epiphyllum sp. (Pinkley 1969; Rivier & Lindgren 1972)
Opuntia sp.[1] (Rivier & Lindgren 1972)
CARYOCARACEAE
Anthodiscus pilosus Ducke (McKenna *et al.* 1986)
CELASTRACEAE

Maytenus ebenifolia Reiss (Luna 1984A; Luna 1984B)

CYCLANTHACEAE

Carludovica divergens Ducke (Luna 1984A)

CYPERACEAE

Cyperus digitatus Roxburgh (McKenna *et al.* 1986)
Cyperus prolixus Humboldt, Bonpland et Kunth (McKenna *et al.* 1986)
Cyperus sp. (Pinkley 1969; Rivier & Lindgren 1972)

DRYOPTERIDACEAE

Lomariopsis japurensis (Martius) J. Sm. (Pinkley 1969; Rivier & Lindgren 1972)

ERYTHROXYLACEAE

Erythroxylum coca Lamarck var. *ipadú* Plowman[2] (Wilbert 1987)

EUPHORBIACEAE

Alchornea castanaefolia (Willdenow) Just. (Luna 1984A; Luna 1984B)
Hura crepitans L. (Luna 1984A; Luna 1984B)

GNETACEAE

Gnetum nodiflorum Brongniart (Schultes & Raffauf 1990)

GUTTIFERAE

Clusia sp. (Rivier & Lindgren 1972; Schultes & Raffauf 1990)
Tovomita sp. (Luna 1984B)
Vismia guianensis (Aublet) Choisy (Luz 1995)

LABIATAE

Ocimum micranthum Willdenow (Pinkley 1969)

LECYTHIDACEAE

Couroupita guianensis Aublet (Luna 1984A; Luna 1984B)

LEGUMINOSAE

Bauhinia guianensis Aublet (Luna & Amaringo 1991)
Caesalpinia echinata Lamarck (Luna 1984A)
Calliandra angustifolia Spruce ex Bentham (Luna 1984B)
Campsiandra laurifolia Bentham (Luna 1984A)
Cedrelinga castaneiformis Ducke (Luna 1984B)
Erythrina glauca Willdenow (Luna 1984B)
Erythrina poeppigiana (Walpers) Cook (McKenna *et al.* 1986)
Pithecellobium laetum Bentham (Luna 1984B)
Sclerobium setiferum Ducke (McKenna *et al.* 1986)
Vouacapoua americana Aublet (Luna 1984B)

LORANTHACEAE

Phrygilanthus eugenioides (L.) HBK (Pinkley 1969; Rivier & Lindgren 1972)

Phrygilanthus eugenioides (L.) HBK var. *robustus* Glaz. (McKenna *et al.* 1986)
Phthirusa pyrifolia (HBK) Eichler (Luna 1984A; Luna 1984B)
MALPIGHIACEAE
Diplopterys cabrerana (Cuatrecasas) Gates[1] (Agurell *et al.* 1968B; Der Marderosian *et al.* 1968; Pinkley 1969; Poisson 1965; Schultes 1972C)
Diplopterys involuta (Turczaninow) Niedenzu = *Mezia includens* (Bentham) Cuatrecasas[4] (Schultes 1983B)
Mascagnia psilophylla (Jussieu) Grisebach var. *antifebrilis* Niedenzu[1] = *Cabi paraensis* (Jussieu) Grisebach; *Callaeum antifebrile* (Grisebach) Johnson (Schultes 1957A)
MARANTACEAE
Calathea veitchiana Veitch ex Hooker *fil.* (Schultes 1972C)
MENISPERMACEAE
Abuta grandifolia (Martius) Sandwith (Luna 1984B)
MORACEAE
Coussapoa tessmannii Mildbread (McKenna *et al.* 1986)
Ficus insipida Willdenow (Luna 1984B)
Ficus ruiziana Standley (McKenna *et al.* 1986)
Ficus sp. (Luna 1984B)
MYRISTICACEAE
Virola sp. (Luna 1984B)
Virola surinamensis (Roland) Warburg (Luna 1984A; Luna 1984B)
NYMPHIACEAE
Cabomba aquatica Aublet (McKenna *et al.* 1986)
PHYTOLACCACEAE
Petiveria alliacea L. (Luna 1984B)
PIPERACEAE
Piper sp. (Schultes & Raffauf 1990)
POLYGONACEAE
Triplaris surinamensis Chamisso (Luna 1984A; Luna 1984B)
Triplaris surinamensis Cham. var. *chamissoana* Meissner (McKenna *et al.* 1986)
PONTEDERIACEAE
Pontederia cordata L.[4] (Schultes 1972C)
RUBIACEAE
Calycophyllum spruceanum (Bentham) Hooker *fil.* ex Schumann (Luna 1984A)
Capirona decorticans Spruce (Luna 1984B)
Guettarda ferox Standley (McKenna *et al.* 1986)

Psychotria carthaginensis Jacquin[1] (Luna 1984A; Pinkley 1969; Schultes 1972C)
Psychotria psychotriaefolia (Seemann) Standley (Pinkley 1969; Prance 1970)
Psychotria "batsikawa" (Der Marderosian *et al.* 1970; Rivier & Lindgren 1972)
Psychotria "nai kawa" (Der Marderosian *et al.* 1970)
Psychotria "pishikawa" (Rivier & Lindgren 1972)
Psychotria viridis Ruíz et Pavón[1] (Luna 1984A; Pinkley 1969; Prance 1970)
Rudgea retifolia Standley (Schultes 1985C; Schultes & Raffauf 1990)
Sabicea amazonensis Wernham (Hugh-Jones 1979; Schultes 1985C; Schultes & Raffauf 1990; Schultes & Raffauf 1992)
Uncaria guianensis (Aublet) Gmelin (McKenna *et al.* 1986)

SAPINDACEAE

Paullinia yoco Schultes et Killip[2] (Langdon 1986)

SCHIZAEACEAE

Lygodium venustum Swartz (Pinkley 1969; Rivier & Lindgren 1972)

SCROPHULARIACEAE

Scoparia dulcis L. (Luna 1984B)

SOLANACEAE

Brugmansia insignis (Barbosa-Rodrígues) Lockwood ex Schultes[1] (Schultes & Raffauf 1990)
Brugmansia suaveolens (Humb. et Bonpl. ex Willd.) Berchtold et Presl[1] (Dobkin de Ríos 1970B; Luna 1984A; Luna 1984B; Rivier & Lindgren 1972)
Brunfelsia chiricaspi Plowman[1] (Plowman 1977)
Brunfelsia grandiflora D. Don[1] (Plowman 1977; Schultes & Raffauf 1990)
Brunfelsia grandiflora D. Don subsp. *schultesii* Plowman[1] (Luna 1984B; Pinkley 1969; Plowman 1977; Schultes & Raffauf 1990)
Capsicum sp. (Rivier & Lindgren 1972; Schultes & Raffauf 1990)
Iochroma fuchsioides (HBK) Miers[1] (McKenna *et al.* 1986)
Juanulloa ochracea Cuatrecasas[4] (Schultes 1972C)
Nicotiana rustica L.[1] (Luna 1984B; Wilbert 1987)
Nicotiana tabacum L.[1] (Luna 1984B; Schultes 1972C; Wilbert 1987)

VERBENACEAE

Cornutia odorata (Poeppig et Endlicher) Poeppig (McKenna *et al.* 1984A)
Vitex triflora Vahl (McKenna *et al.* 1986)

VIOLACEAE

Rinorea viridiflora Rusby[4] (Schultes & Raffauf 1990)

NOTES

[1] These *ayahuasca* additives are known entheogenic plants, many of which are at times used alone for their psychoptic effect, in absence of *ayahuasca*.

[2] These *ayahuasca* cohorts are known stimulants, used alone and as *ayahuasca* additives. In the latter case, their function appears to be counteracting the marked soporific effects of *ayahuasca*, so shaman or patient will not fall asleep during the session. Both *Ilex guayusa* and *Paullinia yoco* are known to be abundant sources of the stimulant caffeine (Lewis *et al.* 1991; Schultes 1986A; Schultes & Raffauf 1990), and *Erythroxlum coca* var. *ipadú* is a known source of the stimulant cocaine (Holmstedt *et al.* 1971; Plowman 1981).

[3] It was recently reported that a species of *Spathiphyllum* is burned and the ash leached with water to yield a powder for coating "edible" pellets of *Virola* resin used by the Witoto Indians of the Colombian Amazon (Schultes & Raffauf 1990). See: Chapter 3, "Chemistry of Entheogenic *Virola* Snuffs."

[4] These species have not been reported to be used as *ayahuasca* additives, but are presumed to have been so used, because they are sometimes known by the name *ayahuasca* or *chacruna* or are otherwise somehow related to the famous potion (Schultes 1972C; Schultes 1985C; Schultes & Raffauf 1990).

* This Table lists plant species reportedly used as additives or "admixtures" to entheogenic *ayahuasca* potions in Amazonia. In many cases, the additives are said to "heighten and lengthen" the visionary properties of the brews (Schultes & Hofmann 1980). In other cases, additive plants are stimulants whose effect counteracts the soporific properties of the simple extracts of *Banisteriopsis caapi* (Furst 1976; Schultes & Raffauf 1990). Finally, some additives appear to be therapeutic (Luna 1984A; Luna 1984B; Luna & Amaringo 1991; McKenna *et al.* 1986) and probably do not exert psychoactive effects. Many of the plants listed here are simply unknown chemically and the rationale for their use in *ayahuasca* is obscure. Certainly some of these unknown plants will prove to be psychoactive. The chemistry of 56 species of *ayahuasca* additive plants has recently been reviewed by D.J. McKenna and colleagues, who aptly characterize the Amazonian *ayahuasca* complex as a "traditional pharmacopoeia" (McKenna *et al.* 1986). There may be some duplication in this table. For example, Luna (1984A) reported a *Tabebuia* species as *ayahuasca* additive, then two years later reported *Tabebuia heteropoda* as additive (McKenna *et al.* 1986). The *Cyperus* species reported as *ayahuasca* admixture two decades ago (Pinkley 1969; Rivier & Lindgren 1972) may be either *C. prolixus* or *C. digitatus* reported subsequently (the former in the English version and the latter in the Spanish of McKenna *et al.* 1986). Similarly, the *Ficus* species Luna (1984B) reported may be *F. ruiziana* he reported two years later (McKenna *et al.* 1986).

CHAPTER FIVE
Psilocybine–Psilocine–Baeocystine: The Teonanácatl Complex

> The *curanderas*… had now taken a total dosage of 30 mg psilocybin. After about ten more minutes the mushroom spirit began to work. María Sabina started to chant…
>
> **Albert Hofmann**
> *Teonanácatl* (1978)

On the evening of 11 October 1962, near the remote Mexican village of Huautla de Jiménez, in the Sierra Madre Oriental of Oaxaca, the Swiss chemist Albert Hofmann gave 30 milligrams of synthetic psilocybine each to María Sabina, her daughter, and another Mazatec shaman. Hofmann also gave 10 milligrams of psilocybine to R. Gordon Wasson, who seven years earlier had become the first outsider ever purposefully to ingest the sacred mushrooms of México, when he was initiated into the sacred Mystery by María Sabina. Hofmann had obtained specimens of María Sabina's mushrooms through Wasson, and in his laboratory at Sandoz LTD. in Basel had succeeded in isolating and characterizing the active principles, which he named *psilocybin(e)* and *psilocin(e)*. Hofmann had prepared both drugs synthetically in Switzerland, and came to México with "the spirit of the mushrooms in the form of pills," in hopes of giving the novel drug to a shaman experienced in the use of the mushrooms (Hofmann 1978B). Under the influence of the psilocybine pills, María Sabina sang a *velada* (a "night vigil," the Spanish word used by the Mazatec Indians to describe a mushroom curing ceremony) for Wasson, Hofmann and his wife Anita, and Irmgard Weitlaner Johnson, one of the first outsiders ever to attend such a mushroom ritual. Although the synthetic psilocybine took somewhat longer to act, María Sabina later said there was no difference between Hofmann's pills and the mushrooms. Besides dramatically and conclusively demonstrating the validity of Hofmann's chemical work, María Sabina's historic testing of psilocybine was a classic scientific experiment, unparalleled in the long history of pharmacognosy.[1]

Two years earlier, Timothy Leary, an obscure lecturer in psychology at Harvard University, had ingested Wasson's entheogenic mushrooms in Cuernavaca. He experienced "a maelstrom of transcendental visions" which led him, on his return to Harvard, to commence research on entheogenic drugs. Leary obtained a supply of Hofmann's psilocybine (which was distributed by Sandoz under the trade name *Indocybin*) and began experiments with the drug. Leary and his colleagues administered psilocybine to prisoners, in an attempt to achieve true rehabilitation, and to divinity students, many of whom were to have religious experiences (Leary 1968). Since Leary and his colleagues were known to ingest psilocybine and other entheogens themselves, and because the use of the drugs quickly escaped the nebulous confines of the laboratory (Kreig 1967; Leary 1968; Weil 1963B), this promising line of research came to be an embarrassment to the staid Harvard administration, and Leary and his colleague Richard Alpert found their contracts terminated in 1963.

This sensational incident received considerable attention in the press, and entheogenic drugs became an important *cause célèbre* of the sixties. Although Leary had cut his teeth on the mushrooms and psilocybine, he soon graduated to the more potent LSD. Leary began actively to proselytize for the use of LSD, and his famous *dictum* "turn on, tune in, drop out" became a byword of the times. The government chose to proselytize against LSD, and the mushrooms and psilocybine were all but forgotten in the resulting fracas. Nonetheless, a good deal of research was conducted with psilocybine, which showed sterling promise in clinical psychiatry (Alhadeff 1962; Delay *et al.* 1959A; Gilberti & Gregoretti 1960; Gnirss 1959; Heimann 1961; Heimann 1962; Hollister 1961; Leuner & Holfeld 1962; Passie 1995; Rinkel *et al.* 1960; Wilkins *et al.* 1962). Although laws against entheogenic drugs soon cut off this research prematurely, psilocybine was to emerge as the entheogen of choice in the seventies, and it is to the story of a remarkable resurgence of interest in an ancient sacrament that I turn in this chapter.

PRE-COLUMBIAN PERSPECTIVES

Our earliest sources of information about the sacred mushrooms of México date from the century following the bloody conquest of the Aztec empire in 1521 (Wasson 1980; Wasson & Wasson 1957A). An educated Indian, by the name of Tezozómoc, writing in Spanish in 1598, described the ingestion of inebriating mushrooms at the coronation of Moctezuma II in 1502 (Tezozómoc 1975).[2] Moctezuma was the last ruler of the Aztecs, and was destined to die an ignominious death in 1520, a prisoner in his own capital (Prescott 1843). Of his coronation, Tezozómoc wrote: "...they gave the strangers mountain [wild] mushrooms to eat, on which they became inebriated, and with this they entered into the dance..." (Wasson 1980; Wasson & Wasson 1957A).

The mushrooms are depicted in Mexican art that survived the conquest. They figure most prominently in the Mixtec *Codex Vindobonensis* (Caso 1963), the Aztec *Magliabechiano Codex*, and the famous Tepantitla frescoes of the great metropolis Teotihuacan (Caso 1942; Wasson & Wasson 1957A), which may also depict the *ololiuhqui* plant (see Chapter 2) or even the water lilies (see Appendix B; Emboden 1982; Furst 1974A).[3] Over 200 stone icons have been discovered in Central America, carved in the shape of mushrooms, with human or animal figures emerging from the "stems." It has been suggested that these "mushroom stones" were emblematic of the sacred mushroom cult in the Maya area (De Borhegyi 1961; De Borhegyi 1962; Lowy 1971; Lowy 1975; Mayer 1977A; Ohi & Torres 1994; Puharich 1959B; Wasson 1980; Wasson & Wasson 1957A; Wasson & Wasson 1958). These and other artistic representations (De Borhegyi 1963) show that the Indians esteemed the mushrooms with the utmost awe and reverence. Although modern shamanic use of these entheogenic mushrooms among the Mayans has not been observed, an archaic dictionary of the Cakchiquel language by Friar Tomás de Coto (Coto 1983) nevertheless referred to *k'aizalah ocox* and *xibalbaj ocox*, mushrooms that made one lose one's judgement, and to *qu'ec c'im* [*kek qim*] *ti qhuhiriçan*, mushrooms "that inebriate" (Garza 1990; Mayer 1977A). It has also been reported that Lacandón shamans made offerings of *Psilocybe* [*Stropharia*] *cubensis* and *Panaeolus venenosus* (=*Panaeolus subbalteatus*) to their gods in sacred places, but they have not been observed to ingest these psilocybian species (Robertson 1973; Thompson 1977).

Quite a different attitude was expressed by Spanish friars like Sahagún to these "harmful little mushrooms that intoxicate the same way as wine" (Sahagún 1950; Sahagún 1982). The mushroom cult was branded as idolatrous, and the most stern efforts were made to expurge the unholy communion. As friar Motolinía put it:

> They called these mushrooms *teunamacatlh* in their language, which means 'flesh of God,' or of the Devil that they worshipped, and in this manner, with this bitter food, they received their cruel god in communion. (Knauth 1962; Motolinía 1971; Wasson 1980; Wasson & Wasson 1957A)

Teunamacatlh or *teonanácatl* was the name of the mushrooms in Náhuatl, the language of the Mexica or Aztecs (a subgroup of Nahua Indians). This word would translate more accurately as "wondrous mushroom" or "sacred mushroom." The pharmacotheon was also known more prosaically as *teyhuinti-nanácatl*, "inebriating mushroom" (Wasson 1980; Wasson & Wasson 1957A).

We learn from the writings of the Spaniards that the mushrooms were bitter, induced visions, and that several distinct species were known to the Indians. Of the effects of the mushrooms they had much to say, but their extravagant and lurid accounts are obviously hearsay, and we can be certain no personal experience underlies them. For this was the age of witchcraft, and in 1620 the Holy [*sic*] Office of the Inquisition formally decreed in México City that the ingestion of inebriating plants was a heresy. The Church in fact relentlessly persecuted the Mexican entheogen use (Del Pozo 1975). Bigots like Br. Hernando Ruiz de Alarcón even tortured Indian shamans, in an attempt to extract the secrets of their "diabolical" rites (López Austin 1967; Ruiz de Alarcón 1953; Wasson 1980; Wasson *et al.* 1974). In response to this execrable behavior, the wondrous mushroom became the *arcanum arcanorum*, the "secret of secrets," to those few shamans who continued to practice the ancient rites in remote areas. With the passing centuries, the bigotry of the Spanish friars was forgotten, and their few obscure accounts remained little more than bizarre curiosities of a bygone era. Latter-day "evangelists" of multifarious Protestant faiths have taken up where the Catholic Church left off, continuing to wage a vigorous holy war on the entheogenic mushrooms (Hoogshagen 1959; Pike 1960; Pike & Cowan 1959). As one missionary put it succinctly: "the partaking of the divine mushroom poses potential problems in relation to the Christian concept of the Lord's Supper" (Pike & Cowan 1959). Indeed it does... (Ott 1995B)

THE REDISCOVERY OF *TEONANÁCATL*

By the turn of the century, the existence of vision-producing mushrooms was almost completely unknown to the world. True, some few writers, mostly physicians, had described cases of accidental inebriations with entheogenic mushrooms (Wasson 1959B), but these were rare, and never connected with the sixteenth century Mexican reports.[4] It did appear that the Catholic Church had succeeded in exterminating the Mexican use of *teonanácatl*. Indeed, in 1915, a respected ethnobotanist named W.E. Safford advanced the preposterous theory that visionary mushrooms had *never* existed, that the early Spanish chroniclers had been misled by the Indians, and that *teonanácatl* referred merely to the *péyotl* cactus (see Chapter 1) in the dried state (Safford 1915; Safford 1921C). For more than twenty years, this theory was tacitly accepted, until it was finally laid to rest in 1937–1939 (La Barre 1938; Schultes 1937B; Schultes 1939; Schultes 1940; Schultes 1961; Schultes 1965).[5]

An Austrian-born ethnobotanist working in México, Blas Pablo Reko, was the first to take issue with Safford's thesis (Reko 1919; Schultes 1978; Wasson 1963). Robert J. Weitlaner, an anthropologist working in México, also born in Austria, became the first outsider in modern times to handle specimens of *teonanácatl.* These specimens were given to Reko, who sent some material to Richard Evans Schultes, then a young graduate student at Harvard University. The material unfortunately deteriorated in transit, and Schultes was unable to identify it, beyond the genus *Panaeolus* (Schultes 1939; Schultes 1940; Schultes 1978).[6] Undaunted, Schultes then teamed up with Reko in 1938, and traveled to Huautla de Jiménez, the remote Oaxacan village where Weitlaner had obtained the mushrooms. Schultes and Reko succeeded in collecting good specimens of *teonanácatl*, which were ultimately shown to represent three species in three genera: *Panaeolus sphinctrinus* (=*P. campanulatus* var. *sphinctrinus*), *Psilocybe* [*Stropharia*] *cubensis* and *Psilocybe caerulescens* (Heim & Wasson 1958; Hofmann 1987; Mayer 1975; Ott 1978B; Ott & Bigwood 1978; Schultes 1939; Schultes 1940; Singer 1949; Wasson & Wasson 1957A).

That same year, Weitlaner's daughter Irmgard, and her future husband Jean Bassett Johnson, became the first outsiders in modern times to attend a mushroom curing ceremony. This also took place in Huautla de Jiménez. Although these pioneering anthropologists observed the use of the mushrooms, they did not themselves partake of them (Johnson 1939A; Johnson 1939B; Weitlaner Johnson 1990). The Second World War then disrupted the impending rediscovery of the mushroom cult. Johnson was killed in combat in North Africa in 1944, and Schultes was diverted to South America to study rubber trees at the behest of the U.S. government. Reko applied himself to other studies until his death in 1953, and the mushroom cult began again to lapse into oblivion (Ott 1978B).

Then, on 19 September 1952, the dedicated amateur ethnomycologists Valentina Pavlovna Wasson and R. Gordon Wasson received a communication from the poet Robert Graves, who enclosed a brief article (Heizer 1944) which referred to the use of inebriating mushrooms in México, and cited Schultes' 1939 paper on *teonanácatl.* Coincidentally, that same week they received a drawing from Giovanni Mardersteig, their printer, of a Central American mushroom stone he had seen and sketched in the Museum Rietberg in Zürich. The Wassons' work had led them to surmise that our remote ancestors had worshipped mushrooms (see Chapter 6), and they immediately resolved to turn their attention to México, to attempt to identify these mushrooms and especially to experience their effects (Wasson & Wasson 1957A).

So it came about, after a thorough review of the accounts of the sixteenth century friars and study of the field work of Schultes, Reko (whom they were able to contact by letter shortly before his death), the Johnsons and Weitlaner, that the Wassons made their first field trip to México in the summer of 1953. That year, and the following summer, they were able to learn precious bits of information about the mushrooms, and to obtain a few samples. Gordon Wasson sampled some of these in 1954, but the dose proved inadequate (Wasson & Wasson 1957A).

Finally, on 29 June 1955, Gordon Wasson and his photographer Allan Richardson were able to collect a large quantity of *Psilocybe caerulescens*, one of the mushrooms Schultes and Reko had collected in Huautla in 1938. That same day, Wasson and Richardson were introduced to María Sabina, a *curandera sin mancha*, a "shaman without blemish," who agreed to perform a *velada* for them that night. Wasson was delighted when María later offered him six pairs of the mushrooms in the home of Cayetano García. Richardson was less than delighted to receive the same dose, for he had promised his wife not to allow any of the "nasty toadstools" to pass his lips. He nevertheless gamely partook of them, and María Sabina herself ingested thirteen pairs, her customary dose. The visionary effects of the mushrooms were a revelation to Wasson, explaining how and why our remote ancestors might have worshipped mushrooms (Benítez 1964; Estrada 1977; Ott 1978B; Richardson 1990; Wasson 1980; Wasson & Wasson 1957A; Wasson *et al.* 1986).

Thus it came about that 434 years after the conquest of México, the pharmacotheon was rescued from oblivion, in the nick of time, just as the cult was nearing its final stages of senescence. Wasson sent specimens of the mushrooms to the renowned French mycologist Roger Heim, who subsequently made his first field trip to México with the Wasson group in the summer of 1956. Heim and the Wassons studied together in México until 1962, finally identifying some twenty species of entheogenic mushrooms, most of which were new to science (Heim & Wasson 1958; Ravicz 1960; Stresser-Péan 1990; Wasson 1961).[7]

CHEMISTRY OF *TEONANÁCATL*

Following the 1956 field trip, Heim returned to Paris with specimens and cultures of various species of *teonanácatl* (Heim 1957C). He and his colleague Roger Cailleux were able to cultivate and fruit many of these species in Paris (Heim & Cailleux 1957; Heim & Wasson 1958). They were especially successful with *Psilocybe mexicana*, and

Heim sent specimens of this cultivated mushroom to two pharmaceutical companies in the United States for chemical analysis. He also gave specimens to one of his colleagues in Paris for chemical study. Since all three laboratories were unable to isolate the active principle(s), Heim decided to send the same mushrooms to Albert Hofmann of the Swiss pharmaceutical firm Sandoz LTD. Hofmann received some 100 grams of dried *P. mexicana* early in 1957, and attempted to isolate the active principles using animal assays to evaluate his fractions. These assays proved ambiguous, and doubts arose as to whether the material cultivated and dried in Paris was indeed psychotropic, leading Hofmann to ingest the mushrooms himself, to ascertain whether they were in fact active. They were (Hofmann 1978B), and thenceforth Hofmann and his assistants tested their extracts on themselves, using the "Heffter Technique" (Ott 1994A), the procedure that had earlier been used by Heffter with *péyotl* (see Chapter 1). Hofmann soon isolated two active principles, which he named psilocybin(e) and psilocin(e) (Heim & Wasson 1958; Hofmann 1960; Hofmann 1978B; Hofmann *et al.* 1958; Hofmann *et al.* 1959; Weidmann *et al.* 1958).[8]

Arthur Brack and Hans Kobel, two of Hofmann's colleagues, were able to grow large quantities of *P. mexicana* sclerotia and mycelia in the Sandoz laboratories, from which Hofmann isolated several grams of psilocybine and centigrams of psilocine. With this material, he was able to determine the chemical structures of both compounds, and to verify these by synthesis. Psilocybine was found to be 4-phosphoryloxy-*N,N*-DiMethylTryptamine, and psilocine 4-hydroxy-*N,N*-DiMethylTryptamine (Heim & Wasson 1958; Heim *et al.* 1958; Hofmann 1978B; Hofmann *et al.* 1959).

At this writing, psilocybine (and in some cases psilocine) are known to occur in at least 98 species of mushrooms in 15 genera, found throughout the world (see Table 4 for list and references and Allen *et al.* 1992). In 1968, the two psilocybine analogues 4-phosphoryloxy-*N*-methyltryptamine (baeocystine) and 4-phosphoryloxytryptamine (norbaeocystine) were isolated from *Psilocybe baeocystis* (Leung 1967; Leung & Paul 1968). Baeocystine has since been found in at least 36 species of psilocybian mushrooms in 9 genera (see Table 5 for list and references). Baeocystine is entheogenic in 10 mg doses and norbaeocystine is likely also entheogenic (Gartz 1992A), but their human pharmacology has not yet been described in the literature in detail, only in a brief report that 4 mg of baeocystine produced "a mild hallucinosis of 3 hours' duration" (Gartz 1993). Stafford (1983) incorrectly reported that norbaeocystine was 4-hydroxy-*N*-methyltryptamine. This probable entheogen (Cerletti *et al.* 1968), however, is as yet unknown from mushrooms, although it has been conjectured to be a metabolic precursor to baeocystine (Repke *et al.* 1977A), and despite the fact that the probable entheogen 4-hydroxytryptamine (Cerletti *et al.* 1968) has been found in *Psilocybe baeocystis* and *P. cyanescens* (Repke *et al.* 1977A). Verily, the list of psilocybian mushrooms grows longer by the year (having increased by 8 species since the first edition of this book in 1993), and the psilocybine-type indoles have proven to be the most widely-distributed of all known mushroom toxins.

EFFECTS OF PSILOCYBINE AND PSILOCINE

Psilocybine produces psychoptic effects in human beings at doses ranging from 5–50 milligrams. The highest dose reported to have been given to a human subject is 120 mg (Fisher 1963), and the "maximum safe dose" has been said to be 150 mg (Brown 1968). Following oral ingestion, the onset of the inebriation is much more rapid than with mescaline or LSD, the major effects usually commencing within about 30 minutes. The inebriation lasts from 3–6 hours, depending on dose (Salgueiro 1964; Shulgin 1980A). Despite these differences in pharmacodynamics, the peak effects of psilocybine are remarkably similar to peak effects of mescaline and LSD. As psychotherapist S.M. Unger commented: "it is now rather commonly adjudged that the subjective effects of mescaline, LSD-25, and psilocybin are similar, equivalent, or indistinguishable" (Unger 1963).

After ingestion, psilocybine is dephosphorylated to psilocine, which then evokes psychoptic effects, and is subsequently excreted substantially unaltered in the urine (Blaschko & Levine 1960; Bocks 1967; Gilmour & O'Brien 1967; Horita 1963; Horita & Weber 1961A; Horita & Weber 1961B; Horita & Weber 1962; Kalberer *et al.* 1962). Psilocine ingested by itself will produce identical effects and, lacking the inactive phosphoryl group of psilocybine, is about 1.4 times the potency—that is, it has equimolar potency (Wolbach *et al.* 1962B).

Peak effects are characterized by auditory and visual alterations and profound synaesthesia (Delay *et al.* 1958; Heim 1957D; Heim & Thévenard 1967; Heim & Wasson 1958; Heim *et al.* 1967; Michaux 1960). These effects are very similar to peak effects of LSD and mescaline, and psilocybine has been demonstrated to produce cross-tolerance with LSD (Abramson *et al.* 1960; Isbell 1959; Isbell *et al.* 1961). Flushing of the skin and slight increase in body temperature are common side-effects of psilocybine inebriation (Cerletti 1959). The psilocybine-containing mushroom *Panaeolus subbalteatus* has been reported to exert an antiviral effect against poliomyelitis virus in mice (Cochran & Lucas 1959), and other potential medicinal effects of the psilocybine-containing mushrooms have been conjectured (Peele 1985; Stamets & Chilton 1983). The ancient Aztecs employed psilocybian mushrooms medicinally, as a topical treatment for gout (in combination with *ololiuhqui* and *Datura* spp.), and orally in treatment of an "aquatic fever" (as a component of a super-entheogen, in combination with *péyotl*, *ololiuhqui* and *Datura* spp.; Sahagún 1950)! However, these Aztec entheogenic plants were probably mostly taken by the shaman/physician or *pahini* ("[s]he who consumes medicine") as a divinatory aid in the diagnosis of the natural or magical causes of illness, the sort of use Wasson found common among contemporary Mazatec and other Mexican shamans like María Sabina (Estrada 1977; Ortíz de Montellano 1990; Wasson *et al.* 1974).

Numerous semi-synthetic derivatives of psilocybine and psilocine have been prepared by Hofmann's group (Troxler *et al.* 1959), some of which have visionary activity. The most interesting are the diethyl-derivatives of both drugs (called CY-19 [or CEY-19] and CZ-74 respectively). These compounds exert the same psychoptic effects as psilocybine and psilocine, but their duration of action is only 2–4 hours, making them more desirable than the natural compounds for medicinal use (Leuner & Baer 1965; Passie 1995). Recently cultures of *Psilocybe* [*Stropharia*] *cubensis* fed *N,N*-DiEthylTryptamine (DET; see Chapter 3) were shown to produce high amounts of CZ-74 (up to 3.3%) and traces of CY-19 (Gartz 1989C). American chemist D.B. Repke and colleagues have synthesized a great number of psilocine derivatives (Grotjahn 1983; Repke & Ferguson 1982; Repke *et al.* 1977B; Repke *et al.* 1981), but so far there has been only one report of human pharmacology of a couple of these intriguing compounds (Repke *et al.* 1985), many of which must be visionary.[9]

PSILOCYBINE AND *TEONANÁCATL* AS LUDIBLE DRUGS

On 13 May 1957, R. Gordon Wasson revealed his rediscovery of the sacred mushrooms of México, in a beautifully-illustrated piece for *Life* magazine (R.G. Wasson 1957). His article "Seeking the Magic Mushroom" for the first time brought awareness of entheogenic mushrooms to the general public. The title (coined by the editors of *Life* over Wasson's objections—he had negotiated, besides a $10,000 fee, absolute editorial control over the article with Time-Life chairman H. Luce, who nevertheless reserved the right to title the piece) caught the popular fancy, and the entheogenic mushrooms were thenceforth known as "magic mushrooms." A week after the appearance of the *Life* article, Valentina P. Wasson, a physician, published her article "I Ate the Sacred Mushrooms" in *This Week Magazine*, a newspaper supplement (on the cover of which she was featured, clad in her physician's white coat; Palmer & Horowitz 1982; V.P. Wasson 1957). The Wassons' popular articles served to publicize *Mushrooms Russia and History*, a book covering 30 years of their "ethnomycological" research (Wasson & Wasson 1957A). The beautifully-illustrated and finely-printed book—a true masterpiece—appeared in a limited edition of 512 copies (designed and printed in his *Dante* typeface on handmade paper by the great typographer Giovanni Mardersteig at the Stamperia Valdonega in Verona; with 26 color plates of Jean-Henri Fabre's watercolors), and has never been reprinted. The book originally cost $125 for the two-volume boxed set, but the publishers doubled that price two weeks after release (Wasson 1977; Wasson 1985). The entire edition sold out before the end of 1957, and the book has since sold for as much as $6500 *per* copy, while one of the authors (RGW) was still living, making it one of the most valuable books ever by a living writer (Horowitz 1994). The Wassons also published a phonograph recording of a mushroomic ceremony with María Sabina, taped in Huautla de Jiménez in 1956, complete with commentary and a partial transliteration and translation (Wasson & Wasson 1957B; see Estrada 1977; English trans., 1981).

While *Mushrooms Russia and History* was a scholarly *tour de force* and a pioneering work in the discipline of ethnomycology, the article in *Life* and the later article in *This Week* introduced the mushrooms to the world (Riedlinger 1990). The *Life* article was accompanied by water-color paintings of the more important species, and Gordon Wasson's moving descriptions of the effects of the fungal entheogen. The article also ran in the Spanish-language edition of *Life*, and later was part of a Time/Life book (Wasson 1965). She being a physician, Valentina's article carried the weight of medical authority, and referred to possible medical uses of the fungal entheogen (V.P. Wasson 1957). Shortly after the appearance of these three pioneering publications, outsiders began to make the pilgrimage to Huautla de Jiménez, in search of the mushroomic experience (this in spite of the fact that the Wassons called the Mazatec Indians "Mixetecos" in their articles, and Gordon Wasson gave María Sabina the alias Eva Méndez; De Solier 1965; Tibón 1983). María Sabina suddenly became the high-priestess of a modern mushroom cult, quite different from its hoary ancestor (Estrada 1977; Ott 1975A).

Soon the mushrooms were profaned, reduced merely to articles of the tourist trade. Would-be shamans staged spurious mushroom *veladas* for the benefit of the eager tourists (Herrera 1967; Ott 1975A; Ott 1978B). The mushrooms came to be widely and conspicuously sold, the tourist lucre overcoming the veils of reticence inculcated by four centuries of Spanish persecution. Postcards depicting the mushrooms and María Sabina, and sleazy clothing embroidered with mushroom motifs became mainstays of the burgeoning tourist trade in one of México's poorest areas (Ott 1975A). María Sabina herself pronounced a fitting epitaph for the dead cult:

> Before Wasson, I felt that the mushrooms exalted me. Now I no longer feel this... from the moment the strangers arrived... the mushrooms lost their purity. They lost their power. They decomposed. From that moment on, they no longer worked. (Estrada 1977; Liggenstorfer & Rätsch 1996).

In the early sixties the Mexican authorities took some steps to curb this mushroomic tourism. Soldiers were stationed in Huautla, and busloads of foreign pilgrims were from time to time deported. María Sabina and other *curanderos* were accused of pandering to the illicit tourist trade and some, like María, even served jail sentences in Oaxaca City (Estrada 1977). The persecution waned, however, and by the mid-seventies the troops were nowhere in sight and the mushroom trade was flourishing (Ott 1975A). Although knowledge of this fungal trade diffused largely by word-of-mouth in the United States and Europe, crackpot articles with sensational descriptions of "the devil's drugs that cause visions, orgies and insanity" were published as early as October 1957 (Goodman 1957; Herald 1958). The first such article appeared in *Fate* magazine (infamous for having originated the great UFO boom in the late forties), and this was attributed to Dr. Steven R. De Borhegyi, "as told to Thor Goodman." De Borhegyi, an archaeologist, was one of the Wassons' collaborators, and had made a chart (*"Mushroom Stones" of Middle America*) of pre-Columbian "mushroom" sculpture for *Mushrooms Russia and History*. He told Gordon Wasson he had nothing to do with the phony *Fate* article (Wasson 1977). The mushrooms even found their way into the syndicated comic strip *Gordo*, in which *Psilocybe* [*Stropharia*] *cubensis* was clearly depicted, and its use attributed to the Wassons' imaginary "Mixeteco Indians" (Arriola 1957).

The 1968 publication by Carlos Castaneda of *The Teachings of Don Juan: A Yaqui* [*sic*] *Way of Knowledge* must have gone a long way to stimulate interest in entheogenic mushrooms in the United States and elsewhere (Castaneda 1968). Castaneda alleged that Don Juan, supposedly a Mexican shaman, ingested psychoptic mushrooms (*honguitos*) in a mixture he called *humito*, the "little smoke." Curiously, Castaneda reported that Don Juan dried the mushrooms for a year, at which time they were reduced to a powder that was smoked with five other "dry plants." This is highly improbable. When dried, the mushrooms do not become powder, and it is likely that after a year of being kept inside a gourd would have lost much (if not all) of their potency. Although the use of entheogenic mushrooms has been reported among many different Mexican indigenous groups, the Yaqui are not among them. Nowhere are the mushrooms smoked... nor are they very effective when so used.

Although Castaneda in *The Teachings of Don Juan* talked about the "smoke" flowing into his mouth, commenting that this smoke was like "menthol" (referring to his first experience with smoking the mushrooms), in the introduction to his 1971 sequel *A Separate Reality: Further Conversations with Don Juan* he averred that smoking the dried mushroom mixture involved "ingesting" the mushroom powder, which didn't even incinerate (Castaneda 1971)! Our dismay at this lack of consistency (it had apparently been pointed out to Castaneda that his report was suspect and anomalous) turns rapidly to chagrin when we reflect that Castaneda claimed that the effect of the mixture was immediate. When ingested, psilocybian mushrooms require at least 15 minutes to act, often more than half an hour. Of course, part of the effect could be attributed to the five species of "dry plants" smoked/ingested with the mushrooms. Castaneda, however, did not identify these plants, and drew attention only to the mushrooms, which he identified as "possibly" *Psilocybe mexicana* (in *The Teachings of Don Juan*) and simply as a mushroom species belonging to the genus "*Psylocebe*" [*sic*] in the sequel (Castaneda 1971). Strangely, Castaneda, who wrote a third book *Journey to Ixtlan* first as his doctoral thesis in anthropology at UCLA (Castaneda 1972), was never asked by his professors to submit voucher specimens of any of the plants whose use he described (see Chapter 4, Note 5)!

R. Gordon Wasson reviewed these three books in *Economic Botany* (and went on to review Castaneda's fourth literary offering as well; Castaneda 1974), and said of *A Separate Reality*: "occasionally there is a faint trace of authenticity in these pages, submerged in a welter of science fiction badly written" (Wasson 1972A). He corresponded with Castaneda, who promised to send him "a dab" of the mushrooms, a promise which was never fulfilled. Castaneda also wrote Wasson that the mushrooms grew on "dead trunks of trees," and that he had collected the same species in Oaxaca, Durango and near Los Angeles (Wasson 1977)! It must be said that no known psilocybian mushroom would satisfy these criteria, and until Castaneda produces specimens for identification, I, like Wasson, will take his accounts to be "science fiction badly written." It has been shown definitively that Castaneda invented the Don Juan stories (De Mille 1976; De Mille 1979; De Mille 1980; Furst 1990) and his books are currently catalogued by the Library of Congress and Castaneda's own publisher as they should be, as *fiction*. Castaneda's protagonist Don Juan must be the most famous literary character since Sherlock Holmes! Nevertheless, the faithful still continue to regard Castaneda as Don Juan's prophet, and as late as 1988, a review of *The Power of Silence: Further Lessons of Don Juan* (Castaneda 1987) appeared in *Shaman's Drum* magazine, with nary a mention of the fictitious nature of the work (Dunn 1988). There can be no doubt, however, that this provocative bit of science fiction greatly stimulated popular interest in the sacred mushrooms of México, and for that reason I give it so much attention here.

The same can be said for Timothy Leary's 1968 book *High Priest* (Leary 1968). This book contained a chapter describing his first entheogenic experience, with psilocybian mushrooms, in Cuernavaca in 1960. This chapter featured *marginalia* consisting of extensive quotations from R. Gordon Wasson's startling and moving 1961 paper on the entheogenic mushrooms, subtitled "An Inquiry into the Origins of the Religious Idea among Primitive [*sic*] Peoples" (Wasson 1961). Like Castaneda's books, Leary's was to give the Wassons' ideas a far wider audience than they had enjoyed in the scientific literature. Similarly, a 1973 book of little scientific value was to stimulate laypersons to go forth *In Search of the Magic Mushroom* (Sandford 1973).

Throughout the sixties and seventies, chemical research was showing that mushrooms producing psilocybine (and sometimes also psilocine) were cosmopolitan (see Table 4). *Psilocybe* [*Stropharia*] *cubensis*, one of the first species of *teonanácatl* collected, was found to be widely distributed in semi-tropical areas of the world, and dozens of mushroom species of north-temperate zones were shown to contain psychoptic compounds (Guzmán & Ott 1976; Guzmán *et al.* 1976; Ott & Bigwood 1978; Pollock 1974; Pollock 1975A; Pollock 1976; Stamets 1978; Stamets 1996).

A well-researched booklet appeared in 1968, with procedures for synthesizing "psilocyn" [*sic*][10] and growing mycelium of psilocybian mushrooms for extraction (Brown 1968). This pioneering booklet was illustrated with a water-color painting of *Psilocybe hoogshagenii*, rather fantastically copied from a *black-and-white* photograph of *dried* specimens in the mycological literature (Heim & Wasson 1958).

There is, however, no evidence that psilocine or psilocybine were ever synthesized or extracted on a commercial scale for black-market sale. Before 1965, Sandoz had distributed psilocybine as a research drug (Cerletti 1965)—its demonstrated utility in psychotherapy was recently reviewed (Passie 1995). Some of this *Indocybin* (also known as CY-39) was diverted for extra-laboratory use (Weil 1963B; Weil 1972); however, when psilocybine became a controlled substance in 1965, the American subsidiary of Sandoz in New Jersey (of which Gordon Wasson was a director) surrendered all its *Indocybin*, psilocine, CZ-74 and CY-19 [or CEY-19] to the government. Psilocybine and psilocine disappeared from the illicit market, soon to be replaced by a variety of spurious preparations, usually commercial edible mushrooms adulterated with LSD or PCP (phencyclidine or *Sernyl*). These preparations were generally frozen or fermented in honey, to render them a rotting black mess not readily identifiable as the garden-variety *Agaricus* (Badham 1984; Brown & Malone 1973A; PharmChem 1973). B. Ratcliffe proposed the binomial *Pseudopsilocybe hofmannii* for these LSD-laced edible mushrooms. As was the case with "organic mescaline" (see Chapter 1), some elaborate folklore grew to surround "psilocybine mushrooms" or "organic psilocybine," despite the fact that hardly anyone had tried the real thing, and the vast majority of preparations were simply LSD or PCP under an assumed name! Recently, it has been reported that LSD is used in place of psilocybian mushrooms in some Thai restaurants offering "magic mushroom" omelettes to tourists (Allen & Merlin 1992A); and *shiitake* mushrooms (*Lentinus edodes*) adulterated with LSD have appeared on the black market in Europe (Stahl *et al.* 1978).

Summarizing analyses of 284 putative psilocybine samples made in 4 different American laboratories, Brown and Malone reported only 10 samples, all of them dried mushrooms, actually contained psilocybine (3.5%); none (0%) contained synthetic or isolated psilocybine. Of the remaining samples, 184 (64.8%) contained LSD (3 of these were *Agaricus* mushrooms spiked with LSD); 32 contained LSD plus PCP (11.3%); 16 (5.6%) contained PCP only; and 6 (2.1%) contained other compounds including "STP" or DOM (see Chapter 1), LSD or DMT plus amphetamines, and one sample actually contained mescaline (Brown & Malone 1973A)! Thus the hapless consumer buying a tablet or capsule alleged to contain psilocybine had no chance whatever of getting the real thing, better than an 80% chance of getting LSD, and was more likely to get synthetic mescaline than psilocybine!

In 1970 Enos published the first "field guide" to North American entheogenic mushrooms (Enos 1970). This tacky pamphlet described 15 species, each illustrated with useless water-color paintings showing nothing so much as the fact that the author had never actually seen most of the mushrooms. Two of the illustrations were copied from Wasson's *Life* article, and the remainder from line drawings in the mycological literature (which were then obtusely colored according to verbal descriptions of colors in the mycological literature!). Despite these shortcomings, the Enos pamphlet was to stimulate awareness that entheogenic mushrooms grew outside of México, and was to get people out looking for them.

An equally slipshod pamphlet followed in 1972, which for the first time presented color photographs of an American entheogenic mushroom, in this case *Psilocybe* [*Stropharia*] *cubensis*, which the naive author mistook for two species, including *Panaeolus subbalteatus*, which looks nothing like *P. cubensis* (Ghouled 1972)! A spate of "field guides" followed, the information and the illustrations improving considerably (Cooper 1977; Haard & Haard 1975; Menser 1977; Norland 1976; Ott 1976B; Ott 1979B; Ott & Bigwood 1978; Stamets 1978; Stamets 1996). The authors of some of the books were able to learn the correct identifications of many of North America's entheogenic species from G. Guzmán, a Mexican mycologist specializing in *Psilocybe*, at the "International Conference on Psychotropic Fungi" in Tenino, [10–9–0] Washington (29–31 October 1976).[11]

As a result of widespread dissemination of identification information, the modern cult of entheogenic mycophagy became firmly entrenched in the United States. The Pacific Northwest became a center of entheogenic mushroom use, as did the Gulf Coast area and Hawai'i (Allen 1992A; Allen & Merlin 1989; Dawson 1975; Merlin & Allen 1993; Ott 1975A; Ott 1976B; Ott 1978C; Ott 1979B; Pollock 1974; Stamets 1996; Weil 1977A). "Mushroom tourism" remains popular in México and South America (G. Bauer 1992; Mandel 1992). Moreover, the modern cult was established in Australia, Indonesia, Bali, Samoa, Thailand, New Zealand and Africa (Aberdeen & Jones 1958; Allen 1991; Allen & Merlin 1992A; Allen & Merlin 1992B; Allen *et al.* 1991; Cox 1981; Gartz & Allen 1993; Guzmán *et al.* 1993; Pollock 1975A; Pollock 1976; Southcott 1974; Stamets 1996), and later began to appear in Europe (Bauereiß 1995; Carter 1976; Cooper 1977; Festi 1985; Gartz 1986E; Gartz 1993; Haseneier 1990; Krötenstuhl 1992; Ott & Bigwood 1985; Pagani 1993; Samorini 1990; Samorini 1992B; Samorini & Festi 1989; Stamets 1996). By fall 1975, wild entheogenic mushrooms were appearing on the illicit drug market in California and Oregon (Ott 1975A; Weil 1977A). As the Reagan Dark Ages descended in the 1980s, there was little further publication of information regarding psilocybian mushrooms, notable exceptions being two books aimed at young readers, *Chocolate to Morphine* (Weil & Rosen 1983) a sort of encyclopedia of "mind-active" drugs, and anthropologist P.T. Furst's *Mushrooms: Psychedelic Fungi* (Furst 1986), one volume in a 25-tome *Encyclopedia of Psychoactive Drugs*. Lately "hip" travelers may opt for joining entheogenic "exotic mushroom" tours to Thailand (interesting that the word "exotic," once used as a euphemism for "erotic" in newspaper adverts for "pornographic" films, now does extra duty as a euphemism for "entheogenic"; Allen 1992B).

It was, however, the development of cultivation technology which was truly to bring entheogenic mushrooms to the illicit drug market. As mentioned previously, this technology was pioneered by Heim and Cailleux in Paris and by Brack and Kobel in Basel in the late fifties (Heim & Wasson 1958; Hofmann 1978B; Hofmann *et al.* 1959). Their procedures, however, were published only in the European scientific literature, and in the 1958 Heim and Wasson book, which was written in French (besides being rather expensive and unavailable in the U.S.). Accordingly, this pioneering work had no direct impact on modern entheogen use. The above-mentioned books by Brown (1968) and Enos (1970) included procedures for cultivating the mycelia of psilocybian mushrooms, which techniques were derived from the work of Heim and Cailleux. These two pamphlets did not, however, deal with production of fruit bodies (mushrooms) in culture, and there is no evidence that they had any significant impact on the illicit market. Moreover, it has recently been found that mycelial cultures of *Psilocybe* [*Stropharia*] *cubensis* contain less psilocybine than the fruiting bodies or mushrooms (Gartz 1989F), suggesting bulk mycelial culture would be an inefficient way to produce psilocybine. Similar studies showed that the mushroom caps contain higher levels of alkaloids than the stems in both *P. cubensis* and *Panaeolus subbalteatus* (Gartz 1987C; Gartz 1989B), and that small-sized mushrooms may be the most potent in the case of *Panaeolus subbalteatus* (Gartz 1989B). This is not surprising, as the rapid growth of mushrooms from *primordia* is by addition of water, and the resultant swelling may rupture some cells, contributing to oxidative decomposition of psilocine to an inactive blue pigment.

Then in 1976 J. Bigwood, D.J. McKenna, K. Harrison McKenna and T.K. McKenna published a booklet detailing an effective method for producing psilocybian mushrooms in culture in high yield (Oss & Oeric 1976). These authors adapted San Antonio's technique (for producing edible mushrooms by casing mycelial cultures on a rye-grain substrate; San Antonio 1971) to the production of *Psilocybe* [*Stropharia*] *cubensis* (for a review of this and other methods of producing psilocybian mushrooms see Ott & Bigwood 1978; Stamets 1993; Stamets & Chilton 1983). The new technique involved the use of ordinary kitchen implements, and for the first time the layperson was able to produce a potent entheogen in her or his own home, without access to sophisticated technology, equipment or chemical supplies. The Bigwood and McKenna book was illustrated with Bigwood's step-by-step photographs and color plates of the final product. It became one of the best-selling countercultural drug books ever published, and is still in print, in an edition lacking Bigwood's superb photographs. It is ironic that rye, one of the most common hosts for the parasitic ergot fungus from which was derived LSD and the ancient Eleusinian *kykeon* potion, came to be the primary substrate for modern production of psilocybian mushrooms. Indeed, inasmuch as the rye used to produce psilocybian mushrooms invariably contained small amounts of ergot (a small handful can be picked from a 100-pound sack of "organic rye"), it can be said that ergot, too, served as a substrate for modern production of psilocybian mushrooms!

A spate of cultivation guides followed on the heels of the Bigwood/McKenna book (Harris 1976; Pollock 1977; Stamets 1978; Stevens & Gee 1977). Some of the writers of these cultivation guides expanded their earnings by selling spore prints of *Psilocybe* [*Stropharia*] *cubensis* (and later other species) along with cultivation supplies and tools, at grossly inflated prices. While amateur cultivation began to be a widespread hobby, the main impact of this enterprise has been a decentralization of production in the illicit entheogen market. Although many cultivators disclaimed a profit motive, once they appreciated how much labor was involved, and began to see how readily this labor could be turned into cash, profit became a primary concern. Some growers, using the same or similar techniques, went on to the cultivation of other species of edible and medicinal mushrooms (as detailed in Stamets 1993; Stamets & Chilton 1983). A recent article described the experimental use of the plant growth hormone 22*S*,23*S*-homobrassinolide, which provoked a two- to threefold increase in growth rate of *P. cubensis* mycelia (Gartz *et al.* 1990).

Thus a considerable market for *Psilocybe* [*Stropharia*] *cubensis* came into being. The mushrooms were generally sold dried and sealed in plastic wrappers. In San Francisco, the typical packet contained five grams of mushrooms, equivalent to roughly 25 milligrams of psilocybine (Bigwood & Beug 1982), representing a good dose, assuming a potent strain was being cultivated. The mushrooms have been sold for $2–$5 *per* gram, or $10–$25 *per* dose. Petri dishes covered with mycelia of *P. cubensis* are also commodities, worth about $25. "Mason jars" (American one-quart [946 ml] home-canning jars) of grain substrate permeated with mycelia are worth about $10 each; spore prints have sold for $5–$10 apiece (Shawcross 1981).

MODERN USE OF *TEONANÁCATL*

Wise prospective users reject immediately any black-market pills or capsules alleged to be psilocybine or "organic psilocybine." There is no synthetic material on the illicit market, nor is it at all likely that the genuine article will appear. Such preparations are invariably misrepresented—adulterated with LSD, PCP, or are simply inert—a "ripoff," in any case.

Informed would-be entheogenic mycophagists are also highly sceptical of alleged "psilocybine mushrooms." If these are frozen, chopped, shredded, or cured in honey,[12] one can be almost certain that they are *not* genuine. Freezing fresh psilocybian mushrooms is perhaps the best way *not* to preserve their activity, besides complicating storage. There is only one reason a pharmacopolist might freeze mushrooms: to render them an amorphous mess so the prospective sucker would not realize what they are—garden-variety mushrooms with unknown adulterants. The same goes for curing mushrooms in honey. Chopping or shredding dried mushrooms will likewise accelerate the oxidative degradation of the active principles. Once again, the rationale for these procedures is to deceive the naive buyer into believing the mushrooms are psilocybian, when in fact they are something else—

a fraud! Should one encounter any such specious and spurious preparations, (s)he ought to eschew them and express *extreme* displeasure to the would-be vendor.

Psilocybine is found on the black market only in the form of whole dried mushrooms. Almost invariably the species sold is *Psilocybe* [*Stropharia*] *cubensis*, cultivated specimens of which are long and slender, having a whitish stem and yellowish cap. The discriminating buyer will look for blue staining where the stem has been handled in the fresh state, and especially in the cross-section, where the mushroom has been cut off at the base. This is the veritable signature of the black-market psilocybian mushroom. The buyer can generally expect to see a dark, diaphanous ring around the upper portion of the stem. As mentioned, the mushrooms are generally sealed in plastic bags for protection from moisture.

Should one encounter fresh mushrooms in the field, (s)he ought be certain of identification before ingesting them (for identification information and color plates of the most important North American species, see Ott & Bigwood 1978; for European species, see Gartz 1993; Ott & Bigwood 1985). Guzmán has published a monograph of *Psilocybe*, which has many color plates and refers to color plates in other publications (Guzmán 1983). While many people will eat the mushrooms fresh in the field, this unhygienic practice is not recommended. Some of the mushrooms grow in or near dung, fragments of which may cling to the mushroom flesh. For safety, the wise user chooses only fresh, healthy specimens, free from insects, eschewing the rotten ones. These are washed thoroughly before ingestion, and the conscientious consumer will cut off the base of each specimen first.

For storage the mushrooms are air-dried at about room temperature (a food drier or screen placed near a heating register are commonly used). Prolonged heating and high temperatures are to be avoided. When the mushrooms are crisp they are sealed in moisture-proof containers, under nitrogen at times. They are then stored in a freezer, and will keep for many months with minimal diminution in potency. The mushrooms are not frozen without first drying them (as they quickly become inactive), and are not to be preserved fresh in honey (the result is a disgusting, fermenting mess). If storage is intended for only a few days, the fresh mushrooms may simply be refrigerated like other vegetables (or meats?).

Some species of psilocybian mushrooms have a not-disagreeable flavor and may be eaten neat, but the majority of species have a strong acrid taste which, while not bitter, some find to be revolting and quite as difficult to tolerate as the taste of *péyotl*. To overcome this, epicurean consumers blend "smoothies" with raw or dried psilocybian mushrooms, using strong-flavored fruit or chocolate to kill the taste. Hot cocoa in water or milk is a common vehicle, providing good flavor as well as historical authenticity (in ancient México, *teonanácatl* was often ingested with honey and cacao bean preparations called *cacáhuatl*).[13] The smoothie technique has the added advantage of enabling the entheogenic mycophagist accurately to apportion the available mushrooms among several users. It is difficult to gauge dosages when working with mushrooms of different species, sizes and/or states of hydration. Simply mixing the whole in a blender with juice or milk, then dispensing equal volumes to all communicants will invariably result in each getting precisely the same dose. Moreover, in the case of dried mushrooms, blending them before ingestion seems to foster more efficient absorption of the active principles. Apparently the dried mushrooms are not easily digested, especially if not thoroughly masticated, whereas blending will break up the mushroom tissue and cause the water-soluble psilocybine to go into solution (*N.B.* psilocine is scarcely water-soluble). Of course, the mushrooms are blended only immediately prior to ingestion. Some users prefer simply to *sauté* the mushrooms in butter, and to eat these over toast or crackers. The light sautéing over low heat will not significantly diminish the potency of the mushrooms.[14]

Some users experience slight nausea as a side-effect of psilocybine inebriation. This is usually mild and transient, and will soon pass. The nausea is probably due to the disagreeable flavor of the mushrooms, and to the fact that this taste repeats itself after ingestion when one belches (Ott & Pollock 1976A). Some users eat fruit or chocolate after the mushrooms to counteract this mild discomfiture.

NOTES

[1] Hofmann left María Sabina with a bottle of 5 mg psilocybine pills, and she "expressed her thanks for the gift, saying that she would now be able to serve people even when no mushrooms were available" (Hofmann 1978B). This is perhaps the only case on record in which a natural-products chemist has returned to the source—the shaman or traditional healer whose information led to the scientific discovery of a novel drug—with the fruits of her or his labor. In giving psilocybine pills to María Sabina, Hofmann was sharing the fruits of a discovery with *an equal partner* in that discovery. While it is a concept alien to modern science, in every respect María Sabina was a collaborator in the work that led to the discovery of psilocybine and psilocine and, as such, entitled to share in the rewards, whether they be recognition merely, or financial gain. In the case of psilocybine, there was no financial gain for Hofmann or Sandoz (who had distributed the drug *gratis* for investigative

purposes, and never brought it formally to market), and it can be said that María Sabina shared the recognition through Wasson's and Hofmann's giving her credit—she became famous in México, a sort of comic-book super-heroine, the subject of drama. When she died, her obituary ran in *South: The Third World Magazine*, an international newsmagazine (Anon. 1986; Palmer & Horowitz 1982). This is the exception, not the rule. An American ethnobotanist has recently suggested (Posey 1990) that intellectual property rights to new pharmaceutical discoveries based on information from traditional healers be recognized for the healers, as they are for the chemists who isolate the active compounds. Posey proposed developing mechanisms for sharing royalties with shamans and healers whose knowledge proves valuable, both out of simple fairness, and as a way to make traditional shamanism a profession with a future, thus helping to preserve information in danger of being lost to acculturation, information which is without question invaluable. I applaud Posey's stance, and commend Hofmann for making the first steps in the direction Posey outlined, 30 years ahead of time. An incipient American pharmaceutical company, Shaman Pharmaceuticals, has advocated precisely this practice, and has hired conservation biologist Steven King as Vice-President for "Ethnobotany and Conservation." It remains to be seen whether this company will realize any profits to share with the shamans of the firm's name. Meanwhile, the decidedly profit-making Merck pharmaceutical company signed a "chemical prospecting" agreement with Costa Rica's INstituto Nacional de BIOdiversidad (INBio) with a one million dollar advance payment. In exchange for drug-development rights to organisms in forested land which INBio is conserving as is, Merck is training Costa Rican scientists and has donated chemical equipment. Merck reportedly will pay royalties to INBio of from 1–3% on new drugs developed from the reserve, and half of the income is earmarked for conservation activities in Costa Rica (Roberts 1992A). Other countries and companies are seeking to emulate Merck/INBio, and there has been a welcome revival of interest in natural products research in the pharmaceutical industry (Roberts 1992A; Roberts 1992B). It is important that government agencies not cripple excessively international trade in this area. The attempt by the Mexican government to fix prices and profiteer on trade in steroid precursors originally derived from Mexican plants led foreign pharmaceutical companies to find alternatives, and in a few years' time, the bottom fell out of what had been a thriving Third World pharmaceutical market (Djerassi 1992). Eventually, the company Syntex, founded in México on the basis of maverick American chemist R. Marker's method for producing hormonal pharmaceuticals from plant-derived steroid precursors, moved its headquarters to California, frightened off by the Mexican government's high-handedness and persistent threats to nationalize the Mexican pharmaceutical industry. Today México, which had pioneered this technology, is a bit-player in this market.

[2] Wrongly known as MONtezuma in the English-speaking world, such as in the familiar refrain from the U.S. Marine Corps' battle hymn "From the halls of Montezuma..." the Aztec monarch's name was actually given as *Motecuhzoma* by sixteenth century Spanish chroniclers. In México today, as in scholarly literature, he is known as Moctezuma II.

[3] Perhaps the best-known Mexican murals depicting entheogenic plant motifs are those of

Tepantitla, in the great Teotihuacan complex, which was already a hoary ruin when the Aztecs arrived in the Valley of México *circa* the thirteenth century. In their pioneering work *Mushrooms Russia and History*, V.P. and R.G. Wasson drew attention to motifs representing entheogenic mushrooms in the Tepantitla mural segment showing Tláloc, the Toltec rain god, and Tlalocan, the watery paradise or Elysian Fields of Mesoamerican mythology (Wasson & Wasson 1957A). The Wassons' interpretations of this particular scene rested in part on an earlier analysis of the scene by Mexican iconographic expert A. Caso (Caso 1942), who later put his *imprimatur* on some of the Wassons' identifications of mushrooms in Mexican codices (Caso 1963). More recent studies of the Tepantitla murals have concluded that the aquatic deity depicted is not Tláloc (Pasztory 1974), and a widely-held alternate interpretation is that a female deity is represented (Kubler 1967). The Wassons' identification of mushroom motifs in this scene has also been disputed; water lilies being an alternate interpretation (see Appendix B; Emboden 1982). In any case, a dominant motif in the Tepantitla murals, found also in carvings at the Palace of Quetzalpapálotl in Teotihuacan, is that of "disembodied eyes"—suggested by Gordon Wasson to be a glyph representing the visionary or entheogenic state (Ott & Wasson 1983; Wasson 1980; Wasson *et al.* 1986). The Tepantitla murals depict disembodied eyes appended to flowers, as well as to eye-drops issuing from these flowers. Clearly, we have here a natural and obvious means of representing graphically entheogenic plants and drops of entheogenic potions issuing from them, what I have called "disembodied eye-drops" (Ott & Wasson 1983). Recently, a collection of mural paintings from Techinantitla at Teotihuacan, which had been looted and illegally removed from México in the 1960s, ending up in the private collection of one H. Wagner, were donated to the Fine Arts Museum of San Francisco, California. Echoing the same motifs found in the Tepantitla murals, the Techinantitla murals depict disembodied eye, mushroom, entheogenic plant and disembodied eye-drop motifs (Berrin 1988). One particularly fine segment shows a feathered serpent from whose mouth issue entheogenic flowers, disembodied eyes and eye-drops, above 12 plants or trees, some of which have drops of entheogenic potion flowing from the flowers, and some of which have disembodied eyes in their stems or trunks. In a recent graphic reconstruction of this and other murals in the looted cache (Amigos 1991; Berrin 1988), it is suggested that the entheogenic marigolds (*Tagetes* spp.; see Appendix B; Siegel *et al.* 1977) are depicted in this mural, and that the plants illustrated may be medicinal or "ritual" species, these authors noting that they are clearly *not* food plants. The authors failed to mention the entheogens, and it is obvious to the *cognoscenti* that we have here painted a visionary scene of entheogenic plants, including perhaps *yyahutli* (*Tagetes* spp.), *mexcalli* (*Agave* spp., source of fermented *octli* or *pulque*, a ritual beverage; see Chapter 6, Note 12), *coaxihuitl* (*Turbina corymbosa*, source of the entheogenic *ololiuhqui* seeds; see Chapter 2), *quauhyetl* or *picietl* (tobaccos; *Nicotiana* spp.; see Appendix A), *toloatzin* (*Datura* spp.; see Appendix A), as well as the unidentified Aztec floral entheogen *poyomatli* (see Appendix B). I would interpret the scene as showing the feathered serpent as the bringer of visions through entheogenic plants (among the Aztecs, Quetzalcoatl had brought the arts of agriculture and medicine to humankind), and/or a component of the entheogenic visions themselves, much as the ancient Mayans depicted "vision serpents" (Schele & Freidel 1990). In this respect, this scene would be analogous to the famous Aztec sculpture of Xochipilli, the "Prince of Flowers," on whose body are carved representations of numerous entheogenic flowers including *quauhyetl* or tobacco, *coaxihuitl* or morning glory, source of entheogenic *ololiuhqui* seeds, and other visionary plants (Fraser 1992; LordNose! 1992; Wasson 1973B; Wasson 1980). This mural and the statue of Xochipilli take on added significance in the light of Wasson's suggestion that "flowers" (*xóchitl* or *ihuinti*) were to the Aztecs a metaphor for the entheogens, as the Aztec poetry refers repeatedly to "flowers that inebriate" (Garibay 1964; Wasson 1980). The Náhuatl metaphor for poetry, *in xóchitl in cuícatl* (literally, "in flower in song"), as the road to truth has also been suggested to represent the entheogens and the fuller view of the world that they bring the seeker of wisdom (Cáceres 1984; León Portilla 1961; Ortíz de Montellano 1990). The *temicxoch* or "flowery dream" of the priests and poets was another metaphor for the entheogenic state, expressed in *tecpillatolli*, the special language of shamans and poets; the divinely-inspired *logos*, the oracular speech of the thaumaturge inebriated with entheogenic plants (depicted in the Teotihuacan murals as "speech scrolls" with appended flowers; Wasson 1980). Another fragment of the Techinantitla murals shows the *logos* or "mouth of god" motif surrounded by mushrooms and shells (or water lilies in Emboden's alternate reading), echoing precisely the miniature painting on a stair riser or "predella" at Zacuala in Teotihuacan (Berrin 1988). Fortunately Wasson published exact copies of this fragment of painting, which was left unprotected from the elements, and has all but disappeared today (Heim & Wasson 1958; Wasson 1980; Wasson & Wasson 1957A). The Techinantitla mural with 12 entheogenic "flowers" may represent the pre-Columbian Mexican pleasure gardens, like the Tezcotzinco gardens of Acolmiztli Nezahualcóyotl, havens for medicinal and exotic flowering plants, especially the entheogenic "flowers," wherein the priests and nobility could have earthly but other-worldly experiences (Nabhan 1989). The Aztecs are credited with the world's first true botanical garden, founded by Moctezuma I in 1467 (Ortíz de Montellano 1990).

[4] In 1917, physician B. Douglas, based on personal (accidental) experience, described the symptoms of his *Panaeolus* inebriation as "purely those of a stimulated nervous system" and noted that the mushrooms could not likely be deadly poisonous (Douglas 1917). Six years later, physician W.W. Ford proposed a new category of mushroom poisoning, "Mycetismus Cerebralis," citing two species of *Panaeolus* now known to contain psilocybine (Ford 1923). In the 1944 review (Heizer 1944) which was destined to steer the Wassons to México, the author associated Ford's "cerebral mycetism" with the *teonanácatl* cult of México, which had recently been ascribed by Schultes to *Panaeolus campanulatus* var. *sphinctrinus* (Schultes 1939). Schultes was the first to make this association in an English-language publication. A 1954 Mexican publication had a brief chapter on *teonanácatl* and referred to the work of Schultes and B.P. Reko (Guerra & Olivera 1954). The Wassons' publication of information on Mexican entheogenic mushrooms elicited additional reports of accidental inebriations (Wasson 1959B).

[5] Shamanic use of entheogenic mushrooms was also traditional in Japan, and the memory of this ancient tradition survived in the penumbra of Japanese cultural consciousness. The eleventh century *Konjaku Monogatari* ("Tales of Long Ago") includes a tale of nuns and

woodcutters who became inebriated in the forest after ingesting *maitake*, "dancing mushrooms" (Wasson 1973A). *Maitake* is now identified with a non-entheogenic species, *Grifola frondosa*. However, as their names suggest, several Japanese species are of known entheogenic potency. The *o-warai-take*, or "big laughing mushroom," is none other than psilocybian *Gymnopilus spectabilis* (see Table 4; Buck 1967; Walters 1965). The *warai-take* or the "laughing mushroom" is the psilocybine-containing *Panaeolus campanulatus* (one of the first species of *teonanácatl* identified in México); and the *shibire-take* or "benumbing mushroom" is *Psilocybe venenata*, known to be entheogenic (see Table 4). There is a Japanese *senryu* poem about the *warai-take*: "It would be nice to make/The *kunikaro*/Eat *warai-take*!" referring to a wish to make the stern *kunikaro*, the feudal lord's straw boss, ingest the "laughing mushrooms" to "lighten up" (Blyth 1973). Several Chinese sources roughly contemporaneous with the *Konjaku Monogatari* describe the effects of the *Hsiao-ch'un* or "laughing mushroom," doubtless one of the Japanese psilocybian species (Blyth 1973; Li 1978; Wasson & Wasson 1957A; Yu 1959). The entheogenic *Amanita* species are known in Japan as *beni-tengu-take* ("scarlet Tengu mushroom," *A. muscaria*); *tengu-take* ("Tengu mushroom," *A. pantherina*); and ***ibo-tengu-take*** ("warted Tengu mushroom," *A. strobiliformis*, from which ibotenic acid gets its name; see Table 6). *Tengu* are mythical creatures, trickster imps associated with the shamanic past, said to get "drunk from eating mushrooms" (Imazeki 1973; Li 1978; Sanford 1972; Wasson 1973A). As in the West, mycological publications of accidental poisonings began to bring these ancient inebriants to scientific attention (Imai 1932). Imazeki and Wasson have written excellent articles on Japanese ethnomycology (Imazeki 1973; Imazeki & Wasson 1973; Wasson 1973A). Another area of interest with respect to traditional psychoactive mushroom use is New Guinea. In the remote Wahgi Valley of New Guinea, an area first penetrated by outsiders in the 1930s, there lives a preliterate people called the Kuma. The first document written about the Kuma makes reference to the fact that the Kuma would ingest a "wild mushroom called *nonda*" which "makes the user temporarily insane" (Heim & Wasson 1965). V.P. and R.G. Wasson described this practice in the opening few paragraphs of the second volume of *Mushrooms Russia and History* (Wasson & Wasson 1957A). Near the end of the following year, R. Singer published a short paper on some specimens he received from the Royal Botanic Gardens at Kew, whence they had been sent by D.E. Shaw. Singer was able to identify one specimen as a new species, which he named *Russula nondorbingi* (Singer *et al.* 1958B). The material Singer received contained also "some other agarics and at least one polypore" and he published a sketchy description of an "*Agaricales* spec." he had recovered from the mixed collection, as well as a photograph of the pickled type specimens of *R. nondorbingi*. Singer, who had learned of the Kuma mushrooms from *Mushrooms Russia and History*, did not quote any ethnological details "since others are undoubtedly much more competent to do so," in a veiled reference to his by then strained relations with the Wassons (Singer *et al.* 1958B; see Note 8 below). Indeed, Heim and Wasson spent three weeks collecting in the Wahgi Valley in 1963 with anthropologist M. Reay (who published a book on the Kuma and a paper on the "mushroom madness"; Reay 1959; Reay 1960) and concluded that Singer's name was a misnomer. Not only did they find eleven different species of "madness" mushrooms, two of which were called *nonda bingi* (not *nondorbingi*), but Singer's *Russula nondorbingi* was not among them (Heim 1963; Heim 1965; Heim 1978;

Heim & Wasson 1964; Heim & Wasson 1965). Heim and Wasson described the following 11 mushroom species as being responsible for *komugl taï* ("mushroom madness" which affects only men) or for the *ndaadl* ("mushroom delirium" which in turn affects only women): *nonda ngam-ngam, Boletus reayi*; *nonda ngamp-kindj kants, Boletus kumaeus*; *nonda gegwants ngimbigl, Boletus manicus*; *nonda kermaipip, Boletus nigerrimus*; *nonda tua-rua, Boletus nigroviolaceus* plus *Boletus flammeus*; *nonda mos, Russula agglutinata* and *R. maenadum*; *nonda wam, Russula psuedomaenadum*; *nonda kirin, Russula kirinea*; and *nonda mbolbe, Heimiella anguiformis* (Heim 1963; Heim 1965; Heim 1966; Heim 1973; Heim 1978; Heim & Wasson 1965). Heim and Wasson concluded that the "mushroom madness" of the Kuma was a non-pharmacological phenomenon (see Appendix B). Although the Kuma attributed the manifestations of madness to the mushrooms, they believe that "those ordained to succumb to it will succumb whether they eat the mushroom or not" (Heim & Wasson 1965). Based on their field research, Heim and Wasson took issue with Singer's conclusion that the Kuma mushrooms cause "cerebral mycetisms" (Singer *et al.* 1958B), although the species *Boletus manicus* has appeared in a compendium of entheogenic plants (Schultes & Hofmann 1979). Nevertheless, Heim reported that trace amounts of three unidentified indolic substances were found in *Boletus manicus*, and in self-experiments with *B. manicus* powder (less than 60 mg) Heim reported "ingestion provoked the apparition of very colorful luminous visions" (Heim 1965; Heim 1978).

[6] Reko and Schultes also sent some material of *teonanácatl* to Swedish pharmacologist C.G. Santesson, who initiated the first chemical and pharmacological studies on the fungal entheogen in 1938. Santesson observed a "semi-narcosis" (*Halbnarkose*) following administration of his extract to frogs and mice, and stated that the presence in his extract of a glucoside was "at least possible" (Santesson 1939). This was as far as Santesson's work on *teonanácatl* was to go. Curiously, Santesson also reported receiving another inebriant (*Rauschdroge*) from Reko and Schultes, namely *Hallimahl*, also a mushroom, also said to be used by the Mexican Indians. After making extracts (alkaloid test negative; presence of glucosides possible) Santesson tested these on frogs, mice and rabbits. Again, he reported a "semi-narcosis" in the frog tests, but not in mice or rabbits. Schultes did not mention the mysterious *Hallimahl* in his 1939 paper on the identification of *teonanácatl*, and in his later history of the identification of *teonanácatl* (Schultes 1978) said Santesson had identified it as *Armillariella mellea*, an edible mushroom. Actually, Santesson had merely said that the name *Hallimahl* sounded like *Hallimasch*, a European name for *Armillariella mellea*. Singer noted this discrepancy, and said *Hallimahl* was likely *Psilocybe mexicana* and *P. cubensis* (Singer 1958A). Singer offered no proof, as no voucher specimens of *Hallimahl* were available, and we shall never know the identity of this inebriant.

[7] In the course of their research on the Mexican entheogenic mushrooms, Wasson and Heim encountered a pair of "narcotic" *Lycoperdon* species in the Mixtec zone of Oaxaca in August 1961. Accompanied by ethnologist R. Ravicz, Heim and Wasson collected a new species, *Lycoperdon mixtecorum*, called *gi'i wa*, the "first-class mushroom" and a well-known species, *L. marginatum*, which their Mixtec informant Agapito called *gi'i sawa*, or the "second-class mushroom" (Heim & Wasson 1962; Heim *et al.* 1967). According to

Agapito, a pair of specimens of either species is taken before sleeping for an hour or an hour and a half, during which time the mushrooms would speak to the subject; in the case of Agapito, predicting an illness and its outcome. During the summers of 1974 and 1975, two groups, led by J.L. Díaz (accompanied in 1974 by C. Álvarez and P. Bremer) and by me (accompanied in 1975 by J. Romano and R. Paniagua) studied with Agapito at his San Miguel Progreso, Oaxaca home. In the course of this work, no fewer than 11 species of "narcotic" mushrooms were pointed-out by Agapito, including *Lycoperdon marginatum* (which Guzmán considered conspecific with *L. candidum*) and *Lycoperdon mixtecorum* (identical to *Vascellum qudenii*, according to Guzmán; Ott *et al.* 1975B). All but one, *Agrocybe semiorbicularis*, were species of puffballs, and the former is very similar morphologically to *Psilocybe mexicana*, which the Mixtecs use ritually (Heim & Wasson 1962), and likely represents a mistake on the part of Agapito, although psilocybine is now known from *Agrocybe farinacea* of Japan (Koike *et al.* 1981). Romano, Paniagua and I severally ingested in separate experiments all ten puffball species identified by Agapito, experiencing no effect whatever, other than nausea and gastrointestinal distress provoked in my two collaborators by a specimen later identified as *Scleroderma verrucosum* (Ott *et al.* 1975B). With the exception of this species, *Agrocybe semiorbicularis*, and a *Rhizopogon* species, specimens of all of Agapito's mushrooms were tested chromatographically against standards of psilocybine and ibotenic acid (known psychoactive agents of entheogenic *Psilocybe* and *Amanita* species respectively), and against *bis*-noryangonin, at that time suspected of being an active agent of *Gymnopilus spectabilis* (Hatfield & Brady 1969; Hatfield & Brady 1971). In no case was any known entheogenic mushroom principle detected, and since the mushrooms had provoked no discernible effects in repeated self-experiments at the doses indicated by Agapito, it was impossible to conduct any further research. We concluded that the "narcotic" mushrooms of the Mixtec were inactive at the prescribed doses. However, Heim cited a report from the United States in 1869 in which a "narcotic influence" was attributed to "meals" of *Lycoperdon*, suggesting the posibility of an activity at higher doses (Coker & Couch 1928; Heim & Wasson 1962; Heim *et al.* 1967). The problem is compounded by the fact that the activity ascribed to these mushrooms, that of inducing dreams, is elusive and difficult to study. Similar activity of the Mexican herb *Calea zacatechichi*, used to induce "lucid dreaming" by the Chontal Indians of Oaxaca, has been categorized as "oneirogenic" (see Appendix B; Mayagoitia *et al.* 1986). R. Bye reported the belief of the Tarahumara Indians of Chihuahua, México, that a *Lycoperdon* species known as *kalamoto* in Tarahumara or *pata de perro* ("dog's paw") may be "used by sorcerers to enable them to approach people without being seen and to make people sick" (see Appendix B; Bye 1979A). This report hints at an association of a *Lycoperdon* species with sorcery. Intriguing German names for *Lycoperdon* species suggest some use of puffballs in European herbalism/witchcraft: *Hexenbeutel* ("witches' bag"); *Hexenei* ("witches' egg"); *Hexenfurz* ("witches' fart"); *Hexenmehl* ("witches' meal"); *Hexenpilz* ("witches' mushroom"); *Hexenpusters* ("witches' breath"); *Hexenschiss* ("witches' shit"); *Hexenschwamm* ("witches' fungus"); and *Hexenstaub* ("witches' dust"; De Vries 1991A). Sundry ethnomedicinal uses of *Lycoperdon* species and other "puffballs" by North American Indians have lately been reviewed (Burk 1983), but in no case was any evidence of entheogenic or ritual use uncovered. The existence of entheogenic Mexican puffball species remains yet to be proved.

[8] During the fruitful collaboration of Wasson in the United States, Heim and co-workers in France and Hofmann and assistants in Switzerland, a shadowy group was conducting similar research in parallel. While Wasson, Heim and Hofmann had purely scientific and (in the case of Hofmann as an employee of Sandoz LTD.), business interests in the Mexican sacred mushrooms, the shadowy group was interested in deriving chemical warfare agents from the mushrooms, or chemical aids to interrogation of "enemy agents." While Wasson, Heim and Hofmann published information in the international scientific literature, the shadowy group was interested in development of a secret chemical arsenal. The United States Central Intelligence Agency (CIA) apparently learned of the existence of the Mexican mushrooms in 1953, when they sent a "young scientist" to México, who returned with plant material, including 4.5 kilograms of *ololiuhqui* (see Chapter 2). The CIA began to plan attempts to obtain samples of the mushrooms, and laid the groundwork for their large-scale cultivation. On 24 June 1953, Morse Allen (then head of ARTICHOKE, predecessor of the CIA's MKULTRA project; see Chapter 2 Note 15) and an associate went to Toughkenamon, Pennsylvania for a three-hour meeting with executives of large commercial mushroom-growing companies, who then agreed to assist the government in large-scale cultivation of poisonous and psychoactive mushrooms (Marks 1979). Sometime early in 1955, after the publication by Heim in French of preliminary articles concerning the Wassons' research in México, the CIA contacted Gordon Wasson, seeking his collaboration. Wasson summarily declined (Forte 1988). On 15 August 1955 Wasson was subsequently contacted by American chemist James Moore, then of Parke, Davis and Company and soon to join the faculty of the University of Delaware. Moore expressed interest in participating in the mushroom research in a "purely scientific" manner, in the discovery of novel compounds in the mushrooms. To persuade Wasson, Moore avowed he could contribute $2000 in grant funds from the "Geschickter Fund for Medical Research, Inc." (Riedlinger 1990). Wasson always assumed Moore's interest was legitimate, until 1979, when J. Marks published *The Search for the "Manchurian Candidate"* based on once-secret information on CIA activities made public following a "Freedom of Information Act" lawsuit (Marks 1979). Marks revealed that the "Geschickter Fund for Medical Research, Inc." was a phony organization, a CIA "front" (see Chapter 2, Note 15), and that Moore was in reality working for the CIA as a sort of "short-order cook who concocted chemical warfare dishes to go" (Marks 1979). Since Wasson had declined to cooperate openly with the CIA, the organization decided to infiltrate his expedition using Moore, whose mission was to obtain information about the mushrooms, and return with specimens, in order to attempt to isolate the active principles of the mushrooms in the United States. Moore didn't fit in well with the group. The expedition photographer Allan Richardson (who along with Gordon Wasson, had been one of the first outsiders to ingest the Mexican sacred mushrooms) commented: "at that time, all we knew was that we didn't like Jim. Something was wrong with him… I avoided him and we went our separate ways" (Richardson 1990). Marks commented that everyone "reveled" in the "primitiveness" of the expedition except for Moore, who didn't seem to enjoy himself (Marks 1979). Although Moore ingested the mushrooms in a *velada* with María Sabina, he did so reluctantly (Wasson 1977). Marks quoted Moore as saying he felt the hallucinogenic effect, which he rather described as a noisome "disoriented" state (Marks 1979). Moore did, however, succeed in

collecting specimens of the entheogenic mushrooms for his planned chemical research, and S. Gottlieb, head of the Chemical Division of the CIA's Technical Services Office, felt it possible that the CIA might obtain a new chemical warfare agent which could be kept an "Agency secret." This was not to be, however. Moore did not succeed in isolating the active principles, for he was relying on animal assays to evaluate his fractions of the mushrooms, and was unwilling to test them on himself. Albert Hofmann, meanwhile, obtained 100 grams of dried *Psilocybe mexicana* cultivated by Heim and Cailleux in Paris early in 1957. Using self-experiments to evaluate fractions of the mushrooms, Hofmann soon isolated the active principles, as discussed above (see Chapter 2, Note 13). Before sending the mushrooms to Hofmann, Heim had sent material to two American pharmaceutical companies, Smith, Kline & French and Merck, Sharp & Dohme, as well as to a French chemist in his Museum. These groups failed to isolate the active principles for the same reason Moore did—unwillingness to use themselves as "human guinea pigs" for the experiments. The CIA also collected large amounts of *ololiuhqui* seeds in México (see Chapter 2). These were entrusted to chemist W.B. Cook of Montana State College (who was later to look for the active principles of *Amanita muscaria* as explained in Chapter 6; Subbaratnam & Cook 1963) for isolation of the active principles. As we saw in Chapter 2, however, Wasson and Hofmann solved the chemistry of *ololiuhqui* in 1960, again frustrating the CIA in its desire to amass a secret chemical arsenal (although Cook published a paper on the isolation of an inactive glucoside from *ololiuhqui*, he was "scooped" by other researchers, who named the compound turbicoryn; Cook & Kealand 1962; Pérezamador & Herrán 1960). There were other groups interested in the Mexican mushrooms. Gastón Guzmán, Mexican mycologist and leading authority on the taxonomy of Mexican fungi, at the time a young graduate student, mentioned he was asked by "some Swiss pharmaceutical companies" in 1956 to help collect entheogenic mushrooms (Guzmán 1990), and he was hired as a consultant by the Swiss firm Geigy (Guzmán 1976). Guzmán was soon to become involved in the following year as field assistant to Rolf Singer, a mycologist sent to México by the "Bertram and Roberta Stein Neuropsychiatric Research Program, Inc." of Chicago. The director of the program, Chicago psychiatrist Sam I. Stein had a personal interest in the mushrooms. He had suffered a strange experience in March 1949 (Singer later incorrectly gave the date as 1941; see Singer 1982), after eating what he thought were *Agaricus bisporus*, commercially-grown edible mushrooms (Stein, in Singer *et al.* 1958B). About six hours later, Stein developed cramps and diarrhea, and after 12 hours had elapsed "cerebral intoxicating effects commenced." These latter effects intensified over a period of days, and lasted "over four months" (Stein, letter to Rolf Singer dated 24 November 1956; this and other letters quoted below from the files of the "Tina and Gordon Wasson Ethnomycological Collection," Harvard Botanical Museum). While this effect does not sound at all like accidental psilocybian mushroom poisoning, Stein suspected that the mushrooms may have been contaminated with the "weed" *Panaeolus subbalteatus* (=*Panaeolus venenosus*), known to crop up in commercial mushroom growing houses and known to have been responsible for at least one case of accidental inebriation from eating commercially-grown edible mushrooms (Murrill 1916; Singer & Smith in Singer *et al.* 1958B; Verrill 1914). Stein subsequently went to the Field Museum in Chicago in 1952, and there met Rolf Singer who worked at the Field Museum at the time (Stein later gave the date as 1953; see Stein 1960). Stein proposed that *Panaeolus subbalteatus* was the possible cause of his poisoning in 1949, and suggested the existence of "a probable cerebral excitatory factor in *Panaeolus* mushrooms" (Stein, letter to Singer dated 24 May 1956). Some years passed, during which Singer became the head of the Botany Department of Instituto Miguel Lillo at the Tucumán National University of Argentina, where Stein again contacted him in a letter dated 24 May 1956, enclosing a synopsis of the research program of the "Bertram and Roberta Stein" foundation, and a list of mushrooms in which the group was interested. Singer's reply, dated 2 June 1956, stated "I recommend you read a recent paper on this by Heim (Institut de France, Acad. des Sciences, Comptes rendus 242, 965, 1385, 1956) and get in touch with Mr. Gordon Wasson of New York" (Wasson 1982A). Stein subsequently wrote to the Wassons, receiving a reply from Valentina P. Wasson dated 18 November 1956 stating: "we know only one way to get the hallucinogenic species: to go and look for them... The quest is expensive, uncomfortable, exciting, and possibly dangerous." Stein then wrote to Singer (24 November 1956), sending a copy of Valentina's letter and offering Singer a job as mycological collaborator to the Stein group. In his response dated 2 December 1956, Singer accepted in principle, proposing "a trip as suggested by Mrs. Wasson in order to get (1) plenty of fruiting bodies of the species concerned for analytical work (2) cultures from this material (3) scientific herbarium material in order to straighten out the taxonomy of the species concerned by comparing them with the material preserved in Paris (Heim is a friend of mine)." Singer stated that, if there were no hurry, he would prefer to make the proposed field trip in 1958. In this interesting letter, Singer also mentioned that he had "an additional job as registrar of the Selective Service here" (that is, he was working for the [Argentine?] government registering young men for military conscription in Argentina!). Stein responded on 14 December: "I should like you to arrange for you to go to Mexico to secure mushrooms. Perhaps you could do this in the next several months." Funding was arranged, and Singer flew to México in July 1957, contracted the services of Guzmán and M.A. Palacios (not M.E. Palacios as in Singer 1982) and commenced work. Singer's group, using as guide a notebook in which had been pasted Heim's water-color illustrations of the mushrooms from Wasson's *Life* article (R.G. Wasson 1957) along with descriptions of the mushrooms from Heim's early French papers (Heim 1956A; Heim 1956B; Ott 1978A), followed so closely in the footsteps of the Wassons and Heim, as to overtake them—Singer met Wasson for the first and only time on 15 July 1957 in the remote Mazatec Indian village of San Andrés (see photograph in Singer 1958B). Singer succeeded in collecting a number of the same mushroom species Heim and the Wassons had collected, as well as cultures, then went to the U.S. and began work on the material with A.H. Smith of the University of Michigan. Singer and Smith published two papers *out-of-order* "through financial assistance of the NSF [National Science Foundation] and the University of Michigan herbarium" in *Mycologia* (Singer 1958A; Singer & Smith 1958B) along with a short paper (Singer & Smith 1958A) giving Latin descriptions and names for seven novel species of *Psilocybe*, including two Singer had collected in México. One of these was *Psilocybe muliercula* and Singer and Smith's paper naming this species appeared on 4 April 1958, 25 days before Heim's Latin description of the mushroom as *Psilocybe wassonii* (Heim 1958). Heim, however, had described the mushroom in French six months earlier, on 18 November 1957 (Heim 1957A) and announced his intention to name the mushroom for the Wassons. Singer learned of this mushroom from the work of the Wassons and Heim, and *did not collect specimens in the field.* He purchased specimens in a market on 30 July 1957, *per* information gleaned from the Wassons and Heim. Singer went ahead and published the name *Psilocybe muliercula*, knowing his "friend" Heim, who had collected it first, intended to name it for the Wassons. His name unfortunately had precedence, as it appeared with Latin description 25 days in advance of Heim's paper naming it *P. wassonii*. It was my refusal to accept the Singer and Smith name that precipitated a series of polemics on the subject (Ott 1976B; Ott 1978A; Ott 1979B; Ott 1990; Singer 1982; Smith 1977; Wasson 1982A). In his feeble defense (Singer 1982), Singer tacitly admitted he was unaware that James Moore, who visited Singer and Smith in Ann Arbor, Michigan during this time, was working for the CIA (Marks 1979), and Moore kept Wasson apprised of Singer and Smith's activities in Ann Arbor, including how Singer was "panting with impatience" over the slow appearance of Heim's papers (Wasson 1982A). Stein, meanwhile, became so disgusted at what he felt was Singer's mistreatment of the Wassons and Heim, that he apologized to Wasson on Singer's behalf, and sent him copies of his correspondence with Singer, which is how they came to be available for examination (Wasson 1977). Heim and the Wassons all felt that Singer's behavior was ungentlemanly (Wasson 1982A). Singer has made many inaccurate statements about the mushrooms, such as saying that they provoke "a temporary narcotic state of hilarity" and are "poisonous when used in excess" (Singer 1949); claiming that their use was reported by "the Spanish conquistadores" who never mentioned them (Singer 1957); saying the Japanese species *Psilocybe subaeruginascens* "caused ten deaths in 1929 alone" (supposedly in Japan—in reality this mushroom, once used traditionally in Japan, has never been reported to cause even a *single* death; Imai 1932; Singer & Smith 1958B); alleging that one Mexican species was "called 'birdies' by the Indians because they made one sing happily" (Singer 1957); *etc.* In general, he had long represented himself as an authority on the subject, 'though he confided to R.G. Wasson: "you have experiences which go far beyond my own (who cowardly refrained from eating the *Psilocybes*)" (Singer, letter to Wasson dated 12 August 1957). Later, on 7 July 1969, Singer ingested entheogenic mushrooms in a hotel in Huautla, about which Wasson commented: "Singer was going through with it just to be able to say he had had the experience, that he could condemn it with authority, right from the horse's mouth. That he was loath, not eager, to take the mushrooms is proved by his unwillingness in 1957, 12 years earlier, to take them" (Wasson, letter to me dated 3 February 1976). Stein, meanwhile, got his mushrooms and his foundation funded research at the University of Michigan (Singer and Smith and mycologist R.W. Ames), at the University of Illinois, at an unidentified "commercial firm" and at the University of Pennsylvania (Singer 1959). At the last-named institution, Leon R. Kneebone grew "satisfactory quantities" of at least 5 species of entheogenic mushrooms in large-scale greenhouse conditions: *Psilocybe cubensis* (photograph in Singer 1958B); *Panaeolus subbalteatus* (photograph in Singer *et al.* 1958B—Kneebone had already grown "a sizable amount... upon his first try" of this species before receiving cultures from Singer; Stein 1960); *Panaeolus* [*Copelandia*] *cyanescens* (Kneebone 1960); *Panaeolus sphinctrinus* (photograph in Singer 1958A) and *Psilocybe aztecorum* (Kneebone 1960; Singer 1959; Stein 1960). Whether this large-scale cultivation had anything to do with the original CIA interest in cultivating mushrooms in Pennsylvania, or the chemical work of Moore, I do not know. In October of 1957, Stein finally ingested 4 specimens of *Psilocybe mexicana*, but experienced no effect. On 22 December 1957 he fried and ingested 2 specimens (about 5 grams; presumably dry weight) of Kneebone's *Psilocybe cubensis* crop in Chicago. He began to feel "uneasiness" and took 4 drops of *Sandril* (concentrated reserpine solution, equivalent to 0.25 mg) less than 40 minutes after having taken the mushrooms. Stein then drove to the house of a medical colleague, Dr. Jesús de la Huerga, for an examination. There he took a "sip" of liquor which "increased the cerebral distress," then 4 more drops of the reserpine solution, finally driving home with difficulty. Once there he took another sip of liquor and remained outside on a porch in the winter cold. Stein "never felt more 'horrible'" and by 7 hours after ingestion was more or less normal (Stein, in Singer *et al.* 1958B). As might be expected, Stein's experience with *Psilocybe cubensis* "in no way resembled my experience with *Agaricus bisporus*, presumed to have been mixed with fruiting bodies of *Panaeolus subbalteatus*" and "only slightly resembled" his prior experience with "a standard dose of lysergic acid diethylamide." This was the first documented "bad trip" with psilocybian mushrooms (*vide* also: Herrera 1967), and Stein said he wouldn't wish to repeat the experiment; which didn't stop him from giving a psychiatric patient doses of *Panaeolus venenosus* (=*P. subbalteatus*) and *Psilocybe caerulescens* (Stein 1959), despite the fact that this patient was already taking daily doses of four other psychotropic drugs—reserpine, amphetamine, amobarbital and iproniazid! The subject, suffering from "homosexual thoughts" had "strong favorable and euphoriant effects" from *Panaeolus subbalteatus*; *Psilocybe caerulescens* was "much less pleasant" (Stein 1959).

[9] In 1985 D.B. Repke, D.B. Grotjahn and A.T. Shulgin published a paper in the *Journal of Medicinal Chemistry* on the human pharmacology of eight *N*-Methyl-*N*-IsoPropyl-Tryptamines or MIPT (Repke *et al.* 1985). Other such papers have been published; this one was unique in that it may well have been the last of its kind to be published in the war[on drugs]time United States. In the present study, instead of the natural, symmetrical dimethyltryptamines, compounds were made replacing one of the methyl groups with an isopropyl group; a three-carbon group in place of a single-carbon group. One of these compounds, 4-Hydroxy-*N*-Methyl-*N*-IsoPropylTryptamine (4-OH-MIPT) had been among Repke's previously-published series of psilocine derivatives (Repke *et al.* 1981), and one had previously been described by Grotjahn (1983). 4-OH-MIPT, as well as three other compounds (MIPT, 4-MeO-MIPT, and 5-MeO-MIPT) all showed activity in human self-experiments (the remaining 4 compounds described in the paper were all inactive up to 50 mg doses; with all experiments involving oral ingestion). The most active compound was 5-MeO-MIPT, with a 5 mg dose (0.07 mg/kg) producing a three-hour effect commencing in 9–16 minutes. The psilocine analogue, 4-OH-MIPT, was about as active as, but longer-lasting than, the parent compound psilocine, a 10 mg dose (0.14 mg/kg) producing a 6–7 hour effect commencing in 20–35 minutes. Simple MIPT was psychoactive at a 25 mg dose (0.33 mg/kg) with a duration of 3–4 hours and time of onset of 40–50 minutes. The weakest of the 4 psychoactive compounds was 4-MeO-MIPT, with an effective dose of 30 mg (0.40 mg/kg) producing a 2–2.5 hour effect commencing in 45–60 minutes. It is interesting that although 4-OH-MIPT is qualitatively and quantitatively similar to psilocine or 4-OH-DMT,

simple MIPT is somewhat more potent than simple DMT (in the paper it is said to be four times the potency of injected DMT but, as we saw in Chapter 4, in the presence of MAO-inhibitors rendering it orally active, DMT is visionary in 20–30 mg range; see Ott 1994A) and, more importantly, is psychoactive orally without the simultaneous use of MAO-inhibitors. Similarly, 5-MEO-MIPT is somewhat more psychoactive than 5-MEO-DMT (see Chapter 3) and again, unlike the natural parent compound, is psychoactive orally. Only 4-OH-MIPT was reported to be visionary ("hallucinogenic"), with both MIPT and 5-MEO-MIPT being characterized as amphetamine-like with "a general heightening of awareness." 4-MEO-MIPT was reported as being a minor stimulant, and in animal tests, the artificial 4-MEO-DMT was shown to be less active than psilocybine in monkeys and rodents (Uyeno 1969; Uyeno 1971). The psychonautic authors concluded: 1) that the unsymmetrical substitution led to greater oral activity; 2) that a 5-methoxy- group produced increased stimulatory effects "at the expense of visual phenomena"; 3) that the 4-hydroxy- group enhanced "general hallucinogenic profile" while adding a methyl group to this hydroxy-group reduced activity; 4) that 6- and 7-methoxy- substitution abolished activity; and 5) that 5,6-dioxygenation likewise abolished activity (Repke *et al.* 1985). Unfortunately, the "Controlled Substance Analogue Enforcement Act" passed a year after this study was published could be construed as illegalizing any experiments of this type which, involving human self-experimentation, are ethically flawless and promise to advance greatly our limited knowledge of brain tryptamine chemistry (see Chapter 2, Notes 13 and 15, and Chapter 3, Note 2 for a discussion of the ethics of research with psychoactive compounds and of the necessity for human experimentation where entheogenic substances are involved). Since DMT is a normal constituent of human cerebrospinal fluid and might be a neurotransmitter in human brains (Christian *et al.* 1976; Christian *et al.* 1977; Corbett *et al.* 1978), this area of research represents a promising way to study the effects of neurotransmitters on consciousness, and to approach the problem of the possibility of metabolic defects producing "mental illness." To close off such a promising field in the name of a "War on Drugs" is arbitrary and counterproductive—pursuing such a heavy-handed approach to research will ultimately doom the United States pharmaceutical industry to technological inferiority. Instead of being treated as heroes or pioneers, as they should be, scientific psychonauts, to use Ernst Jünger's appropriate term (Jünger 1970), courageously (and generously, since they pay for the work out-of-pocket and not with government grants) doing this sort of research are made to feel like criminals. It is worthwhile noting that the above-mentioned study did not result in the discovery of any new "designer drugs." In no case was an entheogenic compound discovered which exceeded the parent compound (psilocine) in activity. Since that parent compound (or its biochemical precursor psilocybine) occurs in more than 98 species of mushrooms growing all over the world (and likely occurs in at least another 60 mushroom species—see Table 4) and can be had free of charge by anyone willing to go out and pick wild mushrooms, it is ludicrous to suppose that suppressing this sort of important and unique research will be an effective strategy in the quixotic "War on [Users of Certain] Drugs." It is undeniable, however, that such suppression will cripple American pharmaceutical companies in their international competition with capable and well-financed Japanese and European firms, while contributing to the steady and inexorable erosion of personal liberty within the United States.

[10] Owing to bureaucratic error, psilocine came to be classified legally under the misspelling psilocyn, which then has cropped up in the scientific and popular literature. Another example is the persistent legal use of the misspelling *marihuana*, whereas in México this Hispanic name for *Cannabis* is typically rendered *mariguana* or less commonly *marijuana*. In his pioneering booklet describing the synthesis of "psilocyn" Brown made the curious error of characterizing the drug as 6-hydroxy-dimethyltryptamine, rather than the correct designation 4-hydroxy-dimethyltryptamine (Brown 1968).

[11] I organized this conference, which took place at Millersylvania State Park, as well as "The Second International Conference on Hallucinogenic Mushrooms" held at Fort Worden near Port Townsend, Washington from 27–30 October 1977 (an extract published as the book *Teonanácatl: Hallucinogenic Mushrooms of North America*, see Ott & Bigwood 1978; Ott & Bigwood 1985); and also "Hallucinogens in Native American Shamanism and Modern Life" at the Japan Center in San Francisco, California from 28 September to 1 October 1978 (extracts published as a special double issue of *Journal of Psychedelic Drugs*, for which I served as "Guest Editor," see Ott 1979A). The participants in the 1976 conference were: Jeremy Bigwood, Lynn R. Brady, W. Scott Chilton, Gastón Guzmán, Dale T. Leslie, Jonathan Ott, Steven H. Pollock, David B. Repke, Paul Stamets and R. Gordon Wasson; of the 1977 conference: Bigwood, Chilton, Guzmán, David Harnden, Albert Hofmann, Leslie, Ott, Repke, Richard Rose, Carl A.P. Ruck, Richard Evans Schultes, Wasson, Andrew T. Weil and Norman Zinberg; and of the 1978 conference: Bigwood, Chilton, José Luis Díaz, Stanislav Grof, Harnden, Hofmann, Bo Holmstedt, Reid Kaplan, Keewaydinoquay (K.M. Peschel), Weston La Barre, Timothy Plowman, Schultes, Alexander T. Shulgin, Wasson, Weil and Zinberg. Bigwood, Hofmann, Ott, Schultes, Wasson and Weil all contributed to the 1978 book based on the 1977 conference; while Bigwood, Chilton, Díaz, Hofmann, Keewaydinoquay, La Barre, Ott, Plowman, Ruck, Schultes, Shulgin, Wasson and Zinberg wrote articles for the *Journal of Psychedelic Drugs* issue based on the 1978 meeting. These three symposia were the most important meetings on entheogenic plants since the 28–30 January 1967 meeting on psychoactive plants held in San Francisco under the sponsorship of the U.S. National Institute of Mental Health and chronicled in the classic book *Ethnopharmacologic Search for Psychoactive Drugs* (Efron *et al.* 1967; see Chapter 4, Note 7). Schultes, Shulgin, Wasson and Weil were among the faculty for the 1967 meeting, and contributors to the resulting book. Not until the 16–20 November 1992 symposium on "Plantas, Chamanismo y Estados de Conciencia" ("Plants, Shamanism, and States of Consciousness") held in San Luis Potosí, México, were so many experts on entheogenic plants convened for an international conference dedicated to this subject. The proceedings of the San Luis Potosí meeting were published as a special issue (No. 5) of *Integration: Zeitschrift für Geistbewegende Pflanzen und Kultur* and as a book (Fericgla 1994B). A followup meeting was held 3–7 October 1994 in Lleida, Catalunya; the third, "Entheobotany: Shamanic Plant Science," held in San Francisco from 18–20 October 1996.

[12] While one of the sixteenth century accounts of *teonanácatl* states that the mushrooms, *por ser amargos*, "being bitter," were taken with honey, there is no tradition of preserving the mushrooms in honey in México. Indeed, embalming in honey is useless for preservation

of mushrooms. Nevertheless, during a 1976 field trip in the Zapotec zone of Oaxaca, I was surprised to be offered *Psilocybe caerulescens* for sale by a Zapotec Indian family... embalmed in honey! Predictably, this was a "disgusting, fermenting mess, crawling with bugs" (Ott 1979B). It is most unlikely any psilocybine had survived the fermentation, but the resulting metheglin may have possessed a modest amount of ethanol! What a tragic waste... fermenting the pharmacotheon into mead... like transmuting gold to lead! On the other hand, in the *Poetic Eddas* of Norse mythology, we hear of Odin's *Othrörir*, the magic mead which imparted immortality, wisdom and poetry, and of *Mimir's Well* at the base of the world tree *Yggdrasil*, from which flowed a magic mead of wisdom (Metzner 1994; Ott 1995B; Pendell 1995; Rätsch 1996)... but this was the Sierra Zapoteca, and not Scandinavia! I was told that the Zapotec Indian family had learned this honey-embalming practice from the mushroomic tourists, and prepared the mushrooms so to satisfy the tastes of the foreigners! This is an example of how quickly tradition can be corrupted by the sudden exposure of isolated pockets of traditional culture to foreign influences.

[13] As Diego Durán wrote more than four centuries ago, describing the coronation of the Aztec emperor Ahuitzotl *circa* 1486 A.D. "...mention is never made that anyone drank wine of any kind to get drunk, but only woodland mushrooms, which they ate raw, on which... they were happy and rejoiced and went somewhat out of their heads, and of wine no mention is made... mention is only made of the abundance of chocolate that was being drunk in these solemnities" (Durán 1967). For a detailed explication of the ancient Mexican connection between cacao and *teonanácatl*, see my book on the subject (Ott 1985). Henry Munn has underscored the connection between cacao and entheogenic mushrooms in contemporary Mazatec shamanism (Munn 1973). In general, the Aztec cacao potion *cacáhuatl* was used as a vehicle for the administration of entheogens and other medicinal plants. One obscure Aztec entheogen was a flower called *poyomatli* (see Appendix B). Since a passage in Sahagún tells us that *poyomatli* was the flower of a tree called *cacahuaxóchitl* (literally, "flower of cacao"), this has led to speculation that the flower of the cacao tree itself (*Theobroma cacao*) was the entheogenic *poyomatli* (Sahagún 1950). However, the flowers of *T. cacao* are not psychoactive, and Wasson proposed that *poyomatli* was the flower of *Quararibea funebris*, known to this day as *cacahuaxóchitl* in Oaxaca, México, and intimately associated with cacao (see Appendix B; Ott 1985; Wasson 1980). Not only is the flower of *Q. funebris* used in contemporary cacao potions in Oaxaca, but the wood of the tree is also used traditionally in manufacture of the *batidor* and *molinillo*, tools traditionally used for frothing cacao drinks (Rosengarten 1977; Schultes 1957B). Although the flowers of *Q. funebris* do not appear to be entheogenic (Ott, unpublished field notes), a group of unique lactones, the quabalactones, have been isolated from the flowers and suggested to be pharmacologically active (Raffauf & Zennie 1983; Zennie *et al.* 1986). Moreover, a novel alkaloid, funebrine, has been isolated from the flowers, the first alkaloid known from the family Bombacaceae (Raffauf *et al.* 1984). Recently, ethnomedicinal use of the leaves of *Q. funebris* has been reported from México (Zamora-Martínez & Nieto de Pascual Pola 1992). A little-known Peruvian shamanic inebriant, *espingo* (or *ispincu*), has recently been identified by Schultes as the seeds of a *Quararibea* species (Wassén 1979), and *ishpingo* has recently been reported used as an *ayahuasca* additive among Peruvian In-

dians (see Chapter 4; Arévalo Valera 1986), and an additive to entheogenic potions based on mescaline-containing *San Pedro* cacti in South America (see Chapter 1; Polia & Bianchi 1992). *Quararibea putumayensis* is used as an arrow poison plant by the Kofán Indians of South America, and the related genus *Matisia* is the source of plant medicines (Schultes & Raffauf 1990). These findings keep the spotlight on *Quararibea funebris* as a candidate for the lost Aztec entheogen *poyomatli*, whose positive identification remains a *desideratum* of Mesoamerican studies. See entries for *poyomatli* and *Quararibea* in Appendix B.

[14] There are compelling reasons to consider avoiding the ingestion of *any* species of mushrooms raw, which would favor the sautéing technique. Gyromitrin and other methyl-hydrazines (volatile compounds similar to propellants used in space vehicles), have long been known from the "false morel" *Gyromitra esculenta*, and have recently been found to occur in other related mushrooms. These methyl-hydrazines are potentially deadly poisonous and are carcinogenic. However, the false morel is widely eaten and enjoyed, and thorough cooking will drive off the volatile methyl-hydrazines. The less toxic phenyl-hydrazine agaritine has recently been found in high concentrations in the common edible mushroom *Agaricus bisporus* and in many wild species of the genus (Stijve *et al.* 1986). While not as toxic as gyromitrin, agaritine shows some toxicity and is associated with other hydrazines in the mushrooms, some of which are carcinogenic (Toth 1979). Hydrazines have also been found in the Japanese cultivated *shiitake* mushroom, *Lentinus edodes*. Pending further study, prudence would dictate avoiding raw mushrooms as potential sources of carcinogenic hydrazines. There is no evidence of hydrazines in entheogenic mushrooms, but these simply have not been analyzed for such compounds. Absence of evidence is not evidence of absence. I might mention that drying, like sautéing, will eliminate the volatile hydrazines. Cooking or drying, however, will not influence content of metals like cesium and arsenic. Some mushrooms accumulate cesium, and wild mushrooms collected in six European countries in 1988, two years after the Chernobyl nuclear accident (curiously, *chernobyl* is the Russian name for visionary wormwood, *Artemisia absinthium*; see Appendix A), showed variable amounts of radioactive cesium. Quanitites were not high enough to represent a significant health risk (Stijve & Poretti 1990). Edible mushrooms of the genus *Laccaria* and other genera were shown to contain arsenic, also in quantities too low to pose a risk to health (Stijve & Bourqui 1991; Stijve *et al.* 1990). Lately there has been a spate of mysterious deaths from eating apparently edible mushrooms around Moscow. The Russians certainly know their mushrooms (Wasson & Wasson 1957A), and some environmental stress is evidently causing mushrooms traditionally eaten as food to synthesize or sequester toxins.

TABLE 4
PSILOCYBINE-CONTAINING MUSHROOMS*

Agrocybe farinacea	Koike *et al.* 1981
Conocybe cyanopus	Benedict *et al.* 1962A; Benedict *et al.* 1967; Beug & Bigwood 1982; Christiansen *et al.* 1984; Gartz 1985F; Ohenoja *et al.* 1987; Repke *et al.* 1977A
C. kuehneriana	Ohenoja *et al.* 1987
C. siligineoides[1]	
C. smithii	Benedict *et al.* 1967; Repke *et al.* 1977A
Copelandia anomalus	Merlin & Allen 1993
C. bispora	Merlin & Allen 1993
C. cambodginiensis	Ola'h 1968; Ott & Guzmán 1976 [as *Panaeolus*]
C. chlorocystis	Weeks *et al.* 1979
C. cyanescens	Allen & Merlin 1992A; Fiussello & Ceruti Scurti 1972; Heim *et al.* 1966; Heim *et al.* 1967; Ola'h 1968; Ola'h 1970 [as *Panaeolus*]
C. tropicalis	Ola'h 1968; Ola'h 1970 [as *Panaeolus*]
Galerina steglichii	Besl 1993; Gartz 1994
Gerronema fibula	Gartz 1986C[2]
G. swartzii (=*G. solipes*)	Gartz 1986C[2]
Gymnopilus aeruginosus	Hatfield *et al.* 1978
G. liquiritiae	Koike *et al.* 1981
G. luteus	Hatfield *et al.* 1978
G. purpuratus	Gartz 1989A; Gartz 1991; Gartz & Müller 1990; Kreisel & Lindequist 1988
G. spectabilis (=*Pholiota*)	Hatfield *et al.* 1978[2]
G. validipes	Hatfield *et al.* 1977; Hatfield *et al.* 1978
G. viridans	Hatfield *et al.* 1978
Hygrocybe psittacina	Gartz 1986C[2]
Inocybe aeruginascens	Drewitz 1983; Gartz 1985C, 1986D, 1987B; Gartz & Drewitz 1985, 1986; Semerdzieva *et al.* 1986; Stijve & Kuyper 1985; Stijve *et al.* 1985
I. calamistrata	Gartz 1986C[2]
I. coelestium	Stijve & Kuyper 1985; Stijve *et al.* 1985
I. cordyalina var. *cordyalina*	Stijve & Kuyper 1985; Stijve *et al.* 1985
I. cordyalina var. *erinaceomorpha*	Stijve & Kuyper 1985; Stijve *et al.* 1985

Inocybe haemacta	Stijve & Kuyper 1985; Stijve *et al.* 1985
I. tricolor	Gartz 1993
Mycena cyanorrhiza	Allen *et al.* 1992
Panaeolina castaneifolius	Ola'h 1968; Ola'h 1970 [as *Panaeolus*]
P. foenisecii	Fiussello & Ceruti Scurti 1972; Gartz 1985G; Ohenoja *et al.* 1987; Ola'h 1968; Ola'h 1970 [as *Panaeolus*]; Robbers *et al.* 1969
Panaeolus africanus	Ola'h 1968; Ola'h 1970
P. antillarum	Allen & Merlin 1992A
P. ater	Ola'h 1968; Ola'h 1970
P. campanulatus	Fiussello & Ceruti Scurti 1972 [*P. papilionaceus*]
P. fimicola	Ola'h 1968; Ola'h 1970
P. microsporus	Ola'h 1968
P. olivaceus	Ohenoja *et al.* 1987
P. retirugis	Fiussello & Ceruti Scurti 1972
P. sphinctrinus	Heim & Hofmann 1958[9]; Ola'h 1968; 1970
P. subbalteatus	Beug & Bigwood 1982; Fiussello & Ceruti Scurti 1972; Ohenoja *et al.* 1987; Ola'h 1968; Ott & Guzmán 1976; Repke *et al.* 1977A; Stijve & Kuyper 1985; Stijve & De Meijer 1993
Pluteus atricapillus	Ohenoja *et al.* 1987[3]
P. cyanopus	Amirati *et al.* 1989; Gitte *et al.* 1983
P. glaucus	Stijve & De Meijer 1993
P. nigroviridis	Stijve & Bonnard 1986
P. salicinus	Christiansen *et al.* 1984; Gartz 1987A; Ohenoja *et al.* 1987; Saupe 1981; Stijve & Bonnard 1986; Stijve & Kuyper 1985
Psathyrella candolleana	Gartz 1986C; Koike *et al.* 1981; Ohenoja *et al.* 1987[2]
P. sepulchralis[2,4]	
Psilocybe argentipes	Koike *et al.* 1981; Yokoyama 1976
P. atrobrunnea	Høiland 1978[5]
P. aztecorum var. *aztecorum*	Heim & Hofmann 1958; Heim & Hofmann 1958[9]; Hofmann *et al.* 1959
P. aztecorum var. *bonetii*	Ott & Guzmán 1976 [as *P. bonetii*]
P. azurescens	Gartz 1994; Liggenstorfer & Rätsch 1996
P. baeocystis	Benedict *et al.* 1962A, 1962B; Beug & Bigwood

	1982; Leung *et al.* 1965; Repke *et al.* 1977A
Psilocybe bohemica	Gartz & Müller 1989; Semerdzieva *et al.* 1986; Stijve & Kuyper 1985
P. caerulescens var. *caerulescens*	Heim & Hofmann 1958; Heim & Hofmann 1958[9]; Hofmann *et al.* 1959; Stein 1960
P. caerulescens var. *ombrophila*[6] (=*P. mixaeensis*)	
P. caerulipes	Leung *et al.* 1965
P. caeruloannulata	Stijve & De Meijer 1993
P. callosa (=*P. strictipes, P. semilanceata* var. *caerulescens*)	Leung *et al.* 1965 [as *P. strictipes*]; Benedict *et al.* 1967 [as *P. semilanceata* var. *caerulescens*]
P. collybiodes[7]	
P. coprinifacies	Auert *et al.* 1980; Semerdzieva & Nerud 1973; Semerdzieva *et al.* 1986; Wurst *et al.* 1984[5]
P. cordispora[8]	
P. cubensis	Allen & Merlin 1992A; Bigwood & Beug 1982; Gartz & Müller 1989; Heim & Hofmann 1958; Hofmann *et al.* 1959; Repke *et al.* 1977A;
P. cyanescens	Benedict *et al.* 1962A; Beug & Bigwood 1982; Repke *et al.* 1977A; Stijve & Kuyper 1985; Unger & Cooks 1979
P. cyanofibrillosa	Stamets *et al.* 1980
P. eucalypta	Margot & Watling 1981
P. fagicola var. *fagicola*[9]	
P. fimetaria	Benedict *et al.* 1967
P. hoogshagenii var. *hoogshagenii*[10]	Stijve & De Meijer 1993
P. hoogshagenii var. *convexa* (=*P. semperviva*)	Heim & Hofmann 1958; Heim & Hofmann 1958[9]; Hofmann *et al.* 1959 [as *P. semperviva*]
P. kumaenorum[11]	
P. liniformans var. *liniformans*	Stijve & Kuyper 1985
P. liniformans var. *americana*	Stamets *et al.* 1980
P. mairei	Auert *et al.* 1980; Semerdzieva & Wurst 1986
P. mexicana	Heim & Hofmann 1958; Heim & Hofmann

	1958[9]; Hofmann & Troxler 1959; Hofmann *et al.* 1958; Hofmann *et al.* 1959; Stein 1960
Psilocybe natalensis	Gartz 1994
P. pelliculosa	Beug & Bigwood 1982; Repke *et al.* 1977A; Tyler 1961
P. pseudobullacea	Marcano *et al.* 1994
P. quebecensis	Heim *et al.* 1967; Ola'h & Heim 1967
P. samuiensis	Gartz *et al.* 1994; Guzmán *et al.* 1993
P. semilanceata	Benedict *et al.* 1967; Beug & Bigwood 1982; Christiansen & Rasmussen 1982; Christiansen *et al.* 1981; Gartz 1985A; Gartz 1985G; Hofmann *et al.* 1963; Høiland 1978; Jokiranta *et al.* 1984; Mantle & Waight 1969; Ohenoja *et al.* 1987; Repke & Leslie 1977; Repke *et al.* 1977A; Semerdzieva *et al.* 1986; Stijve & Kuyper 1985; White 1979
P. serbica	Moser & Horak 1968; Semerdzieva & Nerud 1973
P. silvatica	Repke *et al.* 1977A
P. stuntzii (=*P. pugetensis* Harris *nom. nud.*)	Beug & Bigwood 1982; Ott & Guzmán 1976; Repke *et al.* 1977A
P. subaeruginascens var. *subaeruginascens*	Koike *et al.* 1981
P. subaeruginosa	Picker & Rickards 1970
P. subcaerulipes[12]	
P. subcubensis	Allen & Merlin 1992A
P. subyungensis	Stijve & De Meijer 1993
P. tampanensis[13]	Gartz *et al.* 1994
P. uruguayensis	Stijve & De Meijer 1993
P. venenata[14]	
P. wassonii (=*P. muliercula*)	Escalante & López 1971; Escalante *et al.* 1973; Heim & Wasson 1958[9]
P. weilii	Stamets 1996
P. yungensis[15] (=*P. acutissima; P. isauri*)	
P. zapotecorum (=*P. candidipes*)	Heim & Hofmann 1958; Heim & Hofmann 1958[9]; Hofmann *et al.* 1959; Ott & Guzmán 1976 [as *P. candidipes*]

NOTES

[1] *Conocybe siligineoides* has not been analyzed chemically, but has been reported to have been used in México as a shamanic entheogen (Heim 1956B) among the Mazatec Indians of Oaxaca, who call this mushroom *ta'a'ya*. The finding of psilocybine/psilocine in three other *Conocybe* species underscores the probability that this is a psilocybian mushroom.

[2] In 1986, German chemist J. Gartz reported the detection of psilocybine and/or psilocine in *Gerronema fibula, G. swartzii, Hygrocybe psittacina, Inocybe cordyalina, Inocybe calamistrata, Inocybe haemacta* and *Psathyrella candolleana* (Gartz 1986C). Baeocystine was also detected in the three *Inocybe* species and *Psathyrella candolleana*. A subsequent paper challenged some of these results, finding no psilocybine/psilocine in three specimens of *Gerronema fibula* and one specimen of *G. swartzii* (reported as species of *Rickenella*); nor in 5 specimens of *Psathyrella candolleana*, nor in 5 specimens of *Hygrocybe psittacina* var. *psittacina*, nor in a single specimen of *H. psittacina* var. *californica* (Stijve & Kuyper 1988). Furthermore, another analysis of *Inocybe calamistrata* had failed to detect psilocybine/psilocine (Stijve *et al.* 1985). The status of *G. fibula, G. swartzii, H. psittacina* and *I. calamistrata* as psilocybian mushrooms is thus in doubt, but it should be noted that there are two independent confirmations of psilocybine/psilocine in *Psathyrella candolleana* (Koike *et al.* 1981; Ohenoja *et al.* 1987; see also Note 4 below) and likewise two independent confirmations of psilocybine/psilocine in *Inocybe cordyalina* and *I. haemacta* (Stijve & Kuyper 1985; Stijve *et al.* 1985). In their 1988 paper, Stijve and Kuyper also reported that three specimens of *Gymnopilus spectabilis* were devoid of psilocybine or psilocine, and a recent paper challenged the inclusion of this species among the psilocybian mushrooms (Allen *et al.* 1992), alleging that the report of psilocybine in this species (Hatfield *et al.* 1978) involved a misidentification. This paper referred to two studies (Christiansen *et al.* 1984; Koike *et al.* 1981) which found three specimens of *G. spectabilis* (one from Norway and two from Japan) to be devoid of psilocybine/psilocine. On the other hand, the Japanese name for this species, *o-warai-take*, "big laughing mushroom," suggests the folk knowledge of entheogenic properties in Japan (Imazeki 1973). In their index of "known species of the hallucinogenic fungi," Allen *et al.* (1992) exclude from their list *Agrocybe farinacea*, although they note it has been reported to contain psilocybine (Koike *et al.* 1981) and mistakenly attribute confirmation of this analysis to a later paper, which reported traces of psilocybine in an unidentified *Agrocybe* species (Ohenoja *et al.* 1987). *Agrocybe farinacea* should certainly have been included in their table, as there is no negative report; in contrast to *Panaeolina foenisecii*, which was included in their table and for which there is positive and negative evidence (at least five studies have found this species to be psilocybian—see entry in table for references). In spite of the evidence for this species as "psilocybine latent" (as Ola'h designated it), Allen and Merlin (1991) claim to have "proven" that it is not psilocybian. Finally, in the 1992 index by Allen *et al.*, the authors likewise omit *Panaeolus microsporus*, despite noting that cultured specimens have been found to contain psilocybine (Ola'h 1968). On the other hand, this index of species "scientifically determined as psilocybian" includes 46 species of *Psilocybe*, 3 species of *Gymnopilus* and 2 species of *Copelandia* which have not been chemically determined to contain psilocybine/

psilocine, nor reported to be used traditionally as inebriants—they were added to the list because of taxonomic affinity to known psilocybian species and/or the presence of the bluing reaction. I have listed these species, and a few others, as "probable psilocybian species" in the note at the end of this table. In only a few cases is there modern bioassay information which confirms these species to be psychoactive.

[3] Horak (1978) had reported that the Banza people of Central Africa consumed the acrid-smelling and bitter-tasting *Pluteus atricapillus* var. *ealensis*, known as *losulu* by the Eala people of Zaïre, or *abanda* by the Banza. No details were given, but since *P. atricapillus* is known to contain psilocybine/psilocine (Ohenoja *et al.* 1987), we must allow for the possibility that the Banza were making entheogenic use of variety *ealensis*, which from the description would appear to be less than delectable.

[4] *Psathyrella sepulchralis* was reportedly used as an entheogen by Zapotec Indians of Oaxaca, México (Singer *et al.* 1958A). Ott and Guzmán (1976) later analyzed two collections, including the type (aged 19 and 8 years) but failed to detect psilocybine or psilocine. Guzmán later suspected the Zapotec informants had mistaken this species for *Psilocybe zapotecorum* (Ott & Guzmán 1976), but the subsequent finding by three different groups of psilocybine in *Psathyrella candolleana* suggests that fresh *P. sepulchralis* also may contain psilocybine/psilocine. On the other hand, a recent analysis (Stijve & Kuyper 1988) of five specimens of *Psathyrella candolleana* for psilocybine was negative, and a subsequent list of psilocybian mushrooms neglected to include any species of *Psathyrella* (Allen *et al.* 1992; see also Note 2 above).

[5] Guzmán felt that the specimen analyzed by Høiland as *Psilocybe atrobrunnea* was more likely referable to *P. serbica* or *P. callosa* (Guzmán 1983), both known psilocybian species. A Czechoslovakian species found to contain psilocybine, *Psilocybe coprinifacies* (sometimes placed in *Hypholoma* or *Stropharia*) may be synonymous with *Psilocybe atrobrunnea* (Guzmán 1983; Semerdzieva & Nerud 1973), but Guzmán has recently included both species in a list of psilocybian mushrooms (Allen *et al.* 1992). Some European mycologists consider *Psilocybe coprinifacies* and *P. serbica*, as well as *P. bohemica* and *P. mairei* all to be conspecific with *P. cyanescens* (Gartz 1993; Krieglsteiner 1984), although "complete reproductive barriers" between strains of *P. cyanescens* and *P. bohemica* based on single-spore isolates (or monokaryons) have been demonstrated, showing these two, at least, are in fact distinct species, reproductively isolated (Allen *et al.* 1992).

[6] *Psilocybe caerulescens* var. *ombrophila* (=*P. caerulescens* subsp. *mazatecorum* var. *ombrophila*; *P. caerulescens* var. *mazatecorum* f. *ombrophila*; *P. mixaeensis*) has not been studied chemically. However, this bluing species is undoubtedly psilocybian, as it has been reportedly used as an entheogen by the Mixe of Oaxaca, México, under the name *kongk* (Heim & Wasson 1958; Lipp 1991). Guzmán's *Psilocybe caerulescens* var. *caerulescens* incorporates the following five taxa: *Psilocybe mazatecorum*, *P. caerulescens* var. *mazatecorum*, *P. caerulescens* var. *mazatecorum* f. *heliophila*, *P. caerulescens* var. *nigripes* and *P. caerulescens* subsp. *caerulescens* var. *albida*.

[7] *Psilocybe collybioides*—Southcott (1974) reported that Rickards had found psilocybine in this Australian species, but Guzmán (1983) then doubted this identification, feeling the material analyzed was more likely referred to *P. australiana*, *P. eucalypta* or *P. tasmaniana*. Undoubtedly, all of these bluing Australian species are psilocybian, but only *P. eucalypta* has been proven chemically to be so (Margot & Watling 1981). *Psilocybe australiana* and *P. tasmaniana* have recently been reported used for visionary effects in Australia, and *P. tasmaniana* from New Zealand is said to be psychoactive (Allen *et al.* 1991). Nevertheless, Margot and Watling (1981) failed to detect entheogenic compounds in either *P. australiana* or *P. tasmaniana*. Stamets tentatively (1996) listed all three species as psychoactive.

[8] *Psilocybe cordispora* has yet to be submitted to chemical analysis, although it probably contains psilocybine/psilocine, since its use an an entheogen by the Mixe and Mazatec Indians of Oaxaca, México has been reported (Heim 1956B). The Mixe call this mushroom *atka't* (Lipp 1990), and a typical dose for shamanic divination is reported to consist of 12–13 pairs (Lipp 1991; Miller 1966).

[9] *Psilocybe fagicola* var. *fagicola* as yet has not been studied chemically, but likely contains psilocybine and/or psilocine. Heim and Cailleux (1959) reported this species as being "evidently hallucinogenic" based on information regarding a collection they made near Zacatlamaya, México.

[10] *Psilocybe hoogshagenii* var. *hoogshagenii*—Guzmán (1983) has designated two varieties of Heim's *P. hoogshagenii* (the latter var. *convexa* originally described as *P. semperviva* by Heim and Cailleux). Variety *convexa* (=*P. semperviva*) was found by Hofmann and Heim to be one of the Mexican entheogenic mushrooms with the highest concentration of psilocybine/psilocine (0.6% psilocybine, 0.1% psilocine; Heim & Hofmann 1958; Heim & Hofmann 1958[9]; Hofmann *et al.* 1959). Rubel and Gettelfinger-Krejci (1976) describe diagnostic use of this mushroom among the Chinantec of México. The Mexican Mixtec Indians also make divinatory use of this species, ingesting six pairs of variety *hoogshagenii* (Lipp 1991), recently shown to contain both psilocybine and psilocine (Stijve & De Meijer 1993).

[11] *Psilocybe kumaenorum*—While studying the so-called "mushroom madness" of the Kuma of New Guinea (see Chapter 5, Note 5 and Appendix B), Heim and Wasson collected this bluing *Psilocybe* and described it as being entheogenic (Heim 1978; Heim *et al.* 1967), with the native name being given as *koull tourroum* or *koobl tourrum*. It is undoubtedly psilocybian, and is close to the known psilocybian species *P. zapotecorum*. It has recently been reported as used for ludible purposes in New Zealand, along with the related species *P. novaezealandiae*, and is possibly also so used in Australia (Allen *et al.* 1991). Guzmán, however, recently referred to *P. novaezealandiae* as "non-bluing" and placed it in section *Pratensae* Guzmán, in which no known psilocybian species are found (Guzmán *et al.* 1991). The status of this species as an entheogenic mushroom is thus in doubt, despite the report of ludible use in New Zealand.

[12] *Psilocybe subcaerulipes* has been reportedly tested for entheogenic properties by a Japanese

mycologist and three students (Yokoyama 1973) with positive results. It undoubtedly contains psilocybine/psilocine, but has not been tested chemically. Yokoyama later considered the mushroom he tested to be *P. argentipes*, which was subsequently shown to contain psilocybine (Koike *et al.* 1981).

[13] A single specimen of *Psilocybe tampanensis*, collected near Tampa, Florida, was the basis for cultures and commercial cultivation kits sold in countercultural drug magazines (Pollock 1979). This bluing species was recently reported to contain psilocybine and psilocine in cultivated sclerotia (Gartz *et al.* 1994; Guzmán & Pollock 1978; Peele 1985).

[14] *Psilocybe venenata*—As *Stropharia caerulescens*, Imai (1932) had reported this species from Japan as provoking "a special intoxication," describing two cases. *P. venenata* has not been studied chemically, but is doubtless psilocybian (Matsuda 1960). Under the name of the related species *P. subaeruginascens* (since then separated by Guzmán into two varieties, var. *subaeruginascens* and var. *septentrionalis*; Guzmán 1983), Singer and Smith (1958B) mistakenly attributed ten deaths in Japan to this species, which in reality has caused no deaths. A Hawai'ian death attributed to psilocybian mushrooms in 1972 (Pollock 1974) has been reported to have been in reality a heroin overdose (Allen 1988). There is the possibility of confusing psilocybian mushrooms with deadly amatoxin-containing *Galerina* species (Ott 1979B; Rold 1986; Stamets 1996). Psilocybian mushroom "field guides" have therefore included color plates of poisonous *Galerina* species for comparison purposes (Menser 1977; Ott 1976B; Ott 1979B; Stamets 1978; Stamets 1996). There is at least one death on record, caused by mistaking *Galerina* for *Psilocybe* (Allen 1988; Beug & Bigwood 1982).

[15] *Psilocybe yungensis* (=*P. acutissima*; *P. isauri*)—Although Hofmann failed to detect psilocybine or psilocine in dried material from Oaxaca, México (Heim & Cailleux 1959; Heim & Wasson 1958), this species has been reportedly used as an entheogen by the Mazatec and Mixe, and undoubtedly contains psilocybine and/or psilocine. R.G. Wasson described this species as entheogenic after ingesting it during July 1958 in Río Santiago, Oaxaca (Heim & Wasson 1958; Wasson 1959A). In the seventeenth century, Jesuit missionaries in the Peruvian Amazon reported the use by the Yurimagua Indians of an entheogenic potion made from "mushrooms that grow on fallen trees" (Schultes & Hofmann 1980). This may be referable to the lignicolous *P. yungensis*, currently known from Colombia, Ecuador and Bolivia in South America, but thus far not collected in Perú, which is certainly within its range (Guzmán 1983). Another possibility for the Yurimagua entheogen is the *Dictyonema* species collected by Davis and Yost, a "tree fungus" said to have been used by ancestral Waorani shamans as an entheogenic inebriant in Amazonian Ecuador, under the name *nenendape* (Davis & Yost 1983A). As a third candidate, Gartz recently proposed the lignicolous psilocybian *Gymnopilus purpuratus* from South America for the Yurimagua entheogenic mushroom (Gartz 1993). Mushroom motifs on gold Darien pectorals from Colombia and on a gold Quimbaya figurine, together with mushrooms on the "foreheads" of two Mochica pots in the form of human heads, have been interpreted as representing ancient traditional use of entheogenic mushrooms in South America (Emmerich 1965; Schultes 1977B; Schultes & Bright 1979).

* This table lists all of the known psilocybine- (and/or psilocine-) containing mushrooms meeting one or both of the following criteria: 1) chemical analysis (isolation and/or detection of psilocybine/psilocine by standard methods like Thin-Layer Chromatography [TLC], High-Pressure Liquid Chromatography [HPLC], *etc.*); and 2) report of autochthonous use as shamanic inebriant by field workers and/or self-experimentation by reliable investigators. In the case of the genus *Psilocybe*, in which about half of the proven psilocybian species occur, the taxonomic classification of Guzmán (1983) has been followed. In the case of the genera *Panaeolus*, *Panaeolina* and *Copelandia*, I have adhered to the classification system of Guzmán and R. Singer, as expressed in a recent index of known psilocybian mushrooms (Allen *et al.* 1992). Guzmán (1983) and Allen *et al.* (1992) have all listed as "hallucinogenic [*sic*] species" (based on morphological affinity with known psilocybian species and on the presence of the bluing reaction in fresh or dried material; Gartz 1985D; Levine 1967), an additional 40 *Psilocybe* taxa for which proof of psilocybine/psilocine content or entheogenic use is lacking. These additional probable psilocybian species are: *Psilocybe acutipilea, angustipleurocystidiata, armandii, australiana, banderillensis, brasiliensis, brunneocystidiata, carbonaria, columbiana, dumontii, fagicola* var. *mesocystidiata, farinacea, fuliginosa, furtadoana, galindii, goniospora, graveolens, heimii, herrerae, inconspicua, jacobsii, lonchophorus, mammillata, ochreata, papuana, pintonii, pleurocystidiosa, plutonia, rzedowskii, schultesii, singeri, subaeruginascens* var. *septentrionalis, subfimetaria, tasmaniana, uxpanapensis, veraecrucis, wassoniorum, weldenii, wrightii* and *xalapensis*. Furthermore, several recent papers regarding suspected entheogenic species of Australia, New Zealand and elsewhere, have mentioned the following 14 additional bluing species which are probably psilocybian (Allen *et al.* 1991; Allen *et al.* 1992; Guzmán *et al.* 1988; Guzmán *et al.* 1991; Merlin & Allen 1993): *Copelandia mexicana, C. westii, Gymnopilus braendlei, G. intermedius, G. leteoviridis, G. purpuratus* var. *pampeanus, G. subpurpuratus, Mycena amicta, M. cyanescens, M. pura, Psilocybe aucklandii, P. barrerae, P. novaezealandiae* and *P. sanctorum*. Finally, in Guzmán's recent supplement to his monograph of *Psilocybe*, an additional five bluing species of this genus are described: *Psilocybe aquamarina, P. chiapanensis, P. meridensis, P. moseri* and *P. subtropicalis* (Guzmán 1995); and a recent paper named a new bluing species from New Zealand: *Psilocybe makarorae*, doubtless psilocybian (Johnston & Buchanan 1995). Adding these 60 probable psilocybian species to the 98 known psilocybian species gives a total of at least 158 species of psilocybian mushrooms worldwide. Of the above-cited probable psilocybian species, Paul Stamets, in his excellent new field guide to *Psilocybin* [*sic*] *Mushrooms of the World*, lists the following nine species as being "probably" psychoactive: *Psilocybe aucklandii, P. australiana, P. brasiliensis, P. herrerae, P. makarorae, P. mammillata, P. subfimetaria, P. tasmaniana* and *P. wassoniorum* (Stamets 1996). *Naematoloma popperianum*, collected near San Francisco, California, turns blue-green on bruising, and has been suggested to be psilocybian (Singer 1973; Singer 1978), but chemical evidence is lacking, and psilocybine is unknown from the genus *Naematoloma* (Stamets 1978), although *Psilocybe cubensis* was collected in Vietnam early in this century and at first classified as *Naematoloma caerulescens* (Guzmán 1983; Patouillard 1907). Sometimes *Psilocybe cubensis* may be classified as a *Stropharia* species (Ott & Bigwood 1978; Heim & Wasson 1958), but analyses of numerous other *Stropharia* species have failed to detect psilocybine/psilocine (Gartz 1985D), arguing for classification of this species within *Psilocybe* (Stamets 1996).

TABLE 5
BAEOCYSTINE-CONTAINING MUSHROOMS*

Species	References
Conocybe cyanopus	Repke *et al.* 1977A
C. smithii	Repke *et al.* 1977A
Copelandia cambodginiensis	Merlin & Allen 1993
C. chlorocystis	Weeks *et al.* 1979
C. cyanescens	Allen & Merlin 1992A
Galerina steglichii	Besl 1993; Gartz 1994
Gymnopilus purpuratus	Gartz 1989A; Gartz 1991; Gartz 1992B
Inocybe aeruginascens	Gartz 1987B; Gartz 1989D; Stijve & Kuyper 1985[1]
I. calamistrata	Gartz 1986C
I. coelestium	Stijve & Kuyper 1985
I. cordyalina var. *cordyalina*	Gartz 1986C; Stijve & Kuyper 1985
I. cordyalina var. *erinaceomorpha*	Stijve & Kuyper 1985
I. haemacta	Gartz 1986C; Stijve & Kuyper 1985
Panaeolus antillarum	Allen & Merlin 1992A
P. subbalteatus	Gartz 1989B; Repke *et al.* 1977A; Stein *et al.* 1959[?]; Stijve & Kuyper 1985
Pluteus salicinus	Gartz 1987A; Stijve & Bonnard 1986; Stijve & Kuyper 1985
Psathyrella candolleana	Gartz 1986C
Psilocybe azurescens	Gartz 1994; Liggenstorfer & Rätsch 1996
P. baeocystis	Leung & Paul 1968, 1969; Repke *et al.* 1977A[2]
P. bohemica	Gartz & Müller 1989; Stijve & Kuyper 1985
P. cyanescens	Repke *et al.* 1977A; Stijve & Kuyper 1985
P. cubensis	Allen & Merlin 1992A; Repke *et al.* 1977A
P. hoogshagenii	Stijve & De Meijer 1993
P. liniformans	Stijve & Kuyper 1985
P. mexicana	Gartz 1994
P. natalensis	Gartz 1994
P. pelliculosa	Repke *et al.* 1977A
P. samuiensis	Gartz *et al.* 1994; Guzmán *et al.* 1993
P. semilanceata	Gartz 1985A; Gartz 1986B; Gartz *et al.* 1994; Høiland 1978; Repke & Leslie 1977; Repke *et al.* 1977A; Stijve & Kuyper 1985; White 1979[2]
P. silvatica	Repke *et al.* 1977A

Psilocybe stuntzii	Repke *et al.* 1977A
P. subcubensis	Allen & Merlin 1992A
P. subyungensis	Stijve & De Meijer 1993
P. uruguayensis	Stijve & De Meijer 1993
P. weilii	Stamets 1996
P. zapotecorum	Stijve & De Meijer 1993

NOTES

[1] *Inocybe aeruginascens* was also found to contain another indole alkaloid, aeruginascine (Gartz 1987B; Gartz 1989D) in concentrations similar to levels of psilocybine and baeocystine. According to Gartz, the novel compound "very probably contains phosphate" (Gartz 1992A). This would rule out 4-hydroxytryptamine, already known from *Psilocybe baeocystis* and *P. cyanescens* (Repke *et al.* 1977A) as the possible identity for aeruginascine. Aeruginascine gives a different persistent color after exposure to Ehrlich's reagent than does psilocybine or baeocystine, and the mushroom is known to stain greenish-blue, not the *cyan* blue common to psilocybian mushrooms. Moreover, Gartz reported that aeruginascine "seems to modify the pharmacological action of psilocybine to give an always euphoric mood during ingestion of the mushrooms" (Gartz 1989D). Thus *Inocybe aeruginascens* contains at least three active indole alkaloids: psilocybine/psilocine; baeocystine and aeruginascine. Aeruginascine is, like psilocybine, converted to psilocine by incubation with phosphatase, and it may be a methylphosphate ester of psilocine (Gartz 1992A).

[2] *Psilocybe baeocystis* (Leung & Paul 1968) and *Psilocybe semilanceata* (Gartz 1992A; Høiland 1978) also contained norbaeocystine, 4-phosphoryloxytryptamine. Repke *et al.* (1977A) reported their detection of traces of an indolic compound that "very likely is norbaeocystin" in cultivated *Psilocybe semilanceata* and in *Conocybe smithii* collected in Washington state.

* Baeocystine or 4-phosphoryloxy-*N*-methyltryptamine is an analogue of psilocybine in which a methyl group is missing. It is the phosphoryl derivative of 4-hydroxy-*N*-methyltryptamine; just as psilocybine is the phosphoryl derivative of 4-hydroxy-*N,N*-dimethyltryptamine (psilocine). Both psilocine and 4-hydroxy-*N*-methyltryptamine are psychoactive (Cerletti *et al.* 1968), and Gartz found baeocystine to be psychoptic at a 10 mg dose (Gartz 1992A). Norbaeocystine is the phosphoryl derivative of 4-hydroxy-tryptamine, which is also known to possess psychotropic effects in animals (Cerletti *et al.* 1968), and has been found to occur in *Psilocybe baeocystis* and *P. cyanescens* (Repke *et al.* 1977A). Norbaeocystine is thus also likely to be a visionary compound, assuming *in vivo* dephosphorylation of norbaeocystine to 4-hydroxytryptamine. Norbaeocystine and baeocystine are thought to be precursors to psilocybine. It has been shown that *Psilocybe cubensis* mycelial cultures can biosynthesize psilocine from tryptamine (involving both a 4-hydroxylation and *N,N*-methylation; Gartz 1985I; Gartz 1989E), and the biochemical hydroxylation at the 4-position of tryptamine, tryptophan and indole has been described (Gartz 1985E; Gartz 1985H). Baeocystine surely contributes to the effects of several species.

PART THREE
Isoxazole Derivatives

CHAPTER SIX
Ibotenic Acid–Muscimol: The Primordial Pangk and Amrta

> Unsteadiness continued to increase... I felt that any sudden movement might cause my head to roll off my shoulders. The field of vision began to rotate slowly... I was able to read only laboriously since each word on the printed page was moving about aimlessly.
>
> **W. Scott Chilton**
> *The Course of an Intentional Poisoning* (1975)

With these words the American chemist Scott Chilton described the peculiar effects of ingesting 93 milligrams of ibotenic acid, a crystalline alkaloid he and I had isolated from the mushroom *Amanita pantherina* in his Seattle laboratory. This was the largest dose of ibotenic acid ever ingested. Within three hours of swallowing the drug, Chilton became highly inebriated, and experienced strange alterations of perception, dizziness and muscle twitches, culminating in a heavy, drugged sleep (Chilton 1975). Chilton and I had been conducting chemical studies of *Amanita pantherina* and *A. muscaria*, as well as interviewing persons accidentally inebriated by these common Washington mushrooms, and he published the results of his bioassay experiment to draw attention to the fact that ibotenic acid (and its active form, muscimol) was the active principle of the fly-agaric, perhaps the world's best-known entheogen.

Although ibotenic acid and muscimol have never been available on the illicit drug market,[1] widespread ludible use of *Amanita muscaria* and *A. pantherina* began in the United States in the late sixties and early seventies. There is reason to believe that the fly-agaric, *A. muscaria*, has been used by humankind longer than any other entheogenic plant, and its use can be traced back linguistically to about 4000–6000 B.C.[2] Common motifs in European fairy-tales have been interpreted as metaphors for the fly-agaric, known to this day as the *Glückspilz* (lucky mushroom) and *Narrenschwamm* (jester's mushroom) in German, testifying to folk knowledge of the inebriating potential of this cosmopolitan species (W. Bauer 1992; De Vries 1991C; Golowin 1973; Golowin 1991). The philosophers' stone of alchemy and the Holy Grail, as well as Aladdin's famous magic lamp, are all considered to be metaphors for *Amanita muscaria* (Bauer 1991A; Bauer 1991B; Heinrich 1995). A saying in German, "*er hat verrückte Schwammerln gegessen*" ("he has eaten crazy mushrooms") is still sometimes used in Austria (Gartz 1993), as is the corresponding phrase in Hungarian, employing the term *bolond gomba* ("fool's mushroom"; Wasson 1986). In this concluding chapter, I will examine the ancient and recent history of the fly-agaric and document the modern studies which have led to a resurgence in its use.

THE PRIMORDIAL *PANGK*: *AMANITA MUSCARIA* IN SIBERIA

In 1730 a Swedish colonel named Filip Johann von Strahlenberg, who had been for twelve years a prisoner of war in Siberia, published an detailed account of life among the Siberian peoples. In a discussion of the Koryaks of the Kamchatka Peninsula (on the Bering Sea), von Strahlenberg stated:

> When they make a Feast, they pour Water upon some of these Mushrooms, and boil them. Then they drink the Liquor, which intoxicates them...

This inebriating mushroom he identified as *Muchumor* or *mukhomor*, the Russian name for *Amanita muscaria*. He further stated:

> The poorer Sort, who cannot afford to lay in a Store of these Mushrooms, post themselves, on these Occasions, round the Huts of the Rich, and watch the Opportunity of the Guests coming down to make Water; And then hold a Wooden Bowl to receive the Urine, which they drink off greedily, as having still some Virtue of the Mushroom in it, and by this way they also get Drunk.

This must have seemed an astonishing report when it was first published in Stockholm (an English edition appeared in London in 1736), but it was soon fully corroborated. In 1755 and 1774, Stepan Krasheninnikov and Georg Wilhelm Steller, both members of a Russian expedition to the Kamchatka Peninsula, published descriptions of the area, which confirmed von Strahlenberg's accounts of mushroom inebriation and urine ingestion. Steller went so far as to say: "the urine seems to be more powerful than the mushroom, and its effect may last through the fourth or the fifth man" (for these and other accounts, see: Diószegi 1963; Diószegi 1968; Geerken 1992; Michael 1963; Rosenbohm 1991B; Wasson 1968). This unique form of urinary drug-recycling must be attributed to the scarcity of *Amanita muscaria* in Siberia, and the lack of any other indigenous psychotropic plants. The fly-agaric was alleged to be worth as much as one reindeer *per* mushroom!

Throughout the eighteenth, nineteenth and into the twentieth century, Siberian fly-agaric and urine ingestion was reported by more than a score of writers, some of them reputable botanists and anthropologists. These reports placed the ingestion of the mushroom among the Koryak, Chukchi, Yukagir and Kamchadal tribes of the Kamchatka Peninsula, and also among numerous tribes of central Siberia, living near the Ob and Yenisei Rivers (Wasson 1967A; Wasson 1968; Wasson & Wasson 1957A). The mushroom was not used strictly for ludible purposes: the fungal drug was also used by shamans, to get themselves "into an exalted state to be able to talk to the gods" (as S.K. Patkanov commented, in reference to the Irtysch-Ostyak in 1897), and such ritual use was described both in central Siberia and on the Kamchatka Peninsula. At the turn of the century, the Jesup North Pacific Expedition established that the mushroom was still in use on Kamchatka, but after Bogoraz's and Jochelson's accounts of the expedition published in the first decade of the twentieth century, there followed eight decades of virtual silence on fly-agaric eating in Siberia. It had been the official policy of the Soviet government that there was no drug use in the Soviet Union (excepting, of course, moderate use of alcoholic beverages!), and little further information was published. As an ethnomycological fruit of *glasnost*, however, Estonian mycologist Maret Saar recently published two papers on Siberian ethnomycology. In one (Saar 1991A) Saar averred that among the Khanty (=Ostyak) of the Ob River area, traditional *Amanita muscaria* use continues "its episodical existence even now," citing personal field work. Furthermore, citing personal communications from Y. Batyanova, V. Lebedev and Y. Simchenko, of the Institute of Ethnography of the Soviet Academy of Sciences, Saar informed us that "the custom of AM [*A. muscaria*] consumption is still alive" on the Kamchatka Peninsula (Saar 1991A). In an accompanying paper (Saar 1991B), this author described medicinal use of *A. muscaria* by the Khanty for "psychophysical fatigue" and in a case of venemous snakebite. An earlier report had chronicled external use of an infusion of *A. muscaria* among Russian and Ukrainian settlers in the extreme Southeast of the former U.S.S.R., to treat joint ailments (Moskalenko 1987). The settlers continue to use the traditional Russian name for the fly-agaric, *mukhomor*.[3] In a similar vein, the fly-agaric, called *Agaricus muscarius*, has long been used as a homeopathic remedy (a tincture of 35 g *Amanita muscaria* in 100 ml solution) for depression, tics, epilepsy, *etc.*, and in combination with tincture of *Mandragora* root as a remedy for Parkinson's disease (Villers & Thümen 1893; Waldschmidt 1992).

CHEMISTRY OF ENTHEOGENIC *AMANITA* SPECIES

In 1869, two German chemists published a book on the properties of muscarine, a toxic alkaloid they had isolated from *Amanita muscaria* (Holmstedt & Liljestrand 1963; Schmiedeberg & Koppe 1869). For almost a century, muscarine was believed to represent the main toxic principle of the fly-agaric. This, in spite of the marked difference between fly-agaric and muscarine intoxication. Muscarine causes profuse salivation, lachrymation and perspiration, and is not psychoactive.[4] These symptoms of a stimulated autonomic nervous system are generally not seen in fly-agaric inebriation. Moreover, the concentration of muscarine in European specimens of *Amanita muscaria* was shown to be exceedingly low, only about 0.0003%, by no means high enough to account for the remarkable activity of this mushroom (Eugster 1956; Eugster 1959).

The problem was complicated when Schmiedeberg isolated a base from a sample of commercial muscarine that counteracted muscarine's cardiac depression. Since atropine and related alkaloids (from *Atropa belladonna* and the psychoactive *Mandragora* and *Brugmansia* species; see Appendix A) have this "anti-muscarinic" effect, this new compound came to be called *Pilzatropin* ("mushroom atropine") or alternately *muscaridine* (it has also been called "myceto-atropine" and "mycoatropine"; Tyler 1958A). Further confusion resulted when in 1955 it was reported that *Pilzatropin* was in fact an isomer of atropine, *l*-hyoscyamine, supposedly isolated from South African *Amanita muscaria* and *A. pantherina* (Lewis 1955). To make matters yet more confusing, bufotenine or 5-HydrOxy-*N,N*-DiMethylTryptamine (5-OH-DMT; see Chapter 3) was reported as an entheogenic principle of *A. muscaria* (Wieland & Motzel 1953). Subsequent work has failed to substantiate the presence either of *l*-hyoscyamine or of bufotenine in *A. muscaria*, and the evidence indicates that these reports were most likely in error (Brady & Tyler 1959; Saleminck *et al.* 1963; Talbot & Vining 1963). In 1963, American chemist W.B. Cook of Montana State College (who had earlier worked for the CIA on phytochemistry of *ololiuhqui* seeds from México; see Chapter 5, Note 8) published a preliminary paper regarding pharmacologically-active extracts from *A. muscaria* (Subbaratnam & Cook 1963).

Finally, in 1964, the true visionary principles of the fly-agaric were isolated almost simultaneously in three laboratories—in Japan (Takemoto *et al.* 1964A; Takemoto *et al.* 1964B; Takemoto *et al.* 1964C), England (Bowden & Drysdale 1965; Bowden *et al.* 1965) and Switzerland (Catalfomo & Eugster 1970; Eugster 1967; Eugster 1968; Eugster 1969; Eugster *et al.* 1965; Müller & Eugster 1965). These new compounds were isolated with the assistance of a fly-killing test, a fly-stunning test, and a mouse-narcosis-potentiating test respectively. In 1967, international agreement was reached as to nomenclature, and the compounds were named ibotenic acid[5] and muscimol (earlier called *agarin[e]* or *pantherine*; Eugster & Takemoto 1967; Gagneux *et al.* 1965A; Good *et al.* 1965). Ibotenic acid was found to be *alpha*-amino-3-hydroxy-5-isoxazole acetic acid; and muscimol its decarboxylation byproduct 3-hydroxy-5-aminomethyl isoxazole (Eugster 1967; Gagneux *et al.* 1965B; Kishida *et al.* 1966; Konda *et al.* 1985; Lund 1979; Sirakawa *et al.* 1966). The isoxazole ring (5-atoms: oxygen and nitrogen adjacent) is uncommon in natural products and drugs, but found in the MAO-inhibitor isocarboxazid or *Marplan* (see Chapter 4; Budavari *et al.* 1989). A novel, pharmacologically-active isoxazolic compound, premnazole, was recently isolated from two species of plants in the family Verbenaceae, used in Ayurvedic medicine (Barik *et al.* 1992). In addition, a rearrangement product of ibotenic acid, muscazone, has been isolated from Swiss *A. muscaria* (Eugster *et al.* 1965; Fritz *et al.* 1965; Reiner & Eugster 1967) as well as from American *A. pantherina* (Ott, unpublished). Muscazone is readily prepared from ibotenic acid (Chilton & Ott, unpublished; Göth *et al.* 1967), may be an artifact of isolation procedures, and is of dubious psychoactivity. It is likely that either ibotenic acid or muscimol represents the *Pilzatropin* isolated by Schmiedeberg a century ago. A potentially psychoactive *beta*-carboline compound, methyltetrahydrocarboline carboxylic acid (MCTHC; 1-Methyl-3-Carboxyl-TetraHydro-β-Carboline) has been isolated in low concentrations from European *A. muscaria* (Matsumoto *et al.* 1969). This compound is of unknown pharmacology, however, and Chilton and I were unable to detect this substance in North American *A. muscaria* (Chilton & Ott 1976). Two other compounds of obscure pharmacology, stizolobic acid and stizolobinic acid (also found in edible seeds of *Stizolobium* [*Mucuna*] species), have been isolated in good yield from *Amanita pantherina* (Chilton *et al.* 1974; Chilton & Ott 1976; Saito & Komamine 1978; Ott, unpublished laboratory data). These compounds have been proposed to be feeding deterrents in insects (Janzen 1973), and were found to have such activity against *Spodoptera* but not a *Callosobruchus* species (Fellows 1984).

Besides *Amanita muscaria*, ibotenic acid and muscimol have been isolated from

A. strobiliformis (Takemoto *et al.* 1964A) and *A. pantherina* (Chilton & Ott 1976; Takemoto *et al.* 1964C; see Table 6). Both have been detected in *A. cothurnata* (=*A. pantherina* var. *multisquamosa*), *A. gemmata* (Beutler & Der Marderosian 1981; Chilton & Ott 1976), *A. regalis* (Bresinsky & Besl 1990) and var. *alba* and *formosa* of *A. muscaria* (Benedict *et al.* 1966; Beutler & Der Marderosian 1981; Chilton & Ott 1976). These unusual amino acids are not known to occur in any other plants.[6]

EFFECTS OF IBOTENIC ACID AND MUSCIMOL

Ibotenic acid evokes psychoptic effects in human beings at doses ranging from 50–100 mg (Chilton 1975; Theobald *et al.* 1968). An equivalent effect is produced by 10–15 mg of muscimol (Theobald *et al.* 1968; Waser 1967). After oral ingestion, the onset of the inebriation is rather slow, and generally 2–3 hours elapse before the full effects are felt (Chilton 1975). This delayed response has also been reported following ingestion of *Amanita pantherina* (Ott 1976A). The effects last for 6–8 hours, depending on dose. Effects are characterized by visual distortions, loss of equilibrium, mild muscle twitching (*not* convlusions, as has erroneously been reported), and altered auditory and visual perception (Chilton 1975; Ott 1976A).

It would appear that muscimol is the psychoactive constituent, and that following ingestion of ibotenic acid, a fraction of the material decarboxylates to muscimol, which then produces the inebriation. After oral ingestion of ibotenic acid, a substantial percentage of the drug is excreted unaltered in the urine, but small amounts of muscimol are also excreted (Chilton, unpublished). This mechanism would potentially explain the Siberian urinary drug-recycling practice. After ingestion of the mushroom, the celebrant would excrete substantial amounts of ibotenic acid in her or his urine. A second user ingesting the urine of the first, would cause some of the ibotenic acid again to be decarboxylated to muscimol during digestion, producing inebriation when that muscimol was absorbed; and the bulk of the ibotenic acid would in turn be re-excreted in her or his urine. Thus a 100 mg dose of ibotenic acid might potentially represent four or five 10–15 mg doses of muscimol, and Steller's 1774 report that one dose of mushrooms could be recycled through four or five individuals is certainly feasible. Muscimol itself probably does not play a significant role in urinary drug recycling, since it was found that only a small percentage of injected muscimol was excreted in the urine of mice (Ott *et al.* 1975A). This hypothesis has yet to be verified quantitatively in human beings, 'though it has been demonstrated qualitatively in preliminary experiments (Chilton 1979).

MODERN PUBLICATIONS ON *AMANITA* INEBRIATION

In 1860, the British naturalist Mordecai Cubitt Cooke published in London a book entitled *The Seven Sisters of Sleep*, an historical study of psychoactive drugs, which had a chapter devoted to the Siberian mushroom cult (Cooke 1860). Two years later, Lewis Carroll began to write his incomparable *Alice's Adventures in Wonderland*, which must have drawn inspiration from Cooke's accounts of the wondrous mushroom of Siberia. Cooke had called attention to the many Siberian reports that stated that fly-agaric ingestion provoked *macropsia* (a tendency to see objects larger than life) suggesting perhaps the opposite effect of *micropsia*, and surely this inspired the shrinking and expanding properties of the mushroom in Alice's dream.[7]

The Siberian mushroom cult surfaced again in 1936, when Victor A. Reko, an Austrian journalist, made the unfounded statement that *Amanita muscaria* represented the *teonanácatl* of México, which we discussed at length in the preceding chapter (Reko 1936). Reko even invented the variety *mexicana* of *A. muscaria* and a hypothetical species, *A. mexicana*. He must have been inspired by some accounts of the Siberian mushroom cult, but his suggestion was pure conjecture (see Chapter 2, Note 10). More recently, attempts have been made to link *A. muscaria* with the Mexican cult of *teonanácatl* (Anon. 1975; Lowy 1972; Lowy 1974; Lowy 1977; Lowy 1980; Wasson *et al.* 1986).[8] There is little proof, however, that *Amanita* species have ever been used as inebriants in Náhuatl México, and *teonanácatl* has been shown to represent a complex of psilocybian mushroom species (see Chapter 5). On the other hand, evidence is coming to light implicating *Amanita muscaria* in the Meso-American entheogen complex, evidence which will be discussed in detail below.

A few other modern writers commented on the Siberian *Amanita* cult, but by and large, the obscure accounts of Siberian travelers remained so. The Wassons' publication of *Mushrooms Russia and History* in 1957 was destined to change all that (Wasson & Wasson 1957A). For thirty years these pioneering ethnomycologists had sought an explanation for the rift which divided cultures into two camps with respect to attitudes toward mushrooms. Valentina Pavlovna Wasson (a Russian) and R. Gordon Wasson (an American of Anglo-Saxon extraction) learned that their respective marked attitudes toward fungi (hers of love and adoration, his of hatred and repugnance) mirrored the attitudes of their respective peoples, and that all cultures were either *mycophilic* or *mycophobic*, neologisms they devised to characterize both extremes. They embarked in the late 1920s on an ambitious study of mushroom names in the Indo-European vocabularies, in an attempt to descry the attitudes toward mushrooms that the names conveyed. Among other things, they learned that *Amanita muscaria* was the archetypal "toadstool" and that the hatred of the *myco-*

phobes was concentrated on this single species. They came to conceive of a time in our remote past when our ancestors had worshipped mushrooms. They knew not which mushrooms nor why they had been the object of worship, but felt this could explain mycophilia and mycophobia—in some cultures, the worshipful attitude survived in adoration of fungi, while in others the tabus which must have attended mushroom worship (or *mycolatry*, as Gordon Wasson was much later to call it) lived on in hatred and fear of all fungi (Wasson & Wasson 1957A).

Then they learned of the Siberian use of *Amanita muscaria* in shamanic rituals, and their "bold surmise" was vindicated. In *Mushrooms Russia and History* the Wassons presented a review of eighteenth and nineteenth century reports of mushroom inebriation in Siberia. This remarkable book was destined to stimulate modern awareness of the entheogenic potential of *Amanita muscaria*, even 'though only 512 copies were printed.

An American physician, Andrija Puharich, must be credited with first popularizing the Wassons' discoveries regarding *Amanita muscaria*. In 1959 he published a book entitled *The Sacred Mushroom: Key to the Door of Eternity*, which alleged that *A. muscaria* was used as a sacred drug in ancient Egypt (Puharich 1959A). Puharich had read *Mushrooms Russia and History* and communicated with Gordon Wasson,[9] but his sensational book did not do justice to the field of ethnomycology. Puharich based his allegations about ancient Egyptian entheogenic mushroom use on information derived from "hypnotic trances" of supposed "psychics"! He offered not a shred of scientific proof. He tried to lend verisimilitude to his book by discussing "scientific" attempts to cultivate *Amanita muscaria* and study its chemistry in his Maine laboratory. But no informed scientist would have attempted to cultivate *A. muscaria* on mule dung as Puharich did (predictably without success), or made the absurd statement that this mushroom grew in animal dung (Puharich 1959A). Nothing could be farther from the truth—no *Amanita* species is associated with dung. The mushroom is actually symbiotic with roots of trees, and has never been fruited in culture. Even a mushroom associated with dung could hardly have been expected to respond to the crude methods Puharich described. His alleged chemical experiments likewise give the informed reader pause. He supposedly studied the distribution of muscarine, bufotenine and atropine in *A. muscaria*, and determined that the highest concentration of these toxins was found in the red membrane of the mushroom cap and in its white "warts." As we have noted, neither bufotenine nor atropine occurs in *A. muscaria*, and muscarine is a trace constituent (Puharich must have been misled by preliminary reports in the chemical literature, which we discussed above). How curious that Puharich did not publish his observations in the chemical literature but only in a sensational book intended, I submit, to capitalize on the painstaking work of the Wassons. Either Puharich invented the whole business of chemical experiments, or he was a very inept chemist. I suspect that the former possibility accurately states the case. In spite of the dearth of useful or reliable information in Puharich's book, it must be credited with stimulating modern use of *A. muscaria*. Although Puharich got his ideas from the Wassons, the 512 copies of their epochal book quickly sold out and became collector's items, while Puharich's fanciful book was widely sold, and was still in print in the 1980s.

Another popular source, the 1966 edition of pioneering underground LSD chemist B. Roseman's hand-lettered *LSD: The Age of Mind* (Roseman 1966), had a chapter devoted to "America's Sacred Mushroom: Fly Mushroom (*Amanita muscaria*)." Regrettably this was a distillation of the inaccurate and fanciful writings of Puharich and Victor Reko (incorrectly named *Reka* in the book), and the effects of *A. muscaria* were wrongly attributed to muscarine, bufotenine (calling the latter "a violent hallucinogen"), and "atropine type." The author incoherently concluded that "the predominant, active principle is of an atropine-type origin," inexplicably noting that "in larger amounts of *muscaria*, it is customary to have a hypodermic loaded with atropine available"! The bewildered reader was left wondering to whose custom the author was referring... A recent catalogue (Horowitz 1992) described a manuscript poem called *Amanita's Hymnal* by one G. Quasha, written in 1971 and evidently still unpublished.

Valentina Pavlovna Wasson died of cancer at the end of 1958, and Gordon Wasson continued the ethnomycological research alone. In 1963, freshly retired from his position as Vice-President of J.P. Morgan & Co., he began studies in the Orient, which continued for more than five years and resulted in the publication of *Soma: Divine Mushroom of Immortality* (Wasson 1968), which profoundly influenced modern consciousness of the entheogenic potential of the fly-agaric. This book was published in 1968 in den Haag, in a magnificent limited edition of 680 copies, printed by Giovanni Mardersteig in his *Dante* typeface on handmade paper especially watermarked with an outline of *A. muscaria*. Priced at $200 or 720 Dutch guilders a copy, the edition quickly sold out, and two years later a $15 hardbound edition appeared, followed by a $7.50 paperback—these popular editions being splendid facsimiles of the original. Recently the trade paperback edition has sold for as much as $70, with the *de luxe* edition commanding as much as $2250!

In this lavishly-illustrated masterpiece of the bookmaker's art, Wasson proposed that the god-plant *Soma* of the ancient Aryan civilization was the fly-agaric. The Aryans swept down from the north into what is now Pakistan and northern India in the second millennium B.C., and settled in the Indus Valley. They composed a canon of sacred hymns called the *Vedas*, which have become the foundation of Hinduism. The earliest of the four *Vedas*, the *RgVeda*, deals at length with *Soma*, which was at once a god, a plant, the juice of the plant, and the urine of a priest who had ingested the plant! The plant was described as being red,[10] juicy and fleshy, and no mention is made in the hymns of leaves, roots, seeds or flowers. As Wasson's beautiful photographs amply demonstrated, *Amanita muscaria* was a plausible candidate for *Soma* (Wasson 1967A; Wasson 1967B; Wasson 1968; Wasson 1970A; Wasson 1970B; Wasson 1971; Wasson 1972B; Wasson 1972C; Wasson 1972E; Wasson 1978). It is significant that the Aryans came into India from the north, from the direction of Siberia, where *A. muscaria* had been used since remotest prehistory. As in Siberia, the Aryan *Soma* ritual also appeared to involve the ingestion of the urine of someone who had eaten the mushroomic entheogen.

Wasson further proposed that the sacred plant *Haoma* of the Iranians (who also descend from the Aryans) was originally the fly-agaric, although today *Haoma* is identified with *Peganum harmala* (see Chapter 4, especially Note 2).[11] He suggested that the famous *Ling Chih* of Taoist art (today identified with the mushroom *Ganoderma lucidum*), the "Divine Mushroom of Immortality," was a mythic representation of *Soma*, of which the Chinese had heard legendary accounts. Wasson proposed that the fly-agaric was the "Herb of Immortality" of the ancient Sumerian "Epic of Gilgamesh," one of the oldest written texts we possess (Heidel 1946). Wasson's book came just two years after a prominent American chemist, surveying "habit-forming [*sic*] plants" in search of *Soma* (Tyler 1966), had concluded that either the Aryans were guilty of "gross exaggeration" or the true *Soma* had remained "hidden from modern man" (at least it remained hidden from those who conceived of sacred inebriants as "habit-forming plants"!). That same year an Indian researcher had settled on the wretched *Ephedra vulgaris*, source of the decidedly unholy ephedrine, as the ancient entheogen (Srivastava 1966).

Wasson appended to his book an exhaustive study of the fly-agaric in Siberia, including reproductions of all of the accounts he could locate of Siberian travelers and explorers, and an essay on "The Post-Vedic History of the Soma Plant" by Wendy Doniger (O'Flaherty), then a student and now a prominent Vedic scholar. Most Vedists and ethnologists accepted Wasson's identification of *Soma* (Ingalls 1971; Kramrisch 1972; Kuiper 1970; La Barre 1980C). One prominent exception was J. Brough, who excoriated Wasson in a 31-page review (Brough 1971). This elicited a second publication by Wasson, *Soma and the Fly-Agaric: Mr. Wasson's Rejoinder to Professor Brough*, in which he answered all of Brough's objections, and presented new evidence not found in the original book (Wasson 1972B). A recent article supported Wasson's theory with novel interpretations of the *RgVeda* (Heinrich 1992) and a later book posited *A. muscaria* as the philosophers' stone (Heinrich 1995).

The concluding section of Wasson's book was a recapitulation of the thesis he and his wife had adumbrated eleven years earlier in *Mushrooms Russia and History*. This conceived of a time when early human beings, foraging for their food, learned of the entheogenic potential of the fly-agaric and other plants. This was the "Age of Entheogens," as Wasson dubbed it in 1980 (Ott 1995B). The fly-agaric became the focus of Siberian shamanism and, as it grew in symbiotic association with birch, birch became the "World Tree" or the "Tree of Life" of Siberian folklore (see Eliade 1951, for a discussion of the Tree of Life[12]). From Siberia, the mushroom cult spread in prehistory, becoming the progenitor of today's religions. Nearly 4000 years ago, the Aryans brought the entheogen cult into India, and the Hindu religion evolved from it. The Aryans brought the cult to the Middle East, *Soma* became *Haoma*, and the entheogen cult reached the New World with the early human beings at least 12 millennia ago via the land bridge over the Bering Sea.[13] Evidence is now coming to light implicating the cult of *Amanita muscaria* in contemporary North American Indian shamanism, a use that is definitely traditional, among the Ojibway or Ahnishinaubeg of the Great Lakes area (Keewaydinoquay 1978; Keewaydinoquay 1979; Keewaydinoquay *et al.* 1990; L'Allemant 1626; Navet 1988; Schwartz 1972; Wasson 1979A; Wasson *et al.* 1980A), as well as among the Dogrib Indians of the Canadian Northwest Territories (Halifax 1979; Larsen 1976). As in Siberia, the unusual practice of ingesting the urine of a person inebriated by *Amanita muscaria* seems to have been a feature of North American use, at least among the Ahnishinaubeg or Ojibway (Bourke 1936; Wasson *et al.* 1980A). An Ahnishinaubeg shaman named Keewaydinoquay [M. Peschel] collaborated with Wasson on the documenting of her tribe's use of *Amanita muscaria*, known as *miskwedo* in Ojibway (Keewaydinoquay 1979; Wasson *et al.* 1980A). Although evidence is being elucidated implicating the fly-agaric in traditional Mexican and Guatemalan shamanism, in Meso-America mycolatry came to center around the psilocybian mushrooms, which in that region are generally more abundant and common than is *Amanita muscaria*.[14]

In the Epilogue to his revolutionary book on *Soma*, Wasson went so far as to suggest that the "Tree of Life" and the "Tree of the Knowledge of Good and Evil" of *Genesis* were in fact one tree, and represented the Siberian birch, and that the "fruit" of the tree was none other than the fly-agaric, growing in symbiosis with the birch. In *Genesis*, as in Siberia, the serpent was the spirit of the "Tree of Life." Wasson underscored this thesis in *Persephone's Quest: Entheogens and the Origins of Religion*, his final book, one published, alas, posthumously (Wasson 1968; Wasson *et al.* 1986).

Once again, a more profit-minded writer was to capitalize on Wasson's ideas, as Puharich had done more than a decade earlier. In this case, a philologist named John M. Allegro hastily published a book entitled *The Sacred Mushroom and the Cross*, which purported to demonstrate that Jesus was a mushroom, the fly-agaric, and that the *New Testament* had been written in an elaborate code designed to conceal the sacred mushroom cult from the Romans (Allegro 1970)! Shades of Puharich! The only evidence Allegro offered was linguistic. Since I am not an expert in Biblical philology, I will not attempt to evaluate his arguments. It should be noted, however, that specialists in the study of Biblical languages have unanimously rejected Allegro's thesis, and the fundamental assumptions that underlie it (see, for example, the reviews of Jacobsen 1971 and Richardson 1971). It is probably significant that Allegro, a recognized Biblical scholar, did not present his theory in any scholarly publication, but only in a sensational mass-market book, clearly designed to appeal to the popular audience and not to scholars.[15] I submit that Allegro, like Puharich, was simply trying to capitalize on Wasson's revolutionary ideas. Like Puharich, Allegro contributed little or nothing of value to the field of ethnomycology, but did succeed in increasing popular awareness of the psychoactive potential of the cosmopolitan mushroom *Amanita muscaria.*

MODERN INTEREST IN *AMANITA* SPECIES

As a result of Wasson's pioneering work, and the sensationalized offshoots of Puharich and Allegro, modern ludible consumption of *Amanita muscaria* began to appear in the United States (Haard & Haard 1975; Ott 1976A; Ott 1976B; Pollock 1975B; Weil 1977A) and in Great Britain (Cooper 1977). In Canada, A. McDonald reported "brisk" sales of Canadian *A. muscaria* in a Toronto health-food store at $15 *per* ounce. The "very favorable" experiences of users were in marked contrast to McDonald's personal experiments with California *A. muscaria* on himself and on six volunteers who suffered nausea and distinct muscarinic symptoms (McDonald 1978; McDonald 1980). Chemical studies cited above had shown that North American *A. pantherina* was more potent that *A. muscaria*, and this fact became known to users, some of whom came to prefer *A. pantherina* (Cooper 1977; Ott 1976A; Ott 1976B; Weil 1977A). This modern ludible use has been reported specifically in Washington, Oregon, California, the Rocky Mountain states and Alaska, but there is evidence that *Amanita* species are enjoyed as ludible entheogens on the East Coast and in other parts of the United States. A 1972 book (Coyote Man & Brother William 1972) extolled the virtues of modern "ritual" use of *Amanita muscaria* and *A. pantherina.* A recent book published in Catalán and translated into Spanish described modern entheogenic use of *A. muscaria* in the mountains of Catalunya, Spain, where ludible use of this drug appears to have been traditional (Fericgla 1985; Fericgla 1992). In response to the modern resurgence of interest in this ancient sacrament, magazine articles have appeared in the past twenty years, depicting the mushrooms and praising their virtues (Ott 1977A; Ott 1977B; Robbins 1974).

Against this backdrop of intentional use of *Amanita pantherina* and *A. muscaria*, it is ironic to note that these two species are widely involved in accidental mushroom poisoning cases. In the Pacific Northwest, in fact, these mushrooms are more commonly implicated in accidental mushroom poisoning than are any other species! A recent reprint of a 1949 paper described 18 cases of *A. pantherina* poisoning in Germany (Leonhardt 1992) and there are cases of mass poisonings in southern Germany (John 1935) and of accidental poisonings elsewhere (Gelfand & Harris 1982). Many of these cases result in hospitalization, and the inevitable recovery of the unfortunate victim is usually ascribed to the wonders of modern medicine (Ott 1977A). Interestingly, opossums (*Didelphis marsupialis*) are also susceptible to accidental poisoning by *Amanita muscaria.* This mushroom, as well as the edible *Calvatia gigantea*, proved to be a popular food with test animals, all of whom ate both species with great relish. Six of the nine test animals subsequently became ill after consuming fly-agarics, however. Although the animals consumed all of the fly-agarics offered to them in the first trial, after becoming ill from the mushrooms, four of the nine animals refused to touch them a day later, and the remaining five animals only gingerly picked over their second meal of *Amanita muscaria.* The fly-agaric poisoning made a lasting impression on the opossums, five of whom refused fly-agarics offered them 70 days later. When the researchers, emulating dishonest drug dealers who have been known to dose edible mushrooms with LSD (see Chapter 5), adulterated *Calvatia gigantea* with the fly-agaric toxin muscimol, five of the nine animals learned to avoid eating this mushroom once it had made them ill (Camazine 1983)! This experiment proves that, at least in the case of opossums, muscimol in mushrooms serves as an effective "feeding deterrent."

While some human beings seek out the muscimol-containing mushrooms on purpose, the drug would appear to be an effective feeding deterrent in others! Seeking to learn why the same mushrooms, in the same area, could send psychonautic users on a much-desired "trip," while sending poisoning victims on a decidedly unwanted trip to the hospital, I have undertaken a survey of intentional *versus* accidental use of *A. muscaria* and *A. pantherina* in Washington state (Ott 1976A). The poisoning victims (who believed they were eating edible mushrooms), on first experiencing subjective effects of *Amanita* inebriation, typically felt they had eaten deadly poisonous mushrooms, and hence were in peril of their lives. One man even 'phoned his lawyer to make out his will, before calling for medical attention! The worried reactions of friends and relatives confirmed this impression, which is hardly conducive to pleasant sensations. Many were taken to hospitals, there subjected to the decidedly unpleasant experience of gastric lavage (or gavage—pumping the stomach). Some were treated with atropine, which is known to potentiate the effects of ibotenic acid and muscimol (the alert reader will recall that these toxins exert atropine-like effects, and were once called *Pilzatropin*; Stuntz *et al.* 1972; Tyler 1958A). This treatment, of course, could only have intensified the effects.

Meanwhile, those who ingested the mushrooms purposefully, actively seeking the inebriation, entertained no fear for their lives, and found the experience to be quite pleasant. Clearly, the bad reactions of accidental poisoning victims were a product of improper set and setting and, in some cases, of excessive dosage. Having ingested both *Amanita pantherina* and *A. muscaria*, as well as both pure ibotenic acid and pure muscimol, I state this with confidence. Yet many mycologists, having no understanding of the influence of set and setting on entheogenic drug experiences, have responded in true mycophobic fashion, by labelling these mushrooms as dangerous, even deadly (see for example, Miller 1972, on *A. pantherina*).[16] Some supposedly "hip" writers of field guides for entheogenic mushroom users have fallen prey to this *Amanitaphobia*, and have cautioned their readers to avoid *Amanita pantherina* and *A. muscaria*, and to stick to the psilocybian mushrooms (Haard & Haard 1975; Menser 1977)![17]

True, one death has been attributed to each of these entheogenic *Amanita* species in the United States (Buck 1963; Hotson 1934). But there are only these two cases on record which reliably attribute deaths to these mushrooms alone. I know of no other cases here or in Eurasia, and should be grateful if anyone could point to some other cases (many writers have cited the case of Cagliari 1897, in which the reporter suspected that other species had been eaten, thus disqualifying the case). Both of the recorded deaths involved old and infirm individuals. Almost any drug, medicinal or ludible, could cause death when given to the wrong person at the wrong time. How many deaths have been caused by penicillin or aspirin? In evaluating the safety of a drug, we must look at its effects in a large population, not dwell on one or two idiosyncratic cases. Hundreds of accidental intoxications with entheogenic *Amanita* species are on record, and surely there have been untold thousands of intentional ingestions of these mushrooms, all resulting in no harm to the user. In the report of the fatal poisoning involving *A. pantherina*, another accidental inebriation was described, involving a young (35-year-old) couple. Despite being dosed in the hospital with morphine and atropine (the latter surely *potentiating* the effects of the ibotenic acid/muscimol from the mushrooms) along with ten drops of the abovementioned homeopathic tincture *Agaricus muscarius* (a tincture of *A. muscaria* probably containing *an additional dose* of ibotenic acid/muscimol), both recovered quickly and fully (Hotson 1934). Writing in the *Journal of the American Medical Association*, a noted medical authority on mushroom poisoning, Dr. Robert W. Buck stated (Buck 1963):

> Deaths following the ingestion of *Amanita muscaria* have not been documented sufficiently to permit the conclusion that this is a lethal mushroom when ingested by healthy persons. In two cases of ingestion of considerable quantities of both raw and cooked mushrooms, the patients experienced some discomfort but recovered quickly and completely.

We have seen that *Amanita muscaria* was an esteemed and valuable drug in Siberia, which would hardly have been the case, were it deadly. Obviously, the mycologists (many of whom are notoriously mycophobic) have erred on the side of caution. *Amanita muscaria* and *A. pantherina* are definitely *not* deadly and, when used intelligently, are decidedly *not* dangerous.

CONTEMPORARY USE OF ENTHEOGENIC *AMANITA* SPECIES

Neither ibotenic acid nor muscimol has ever appeared on the illicit drug market. So far as I know, *Amanita pantherina* and *A. muscaria* have only rarely been sold on the black market, as in the case of the Toronto health-food store mentioned above (McDonald 1978). Hence it is unlikely that the prospective user might acquire this drug from his friendly local pharmacopolist. Only by collecting the mushrooms in the field might the would-be entheogenic mycophagist obtain this fungal drug.

One should be very careful with field identification when collecting *any* mushroom to be eaten. This is especially true in the present case, to avoid confusing *Amanita muscaria* or *A. pantherina* with one of their potentially lethal cousins. The deadly toxins *alpha*-amanitin and phalloidin (and related cyclic polypeptides) have been thus far shown to occur in toxic amounts in seven North American *Amanita* species: *A. phalloides, A. bisporigera, A. verna, A. virosa* (Tyler *et al.* 1966; Yocum & Simons 1977), *A. ocreata* (Horgen *et al.* 1976), *A. tenuifolia* (Block *et al.* 1955) and *A. suballiacea* (Stark *et al.* 1973). An excellent review of the toxicity of these mushrooms has been published (Hatfield & Brady 1975). All of these species are potentially deadly poisonous, and should be assiduously avoided by the mycophagist.[18] I strongly advise that one familiarize oneself thoroughly with the distinguishing characteristics of *A. muscaria* and *A. pantherina* before attempting to collect *Amanita* species for ingestion (this goes also for the common and delicious edible species *Amanita caesarea*). Happily, the two entheogenic species have red to yellow and brown to tan caps respectively, and are easily distinguished from their deadly cousins, which have white or (in the case of *A. phalloides*) greenish caps. Moreover, the volva of *A. muscaria* and *A. pantherina* is distinctive. I recommend that the reader consult an illustrated field guide to mushrooms (for example Miller 1972, or Haard & Haard 1975, which have excellent photographs, although much of the information on toxicity in these books is erroneous) before attempting collection of entheogenic *Amanita* species (see also Menser 1977, and Ott 1979B for comparative photographs of deadly and entheogenic *Amanita* species). *Under no circumstances should one ingest an* Amanita *species that is all white or has a greenish cap!*

The entheogenic *Amanita* species are sometimes eaten in the field, but this unhygienic practice is not to be recommended (see Chapter 5, Note 14). The wise user chooses only the freshest specimens, and these are washed thoroughly, perhaps sautéed in butter before ingestion. Some users air-dry and store the mushrooms for later use, preferring to ingest only the caps, as the fleshy stems are often infested with larvae. I have observed the practice of drying the mushroom caps and smoking them (Ott 1975B), and have shown that the smoke of the burned caps contains muscimol, and is definitely inebriating (Ott, unpublished laboratory notes). Some users even separate the red pellicle from the mushroom caps, and dry this for later smoking. This uncommon practice results in a more rapid effect of shorter duration than the more customary method of eating the mushrooms. There are three sketchy reports of ethnomedicinal smoking of *A. muscaria*. In Afghanistan, a dried extract of the fly-agaric, under the name *tshashm baskon* ("eye opener") is smoked as a treatment for psychosis in the Shetul Valley (Mochtar & Geerken 1979), and there are two reports from México (Puebla and Chiapas) of the smoking by shamans of a mixture of tobacco with dried *A. muscaria* caps as an aid in diagnosis (Knab 1976–1978; Rätsch 1987).

Some users stick to *Amanita pantherina* and avoid *A. muscaria*—not only is

North American *A. muscaria* less potent, but some have reported muscarinic reactions to it (McDonald 1978; T.K. McKenna 1992; Ott 1976A), which might be unpleasant. It is possible that North American specimens contain higher concentrations of muscarine than does European material. Extreme caution with dosages of the entheogenic *Amanita* species is necessary. The optimal dose range is very narrow (Haard & Haard 1975; Ott 1976A). If exceeded, it can put the user in a dreamy, perhaps comatose state, and cause him to sleep through the entire effect. In one personal experience, a very small amount of *A. pantherina* (about one-half cup of sautéed material) was sufficient to produce a strong psychoptic effect in me, while half again as much (*i.e.* three-fourths of a cup) produced a frightening dissociative reaction in another person (Ott 1976A). Should one wish to experiment with these entheogenic *Amanita* species, one should ingest a small amount at first, waiting several hours before augmenting the dose, if necessary (2–3 hours are generally required for the full effects to manifest themselves). By a small dose, I mean no more than one small to medium-sized mushroom cap. When dried, the mushrooms may actually *increase* in potency for a few months, as drying causes decarboxylation of ibotenic acid to the much more potent muscimol (Repke *et al.* 1978).

Under no circumstances should one ingest these mushrooms outdoors in a remote place (in contrast to the instructions of Haard & Haard 1975), or when one must drive an automobile or interact in a social environment. They should be used only in a safe, secure environment, where one may not hurt oneself or others. During peak inebriation, experienced users will lie still, as equilibrium and balance are drastically undermined, as in advanced stages of alcohol intoxication. As with other entheogenic drugs, transient nausea is occasionally reported as a side effect of the inebriation. Such episodes require no special treatment, as they will quickly pass. In my experience, these mushrooms are pharmacologically unique. While the inebriation may be bizarre and overpowering, the user prepared for the experience can find it singularly enjoyable and rapturous. Although most entheogenic mycophagists prefer the psilocybian species, not a few are fonder of the entheogenic *Amanita* species, which are safer than their psilocybian cousins in one important respect—being legal, the prospective user need not worry about disastrous legal repercussions ensuing from their simple possession and use.

NOTES

[1] Both ibotenic acid and muscimol have become standard tools in neurochemical research, considerable interest having been stimulated by the initial neurochemical studies of the two novel drugs (König-Bersin *et al.* 1970; Waser 1971A; Waser 1971B; Waser & Bersin 1970). I introduced both compounds to the scientific research market in 1976. Although these are not controlled substances, in contrast to many of the entheogenic drugs discussed in this book, it is highly unlikely that the pure compounds have been "diverted" for extra-laboratory use, owing to their high prices. Ibotenic acid sells to the end-user for $462.70 for 10 mg, or $4627.00 for a 100 mg dose! Muscimol is quite a bit cheaper, but still selling for $81.90 for 10 mg, a good dose (Sigma Chemical Co., 1996). Moreover, such compounds are not sold to the general public, and are labeled "for laboratory use only... not for drug, household or other uses."

[2] Since the ancient Eurasian word for *Amanita muscaria*, *pangk*, and ancient words for inebriation in Finno-Ugrian languages, such as *pagal*, derive from the same root (the literal meaning of *pagal* is "bemushroomed"), and these words have a common ancestor in what the linguists call Uralic, it can be said that knowledge of the inebriating properties of *A. muscaria* goes back at least to the early time when Uralic split into two linguistic branches—Samoyed and Finno-Ugrian—about 6000 years ago (Wasson 1968). To the European observers, with their own cultural context regarding inebriation, the Siberians were "drunk" on mushrooms! The Siberians were equally surprised to discover that the Europeans were becoming "bemushroomed" with firewater (Wasson 1968; see also Chapter 1, Note 5)! Archaeologically, mushroom inebriation in Siberia can be traced back at least 3000 years, with the discovery by N.N. Dikov of peculiar petroglyphs on the banks of the Pegtymel′ River, which drains into the Arctic Ocean, in the Chukotka region. These petroglyphs depict mushrooms and anthropomorphic figures with mushrooms appended to their heads. The petroglyphs are found in the territory of the Chukchi, one of the Siberian peoples who traditionally used *Amanita muscaria* (Wasson 1968; Wasson *et al.* 1986). Anthropomorphic figures holding and sprouting mushrooms are also known from sixteenth century Mexican codices (Wasson 1980) and rock paintings of Tassili in Algeria, which may be far older than the Chukotka petroglyphs (Lajoux 1963; Lhote 1959; McKenna 1988; T.K. McKenna 1992; Samorini 1989; Samorini 1992A; see Giorgio Samorini's papers for illustrations). Motifs in Swedish rupestrian art have also been interpreted as referring to shamanic use of entheogenic mushrooms (Kaplan 1975).

[3] Just prior to the Russian invasion of Afghanistan, a curious paper appeared from Kabul on "The Hallucinogens Muscarine [*sic*] and Ibotenic Acid in the Central Hindukush," written in German (Mochtar & Geerken 1979). This "Contribution on Folk-Medicinal Mycology" referred to ludible and medicinal use of *Amanita muscaria* in the Shetul Valley of Afghanistan. The use of the mushroom was described by "older inhabitants of this remote mountain valley" during field trips in the 1960s and early 1970s. The authors did not observe any use of the mushroom, supposedly called *nan-e-saghta* or "raven's bread," but it was said to be dried, powdered, then boiled with whey from goat's milk cheese and

fresh *Berspringskraut* (*Impatiens noli tangere*) to yield a drink called *bokar*. *I. noli tangere* is also known in Germany as *Hexenkraut* "witches' herb" (De Vries 1991A). Henbane (*Hyoscyamus niger*) was added and the mixture applied topically in massage. Another Shetul name for *A. muscaria* is *tshashm baskon*, "eye opener." Medicinal use of the mushroom was described for psychosis (oral ingestion) and for frostbite (topical application). The authors noted that extracts of the mushroom (presumably dried) were smoked in cases of psychosis. Ritual use of *A. muscaria* in the Philippines was recently reported (Rätsch 1992).

4 Muscarine was the first toxic compound to be isolated from a mushroom, and worldwide, most cases of accidental mushroom poisoning are attributable to muscarine-containing species (Eugster 1956; Eugster 1959; Eugster & Waser 1954; Waser 1961). Most muscarine-containing mushrooms are found in the genus *Inocybe*. Some 50 species of *Inocybe* contain toxic amounts of muscarine, as do 4 species of *Clitocybe*, and trace amounts are found in 13 other genera, including *Amanita* (Chilton 1978). As much as 0.5–1.0% muscarine (as dry weight) is found in *Inocybe obscuroides* and *I. napipes*, which is some 3000 times the quantity isolated from European *Amanita muscaria* by Schmiedeberg and Koppe (Chilton 1978; Schmiedeberg & Koppe 1869). Six species of *Inocybe* have been reported to contain psilocybine and baeocystine (see Tables 4 and 5), and 92 specimens of the best-known of these, *I. aeruginascens*, were found to be devoid of muscarine, nor have muscarinic symptoms been reported to accompany accidental or intentional inebriations with any of the psilocybian *Inocybe* species (Gartz 1986A). Another study found five *Inocybe* species known to contain psilocybine and/or baeocystine (see Tables 4 and 5) to be devoid of muscarine (Stijve *et al.* 1985). Muscarine was also one of the first neurochemicals available for research, and it was found to bind to the acetylcholine receptor in the peripheral nervous system, an effect which came to be called "muscarinic." In this respect, its pharmacology is opposite to that of atropine (from *Atropa belladonna* and other Solanaceae; see Appendix A) which, like muscarine, binds to the acetylcholine receptor where, unlike muscarine, it does not activate the receptor. Atropine is widely used as an antidote to mushroom poisoning cases involving muscarine. In the case of muscarinic *Inocybe* or *Clitocybe* poisoning, this treatment is indicated and effective. It is *contraindicated* in the case of *Amanita muscaria* or *A. pantherina* poisoning, which involves ibotenic acid and muscimol, compounds which exert an atropine-like activity, and were indeed once designated *Pilzatropin*, "mushroom atropine" (Stuntz *et al.* 1972; Tyler 1958A).

5 Ibotenic acid derives its name from the Japanese name for *Amanita strobiliformis* (from which it was first isolated; see Takemoto 1964A), ***ibo-tengu-take*** "warted Tengu mushroom" (Imazeki, 1973). As explained in Note 5, Chapter 5, there is an ancient tradition of entheogenic mushroom use in Japan, and the entheogenic *Amanita* species are identified with the *Tengu*, trickster imps said to "get drunk from eating mushrooms" (Imazeki 1973; Wasson 1973A). There is a sixteenth century *haiku* poem by M. Shiki referring to the *tengudake* or *Amanita pantherina*, as some sort of inebriant: "Teetotalers/Must be afraid of it,/ The *tengudake*" (Blyth 1973).

6 Dihydro-ibotenic acid or tricholomic acid (see Table 6) has been isolated from *Tricholoma*

muscarium (called in Japan *haetori-shimeji* or "fly-killer mushroom"), a species traditionally used in Japan as an insecticide (Takemoto 1961; Takemoto & Nakajima 1964). This compound would appear to lack acute human toxicity, as *T. muscarium* is considered to be edible in Japan and is much sought after for the table (Imazeki 1973). I have detected this compound in other common edible mushrooms of the Tricholomataceae (Ott, unpublished laboratory data), and it is also known from *Tricholomopsis rutilans* (Yamotodani & Yamamoto 1969). It is possible, however unlikely, that tricholomic acid has long-term toxic effects in regular consumers of these mushrooms, since at least one tricholomic acid-containing species, *Pleurotus ostreatus*, has been reported to show some toxicity (Al-Deen *et al.* 1987). Since ibotenic acid and tricholomic acid have been patented in Japan as flavor-enhancers (both are structural analogues of glutamic acid, the monosodium salt of which [MSG] is widely used as a flavor-enhancer), it is probable that tricholomic acid is at least in part responsible for the "fifth flavor" (apart from bitter, salty, sour and sweet) which the Japanese call *umami* and much esteem (Chilton 1978; Kirimura *et al.* 1969; Younger 1992). It is probable that tricholomic acid occurs in the *shiitake* mushroom, *Lentinus edodes*, the classic *umami*-flavored food, as this species is also in the Tricholomataceae. I have detected tricholomic acid in the *umami*-flavored *Pleurotus ostreatus*, and it is probable that it occurs in at least four other species of this genus, likewise in the Tricholomataceae. These mushrooms have been found to be carnivorous, to possess a neurotoxin which immobilizes soil nematodes, allowing hyphae of the mushroom to penetrate and digest the animals (Thorn & Barron 1984). This effect is probably due to the insecticidal tricholomic acid.

7 Wasson and Wasson (1957A) have suggested that Carroll was inspired by references to the Siberian mushroom use in Cooke's *A Plain and Easy Account of the British Fungi*, thought to have been published in 1862, as a review appeared in *The Gardener's Chronicle and Agricultural Gazette* on 4 October 1862, just over a month before Carroll started to write *Alice*. I suggest Cooke's 1860 book as a more likely source of Carroll's inspiration, as it dealt at greater length with the Siberian mushroom cult (Cooke 1860). Schultes and Aldrich (1990) and T.K. McKenna (1990) independently arrived at the same conclusion, which Gordon Wasson himself first suggested in print in 1979 (Wasson 1979B).

8 Andrija Puharich has even claimed that he was told by Chatino shamans in Oaxaca that *Amanita muscaria* was one of the entheogenic mushrooms in use among the Chatino (Puharich 1962). Bill Upson, who served as Puharich's translator in the Chatino country, later told Wasson that no such information was imparted in his presence (Wasson 1963). Wasson wrote: "after the Puharich statement had appeared, I gave Bill [Upson] a photograph in color of *Amanita muscaria*, and he returned to Juquila and Yaitepec... to sound out Chatino villagers as to the use they made of it. The results were uniformly and unanimously negative." As we will see below, there are reasons to doubt the veracity of some of Puharich's ethnomycological pronouncements.

9 In his 1959 book, Puharich described meeting R. Gordon Wasson on 12 February 1955 and commented that he was dealing with an "expert." Puharich recounted how Wasson had

witnessed a *curandero* ingesting entheogenic mushrooms on 15 August 1953 in Huautla de Jiménez, and referred the reader to *Mushrooms Russia and History*. What most impressed Puharich was Wasson's mention of apparent divinatory powers conferred on the shaman by the mushrooms. In an ominous note, Puharich, at the time a Captain in the U.S. Army (who had lectured at the Pentagon for the "Advisory Group on Psychological Warfare and Unconventional Warfare") said he felt it was his "duty" to inform his military superiors of the information Wasson had given him, supposedly receiving Wasson's permission to do so. Whether this had anything to do with the 1956 infiltration of Wasson's Mexican research expedition by a CIA "mole" (Marks 1979; Singer 1982; Wasson 1982A) I do not know. Early in June 1955, Puharich again met Wasson, who informed him of his forthcoming expedition to México later that month (which was to produce a breakthrough, the initiation of Wasson and photographer Allan Richardson to the use of the mushrooms by María Sabina on the night of 29–30 June), even inviting Puharich to participate! Puharich "regretfully declined" and proposed setting up "some sort of extrasensory perception experiment." Wasson was to send a telegram alerting Puharich as soon as he had arranged for a *curandero* to try to communicate "telepathically" with Puharich and his research subjects in Maine. Puharich reported receiving a letter from Wasson on 29 June 1955, saying he was leaving México City *en route* to Huautla. The mail must have been fast, for Wasson left for Huautla on Monday 27 June, arriving the next day! The breakthrough *velada* with María Sabina took place on Wednesday 29 June, lasting through the night to the morning of Thursday 30 June (Wasson & Wasson 1957A). Puharich reported that the *velada* had taken place on the night of 30 June, a mistake, and that night in Maine began attempts to receive the "telepathic" communications. None were sent nor received, and Puharich considered the experiment a "great disappointment" (Puharich 1959A). Wasson never mentioned the episode, and cited Puharich's books without comment in his 1963 bibliography of psilocybine and *teonanácatl* (Wasson 1962A). See the preceding note for further information on Puharich. In an Appendix to his 1967 book on entheogenic mushrooms, Heim reported on the "Experiences of Mr. H.K. Puharich" among the Chatino Indians of Oaxaca (Heim *et al.* 1967). Henry K. Puharich (described as a physician from Carmel, California) is far better known as physician-writer Andrija Puharich, author of *The Sacred Mushroom: Key to the Door of Eternity* (Puharich 1959A). Later, an American psychiatrist reported "telepathic" experiences following ingestion of *Amanita pantherina* (Metzner 1970; Paul 1966).

[10] *Hari*, the color description of *Soma* in the *RgVeda*, is a matter of controversy. In his 1968 book, Wasson claimed *hari* meant red, as it was also the color of fire and of the sun, and mentioned it was cognate with *hiranya* in Sanskrit, "golden" (Wasson 1968). In his review, Brough had claimed that for *hari*, "red is absolutely excluded" (Brough 1971). Wasson had based his interpretation on an analysis of his argument by Vedist Louis Renou (Wasson 1972B). In 1974, the Vedist H.W. Bailey, Brough's predecessor at Cambridge University, published a paper on the meaning of the Khotan Saka word *zar*, cognate to Vedic *hari* (Bailey 1974). Without mentioning this *Soma* controversy, Bailey stated: "here *hari-*, *harit-*, *harita-* has the same wide range from red through orange to yellow and green" (Wasson 1978). Allowing for differences in scholarly opinion, it can hardly be said that

"red is absolutely excluded" for *hari* and for *Soma*, and Wasson's theory remains plausible as to the color of *Soma*. It must also be mentioned that *Amanita muscaria* likewise has a wide color range "from red through orange to yellow" and even white (Miller 1972), and that the white and yellow varieties (*alba* and *formosa* respectively), like the red variety *muscaria*, are psychoptic (see Table 6; Benedict *et al.* 1966; Beutler & Der Marderosian 1981; Chilton & Ott 1976).

[11] Some argue *Haoma* was always *Peganum harmala*, as was *Soma*. This has been championed chiefly by D.S. Flattery and M. Schwartz (Flattery & Schwartz 1989; see Chapter 4, Note 2). However, proponents of this theory must confront increasing new evidence that Aryan *Soma* was a mushroom. Vedist H.W. Bailey proposed a new etymology for *"Som-a"* making the word cognate with the Indo-European mushroom words *fungus* (Latin), *Schwamm* (German), *spongia* (Greek), *etc.* (Bailey 1972; Wasson & Wasson 1957A). Schwartz, of course (Flattery & Schwartz 1989) took issue with this etymology, but there will always be differences in scholarly *opinion* regarding archaic etymologies. Arguing from the Iranian literature, Iranianist Ilya Gershevitch had already concluded that one would have arrived at a hallucinogenic mushroom as *Haoma* / *Soma* even if one had not heard of Wasson's book, merely by "cool reasoning" (Gershevitch 1974). While Schwartz leaned on some of Gershevitch's arguments and cited his paper, he failed to mention the key conclusion of the paper, which had ended up supporting Wasson's theory! Both Flattery and Schwartz suggested it would be unlikely *Soma* were a mushroom since the drug was clearly pressed, and extraction by pressing would be unnecessary if, as in the case of a mushroom, equivalent results might be had simply by chewing the plant (Flattery's section §45; Schwartz's section §186). The same argument was made by J. Brough (1971) and answered by Wasson (1972B), however, who had observed Mixtec Indians in México grinding psilocybine-containing mushrooms on a *metate*, although presumably chewing the mushrooms well would have yielded the same results, and the ancient Náhuatl poetry speaks of the "liquor of the inebriating mushrooms" (Wasson 1963; Wasson 1980). Moreover, since drying is known to result in almost complete decarboxylation of ibotenic acid to the more-potent muscimol (Repke *et al.* 1978), the common practice in Siberia of drying *Amanita muscaria* prior to use has a pharmacological rationale. There are references in the *RgVeda* to the rehydration of the (presumably dry) *Soma* plant, prior to its subsequent pressing (Wasson 1968; Wasson 1972B), and just such a practice has been observed with *Amanita muscaria* in Siberia. In *Soma and the Fly-Agaric* (Wasson 1972B), Wasson bolstered his case by suggesting that a deity mentioned seven times in the *RgVeda*, *Aja Ekapad*, literally "the Not-born Single-foot" is none other than *Soma* in another guise (see also Wasson 1978). Recalling that Parjanya, God of Thunder, was the father of *Soma*, we see here a clear-cut reference to *Amanita muscaria*, known to this day by the Quiché of Guatemala as *kakuljá* (Lowy 1974), the "lightningbolt," and known in the ancient Quiché *Popol Vuh* as *kakuljá hurakan*, the "lightningbolt one-leg"! (see Note 13 below; Wasson *et al.* 1986). The universal association of seedless ("not-born") mushrooms with lightning was explored by Wasson in his first ethnomycological publication (Wasson 1956; Wasson *et al.* 1986). Of *Aja Ekapad* Flattery and Schwartz had nothing to say. The primary substitute for *Soma*, mentioned in the *Tandya Brahmana* and called in Sanskrit *putika* (Doniger O'Flaherty 1968;

Kramrisch 1975) was proven by Heim and Wasson to have been a mushroom—during field work among Santal tribes in 1967 in Orissa, India, they had collected and studied a mushroom (*Scleroderma bulla = S. hydrometrica* var. *maculata*) known as *putka*, the mushroom "endowed with a soul," which was none other than the Sanskrit *putika*, the primary *Soma* substitute (Heim & Wasson 1970). The careful reader will recall that in 1975 the Mixtec informant Agapito had identified *Scleroderma verrucosum* as a "dream-inducing" mushroom, but it was not found to be entheogenic, and turned out to provoke gastrointestinal distress rather than dreams (see Chapter 5, Note 7 and Ott *et al.* 1975B). Santali nouns are either "animate" or "inanimate," "animate" meaning "endowed with a soul"—all animals are animate; all plants inanimate, with the sole exception of *putka*, the only plant "endowed with a soul" (Heim & Wasson 1970). As Kramrisch wrote: "The identification of Putika, the Soma surrogate, supplies strong evidence that Soma indeed was a mushroom... That Putka-mushrooms should be known, to this day, as 'endowed with a soul' witnesses amongst the Santal of Eastern India a memory of the numinous emanating from the indigenous Indian *Soma* substitute." *Putka* is one of the few Sanskrit words in the non-Indo-European Santali language and in this case absent from modern spoken Hindi. *Putka* is cognate with English *putrid*, "stinking," in reference to the mushroom which, when old, "stinks like a cadaver." In their book, Flattery and Schwartz dismissed the *putka* evidence out of hand (Flattery & Schwartz, §8 Note 5), accepting as writ Kuiper's *opinion* that there is no etymological relationship between *putka* and *putika* (but failing to mention that Kuiper tentatively *accepted* Wasson's *Soma*–mushroom theory; see Kuiper 1970), and had no explanation for the fact that the Santal *putka* was "endowed with a soul." Wasson later equated *putka*, as *Soma* substitute, with the *sukara-maddava* (translated either as "mushrooms" or "pork," this is a hapax in Pali, and a source of controversy among Buddhist scholars), the last meal of the Buddha, served him *circa* 483 B.C. in Pava. It is strange that the Buddha would have eaten either mushrooms or pork, as both are strictly forbidden Brahmans, and Wasson convincingly showed *putka* to have been the *sukara-maddava*, the Buddha's last meal the *Soma* surrogate (Wasson 1982B; Wasson *et al.* 1986). Indeed, according to the ancient Brahmanic *Laws of Manu*, mushrooms are forbidden to Brahmans, and eating them is said to be tantamount to murdering another Brahman—a tabu perhaps deriving from ancient sacramental use of the fungal entheogen *Soma* (Wasson 1982B). Schwartz devoted 12 sections (§240–§251) to a convoluted analysis of *pata-* of the *AtharvaVeda* and *sukara maddava*, finally concluding the whole business had no "real relevance" to the problem of *Soma's* identity (Flattery & Schwartz 1989). Perhaps the situation was best summed up by Wendy Doniger (O'Flaherty): "As an Indologist... I still feel that the broader hypothesis—that Soma was an entheogen—is more significant than the narrower one—that it was a mushroom. Over the years, however, the new evidence that RGW has brought to light, particularly the evidence linking the Buddha's last meal to Soma through the double links of the Vedic *Putika* and the Santal *putka*, does in fact make it seem likely that Soma was a mushroom, as RGW believed from the first moment, and, when we recall the religious role of urine mentioned above, specifically the fly-agaric" (Doniger O'Flaherty 1982; then reprinted in Doniger 1990; Wasson *et al.* 1986). Recent translations of 11th to 12th century Tibetan Buddhist hagiographies (themselves translated from Sanskrit) of 2nd to 9th century adepts divulged the full gamut of Eurasian fly-agaric motifs (not-born, Tree of Life, elixir of immortality, urine as elixir, single eye) related to an ambrosial alchemical elixir of enlightenment, apparently the *Soma* potion, strongly supporting Wasson's hypothesis (Hajicek-Dobberstein 1995). The religious role of urine and association of entheogenic urine with *Soma* (see Chapter 4, Note 2), would not rule out the entheogenic psilocybian mushrooms as candidates for *Soma*, particularly the golden-yellow-capped *Psilocybe* [*Stropharia*] *cubensis*. Following ingestion of psilocine, substantial amounts (25%) of this entheogen were excreted in the urine (Kalberer *et al.* 1962; see Chapter 5). Since psilocybian mushrooms contain mostly psilocybine, which is dephosphorylated to psilocine *in vivo* (Horita & Weber 1962), their ingestion may result in excretion of significant quantities of entheogenic psilocine in the urine. Thus, according to Wendy Doniger's criteria, if *Soma* likely were a mushroom, and entheogenic urine is a prerequisite for *Soma*, then either *Amanita muscaria* or the psilocybian mushrooms fill the bill. Although Wasson and Heim had considered this possibility (Heim & Wasson 1970; Riedlinger 1993), the first openly to postulate the psilocybian mushrooms as *Soma* were mycologists Schroeder and Guzmán (1981). Recently T.K. McKenna has advanced *P. cubensis* as *Soma* candidate (T.K. McKenna 1992), muddying the waters by suggesting it might have been combined with *Peganum harmala*! McKenna objected to Wasson's proposal of *Amanita muscaria* as *Soma*, saying that muscimol, the psychoactive principle, "has been described as merely an emetic and a sedative," citing only the *Merck Index* (Budavari *et al.* 1989), which is a source for chemical, not pharmacological information. He went on to say "human exposure to muscimol is not described in the literature," bemoaning the "queasy illogic that overtakes the academic mentality in the presence of questions revolving around self-induced changes in consciousness." I don't know to what literature McKenna is referring, but P.G. Waser described three self-experiments with muscimol (5, 10 and 15 mg doses) almost 30 years ago (Waser 1967; Waser & Bersin 1970), mentioning "disturbance of visual perception, illusions of colour vision" 'though his hallucinations were not "as vivid and colourful as with LSD." In 1968, the group of W. Theobald described the effects of 7.5 mg muscimol in six human volunteers, and of 10 mg in three subjects (Theobald *et al.* 1968) and compared and contrasted the effects with those of psilocybine and "*ololiuqui.*" McKenna concluded that "the rapturous visionary ecstasy that inspired the Vedas... could not possibly have been caused by *Amanita muscaria*" based on his own limited experience and that of an unnamed colleague. His soundings of the literature have been cursory, for he ignored Pollock's report of "a profound euphoric state of consciousness" after consuming four caps of Alaskan *A. muscaria* (Pollock 1975B). Similiarly, McKenna failed to mention my 1976 report of entheogenic effects following ingestion of Washington state *A. pantherina* (which also contains ibotenic acid and muscimol) and *A. muscaria* (Ott 1976A), and appeared to be unaware of an obscure book describing entheogenic experiences with the fly-agaric (Coyote Man & B. William 1972). He did not cite a Danish book, which has gone through four editions, and refers to "hallucinogenic" effects of fly-agaric in human experiments (Larris 1980). He likewise seemed unaware of a 1985 book published in Catalán by Spanish researcher J. Fericgla, who described distinct visionary effects (adopting the term *enteògens* in Catalán) following ingestion of two dried specimens of *Amanita muscaria* from La Molina, Catalunya, where use of *A. muscaria* appears to be traditional (Fericgla 1985; Fericgla 1992). Also ignored was F. Festi and A. Bianchi's report of self-experiments with *A. muscaria*, which was reiterated in a paper appearing after McKenna's book (Festi & Bianchi 1991; Festi & Bianchi 1992), accompanied by another paper describing self-experiments leading to entheogenic effects (Römer 1992). A 1991 book in German also made reference to decidedly visionary experiences with *A. muscaria* (Bauer *et al.* 1991; Wagner 1991B). Given the very limited nature of McKenna's research on the subject, and his own admittedly limited experience, his conclusions are premature, to say the least. Based on my own self-experiments with *A. muscaria* and *A. pantherina*, as well as with pure ibotenic acid and muscimol, I would say that the drug is quite capable of having produced "the rapturous visionary ecstasy that inspired the Vedas," far more so than the seeds of *Peganum harmala*, a *Valium*-like drug (as we saw in Chapter 4). McKenna "confessed" to being impressed by the proposal of *P. harmala* as *Soma*, and claimed harmaline-rich extracts of the *harmel* seeds might "give a reliable and ecstatic hallucinogenic experience," despite Naranjo's finding that the drug "was usually associated with dizziness or general malaise," and provoked "intense vomiting" and other physical discomforts... hardly likely to induce "rapturous visionary ecstasy." In any case, McKenna mentioned no personal experiments with *P. harmala* seeds. McKenna seemed to conceive of the true *Soma* as *Psilocybe cubensis*, with *P. harmala* as a later substitute, which is how Wasson conceived of the latter. It should be mentioned that in their Santal research, Heim and Wasson were told of the use by the Santals of an entheogenic mushroom growing in cow dung and meeting the description of *Psilocybe cubensis*, which they were unable to collect owing to unseasonably dry weather (Heim & Wasson 1970). The association of this mushroom, which is considered to be indigenous to Southeast Asia, with cow dung could help explain the cow's sacred status in India (Wasson *et al.* 1986). Like some of the Vedic gods (Krsna, Visnu), this mushroom also turns blue... Although *Psilocybe cubensis* has not as yet been reported from India, the coprophilous psilocybian species *Panaeolus campanulatus* (as *P. papilionaceus*) and *Copelandia cyanescens* have been collected there, as well as the cosmopolitan psilocybian *Psilocybe semilanceata* (Bhide *et al.* 1987; Gerhardt 1990). An apparently psychoactive species tentatively identified (on the basis of photographs) as either *Psilocybe cubensis* or *P. subcubensis* is known from Nepal (Schroeder & Guzmán 1981). A recent publication reported the collection and detection of visionary tryptamines in four mushroom species from Thailand: *Psilocybe cubensis*; *P. subcubensis*; *Copelandia cyanescens* and *Panaeolus antillarum* (Allen & Merlin 1992A), and another paper reported a new psilocybine-containing species from Thailand, *P. samuiensis* (Guzmán *et al.* 1993). *Copelandia cyanescens*, as well as the related species *C. cambodginiensis* and *C. tropicalis* are known from Cambodia and elsewhere in Southeast Asia (Ola'h 1968) and in Hawai'i (Allen & Merlin 1989). *Psilocybe cubensis* was collected in Vietnam in 1907 and reported as *Naematoloma caerulescens* (Guzmán 1983). Finally, it is important to note that *Amanita muscaria* was not the sole entheogenic mushroom reported from Siberia. A. Kannisto, researching among the Vogul living near the Upper Lozva River in the first decade of the twentieth century reported: "the term *pa:ηχ* refers to a small mushroom (not the beautiful many-colored fly-agaric) that grows at the base of a tree stump... shamans dry and eat them" (Wasson 1968). I.A. Lopatin reported in personal correspondence to Wasson (dated 28 January 1963 and 19 July 1966) that in the Chukotka region of Siberia (the northeast, where live the Chukchi, Koryak, Kamchadal and Yukagir *pa:ηχ* users), "mushroom species other than the fly-agaric are used for their psychic effects" (Wasson 1968), and *Psilocybe semilanceata* appears in Russian fairy-tale illustrations (Haseneier 1992). See Ott 1994B for a review of the literature on identification of *Soma*.

[12] We are indebted to Eliade for his exhaustive study of shamanism, *Shamanism: Archaic Techniques of Ecstasy* (Eliade 1951) and his subsequent book *Yoga: Immortality and Freedom* (Eliade 1954). However, Eliade was anything but an expert on the ethnopharmacological aspects of shamanism and was apparently unfamiliar with entheogens. In Wasson's original publication on *Soma* (Wasson 1968), he devoted eight pages in the "Exhibits" section to reproducing passages from both of Eliade's books referring to shamanic inebriants. In the book on yoga, Eliade stated that "intoxication by drugs (hemp, mushrooms, tobacco *etc.*)" was a recent phenomenon representing "a decadence among the shamans of the present day" (Eliade 1954). No references were cited, and in four separate passages of his book on shamanism, Eliade had stated the same thing, that "the use of intoxicants (alcohol, tobacco, *etc.*) is a recent innovation and points to a decadence in shamanic technique" (Eliade 1951), again offering no references to substantiate his views. His position seems to have been a moralistic one: "narcotics [*sic*] are only a vulgar substitute for 'pure' trance" (Eliade 1951). As Wasson pointed out, Eliade was committing an anachronism by throwing mushrooms in with alcohol and tobacco when discussing shamanic "narcotics" (see Chapter 4, Note 1 for a discussion of the pejorative use of the word *narcotic* in this context). As we have outlined in Note 2 above, on linguistic grounds the Siberian use of mushrooms for inebriation can be traced back at least 6000 years, and petroglyphs discovered at the time of the publication of Wasson's *Soma* document the use of mushrooms for inebriation by the Chukotka peoples at least 3000 years ago (Wasson *et al.* 1986). On the other hand, distilled alcohol (discovered in the West around 1100 A.D. in Italy; see Forbes 1948) and tobacco (a New World shamanic plant; see Appendix A) were unknown in Siberia until after contact with the outside world, which commenced sometime around 1580 A.D. with Yermak's invasion of Siberia (Wasson 1968). While Eliade's comments on degeneration of shamanism represented by the use of distilled alcohol may have some truth in them, there are contexts in which the use of alcohol may be entheogenic (Escohotado 1989A; Pendell 1995), and as a concentrated form of pharmacological power, distilled alcohol may fit in well with the shamanic world-view. Indeed, in his first contacts with María Sabina in México, Wasson found *aguardiente*, "fire water" to be part of María's pharmacological repertory which had become one of the typical forms of payment to the Mazatec thaumaturge (Wasson & Wasson 1957A; Wasson *et al.* 1974). The use of *aguardiente* by South American *ayahuasqueros* is well known (Ott unpublished), and there is an established shamanic role for alcoholic inebriation from fermented *chicha* beverages in Amazonia (Schultes & Raffauf 1992). Of course, this could be deemed by Eliade to represent a "degeneration" of the pre-conquest shamanic technique; but in one of the surviving pre-conquest Mexican codices, the Mixtec *Codex Vindobonensis*, there is clearly represented a ritual role for *pulque* or alcoholic *Agave* beer (see Chapter 1, especially Note 5), which parallels a similar representation of ritual use of entheogenic mushrooms in another panel of the same codex (Caso 1963; Gonçalves de Lima 1956; Wasson 1980), and *Agave* is illustrated along with entheogenic plants in the Techinantitla murals (see

Chapter 5, Note 3). The ancient Aztecs worshipped a god of *octli* or *pulque*, Tezcatzóncatl, and alcoholic beverages were used in Mayan shamanism (Cuéllar 1981; Garza 1990). Although *pulque* was an important and nutritious food to the ancient Aztecs and had ritual importance, drunkenness was not tolerated—drunkenness was a capital offense for a priest or noble, and commoners were executed for a second offense (having their heads shaved for a first offense). Only elderly people who had discharged their duty to the state were permitted to become inebriated with alcohol (Ortíz de Montellano 1990). Moreover, ritual use of *pulque* may have involved *teoctli* or "wondrous *pulque*," fortified with entheogens, like ancient Greek wines (Gonçalves de Lima 1956; see Chapter 2, Note 17). As for tobacco, it was (and remains) the shamanic drug *par excellence* in the New World (Wilbert 1991; see also Chapter 4 on "*Ayahuasca* Admixtures" and Appendix A), and its adoption by Siberian shamans represented, as Wasson said "recapturing for it the religious meaning that it has always had for the American Indians" (Wasson 1968). Is this degeneration? I think not—hardly any human culture developed in isolation from other groups, and shamanism, like many aspects of culture, is a living, growing institution. It is natural that Siberian shamans adopt the drug their American fellows had been using for millennia in quite similar contexts (as Eliade's work made manifest), and can be seen as a healthy growth of their technique, rather than as degeneration. In the case of the mushrooms, Eliade missed the mark completely. Instead of seeing shamanic use of the fly-agaric and other entheogenic mushrooms (see preceding note) as the very essence and ground of Siberian shamanism, and finding in the ecology of *Amanita muscaria* the genesis of many beliefs and practices regarding the World Tree so important to Siberian shamans, beliefs which were so carefully documented in his lengthy book, Eliade, blinded by his moralistic prejudice against "narcotics," had failed to see the forest for the trees, and was unable to perceive the breathtaking vista which presented itself to Wasson a decade and a half later (Wasson 1968). What to Eliade was "degenerate" and "a vulgal substitute" was to Wasson "religion pure and simple, free of Theology, free of Dogmatics, expressing itself in awe and reverence and in lowered voices, mostly at night, when people would gather together to consume the Sacred Element" (Wasson *et al.* 1986). In an interview with Wasson just over a year before his death, religious philosopher R. Forte brought up the subject of Eliade (Forte 1988). Wasson and Eliade never met, nor had they any correspondence, although Eliade finally cited Wasson's *Soma* theory in his history of religious ideas, and belatedly acknowledged the role of entheogenic drugs in religion (Eliade 1976). Forte, who had been a graduate student at the University of Chicago Divinity School, studying under Eliade, had arranged to interview his elderly professor on the subject of "sacred substances and the history of religion." When Forte arrived "with twelve pages of quotations from just a few of his books pertaining to sacred plants or elixirs in the history of religion" and "a good list of questions," Eliade evidently did not wish to be interviewed on the subject. Under questioning, Eliade first stated, "I do not know anything about them"; finally, when asked if there were something about the topic which put him so obviously ill-at-ease, he threw up his hands and concluded: "I don't like these plants!" (Forte 1988).

[13] There is considerable controversy regarding the human colonization of the New World, but the evidence strongly indicates the first peopling of Beringia (whence the migrations

came) around 12,000 years B.P., coinciding with the sudden appearance there of trees, first dwarf birch (*Betula nana*) around 14,000–12,000 B.P., then aspen, poplar, spruce and other trees (Hoffecker *et al.* 1993). It is thought that prior to this time inadequate fuel wood (and forage for hunted animals) prevented sustained colonization by human beings. The earliest documented human habitation sites in Beringia predate by at least a century the earliest well-documented and widely-accepted indices of human settlement elsewhere in the New World (the so-called Clovis culture). It is perhaps significant in this context that dwarf birch, the first tree to have colonized extensively the "land bridge" of Beringia, is, like all birches, a common symbiont for *Amanita muscaria* in present-day Kamchatka, part of central Beringia (Wasson 1968). So closely related is the mushroom to the dwarf birch, that Karl von Dittmar described in the mid-nineteenth century how the Koryak and Chukchi of Kamchatka would carry their dried *Amanita muscaria* pieces in boxes made of dwarf birch (see Wasson 1968). This begs the question: might not early human settlers plausibly have followed the trail of *A. muscaria*, as well as of fuel wood and game animals, across the land bridge into eastern Beringia or the New World? Might it not have been the presence of their revered entheogen in central Beringia which first attracted human beings to the area? We must recall that even in modern times, despite sparse human habitation of Kamchatka, *Amanita muscaria* was always rare and valuable—A. Erman reported in the early nineteenth century that the Koryaks "often paid a reindeer for a single dried piece" (see Wasson 1968). Given the known importance of shamanic inebriants in preliterate cultures, lack of *Amanita muscaria* in Beringia prior to 12,000 B.P. could be seen as a *spiritual* barrier to migration, quite as important as the material barrier of scarcity of fuel wood and game. We have evidence that the Aryans who migrated south into India four millennia ago were preoccupied with problems of trade for *Soma* with the Dasyus, peoples who still inhabited the mountains where it grew and which the Aryans had abandoned (Wasson 1968). Much as reindeer were traded for *Amanita muscaria* in Kamchatka, the *Satapatha Brahmana* describes the Aryans trading a cow for *Soma*, attesting to its value (for purposes of the present discussion, it matters not whether *Soma* was *Amanita muscaria*). The recent discovery of a 5200–5300 year old corpse locked in ice in Austria (Seidler *et al.* 1992) has led to speculation that the cause of death by freezing may have resulted from overindulgence in "prehistoric *Schnapps*" (McManus & Seidler 1992). However, no remains of a suitable container for the *Schnapps* have been found, leading to speculation that a pair of dried mushrooms the ice man—since named Ötzi—was carrying strung on a leather thong may have been the cause of a fatal inebriation. Indeed, V.G. Bogoraz, a Russian anthropologist who accompanied the Jesup North Pacific Expedition to Kamchatka at the start of the twentieth century, reported that the Koryaks would dry fly-agarics, after which they were "strung together in threes," and even today dried *Amanita muscaria*, which may still be carried on leather thongs, is used in Siberia and Kamchatka against fatigue—"when a hunter goes to a far-away forest for a long time and gets tired there… he will eat dried *Amanita muscaria* and get kind of drunk. After that he will feel well again and can resume hunting" (Saar 1991A). Might not Ötzi have eaten psychoactive mushrooms from his thong, in a similar attempt to revive his flagging spirits, an attempt which proved unsuccessful? The pair of dried mushroom pieces found with him, however, were not pieces of *Amanita muscaria*, but rather have been identified as *Piptoporus betulinus*, a mushroom known to contain antibiotic, but not entheogenic compounds (Pöder *et al.* 1992). It may be, however, that Ötzi's thong had also contained *Amanita muscaria* or some other entheogenic mushroom, which were consumed in an unsuccessful attempt to ward off fatigue. Or have we here a pointer to a new entheogenic species (for which, see also: Blanchette *et al.* 1992; Stone 1992)?

[14] In Guatemala, on the other hand, the Quiché Maya call *Amanita muscaria kakuljá* or "lightningbolt" (Lowy 1974). In the famous *Popol Vuh* of the Quiché Maya (an ancient Quiché manuscript of unknown authorship and date, transliterated shortly after the conquest with Latin characters, given to Dominican friar Francisco Ximénez early in the eighteenth century; Ximénez transcribed the Quiché text and translated it into Spanish; the original copy has not been seen since), we learn of a trinity of Quiché gods: *kakuljá hurakan*, "lightningbolt one-leg"; *chipi kakuljá*, "dwarf lightningbolt"; and *raxa kakuljá*, "green lightningbolt"—of which *kakuljá hurakan* was the most important (Recinos 1947; Tedlock 1985). Wasson has proposed that these might represent a trinity of entheogens, that *kakuljá hurakan* is *Amanita muscaria* (as Lowy's work would indicate); whereas the "dwarf lightningbolt" *chipi kakuljá* refers to the smaller entheogenic psilocybian mushrooms (see Chapter 5), and the "green lightningbolt" *raxa kakuljá* is none other than the Aztec snake plant, the morning glory *Turbina corymbosa*, source of the entheogenic *ololiuhqui* seeds discussed in Chapter 2 (Wasson 1986; Wasson 1995). In his translation of the *Popol Vuh*, D. Tedlock supported the interpretation of Wasson, adding bits of further evidence. In Quiché, the stipe or stem of a mushroom is called *rakan*, "leg," lending credence to the interpretation of the "lightningbolt one-leg" as the "lightningbolt" mushroom with one "leg." Tedlock further gives *nanáhuatl* as another name for *kakuljá hurakan*, saying that "*Nanahuatl* means 'warts' in Nahua, which suggests the appearance of the *muscaria* when the remnants of the veil still fleck the cap" (Tedlock 1985). P. Furst has also suggested that *A. muscaria* corresponds more closely than the psilocybian mushrooms to the physiognomy of the mushrooms depicted on the Mayan "mushroom stones" (see De Borhegyi 1961; Furst 1976; Heim & Wasson 1958; Lowy 1971; Mayer 1977A; Ohi & Torres 1994; Wasson 1980 and Wasson & Wasson 1957A for illustrations), and has discovered in Nayarit a *terra cotta* mushroom figurine unmistakably sporting *A. muscaria's* characteristic "warts" (for photograph, see Wasson *et al.* 1986). Guzmán also published photographs of a mushroom stone from Pátzcuaro, Michoacán, the Purépecha region of México, clearly depicting *A. muscaria*, replete with "warts" and a characteristic volva, with a "death's head" carved on one side (Guzmán 1990; Guzmán 1992). In an unpublished manuscript dated 1976–1978, Náhuatl scholar T. Knab reported use of dried *Amanita muscaria* caps by a shaman in the Valley of Puebla. The caps were ground and mixed with tobacco for ingestion or smoking to "purify" the air and diagnose illness (Knab 1976–1978). Recently similar smoking of dried *A. muscaria* with tobacco among Mayan Indian groups has been reported (Rätsch 1987), and a parallel ethnomedicinal smoking of dried extracts of *A. muscaria* has been reported from the Shetul Valley of Afghanistan (Mochtar & Geerken 1979). Although generally held to be toxic (De Avila *et al.* 1980), an ethnomycological study in Durango, México, revealed that the Southern Tepehuan Indians classify the entheogenic *Amanita muscaria* and *A. pantherina* as *maimda'kam*, "mushrooms that make people feel dizzy or

drunk" (Elizondo 1991). Some of these new discoveries led Wasson to reappraise his stance on the importance of the fly-agaric in Mesoamerica, and led him to postulate that Huitzilopochtli, the "black Tezcatlipoca" was the Mexican equivalent of *kakuljá hurakan*—for he is also one-legged (Wasson *et al.* 1986)! These Mesoamerican one-legged god images harken back to the ancient Indian *Soma* cult, for in the *RgVeda,* the *Soma* plant, most likely a mushroom and possibly *A. muscaria,* is referred to as *Aja Ekapad,* the "Not-born Single-foot" (Wasson 1972B)! Thus it can be said that there most likely was an ancient tradition of entheogenic use of *Amanita muscaria* in Mesoamerica (Wasson 1995). In México this may have given way largely to the use of the far more abundant *Psilocybe* and related psilocybian mushrooms discussed in Chapter 5.

[15] Allegro's book was originally serialized in an English tabloid of sensationalist stripe (*The News of the World*), a far cry from the peer-reviewed scholarly literature he normally favored. Allegro never addressed his theory to fellow specialists in Biblical philology. Allegro was paid the princely sum of £30,000 for first serialization rights (Wasson in Forte 1988) and at the time was apparently hard-pressed to pay some debts (Wasson 1977). It is difficult to escape the conclusion that he wrote *The Sacred Mushroom and the Cross* to make a fast buck. As Wasson later commented, "I think that he [Allegro] jumped to unwarranted conclusions on scanty evidence. And when you make such blunders as attributing the Hebrew language, the Greek language, to Sumerian—that is unacceptable to any linguist. The Sumerian language is a parent to no language and no one knows where it came from" (Wasson in Forte 1988). This and several other points were made in the reviews of Jacobsen and Richardson (1971); see also the criticisms of Jacques (1970). Nevertheless, Allegro's specious theory continues to be taken seriously by some students of entheogenic mushrooms (Haseneier 1992; Klapp 1991), and a recent German anthology on the fly-agaric (Bauer *et al.* 1991) was dedicated to John Marco Allegro.

[16] Even the normally-accurate popular science monthly *Scientific American* depicted *Amanita muscaria* among other species on its cover, with the subtitle "Deadly Mushrooms" (Litten 1975). A recent book contained the unfounded statement: "normally, 10 or more specimens of Fly-Agaric can be fatal" (Lincoff & Mitchel 1977). No reference was given, and I would like to see the evidence on which this statement is based.

[17] Haard and Haard stated of the entheogenic *Amanita* species: "eating these mushrooms is akin to befriending a wolverine" (Haard & Haard 1975). Since I have never befriended a wolverine, I cannot comment on this comparison. These authors make the unfounded statement "in Germany, where such poisonings are frequent, death rates of 5.5% and 1.54% are known for *A. muscaria* and *A. pantherina* respectively"; then contradict themselves on the same page (p. 100) by saying "actually, documented deaths from *A. muscaria* poisoning are rare or non-existent"! No references were cited, and I challenge Haard & Haard to point to *any* German deaths from the entheogenic *Amanita* species. On page 99, these authors claimed of the psychoactive *Amanita* species: "an average concentration (of ibotenic acid and muscimol) of 70 mg/g fresh mushrooms is typical." This would be equivalent to 70 grams of ibotenic acid/muscimol *per* kilogram of fresh mushrooms. In

more than ten years of commercial isolation of ibotenic acid from Washington state *A. pantherina*, the highest yield I ever attained was 18.2 grams ibotenic acid from 55 kilograms of fresh *A. pantherina* collected near Tenino, Washington in May 1986—this amounts to only 330 milligrams of ibotenic acid *per* kilogram of fresh mushrooms (Ott 1980). Takemoto *et al.* (1964C) isolated 220 mg of ibotenic acid *per* kilogram of Japanese *A. pantherina*; Repke *et al.* (1978) detected the equivalent of 50 mg of ibotenic acid *per* kilogram of *A. pantherina* (also from Tenino, Washington; expressed as fresh weight); whereas Benedict *et al.* (1966) detected about 460 mg *per* kilogram of combined ibotenic acid/muscimol from *A. pantherina* of Tenino, Washington. Japanese *A. pantherina* was recently shown to contain 660 mg ibotenic acid plus 280 mg muscimol *per* kilogram (Yamaura & Chang 1988). Thus Haard & Haard overstated the toxicity of these mushrooms by about 75–200-fold! The minimum lethal dose in mice was estimated to be 21.5 g fresh *A. pantherina per* kilogram body weight, or some 1.50 kg fresh mushrooms for a 70 kg human being (Yamaura & Chang 1988). Haard and Haard's information on the toxicity of the *Psilocybe* mushrooms is scarcely better. First, with no references, they state "occasionally persons accustomed to collecting *P. semilanceata* discover some *P. baeocystis* or *P. strictipes*. One could have an interesting evening with twenty to forty *P. semilanceata* but this many *P. baeocystis* and possibly *P. strictipes* would be a potentially lethal overdose." Later, they state: "on a gram per gram basis it [*Psilocybe cubensis*] is considered relatively weak, about the same as *P. cyanescens*." However, in quantitative analyses of Pacific Northwest *Psilocybe* species, it was found that *P. cyanescens* was the most potent species tested, containing from 6.6–19.6 mg psilocybine/psilocine *per* gram of dried mushroom (14 specimens tested), while the "potentially lethal" [*sic*] *P. baeocystis* contained 1.5–14.4 mg psilocybine/psilocine *per* gram of dried mushroom (7 specimens tested), and cultivated *P. cubensis* contained 5.0–14.3 mg psilocybine/psilocine *per* gram (15 specimens tested; Beug & Bigwood 1982; Bigwood & Beug 1982). One possible explanation for this discrepancy is the fact that what Haard and Haard described as *P. cyanesans* [*sic*], of which they published a color photograph as Plate XXII, is clearly *P. stuntzii*, which has a persistent annulus (Guzmán 1983; Guzmán & Ott 1976; Haard & Haard 1975; Ott 1976B; Ott 1979B; see also Ott & Pollock 1976B; Weil 1977A). In contrast to the highly potent *P. cyanescens*, *P. stuntzii* may indeed be one of the weaker of the psilocybian mushrooms, showing from 0–4.2 mg psilocybine/psilocine *per* gram dried mushroom, based on testing 4 specimens (Beug & Bigwood 1982). It is difficult to imagine why Haard & Haard considered *P. baeocystis* to be potentially lethal. True, the death of one child in Oregon has been attributed to this species (McCawley *et al.* 1962), the only fatality ever blamed on a psilocybian mushroom (excluding here the incorrect attribution of ten fatalities to *Psilocybe subaeruginascens* or *P. venenata*; by Singer & Smith 1958B and see Table 4; and the 1972 Hawai'ian death attributed in the press to psilocybian mushroom poisoning, which has been shown probably to have involved an overdose of heroin; Allen 1988; Pollock 1974). Identification of the causative agent in the Oregon death as *Psilocybe baeocystis* was far from certain, however. The paper describing the death reported three separate episodes of poisoning involving two adults (aged 30 and 35) and four children (aged 4,4,6 and 9). In only one of the three episodes "was it possible to make a specific botanical classification," and that was based on identification of mushrooms cultivated "from the same mycelial spawn" (presumably dug up from the lawn in Milwaukie, Oregon or Kelso, Washington, where the toxic mushrooms had been gathered)! This procedure is virtually worthless, since the mycelia of any number of different mushroom species could have been present in the soil! The adults in the case experienced a "cheap drunk" which may have been due to a psilocybian mushroom. The children, however, developed fevers and convulsions, symptoms never observed with psilocybian mushrooms, leading to death in one case (one child, however, "despite the presumably unpleasant experience of gavage, ate a single mushroom five days later with mild recurrence of the typical symptoms"!). The authors were able to mimic this syndrome with administration of large amounts (15 mg/kg) of psilocybine by intraperitoneal injection into two puppies—this would be equivalent to nearly a half gram of psilocybine in a 30 kg child, or about half a kilogram of *P. baeocystis* (the maximum dose estimated to have been ingested by the children was about 15 grams, which could have contained as much as 20 mg of psilocybine/psilocine, using the maximum values detected in this species; Beug & Bigwood 1982; McCawley *et al.* 1962). For all the defects of this report, it is at least suggestive that psilocybian mushrooms might provoke an anomalous reaction in children, leading to hyperthermia and convulsions, possibly with fatal sequelae; even 'though psilocybine is remarkably non-toxic in adults and experimental animals. In any case, entheogenic drugs like psilocybine should never be given to children under any circumstances. A European case of *Copelandia* [*Panaeolus*] *cyanescens* poisoning led to non-fatal convulsions in a child victim (Heim *et al.* 1966), lending credence to psilocybine/psilocine as the causative agent in the Oregon death (McCawley *et al.* 1962).

[18] It is estimated that the death rate for human beings accidentally poisoned by the amatoxin-containing *Amanita* species is about 50%, and treatment is typically supportive and symptomatic. Sometimes hemodialysis may be performed, to attempt to filter the cyclic peptide toxins from the blood. Recently, European physicians have had some success in treatment of amatoxin poisoning using "anti-hepatotoxic" compounds from the milk thistle, *Silybum marianum*. A crude extract of flavolignans from *S. marianum* seeds, called silymarin (trade name *Legalon*) has proven useful in amatoxin poisoning cases. In a recent trial of one of the flavolignans, silybin, in 60 patients poisoned by amatoxin-containing *Amanita* species, there were no deaths (see Der Marderosian & Liberti 1988 and Foster 1991 for a summary of this exciting work).

TABLE 6
ISOXAZOLE-CONTAINING MUSHROOMS*

I. IBOTENIC ACID-CONTAINING:

Amanita cothurnata	Beutler & Der Marderosian 1981 [as *A. pantherina* var. *multisquamosa*]; Chilton & Ott 1976
A. gemmata	Benedict *et al.* 1966; Beutler & Der Marderosian 1981; Chilton & Ott 1976[1]
A. muscaria	Bowden *et al.* 1965; Eugster *et al.* 1965; Eugster 1967; Takemoto *et al.* 1964C
A. muscaria var. *alba*	Benedict *et al.* 1966
A. muscaria var. *formosa*	Benedict *et al.* 1966; Beutler & Der Marderosian 1981; Chilton & Ott 1976
A. pantherina	Benedict *et al.* 1966; Beutler & Der Marderosian 1981; Chilton & Ott 1976; Takemoto *et al.* 1964C Yamaura & Chang 1988
A. regalis	Bresinsky & Besl 1990
A. strobiliformis	Takemoto *et al.* 1964A[2]

II. TRICHOLOMIC ACID-CONTAINING:

Pleurotus ostreatus	Ott, unpublished laboratory data[3]
Tricholoma muscarium	Takemoto 1961; Takemoto & Nakajima 1964[4]
Tricholomopsis rutilans	Yamatodani & Yamamoto 1969

NOTES

[1] While the group of Benedict reported finding isoxazoles only in "intermediates" between *Amanita pantherina* and *A. gemmata*, and not in pure *A. gemmata* (Benedict *et al.* 1966), two groups subsequently detected ibotenic acid and muscimol in Washington State *A. gemmata* (Chilton & Ott 1976) and muscimol in two Pennsylvania collections (Beutler & Der Marderosian 1981). There is a French report of a psychotropic "poisoning" caused by this species, which was ingested together with another mushroom, prompting a self-experiment with *A. gemmata*, which gave the same experience as the original accidental intoxication (Cornué 1961).

[2] Although ibotenic acid had originally been isolated from Japanese *Amanita strobiliformis* (Takemoto *et al.* 1964A), two groups subsequently failed to detect the compound in a Tennessee collection of this cosmopolitan species (Benedict *et al.* 1966), nor in Swiss material, nor in a collection from California (Chilton & Ott 1976).

[3] Widespread cultivation of this cosmopolitan, savory mushroom has begun in recent years, making the "oyster mushroom" a common sight both in Mexican and American supermarkets (Stamets & Chilton 1983). Using thin-layer chromatographic analysis and an authentic sample of tricholomic acid kindly provided by T. Takemoto of Japan, I found that tricholomic acid was a constituent of North American cultivated *Pleurotus ostreatus* (Ott, unpublished laboratory data, October 1984). Indeed, this flavor-enhancing analogue of Monosodium Glutamate (MSG) probably contributes substantially to the wonderful flavor of this mushroom, considered by some to be one of the best of all edible mushrooms. While tricholomic acid does not appear to provoke acute toxic effects in human beings, the human pharmacology of this dihydro- derivative of ibotenic acid is completely unknown. Tricholomic acid is most decidedly an insecticide, and *P. ostreatus* (and other members of the genus *Pleurotus*) is known to be a carnivorous mushroom—the fungal hyphae secrete a neurotoxin which immobilizes soil nematodes, allowing them to be penetrated and digested by hyphae (Thorn & Barron 1984). My research would indicate that the insecticidal tricholomic acid is a most probable candidate for the *Pleurotus* nematode neurotoxin. It is interesting to note that, like *Tricholoma muscarium* (see following note), *Pleurotus ostreatus* is a "fly-killer mushroom." While analyzing extracts of the oyster mushroom against standards of tricholomic acid in my laboratory in Washington State in October 1984, I observed that both the *Pleurotus* extract and the tricholomic acid standard solution attracted and killed flies. After standing open in my laboratory for 24 hours (with a door opened to the outdoors), I counted no fewer than nine dead flies in the *Pleurotus* extract which was found to contain tricholomic acid, and a single fly even squeezed through the tiny opening of the screw-cap vial in which the small amount of tricholomic acid solution was kept, and there met his death! Although tricholomic acid-containing mushrooms are widely eaten and considered choice, nevertheless there is evidence that *Pleurotus ostreatus* may be toxic if eaten fresh in large quantities. Toxic reactions to eating Iraqi *Pleurotus ostreatus* (voucher specimens identified by mycologist D.N. Pegler at Royal Botanic Gardens in Kew, Surrey, England) led to pharmacological studies

in mice of a room-temperature aqueous extract. Following large oral and intraperitoneal doses of the extract, the mice showed severe hepatotoxicity and hemorrhages in intestine, liver, lung and kidney leading to death (Al-Deen *et al.* 1987). The average lethal dose in the mice would be equivalent to 2.8 kg fresh mushrooms for a 70 kg human being. The authors of the study suggested the possibility that pleurotolysin (Bernheimer & Avigad 1979), a toxic protein, might have been responsible, but there exists the possibility that tricholomic acid plays a role in the toxicity of this species, and that smaller quantities of fresh mushrooms might provoke some toxicity.

[4] Under the name *haetori-shimeji, Tricholoma muscarium* has a long history of use as a household insecticide in Japan (Imazeki 1973; Takemoto 1961). Using a fly-killing assay, Takemoto's group succeeded in isolating tricholomic acid from this mushroom (Takemoto 1961). A similar assay was employed three years later to isolate ibotenic acid from *Amanita strobiliformis* (Takemoto *et al.* 1964A). The British group of K. Bowden employed a fly-stunning test, which enabled them also to isolate ibotenic acid from *Amanita muscaria* at about the same time (Bowden & Drysdale 1965; Bowden *et al.* 1965). The latter species, known as *Amanite tue-mouche* in French ("fly-killer Amanita") or *Fliegenschwamm* ("fly-agaric") in German, has long had a reputation as a fly-killer in Europe. The earliest reference to insecticidal use of the fly-agaric was in the 13th century *De Vegetabilibus* of Albertus Magnus, but this reputation was sealed when Linnaeus himself had placed this practice in Sweden in *Flora Svecica.* However, there exists no firm evidence the fly-agaric was ever used traditionally in Europe as a flycide, nor that there was much concern about insects in general, nor demand for insecticides in Europe until modern times. V.P. and R.G. Wasson have argued that the "fly" in the *Amanita* had nothing to do with the use of the mushroom as an insecticide, that rather it was the "fly" of demonic possession, a linguistic reflection of the inebriating potency of *A. muscaria* and its shamanic and religious past, filtered through the dark glasses of mediaeval religious intolerance (Wasson & Wasson 1957A). It is interesting to note that, like *Tricholoma muscarium, A. muscaria* is eaten in Japan as food and much esteemed. Near Ueda in Nagano Prefecture, large quantities of *A. muscaria* are gathered and soaked in brine for 12 or 13 weeks, then rinsed repeatedly before ingestion (Imazeki 1973). A parallel culinary use of *A. pantherina* has been reported from the state of Washington in the U.S., where some users boil the mushrooms and discard the water before canning them. Although in Japan the *A. muscaria* eaters are aware that the mushroom in the fresh state "is somewhat inebriating" (Imazeki 1973), at least some of the Washington State users of *A. pantherina* as food are unaware of the toxicity of fresh specimens (Chilton 1979; Ott 1979B).

* This table lists mushroom species known to contain unusual isoxazole amines. The mushrooms in the first section are all definitely entheogenic (see Coyote Man & Brother William 1972; Fericgla 1985; Fericgla 1992; Festi & Bianchi 1992; Heinrich 1992; Heinrich 1995; Larris 1980; Leonhardt 1992; Ott 1976A; Pollock 1975B) and these contain as active principles the amino acid ibotenic acid (named for ***ibo-tengu-take,*** the Japanese common name for *Amanita strobiliformis*, from which it was first isolated, and relating the mush-

room to the mythical *Tengu*, trickster imps reputed to "get drunk from eating mushrooms"; see Chapter 6, Note 5 and Imazeki 1973) and its decarboxylation product, muscimol (Chilton 1975; Theobald *et al.* 1968; Waser 1967). Muscazone, a rearrangement product of ibotenic acid, was first isolated from Swiss *A. muscaria* (Eugster *et al.* 1965) and has since been isolated likewise from American *A. pantherina* (Ott, unpublished laboratory data). This compound may be an artefact of the isolation procedures, and is of dubious psychoactivity (Ott, unpublished laboratory data). Muscimol was earlier known as *agar-in(e)* or *pantherine*, and either muscimol or ibotenic acid likely represents the *Pilzatropin* first isolated by Schmiedeberg more than a century ago (Tyler 1958A). The second section of the table lists mushrooms containing dihydro-ibotenic acid or tricholomic acid. First isolated as the insecticidal principle of *Tricholoma muscarium* (known in Japan as *haetori-shimeji* or "fly-killer mushroom"), this compound evidently lacks acute human toxicity, as the *haetori-shimeji* is considered edible in Japan and is much esteemed for the table (Imazeki 1973; Takemoto 1961). Both ibotenic acid and tricholomic acid are potent flavor-enhancers and are analogues of the well-known flavor-enhancer MonoSodium Glutamate (MSG), first isolated from *Laminaria japonica* (Ikeda 1908), a Japanese seaweed used as a condiment (Barinaga 1990A; Ikeda 1908; Xia & Abbott 1987). Just like ibotenic acid, tricholomic acid is active at glutamic acid synapses in brains of experimental animals (Shinozaki & Konishi 1970), making it a candidate for ibotenic acid-like psychoactivity. As outlined in Chapter 6, Note 6, tricholomic acid may represent the essence of *umami*, the "fifth flavor" esteemed in Japan and especially identified with *shiitake*, *Lentinus edodes*, a mushroom in the same family (Tricholomataceae) as *Tricholoma muscarium*, which must also contain the delectable *umami*-flavored tricholomic acid. In their pioneering book *Mushrooms Russia and History*, Gordon and Tina Wasson reported the contemporary use in Sweden of pieces of caps of *Amanita muscaria* as flavor-enhancers in dishes of wild mushrooms (Wasson & Wasson 1957A).

PART FOUR

Appendices, Bibliography, Index
Acknowledgements

APPENDIX A
Sundry Visionary Compounds

1. ASARONES AND *ACORUS CALAMUS*

Asarones, *trans-* and *cis-* isomers of 2,4,5-trimethoxy-1-propenylbenzene (α-asarone and β-asarone respectively) are the volatile active compounds from the rhizome of sweet flag, *Acorus calamus*, a cosmopolitan marsh plant traditionally used medicinally in both the New and Old Worlds. Several North American Indian groups employed sweet flag rhizomes as a tonic and stimulant (Morgan 1980; Motley 1992) and under the names *bach* and *ugragandha* these rhizomes have been used in traditional Ayurvedic medicine as a sedative and also for neurological complaints (Vohora *et al.* 1990) and by the Ainu of Japan as an anthelmintic (Mitsuhashi 1976). In Nepal *A. calamus* preparations are used as nerve tonics (Singh *et al.* 1979) and the plant is used for oral infections (Bhattarai 1992) and against coughs (Joshi & Edington 1990). The Akha of Thailand use a related species, thought to be *A. gramineus*, chewing the rhizome for stomachache (Anderson 1986A), much as the Bontoc of the Philippines use a stem tea of *A. calamus* (Bodner & Gereau 1988). The isomers of asarone, like mescaline, are trimethoxybenzene derivatives, and amination of asarone yields the psychotropic compound TMA-2 (see Chapter 1). The asarones are also found in roots of *Asarum europaeum* and *A. arifolium*, from which they were first isolated in 1899, and in bark of *Guatteria gaumeri* (Tena-Betancourt *et al.* 1987). Richard Spruce observed the use of the bark juices of various *Guatteria* species as "glues" mixed with dart poisons in South America (Bisset 1992A). A related compound from anise and fennel seeds, anethole, has been proposed to have visionary effects (Albert-Puleo 1980).

The wild muskrat of North America, *Ondatra zibethica*, is a voracious consumer of sweet flag rhizomes, and several indigenous groups associated the plant with the muskrat. Thus it is called "muskrat root"—*moskwas'wask*, in Abnaki Algonquian, *muskwe s uwesk* in Penobscot, *weekas* in Cree, *etc.* Muskrat furs were an important trade item for the Indians in the colonial period, and these furs were of considerable economic importance to the Hudson Bay Company (Morgan 1980). In 1892, in the territory of the Cree, R. Strath reported: "large bundles of this plant can be seen hanging in every tepee... A piece of root is carried by every tripper on his hunts and trips for the Hudson Bay Company and when feeling exhausted by hunger or fatigue, a small piece slowly chewed will restore the flagging energies is a most wonderful manner" (Strath 1903). There are many reported medicinal uses of sweet flag in North America, as a cold and respiratory remedy among the Maritime Indians, for example (Chandler *et al.* 1979; Moerman 1986), and the plant inspired Walt Whitman to compose 39 "Calamus poems" (Morgan 1980). The aromatic rhizomes were also used as a stimulant for horses and as an attractant for fish. There is a report of Cree Indian chewing of the root for entheogenic effects (Moerman 1986; Smith 1973), which may refer to the fact that two persons living among the Cree in the 1960s experimented on five occasions with large doses of the rhizomes—about 10 inch pieces, roughly ten times the Cree stimulant dose. They reported experiences similar to LSD, which both had tried (Hoffer & Osmond 1967). The Cree use of sweet flag rhizome as a stimulant stands in marked contrast to its traditional use in Ayurvedic and Thai medicine as a sedative (Ponglux *et al.* 1987; Vohora *et al.* 1990) and similar use in traditional Tibetan psychopharmaceutical preparations (Tsarong 1991). In Europe on the other hand, sweet flag was reported as an ingredient of three distinct archaic recipes for psychotropic witches' "flying ointments" (Hansen 1978). Dioscorides described the use of *Acorus calamus* in a medicinal incense called *kuphi*, and a similar preparation was mentioned in the ancient Egyptian Ebers papyri (Negbi 1992). American anthropologist R. Kaplan reported the use of a purgative potion containing *A. calamus* rhizomes, before being given *miskwedo* (*Amanita muscaria*; see Chapter 6) by the Ahnishinaubeg (Ojibway) shaman Keewaydinoquay [K.M. Peschel] (Wasson *et al.* 1980A).

Pursuing the sedative principles of sweet flag rhizomes led to the isolation of α- and β-asarone (Baxter *et al.* 1960; Keller & Stahl 1982), and these compounds were shown to have sedative effects similar to reserpine and chlorpromazine (Sharma *et al.* 1961), and anticonvulsive activity (Chauhan *et al.* 1988). Recently an ethanolic extract of Asian *A. calamus* rhizomes was shown to have effects similar to those of α-asarone, but with significant differences, suggesting the presence of other active compounds (Vohora *et al.* 1990). Despite the known sedative properties of asarone, and in part owing to the lack of other known active compounds in the plant, α- and β-asarone have been proposed as possible entheogenic principles of the Cree *Acorus calamus* rhizomes (Schultes & Farnsworth 1980; Schultes & Hofmann 1980).

β-Asarone is a known carcinogen, and its use as a food additive has been banned in the United States, although the drug was listed as a stimulant in the *U.S. Pharmacopœia* from 1820–1916 and in the *National Formulary* from 1936–1950 (Kindscher 1992). Recent research, however, casts considerable doubt on the identification of the asarones as active agents in North American sweet flag strains. The asarones appear to be important constituents only of the Asian sweet flag strains, whereas the North American strains used as stimulants and reportedly visionary do not contain asarones (Foster & Duke 1990; Keller & Stahl 1982; Tyler 1987). This might explain why the asarone-rich Indian sweet flag is used as a sedative, while asarone-free North American strains of the plant rather have stimulant properties. It has been proposed that *A. calamus* is an Old World plant introduced into North America during the colonial period, and that the indigenous, stimulant strains in Canada are more properly designated as a distinct species, *A. americanus* (Packer & Ringius 1984). This could account for the pharmacological differences between American and European sweet flags. Further research is needed to determine the stimulant principle(s) of North American *A. calamus*. The lone report of LSD-like properties of large doses of North American sweet flag rhizomes certainly requires confirmation, and the visionary principle(s) of this strain, if any, probably remain to be isolated. Various sesquiterpenoids of unknown pharmacology have been identified in European sweet flag oil (Rohr *et al.* 1979).

II. ATROPINE, HYOSCYAMINE, SCOPOLAMINE—THE VISIONARY TROPANES

The most widespread and most widely-used class of vision-inducing plants belong to the family Solanaceae, which has more than 16 genera containing psychotropic compounds (Heimann 1952). At least eight of these genera possess species used traditionally for their content of visionary tropane alkaloids, principally hyoscyamine, scopolamine (synonym: hyoscine) and atropine (*d,l*-hyoscyamine): 1) *Atropa*; 2) *Brugmansia*; 3) *Datura*; 4) *Hyoscyamus*; 5) *Latua*; 6) *Mandragora*; 7) *Methysticodendron*; and 8) *Solandra*. In addition, there are three genera of solanaceous visionary plants whose chemistry is poorly known: 1) *Brunfelsia*; 2) *Iochroma*; and 3) *Petunia*; of which *Iochroma* is alkaloid-positive and probably will be shown also to possess tropane alkaloids. *Brunfelsia* appears to belong to a separate chemical category. The chemically-obscure solanaceous *Juanulloa ochracea* is a suspected additive to *ayahuasca* potions in Amazonia (see Chapter 4; Schultes & Raffauf 1990). The genera *Nicotiana* and *Duboisia* will be treated in a separate section below. All of the above genera have a rich history of use as inebriants, and the entheobotany and chemistry of each will briefly be treated here.

ATROPA: *Atropa belladonna*, for which ATROPine and TROPane alkaloids are named, also called "deadly nightshade," was widely used as an ingredient of witches' "flying ointments" in mediaeval Europe (Bauereiß 1995; Clark 1921; de Vries 1991A; Hansen 1978; Harner 1973C; Johnson 1957; Lewin 1924; Mann 1992; Mehra 1979), and was once used by Italian women to dilate their pupils to enhance their beauty, hence the name *belladonna* "beautiful woman" (Camilla 1995; Heiser 1987). The ancient Greeks knew of the inebriating potential of this plant, and may have added it to their wines of legendary potency (Mann 1992; Wasson *et al.* 1978; see Chapter 2, Note 17). Today it is used in Morocco as an aphrodisiac and "memory stimulant" (Bellakhdar *et al.* 1991), although one of its constituent alkaloids is known to *impair* human serial learning (Sitaram *et al.* 1978). In Nepalese ethnomedicine, *A. belladonna* is used as a sedative (Singh *et al.* 1979). *A. belladonna* contains roughly 0.4% alkaloids in the leaves, 0.5% in the roots and 0.8% in the seeds. The principal alkaloid is hyoscyamine, with lesser amounts of scopolamine, and trace amounts of other tropane alkaloids as well as traces of nicotine (Evans 1979; Schultes & Hofmann 1980).

BRUGMANSIA: The genus *Brugmansia* contains a half-dozen species of small trees, which were earlier classified as "tree *Daturas*" (Barclay 1959; Bristol 1966B; Bristol 1969; Lockwood 1973A; Lockwood 1973B; Lockwood 1979). All species are native to South America, and are found as cultivars as far north as México, where they are commonly known as *floripondios* and are sometimes used as inebriants, for example, among the Mixe, who make a hot-water infusion of three flowers of *B. candida* for divinatory purposes (Lipp 1990; Lipp 1991). There is use of *Brugmansia suaveolens*, which grows well in the tropical lowlands, as a shamanic inebriant in the Amazon, sometimes as an additive to *ayahuasca* (see Chapter 4; Schultes 1979E; Schultes & Raffauf 1992). Siona and Secoya Indians of Ecuador employ *Brugmansia* x. *insignis* alone as an entheogen, and as an *ayahuasca* admixture (Vickers & Plowman 1984), as do Quichua shamans (Chango *et al.* 1984). The majority of the use of the *Brugmansia* species as inebriants, however, is in the Andes, from Colombia south to Chile (Walton 1970). A recent article described representations of *Brugmansia* flowers on pre-Columbian spindle whorls from the Colombian Quimbaya culture (McMeekin 1992), and *B. vulcanicola* is depicted in pre-Columbian art (Schultes & Bright 1977). In the Sibundoy Valley, in the Colombian Putumayo, there exist numerous "atrophied or aberrant strains" of *Brugmansia aurea*, valued by shamans for their potent entheogenic properties. Two of these strains, known as *kinde borrachero* and *munchiro borrachero*, were recently described in a photo-essay on Amazonian medicinal plants (Schultes & Raffauf 1992). Some *Brugmansia* species are used therapeutically, such as *B. sanguinea*, which has also been reported to be employed as an entheogen in Perú under the name *misha toro* (Polia & Bianchi 1992; Schultes & Raffauf 1990). The preparation of inebriants from these plants varies from place to place but usually involves infusions of leaves and stems or pulverized seeds. The major alkaloid in *Brugmansia* is scopolamine, which may make up from 31–60 percent of the alkaloidal fraction, normally representing from 0.3–0.55% of dry weight. Lesser amounts of norscopolamine, atropine, meteloidine, and other tropane alkaloids occur in *Brugmansia* species (Bristol *et al.* 1969; Evans *et al.* 1965). *B. sanguinea* var. *vulcanicola* was shown to produce up to 0.83% tropane alkaloids, making this one of the most potent sources known for these valuable medicaments (Rivera *et al.* 1989). Similar levels were also found in *B. candida* and *B. aurea* (El Imam & Evans 1990). There now exists the commercial cultivation of *Brugmansia sanguinea* in Ecuador for scopolamine (or hyoscine) production (Evans 1989).

BRUNFELSIA: Various *Brunfelsia* species, especially *B. grandiflora* (once reported as *B. maritima*; Plowman 1977) and *B. chiricaspi* are used as inebriants in Amazonia, generally as admixtures to *ayahuasca* in Ecuador and Perú (Plowman 1973; Plowman 1974; Plowman 1977; Plowman 1980; Schultes 1979E). The chemistry of these visionary plants has not been fully worked out, but no tropane alkaloids are yet known from this genus, although "mandragorine" (see *Mandragora* below) was reported from roots of *manacá, Brunfelsia uniflora* (see Plowman 1977 for a review of *Brunfelsia* chemistry). A non-nitrogenous psychotropic compound, scopoletin, a coumarin, has been isolated from *B. grandiflora, B. uniflora* and other species (Mors & Ribeiro 1957; Plowman 1977; Schultes & Hofmann 1980). A convulsant principle, brunfelsamidine, has been reported in *B. grandiflora* (Lloyd *et al.* 1985).

DATURA: Plants of the genus *Datura* have a long tradition of use as inebriants in both the New and Old Worlds (Barclay 1959; Johnson 1972; Litzinger 1981; Safford 1921A; Safford 1921B; Safford 1922; Weil 1977B). *Datura metel*, called *dutra* or *dhatura* in India, has long been in use as an inebriant, and in the seventeenth century was reportedly used by women in Goa to drug men senseless in order to "prosecute their delights" on them (J.A. De Mandelslo in Schleiffer 1979). *Datura* is a sacred plant in Kashmir, but its seeds are used by bandits "for stupefying victims" (Shah 1982). Sometimes *Datura* species may be added to *kava* (see below) in Fiji, out of malice

(Singh 1992). In Nepal, the plant is used as a sedative (Singh *et al.* 1979), and in contemporary Morocco, *D. stramonium* continues to be used for its narcotic properties (Bellakhdar *et al.* 1991). *Datura* species were used in beers and palm wines in Africa "to add a stupefying or narcotic effect" (Oliver-Bever 1983). On a less concupiscent or malicious note, in ancient México *Datura* species, called *toloache* or *toloatzin*, were used in divination and healing (Furst 1976), a use which continues among the Mixe (Lipp 1990; Lipp 1991) and the Tarahumara, who call the plant *dekuba* or *wíchuri* (Bye 1975; Bye 1979A; Furst & Myerhoff 1972). *D. stramonium* or "Jimson weed" got its name from the colony of Jamestown, Virginia, following a famous episode in which soldiers at that colony unknowingly made a soup of the herb (Heiser 1987). *Datura stramonium* may have been used as an inebriant by certain Algonquian tribes of northeastern North America, under the name *wisakon*, a name which may refer to many different plants (Merrill & Feest 1975). The major shamanic use of *Datura* species was concentrated in northern México and in the American southwest. The following groups were reported to use *D. meteloides* or other *Datura* species as an inebriant: Apache (Reagan 1929); Coahuilla (Barrows 1967); Costanoan (Bocek 1984); Hopi (Whiting 1939); Kawaiisu (Zigmond 1981); Mahuna (Romero 1954); Kayenta Navaho (Wyman & Harris 1951); Ramah Navaho (Hill 1938; Vestal 1952); Paiute and Shoshoni (Train *et al.* 1941); and Zuni (Stevenson 1915). The Chumash Indians of California made ritual use of *Datura* species such as *D. wrightii* (Applegate 1975; Grob & Dobkin de Ríos 1992; Timbrook 1984; Timbrook 1987; Timbrook 1990), and the use of *Datura* species in initiatory ceremonies has been reported among the Luiseño Indians and other groups of southern California (Furst 1976; Sparkman 1908). Chumash murals thought to be 5000 years old (Hyder & Oliver 1983) have been interpreted to represent ritual use of *Datura* species (Campbell 1965). Mediaeval European use of *Datura* in witches' "flying ointments" (Clark 1921; De Vries 1991A; Hansen 1978; Harner 1973C; Lewin 1924; Mehra 1979) has been echoed in Castaneda's fictitious account of similar use, supposedly among the Yaqui of northern México (Castaneda 1968). *Datura* species generally contain principally hyoscyamine, scopolamine, meteloidine and other tropane alkaloids, in concentrations as high as 1.2% in fruits of *D. metel* (Al-Yahya & Evans 1975; Dieckhofer *et al.* 1971; Leary 1970; Schultes & Hofmann 1980). *Datura metel* root was used for its high alkaloid content in ancient China as an arrow poison (Bisset 1979).

HYOSCYAMUS: The famous henbane or *Hyoscyamus niger* was known to the ancient Greeks as an inebriant, and was probably an additive to Greek wines (Wasson *et al.*

1978; see Chapter 2, Note 17) and to Germanic beers (Rätsch 1996). Native to Europe, henbane (Spanish: *beleño*) was also a common ingredient in witches' "flying ointments" (Bauereiß 1995; Clark 1921; de Vries 1991A; Harner 1973C; Hansen 1978; Lewin 1924; Mehra 1979). Henbane juice was employed as an arrow poison by the ancient Gauls (Hansen 1978). To this day, henbane is used in Moroccan ethnomedicine as a narcotic and a dental analgesic (Bellakhdar *et al.* 1991), and henbane was a part of the ancient Chinese pharmacopœia (Li 1978). The main alkaloid of henbane is hyoscyamine (Evans 1979; Geiger & Hesse 1833), and it also contains significant amounts of scopolamine. The roots are the most active part, containing up to 0.16% alkaloids (Henry 1949; Schultes & Hofmann 1980). *Hyoscyamus niger* is smoked with tobacco in southern Kashmir "as an hallucinogen" (Shah 1982) and *H. boveanus* flowers were used in the same fashion by Bedouins of the Egyptian desert (Goodman & Hobbs 1988). *Hyoscyamus reticulatus* has been reported as a traditional "psychodysleptic" in Afghanistan (Younos *et al.* 1987), where *H. niger* is reportedly also mixed with *Amanita muscaria* as a topical remedy (see Chapter 6, Note 3; Mochtar & Geerken 1979). In Nepalese ethnomedicine, *H. niger* is employed as a sedative (Singh *et al.* 1979). *Hyoscyamus albus*, *H. aureus*, *H. reticulatus* and *H. senecionis* all showed high concentrations of tropanes, while the most potent species was *H. muticus* and *H. pusillus* contained only traces of alkaloids (Pelt *et al.* 1967).

IOCHROMA: Various species of *Iochroma*, especially *I. fuchsioides*, have been reportedly used by the Kamsá Indians of Colombia as shamanic inebriants (Schultes 1979E). Fresh leaf, root and bark infusions are drunk by Kamsá shamans (Schultes & Raffauf 1992; Shemluck 1990). The plant has also been reportedly used as an *ayahuasca* additive (McKenna *et al.* 1986; Ott 1994A; Schultes 1972B). Field tests on leaves of *I. fuchsioides* have indicated the presence of alkaloids, but these have not been identified. It is probable this species contains entheogenic tropane alkaloids (Schultes 1977A; Schultes & Hofmann 1980), but so far, only content of non-visionary withanolides of obscure pharmacology has been reported (Shemluck 1991).

LATUA: The one species in this genus, *Latua pubiflora*, was evidently used once by shamans in Valdívia province, Chile (Schultes 1979E). The plant is still known in Chile as *latué* (also rendered *latúe* or *latuy*), "that which kills," or *árbol de los brujos*, "sorcerer's tree." The leaves of *L. pubiflora* have been found to contain 0.18% hyoscyamine and lesser amounts of scopolamine (Bodendorf & Kümmer 1962; Plowman *et al.* 1971; Schultes 1979D; Schultes & Hofmann 1980). The plant is sometimes called *Latua venenosa* or *Lycioplesium pubiflorum* (Plowman *et al.* 1971).

MANDRAGORA: *Mandragora officinarum*, or mandrake, was a prominent ingredient in witches' "flying ointments" (Clark 1921; De Vries 1991A; Hansen 1978; Harner 1973C; Lewin 1924; Mehra 1979; Thompson 1968). Mandrake was reputed in Europe to be an aphrodisiac, and was widely used in philtres or love potions, a use also mentioned in the Bible (Hansen 1978; Heiser 1987; Lehane 1977). Shakespeare's Cleopatra ordered "Give me to drink mandragora/That I might sleep out this great gap of time/My Anthony is away." An ancient Egyptian myth of the sun god Ra describes brewing of mandrake beer (Rätsch 1996; E.A. Wallis Budge in Schleiffer 1979). Mandrake was also an ingredient in ancient Greek wines (Wasson *et al.* 1978; see Chapter 2, Note 17), and Dioscorides and Pliny described use of mandrake wine as a surgical anesthetic (Stillman 1922). *Mandragora autumnalis* is employed for narcotic properties in contemporary Moroccan ethnomedicine (Bellakhdar *et al.* 1991). Hyoscyamine is the major mandrake alkaloid, lesser amounts of scopolamine and atropine, plus traces of cuscohygrine or "mandragorine" are present (Evans 1979; Hesse 1901; Jackson & Berry 1979; Phokas 1959; Schultes & Hofmann 1980; Staub 1962). Rätsch (1994) has recently published a superb review of mandrake history.

METHYSTICODENDRON: This genus has but one species, *Methysticodendron amesianum* found only in the Sibundoy Valley of Colombia. An infusion of the leaves of this species, known as *mitskway borrachero* "jaguar inebriant" or *culebra borrachera*, "serpent inebriant" is taken by Kamsá shamans for divinatory healing (Schultes 1955; Schultes 1979E; Schultes & Raffauf 1992). It has been questioned whether *M. amesianum* deserves generic rank, or is rather a viral-infected, mutant species of *Brugmansia* (Bristol 1966B; Bristol 1969). The leaves of this plant contain 0.3% alkaloids, of which 80% is scopolamine, with lesser amounts of atropine and other alkaloids (Pachter & Hopkinson 1960; Schultes & Hofmann 1980).

PETUNIA: A sketchy report ascribed visionary properties to an unspecified species of *Petunia* in highland Ecuador. Known as *shanín* in Ecuador, the plant was later identified as *Petunia violacea* (Alvear 1971), but chemical analysis detected no alkaloids in this species (Butler *et al.* 1981).

SOLANDRA: Two species of *Solandra*, *S. guerrerensis* and *S. guttata* are used as visionary inebriants by the Huichol Indians of northern México, who call the plant *kiéri* or *kiéli*. Inebriating infusions are prepared from juice of the branchlets (Furst 1976; Furst 1989; Furst 1995; Knab 1977; Knab 1976–1978). Under the name *hueipatl* or *tecomaxóchitl*, this plant was an important inebriant to the ancient Aztecs (Garza

1990). Preliminary chemical studies have shown the presence of tropane alkaloids in concentrations of approximately 0.15%. Atropine, hyoscyamine and other tropane alkaloids were identified (Evans *et al.* 1972).

Several of the above-mentioned plants containing tropane alkaloids were part of what Hansen called *The Witch's Garden* (*Heksens Urtegård* in Danish), and figured as prominent ingredients in the famous "flying ointments" or "witches' salves" (*Hexensalben* in German): *Atropa*, *Datura*, *Hyoscyamus* and *Mandragora* (Clark 1921; De Vries 1991A; Hansen 1978; Harris 1974; Mehra 1979). One of the first individuals to suggest that the "flights" of fancy of the European witches were in fact drug-induced visions was the Spanish physician, A.F. De Laguna in the sixteenth century (Mann 1992; cited in Schleiffer 1979). The best-known "rationalist" critics of the Inquisition against witchcraft were Johann Weyer (Wierus), author of the famous *De Praestigiis Daemonum* and Reginald Scot, who published recipes for the witches' ointments (Cohn 1975; cited in Schleiffer 1979; Szasz 1970). Giovanni Battista Della Porta is perhaps one of the first actually to have experimented with the ointments—"when I was a young man, I tried these things on my Chamber-Fellows"—in the sixteenth century (which must have made him quite popular around the dorm!), and De Laguna also experimented on the "wife of the public executioner" (cited in Schleiffer 1979). In modern times, Karl Kiesewetter was the first to experiment with the ointments (Kiesewetter 1892), and this intrepid psychonaut died as a consequence of one self-experiment (Hansen 1978). In Germany, Siegbert Ferckel and Will-Erich Peuckert have conducted modern experiments with "flying ointments" prepared according to old recipes (Ferckel 1954; Mann 1992; Peuckert 1960) and Gustav Schenk conducted a self-experiment with henbane seeds (Schenk 1954, quoted in Mann 1992 and Schleiffer 1979). Ferckel, Schenk and Peuckert experienced distinct sensations of flying after anointing themselves with the ointments (in Schenk's case, the vapors of burned henbane seeds were inhaled), and Castaneda also described a similar fictitious experience with *Datura* (Castaneda 1968). These intriguing experiments account for the consistency in the testimony of many accused "witches" throughout Europe over several centuries, for their "flying ointments" were indeed capable of inducing distinct flights of visionary fancy, following topical application leading to percutaneous absorption of their constituent tropane alkaloids.

In modern medicine atropine, hyoscyamine and scopolamine are all used as "anticholinergic" agents—drugs to block the action of acetylcholine, a neuromuscular transmitter substance (Der Marderosian & Liberti 1988; Hall *et al.* 1977; Metzner 1967; Morton 1977). Clinically, they are used as spasmolytics in cases of gastroenteritis, in peptic ulcer and spastic colitis; in ethnomedicine tropane alkaloid-containing drugs have been used as anti-asthmatics (Ponglux *et al.* 1987). Atropine is used as an antidote in poisonings involving substances which exert a cholinergic effect, such as the mushroom poison muscarine (see Chapter 6, Note 4) and some insecticides. All three compounds are very toxic, and are used medicinally in doses of around a quarter of a milligram. Commercially the alkaloids are obtained from *Hyoscyamus* and *Duboisia* species (see section on nicotine, below; Morton 1977) and *Brugmansia candida* has been suggested to be an alternate source of hyoscine or scopolamine (Griffith 1976), while *B. sanguinea* is now being grown commercially for that pourpose (Evans 1989). Scopolamine has won fictional fame as the cloak-and-dagger "truth serum" of countless movies, and indeed it was tested by German doctors and their American counterparts as an interrogation aid, and was not found to be especially effective (Lee & Shlain 1985). Scopolamine has in fact been shown to *impair* serial learning in human beings at 0.5 mg doses (Sitaram *et al.* 1978). Twelve different species of tropane-alkaloid-containing plants are used in traditional Chinese medicine. Besides species of *Datura*, *Hyoscyamus* and *Mandragora*, species of *Atropanthe*, *Physochlaina*, *Przewalskia* and *Scopolia* are employed (Peigen & Liyi 1983). Tropane alkaloids are known also from the solanaceous genera *Anthocercis*, *Anthotroche*, *Crenidium*, *Cyphanthera*, *Grammosolen* and *Symonanthus* (El Imam & Evans 1984; Evans & Ramsey 1983; Festi 1995). *Solanum hirtum*, of unknown chemistry, is used as a tobacco substitute by South American Yanoamá Indians, under the name *tupiro* (Wilbert 1987).

Perhaps inspired by the fantastic accounts of Castaneda (1968), there have been some modern experimenters with tropane alkaloid-containing *Datura* species (Ott 1979B). The 1972 booklet, *Get The Buzzzon* mentions "nowdays [*sic*], new generation people have begun to experiment with toloache" and describes several such experiments with *Datura*, including ingesting roots and seeds, tea of seeds, fruits and cigarettes of leaves (Coyote Man & B. William 1972). There have been recent reports of the use of *Hyoscyamus niger* by children in Turkey in a dangerous sort of game—two deaths have resulted (Tugrul 1985). A recent fatality from drowning in the United States was attributed to disorientation following intentional ingestion of flowers of a "tree *Datura*" (Hayman 1985). *Datura stramonium* and *D. metel* are known as *concombre zombi*, "*zombi's* cucumber" in Haiti, and are reportedly used by sorcerers or *bokors* as an antidote to the stupefying and death-simulating "*zombi* powder," which consists of a variety of toxic plants and animals, especially tetrodotoxin-containing puffer fish and the toxic toad, *Bufo marinus* (see Chapter 3 and Appendix B; Davis 1983C; Davis 1983D; Davis 1988A). The role of tetrodotoxin in the *zombi* phenomenon has been questioned (Anderson 1988; Booth 1988A; Davis 1988B; Davis 1989), and indeed the evidence for this is sketchy. The pharmacognostical aspects of the Haitian *zombi* phenomenon have been explored in a popular book (Davis 1985), which was used as the basis for a sensational science-fiction film. A parallel use of nicotine- and tropane alkaloid-containing *Duboisia myoporoides* as an antidote to ciguatera poisoning from toxic fish was reported from New Caledonia (see section on nicotine below; Dufva *et al.* 1976).

III. IBOGAINE, TABERNANTHINE, VOACANGINE—FROM *EBOKA* TO *SANANHO*

One of the most intriguing of the Old World visionary plants is *Tabernanthe iboga*, source of the indole alkaloid ibogaine and related ibogane compounds (Haller & Heckel 1901). *Tabernanthe* is in the Apocynaceae or dogbane family, and ibogaine was reported in *Tabernanthe pubescens* (= *T. iboga*; Mulamba *et al.* 1981), in *Voacanga schweinfurthii* var. *puberula* (Richard *et al.* 1983), in other *Voacanga* species (Hedberg *et al.* 1982); in ten species of the related *Tabernaemontana* genus, including *T. citrifolia* (= *T. pandacaqui*; Abaul *et al.* 1989; Van Beek *et al.* 1984); and is the major alkaloid of the bark of *Tabernaemontana* [*Sarcopharyngia*] *crassa* (Batchily *et al.* 1986; Van Beek *et al.* 1985). Ibogaine is also reported from *Daturicarpa* [*Tabernanthe*] *elliptica* (Bruneton *et al.* 1976); *Ervatamia orientalis* (= *Tabernaemontana pandacaqui*; Knox & Slobbe 1975); *Pagiantha* [*Tabernaemontana*] *cerifera* (Bert *et al.* 1989); and *Trachelospermum jasminoides* (Atta-Ur-Rahman *et al.* 1988)—all Apocynaceae—as well as in various species of *Alstonia* and *Stenosolen*. Voacangine (carbomethoxy-ibogaine) is known from *Tabernanthe iboga* as well as various species of *Voacanga* (Janot & Goutarel 1955; Richard *et al.* 1983; Thomas & Biemann 1968) and from 35 species of *Tabernaemontana* (Van Beek *et al.* 1984). Ibogaine isomer tabernanthine also occurs in *T. iboga*, and this compound is known from two species of *Tabernaemontana* (Van Beek *et al.* 1984). Ibogamine is another constituent of *T. iboga* found in *Voacanga* species (Hedberg *et al.* 1982) and in numerous species of *Tabernaemontana* (Van Beek *et al.* 1984). While ibogaine is considered a principal active agent of *T. iboga*, mainly responsible for its stimulant and visionary properties (Gaignault & Delourme-Houdé 1977), voacangine, tabernanthine and ibogamine have shown properties similar to ibogaine in animal experiments (Bert *et al.* 1988; Zetler *et al.* 1968), and may contribute to the visionary effects of *T. iboga*.

The first report of the use of *Tabernanthe iboga*, or *eboka*, was in 1864, and there were other reports of its use in Gabon and the Belgian Congo as a stimulant and aphrodisiac (Pope 1969). In 1903 *eboka* was first reported as a visionary plant and the object of cultic use in the Congo (Schleiffer 1979; Schultes & Hofmann 1980). A detailed account of the Bwiti cult of *eboka* in Gabon has been published (Fernandez 1972; Fernandez 1982). Initiates to the Bwiti cult eat the powdered root bark of *eboka* in massive doses, from 15–50 times the normal threshold dose of 20 grams, the latter thought to contain about 75–125 mg of ibogaine. The initiation dose, said to "break open the head" thus may contain as much as 6.25 grams of ibogaine, and not surprisingly, breaking open the head has occasionally resulted in the deaths of initiates (Fernandez 1972)! At the lower dose, the drug apparently does not produce visions, but does have a pronounced stimulating effect (Fernandez 1972; Schleiffer 1979). A mushroom called *duna* figures in the mythology of the Bwiti religion, and evidence was recently brought to light suggesting the yet-unidentified mushroom may be psychoactive and used to induce visions and in sorcery (Samorini 1992C).

While the *Tabernaemontana* species which contain ibogaine and related indole alkaloids have manifold medicinal uses in various parts of the world, they do not seem to have a tradition of use as inebriants, with the exception of *T. coffeoides*, which contains voacangine and is used as a stimulant in Madagascar; *T. muricata* of unknown chemistry (alkaloid-positive) and used as a stimulant in the Colombian Amazon (Schultes 1979A); and *T. dichotoma*, which contains an isomer of iboxygaine, and is known in India as a deliriant drug (Van Beek *et al.* 1984). *Tabernaemontana divaricata* and *T. pandacaqui* (as *T. citrifolia* reported to contain ibogaine) are used as sedatives and analgesics in Thai ethnomedicine and extracts of various parts of both species have been shown to have sedative and analgesic properties in pharmacological tests (Taesotikul *et al.* 1989). *Sananho*, a *Tabernaemontana* species, is a known ingredient of South American dart poisons (Bisset 1992A), and under the name *tsicta*, *T. sananho* and other *Tabernaemontana* species are used in Ecuadorian ethnomedicine (Kohn 1992). *Tsicta* is used as a hunting aid, to sharpen the senses. After weathering the initial disagreeable effects of a tea of *tsicta* bark, the user becomes more sensitive and aware (Miller 1993), mirroring reported effects of "hunter magic" made from skin secretions of toxic frogs (Amato 1992; see Chapter 3). There is evidence that some *Voacanga* species are used as stimulants in Africa (Montgomery 1990); *V. bracteata* may be so used in Gabon (De Smet 1996). An unidentified *Tabernaemontana* from Amazonia is used as an *ayahuasca* admixture (see Chapter 4; Schultes & Hofmann 1979), along with three other Apocynaceae: *Himatanthus sucuuba*, *Malouetia tamaquarina* and *Mandevilla scabra* (Bisset 1992B; Luna 1984B; Luna & Amaringo 1991). An infusion of leaves of *Tabernaemontana heterophylla* is used as a tonic for elderly people in the Brasilian Amazon region (Schultes 1979A).

First isolated in 1901, ibogaine saw early, limited medical use as an antidepressant (Furst 1976) and psychotherapist C. Naranjo has experimented with the pure compound and with *T. iboga* extracts as adjuncts to psychotherapy. Naranjo found the drug to have certain benefits, particularly in eliciting fantasies and memories (Naranjo 1973A). Because of limited availability, there has been little modern experimentation with ibogaine or *eboka* as a ludible drug. Stafford reproduced the account of one psychonaut, mentioning ibogaine seems to have been synthesized on occasion for the U.S. black market, the drug appearing in reports of PharmChem Laboratory's analysis service (Stafford 1983), although this probably involved isolated, not synthetic, material. Lack of availability of ibogaine did not deter the U.S. government from illegalizing it, currently listed on Schedule I, along with LSD, DMT, psilocybine and others. Supplies of imported *Tabernanthe iboga* root have been available on the black market of the Pacific coast of the U.S., and tinctures of *eboka* root have found a place in European phytomedicine, sold over the counter in pharmacies as homeopathic remedies. Ibogaine has been suggested as therapy for opiate addiction, a dubious proposition. In studies of this phenomenon, it was shown that the active metabolite of ibogaine was 12-hydroxy-ibogamine (Mash *et al.* 1995).

IV. NICOTINE, TOBACCOS AND *PITURI*

Nicotine, the active and addictive principle of the ubiquitous tobacco, is not generally thought of as an inebriant capable of inducing visions. The low nicotine content of modern pre-rolled cigarettes, indeed, is insufficient for visionary experiences, sufficing only to provide mild stimulation to the smoker, and relief from the withdrawal symptoms occasioned by tobacco addiction (Byrne 1988; Schelling 1992). Nevertheless, tobacco was the shamanic inebriant *par excellence* throughout the Americas, and *Nicotiana tabacum* (source of modern cigarette, cigar and pipe tobaccos) and *N. rustica* (used in *bidis*) were the most important species. According to tobacco expert J. Wilbert, in Amazonia "*Nicotiana* figures as a transformation agent side by side with *Anadenanthera*, *Banisteriopsis*, *Trichocereus pachanoi*... and *Virola* in the were-jaguar complex and lycanthropy in general." Moreover, tobacco preparations are one of the most common and widespread additives to entheogenic *ayahuasca* brews (see Chapters 1, 3 and 4), and many shamans, like those of the Záparo tribe "take *ayahuasca*... to see better but believe that their true power derives from tobacco" (Schultes & Hofmann 1979; Schultes & Raffauf 1990; Wilbert 1987; Zethelius & Balick 1982). The ingestion of tobacco is an integral part of shamanic training throughout Amazonia (Alarcón 1990; Schultes & Raffauf 1992). In México, the Tarahumara Indians "consider tobacco next in importance to '*híkuri*'" or *péyotl*, and "more powerful than '*dekuba*' (*Datura*)" (Bye 1979A). Besides *N. tabacum* and *N. rustica*, the Tarahumara Indians also smoke ritually *N. trigonophylla* (Bye 1979A) a species of wild tobacco likewise used by the Hopi Indians (Whiting 1939). In the Old World, Australian Aborigines used another nicotine-containing plant called *pituri*, *Duboisia hopwoodii*, as a masticatory for stimulant purposes and as a shamanic inebriant (Cawte 1985; Watson 1983; Watson *et al.* 1983). Although it is primarily a New World genus, there are several Old World species of tobacco (in the South Pacific, Australia and Africa; see Feinhandler *et al.* 1979; Goodspeed 1954). Nicotine occurs in a handful of other plants, and has been reported as a trace constituent of *coca* leaves, a report which has not been confirmed (Novák *et al.* 1984). Australian Alyamara Aborigines chewed (together with alkaline ash) dried leaves of several *Nicotiana* species "for their narcotic effect"—*N. benthamiana*, *N. gossei*, *N. ingulba*, *N. megalosiphon* and *N. velutina*. They made similar use of the related *Goodenia lunata*. Leaves of some of these wild tobaccos were also macerated and added to tiny water holes in rocks to stun and facilitate capture of birds drinking from them (O'Connell *et al.* 1983). *Nicotiana ingulba* was reportedly used as an inebriant by the Binbidu people of Australia (Thomson 1961).

The ethnopharmacognosy of tobacco in South America has been summarized in a recent book by J. Wilbert, *Tobacco and Shamanism in South America* (Wilbert 1987). Wilbert had earlier detailed the shamanic use of tobacco among the Warao Indians of Venezuela (Wilbert 1972; Wilbert 1975). First observed by Europeans on Columbus' first voyage, tobacco use was found to be nearly universal among New World Indian groups. While smoking is the best-known means of ingestion of tobacco, for shamanic inebriation it has also been employed as a masticatory, in potions, in "lickable" oral preparations (*ambíl* and *chimó*; Kamen-Kaye 1971; Kamen-Kaye 1975; Schultes 1945), as a snuff (Gorman 1993), and in clysters or enemas. Smoking is by far the most common method of tobacco administration in South America, being cited by Wilbert in 233 Indian tribes; followed, in order of prevalence, by tobacco potions (64 tribes), masticatories (56 tribes), snuffs (53 tribes), "lickable" preparations (16 tribes), with only two tribes reported to have used tobacco clysters (Wilbert 1987). The use of tobacco enemas was also mentioned in N. Monardes' classic 1574 treatise on New World medicinal plants, recently reprinted (Monardes 1990). In all cases, large doses of potent tobaccos are employed to achieve visionary trance states, and the known effects of severe nicotine intoxication, leading to visual alterations called tobacco amblyopia, appear to be an integral component of shamanic vision among South American indigenous groups (Wilbert 1987; Wilbert 1991). Not confined to South America, the ritual use of tobacco, both *Nicotiana rustica* or *picietl* and *N. tabacum* or *quauhyetl*, was extremely important in pre-Columbian México and survives there to this day (Furst 1976; Garza 1990; Robicsek 1978; Schele & Freidel 1990; Schele & Miller 1986). Temperate-zone North American indigenous groups also used *N. rustica* and other tobacco species as shamanic inebriants, such as the Costanoan Indians of California, the Kawaiisu of Utah and the Pima, who used *Nicotiana bigelovii* (Bocek 1984; Zigmond 1981) and the Chumash who used that species as well as *N. attenuata* (Timbrook 1984; Timbrook 1987; Timbrook 1990). *N. attenuata* has been found in ancient reedgrass "cigarettes" from Arizona, and was used by Hopi, Pima, Yuma, Zuni, Washoe and Southern Paiute Indians (Adams 1990). *N. attenuata* was used traditionally as far north as Canada, for example by the Thompson Indians (Turner *et al.* 1990).

While β-carboline ingredients have been proposed to explain the use of tobacco as a shamanic inebriant (Janiger & Dobkin de Ríos 1976), the tobacco species important in shamanism contain nicotine and sometimes lesser amounts of nornicotine, and these compounds are the most important in tobacco pharmacology. As J. Wilbert summarized it: "native interest in tobacco centers on the nicotine alkaloid it contains. A comparison of the ethnographical record of tobacco use with the results of experimental and clinical studies indicates that nicotine pharmacology tends to confirm a number of therapeutic practices and basic beliefs of tobacco shamanism in South America" (Wilbert 1991). Nicotine, first isolated in 1807, is extremely toxic, and one or two drops of pure nicotine (60–120 mg) placed on the skin are sufficient to kill an adult human being. A typical cigar contains enough nicotine to kill two people, were it injected into their bodies (Larson *et al.* 1961). Indeed, *Nicotiana* species have been used as dart-poison ingredients in South America (Bisset 1992A) and there is at least one human fatality on record from mistaken consumption of the leaves of "desert tobacco," *N. trigonophylla* (a species which was used traditionally by the Pima and Yuma Indians; Adams 1990), while leaves of the anabasine-containing *N. glauca* have also caused fatalities (Castorena *et al.* 1987; Turner & Szczawinski 1991). Contemporary Huichol Indians of México prepare an inebriating smoking mixture called *ye-tumutsáli*, of *Nicotiana rustica* with *yahutli* (also rendered as *yyahutli* or *yauhtli* and also called *pericón*) or *Tagetes lucida*, relative of *T. erecta* or *zempoalxóchitl* (see Appendix B; Siegel *et al.* 1977), and a "psychotomimetic" snuff of *N. tabacum* with *Sterculia* ash added has been reported from Surinam and French Guiana (Plotkin *et al.* 1980). "Hallucinogenic" use of tobacco in Mesoamerica has been summarized briefly in a recent article (Elferink 1983).

The use of *pituri*, cured leaves of *Duboisia hopwoodii*, as a stimulating and inebriating masticatory by the Australian Aborigines was reported in the 1860s by members of an ill-fated group of explorers under W.J. Wills, all but one of whom died of starvation in 1861. They called it *bedgery*, *pedgery* and *pitchery* and described it as being "highly intoxicating," adding that "after chewing it for a few minutes I felt quite happy and perfectly indifferent about my position" (W.J. Wills and A. Morehead cited in Schleiffer 1979). This is quite a testimonial, considering the "position" of the author was grave—he was starving and watching all of his companions on the expedition die of starvation! Samples of *pituri*, as well as leaves of *D. hopwoodii*, have been shown to contain high concentrations of nicotine, as much as 5%, and nornicotine and related alkaloids have been found in the leaves of the plant. The roots of *D. hopwoodii* have been found to contain hyoscyamine and scopolamine, besides nicotine, nornicotine and related alkaloids. An 80-year-old sample of *pituri* was shown to contain 0.5% nicotine and 0.2% metanicotine with traces of other alkaloids (Watson *et al.* 1983). A related species, *Duboisia myoporoides* is used by natives of New Caledonia as an antidote to poisoning from toxic fish, called ciguatera poisoning (Bourdy *et al.* 1992). The leaves of this species are ingested to counteract the poisoning, and have been shown to contain nicotine, nornicotine, atropine and scopolamine. It was estimated that two mouthfuls of the leaves would contain roughly 50 mg of nicotine and 20 mg of scopolamine (Dufva *et al.* 1976). The Australian Aborigines have also been observed to chew leaves of wild *Nicotiana* species, which presumably contain nicotine, for stimulatory purposes (Peterson 1979).

V. *KAVA*–PYRONES AND PSYCHOACTIVE *PIPER* SPECIES

The *kava*-pyrones (or *kava*-lactones) are a group of non-nitrogenous compounds isolated from the roots of *Piper methysticum*, from which an inebriating beverage, *kava* (known in Fiji as *yaqona* or *yagona* and pronounced *yangona*) was traditionally prepared throughout Oceania (Barrau 1957; Brunton 1989; Cawte 1985; Cox 1992; Gatty 1956; Hough 1904; Lebot 1991; Lebot *et al.* 1992; Singh 1992). While it has been claimed that the word *kava* derives from the Sanskrit word for inebriating potion, *kasya* (Steinmetz 1960), the name much more likely comes from the Polynesian name for the source plant, *ava* (Lebot & Lévesque 1989). On the other hand, it has been argued that the Polynesians originated in southern India, and the *kava* ceremony has been compared to the famous Vedic *Soma* sacrifice (see Chapter 6;

Williamson 1939). Methysticin was the first active compound isolated from *kava* in 1860–1861 (Cuzent 1861; Gobley 1860), and at least five other active pyrones (out of at least 19) are known from the plant: dihydromethysticin, kawain, dihydrokawain, yangonin and desmethoxyyangonin (Duve 1981; Hänsel 1968; Jössang & Molho 1967; Jössang & Molho 1970; Keller & Klohs 1963; Klohs 1967; Lebot & Lévesque 1989; Lewin 1886; Meyer 1967; Saüer & Hänsel 1967; Sengupta & Ray 1987; Smith 1983; Smith *et al.* 1984; Young *et al.* 1966). Yangonin occurs also in *Ranunculus* species, and *bis*-noryangonin has been detected in several species of mushrooms, including the entheogenic psilocybian *Gymnopilus spectabilis* (see Chapter 5; Hatfield & Brady 1969; Hatfield & Brady 1971; Ott 1976B). A novel pyridone alkaloid, pipermethystin, is known from *kava* leaves (Smith 1979), and a Hawai'ian strain, called "black *kava*," is said to be one of the most potent, the leaves being as potent as the roots of ordinary strains (Facciola 1990). There also exists a Hawai'ian strain called *Lehua kava*, "red *kava*," yet more potent that the black (Montgomery 1990).

The use of the inebriating beverage *kava* was first documented by Europeans when Captain James Cook visited the Sandwich Islands (Hawai'i) in 1768 (Schleiffer 1979) and the plant was described botanically by J.G.A. Forster, a botanist who accompanied Cook on his second voyage from 1771–1775 (Lebot 1991). Today strictly a cultivar, the wild precursor of *kava* is thought to be *Piper wichmannii* (Cox & Banack 1991; Lebot 1991), which is the only wild species of *Piper* known to contain the *kava* pyrones (Chew 1972; Lebot & Lévesque 1989). This wild species is held to have been used by the ancestors of today's *kava* drinkers, and is still sometimes used as an admixture (Lebot *et al.* 1986). *Piper wichmannii* was reportedly used in New Guinea to "counter magic" (Telban 1988) and *P. subpeltatum* is used in love charms in Madagascar (Beaujard 1988). *Kava* is also drunk as an inebriant in Samoa (Cox *et al.* 1989; Grattan 1948; Holmes 1967), the New Hebrides (Gajdusek 1967), Tonga, Fiji, Tahiti, the Caroline Islands in Micronesia as far west as Uvea (Kirch 1978), and on many islands in Melanesia (Banack 1991; Ford 1967; Schleiffer 1979). The recent introduction of *kava* to Australian Aborigine groups as a sort of replacement therapy for alcohol has led to enthusiastic use, and now *kava* itself is considered there to be a "drug of abuse" (Cawte 1985; Prescott & McCall 1988).

The roots of the cultivated *kava* plant were traditionally chewed and expectorated, after which the diluted mash was mixed and filtered prior to drinking (Lebot 1991; Schleiffer 1979). This method is still practiced in the New Hebrides (Gajdusek 1967), whereas in Samoa and elsewhere the more modern method, said to yield a less potent preparation, is to grind or pulverize the roots rather than chew them (Holmes 1967; Lebot 1991). In Lau, Fiji, labor strife among canoe builders may be avoided by discussing the next day's work assignments around the evening *kava* bowl (Banack & Cox 1987). While the most prominent use of *kava* is as an inebriant (Ford 1967; Gajdusek 1967; Holmes 1967; Schleiffer 1979), it is used medicinally in ethnogynecology in Tonga (Singh *et al.* 1984), and also against stings and inflammations (Whistler 1991), and is commonly used medicinally in Hawai'i as well (Abbott & Shimazu 1985). "Maori" healers in the Cook Islands use *kava* extract medicinally for urinary-tract ailments (Whistler 1985), whereas in Samoa *kava* is used as a remedy for venereal disease (Uhe 1974). Fungistatic activity has been demonstrated for *kava* extracts, justifying reported ethnomedicinal use as a topical antiseptic (Hänsel *et al.* 1966). Ethnomedicinal use of *kava* throughout the Pacific has been summarized in a recent table (Lebot 1991). In Tonga, fish poisons are associated with *kava*, such as *kavahaha* or "fish *kava*" (*Derris trifoliata*), and *kavafisi* or "*kava* from Fiji" (*Tephrosia piscatoria*; Rickard & Cox 1986).

While the major effect of the *kava* beverage is as a sort of euphoriant tranquilizer, a type of alcoholic cocktail without the hangover (Kretszchmar 1970; Lebot 1991; Lewin 1924), the drug was also used ceremonially in connection with religious cults (Cox & Banack 1991; Lebot 1991; Schleiffer 1979), and in Hawai'i its use was once associated with the *kahunas*, shaman/priests (Titcomb 1948). *Kava* potions have been used ritually as an offering to the ancestors or the gods (Lebot 1991). The potion has been said to evoke effects like LSD or psilocybine in high doses (Hoffer & Osmond 1967). The active pyrones isolated from *kava* have shown muscle-relaxant properties (Meyer 1967), as do extracts of the root (Buckley *et al.* 1967). *Kava* extracts have been shown to effect muscle relaxation by a mechanism similar to that of local anesthetics (Singh 1983). Some pharmaceutical companies became interested in the potential of *kava* compounds as medicinal tranquilizers, and, on the basis of electrophysiological comparisons with LSD, the drug was described as a "weak psychotogen" or a weak LSD-type compound (Marrazzi 1967). Human and animal studies found dihydromethysticin to be the most active tranquilizer in *kava*, but relatively weak—doses of 800–1200 mg were needed in human beings, causing side-effects including allergic skin reactions, leading pharmaceutical researchers to conclude "further study of Kava as a modern medicinal agent would not appear to be needed" (Pfeiffer *et al.* 1967). Although visual alterations were reported in a single human subject following ingestion of 600 ml of *kava* prepared according to the traditional method in Fiji, these were "consistent with those of drugs with an action similar to cocaine" (Garner & Klinger 1985), and we have seen *kava* was reported to exert an effect like that of local anesthetics, of which cocaine is the prototype (Singh 1983). Furthermore, *kava* specialist V. Lebot recently stated: "the effect felt on consuming *kava* is so close to the one produced by an extract of coca leaves..." which, of course, contain cocaine (Holmstedt *et al.* 1978; Lebot 1991). Perhaps the most significant *datum* is the testimony of Polynesian experts P.A. Cox and L. O'Rourke: "as consumers of *kava* we believe its alleged hallucinogenic properties are more apocryphal than real" (Cox & O'Rourke 1987).

Although the pharmaceutical companies turned their backs on *kava*, it has found a place in modern herbal medicine. *Kava* extract is an ingredient of a German herbal sedative called *Kavo Sporal*, and *Fink Cysto Capsules*, a local anesthetic used to treat bladder disorders in herbal therapy, contain *kava* extract (Weiss 1988). Similarly, a French product, *Kaviase*, contains *kava* extracts, and the Swiss *Kavaform* contains synthetic kawain (Lebot 1991). *Kava* extract is an ingredient in a hair conditioner called *Kava!*, which would appear to be an unfelicitous marketing scheme, given the propensity of *kava* potions to provoke *kani kani* or skin lesions in heavy users—wait until some unfortunate bather breaks out in a rash following use, or until some careless youth decides to drink half a bottle of the *nostrum*! *Kava* extracts have become popular herbal tranquilizers in the United States (Stafford 1983), and there is apparently some renewed interest on the part of pharmaceutical companies in the drug (Montgomery 1990). Much of the world's supply comes from Fiji, where 2400 hectares are planted with *Piper methysticum*, earning farmers there U.S. $20 million annually (Duve & Prasad 1983).

A Samoan ethnomedicine thought to be *Piper graefei* was pharmacologically active, as was *P. methysticum* (Cox *et al.* 1989). *Piper sarmentosum* of West Sumatra was shown to contain alkaloids (Arbain *et al.* 1989). Fruits of "false *kava*," *Macropiper latifolium*, are used as an antidote to ciguatera poisoning in Vanuatu (Bourdy *et al.* 1992) as well as in ethnogynecology (Bourdy & Walter 1992); while *M. excelsum*, as *kawa kawa*, is a New Zealand Maori ethnomedicine (Brooker *et al.* 1981). *Piper sanctum* or *acuyo* is a Mexican plant having ethnogynecological and urinary-tract medicinal uses similar to those of *kava* in Oceania (Díaz 1976). Another Mexican *acuyo*, *P. auritum* (which contains safrole; Gupta *et al.* 1985; Zulueta Rodríguez 1988), is a condiment with similar medicinal uses (Díaz 1976), used along with *P. umbellatum* in Chinantec Indian ethnogynecology (Browner 1985). In Panamá, *P. auritum* leaf is used to lure and trap fish, and then to feed the trapped fish—resulting in pre-seasoned fish fillets (Joly 1981)! Cabecar and Guaymí Indians of Central America use a tea of *P. auritum* leaves to treat abdominal pains, whereas the Cabecar use *P. marginatum* (safrole-containing; Díaz & Gottlieb 1979) leaf infusions for headache (Hazlett 1986). In Guyana, leaves of *P. obliquum* may be applied topically against headaches and to treat other pains (Austin & Bourne 1992). *Piper pellucida* stem tea is used by the Lahu of Thailand to treat menstrual difficulties (Anderson 1986B). In Brasil, three species of *Piper*—*P. abutiloides*, *P. cincinnatoris* and *P. lindbergii* are used as analgesics (Costa *et al.* 1989).

The leaf of *Piper betle* is masticated throughout Southeast Asia and in Oceania together with the stimulant *Areca catechu* or *betel*, source of arecoline (Balasubrahmanyam & Rawat 1990; Sen *et al.* 1989). *Piper betle* leaf is also used in Chinese, Thai and in Vietnamese traditional medicine (Nguyen & Do 1991; Ponglux *et al.* 1987), and extracts of *betle* leaf have recently been shown to possess anti-tumorigenic properties (Bhide *et al.* 1991). *Piper betle* is currently being cultivated near Fresno, California to supply the U.S. *betel*-chewing market (Shulgin 1992).

Two *Piper* species, *P. longum* and *P. nigrum* are reportedly used in traditional Tibetan and Nepalese psychopharmacological preparations (Singh *et al.* 1979; Tsarong 1991) as well as in Ayurvedic medicine (Johri & Zutshi 1992). The Mikir of India use the chemically-obscure *Piper attenuatum* in various ceremonies of worship, suggesting psychoactivity (Jain & Borthakur 1980). Many *Piper* species are used medicinally in Amazonia, and *P. interitum* would appear to be psychoactive—the roots and leaves of this species are used by the Kulina Indians of Perú as a tobacco substitute (Davis & Yost 1983B; Schultes & Raffauf 1990). Similarly, the Yanoamá Indians employ *Piper cryptodon*, under the name *holehole be*, as a tobacco substitute (Wilbert 1987). An unidentified *Piper* is used by the Canelos Indians of Ecuador as a stimulant, under the name *guayusa* (the name of *Ilex guayusa*, a caffeine-containing holly; Schultes & Raffauf 1990). *Piper bartlingianum*, used in ethnomedicine (Boom 1987), was reported from Surinam in the eighteenth century as an ingredient of the dart poison *woorara* (Bisset 1992A; Reis Altschul 1973). An unspecified species of *Piper* has been cited as an *ayahuasca* admixture plant (Schultes & Raffauf 1990).

VI. SALVINORIN A AND *SKA PASTORA*

The salvinorins are a class of non-nitrogenous diterpenes isolated from a little-known Mexican entheogenic plant, *Salvia divinorum*, a member of the Labiatae or Lamiaceae, the mint family. Similar diterpenes such as salviarin and splendidin have been isolated from *Salvia splendens* and other *Salvia* species (Savona *et al.* 1978; Savona *et al.* 1979), and these *Salvia* diterpenes represent a novel class of psychoactive compounds. Loliolide, an ant repellent, has recently been isolated from *Salvia divinorum* (Valdés 1986). *Salvia occidentalis* is reportedly used for analgesia by Panamanian Cuna Indians (Duke 1975). *Salvia persepolitana* was once proposed as a candidate for the ancient Iranian entheogen *Haoma* (see Chapter 4; Doniger O'Flaherty 1968). Even the common culinary sage *Salvia officinalis* has been said to provoke "intoxication and giddiness" if smelled for a prolonged time (Duke 1987). Colforsin (commonly known as *forskolin* and its diastereomer *coleonol*) is a related diterpene from another medicinal plant of the Lamiaceae family, *Coleus barbatus*, widely known as *C. forskohlii* (Ammon & Müller 1985; Valdés *et al.* 1987B), and has been shown to have hypotensive effects (Dubey *et al.* 1981). Two species of *Coleus* not indigenous to México, *C. blumei* and *C. pumila*, are considered by some Mazatec Indian shamans to belong to the same "family" as *Salvia divinorum*, but are of unknown chemistry and pharmacology (Wasson 1962B). *Coleus blumei* is used in Samoan ethnomedicine as a remedy for elephantiasis (Uhe 1974). A *Coleus* species was reportedly used by the Nekematigi of New Guinea to treat headaches (Johannes 1975). A species of Amazonian mint, *Ocimum micranthum*, has been reported as an additive to entheogenic *ayahuasca* potions (see Chapter 4; Schultes & Hofmann 1979), and *Mentha pulegium* was an ingredient of the entheogenic *kykeon* potion of the Eleusinian Mysteries (Wasson *et al.* 1978).

J.B. Johnson, the first anthropologist to observe use of entheogenic mushrooms in México in 1938 (see Chapter 5) also mentioned the existence of a visionary infusion made from a leaf he called *hierba María* (Johnson 1939A), and Blas Pablo Reko, a pioneer in studies of Mexican entheogens (see Chapter 2, Note 10) collected some material of a divinatory leaf (unsuitable for botanical identification) in the Mazatec zone of México (B.P. Reko 1945). In 1952, Robert J. Weitlaner described a curing ceremony in which *yerba de María* was employed, and in 1960–1962 R. Gordon Wasson made several collections of this plant, observed its use, and ingested it himself. Finally in 1962, Wasson and Albert Hofmann collected flowering material of the mysterious entheogen, which Epling and Játiva identified as a new species, *Salvia divinorum* (Epling & Játiva-M. 1962; Wasson 1962B). During their 1962 expedition, Wasson and Hofmann's wife Anita ingested juice of the leaves in the course of a curing ceremony on 9 October, and Hofmann himself ingested juice of the leaves on the night of 11 October, when he introduced María Sabina to his 5 mg pills of synthetic psilocybine (see Chapter 5). Although Anita Hofmann received the juice of only three pairs of leaves, she reported "striking, brightly bordered images" and after ingesting the juice of just five pairs of leaves, Albert Hofmann described "mental sensitivity and intense experience, which, however, was not accompanied by hallucinations." Hofmann returned to Switzerland with fresh juice of the leaves preserved in alcohol for chemical analysis (Hofmann 1980; Hofmann 1990). The active principle appeared to be unstable, for Hofmann was unable to detect any activity in the juice he took to Switzerland, and therefore did not attempt to isolate the active principles.

Two decades later, Ortega and colleagues isolated a novel compound which they called salvinorin from leaf of *S. divinorum* (Ortega *et al.* 1982). Two years later, Valdés and colleagues isolated two diterpenes from *S. divinorum*, which they named divinorins A and B (Valdés *et al.* 1984). Since divinorin A is identical to the previously-isolated salvinorin, the two compounds are properly named salvinorin A and salvinorin B (Valdés *et al.* 1987A). Salvinorin A is psychotropic and produced effects in animals similar to those of mescaline, and there appear to be other active diterpenes in the plant (Valdés 1983; Valdés *et al.* 1987A). However, the primary effect of salvinorin A was sedative, and both groups isolated it from dried leaves.

In 1962 R.G. Wasson summarized his findings on the ethnopharmacognosy of *Salvia divinorum* in the Mazatec zone of México, where the plant is called *Ska Pastora* or *Ska María Pastora*, *hojas de la Pastora* or *hojas de María Pastora*, "leaves of the Shepherdess" or "leaves of Mary Shepherdess" (Wasson 1962B). This Mazatec name seemingly shows a Catholic influence, although the Biblical Mary was not a shepherdess, and no shepherdess figures in Catholic iconography. Wasson described the effects of *Ska Pastora* leaves, which he first ingested on 12 July 1961 in Ayautla, Oaxaca. The leaves are customarily taken in pairs, and the Indians would "consume the leaves by nibbling at the dose with their incisor teeth," which Wasson was unable to do, owing to their extremely bitter taste, and 34 pairs of the leaves were squeezed to extract their juice, then diluted with water. Wasson stated that "the effect of the leaves came sooner than would have been the case with the mushrooms, was less sweeping, and lasted a shorter time. There was not the slightest doubt about the effect, but it did not go beyond the initial effect of the mushrooms—dancing colors in elaborate, three-dimensional designs" (Wasson 1962B). The following year, Wasson published a few more details on the use of *S. divinorum*, including the proposal that the plant represented the ancient Aztec drug *pipiltzintzintli* (Wasson 1963). One further detail was the practice of crushing the leaves on a metate to extract their juice, done for "toothless" persons, whereas the customary method of ingestion was to nibble the leaves (Wasson 1962B; Wasson 1963). The practice of nibbling rolled-up "cigars" of the leaves is still common in the Mazatec zone of Oaxaca (Blosser 1991; Mayer 1977B), and sometimes a potion is made by triturating the crushed leaves in water (Valdés *et al.* 1983; Valdés *et al.* 1987A). Besides Wasson's astute suggestion that *Ska Pastora* represents the ancient Aztec *pipiltzintzintli*, it has also been conjectured that *Salvia divinorum* is depicted in the headdress of a "death god" painted on one panel of the ancient Mayan *Dresden Codex* (Emboden 1983A).

The most complete ethnographic study of *Ska Pastora* is that of Valdés and colleagues, who described the use of the juice of *S. divinorum* in doses of from 20–80 pairs of leaves—50–200 grams; 20 pairs is a "beginner's dose" (Valdés *et al.* 1983), and the Valdés group have described personal visionary experiences provoked by the drug (Valdés *et al.* 1983; Valdés *et al.* 1987A). Given this dose range, it is surprising Anita Hofmann experienced visionary effects following the ingestion of juice of only three pairs of leaves (Hofmann 1980; Hofmann 1990). In her biography, María Sabina described her use of *Ska Pastora* "when the mushrooms are not available" (Estrada 1977), and some have considered the leaves of Mary Shepherdess to be an inferior entheogen. Much of this attitude may be due to the former necessity of consuming large quantities of the fresh leaves to experience distinct effects, and the evident instability of the active principle—the juice is said to retain its activity for only one day, and the leaves may be kept fresh for a week if wrapped in other leaves (Valdés *et al.* 1983). Since salvinorin A was found to have sedative effects in mice, there was doubt whether it represented the decidedly stimulating visionary principle of the leaves. Some consider *Ska Pastora* to be the entheogen *par excellence* (Bigwood 1978), and there is a modern market for live *S. divinorum* plants, "sage of the seers" in the U.S., although an American expert on herbs stated "for me the leaves produced hardly noticeable effects... and I predict that *Salvia divinorum* will never become a popular subculture euphoric" (Foster 1984).

In 1975 I observed the smoking of freshly-dried leaves of *S. divinorum*, brought fresh from the Mazatec country, by young marijuana users in México City, a use later reported by Díaz (Díaz 1975). I personally verified that such smoking did indeed produce a short-acting effect, and this peculiar, non-Indian use of the plant still exists today (Blosser 1991; Pendell 1992; Pendell 1995). Based on several self-experiments, Díaz classified *S. divinorum*, with marijuana and *Calea zacatechichi*, as an "oneirogenic" or dream-inducing plant (see Appendix B; Mayagoitia *et al.* 1986), as "cognodysleptics"—drugs inducing "a greater vividness discernible in all sensorial spheres" (Díaz 1979). Díaz rejected Wasson's identification of *S. divinorum* as the Aztec *pipiltzintzintli*, suggesting instead that marijuana, *Cannabis sativa*, corresponded to the ancient drug (Díaz 1975; Díaz 1977; Díaz 1979). Marijuana (see below), however, is universally regarded as a post-contact introduction to the New World, and Schultes and Hofmann rightly deemed Díaz's proposal "more than highly unlikely" (Schultes & Hofmann 1980). *Salvia divinorum* is easily cultivated (Valdés *et al.* 1987A), and is in fact unknown outside of cultivation, existing only in a few isolated garden patches in the Sierra Mazateca, although its cultivation in the United States and elsewhere is becoming more and more common in recent years.

Some Mazatec Indians believe the plant is foreign to their region of the Sierra Madre Oriental (Wasson 1962B) and we know not whence it came, as no wild populations have been discovered, and the wild progenitor is unknown, although the plant was said most closely to resemble the wild Mexican species *Salvia cyanea* (Epling & Játiva-M. 1962). Indeed, the assertion of the Mazatec Indians that the plant is inactive when dried is false—the leaves are known to preserve their activity in the dried state for a considerable time. The Mazatecs seem unaware of the activity of the plant when smoked, 'though they may have learned of this recently from outsiders, some of whom have treated it as a sort of marijuana. Smoking five or six puffs of the dried leaves in rapid succession yields a mild effect similar to that of ingesting the fresh leaves, which commences at about the fifth or sixth inhalation and lasts for one to two hours. My colleagues and I have recently found that it is unnecessary to swallow the leaves or their juice, and that the most efficient absorption of the psychoptic principle(s) takes place in the mucous membranes of the mouth. As few as six leaves well-chewed and held as a quid in the mouth (in the manner in which *coca* is chewed) may lead to a visionary effect commencing in about ten minutes and lasting one to two hours (Ott 1995A; Siebert 1994; Valdés 1995). Although the two groups that first isolated salvinorin A did not report on its human pharmacology, recent studies have shown this compound to be the most potent natural entheogen known, active sublingually or *via* smoking at doses as low as 100–200 mcg (Ott 1995A; Siebert 1994). My conjecture that the plant might contain psychoactive thujones (see below) known from other *Salvia* species proved to be false—steam distillation failed to isolate thujones from fresh leaves of *S. divinorum* (Ott 1995A). In an earlier attempt at crossing two strains of this plant, seeds resulted, but these were unfortunately killed by overheating in a greenhouse before their viability could be assessed (Valdés *et al.* 1987A). A recent cross-pollination study resulted in only 3% seed set, leading to the conclusion that *Salvia divinorum* was a hybrid; although the prospective parent species remain unknown (Reisfield 1993). Our Lady Mary Shepherdess continues to attract more and more devotees, from whom she continues, nevertheless, to guard secrets (Pendell 1995).

VII. TETRAHYDROCANNABINOLS AND *CANNABIS* SPECIES

The tetrahydrocannabinols are non-nitrogenous active principles of marijuana, *Cannabis* species (Joyce & Curry 1970; Weil *et al.* 1968). They are a subgroup of the cannabinoids, monoterpene compounds, of which more than 50 have been isolated from *Cannabis* and its preparations (Mechoulam 1973; Schultes & Hofmann 1980). The principal active cannabinoid component would appear to be (–)-Δ^1-3,4-*trans*-tetrahydrocannabinol (Δ^1-THC), first isolated in 1964 (Gaoni & Mechoulam 1964), and a second active isomer, occurring in lesser amounts, (–)-Δ^6-3,4-*trans*-tetrahydrocannabinol (Δ^6-THC), was isolated in 1966 (Hively *et al.* 1966). In fresh *Cannabis* plants, these and other cannabinoids may exist principally or exclusively as their corresponding carboxylic acids (THC acids), which are converted to the active, neutral cannabinoids on drying, storage, heating, combustion, or during chemical analysis (Schultes & Hofmann 1980). In the case of Δ^1-THC, there exist two carboxylic acid forms, Δ^1-THC acid A (4′-carboxy) and Δ^1-THC acid B (6′-carboxy), of which the former is the more common (Schultes & Hofmann 1980). Whereas Δ^6-THC is normally a trace constituent, it exists in "considerable amounts" in some *Cannabis* samples (Mechoulam 1973). This varying ratio of two active isomers of THC may in part acount for varying effects in batches of *Cannabis,* and there are other chemical differences (such as the ratio of THC acids to neutral cannabinoids) which may be of importance (Mechoulam 1973). Moreover, cannabinol and cannabidiol both show neurochemical activity, and cannabidiol in particular may be responsible for depressant effects of some *Cannabis* preparations (Paton & Pertwee 1973A). The complex chemistry of *Cannabis* species has been reviewed by Schultes and Hofmann (1980) and in greater detail by Mechoulam (1973). The active dose of Δ^1-THC has been estimated to be from 3–30 mg (Mechoulam 1973; Schultes & Hofmann 1980), and the pharmacology of the tetrahydrocannabinols has been reviewed (Kettenes-van den Bosch & Salemink 1980; Mason & MacBay 1985; Nahas 1976; Starks 1977), as has the recent status of *Cannabis* research (Husain & Khan 1985). Although unstable, THC and other cannabinoids were detected in 90-year-old dried marijuana (Harvey 1990). The function of these secondary compounds in the living plant is obscure, but stress appears to cause *Cannabis* plants to produce more cannabinoids (Haney & Kutscheid 1973; Latta & Eaton 1975).

Recent study of the THC receptor in brains led to the isolation of arachidonylethanolamide, the endogenous ligand of the receptor (the natural substance in the brain which normally binds to the receptor which THC activates). The compound was named *anandamide*, from *ananda*, Sanskrit for "bliss." It is probable that this important finding constitutes the discovery of a new class of neurotransmitters which mediate relaxation (and perhaps even bliss!) in mammalian brains (Barinaga 1992; Devane *et al.* 1992).

The tetrahydrocannabinols are known only from *Cannabis* species. There is considerable taxonomic controversy as to whether there are one or more species of

Cannabis. The polytypic concept of the genus has been advanced by Schultes and co-workers (Schultes *et al.* 1974) and independently by others (Anderson 1974; Anderson 1980; Emboden 1974). These botanists conceive of three species: *Cannabis sativa* (tall and laxly-branched; Shawcross 1982), *C. indica* (short and very densely-branched) and *C. ruderalis* (very short and not or sparsely-branched), having morphological, ecological and chemical differences. Crossbreeding of so-called *Cannabis sativa* and *C. ruderalis* yielded hybrids intermediate in THC content (Beutler & Der Marderosian 1978). On the other hand, Small and Cronquist and Quimby and colleagues have championed the monotypic concept of the genus, accepting only the species *Cannabis sativa* with two subspecies, each with two varieties—*Cannabis sativa* subsp. *sativa* var. *sativa* and var. *spontanea*; and *Cannabis sativa* subsp. *indica* var. *indica* and var. *kafiristanica* (Quimby *et al.* 1973; Small 1975C; Small & Cronquist 1976; Small *et al.* 1975). The argument turns on factors other than taxonomic—Small has stated that taxonomy must "serve the needs of society"—that is, that since the anti-marijuana laws were written assuming there was one species of marijuana which is specifically mentioned in the statutes, then taxonomists should not rock the boat, suggesting there are several species, thereby undermining the strictures against marijuana (Small 1975A; Small 1975B; Small 1976)! Both sides of the argument have recently been summarized (Emboden 1981A), and recent research of *Cannabis* morphology, chemotaxonomy and genetics is uncovering new evidence which supports a polytypic concept of the genus (Hillig 1993). Regardless of how many species of *Cannabis* there are, all active strains contain the tetrahydrocannabinols, which occur throughout the plant, even in the pollen (Paris *et al.* 1975), and these are not found outside the genus.

The history of *Cannabis* is long and complex, and will be only briefly adumbrated here. Textiles made of *Cannabis* fibers (hemp) are known from China, dating back 6000 years (Li 1974B). Clear mention of the psychotropic properties of *Cannabis* is found in the herbal *Pen Ts'ao Ching*, compiled in the first century A.D. but traditionally attributed to a legendary emperor *circa* 2700 B.C. (Emboden 1972A; Li 1974A; Touw 1981). *Cannabis* has long enjoyed a ritual role in India (Aldrich 1977), and the plant was mentioned in the *Atharva Veda* as a sacred inebriant created, along with the *amrta* or the *Soma* potion (see Chapter 6) when the gods churned the oceans (Sharma 1977; Touw 1981). *Cannabis* preparations, sometimes called *vijaya* (or *bijaya*), "victory" in Sanskrit (Marglin 1985), are especially sacred to Shiva, and occur in three forms: *bhang*, a preparation of leaves used in beverages such as *bhang lassi* and taken by devout Hindus before visiting important temples, *ganja* or flower-tops and *charas* or pure resin, both of which are smoked, typically in a *chillum*, a straight pipe held vertically (Carstairs 1954; La Barre 1980B). *Cannabis* preparations figured prominently in ritual worship of the pre–Vedic Indian tribal god Jagannath in the Jagannath Mandir in Puri, Orissa (Marglin 1985). The Hindu ritual use of *Cannabis* has been summarized by Swami Agehanandra Bharati (cited in Schleiffer 1979). *Cannabis* is widely used in Asian ethnomedicine, for example as a sedative and analgesic in Thailand (Ponglux *et al.* 1987) and topically for dermatological conditions by the Khasi and Garo tribals of Meghalaya, India (Rao 1981). In Haryana, India, *C. sativa* leaves are taken orally with honey for cough (Lal & Yadav 1983), while in Nepal, leaf juice is employed as a vulnerary (Bhattarai 1992). A pangæan summary of *Cannabis* entheobotany has been compiled (Bennett *et al.* 1995).

In the western world, *Cannabis* was mentioned by Herodotus in the fifth century B.C., said to be thrown on hot rocks in sweat lodges by the mysterious Scythians, who would thereby become inebriated inhaling the vapors (Brunner 1977; Schleiffer 1979). The ancient physicians Dioscorides and Galen referred to the use of *Cannabis* in medicine, and there is evidence for its use as an inebriant in the classical world (Andrews & Vinkenoog 1967; Emboden 1972A; Escohotado 1989A). *Cannabis* came to have the greatest social and ritual importance in the Arabian world, and Marco Polo first brought the use of *Cannabis* as an inebriant in the Arabian world to the attention of Europeans in the thirteenth century. Polo described a mysterious "Old Man of the Mountain" with a fantastic garden full of delights including beautiful young women, to which he would lead drugged men, thereby convincing them that he possessed the key to paradise. Thus winning their allegience, he employed them as assassins. Tradition has it that the old man was none other than Hasan Sabah, the drug *hashish*, the sect the Hashishins, from which the modern word *assassin* derives. Rudolf Gelpke has attempted to separate fact from fiction in the elaborate legend of the "Old Man of the Mountain" (Gelpke 1966A; Gelpke 1966B). There is no doubt, however, of the importance of *Cannabis* in the Arabian world, the drug is mentioned by Scheherazade in *A Thousand Nights and One Night* (Emboden 1972A), and has been associated with the esoteric Sufi sect of "whirling dervishes" (Friedlander 1975; Gelpke 1966A; Lewin 1924). To this day, most of Europe's *hashish* comes from the Moroccan Rif, where the drug is known as *kif* (Benabud 1957; Cherniak 1979; Joseph 1973; Mikuriya 1970). The African history of *Cannabis* has been summarized (Du Toit 1980).

In 1845, J.-J. Moreau (de Tours) published the first scientific study of *Cannabis* in Paris, including psychonautic bioassays on himself and on residents of Egypt (Moreau 1845). Moreau was at the center of a Parisian literary circle called "Le Club des Hachichins," at whose meetings a confection of *hashish* called *dawamesk* was freely consumed. Two prominent members were the French poet Charles Baudelaire, whose book *Les Paradis Artificiels*, "the artificial paradises" poetically described the effects of opium and *hashish* (Baudelaire 1860) and also the French writer Théophile Gautier, who wrote two articles describing his *Cannabis* experiences (Gautier 1961; Strausbaugh & Blaise 1991). American poet Bayard Taylor's accounts of his *hashish* experiments preceded those of Baudelaire by some five years (Hayter 1968; Taylor 1961). Perhaps the most famous literary work on *Cannabis* is the classic *The Hasheesh Eater: Being Passages from the Life of a Pythagorean* by American Fitz Hugh Ludlow, who described personal experiences with large doses of tincture of *Cannabis indica* prepared by Tilden & Co. for the apothecary trade (Ludlow 1857). Another well-known experimenter with *hashish* was Walter Benjamin (Benjamin 1972). The modern literature on *Cannabis* is voluminous and will not be reviewed here.

Thanks to the literary efforts of Gautier, Taylor, Baudelaire, Ludlow and others, the use of *Cannabis* spread beyond its traditional domains, and for the past century and a half there has been use of the drug by esoteric circles in western society. In the United States, use of marijuana was associated with migrant Mexican laborers and small circles of black musicians until the 1950s, when its use by adherents to the Beat movement first brought access to the drug to other echelons of American society. *Cannabis* use became an integral feature of the "Psychedelic Age" of the sixties, and by the advent of the seventies, at least 24 million Americans had tried the drug (Grinspoon 1977; National Commission on Marihuana [*sic*] 1972). A National Institute on Drug Abuse survey in 1988 found at least 12 million regular users (12 years of age or older) of marijuana in the American population (Goldstein & Kalant 1990). Thanks to vigorous police efforts to suppress smuggling of *Cannabis* preparations into the United States, and diffusion of cultivation technology, the U.S. has become one of the world's leading producers and a leading consumer of *Cannabis*. Another result has been the breeding of super-potent strains of marijuana hitherto unknown in the world (Ott 1992A). There have been many books detailing methodology of *Cannabis* cultivation, and the first was probably *The Cultivator's Handbook of Marijuana* (Drake 1970; see also Frank & Rosenthal 1974; Irving 1978; Mountain Girl 1977). Apart from its universal use as an inebriant, marijuana has become somewhat widely used as a medicinal agent, principally for controlling the extreme nausea which is a side-effect of cancer and AIDS chemotherapy, and for reducing intraocular pressure in sufferers of glaucoma (Roffman 1982; Zinberg 1979). The marked effectiveness of smoked marijuana and orally-ingested Δ^1-THC as anti-nausea medications, and of smoked marijuana as a glaucoma treatment has forced modifications in anti-drug statutes, and exceptions permitting medicinal use of *Cannabis* in certain cases. However, the U.S. government, not wishing to give mixed signals in the case of marijuana (preferring instead to allow needless human suffering), has stopped the distribution of the drug to new cancer, AIDS or glaucoma patients. Capsules of THC (*Marinol*) will still be available (Blumenthal 1992). The legal situation, as well as the utility of marijuana in modern medicine, has been outlined in two recent books (Grinspoon & Bakalar 1993; Roffman 1982). *Cannabis* has been proposed as a therapeutic agent in the treatment of alcoholism (Mikuriya 1971; Mikuriya 1973). Marijuana's value in medicine and the sheer number of illegal users of the drug as an inebriant have been cited by groups like NORML (National Organization for the Reform of Marijuana Laws) in the U.S., which have been campaigning to rescind marijuana prohibition, as a reason to change the laws. After some gains in the seventies, including the state-wide "decriminalization" in Alaska, Oregon, California and elsewhere, a conservative backlash has prompted recriminalization in every case, and with the current hysterical attitude toward illicit drugs, marijuana has come to symbolize and epitomize the scourge of "dangerous drugs," while the once-feared entheogens like LSD and mescaline have been all but forgotten. Marijuana is without doubt one of the most widely-employed visionary drugs in the world, with hundreds of millions of users (Rubin 1975).

VIII. THUJONES AND VISIONARY *ARTEMISIA* SPECIES

Thujones are non-nitrogenous terpenoid constituents of the volatile oils of several plants, notably *Thuja occidentalis* (from which they were first isolated), *Artemisia absinthium* and other *Artemisia* species, *Salvia officinalis* or sage, and tansy, *Tanacetum vulgare*. Common synonyms are absynthol (or absinthol), salvanol (or salviol) and tanacetone (Albert-Puleo 1978). There are two stereoisomers, α-thujone (*l*-thujone) and β-thujone (*d*-thujone or *d*-isothujone). An Argentinian strain of *Artemisia absinthium* was recently found to contain 59.9% β-thujone in the essential oil, along with only 2.3% α-thujone (Sacco & Chialva 1988). The essential oil of commercial sage, normally *Salvia officinalis*, may contain from 14–67% thujones. Sometimes commercial sages consist also of *S. triloba*, however, whose essential oil is much lower in thujones, from 1–5.6% (Tucker *et al.* 1980). In southern Italy, the leaves of *S. officinalis* may be smoked with the leaves of *Datura stramonium* as an asthma remedy (De Feo *et al.* 1992). *S. officinalis*, together with *S. lyrata*, was used as a stimulant by North American Cherokee Indians (Hamel & Chiltoskey 1975) while the Hopi Indians made a parallel ludible use of *S. carnosa* (Whiting 1939).

The thujones are best known as principles of oil of wormwood, the essential oil of *Artemisia absinthium*, component of the nineteenth century alcoholic beverages called *absinthe* (Albert-Puleo 1978; Emboden 1983B; Montagne & Vogt 1982; Vogt 1981). Other alcoholic beverages have also been prepared with thujone-containing plants, including *Salvia*- and *Artemisia*-containing ales and beers. Vermouth (*Wermut* is the German name for wormwood, as well as for absinthe and vermouth) traditionally contains small amounts of oil of wormwood (Albert-Puleo 1978). Absinthe was prepared by distilling alcohol over mashed leaves of wormwood, and other common ingredients were *Angelica* root, *Acorus calamus* rhizome (which may contain the psychoactive asarones; see above), cinnamon, fennel seed, star anise (both of which contain anethole, another potentially psychoactive compound; Albert-Puleo 1980) and other plants. The characteristic and much-desired green color of the liqueur, which was supposed to whiten when diluted with water, was sometimes artificially enhanced by addition of indigo and other plants, or toxic metal salts like copper sulfate and antimony chloride (Vogt 1981). In spite of this plethora of ingredients and adulterants, the principal active constituents of absinthe seem to have been alcohol and thujones (Vogt 1981). Owing to structural similarities, it has been proposed that the psychoactive effects of thujones and tetrahydrocannabinols from marijuana (see above) involve binding to the same receptor in the brain (Del Castillo *et al.* 1975; Rice & Wilson 1976), and acute inebriation with absinthe is somewhat similar to *Cannabis* inebriation (Vogt 1981). The gene coding for the THC receptor has recently been cloned, thus it will soon be possible to test this hypothesis (Marx 1990). However, the recent isolation of anandamide, an endogenous ligand of the THC receptor (Barinaga 1992; Devane *et al.* 1992) suggests that it is the hydrocarbon side-chain of THC (which anandamide and THC possess, but thujones lack) that binds to the receptor, making improbable the theory that thujones also bind to this THC receptor (although there may be others).

Absinthe was typically taken in the evenings in Parisian sidewalk *cafés*, and the liqueur was usually placed in a glass, then diluted with some five parts of water which were dripped into the liqueur over a lump of sugar held in a perforated spoon (Vogt 1981). Absinthe use was at first confined to members of the lower classes, but by the mid-nineteenth century its use became fashionable, associated with the intelligentsia and artists, only to become again a working-class drink by the first decade of this century (Conrad 1988; Miller & Koral 1995). Cocaine has experienced a similar trajectory (Grinspoon & Bakalar 1976). Absinthe was once produced in huge amounts, with French production rising to 36 million liters annually in 1910 (Conrad 1988), and in 1878, eight million liters were imported into the United

States (Albert-Puleo 1978). When it became increasingly obvious that the drink was neurotoxic, leading to a syndrome called *absinthism*, it was banned, first in Belgium in 1905, then in Switzerland in 1907, later in the United States in 1912, and finally in France in 1915 (Conrad 1988; Vogt 1981). This prohibition of absinthe was perhaps the prototype for modern legal "control" of drugs. Today only imitation absinthe, called *Pernod*, is available—it contains no thujones, although Spanish *absenta* was never prohibited and "bootleg" absinthe continues to be made in the Val-de-Travers region of Switzerland (Conrad 1988). Despite the banning of wormwood in the United States, sage, which may contain up to 67% thujones in its essential oil, remains on the U.S. Food and Drug Administration's GRAS (Generally Recognized As safe) list, and may be used as a food additive (Tucker *et al.* 1980). There appears to be some modern American interest in absinthe-like beverages, and two American poets, Gary Snyder and Dale Pendell, have composed poems to "Artemisia," as Walt Whitman did to "Calamus" before them (Pendell 1992; Pendell 1995). It is commonly assumed that the thujones were the neurotoxic principles of absinthe, although alcohol also is a potent neurotoxin (absinthe contained from 68–85% alcohol) and significant quantities of copper and antimony salts used as adulterants (particularly in cheap imitation absinthe for the poorer classes) may have been present and responsible for the neurotoxicity. French writer J.-K. Huysmans compared the taste of such *ersatz* absinthe to that of a "metal button slowly sucked" (Conrad 1988). While large doses of injected thujones are unquestionably toxic, modern toxicological studies of thujones, in the quantities present in absinthe, without the copper and antimony adulterants, are needed before concluding that the neurotoxicity associated with absinthism was a consequence of the thujone content. I suspect the copper and antimony salts, as well as the unusually high alcohol content, had more to do with absinthe toxicity than the thujone content. Non-thujone essential oils commonly present in absinthe have also been shown to have convulsant properties and are probably neurotoxic (Millet *et al.* 1980).

Traditionally used medicinally as an anthelmintic, hence the name, "wormwood" has also found application as a uterotonic in ethnogynecology (Albert-Puleo 1978). The drug was known in ancient Greek, Indian and Arab medicine (Fleurentin *et al.* 1983). In India, the drug has been used chiefly as a tonic and stimulant, and it is known to be effective for chronic fevers, and has recently been shown to possess antimalarial activity (Zafar *et al.* 1990), perhaps justifying the French military use of absinthe against fevers in the 1840 Algerian war... strictly for medicinal purposes, of course... (Conrad 1988). *Artemisia absinthium* is indeed used as an antimalarial in traditional Greek ethnomedicine (Malamas & Marselos 1992). A related thujone-containing species, *Artemisia tilesii*, was used traditionally by Alaskan Eskimos to treat skin infections and joint pain of arthritis (Overfield *et al.* 1980), and is still so used in Alaska (Holloway & Alexander 1990). *Artemisia vulgaris* is used as an antipyretic in traditional Thai phytomedicine (Ponglux *et al.* 1987). Extracts of *A. absinthium* have been shown to have antipyretic effects similar in potency to aspirin (Khattack *et al.* 1985). Another thujone-containing species, *Artemisia caerulescens* subsp. *gallica* is used traditionally in Spain as an analgesic, anti-inflammatory and antipyretic, effects which have been verified in pharmacological tests (Morán *et al.* 1989A). The essential oil of this species was also shown to have antimicrobial effects (Morán *et al.* 1989B). Wormwood tea, tincture and extracts are still employed in modern phytotherapy to treat digestive problems and as an anthelmintic (Weiss 1988). Alaskan use of *A. frigida* as a decongestant in steam baths has been reported (Holloway & Alexander 1990), and Mexican-Americans in Colorado chew leaves of this species against stomachache (Bye & Linares 1986).

At least seven *Artemisia* species were employed as traditional analgesics by North American Indians, in decoctions both for internal and external use (Moerman 1986). This analgesic use probably involved volatile thujones—the Zuni smoked or inhaled steam of *A. carruthii* to effect analgesia (Stevenson 1915), while the Cheyenne Indians snuffed crushed leaves of *A. ludoviciana* to treat headaches (Hart 1981; Kindscher 1992). Similarly, the Lahu of Thailand snuff leaves of *A. dubia* to treat headaches and nosebleed (Anderson 1986B), whereas in Nepal juice of this plant is placed on the forehead in treatment of headaches (Joshi & Edington 1990). Some *Artemisia* species were used traditionally as stimulants, and again the volatile thujones were probably involved. Fumes of leaves and flowers of *A. frigida* were inhaled as a stimulant by Potowatomi Indians (Smith 1933), while Thompson Indians used bruised leaves of *A. tridentata* as a stimulating inhalant (Steedman 1928). *Artemisia indica* is used in northeast India as an analgesic—leaves and branches are spread out on a bed to treat body pain (Gangwar & Ramakrishnan 1990), while in Nepal a child with dysentery may be seated over heated plants of this species (Manandhar 1991). Similarly, North American Thompson Indians treated body pains and rheumatism with *A. dracunculus*—a 15 cm thick layer of plants was spread on a bed of red-hot rocks covered with a layer of sand, on which the patient would lie naked, to be covered with a blanket (Turner *et al.* 1990).

Three *Artemisia* species—*A. abrotanum*, *A. cina* and *A. vulgaris*—are known traditionally in Germany as *Hexenkraut*, "witches' herb" (De Vries 1991A; Storl 1996). *Artemisia nilagirica* leaves are reportedly smoked "for hallucination" by the Oraons of West Bengal state, India (Pal & Jain 1989). The volatile oil of the above-ground parts of this species contains α- and β-thujone (Uniyal *et al.* 1985), which probably accounts for the psychoactive effects following smoking. I recently verified by self-experiment that *A. absinthium* leaves are also psychotropic when smoked (Ott, unpublished laboratory notes). Leaf decoctions of *A. nilagirica* are used to treat "brain diseases" in Meghalaya, India (Neogi *et al.* 1989). Infusions of leaf and stem of *A. copa* are said to be "probably hallucinogenic" for users in northern Chile (Aldunate *et al.* 1983). The ancient Aztecs used *Artemisia mexicana* as an inebriant, under the name *itzauhyatl*. The Spaniards called this plant *estaphiate* or *ajenjo* (Spanish for *A. absinthium*) and Jacinto de la Serna spoke of this drug in the same breath as *péyotl* and *ololiuhqui* (De la Serna 1953; Garza 1990). The ancient Aztecs also made medicinal use of *itzauhyatl* (Ortíz de Montellano 1975; Ortíz de Montellano 1990) and under the name *estafiate* or *istafiate*, *A. ludoviciana* subsp. *mexicana* is still an ethnomedicine of Tarahumara Indians and urban Mexicans (Bye 1986A).

APPENDIX B
Putative Entheogenic Species

This appendix contains three annotated lists of putative entheogenic species (with some animals included) mentioned in the recent literature and in well-known publications such as *The Botany and Chemistry of Hallucinogens* (Schultes & Hofmann 1980) and popular books like *Plants of the Gods* (Schultes & Hofmann 1979) and *Narcotic Plants* (Emboden 1979). Some of these are cited within the text, where additional putative entheogenic species may also be found (such as the list of suspected psilocybine-containing mushrooms appended to Table 4, and the list of *ayahuasca*-additive plants in Table 3). For convenience and in the interest of clarity, I have grouped all these putative entheogenic organisms under three headings: I. Probable—species with well-documented phytochemistry or entheogenic use, or with suggestive ethnomedicinal use combined with taxonomic affinity to species containing visionary compounds; II. Possible—entities which have been reported in the literature to be vision-inducing but for which the evidence is slight and for which corroborative chemical evidence is lacking or inconclusive; and III. Doubtful—species reported to be possibly entheogenic in the literature, for which the evidence is suspect, either because the original reports were highly speculative or because self-experiments or chemical study by capable scientists have not resulted in psychoptic effects or the detection of entheogenic compounds. The final category includes a number of cacti which do contain mescaline, a known entheogenic compound, but in such minuscule quantities as to be biologically insignificant (although we cannot rule out the possiblity that other strains of these species with pharmacologically-significant concentrations of mescaline might one day be found). In every case, references are made in the annotations to the text (in parentheses after the botanical name—with the chapter number followed by references to sections or footnotes) and to the scientific literature in the bibliography. As always, other ethnomedicinal uses of these plants are cited, placing them in their broader ethnobotanical context.

I. PROBABLE

Ariocarpus fissuratus; A. agavoides; A. kotschoubeyanus; A. scapharostrus; A. trigonus (1, Note 7): *A. fissuratus* is considered to be a relative of *híkuli* or *péyotl* by the Tarahumara, and is considered by these Indians to produce entheogenic effects (Bye 1979A). Several phenethylamines, but not mescaline, are known from this species (Norquist & McLaughlin 1970). The evidence is less convincing for the other *Ariocarpus* species, and *A. retusus* has been called a "false peyote," and is said to produce noxious effects (Bruhn & Bruhn 1973; Furst 1971; Schultes & Hofmann 1980).

Armatocereus laetus: Under the name *pishicol*, Davis reported this "psychoactive cactus" in a paper on "sacred plants of the *San Pedro* cult" (Davis 1983B).

Balansia claviceps; B. cyperi; B. epichloë (2, Note 4): Shown to produce "several unidentified ergot alkaloids" (Plowman *et al.* 1990), this parasitic fungus is a relative of ergot and commonly infests a species of *Cyperus* used by the Sharanahua Indians of Amazonia as an *ayahuasca* additive (Schultes & Raffauf 1990; see Chapter 4 "Miscellaneous Admixtures"). Among the Siona and Secoya of Ecuador, host plant *Cyperus prolixus* is used as an aid to parturition, which may involve the uterotonic ergoline alkaloids of *Balansia cyperi* (Vickers & Plowman 1984). Similarly, African use of a *Cyperus* species in ethnogynecology may point to infestation by *Balansia cyperi* or another allied ergot-alkaloid-containing mushroom (Veale *et al.* 1992). *Balansia claviceps* and *B. epichloë* likewise contain psychoactive ergoline alkaloids (Porter 1995; Porter *et al.* 1979).

***Bufo alvarius* Girard; *B. marinus* L.** (3, "The Riddle of the Toad"): The Sonoran Desert *B. alvarius* has been shown to produce a number of tryptamines in its skin and cutaneous glands (Deulofeu & Rúveda 1971). The highest concentrations found were of 5-MethOxy-DiMethylTryptamine (5-MeO-DMT, also known as *O*-methylbufotenine), up to 150 mg *per* gram of dried gland tissue; with much lower amounts of bufotenine present (only 5 mg *per* gram of dried gland tissue; Erspamer *et al.* 1965; Erspamer *et al.* 1967). As discussed in Chapter 3, 5-MeO-DMT (one of the principal visionary ingredients of snuffs made both from *Anadenanthera* and *Virola* species) is psychoptic when smoked or injected, and has about four times the potency of DMT (Shulgin 1970; Shulgin in De Smet 1983). Recently there has been entheogenic use of *Bufo alvarius* venom, squeezed out of the parotoid glands of these toads, and a "Church of the Toad of Light" has been formed, with such *B. alvarius* venom as the sacrament (Blosser 1991; Davis & Weil 1992; Krajick 1992;

Montgomery 1990; Most 1984; Weil & Davis 1994). Although the primary component, 5-MeO-DMT, remains legal, trace content of bufotenine, which is listed on Schedule I with DMT, DET, psilocine, LSD, mescaline, *etc.*, makes this toad-venom sacrament a controlled substance, involved in a recent arrest (Boire 1994). While Knab once reported the preparation in Veracruz, México, of a toad venom inebriant based "probably" on *Bufo marinus* (Knab 1974), this species was found to be devoid of 5-MeO-DMT, although it did contain dehydrobufotenine and bufothionine (Erspamer *et al.* 1967). Indeed Knab's heart-throbbing experience following ingestion of the potion was hardly psychoptic. Owing to distortions in the news media, there has arisen the bizarre phenomenon of "toad licking," in some cases involving *B. marinus*, which has resulted in cases of severe poisoning (Pulling 1990). Nevertheless, the venom of this species may be psychoactive when smoked, as is the venom of *B. alvarius*. There was a recent case in which venom of *B. marinus* was smoked (the subject, having heard that *B. alvarius* venom was psychoactive when so used, assumed either that he was dealing with the latter species or that any species of toad was similarly active), leading to psychotropic effects (Blosser 1991). *One should not lick any species of toad, nor ingest toad venoms orally!* This *caveat* applies also to frogs, some tropical species of which produce potent toxins in their skins (Daly & Myers 1973), and venoms scraped from *Phyllobates* frog skins are used by Emberá Indians and other groups as dart poisons (Myers *et al.* 1978). The Amahuaca Indians of Perú rub toad or frog (both *Phyllobates* and *Dendrobates*) venoms into self-inflicted burns for reputed psychoactive effects (Carneiro 1970), and Matsés Indians likewise rub venom of the poisonous frog *Phyllomedusa bicolor* into burns (Gorman 1993). Following drastic and life-threatening effects and a prolonged sedation, this is said to enhance the senses and strength as an aid in hunting, and visionary effects have been reported (Amato 1992). A potent analgesic, epibatidine, has been isolated from the venom of *Epipedobates tricolor* of Ecuador (Bradley 1993). On the other hand, oral ingestion of venoms from *any* species of *Bufo*, *Dendrobates*, *Phyllobates*, *Phyllomedusa* or other toxic amphibian is likely to be fatal or life-threatening. DMT has been found also in marine creatures, such as the gorgonian *Paramuricea chamaeleon* (Cimino & De Stefano 1978), and also in human cerebrospinal fluid (Corbett *et al.* 1978).

Cordyceps capitata; C. ophioglossoides (2, Note 4): These parasitic fungi are relatives of ergot reportedly used in mushroom curing rituals in México (Guzmán 1958; Heim 1957A). Although preliminary chemical studies found the former species to be devoid of psilocybine and psilocine, it was found to contain traces of a "different indolic substance" (Heim & Wasson 1958) which, alas, has not yet been identified.

Coriaria thymifolia: Under the name *shanshi*, this plant is reportedly used for its visionary effects in Ecuador (Naranjo 1969; Schultes & Hofmann 1980). Preliminary chemical studies suggested the presence of a pharmacologically-active glycoside (Naranjo & Naranjo 1961), and the fruits of this plant are known to have provoked accidental poisonings of children (Lewis & Elvin-Lewis 1977). Known by the name *piñan*, these fruits are said to be intoxicating to children if indulged in excessively (Joyal 1987). An "epidemic" of honey poisoning in New Zealand in 1945 was eventually traced to honey made from the honeydew or excrement of a leaf-hopper, *Scolypopa australis* Walker, which had fed on the leaves of the *tutu*, *Coriaria arborea* (Harris & Filmer 1947; Palmer-Jones & White 1949). The toxic agent in the honey, originally called "mellitoxin," was found to be identical to hyenanchin (or hyaenanchin), first isolated from *Hyaenanche globosa*. A second related toxin, tutin, was later found in the honeys and in *C. arborea* (Clinch & Turner 1968; Palmer-Jones 1965; Turner & Clinch 1968). Evidently, tutin from the leaves of *C. arborea* was transformed to hyenanchin during digestion by the leaf-hopper. Since poisoning by the tutin-containing *C. ruscifolia* and by the *C. arborea* honeys involves giddiness, delirium and excitement, it is possible that the active principle of the Ecuadorian *C. thymifolia* may be tutin or hyenanchin, or another related picrotoxin-like substance. *Coriaria atropurpurea* has been classified as "hallucinogenic" in a Mexican catalogue of medicinal plants (Díaz 1976), and has been suggested to represent the Aztec inebriant *tlacopétatl* (Díaz 1979). The chemistry of this species is obscure.

Desfontainia spinosa: This species and its variety *hookeri* are reportedly used as inebriants in Colombia (Schultes 1977c), Chile (Houghton & Manby 1985; Mariani Ramírez 1965; Schultes & Raffauf 1992) and Ecuador (Vickers & Plowman 1984). As *borrachero de páramo*, this plant is used in Colombia as a tea for shamanic diagnosis (Schultes & Hofmann 1980). Known as *chapico*, *michai blanco*, *taique* or *trautrau* in Chile, it is presently being grown as an ornamental in the U.S. (Andoh 1986).

Dictyoloma incanescens: The bark of this rutaceous (the citrus family) species was found to contain low concentrations of 5-MethOxy-DiMethylTryptamine (5-MeO-DMT), with 0.04% (expressed as the picrate salt) obtained by isolation (Pachter *et al.* 1959). There is no evidence of shamanic use of this plant, and the entheogenic 5-MeO-DMT is not active orally in any case (see Chapter 3, "Effects of Entheogenic Tryptamines" and entry below for *Vepris ampody*, mentioning other citrus species).

Dictyophora phalloidea (2, Note 4): This mushroom, which has not been studied chemically, is consumed ritually along with psilocybian *Psilocybe mexicana* by the Chinantec Indians of Oaxaca, México (Heim & Wasson 1958; Wasson 1959A). Roger Heim noted that the mushroom was likewise used in "sorcery" in Thailand, but did not elaborate on this intriguing comment (Heim & Wasson 1958). In a subsequent book, Heim wrote obscurely that *D. phalloidea* was used in Thailand for "criminal poisonings," mentioning also that it was used in "sorcery" by the Tanala and Betsimisaraka of Madagascar, offering no details (Heim 1978). Clearly, more information about this intriguing mushroom is needed.

Echinocereus merkeri; E. salm-dyckianus; E. triglochidiatus (1, Note 7): *E. salm-dyckianus* and *E. triglochidiatus* are considered to be "kinds" of *péyotl* by Mexican Tarahumara Indians (Bye 1975; Bye 1979A), and *E. merkeri* has been reported to contain phenethylamine alkaloids (Agurell 1969B; Bruhn & Bruhn 1973). In his paper on Tarahumara entheogens, Bye mentioned that the entheogenic tryptamine 5-MethOxy-DiMethylTryptamine (5-MeO-DMT) had been detected in *E. triglochidiatus*, which could make this species a potential entheogen, although the compound is not active orally, and the report awaits confirmation (Bye 1979A; McLaughlin 1979).

Ipomoea crassicaulis; I. involucrata; I. littoralis; I. medium; I. pes-caprae (Table 2, Notes 6–8): *Ipomoea crassicaulis* and *I. pes-caprae* are used ethnomedicinally as ecbolics, which would suggest content of ergoline alkaloids found in many other species of the genus (Dagar & Dagar 1991; Zamora-Martínez & Nieto de Pascual Pola 1992). Leaf juice of *I. involucrata* is used as a hemostatic in Sierra Leone, West Africa (MacFoy & Sama 1983), and the Fang of Central Africa consider the juice of whole plants to be a stimulant and "medico-magic" therapy in cases of bewitchment (Akendengué 1992). These uses also suggest content of ergoline alkaloids. Similarly, flowers of *I. littoralis* have been used as a hemostatic, and leaves as a therapy for postpartum pain and as a pediatric anticonvulsant, again suggesting content of ergoline alkaloids which might be psychoactive (Austin 1991; Whistler 1992). In Madagascar, decoctions of *I. medium* leaves likewise are used as a pediatric anti-convulsant, once again pointing to the possible content of ergoline alkaloids in this species (Beaujard 1988).

Mammillaria craigii; M. grahamii* var. *oliviae; M. heyderi; M. longimamma; M. pectinifera; M. senilis (1, Note 7): The Tarahumara Indians reportedly use *M. craigii* as an entheogen, under the name *wíchuri* or *peyote de San Pedro* (Bye 1979A). Other *Mammillaria* species may be called *híkuri* or *peyotillo*, suggesting psychotropic properties. *M. heyderi* and other species contain some phenethylamine alkaloids also found in *Ariocarpus fissuratus* (Bruhn & Bruhn 1973; West & McLaughlin 1973).

Mimosa hostilis **[*M. tenuiflora*]; *M. nigra; M. pudica; M. scabrella; M. verrucosa*** (3, "More DMT Entheogens"): A *Mimosa* species once smoked as a "marijuana substitute" by Nicaraguans is known as *dormilona*, a name commonly applied to *M. pudica* in México and Guatemala (Bigwood 1987; Girón *et al.* 1991; Lazos Chavero & Álvarez-Buylla Roces 1988). This species is used in both the Americas and Asia as a soporific or tranquilizer (Arnason *et al.* 1980; Nguyen & Do 1991), and as a pediatric anticonvulsant in Madagascar (Beaujard 1988). *M. hostilis* and *M. verrucosa* roots were the basis of the Brasilian inebriating drink *vinho da jurema*, and *M. hostilis* is known to contain DMT (Pachter *et al.* 1959; Smith 1977). Although use of *vinho da jurema* has been said to be extinct (Schultes & Hofmann 1980), it yet continues in northeastern Brasil (Da Mota 1987). Since DMT is not active orally (Turner & Merlis 1959), the potion may also contain some MAO-inhibitor (see Chapter 4). Thus far, entheogenic tryptamines are unknown from *M. pudica*, which was used as a soporific drug by the Aztecs, under the name *pinahuihuitztli* (Garza 1990). Infusions of whole *M. pudica* are used ethnomedicinally in the Caribbean against dysentery (Seaforth 1991). The Mexican ethnomedicine *tepescohuite*, *M. tenuiflora* [*M. hostilis*] bark, was shown to contain DMT (Meckes-Lozoya *et al.* 1990), as was bark of Brasilian ethnomedicine *M. scabrella* (De Moraes *et al.* 1990). *M. albida*, used in ethnogynecology by Mexican Tzotzil Indians (Velázquez Díaz 1992), may contain tryptamines, and *M. tenuiflora* roots may also contain β-carbolines.

Mucuna pruriens: There is no evidence of traditional use of this plant as an inebriant, but phytochemical research has shown it contains DMT, DMT-*N*-oxide, 5-MeO-DMT and bufotenine, and that an alkaloid-enriched extract of the plant was pharmacologically-active in rats (Bhattacharya *et al.* 1971; Schultes & Hofmann 1980). It remains to be seen whether the whole plant is visionary in human beings at ordinary doses. This plant is reportedly used as an aphrodisiac and nerve tonic in Brasil (Elisabetsky *et al.* 1992), as an aphrodisiac by the Cuna Indians of Panamá (Duke 1975), and as a remedy for "disorders of the nervous system" in Nepalese ethnomedicine (Joshi & Edington 1990). *Mucuna pruriens* is used as an anthelmintic in tropical West African ethnomedicine (Oliver-Bever 1983), and in the Caribbean is considered to be a poisonous plant (Seaforth 1991). In traditional Indian ethnomedicine, the seeds of this plant are employed as an abortifacient (Nath *et al.* 1992) and aphrodisiac (Schultes & Hofmann 1979), whereas among the Akha of Thailand the leaves and stems are made into a poultice for treating burns (Anderson 1986A).

Pandanus: The fruit of an unidentified species of *Pandanus* is reportedly used as an entheogen in New Guinea (Hyndman 1984; Sinclair 1957; Stone 1984). The nuts of an unidentified *Pandanus* species have been found to contain DMT (Culvenor 1984; Hyndman 1984; Schultes & Hofmann 1980). *Pandanus antaresensis* is used ethnomedicinally in New Guinea as an analgesic and as an antipyretic (Hyndman 1984).

Scirpus (2, Note 4): Under the name *bakánoa*, Tarahumara Indians of México consider this species to be a powerful visionary medicine (Bye 1979A). Chemical studies are wanting (Schultes & Hofmann 1980). Various species of *Scirpus* were used ethnomedicinally by North American tribes, often as ritual emetics (Moerman 1986).

Tabernaemontana coffeoides; T. crassa; T. dichotoma; T. muricata; T. sananho (4, "Miscellaneous Admixtures"; Appendix A, "Ibogaine, Tabernanthine and Voacangine"): Like many members of the Apocynaceae, these species contain stimulating and potentially entheogenic ibogane alkaloids. *T. coffeoides* contains voacangine, among other alkaloids, and is used as a stimulant in Madagascar (Van Beek *et al.* 1984), as is the chemically-obscure species *T. muricata* in Colombia (Schultes 1979A). *T. dichotoma* is known in India as a deliriant drug, and contains alkaloids, including an isomer of iboxygaine (Van Beek *et al.* 1984). Under the name *sananho*, a *Tabernaemontana* species is used as an *ayahuasca* additive (Schultes & Hofmann 1979), and under the same name a species of *Tabernaemontana* is used as an ingredient of South American dart poisons (Bisset 1992A). This might represent *T. sananho*, a species reported to be strongly-positive for alkaloids in field tests (Schultes 1985A) and employed under the name *tsicta* as a hunting aid in Ecuador. Bark extracts of *tsicta* are given both to human hunters and their dogs, to sharpen their senses for hunting, after weathering the initial, disagreeable effects (Miller 1993).

Tagetes erecta; T. lucida (5, Note 3, Appendix A, "Nicotine"): Contemporary Huichol Indians of México prepare a psychoactive smoking mixture called *ye-tumutsáli* from *T. lucida* plus *Nicotiana rustica* (Díaz 1975; Siegel *et al.* 1977). There is evidence that this plant, also called *pericón* and known to the ancient Aztecs as *yyahutli* (also spelled *yahutli* or *yauhtli*), is entheogenic (Elferink 1988; Lozoya 1990), but since it is today smoked with the potent entheogen *N. rustica*, sometimes accompanied by ingestion of *péyotl*, any reported visionary effects are potentially attributable to these known inebriants. Further studies are wanting. *Tagetes lucida* is also used in ethnomedicine by the Tarahumara Indians and by urban Mexicans (Bye 1986A), and the ancient Aztecs likewise made various medicinal uses of the plant (Ortíz de Montellano 1990). Mayan shamans employed *T. lucida* as an inebriant, under the name *xpuhuc* in Yucatecan Maya and *yia* in Quiché (Garza 1990). *Tagetes erecta*, the famous *zempoalxóchitl* of México, has been reportedly used as a sacred inebriant by the Mixe Indians of Oaxaca (Lipp 1990), who make hot-water infusions of nine flowers for divinatory purposes (Lipp 1991). This species is used as a malaria remedy in Madagascar (Rasoanaivo *et al.* 1992). *Tagetes campanulata*, *T. multiflora* and *T. pusilla* are used as gastrointestinal remedies in Argentinian ethnomedicine (Gilberti 1983), as is *T. minuta* in Paraguay (Schmeda-Hirschmann & Bordas 1990).

Tanaecium nocturnum: A psychoactive snuff called *koribo* is prepared by Brasilian Paumarí Indians from roasted, pulverized leaves of this plant with tobacco (Prance *et al.* 1977). Tea of the root-bark is also psychoactive, apparently sedative (Schultes & Hofmann 1980). It has been reported that merely *smelling* the plant has provoked psychoactive effects in researchers (Schultes & Hofmann 1980). The chemistry of this intriguing drug is obscure.

Teliostachya lanceolata* var. *crispa (4, "Miscellaneous Admixtures"): The leaves of this plant are used to make an entheogenic infusion by the Kokama Indians of Perú, with about ten leaves representing a dose (Schultes & Raffauf 1990). Branches of the plant are also used as an *ayahuasca* admixture (Schultes 1972C). There has been little chemical work done on this plant, but McKenna found leaves to be devoid of alkaloids (McKenna *et al.* 1984A). This species is reportedly used as a remedy for stomachache by the Siona and Secoya of Ecuador (Vickers & Plowman 1984).

Tetrapterys methystica; T. mucronata (4, "Entheogenic Potions of Amazonia"): These malpighiaceous shrubs are used by Makú Indians of Brasil and Karapaná Indians of Colombia in the preparation of *ayahuasca*-like potions, and may represent the other "kind" of *caapi* mentioned both by Spruce and Koch-Grünberg (Schultes 1954A; Schultes & Raffauf 1990). Chemical studies are lacking. Gates has recently reclassified *Tetrapterys methystica* as *T. styloptera* (Gates 1986).

Vepris ampody: Leaves and branches of this rutaceous plant were recently shown to be rich in *N,N*-DiMethylTryptamine (DMT). Up to 0.22% DMT has been found in this plant, making it one of the richer known sources of this valuable compound (Kan-Fan *et al.* 1970). Two other rutaceous species, *Limonia acidissima* and *Zan-*

thoxylum arborescens are known to contain DMT (Abu-Zarga 1986; Grina *et al.* 1982). The rutaceous species *Dictyoloma incanescens* (see above) contains small amounts of 5-MeO-DMT in the bark (Pachter *et al.* 1959). Mexican Tzotzil Indians use an extract of *Casimiroa edulis* bark as an ecbolic, and this rutaceous species might also contain DMT (Velázquez Díaz 1992). It was described as a soporific drug by both Sahagún and Hernández, and is today known as *zapote dormilón* and *zapote borracho* ("sleepy sapodilla" or "drunken sapodilla"; Díaz 1976; Garza 1990). Several tryptamine-containing *Mimosa* species are also used ethnomedicinally as soporifics (see entry above and Chapter 3).

II. POSSIBLE

Alchornea castanaefolia; A. floribunda; A. hirtella (4, "Miscellaneous Admixtures"; Appendix A): *A. castanaefolia* has been reported as an *ayahuasca* additive in Perú (Luna 1984A; Luna 1984B), and *A. floribunda* as an additive to African *eboka* potions (Samorini 1993B; Schultes & Hofmann 1980). An early report of indole alkaloid yohimbine in *A. floribunda* (Paris & Goutarel 1958) was not confirmed in a later study (Raymond-Hamet & Goutarel 1965). Alchorneine, isoalchorneine and alchorneinone, novel pyrimidine and imidazole derivatives, have been isolated from roots and leaves of *A. floribunda* and *A. hirtella* (De Smet 1996; Khuong-Huu *et al.* 1972). These are of unknown psychoactivity, but these plants are used in Africa as stimulants and inebriants. Pharmacological tests showed extracts of *A. castanaefolia* had anti-fungal, but not anti-viral nor anti-microbial activity (MacRae *et al.* 1988).

Alternanthera lehmannii (4, "Miscellaneous Admixtures"): This plant is used by Ingano Indians of Colombia as an *ayahuasca* additive, but is of unknown chemistry and pharmacology (Schultes & Hofmann 1980; Schultes & Raffauf 1990).

Amaranthus spinosus: The Lodha of West Bengal, India were recently reported to smoke the powdered, dried root of this plant "for hallucination." Furthermore, "eating paste of roots can cause temporary insanity" (Pal & Jain 1989). This plant was used in North American Cherokee Indian ethnogynecology, and also as a mysterious "ceremonial medicine" (Hamel & Chiltoskey 1975; Moerman 1986).

Arctostaphylos alpina; A. uva-ursi: Ojibway or Ahnishinaubeg Indians smoked the leaves of both of these ericaceous species "to cause intoxication" (Reagan 1928).

Leaves of *A. uva-ursi* were smoked as a "narcotic" by Kwakiutl Indians (Turner & Bell 1973), who made similar use of leaves of the ericaceous *Ledum groenlandicum* or "Labrador tea" (Turner & Bell 1973). Nitinaht Indians called *A. uva-ursi kinnikinnick*, from an Algonquian term for "that which is mixed," as this plant, also known as *bearberry*, was a common ingredient of smoking mixtures (Turner *et al.* 1983), and indeed was said to be "the principal smoking mixture of the Northwest" Indians (Gunther 1981). Leaves of *Taxus brevifolia*, source of the anti-cancer drug taxol and other taxanes (Miller 1980), were sometimes smoked alone or with *A. uva-ursi* by Pacific Northwest Indians, and were "said to make a person dizzy" (Hartzell 1991); Klallam Indians also used *T. brevifolia* as an analgesic (Moerman 1986). *Kinnikinnick* also refers to another plant used in smoking mixtures, *Cornus stolonifera* or "western red-osier dogwood," in the Cornaceae family (Turner *et al.* 1983), this was smoked by Plains Indians for an effect "similar to opium" (Chamberlin 1911; Hart 1976), and bark decoctions were used by North Carrier Indians as a stimulant (Smith 1929). Tarahumara Indians of México make a wine of *Arctostaphylos pundens* (Feest 1983). *A. uva-ursi* contains arbutin, an effective urinary antiseptic (Tyler 1987), and is commonly used in contemporary phytomedicine, often as a diuretic (Weiss 1988). The Ericaceae or heath family, to which belong *Azalea* and *Rhododendron* species, is a source of toxic honeys, some of which provoke inebriation. The most famous case of honey poisoning involved an entire army, described in the fourth century B.C. *Anabasis* of Xenophon (cited in Schleiffer 1979). The toxic honey was from *Azalea pontica*, also called *Rhododendron ponticum* and *Heraclea pontica* (Thresh 1887). Toxic agents of these honeys are glucosides called andromedotoxins or grayanotoxins (Krause 1926; Plugge 1891; Wood *et al.* 1954). Toxic honeys result from *Ledum palustre*, used as an inebriant in Siberia (Brekhman & Sam 1967), due to another toxic glucoside, ericolin, which might be present in the inebriating *L. groenlandicum* of the Kwakiutl (Palmer-Jones 1965). Toxic glucosides from ericaceous honeys may be active principles of the inebriating *kinnikinnicks*. Visionary tropane alkaloids sequestered by bees from nectar of *Atropa belladonna* have also provoked human psychoptic effects following ingestion of toxic honeys (Hazslinszky 1956).

Boophane disticha: The bulb of this amaryllidaceous arrow-poison plant is used as an inebriant in initiatory ceremonies by the Basuto people of South Africa. These bulbs contain 0.31% of a mix of eleven alkaloids of unknown activity, mainly buphanidrine, undulatine, buphanisine, buphanamine and nerbowdine (De Smet 1996).

Caesalpinia sepiaria: As *Yun-shih*, this Chinese vine is said to provoke visions and "communication with spirits" (Li 1978; Schultes & Hofmann 1980), and is said to contain "an alkaloid of unknown structure" (Schultes & Hofmann 1979). *Caesalpinia echinata* has been reported as an *ayahuasca* admixture (Luna 1984A).

Callaeum antifebrile (4, "Entheogenic Potions of Amazonia"; 4, "Chacruna and Chagropanga") = *Cabi paraensis*; *Mascagnia psilophylla* var. *antifebrilis*: See entry under *Mascagnia psilophylla* var. *antifebrilis.*

Canavalia maritima: This plant is reportedly used by sailors as a "marijuana substitute" in México; pyrrolidine alkaloids have been found in the pods (Díaz 1975).

Cardamine concatenata: This species has been referred to as an "Iroquois hallucinogen" used "to mesmerize" (Herrick 1977; Moerman 1986). Little information is available on this plant, and no entheogenic compounds are known from it, nor indeed from any other plant of the family Brassicaceae.

Cecropia mexicana; C. obtusifolia: These moraceous species, known as *guaruma* and widely used in México for various ethnomedicinal indications (Díaz 1976), have been reported in Veracruz, México to provoke a *Cannabis*-like effect following smoking of the dried leaves. Various *Cecropia* species are used in South America as a source of *llipta*—alkaline ash chewed with *coca* (Kamen-Kaye 1971; Schultes & Raffauf 1990; Schultes & Raffauf 1992). We have no information on entheogenic constituents of these two plants, but several other species of Moraceae are involved in South American entheogenic use—species of *Coussapoa* and *Ficus* as *ayahuasca* additives (Luna 1984B; McKenna *et al.* 1986), plus species of *Helicostylis* and *Maquira* (see entries below) to prepare the recondite entheogens *takini* and *rapé dos indios* (Schultes & Raffauf 1990; Wilbert 1987).

Cestrum laevigatum: A *Cestrum* probably referable to this species is sold as a "marijuana substitute" in Brasil under the name *dama da noite* or "lady of the night" (Schultes & Hofmann 1980). No psychoactive compounds are known from this species. *Cestrum parqui* recently appeared in a list of putative Italian psychotropic plants (Festi & Alliota 1990).

Clematis virginiana: A decoction of stems of this species of Ranunculaceae was reportedly used as a wash "to induce strange dreams" by the Iroquois Indians, an "oneirogenic" effect suggested to be "hallucinogenic" (Herrick 1977; Moerman

1986). No chemical data are available, but toxic alkaloids are known from the family (see *Delphinium nudicaule* below). Some *Clematis* species contain skin irritants, and their ingestion can cause burning of the mouth (Turner & Szczawinski 1991). North American Nez Perce Indians used *C. hirsutissima* as a stimulant for horses, apparently involving the local irritant effect of anemonin in peeled root placed in the animal's nostrils (Kern & Cardellina 1983). The plant actually contains protoanemonin, which is converted rapidly to anemonin *in vivo.*

Comandra pallida: This santalaceous species was reportedly used by Kayenta Navaho as a "narcotic" (Wyman & Harris 1951). We have no chemical information on any prospective entheogenic principles.

Coryphantha calipensis; C. compacta; C. cornifera var. ***echinus; C. macromeris; C. palmerii; C. ramillosa*** (1, Note 7): *C. macromeris* and *C. palmerii* have been reportedly used as ritual entheogens (Schultes & Hofmann 1980), and *C. compacta* is considered by the Tarahumara Indians of México to be a "kind" of *péyotl* (Bye 1979A). All of these species contain phenethylamines, including macromerine and normacromerine (Hornemann *et al.* 1973; Sato *et al.* 1973).

Crotalaria sagittalis: The roots of this fabaceous plant were "considered to be a very strong narcotic" by the Delaware-Okl Indians (Tantaquidgeon 1942). Dangerous hepatotoxic pyrrolizidine alkaloids are known from *Crotalaria* species, and their ingestion should thus be avoided assiduously (Turner & Szczawinski 1991).

Cymbopetalum penduliflorum: Known as *xochinacaztli* ("ear-flower") to the Aztecs (Safford 1910; Safford 1911), this aromatic flower was also known as *teonacaztli* ("sacred ear"), of which Sahagún said: "it inebriates like the mushrooms" (Sahagún 1950; Sahagún 1982). It has been suggested that this flower might represent the lost Aztec entheogen *poyomatli* (Díaz 1979; see below). Non-psychotropic, cardioactive alkaloids are known from the South American species *C. brasiliense* (Cavé *et al.* 1984). Today the flowers of *C. penduliflorum* are used as a spice for chocolate drinks, under the name *hueynacaztli* (Bye & Linares 1990).

Cypripedium calceolus (1, Note 7): The "yellow lady's slipper" orchid (as *C. parviflorum*) was reportedly used by Menominee Indians of North America "in sacred bundles to induce dreams of the supernatural" (Smith 1923). This "oneirogenic" effect has been reputed to be "hallucinogenic" (Moerman 1986). No chemical data are available on this plant, which was used also by Cherokee Indians variously as a sedative, analgesic, stimulant and anticonvulsant, suggesting potential psychoactivity (Lewis & Elvin-Lewis 1977; Herrick 1977; Moerman 1986). The leaves may contain irritant compounds (Turner & Szczawinski 1991). See also *Oncidium longifolium* below, another putative entheogenic species of orchid.

Cytisus canariensis: This Old World plant, introduced to México, has been adopted as a shamanic drug by the Yaqui Indians (Díaz, 1979; Fadiman 1965; Schultes & Hofmann 1979). While the plant contains abundant cytisine, this alkaloid is not psychoptic. It is sometimes known in the literature as *Genista canariensis*.

Delphinium nudicaule: Mendocino Indians of California considered this ranunculaceous species to have "narcotic properties" (Chestnut 1902). Toxic aconite-like steroidal alkaloids are known from the genus, and experimentation is not advisable (Turner & Szczawinski 1991). *Delphinium ajacis* is used as a parasiticide, and contains the alkaloid ajacine and related compounds (Tyler *et al.* 1976); while toxic glycosides such as delphinidin are found in *D. virescens* (Kindscher 1992).

Desmodium caudatum; D. gangeticum; D. gyrans; D. lasiocarpum; D. paniculatum; D. pulchellum; D. tiliaefolium; D. triflorum (4, Note 2): *Desmodium gangeticum*, known as *saumya* or *amsúmat* ("rich in *Soma* juice") has been suggested to be an entheogenic plant of India (Flattery & Schwartz 1989). β-Carboline alkaloids are known from some of these species, which likewise contain entheogenic tryptamines (see Chapter 3; Banerjee & Ghosal 1969; Ghosal 1972; Ghosal *et al.* 1972; Ueno *et al.* 1978). However, concentrated decoctions of *Desmodium pulchellum* "were only feebly active" in pharmacological tests in rats and mice, suggesting that these alkaloids occur in subthreshold amounts for psychoptic effects (Ghosal 1972). *Desmodium lasiocarpum* has been reported to be used by the Bontoc people of the Philippines as a "tobacco substitute" but no details were given (Bodner & Gereau 1988). *Desmodium gangeticum* is used in tropical West Africa as an antipyretic and cold remedy (Oliver-Bever 1983). A *Desmodium paniculatum* root infusion was used by North American Houma Indians as a stimulant (Kindscher 1992; Moerman 1986; Speck 1941).

Dimorphandra parviflora: In 1851 Richard Spruce collected this leguminous species in Barra, Brasil, and noted its seeds were used in the preparation of entheogenic *paricá* snuff (see Chapter 3, De Smet & Lipp 1987). We should consider this little-known plant to be a possible entheogen, pending further study. Alkaloids are known from *D. mollis*, which is toxic to cattle (Dos Santos *et al.* 1974).

Elaeophorbia drupifera: The latex of this plant, *ayañ beyem*, was applied, in association with *Alchornea floribunda*, directly to the eyeball by African Fang to elicit "bizarre visions"; but this is said to cause blindness (Emboden 1972B; Fernandez 1972).

Epithelantha micromeris (1, Note 7): Tarahumara Indians of México call this cactus *híkuli mulato* ("the dark-skinned *péyotl*"), and it is reported to be psychoactive (Lumholtz 1902), and said to be used in shamanism (Schultes & Hofmann 1980).

Galbulimima belgraveana: Natives of Papua, New Guinea are said to prepare an inebriant from leaves and bark of this species with *Homalomena* leaves. Although piperidine alkaloids are known from bark of *Galbulimima* (Ritchie & Taylor 1967), no entheogens are known in the New Guinea plant (Schultes & Hofmann 1980).

Gaultheria: A species of *Gaultheria* has been described an an entheogenic plant in Perú (Schultes & Hofmann 1979). No entheogenic principles are known from the genus, many species of which contain flavonoids (Middleton 1992).

Gomortega keule: Chilean Mapuche Indians call this species *keule* or *hualhual*, and consider its fruits to be inebriating (Houghton & Manby 1985; Mariani Ramírez 1965; Schultes 1970A). Chemical studies are lacking (Schultes & Hofmann 1980).

Helichrysum foetidum; H. stenopterum: These species were reportedly used by shamans "for inhaling to get their trance" in Zululand in South Africa (Schultes & Hofmann 1980). Thus far, no entheogenic principles are known from this genus.

Helicostylis tomentosa; H. pedunculata: Bark of this "sacred" tree may be the source of the entheogen *takini* of Surinam, used by Karib and Arawak Indians (Reis & Lipp 1982; Schultes & Raffauf 1990). *Takini* is the latex of *H. tomentosa* or *H. pedunculata*—fumes of latex of both trees were used with tobacco in shamanic initiation among coastal Arawak tribes of South America; the Cariña Indians of Guiana give newly-initiated tobacco shamans two small gourds of *takini* latex (Wilbert 1987).

Hieracium pilocella: Under the name *håret høgeurt*, this plant in the family Compositae was reported in a Danish book on "hallucinogens" to expand consciousness after smoking one or two "joints" (Larris 1980). The psychoactive principle is unknown, and this interesting and legal plant has recently begun to be cultivated in the United States. Under the name "hawkweed," *H. pilocella* was used as an anti-diarrheal by North American Iroquois Indians, and other species of the genus were likewise used by North American Indians as gastrointestinal remedies (Herrick 1977; Moerman 1986).

Homalomena belgraveana: The leaves of *ereriba*, thought to be this species of *Homalomena*, are taken together with leaves and bark of *Galbulimima belgraveana* by natives of Papua, New Guinea to induce an inebriation followed by dreams (Barrau 1962; Schultes & Hofmann 1980). Chemical studies are lacking. *Homalomena cordata* and *H. versteegii* have recently been reported to be employed in New Guinea for "rain magic" and "love magic" respectively (Telban 1988).

Iresine (1, "Chemistry of *Péyotl*"; 4, "Miscellaneous Admixtures"): Species of *Iresine* have been reported both as *ayahuasca* additives (Schultes & Hofmann 1979) and as an additive to *cimora*, an entheogenic potion thought to contain also mescaline-containing *Trichocereus pachanoi*, cactus *Neoraimondia macrostibas*, *Isotoma longiflora*, *Pedilanthus tithymaloides*, and *Brugmansia* species (Cruz-Sánchez 1948; Dobkin de Ríos 1977; Schultes & Hofmann 1980). It has been claimed that the *cimora* potion contains only the *Iresine* species (Friedberg 1959; Friedberg 1960) and, still more recently, that it contains only the *Brugmansia* species, whereas *timora* is the name of the *Iresine* species (Davis 1983B).

Iryanthera longiflora; I. macrophylla; I. ulei (3, "Chemistry of Entheogenic *Virola* Snuffs"): These three myristicaceous plants are used in the elaboration of edible entheogenic pastes by the Bora and Witoto Indians of South America (Davis & Yost 1983B; Schultes & Raffauf 1990). Although an early study found the entheogenic (but orally-inactive) 5-MEO-DMT in *I. ulei* (Holmstedt *et al.* 1980), a subsequent study failed to find tryptamines in the above-mentioned species, nor in *I. crassifolia*, *I. jurensis*, nor *I. paraensis* (McKenna *et al.* 1984B).

Isotoma longiflora (1, "Chemistry of *Péyotl*"): This plant has been reportedly used as an additive to the entheogenic *cimora* potion thought to be based on mescaline-containing *Trichocereus pachanoi* (Dobkin de Ríos 1977; Schultes & Hofmann 1980), an assumption challenged recently (Davis 1983B; Friedberg 1959). Latex of *Isotoma longiflora* is used medicinally by the Cuna Indians of Panamá (Duke 1975).

Jatropha grossidentata: Ayoreo Indians of the Paraguayan Chaco smoke dried roots of this plant, *caniroja*, to "communicate with the spirits" in shamanic initiation. The plant contains diterpenes of obscure pharmacology (Schmeda-Hirschmann 1993).

Juanulloa ochracea (4, "Miscellaneous Admixtures"): As this solanaceous species is called *ayahuasca* in Colombia, it has been suggested to be psychoactive, perhaps once used in *ayahuasca* potions, although such hasn't been reported (Schultes 1972C).

Justicia pectoralis* var. *stenophylla (3, "Chemistry of Entheogenic *Virola* Snuffs"): The leaves of this aromatic plant are used as an additive to entheogenic *epéna* snuffs by various Waiká Indian groups (Chagnon *et al.* 1971; Schultes & Hofmann 1980). Although preliminary tests indicated the presence of DMT (Schultes & Holmstedt 1968), later studies failed to confirm this, and extracts proved to be inactive in animal experiments (McKenna *et al.* 1984A; MacRae 1984; MacRae & Towers 1984B). Quinazoline alkaloids similar to those found in *Peganum harmala* are known from two *Justicia* species used in ethnomedicine by the Tamang of Nepal (Chowdhury & Bhattacharya 1985). Under the name *curía*, powder of *Justicia caracasana* is used as an aromatic additive to a Venezuelan "lickable" tobacco preparation called *chimó*, reminiscent of the *ambíl* so esteemed by Bora and Witoto Indians (Wilbert 1987). Since the name *curía* also refers to *Justicia pectoralis*, it is thought this species likewise is or was an additive to *chimó* (Kamen-Kaye 1971; Kamen-Kaye 1975).

Kaempferia galanga: This condiment in the ginger family, widely used in Asian cuisine, has been reported to be used as an entheogen in New Guinea, under the name *maraba* (Barrau 1962; Schultes & Hofmann 1980). We know nothing of potential entheogenic constituents in this plant.

Kyphosus fuseus: Known as the "dream fish" or "silver drummer fish," this edible fish is reputed to possess *Calea zacatechichi*-like "oneirogenic" or dream-inducing properties, for which it is reportedly eaten by Norfolk Islanders of Melanesia (Halstead 1978; Helfrich & Banner 1960; McCullough 1971; La Barre 1980A). Without citing any references, Stafford (1983) reported the "dream fish" contains 5-MeO-DMT (see Chapter 3); but this compound is not active orally, and even were it present, would not likely contribute to any "oneirogenic" properties. The Hawai'ian "nightmare *weke*," apparently a related mullet, is said to provoke nightmares, should one ingest the brain of this otherwise edible fish (Ching 1991). The mullets *Mugil cephalus* and *Neomyxus chaptalli*, as well as the goatfish *Mulloidichthys samoensis* and

Upeneus arge also provoke this "oneirogenic" syndrome (Helfrich & Banner 1960).

Lagochilus inebrians: An infusion of dried leaves of this plant is taken traditionally by various tribes of Turkestan and is thought to be inebriating (Schultes & Hofmann 1980; Schulz 1959). A diterpene called lagochiline has been isolated from the plant (Abramov 1957). Although possessing pharmacological properties, it is unknown whether this compound is psychoactive, although the discovery of a psychoactive diterpene from *Salvia divinorum* (Ortega *et al.* 1982; Ott 1995A; Siebert 1994; Valdés *et al.* 1984) suggests the possibility.

Leonotis leonurus: Under the name *wild dagga* ("wild marijuana"), flower buds and an exudate of the leaves of this mint species were smoked traditionally in South Africa as an inebriant by the Hottentots (Emboden 1979; Schleiffer 1979). Chemical studies are lacking, and the drug is used as an emmenagogue in Thai ethnomedicine (Ponglux *et al.* 1987).

Leonurus sibiricus: Known as *marihuanilla*, this Old World plant has come to be smoked as a "marijuana substitute" in Chiapas, México (Díaz 1975). The plant apparently contains alkaloids, but no psychoactive principle is known. Seeds and infusions of *Leonurus artemisia*, *L. heterophyllus*, *L. sibiricus* and *L. tartarica* are used in Chinese medicine as emmenagogues, diuretics and vasodilators (Chin & Keng 1992; Hu *et al.* 1980; Keys 1976).

Lobelia tupa: Known in Chile as *tupa* or *tabaco del diablo*, Mapuche Indians have been reported to smoke the leaves of this plant as an inebriant (Duke 1985; Schultes & Hofmann 1980). Piperidine alkaloids not known to be psychoactive are found in this plant, although lobeline is said to exert a nicotine-like activity. *Lobelia inflata* was used ceremonially by North American Crow Indians, and in love magic by Mesquakie and Pawnee Indians (Kindscher 1992).

Lomariopsis japurensis; L. nigropalatea (4, "Miscellaneous Admixtures"): *Lomariopsis japurensis* has been reported to be an admixture to *ayahuasca* (Schultes & Hofmann 1979). Unknown chemically, there is the possiblity that this fern species, which is also used against postpartum hemorrhage by the Quijos Quichua of Ecuador (Marles *et al.* 1988) and *L. nigropalatea*, used as a hemostatic by Makú Indians (Schultes 1985A; Schultes & Raffauf 1990), may contain the vasoconstrictive and entheogenic ergoline alkaloids. We have no chemical data on these fern species.

Magnolia virginiana: Leaves or bark of this North American tree were reportedly snuffed by Rappahannock Indians as a sort of "mild dope" (Moerman 1986; Speck *et al.* 1942). No entheogenic principles are known from this plant. The Mexican *Magnolia dealbata* or *elexóchitl* has been suggested to represent the lost Aztec entheogen *poyomatli* (see entry below; Díaz 1979).

Malouetia tamaquarina (4, "Miscellaneous Admixtures"): Makuna Indians of Colombia add leaves of this apocynaceous plant to *ayahuasca* potions (Schultes & Raffauf 1990); contains alkaloids (Bisset 1992B), but no known entheogenic principles.

Manihot anomala* subsp. *anomala: Paraguayan Ayoreo Indians smoke dried roots of this plant, *sienejna*, to "communicate with the spirits" in shamanic initiation. We've no phytochemical or pharmacological information (Schmeda-Hirschmann 1993).

Maquira sclerophylla (3, "More DMT Entheogens"): Brasilian Indians in the Pariana area once prepared an entheogenic snuff from fruits of this moraceous tree, still known as *rapé dos indios* ("Indian snuff"; Schultes 1984; Schultes & Raffauf 1990). Intraperitoneal injection of extracts caused amphetamine-like stimulation in rats (De Carvalho & Lapa 1990); cardiac glycosides are present (Shrestha *et al.* 1992).

Mascagnia psilophylla* var. *antifebrilis (4, "Entheogenic Potions of Amazonia"; 4, "Chacruna and Chagropanga") = *Cabi paraensis*; *Callaeum antifebrile*: Once reported as a variant type of source plant for *ayahuasca* (Schultes & Raffauf 1990), this malpighiaceous species has just been reported rather as an admixture to *Banisteriopsis* in the potions (Luna & Amaringo 1991). Malpighiaceae expert B. Gates recently reclassified this species as *Callaeum antifebrile*, and determined it was conspecific with *Cabi paraensis* (Gates 1986), which is reported to contain harmine (Mors & Zaltzman 1954; Ríos *et al.* 1965).

Mentha pulegium (2, Postscriptum): This aromatic mint is known to have been an ingredient to the entheogenic *kykeon* potion drunk during the Eleusinian Mysteries in the ancient world, and has been considered to be "mildly psychoactive" (Wasson *et al.* 1978). Peruvian shamans burn the plant as an offering to Pachamama (Wassén 1967; Wassén 1979). No entheogenic principles have been identified.

Mesembryanthemum expansum; M. tortuosum: Under the name *kanna*, these two species are thought to represent the entheogenic drug of that name, the root of which was chewed by the Hottentots of South Africa (Lewin 1924; Schultes & Hofmann 1980). Alkaloids are known from these plants (Popelak & Lettenbauer 1967), but no known entheogenic principles have been identified. As *Sceletium*, *M. expansum* and *M. tortuosum* have been reported as inebriants among the Hottentots and Bushmen of South Africa (Watt & Breyer-Brandwijk 1962).

Mirabilis multiflora: Under the name *so'ksi* or *so'kya*, the root of this nyctaginaceous plant (also known as *Quamoclidion multiflorum*) was reportedly chewed by Hopi medicinemen to "induce vision while making diagnosis" (Whiting 1939). The visionary principle remains unknown, and cultivation has recently begun in the United States. As *maravilla*, it was reported that 1–2 ounces of the root (28–57 g) provoked 30–60 minutes of "gaiety and hyperactivity" followed by "befuddlement" (Moore 1979). Zuni Indians reportedly bake bread with powdered root of *M. multiflora* as an anorexic (Camazine & Bye 1980). Some plants in the genus *Mirabilis* are toxic (Turner & Szczawinski 1991). *Mirabilis nyctaginea* had various medicinal uses among North American Dakota, Omaha and Ponca Indians (Kindscher 1992).

Mitragyna speciosa: Leaves of this plant, as *kratom*, are used as an "opium substitute" in southeast Asia, and it has been suggested to be entheogenic, in part based on content of indole alkaloids like mitragynine (Emboden 1979; Harrison McKenna 1989; Jansen & Prast 1988A; Jansen & Prast 1988B). Whole leaves of *kratom* are stimulating, while mitragynine is a depressant (Shellard 1989), suggesting the pharmacological importance of secondary alkaloids. Further studies are needed to clarify *kratom* ethnopharmacognosy. *Kratom* or *gra-tom* is used as a stimulant and antidiarrheal in Thai ethnomedicine (Ponglux *et al.* 1987). Four African species of *Mitragyna* were devoid of mitragynine, but rich in other alkaloids (Shellard 1983).

Monadenium lugardae: The root of this South African plant was once taken as an aid to divination. Alkaloids have been isolated, but no entheogenic principles are as yet known (De Smet 1996; Watt & Breyer-Brandwijk 1962).

Monodora myristica: The seeds of this annonaceous species, called *pebe*, have been proposed to be psychoactive aids to contacting the "water spirits" in Central Cameroon, Africa (Wagner 1991A). These seeds have been reportedly used as a stimulant and headache remedy by neighboring Central African Pygmies (Motte 1982). They are also a "nutmeg substitute" and it is possible that true nutmeg, *Myristica fragrans* (see Chapter 1), is the psychoactive *pebe* used to contact the "water spirits." The well-known medicinal cucurbit *Momordica charantia* is said to be used as an "antidote" to *pebe*, to break off contact with "water spirits," and is called in Cameroon *ngoko bi ai kâi* (Wagner 1991A). *Momordica charantia* is reported to be very toxic (Turner & Szczawinski 1991), and is used in Caribbean (Reis & Lipp 1982; Seaforth 1991), North American (Lewis & Elvin-Lewis 1977) and Chinese ethnomedicine (Hu *et al.* 1980). More research is needed to clarify the possibility of visionary annonas.

Mostuea gabonica; M. stimulans: Root bark of these loganiaceous plants was chewed in Gabon for an effect like *eboka*, and *M. stimulans* roots contained alkaloids, possibly identical to gelsemine and sempervirine (De Smet 1996).

***Myelobia smerintha* Huebner**: In accounts of his nineteenth century travels in South America, French explorer Augustin de Saint-Hilaire described the use by Malali Indians in Brasil's Minas Gerais province of a larval insect which feeds on bamboo (Saint-Hilaire 1824). The insect, *bichos da tacuara* ("bamboo worms"), was an esteemed food, and Saint-Hilaire followed the example of a guide, breaking off the head and removing the intestinal tube, then sucking the white flesh from the skin. The Indians said that the dried, powdered insects were used as a vulnerary, and that the dried, headless insects (but complete with intestinal tube) were psychotropic, provoking "a kind of ecstatic sleep, which often lasts more than a day, and similar to that experienced by the Orientals when they take opium in excess. They tell, on awakening, of marvelous dreams..." Today the name *bicho da tacuara* refers to the larvae of the moth *Myelobia smerintha*, and it has been proposed that the gut or salivary glands of this insect is "a new hallucinogen" (Britton 1984). This insect perhaps belongs in the category of "oneirogenic" or dream-inducing drugs, of which *Calea zacatechichi* is the prototype (Díaz 1975; Mayagoitia *et al.* 1986), and including *Cymbopogon densiflorus* and the "dream fish" (Schultes & Hofmann 1980).

Neoraimondia macrostibas (1, "Chemistry of *Péyotl*"): This cactus may be an additive to an entheogenic beverage called *cimora*, also said to contain cactus *Trichocereus pachanoi* (Dobkin de Ríos 1977; Schultes & Hofmann 1980). It has been claimed that the beverage contains no cacti, but rather is based on entheogenic *Brugmansia* species (Davis 1983B). *Neoraimondia arequipensis* var. *roseiflora*, once a variety of *N. macrostibas* (Ostolaza *et al.* 1985), was devoid of mescaline (Ma *et al.* 1986).

Nepeta cataria: "Catnip" is psychotropic for cats, especially housecats, but active in most species of Felidae. The volatile fraction contains a number of compounds which are psychoactive in cats, especially nepetalactone, dihydronepetalactone and isodihydronepetalactone (Tucker & Tucker 1988). These lactones are also found in: *Nepeta cataria* var. *citriodora* (=*N. citriodora*), *N. hindostana*, *N. leucophylla*, *N. mussinii*, *N. nepetella* (=*N. lanceolata*) and *N. sibthorpii*, some of which excite cats. A psychoactive monoterpenoid alkaloid, actinidine, is also present; likewise in cat-psychoactive *Actinidia polygama* and *A. kolomikta*, which also contain dihydronepetalactone, isodihydronepetalactone and neonepetalactone. Also present are related cat-active lactones iridomyrmecin and isoiridomyrmecin, originally isolated from cat-attracting ants of the genera *Iridomyrmex*, *Dolichoderus* and *Tapinoma* (some ants also contain dihydronepetalactone; some beetles produce in their defensive secretions actinidine and dihydronepetalactone). Actinidine is also found in *Actinidia arguta*, sap of which is used as an expectorant in Ainu ethnomedicine (Mitsuhashi 1976), whereas decoctions of stem of *A. polygama* are used as sedatives by Russians and Ukrainians (Moskalenko 1987). There are many other cat-psychoactive plants, such as *Valeriana officinalis* (which produces actinidine) and *V. celtica* (containing nepetalactone). *Teucrium marum* is cat-active, with presumably cat-psychoactive ant compounds dolicholactones C and D. The following plants not known for use by cats contain cat-active lactones: *Boschniakia rossica* (boschniakine, boschnialactone, onikulactone); *Menyanthes trifoliata* (mitsugashiwalactone—this is used as gastrointestinal remedy by North American Kwakiutl Indians; Turner & Bell 1973); *Tecoma stans* (actinidine, boschniakine); *T. radicans* (boschniakine) and *Myoporum desertii* (nepetalactone; see Tucker & Tucker 1988 for review of this branch of zoopharmacognosy). Catnip has been used ethnomedicinally by diverse North American Indians, principally as a cold remedy, sedative and gastrointestinal remedy (Moerman 1986), and Cherokee Indians used infusions of the leaves as a stimulant (Hamel & Chiltoskey 1975). Catnip was reported to be psychoactive in human beings following smoking of the dried leaves (Jackson & Reed 1969). It is possible that the cat-psychoactive lactones are responsible, although cats normally are affected by *smelling* the plant (the active compounds being volatile). There have been reports of ritual ingestion of psychoactive ants by California Indians (Blackburn 1976), which may be lactone-containing species, 'though nicotine analogue anabasine occurs in ant venoms (Wheeler *et al.* 1981). *Nepeta hindostana* and *N. elliptica* are ingredients of *shankhapushpi*, an Ayurvedic epilepsy remedy (Dandekar *et al.* 1992); *N. longibracteata* leaves are used in Ladakh "for worship" (Bhattacharyya 1991).

Nephelium topengii: A drug described in a 12th century Chinese source as being vision-producing, *Lung-li*, is considered to be referable to this species (Li 1978;

Schultes & Hofmann 1980). We have no chemical data on this intriguing plant.

Ocimum micranthum (4, "Miscellaneous Admixtures"): This mint species is reportedly used as an *ayahusaca* admixture in South America (Schultes & Hofmann 1979). There exist at least two reports of the ethnomedicinal use of this species in México and Guatemala as an analgesic (Alcorn 1984; Girón *et al.* 1991). Chemical studies are lacking.

Oconenetl: In his sixteenth century account of the ancient Aztecs, Diego Muñóz Camargo spoke of an entheogenic bird called *oconenetl*, saying "eating the flesh of this bird causes one to see visions" (Garza 1990; Muñóz Camargo 1892). The bird remains unidentified. This brings to mind Schultes' report of the South American bird which dines on fruits of the *ayahuasca* additive plant *Malouetia tamaquarina*, and thereby renders its bones toxic to dogs (Schultes 1987A). Recently batrachotoxins were found in skin and feathers of New Guinean birds of the genus *Pitohui* (Dumbacher *et al.* 1992). Similar compounds are known from skin secretions of toxic Colombian *Phyllobates* frogs, some of which are used as dart poisons, and some such frog-skin secretions are rubbed into self-inflicted burns for a sort of psychoactive effect (see entry above for *Bufo alvarius*; Amato 1992).

***Oncidium longifolium* (=*O. cebolleta*)** (1, Note 7): Mexican Tarahumara Indians consider this epiphytic orchid to be a "companion" to the *péyotl* cactus (Bye 1979A), and novel phenanthrene derivatives of unknown pharmacology were recently isolated from the plant (Stermitz *et al.* 1983). *Oncidium carthagenense* and *O. pusillum* are both used ethnomedicinally in México and South America (Alcorn 1984; Schultes & Raffauf 1990).

Osteophloeum platyspermum (3, "Chemistry of Entheogenic *Virola* Snuffs"): Under the name *O. platyphyllum*, this myristicaceous plant was reported to contain DMT, 5-MEO-DMT and bufotenine (Holmstedt *et al.* 1980), but a subsequent analysis found only *N*-methyltryptophan methyl ester (McKenna *et al.* 1984B). Like related species of *Virola* and *Iryanthera*, *O. platyspermum* is used entheogenically, by Quijos Quichua Indians, who ingest sap of this plant with *Tabernaemontana sananho* and a *Brugmansia* species (Bennett & Alarcón 1994). Glycerides and neolignans of unknown pharmacology have been reported from this interesting plant (Fo *et al.* 1984).

Pachycereus pecten-aboriginum (1, Note 7): Young branches of this gigantic cactus are crushed in water by Tarahumara Indians to make a ceremonial beverage called *cawé* or *chawé* (Bye 1979A; Schultes & Hofmann 1980). Phenethylamine alkaloids are reported from this cactus (Agurell *et al.* 1971; Bruhn & Lindgren 1976), but none of these are known to be entheogenic.

Pagamea macrophylla (3, "More DMT Entheogens"): Pulverized leaves of this rubiaceous plant are used as a snuff by Barasana shamans of South America (Schultes 1980; Schultes & Raffauf 1990). No chemical research has been reported on this intriguing plant, whose psychoactive principles remain a mystery.

Pancratium trianthum: Under the name *kwashi*, bulbs of this plant were traditionally rubbed on incisions in the head by South African Bushmen (Schultes & Hofmann 1980). The experience was said to provoke hallucinations. Alkaloids are known from the genus, but this species is obscure chemically. The psychoactive use of this plant among !Kung Bushmen has been questioned (Dobkin de Ríos 1986).

Pernettya furens; P. parvifolia: The fruits of the Ecuadorian species *P. parvifolia*, known as *taglli*, are said to induce hallucinations, and the fruits of the Chilean *P. furens*, known as *hierba loca*, supposedly provoke a *Datura*-like inebriation (Naranjo 1969; Schultes & Hofmann 1980). *Pernettya parvifolia* has been reported to contain andromedotoxins or grayanotoxins, toxic glucosides common in the family Ericaceae (see entry for *Arctostaphylos* spp.; Lewis & Elvin-Lewis 1977).

Petunia violacea (Appendix A, "Atropine, Hyoscyamine, Scopolamine"): Under the name *shanín*, this plant was reportedly used as an entheogen in highland Ecuador (Alvear 1971). Although a preliminary chemical analysis revealed no alkaloids (Butler *et al.* 1981), further study is clearly needed.

Peucedanum japonicum: Used in traditional Chinese medicine, this plant is said to provoke visions (Li 1978; Schultes & Hofmann 1980). Chemical studies are wanting on this interesting plant.

Phytolacca acinosa: This ancient Chinese ethnomedicine was said to be used by sorcerers in antiquity "for seeing spirits" (Li 1978; Schultes & Hofmann 1980). No entheogenic principles are known from this species.

Poyomatli (5, Note 13): In their translation of the Náhuatl *Florentine Codex* of

Sahagún (which was partially translated into Spanish and published as Sahagún's *Historia General de las Cosas de Nueva España*; Sahagún 1950; Sahagún 1982—there are significant differences between the Náhuatl and the Spanish texts), Americans Dibble & Anderson found that the mysterious Aztec floral entheogen *poyomatli* was the flower of *cacahuaxóchitl*, known to the botanist as *Quararibea funebris* (see following entry; Garza 1990; Wasson 1980). However, self-experiments have indicated that flowers of *Q. funebris* are not entheogenic (Ott, unpublished laboratory notes). *Cymbopetalum penduliflorum* or *teonacaztli* (see entry above) was said by Sahagún to inebriate "like the mushrooms" and has also been suggested as a candidate for *poyomatli* (Díaz 1979; Sahagún 1950). This annonaceous plant, also known as *xochinacaztli* and *hueynacaztli*, may still be used as a spice for chocolate drinks, as is *Quararibea funebris* (Bye & Linares 1990). This use may explain why the latter plant is today known as *cacahuaxóchitl*—literally, "flower of cacao," and actual flowers of cacao trees, *Theobroma cacao*, have also been tested for entheogenic effects, with negative results (Ott 1985). Another aromatic flowering tree, in the Leguminosae family, likewise known to the Aztecs as *hueynacaztli*, *Enterolobium cyclocarpum*, has also been suggested as a possible *poyomatli*, as has the aromatic *Magnolia dealbata* or *elexóchitl* (Díaz 1979).

Quararibea funebris (5, Note 13): The flowers of this aromatic tree, a modern-day additive to cacao potions in Oaxaca, México, have been proposed to represent the lost Aztec entheogen *poyomatli* (see previous entry; Ott 1985; Rosengarten 1977; Schultes 1957B; Schultes 1972F; Wasson 1980). Although the flowers have not been found to be entheogenic in preliminary trials, interesting lactones and an alkaloid have been isolated from them (Raffauf & Zennie 1983; Raffauf *et al.* 1984; Zennie *et al.* 1986). A little-known shamanic inebriant from Perú, *espingo* (or *ispincu*), was recently found to represent seeds of a species of *Quararibea* (Wassén 1979). There is the possibility this species, as *ishpingo*, is used as an *ayahuasca* additive by Shipibo-Conibo Indians of Perú (Arévalo Valera 1986). Recently *ishpingo* was also reported as an additive to entheogenic potions based on the mescaline-containing *Trichocereus* cacti in Perú (Polia & Bianchi 1992). *Q. funebris* leaves are used ethnomedicinally in México (Zamora-Martínez & Nieto de Pascual Pola 1992), and *Q. putumayensis* is used by the South American Kofán Indians in the preparation of arrow poisons (Schultes & Raffauf 1990).

Ranunculus acris: It has been proposed that this plant represents the *mao-ken* or *shui-lang* of ancient China, reputed to provoke delirium (Li 1978; Schultes & Hofmann 1980). Protoanemonin occurs in this species (Turner & Szczawinski 1991).

Rhynchosia longeracemosa; R. pyramidalis [***R. phaseoloides***]: The seeds of these leguminous species are known as *piule* in Oaxaca, México. Since *piule* is thought to be a general term for entheogens (it is applied, variously, to entheogenic morning glories and entheogenic mushrooms, and is held to be etymologically related to *péyotl*), it has been speculated that *Rhynchosia* seeds are entheogenic (Díaz 1979; Santesson 1938; Schultes & Hofmann 1980; Wasson 1963). In the Nahua village of Amecameca, México, six pairs of *R. pyramidalis* seeds are ingested with six pairs of *Psilocybe aztecorum* in shamanic healing ceremonies (Wasson & Wasson 1957A).

Rudgea retifolia (4, "Miscellaneous Admixtures"): There is evidence this rubiaceous plant was used in Perú as an *ayahuasca* additive (Schultes & Raffauf 1990), as it has the vernacular name, *chacruna*, of the famous *ayahuasca* additive *Psychotria viridis.*

Senecio calophyllus; S. cervariaefolia; S. grayanus; S. hartwegii; S. praecox; S. toluccanus (1, Note 7): These species are known in México as *peyote*; *S. hartwegii* as *peyote de Tepíc* (Díaz 1975; Schultes 1937B; Schultes & Hofmann 1980). Sesquiterpene lactones and alkaloids are known from the genus, but no visionary principles have been found, nor modern use of the plants as inebriants. While the relationship of these species to *péyotl* in México is obscure, a recent study found that *Senecio elatus* is used in Perú as an additive to potions based on *San Pedro*, the mescaline-containing *Trichocereus pachanoi* (see Chapter 1; Polia & Bianchi 1992). A *Senecio* species, *quimichpatli* or *chochoyatl*, was said to be inebriating (Díaz 1976; Reko 1919).

Sida acuta; S. rhombifolia: Under the name *chichibe*, the former species is reportedly smoked as a "marijuana substitute" in Veracruz, México (Díaz 1975; Schultes & Hofmann 1980). Although ephedrine is known from the genus and might explain any stimulating effects of this plant, we know of no entheogenic principles. *Sida acuta* has been reported as a "mystical medicine" of the Cuna Indians of Panamá (Duke 1975). The Marama of Bangladesh take a bolus of the whole *Sida acuta* plant as a tranquilizing remedy for "uneasiness" (Alam 1992), and root extracts of this species are used as an ecbolic by the Miskito of Nicaragua (Dennis 1988).

Siler divericatum: This ancient Chinese medicine, called *fang-feng*, has been reputed to provoke "madness" (Li 1978; Schultes & Hofmann 1980). Solid information concerning this plant is lacking, and this genus remains to be studied chemically.

Spiraea caespitosum: Kayenta Navaho Indians used this rosaceous plant as a "narcotic" (Wyman & Harris 1951). There are no known entheogenic principles from this species, which is a source of salicylic acid, precursor to aspirin, that derives its name from the genus *Spiraea* (Lewis & Elvin-Lewis 1977).

Stephanomeria pauciflora: Kayenta Navaho Indians used the root of this asteraceous plant as a "narcotic" (Wyman & Harris 1951) but this species is chemically obscure.

Terminalia bellirica: The Lodha of West Bengal, India reputedly eat dried kernels of this plant "for hallucination" (Pal & Jain 1989). The plant's "narcotic properties" have been reported from southeast Asia (Perry 1980), and it is used as an anthelmintic in Chinese ethnomediçine (Sheng-ji 1985), as an antipyretic and laxative in Nepal (Singh *et al.* 1979) and as an asthma remedy in Kerala, India (Pushpangadan & Atal 1986). In traditional Indian ethnomedicine, dried fruits, called *bahera*, are used for stomach disorders, and decoctions of *T. sericea* root have caused deaths in Africa (Lewis & Elvin-Lewis 1977).

Thamnosma montana: An infusion of this rutaceous plant, known commonly as "turpentine broom," was reportedly ingested by Kawaiisu shamans "to go crazy like coyotes" (Moerman 1986; Zigmond 1981). We know no entheogenic principles from this plant, although DMT and 5-MeO-DMT is found in several genera from this family (*Dictyoloma*, *Limonia*, *Vepris*, *Zanthoxylum*).

Tillandsia mooreana; T. purpurea; T. usneoides (1, Note 7): The terrestrial bromeliad *T. mooreana*, known to the Tarahumara as *waráruwi*, is considered to be a "companion" to the *péyotl* cactus by the Tarahumara Indians (Bye 1979A). This *tencho*, as *Tillandsia* species are commonly known in México, was earlier identified by Bye as *Tillandsia inflata* (Bye 1975). We have no information regarding the chemistry or properties of this plant, but flavonoids were recently found in *T. purpurea* (Arslanian *et al.* 1986), a plant depicted on ancient Mochica pottery of northern Perú (Hoyle 1938) in a context suggestive of visionary use (Cabieses 1986). See also Dobkin de Ríos (1977) for other entheogenic plant motifs in Mochica pottery. *Tillandsia usneoides* is used in Brasilian ethnomedicine as an analgesic (Costa *et al.* 1989), and aqueous extracts of this plant are said to evoke "visions" (Da Mota 1987).

Trichocline dealbata; T. exscapa; T. reptans: The rhizomes of these composite species, especially *T. reptans*, were reported by 18th century Jesuit priest Pedro Lozano as inebriating additives to fermented *chicha* beverages made by Calchaqui Indians of Argentina (Zardini 1977). Under the name *coro*, this inebriating drug is said to be used in modern times as an additive to smoked tobacco. Chemical studies are needed to clarify the pharmacognosy of this little-known drug.

Utricularia minor: This little-known plant in the family Lentibulariaceae was recently reported to be "highly intoxicating." Among the residents of the Himalayan province of Ladakh, India, roasted leaves of this plant are steeped in water, then buried for 10–15 days underground in a sealed bottle. Little is known about this drug plant, but it is reputed to be extremely toxic as well—"deaths have been reported" (Navchoo & Buth 1990).

Zornia latifolia: Under the name *maconha brava* ("wild marijuana"), leaves of this plant are smoked in Brasil as a "marijuana substitute" (Schultes & Hofmann 1980). No entheogenic principles are known.

III. DOUBTFUL

Alstonia venenata: This Indian ethnomedicine has been suggested to be entheogenic based on its content of indole alkaloids such as alstovenine and venenatine (Bhattacharya *et al.* 1975; Schultes & Hofmann 1980). The former is said to be an MAO-inhibitor and stimulant, the latter a reserpine-like drug. Since the MAO-inhibitors in *Banisteriopsis* species are not by themselves entheogenic (see Chapter 4), but require admixtures such as DMT-rich *Psychotria viridis*, more specific evidence is required before considering this plant to be entheogenic.

Astrophytum asterias; A. capricorne; A. myriostigma (1, Note 7): These cacti bear a superficial resemblance to *péyotl*, and are known as *peyotillo* in México (Anderson 1980). There is no evidence the resemblance is more than superficial.

Aztekium riterii (1, Note 7): This cactus is associated with *péyotl* owing to a similar appearance (Anderson 1980), but there is no evidence it is entheogenic.

Boletus flammeus; B. kumaeus; B. manicus; B. nigerrimus; B. nigroviolaceus; B. reayi (5, Note 5): These six species of *Boletus* were among the eleven species of "madness inducing" mushrooms used by the Kuma of New Guinea (Heim 1963;

Heim 1965; Heim 1966; Heim 1973; Heim 1978; Heim & Wasson 1964; Heim & Wasson 1965). This was found to be a non-pharmacological phenomenon by Heim and Wasson, and none of these species is known to be entheogenic, although they have been mentioned in articles and books on entheogens (Schultes 1979C; Schultes & Hofmann 1980), even depicted in popular books (Emboden 1979; Schultes & Hofmann 1979). It has been said that *B. manicus* has "somewhat toxic properties" (Schultes & Hofmann 1979). On the other hand, Heim reported "colorful luminous visions" following the ingestion of small amounts of powdered *B. manicus*, and Hofmann detected trace amounts of three unidentified indolic substances in this mushroom (Heim 1965; Heim 1978).

Cacalia cordifolia; C. decomposita (1, Note 7): Both of these composites are known as "peyotes" in México—the former is known as *Peyotl Xochimilcensi* (Díaz 1976; Schultes 1937B). However, they are used as medicinal plants and there is no evidence that they are entheogenic. Sesquiterpene lactones and alkaloids are known from the genus (Schultes & Hofmann 1980).

Calea zacatechichi (5, Note 7): The Chontal Indians of México were said to take an infusion of dried leaves of this plant, which they call *thle-pelakano* ("leaf of god"), then to smoke cigarettes of the same, after which visions were seen in dreams (MacDougall 1968). Much has been written about this dream-inducing activity, which has been dubbed "oneirogenic" (Díaz 1975; Mayagoitia *et al.* 1986; Schultes & Hofmann 1980) or "oneiromantic" (Baudelaire 1860). Although the drug seems to favor dreams in some people (Mayagoitia *et al.* 1986), it has not been found to be entheogenic, based on self-experiments by me and other individuals. As a result of modern interest in "lucid dreaming" (Gackenbach & Bosveld 1990; LaBerge & Rheingold 1990) there has come to be modern experimentation with this "Dream Herb," which has been introduced into cultivation in the United States.

Carnegiea gigantea (1, Note 7): This gigantic *saguaro* cactus is reportedly the basis for a ceremonial fermented beverage (Díaz 1979) and is known to contain tetrahydroisoquinoline alkaloids (Bruhn & Bruhn 1973; Bruhn & Lundström 1976; Bruhn *et al.* 1970; Heyl 1928; Schultes & Hofmann 1980). However, no entheogenic activity has been reported for the cactus, nor have entheogenic alkaloids as yet been isolated from it.

Cymbopogon densiflorus: Like *Calea zacatechichi*, this plant is said to induce dreams.

Shamans in Tanganyika were said to smoke the flowers alone or with tobacco to learn the future in their dreams (Schultes & Hofmann 1979; Schultes & Hofmann 1980). There is no evidence of entheogenic compounds in, or use of this plant.

Erythrina flabelliformis; E. americana: "Extremely tenuous" suggestions that the seeds of these colorful leguminous trees are entheogenic are "open to doubt" (Schultes & Hofmann 1980). In fact, such use has not been observed, nor have any entheogenic principles been isolated from these seeds. They have found use in ethnomedicine (Díaz 1979), and the red flowers are a popular vegetable in México.

Heimia salicifolia: Although alleged of this medicinal plant (Arenas 1987; Bandoni *et al.* 1976) "there is no doubt that it is employed... as an hallucinogen" (Schultes & Hofmann 1980), this datum comes from a suspect source—Victor A. Reko's 1936 book *Magische Gifte* (Reko 1936; see Chapter 2, Note 10). Reko claimed that wilted, crushed leaves of the plant, known in México as *sinicuiche*, were fermented in water then drunk, with hallucinations resulting. However, when Díaz and his collaborators ingested such a preparation, only an uncomfortable hypothermia resulted, and "in no case were there any mental alterations" (Díaz 1975). The hypothermic effects are doubtless due to the content of the alkaloid cryogenine or vertine (Kaplan & Malone 1966; Robichaud *et al.* 1964; Robichaud *et al.* 1965; Schultes & Hofmann 1980). An oral dose of 310 mg vertine (=36–156 g dried plant) provoked no psychotropic effects (Malone & Rother 1994). Vertine and nesodine, a related *sinicuiche* alkaloid, were shown to be aspirin-like inhibitors of the enzyme prostaglandin synthetase, being 2.5 and 2.2 times as potent as aspirin respectively (Lema *et al.* 1986).

Heimiella anguiformis (5, Note 5): Along with several species of *Boletus* and *Russula* cited above and below, *H. anguiformis* was one of the mushrooms related to the "mushroom madness" of the Kuma of New Guinea, which was found to be a non-pharmacological phenomenon (Heim 1963; Heim 1965; Heim 1966; Heim 1973; Heim 1978; Heim & Wasson 1964; Heim & Wasson 1965). Nevertheless, misspelled as *H. angrieformis*, this mushroom was illustrated in *Plants of the Gods* (Schultes & Hofmann 1979) with the implication that it was entheogenic.

Lophophora diffusa (1, Note 6): This close relative of *péyotl* (Anderson 1969; Anderson 1980) has been found to contain only traces of mescaline, with the principal alkaloid being the non-entheogenic peyotline or pellotine (Bruhn & Holmstedt 1974; Schultes & Hofmann 1980). There is no firm evidence that this plant is used as an entheogen, and Díaz reported that experimenters with *L. diffusa* "had a very disagreeable experience" although two "described pleasant effects" (Díaz 1979).

Lycoperdon marginatum; L. mixtecorum (5, Note 7): In 1961, Heim and Wasson were told by a Mixtec informant that these puffballs were dream-inducing (Heim & Wasson 1962; Heim *et al.* 1967). In 1974 a group led by J.L. Díaz, and in 1975 a group led by me studied with the same Mixtec informant, who identified no fewer than 11 species as dream-inducing, ten of these puffballs, including both *Lycoperdon* species reported by Heim and Wasson. In self-experiments followed by chemical tests, we found none of these species to be psychoactive, nor did they contain any known entheogenic mushroom constituents (Díaz 1975; Ott *et al.* 1975B). We concluded that the mushrooms were inactive at the doses prescribed, although "narcotic influence" has been attributed to "meals" of *Lycoperdon* (Coker & Couch 1928), and a *Lycoperdon* species is said to be "used by sorcerers to enable them to approach people without being seen" among the Tarahumara (Bye 1979A). Miscellaneous North American ethnomedicinal uses, none psychotropic, of *Lycoperdon* and other "puffball" species, mainly as hemostatics, has recently been reviewed (Burk 1983).

Nymphaea ampla; N. caerulea: Several publications have alleged entheogenic effects of water lilies, especially these species (Díaz 1975; Dobkin de Ríos 1974; Emboden 1972B; Emboden 1978; Emboden 1979; Emboden 1981B; Emboden 1982; Emboden 1983A; Schultes & Hofmann 1979; Schultes & Hofmann 1980). While this theory is based on analyses of Egyptian and Mayan art, "upon interpretation rather than sound scientific evidence" (Emboden 1982), Díaz reported that Mexican indigenous residents of Chiapas knew of psychoactive properties of *N. ampla* (Díaz 1975). On further investigations around the Lagunas de Montebello, Chiapas, it was determined that the Mexicans had learned of this fact from outsiders who had come to harvest the bulbs of the lilies (Díaz 1975; Ott, unpublished field studies). Díaz's interviews with "a good quantity of mestizo curanderos" were "fruitless"—none used the plant, but many knew of such use by outsiders (Díaz 1975). Many alkaloids are known from *Nymphaea* (Willaman 1961), and Díaz proposed that apomorphine "produces intense neurochemical and behavioral alterations" and may be responsible for entheogenic effects of water lilies (Díaz 1975). However, apomorphine is a synthetic opiate, formed by reaction of morphine and hydrochloric acid, and is a powerful emetic—*in vivo* formation of apomorphine is thought to explain the nausea associated with oral ingestion of morphine and opium—drugs not considered to be entheogenic (the structure given by Díaz is incorrect). There is no evidence whatever that this, or any other alkaloid of *Nymphaea* is entheogenic, and even Emboden, the most prominent champion of water lilies as entheogens, admitted "from my own experiences, I have found that mushrooms with entheogenic properties are superior to any water lily species in provoking the sensation of ecstasis..." (Emboden 1982). Acceptance of these plants as entheogens awaits some chemical or pharmacological proof. Recently it was proposed that *N. ampla*, as *quetzalaxochiatl*, was an inebriant of the ancient Aztecs (Díaz 1979; Garza 1990). Quinault Indians of northwestern United States apply hot rhizomes of *Nuphar polysepalum* to rheumatic joints, and the Makah Indians make similar medicinal use of this related water lily (Gunther 1981). The nearby Nitinaht Indians of Vancouver Island traditionally made a tonic from the rhizomes of this plant (Turner *et al.* 1983). The Bella Coola, Gitksan and Kwakiutl Indians likewise used the plant as an antirheumatic, contraceptive, analgesic and antiasthmatic remedy (Johnson Gottesfeld & Anderson 1988; Moerman 1986; Turner & Bell 1973). Species of *Nymphaea*, *Nelumbo* and *Nelubium* were reportedly used in Indonesian ethnomedicine as diuretics and said to be "more or less narcotic" (Hirschhorn 1983) while *Nymphaea lotus* was used as a food source in tropical West Africa (Oliver-Bever 1983). In Afghanistan, *N. ampla* is used as a cardiac sedative (Younos *et al.* 1987). In Kenya, roots of *N. lotus* are eaten as a food by the Turkana (Morgan 1981). *Nymphaea* species were reported as ingredients in one recipe for witches' "flying ointments" (Hansen 1978).

Obregonia denegrii (1, Note 7): This cactus is sometimes called *peyoti* or *peyotillo* and contains some of the *péyotl* alkaloids (Díaz 1979). It does not contain mescaline, and there is no evidence it bears more than a superficial resemblance to *péyotl.*

Opuntia acanthocarpa; O. basilaris; O. echinocarpa; O. ficus-indica; O. imbricata; O. spinosior (4, "Miscellaneous Admixtures"; Table 1): These cacti were reported to contain traces of mescaline (El-Moghazy *et al.* 1982; Ma *et al.* 1986; Meyer *et al.* 1980; Pardanani *et al.* 1978). The 0.0004–0.01% mescaline found in these cacti is insufficient for visionary effects, and traditional use of these plants as entheogens has not been reported. On the other hand, South American Sharanahua Indians regard a cultivated species of *Opuntia* called *tchai*, to be "hallucinogenic." This cactus may be mixed in *ayahuasca*, making the effects "very strong" (Schultes & Raffauf 1990). There is the possibility that the traces of mescaline found in these *Opuntia* species (several hundred times below typical concentrations of mescaline in *Lophophora williamsii*), may be sufficient to provoke visionary effects in the presence of the MAO-inhibitors of *ayahuasca* (see Chapter 4), just as those compounds can render the orally-inactive DMT entheogenic. Indeed, mescaline appears to be potentiated by the MAO-inhibiting β-carboline alkaloids found in *ayahuasca* (Ott 1994A)

Peganum harmala; Tribulus terrestris (4, "*Harmel... Haoma*?"; 6, Note 11): Although widely depicted in compendia of entheogenic plants (Emboden 1979; Ott 1979B; Schultes & Hofmann 1979; Schultes & Hofmann 1980), and suggested to represent the ancient Aryan entheogen *Soma* (Flattery & Schwartz 1989), there is no historical record of use of *Peganum harmala* as an entheogen. It does contain large quantities of β-carboline alkaloids such as harmine and harmaline, which have been widely considered to be entheogenic. However, human experiments with the pure compounds have failed to demonstrate unequivocal entheogenic effects (Naranjo 1967; Naranjo 1973B), and my own experiments with extracts of *harmel* seeds showed rather *Valium*-type effects than visionary properties (see Chapter 4). A recent sketchy report from Ladakh, India attributed "narcotic" properties to ingestion of powdered seeds of *P. harmala* and the related harmine-containing *Tribulus terrestris* (Navchoo & Buth 1990). There is also a vague report that swallowing *harmel* seeds "induces hallucination and sexual stimulation" in the Near East (Abulafatih 1987; Hooper & Field 1937). In Afghanistan, *P. harmala* is used ethnomedicinally as an antiseptic and hemostatic, while *T. terrestris* is used as a diuretic and spasmolytic (Younos *et al.* 1987).

Pelecyphora aselliformis; P. pseudo-pectinata (1, Note 7): Although known as *peyotillo*, *peyote* or *peyote meco* in México, and having a place in ethnomedicine (Bruhn & Bruhn 1973), there is no record of entheogenic use of *P. aselliformis* in México. It does contain alkaloids, including traces of mescaline, but in quantities insufficient to provoke entheogenic effects (Bruhn & Bruhn 1973; Neal *et al.* 1972). *P. pseudo-pectinata* likewise is known as a "kind" of *péyotl*, and contains some non-entheogenic *péyotl* alkaloids (Bruhn & Bruhn 1973).

Polaskia chende (Table 1): Although not reported to be used as an entheogen, this cactus was found to contain trace amounts (less than 0.01% dry weight) of mescaline (Ma *et al.* 1986). This is several hundred times less than the concentration of this visionary compound in *péyotl*, and this species cannot be considered to be entheogenic.

Pterocereus gaumeri (Table 1): This cactus has not been reported to be used an an entheogen, but was recently reported to contain around 0.01% (dry weight) of mescaline, insufficient, however, to provoke entheogenic effects (Ma *et al.* 1986).

Russula agglutinata; R. kirinea; R. maenadum; R. nondorbingi; R. pseudomaenadum (5, Note 5): The mycologist R. Singer alleged that *R. nondorbingi* caused "cerebral mycetisms," based on identifying it as a new species in a mixed collection of "madness-inducing" mushrooms said to be used by the Kuma of New Guinea (Singer *et al.* 1958B). Not only did Heim and Wasson fail to identify *R. nondorbingi* among the eleven species associated with the "mushroom madness" of the Kuma (which did include four species of *Russula*), but they concluded that this was a non-pharmacological phenomenon (Heim 1963; Heim 1965; Heim 1966; Heim 1973; Heim 1978; Heim & Wasson 1964; Heim & Wasson 1965). There is no evidence that these species, or any other species of *Russula*, are entheogenic, although *R. agglutinata* appeared in a popular compendium of entheogenic plants, misspelled as *R. agglutina* (Schultes & Hofmann 1979).

Sophora secundiflora (1, "North America Hegira"): Based mainly on findings of seeds of this species together with dried *péyotl* and *Ungnadia speciosa* in archaeological remains (Adovasio & Fry 1976), it has been conjectured that the Plains Indian use of *péyotl* supplanted an archaic "red bean cult" based on ceremonial ingestion of *S. secundiflora* seeds (Campbell 1958; Howard 1957; La Barre 1938A; Schultes & Hofmann 1980). Although non-entheogenic alkaloids are abundant in these seeds (Keller 1975; Keller *et al.* 1976), the evidence for their entheogenic use is not strong, and it has been suggested that the "red bean cult" had more to do with use of the seeds as adornment than as entheogens (Merrill 1977).

Stenocereus beneckei; S. eruca; S. stellatus; S. treleasei (Table 1): None of these cactus species have been found to be used as entheogens, but all were recently found to contain trace amounts (around 0.01% dry weight) of mescaline (Ma *et al.* 1986). This quantity is several hundreds of times lower than the mescaline content of *péyotl*, and these species cannot be considered to be entheogenic.

Stetsonia coryne (Table 1): Although this cactus species has been found to contain traces of mescaline (Agurell *et al.* 1971), the concentration is too low for entheogenic effects, and there is no evidence for entheogenic use of this cactus.

Strombocactus disciformis (1, Note 7): Although this cactus bears a superficial resemblance to *péyotl*, and may be known as *peyotillo* (Anderson 1980), it is not known to contain entheogenic compounds, nor has it ever been reported to be used as a traditional entheogen.

Ungnadia speciosa: Based on archaeological juxtaposition of seeds of this plant with dried *péyotl* and seeds of *Sophora secundiflora*, it has been proposed that *U. speciosa* is an entheogenic plant (Adovasio & Fry 1976; Schultes & Hofmann 1980). No entheogenic principles are known from these little-studied seeds, and there is absolutely no evidence for their use as sacred drugs.

IV. ADDENDUM TO SECOND EDITION IN PRESS

Acacia angustissima: In the sixteenth century, Spanish friar Motolinía reported that the Mexican Indians would add "vnas rrayzes," "some roots," to fermenting *pulque* (*Agave* wine) to enhance its inebriating effects (Motolinía 1971). The plant in question, called *ocpatl*, "*pulque* drug," is *Acacia angustissima*, today still known as *palo de pulque*, "*pulque* stick" (Díaz 1976; Gonçalves de Lima 1956). According to one sixteenth century decree proscribing the practice, the plant was cultivated for this purpose. Although we have no chemical information germane to this fortification, which is perhaps obsolete, at least seven species of *Acacia* are known to contain entheogenic tryptamines, which in general are concentrated in the roots and especially root barks (Ott 1994A), and Rätsch reported the addition of *Acacia* bark to West African millet beers; evidently also to enhance their effects (Rätsch 1996). The ancient Mexicans spoke of *teoctli* or "wondrous *pulque*," evidently *Agave* wine fortified with entheogens, and also known as *xochioctli*, "flower *pulque*" or "entheogenic *pulque*" (Gonçalves de Lima 1956; see Chapter 2, Note 17 and Chapter 6, Note 12)—might this not have been *pulque* epoptically enhanced by addition of the roots of *Acacia angustissima* during fermentation?

Lachnanthes tinctoria: Seminole and other southeastern North American Indian tribes used the roots of this common dye-plant in the Haemodoraceae family as a stimulant. Ingestion of the roots of this *spirit weed* or *red root* was said to be invigorating and to provoke eloquence and loquaciousness (Duke 1985). No psychotropic principles are as yet known from this interesting plant.

APPENDIX C

Entheopœia:
Index of Entheogen Chemistry and Pharmacology

1. ASARONES [*Merck Index* 11: 849; 12: 861; see *PIHKAL* No. 157, TMA]

Synonyms: 1,2,4-trimethoxy-5-(1-propenyl)-benzene; asarin; asarum camphor; asarabacca camphor; Asaron

Physical: $C_{12}H_{16}O_3$ molecular weight 208.26; C 69.21% H 7.74% O 23.05%

Isolation: Gatterman, *Berichte Deutschen Chemischen Gesellschaft* 32: 289, 1899 (*Asarum europaeum*); Baxter, *Nature* 185: 466, 1960 (*Acorus calamus*)

Synthesis: Seshadri, *Proceedings of the Indian Academy of Sciences* 32A: 110, 1950; Sharma, *Indian Journal of Applied Chemistry* 32: 236, 1969

Chemistry: *alpha*-asarone, needles from light petroleum, mp 62–63°; bp 296,° pract. insol. in water, sol. in alcohol, ether, chloroform, acetic acid

Pharmacology: reserpine-like, chlorpromazine-like sedative (Sharma, *Nature* 192: 1299, 1961); putative entheogen (Hoffer, *The Hallucinogens*, Academic, 1967)

Legal Status: not controlled

OCH_3 CH_3 CH_3O OCH_3

2. ATROPINE [*Merck Index* 11: 891; 12: 907]

Synonyms: *d,l*-tropyl tropate; endo(±)-α-(hydroxymethyl)benzene-acetic acid 8-methyl-8-azabicyclo[3.2.1]oct-3-yl ester; *d,l*-hyoscyamine; Atropin

Physical: $C_{17}H_{23}NO_3$ molecular weight 289.37; C 70.56% H 8.01% N 4.84% O 16.59%

Isolation: Chemnitius, *J. Praktische Chemie* 116: 276, 1927 (Solanaceae spp.)

Synthesis: Ladenburg, *Justus Liebig's Annalen der Chemie* 217: 75, 1883; Willstäter, *Berichte der Deutschen Chemischen Gesellschaft* 31: 1537, 1898

Chemistry: orthorhombic prisms from acetone, mp 114–116,° slightly soluble in water, alcohol; sulfate monohydrate, powder, mp 190–194,° water sol.

Pharmacology: deliriant (Gosselin, *Clinical Toxicology of Commercial Products*, Williams & Wilkins, 1984)

Legal Status: controlled, prescription drug

CH_3N CH_2OH OOCCH C_6H_5

3. BAEOCYSTINE

Synonyms: 3-[2-(methylamino)ethyl]-1*H*-indol-4-ol dihydrogen phosphate ester; desmethyl psilocybine; 4-phosphoryloxy-*N*-methyltryptamine; Baeocystin; 4-OP-MMT

Physical: $C_{11}H_{15}N_2O_4P$ molecular weight 270.28; C 48.88% H 5.59% N 10.36% O 23.68% P 11.46%

Isolation: Leung, *Journal of Pharmaceutical Sciences* 57: 1667, 1968 (*Psilocybe baeocystis*); Repke, *J. Pharm. Sci.* 66: 113, 1977 (*Psilocybe semilanceata*)

Synthesis: Troxler, *Helvetica Chimica Acta* 42: 2073, 1959; Brenneisen, *Archiv der Pharmazie* 321: 487, 1988

Chemistry: crystals from methanol, mp 254–258° (Leung, *J. Pharm. Sci.* 57: 1667, 1968); mp 245–248° (Repke, *J. Pharm. Sci.* 66: 113, 1977)

Pharmacology: psychoptic in 10 mg oral dose; 4 mg threshold (Gartz, pers. com.); active in animals (Cerletti, *Advances in Pharmacology* 6B: 233, 1968)

Legal Status: not scheduled, but potentially controlled analogue of psilocybine

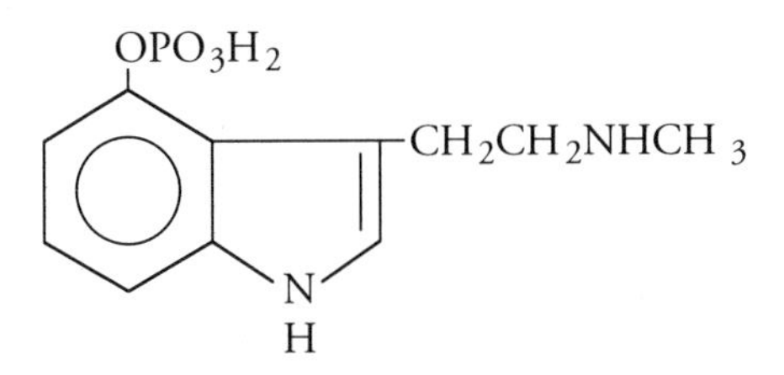

4. BUFOTENINE [*Merck Index* 11: 1467; 12: 1502]

Synonyms: 3-[2-(dimethylamino)ethyl]-1*H*-indol-5-ol; Bufotenin; 5-hydroxy-*N,N*-dimethyltryptamine; *N,N*-dimethylserotonine; Mappin; 5-OH-DMT

Physical: $C_{12}H_{16}N_2O$ molecular weight 204.27; C 70.56% H 7.89% N 13.71% O 7.83%

Isolation: Handovsky, *Arch. Exp. Path. Pharm.* 86: 138, 1920 (*Bufo vulgaris*); Stromberg, *J. Am. Chem. Soc.* 76: 1707, 1954 (*Anadenanthera peregrina*)

Synthesis: Hoshino, *Liebig's Ann. Chem.* 520: 19, 1935; Speeter, *J. American Chemical Society* 76: 6208, 1954; Stoll, *Helvetica Chimica Acta* 38: 1452, 1955

Chemistry: prisms from ethyl acetate, mp 146–147,° pract. insol. in water, sol. in alcohol, dilute acids; methyliodide, prisms from methanol, mp 214–15°

Pharmacology: psychoactive 10–12 mg i.m.; 10 mg i.v. (Turner, *Archives of Neurology and Psychiatry* 81: 121, 1959; Fabing, *Science* 123: 886, 1956)

Legal Status: controlled, Schedule I

HO — $CH_2CH_2N(CH_3)_2$

N
H

5. DIETHYLTRYPTAMINE

Synonyms: 3-[2-(diethylamino)ethyl]-indole; *N,N*-diethyltryptamine; DET; T-9; Diäthyltryptamin
Physical: $C_{14}H_{20}N_2$ molecular weight 216.19; C 77.72% H 9.32% N 12.96%
Isolation: as yet only known as an artificial compound
Synthesis: Barlow, *British Journal of Pharmacology* 14: 99, 1959; Speeter, *Journal of the American Chemical Society* 76: 6208, 1954
Chemistry: crystals from petroleum ether, mp 85–89,° sol. in ether, chloroform; hydrochloride, mp 172–173,° sol. in water
Pharmacology: psychoptic at 1 mg/kg i.m. (Szára, *Proc. Third World Congress of Psychiatry* 1: 670, 1961; Szára, *Archives of General Psychiatry* 15: 320, 1966)
Legal Status: controlled, Schedule I

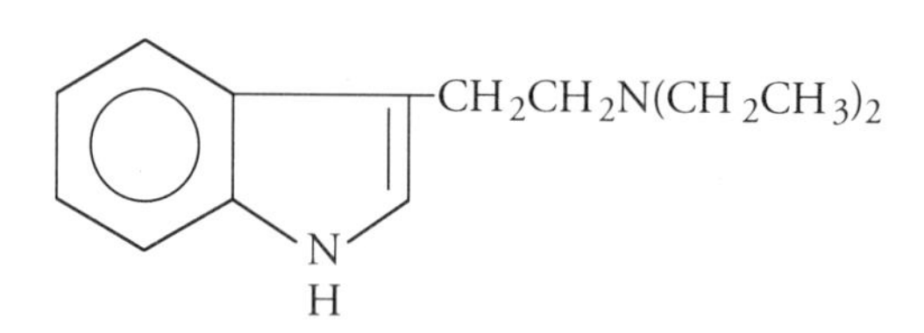

6. DIETHYL-4-HYDROXYTRYPTAMINE

Synonyms: 3-[2-(diethylamino)ethyl]-1*H*-indol-4-ol; 4-hydroxy-*N,N*-diethyltryptamine; CZ-74; 4-OH-DET
Physical: $C_{14}H_{20}N_2O$ molecular weight 232.45; C 72.34% H 8.67% N 12.10% O 6.88%
Isolation: still known only as an artificial compound; but has been biosynthesized
Synthesis: Troxler, *Helvetica Chimica Acta* 42: 2073, 1959
Chemistry: crystals from acetone, mp 104–106°
Pharmacology: psychoptic in same dose range as psilocine (Leuner, *Neuro-Psychopharmacology*, Elsevier, 1965)
Legal Status: not scheduled but potentially controlled analogue of (Schedule I) DET

OH
$CH_2CH_2N(CH_2CH_3)_2$
N
H

7. DIETHYL-4-PHOSPHORYLOXYTRYPTAMINE

Synonyms: 3-[2-(diethylamino)ethyl]-1*H*-indol-4-ol dihydrogen phosphate ester; 4-phosphoryloxy-*N,N*-diethyltryptamine; CY-19; CEY-19; 4-OP-DET

Physical: $C_{14}H_{21}N_2O_4P$ molecular weight 312.31; C 53.84% H 6.78% N 8.97% O 20.49% P 9.92%

Isolation: as yet known only as an artificial compound

Synthesis: Troxler, *Helvetica Chimica Acta* 42: 2073, 1959

Chemistry: crystals from methanol, mp 260–263°

Pharmacology: psychoptic in same dose range as psilocybine (Leuner, *Neuro-Psychopharmacology*, Elsevier, 1965)

Legal Status: not scheduled but potentially controlled as analogue of psilocybine

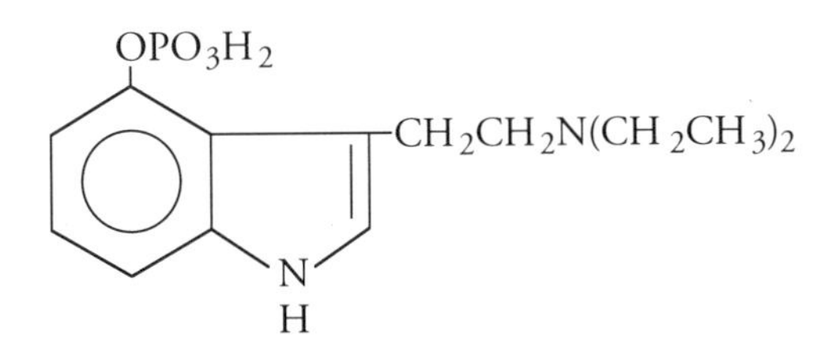

8. DIMETHYLTRYPTAMINE [*Merck Index* 11: 3251; 12: 3311]

Synonyms: 3-[2-(dimethylamino)ethyl]-indole; *N,N*-dimethyltryptamine; DMT; nigerina; nigerine; Dimethyltryptamin

Physical: $C_{12}H_{16}N_2$ molecular weight 188.27; C 76.55% H 8.57% N 14.88%

Isolation: Fish, *J. Am. Chem. Soc.* 77: 5892, 1955 (*Anadenanthera peregrina*); Agurell, *Acta Chemica Scandinavica* 23: 903, 1969 (*Virola theiodora*)

Synthesis: Manske, *Canadian Journal of Research* 5: 592, 1931; Speeter & Anthony, *Journal of the American Chemical Society* 76: 6208, 1954

Chemistry: crystals from ethanol, mp 44.6–46.8,° sol. in dilute acids; picrate, mp 169.5–170.5°; methiodide, mp 216–217°; fumarate, mp 152–152.5°

Pharmacology: psychoptic at 1 mg/kg i.m. (Szára, *Experientia* 12: 441, 1956; Sai-Halász, *Psychiatria et Neurologia* 135: 285, 1958)

Legal Status: controlled, Schedule I

CH2CH2N(CH3)2
N
H

9. DIMETHYL-5-METHOXYTRYPTAMINE

Synonyms: 3-[2-(dimethylamino)ethyl]-5-methoxyindole; 5-methoxy-*N,N*-dimethyltryptamine; 5-MEO-DMT; *O*-methylbufotenine

Physical: $C_{13}H_{18}N_2O$ molecular weight 218.17; C 71.51% H 8.32% N 12.84% O 7.33%

Isolation: Legler, *Die Naturwißenschaften* 50: 94, 1963 (*Anadenanthera peregrina*); Holmstedt, *Arch. Int. Pharmacod. Thér.* 156: 285, 1965 (*Virola theiodora*)

Synthesis: Benington, *Journal of Organic Chemistry* 23: 1977, 1958; Gessner, *Am. Journal Physiology* 203: 167, 1962; Stoll, *Helv. Chim. Acta* 38: 1452, 1955

Chemistry: prismatic crystals from hexane, mp 67.5–68.5°; oxalate, mp 173°; picrate, mp 175–176°; methiodide, mp 183°

Pharmacology: psychoptic at 5–10 mg vaporized (Shulgin in De Smet, *Journal of Ethnopharmacology* 9: 129, 1983)

Legal Status: not controlled

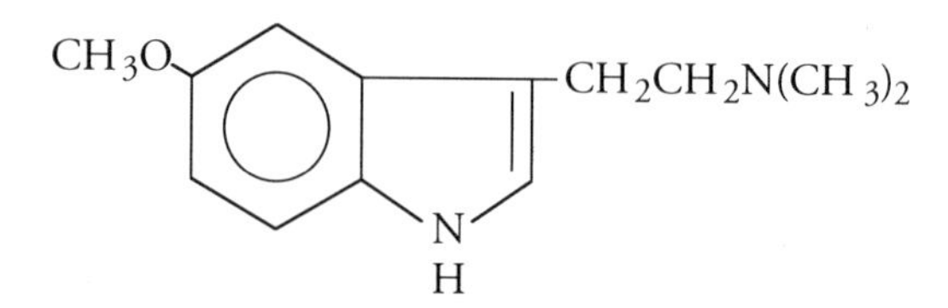

10. DIPROPYLTRYPTAMINE

Synonyms: 3-[2-(dipropylamino)ethyl]-indole; *N,N*-dipropyltryptamine; DPT; Dipropyltryptamin

Physical: $C_{16}H_{24}N_2$ molecular weight 244.38; C 78.64% H 9.90% O 11.46%

Isolation: as yet known only as an artificial compound

Synthesis: Barlow, *British Journal of Pharmacology* 14: 99, 1959; Speeter, *J. Am. Chem. Soc.* 76: 6208, 1954; Vitali, *Bol. Sci. Fac. Chim. Ind.* 17: 84, 1959

Chemistry: hydrochloride crystals, mp 174.5–178,° sol. in water

Pharmacology: psychoptic above 1 mg/kg (Szára, *Feder. Proc.* 20: 885, 1961); psychotherapy at 90–100 mg doses (Grof, *Hum. Encoun. Death*, Dutton, 1977)

Legal Status: not controlled

CH2CH2N(CH2CH2CH3)2
N
H

11. DOB [*PIHKAL* No. 62]; **2C-B** [*Merck Index* 12: 1958; *PIHKAL* No. 20]

Synonyms: 2,5-dimethoxy-4-bromo-phenylisopropylamine; 2,5-dimethoxy-4-bromoamphetamine; PBR

Physical: $C_{11}H_{16}NO_2Br$ molecular weight 274.05; C 48.17% H 5.88% N 5.11% O 11.68% BR 29.16%

Isolation: yet only an artificial compound (Shulgin, *J. Psych. Drugs* 13: 99, 1981)

Synthesis: Shulgin, *Pharmacology* 5: 103, 1971; Sargent, *Neuropharm.* 14: 165, 1975

Chemistry: crystalline HCL salt from isopropanol or ethanol/ether, mp 198–199°; **11A. 2C-B** [2,5-dimethoxy-4-bromo-phenethylamine; α-desmethyl-DOB; *Nexus*; *Erox*; BDMPEA; MFT; $C_{10}H_{14}NO_2Br$ molecular weight 260.13; C 46.17% H 5.42% N 5.38% O 12.30% BR 30.72%] HCL, white or pale pink needles from ethanol, mp 237–239° (dec); HBR, mp 214.5–215°

Pharmacology: DOB psychoptic at 2–3 mg racemate; 1–2 mg *"R"* isomer; toxic at 35–75 mg (Shulgin, *Journal of Psychoactive Drugs* 13: 99, 1981); 2C-B psychotropic at 12–24 mg (Shulgin & Shulgin, *PIHKAL*, Transform, 1991)

Legal Status: DOB controlled, Schedule I; 2C-B controlled, Schedule I

CH_3O NH_2 R Br OCH_3

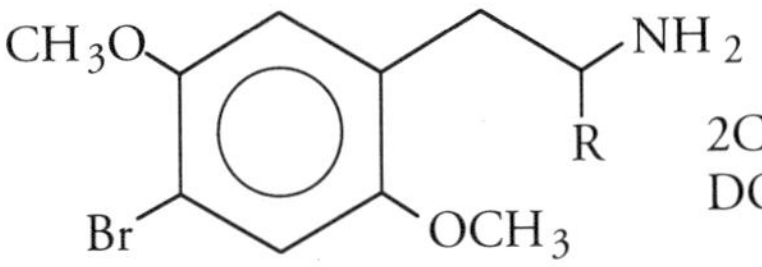

2C-B: R = H
DOB: R = CH_3

12. DOI [*PIHKAL* No. 67]

Synonyms: 2,5-dimethoxy-4-iodo-phenylisopropylamine; 2,5-dimethoxy-4-iodo-amphetamine

Physical: $C_{11}H_{16}NO_2I$ molecular weight 321.16; C 41.14% H 5.02% N 4.36% O 9.96% I 39.51%

Isolation: still known only as an artificial compound

Synthesis: Shulgin & Shulgin, *PIHKAL*, Transform Press, Berkeley, 1991

Chemistry: colorless oil, soluble in ether; hydrochloride, white crystals, mp 200.5–201.5°

Pharmacology: psychoptic at 1.5–3.0 mg peroral (Shulgin, *PIHKAL*, Transform, 1991)

Legal Status: not scheduled; potentially controlled as analogue of (Schedule I) DOB

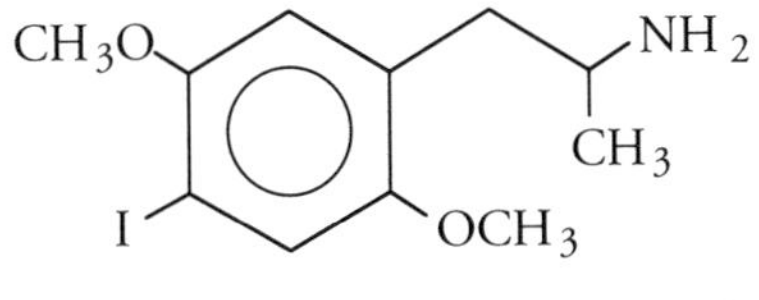

CH_3O NH_2 CH_3 I OCH_3

13. DOM [*PIHKAL* No. 68]

Synonyms: 2,5-dimethoxy-4-methyl-phenylisopropylamine; Serenity, Tranquility, Peace; 2,5-dimethoxy-4-methylamphetamine; STP; Stop The Police
Physical: $C_{12}H_{19}NO_2$ molecular weight 209.16; C 68.85% H 9.16% N 6.69% O 15.30%
Isolation: as yet known only as an artificial compound
Synthesis: Shulgin & Shulgin, *PIHKAL*, Transform Press, Berkeley, 1991
Chemistry: mp 60–61°; sol. in organic solvents; hydrochloride, sol. in water, alcohol, mp 187–188°; sulfate, mp 131°
Pharmacology: Snyder, *Science* 158: 669, 1967; Hollister, *Psychopharmacology* 14: 62, 1969; 3–10 mg psychoptic orally (Shulgin, *PIHKAL*, Transform, 1991)
Legal Status: controlled, Schedule I

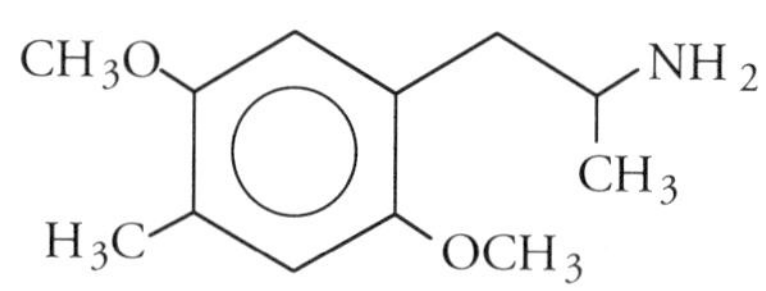

14. ELEMICIN [see *PIHKAL* No. 157, TMA]

Synonyms: 3,4,5-trimethoxy-1-(2-propenyl)benzene
Physical: $C_{12}H_{16}O_3$ molecular weight 208.25; C 69.21% H 7.74% O 23.05%
Isolation: Shulgin, *Ethnopharmacologic Search for Psychoactive Drugs*, U.S. Government Printing Office, Washington, D.C., 1967 (*Myristica fragrans*)
Synthesis: Hahn, *Berichte der Deutschen Chemischen Gesellschaft* 67: 696, 1934; Peart, *Journal of the American Chemical Society* 70: 1747, 1948
Chemistry: bp 175°
Pharmacology: presumed psychoactive component of nutmeg (Shulgin, Truitt, *Ethnopharm. Search Psychoact. Drugs*, U.S. Government Print. Office, 1967)
Legal Status: not controlled

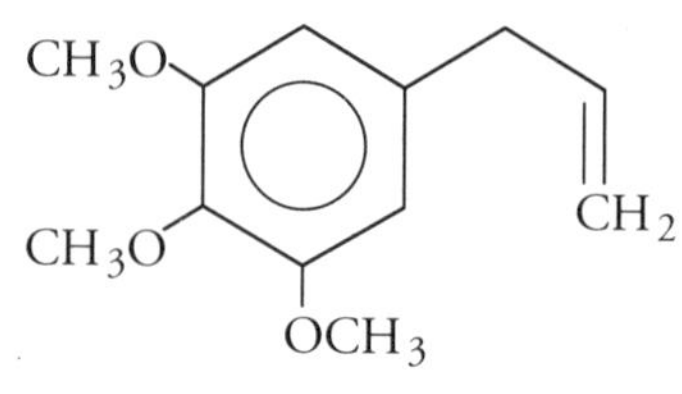

15. ERGINE [*Merck Index* 11: 5505; 12: 5663]

Synonyms: 9,10-didehydro-6-methylergoline-8β-carboxamide; lysergic acid amide, lysergamide; LA-111; Ergin; Lysergsäure amid

Physical: $C_{16}H_{17}N_3O$ molecular wt. 267.33; C 71.89% H 6.41% N 15.72% O 5.98%

Isolation: Hofmann, *Experientia* 16: 414, 1960 (*Turbina corymbosa*); Arcamone, *Nature* 187: 238, 1960 (*Claviceps paspali*)

Synthesis: Smith, *Journal of the Chemical Society* 763, 1932 (degradation of ergot alkaloids); Stoll, *Helv. Chimica Acta* 38: 421, 1955 (from lysergic acid)

Chemistry: prisms from methanol, mp 242° (dec), water sol.; methanesulfonate, prisms from methanol/acetone, mp 232° (dec), slightly sol. in water

Pharmacology: psychoptic at 0.5–1 mg oral (Hofmann, *Botanical Museum Leaflets* Harvard University 20: 194, 1963; Solms, *Praxis* 45: 746, 1956)

Legal Status: controlled, Schedule III

16. ERGONOVINE [*Merck Index* 11: 3600; 12: 3694]

Synonyms: D-lysergic acid-L-2-propanolamide; Ergobasin; ergotocin; ergometrine; ergostetrine; *N*-[α-(hydroxymethyl)ethyl]-D-lysergamide; *Ergotrate*; *Syntometrine*; Ergonovin

Physical: $C_{19}H_{23}N_3O_2$ molecular wt. 325.41; C 70.13% H 7.12% N 12.91% O 9.83%

Isolation: Hofmann, *Bot. Mus. Leaf.* Harv. Univ. 20: 194, 1963 (*Ipomoea violacea*)

Synthesis: Stoll, *Helvetica Chimica Acta* 26: 956, 1943 (from lysergic acid); Kornfeld, *J. of the American Chemical Society* 76: 5256, 1954 (total synthesis)

Chemistry: tetrahedra from ethyl acetate; needles from benzene, mp 162,° sol. in water, alcohols; maleate (*Ermetrine*), mp 167,° sol. in water, alcohol

Pharmacology: psychoptic at 2–10 mg oral (Hofmann, *The Road to Eleusis*, Harcourt Br. Jovan. 1978; Bigwood, *Journal of Psychedelic Drugs* 11: 147, 1979)

Legal Status: controlled, prescription

17. HARMALINE [*Merck Index* 11: 4528; 12: 4644]

Synonyms: 4,9-dihydro-7-methoxy-1-methyl-3*H*-pyrido[3,4-*b*]indole; Harmalin; 3,4-dihydroharmine; harmidine; harmalol methyl ether; Harmidin

Physical: $C_{13}H_{14}N_2O$ molecular weight 214.27; C 72.87% H 6.59% N 13.07% O 7.47%

Isolation: Göbel, *Liebig's Annalen der Chemie* 38: 363, 1841 (*Peganum harmala*); Hochstein, *J. Am. Chemical Society* 79: 5735, 1957 (*Banisteriopsis caapi*)

Synthesis: Späth, *Berichte der Deutschen Chemischen Gesellschaft* 63: 120, 2102, 1930; Spenser, *Canadian Journal of Chemistry* 37: 1851, 1959

Chemistry: prisms, tablets from methanol; octahedra from ethanol, mp 229–231,° slightly sol. in water, alcohol, ether; HCL yellow, sol. in water, mp 212°

Pharmacology: psychoactive above 1 mg/kg i.v. or 4 mg/kg oral (Naranjo, *Ethnopharm. Search Psychoact. Drugs*, U.S. Government Print. Office, 1967); sedative

Legal Status: not controlled, but appears to be "watched"

CH_3O N H CH_3 N

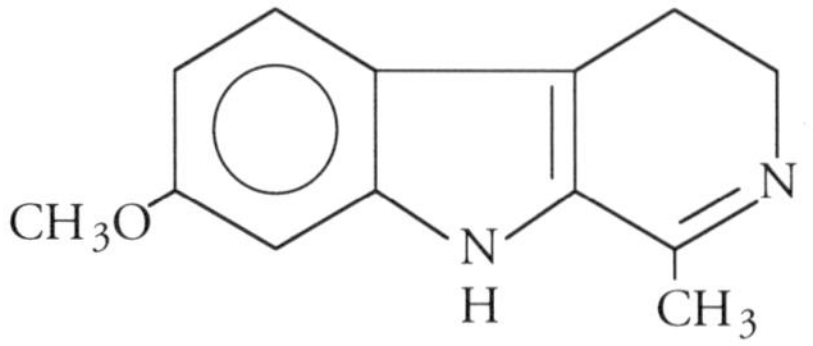

18. HARMINE [*Merck Index* 11: 4531; 12: 4647]

Synonyms: 7-methoxy-1-methyl-9*H*-pyrido[3,4-*b*]indole; banisterine; telepatina; telepathine, yajéina; yajéine; leucoharmine; Banisterin, Harmin

Physical: $C_{13}H_{12}N_2O$ molecular weight 212.25; C 73.57% H 5.70% N 13.20% O 7.54%

Isolation: Fritzsche, *Liebig's Ann. der Chem.* 64: 360, 1847 (*Peganum harmala*); Hochstein, *J. Am. Chem. Soc.* 79: 5735, 1957 (*Banisteriopsis caapi*)

Synthesis: Späth, *Ber. Deut. Chem. Gesel.* 63B: 120, 1930; Harvey, *J. Chem. Soc.* 97, 1938

Chemistry: prisms from methanol, mp 261° (dec), slightly sol. in water, alcohol, chloroform, ether; HCL, mp 262° (dec), 321° anhydrous, sol. in water

Pharmacology: psychoactive above 2 mg/kg i.v.; 8 mg/kg oral (Naranjo, *Ethnopharm. Search Psychoact. Drugs*, U.S. Government Print. Office, 1967); sedative

Legal Status: not controlled, but appears to be "watched"

CH_3O N H CH_3 N

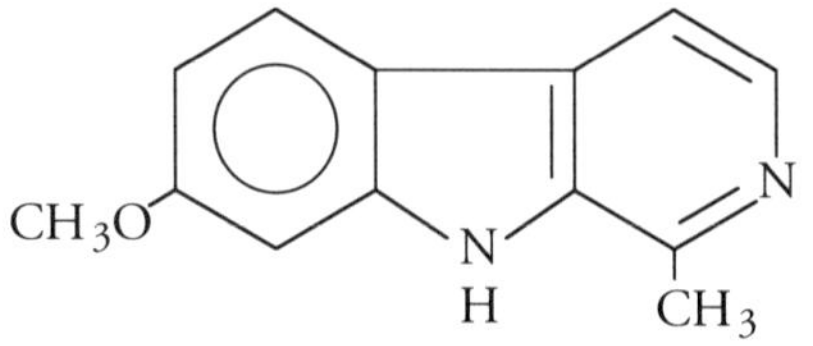

19. HARMINE-1,2,3,4-TETRAHYDRO

Synonyms: 2,3,4,9-tetrahydro-7-methoxy-1-methyl-1*H*-pyrido[3,4-*b*]indole; 1,2-dihydroharmaline; leptaflorine, THH

Physical: $C_{13}H_{16}N_2O$ molecular weight 216.28; C 72.19% H 7.46% N 12.95% O 7.40%

Isolation: Paris, *Bull. Soc. Chim. Fr.* 1957: 780, 1957 (*Leptactinia densiflora*); Hochstein, *J. American Chemical Society* 79: 5735, 1957 (*Banisteriopsis caapi*)

Synthesis: Perkin, *Journal of the Chemical Society* 115: 961, 1919 (racemate)

Chemistry: needles from methanol, mp 198.4–199.8° (*Banisteriopsis R* enantiomer); 198–199° (synthetic racemate), sol. in ethanol, methanol, chloroform

Pharmacology: psychotropic in human beings above 3 mg/kg i.v. or 12 mg/kg oral (Naranjo, *Ethnopharm. Search Psychoact. Drugs*, U.S. Gov't. Print. Off., 1967)

Legal Status: not controlled, but appears to be "watched"

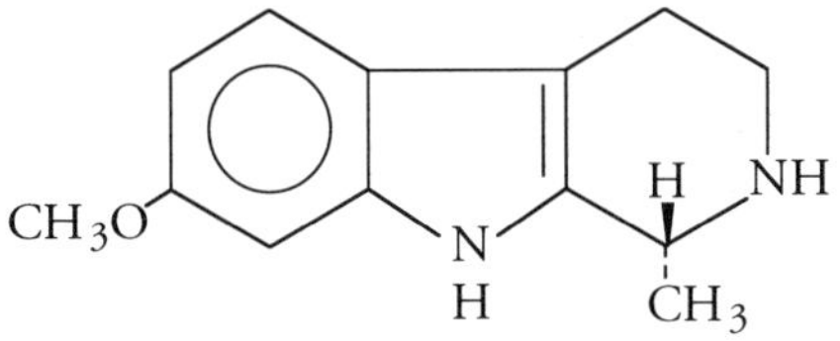

CH3O NH H N H CH3

20. IBOGAINE [*Merck Index* 11: 4806; 12: 4920]

Synonyms: 12-methoxy-ibogamine; Ibogain, *Endabuse* [*sic*]

Physical: $C_{20}H_{26}N_2O$ molecular weight 310.44; C 77.38% H 8.44% N 9.02% O 5.15%

Isolation: Dybowski, *Compt. Rend. Acad. Sci.* 133: 748, 1901 (*Tabernanthe iboga*); Van Beek, *J. of Ethnopharmacology* 10: 1, 1984 (*Tabernaemontana* spp.)

Synthesis: Büchi, *Journal of the American Chemical Society* 88: 3099, 1966; Rosenmund, *Berichte der Deutschen Chemischen Gesellschaft* 108: 1871, 1975

Chemistry: prismatic needles from ethanol, mp 152–153,° sol. in ethanol, ether, chloroform, acetone; hydrochloride, mp 299–300° (dec), sol. in water

Pharmacology: psychoptic above 1 mg/kg (Schneider, *Annals of the New York Academy of Sciences* 66: 765, 1957; Pope, *Economic Botany* 23: 174, 1969)

Legal Status: controlled, Schedule 1

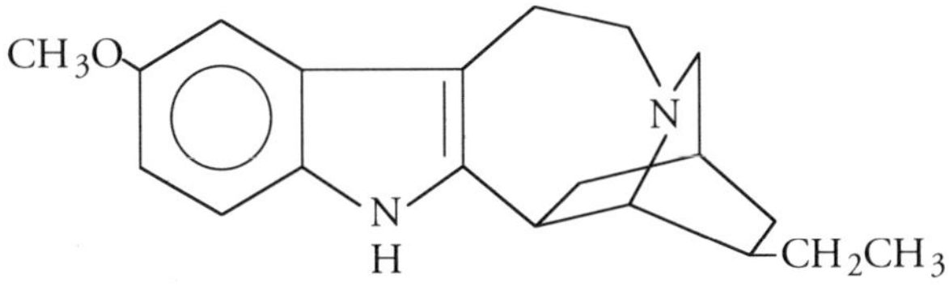

CH3O N N H CH2CH3

21. IBOTENIC ACID [*Merck Index* 11: 4808; 12: 4922]

Synonyms: α-amino-2,3-dihydro-3-oxo-5-isoxazoleacetic acid; Prämuscimol; α-amino-(3-hydroxy-5-isoxazolyl)acetic acid; Pilzatropin; Ibotensäure

Physical: $C_5H_6N_2O_4$ molecular wt. 158.11; C 37.98% H 3.82% N 17.72% O 40.48%

Isolation: Takemoto, *Yakugaku Zasshi* 84: 1186, 1964 (*Amanita strobiliformis*); Eugster, *Tetrahedron Letters* 1813, 1965 (*Amanita muscaria*)

Synthesis: Gagneux, *Tet. Lett.* 2081, 1965; Nakamura, *Chem. Pharm. Bull. Jpn.* 19: 46, 1971; Kishida, *ibid.* 14: 92, 1966; Sirakawa, *ibid.* 14: 89, 1966

Chemistry: crystals from water or methanol, mp 151–152° (anhyd.), 144–146° (monohydrate), sol. in water

Pharmacology: psychoptic above 1 mg/kg (Chilton, *McIlvainea* 2: 17, 1975); flavor-enhancer, neurotoxin

Legal Status: not controlled

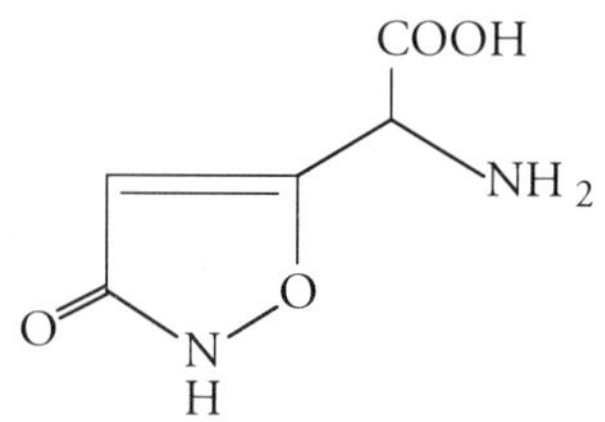

22. KAWAIN [*Merck Index* 11: 5167; 12: 5299]; **DIHYDROKAWAIN**

Synonyms: 5,6-dihydro-4-methoxy-6-(2-phenylethenyl)-2*H*-pyran-2-one; kavain, gonosan

Physical: $C_{14}H_{14}O_3$ molecular weight 230.26; C 73.03% H 6.13% O 20.84%

Isolation: Borsche, *Berichte der Deutschen Chemischen Gesellschaft* 63: 2414, 1930; Hänsel, *Die Naturwißenschaften* 45: 573, 1958 (*Piper methysticum*)

Synthesis: Fowler, *J. Chem. Soc.* 3642, 1950; Kostermans, *Nature* 166: 788, 1950

Chemistry: rods from methanol/ether, mp 105–106,° sol. in acetone, ether, methanol, pract. insol. in water, slightly sol. in hexane; **22A. DIHYDROKAWAIN** [marindinin; $C_{14}H_{16}O_3$ molecular weight 232.27; C 72.39% H 6.94% O 20.66%] crystals from ether, mp 58–60,° sol. in alcohol, chloroform, slightly sol. in ether; practically insol. in water, petr. ether

Pharmacology: muscle relaxant (Meyer, *Ethno. Search Psychoactive Drugs*, U.S. Gov't. Print. Office, 1967); DIHYDROKAWAIN human sedative (Pfeiffer, *ibid.*)

Legal Status: not controlled

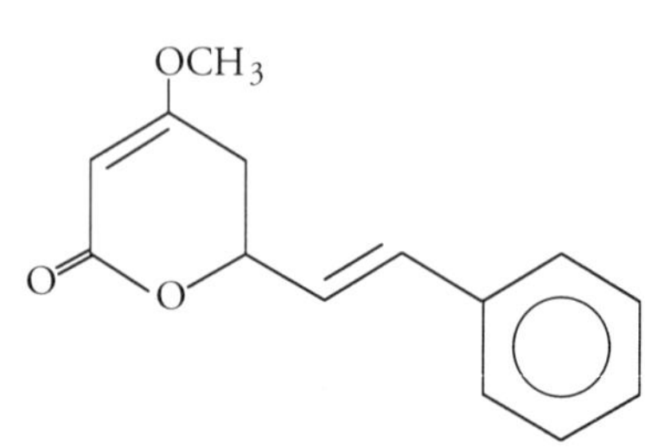

23. LSD [*Merck Index* 11: 5507; 12: 5665]

Synonyms: 9,10-didehydro-*N,N*-diethyl-6-methylergoline-8β-carboxamide; D-lysergic acid diethylamide; Lysergsäure Diäthylamid; LSD; LSD-25; EA-1729; lysergide; *N,N*-diethyl-D-lysergamide; acid; clear light; blotter
Physical: $C_{20}H_{25}N_3O$ molecular wt. 323.44; C 74.27% H 7.79% N 12.99% O 4.95%
Isolation: still only artificial, but probably natural; has been biosynthesized
Synthesis: Stoll, *Helv. Chim. Acta* 26: 944, 1943; Stoll, *Helv. Chim. Acta* 38: 421, 1955
Chemistry: prisms from benzene, mp 80–85°; D-tartrate (*Delysid*) prisms from methanol, mp 198–200,° sol. in water
Pharmacology: psychoptic above 1 mcg/kg (Hofmann, *LSD: My Problem Child*, McGraw-Hill, 1980; Shulgin, *Journal of Psychedelic Drugs* 12: 173, 1980)
Legal Status: controlled, Schedule 1

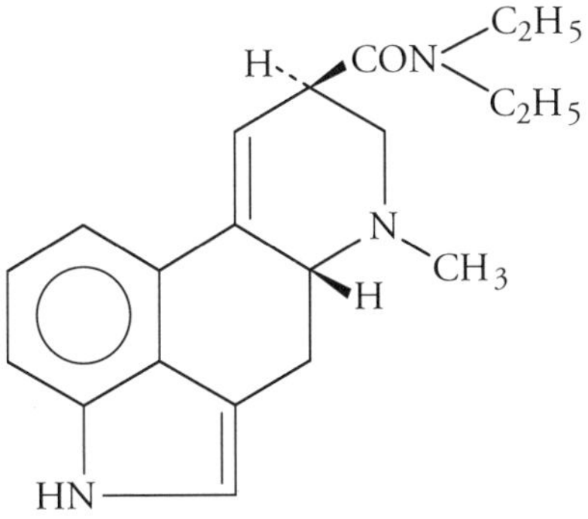

24. MDA [*Merck Index* 12: 5804; *PIHKAL* No. 100]

Synonyms: 3,4-methylene-dioxyphenylisopropylamine; *Amphedoxamine*; 3,4-methylene-dioxyamphetamine, The Love Drug; SKF-5; EA-1298
Physical: $C_{10}H_{13}NO_2$ molecular wt. 179.22; C 67.02% H 7.31% N 7.82% O 17.85%
Isolation: as yet known only as an artificial compound
Synthesis: E. Merck Co., Ger. pat. 274,350, 1914; Shulgin & Shulgin, *PIHKAL*, Transform Press, Berkeley, 1991
Chemistry: oil, bp 80–90°; hydrochloride, crystals from isopropanol, mp 187–8°
Pharmacology: psychoactive above 1–2 mg/kg oral (Alles, *Neuropharmacology*, Macy Found., 1959; Naranjo, *Med. Pharm. Exp.* 17: 357, 1967)
Legal Status: controlled, Schedule 1

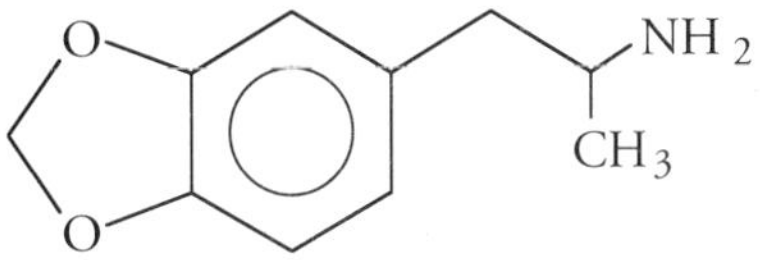

25. MDMA [*Merck Index* 11: 5646; 12: 5806; *PIHKAL* No. 109]

Synonyms: *N*,α-dimethyl-1,3-benzodioxole-5-ethanamine; Adam; 3,4-methylenedioxymethamphetamine; Ecstasy, XTC, MDM, Éxtasis

Physical: $C_{11}H_{15}NO_2$ molecular weight 193.25; C 68.37% H 7.82% N 7.25% O 16.56%

Isolation: still only known as an artificial compound

Synthesis: E. Merck Co., Ger. pat. 274,350, 1914; Kasuya, *Yakugaku Zasshi* 78: 509, 1958; Krajewski, *Acta Polon. Pharm.* 17: 421, 1960

Chemistry: oil, bp 100–110°; HCL (Ecstasy), crystals, mp 148–149,° sol. in water

Pharmacology: psychoactive above 1–2 mg/kg oral (Braun, *Journal of Pharmaceutical Sciences* 69: 192, 1980; Braun, *Arzneimittel-Forschung* 30: 825, 1980)

Legal Status: controlled, Schedule I

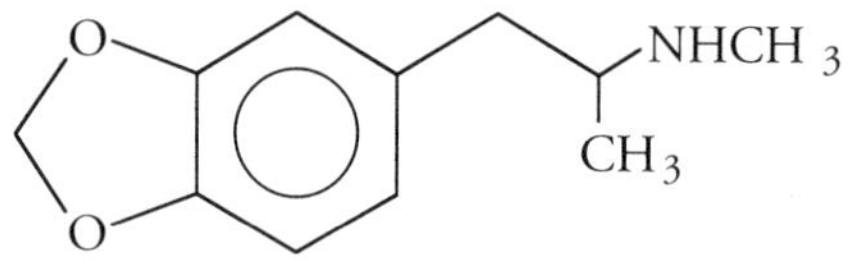

26. MMDA [*PIHKAL* No. 132]

Synonyms: 3-methoxy-4,5-methylenedioxy-phenylisopropylamine; 3-methoxy-4,5-methylenedioxyamphetamine

Physical: $C_{11}H_{15}NO_3$ molecular weight 209.24; C 63.14% H 7.22% N 6.69% O 22.94%

Isolation: still known only as an artificial compound

Synthesis: Shulgin & Shulgin, *PIHKAL*, Transform Press, Berkeley, 1991

Chemistry: hydrochloride, white crystals, mp 190–191°

Pharmacology: psychoactive at oral doses of 100–250 mg (Shulgin & Shulgin, *PIHKAL*, Transform Press, Berkeley, 1991)

Legal Status: not scheduled, but potentially controlled analogue of MDMA

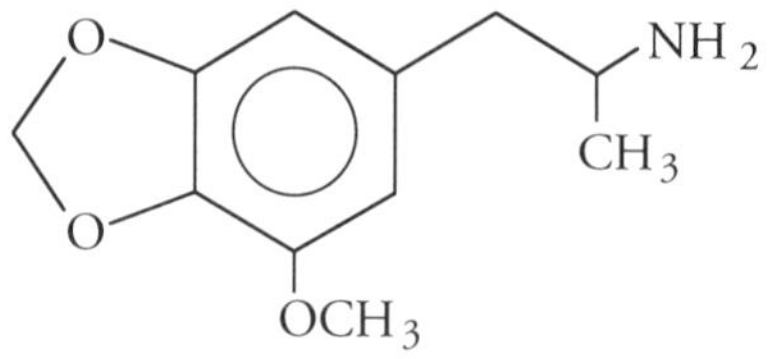

27. MESCALINE [*Merck Index* 11: 5808; 12: 5965; *PIHKAL* No. 96]

Synonyms: 3,4,5-trimethoxy-benzeneethanamine; 3,4,5-trimethoxy-β-phenethylamine; Mezcalin; Mescalin; Meskalin; Mezkalin; EA-1306; M

Physical: $C_{11}H_{17}NO_3$ molecular wt. 211.26; C 62.54% H 8.11% N 6.63% O 22.72%

Isolation: Heffter, *Ber. Deut. Chem. Gesell.* 29: 221, 1896 (*Lophophora* spp.); Poisson, *Annales Pharmaceutiques Françaises* 18: 764, 1960 (*Trichocereus*)

Synthesis: Späth, *Monatshefte für Chemie* 40: 129, 1919; Aboul-Enein, *Acta Pharmaceutica Suecica* 16: 267, 1979

Chemistry: crystals, mp 35–36,° bp 180,° sol. in water, alcohol, chloroform, benzene; HCL, mp 181,° sol. in water; sulfate, mp 183–186,° sol. in water

Pharmacology: psychoptic above 2–3 mg/kg (Heffter, *Arch. Exp. Path. Pharm.* 40: 385, 1898; Anderson, *Peyote the Divine Cactus*, Univ. Arizona, 1980)

Legal Status: controlled, Schedule I

CH3O NH2 CH3O OCH3

28. METHYLERGONOVINE [*Merck Index* 11: 5989; 12: 6147]

Synonyms: 9,10-didehydro-*N*-[1-(hydroxymethyl)propyl]-D-lysergamide; D-lysergic acid(+)-2-butanolamide; methylergometrine; Methylergobasin; Methylergonovin

Physical: $C_{20}H_{25}N_3O_2$ molecular wt. 339.44; C 70.77% H 7.42% N 12.38% O 9.43%

Isolation: still known only as an artificial compound

Synthesis: Stoll, *Helv. Chim. Acta* 26: 956, 1943; Stoll, U.S. pat. 2,265,207, 1941

Chemistry: crystals from benzene, mp 172,° sparingly sol. in water, sol. in alcohol, acetone; maleate (*Methergine*) powder, sol. in water, alcohol, chloroform

Pharmacology: psychoptic above 2 mg (Ott, *Journal of Psychedelic Drugs* 12: 165, 1980); oxytocic at 0.2 mg (Hofmann, *Die Mutterkornalkaloide*, F. Enke, 1964)

Legal Status: controlled, prescription drug

H CH2CH3 H CONH CH2OH N CH3 H HN

29. METHYLISOPROPYL-4-HYDROXYTRYPTAMINE

Synonyms: 3-[2-(methylisopropylamino)ethyl]-1*H*-indol-4-ol; 4-OH-MIPT; 4-hydroxy-*N*-methyl-*N*-isopropyltryptamine
Physical: $C_{14}H_{20}N_2O$ molecular weight 232.45; C 72.34% H 8.67%; N 12.10% O 6.88%
Isolation: still known only as an artificial compound
Synthesis: Repke, *Journal of Heterocyclic Chemistry* 18: 175, 1981
Chemistry: crystals from ethyl acetate/hexane, mp 123–124°
Pharmacology: psychoptic at 10 mg orally (Repke, *J. Medicinal Chem.* 28: 892, 1985)
Legal Status: not scheduled, but potentially controlled as an analogue of psilocine

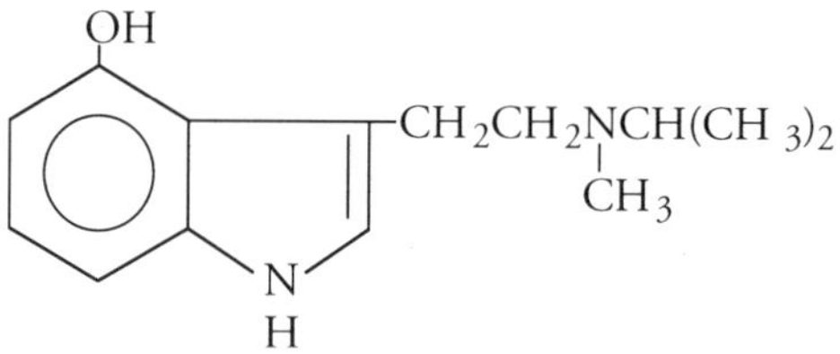

30. METHYLISOPROPYL-5-METHOXYTRYPTAMINE

Synonyms: 3-[2-(methylisopropylamino)ethyl]-5-methoxyindole; 5-MEO-MIPT; 5-methoxy-*N*-methyl-*N*-isopropyltryptamine
Physical: $C_{15}H_{22}N_2O$ molecular weight 246.35; C 73.13% H 9.00% N 11.37% O 6.49%
Isolation: still known only as an artificial compound
Synthesis: Repke, *Journal of Medicinal Chemistry* 28: 892, 1985
Chemistry: hydrochloride, mp 162–163°
Pharmacology: stimulant with "general heightening of awareness" at 5 mg dose orally (Repke, *Journal of Medicinal Chemistry* 28: 892, 1985)
Legal Status: not controlled

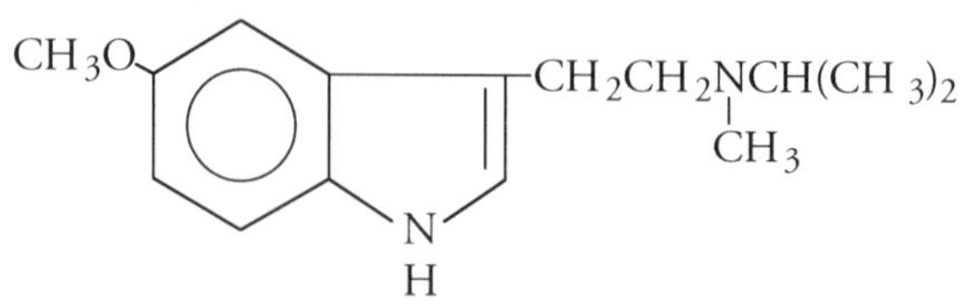

31. METHYSERGIDE [*Merck Index* 11: 6055; 12: 6217]

Synonyms: 9,10-didehydro-*N*-[1-(hydroxymethyl)propyl]-1,6-dimethyl ergoline-8-carboxamide; 1-methyl-D-lysergic acid butanolamide; UML-491

Physical: $C_{21}H_{27}N_3O_2$ molecular wt. 353.46; C 71.36% H 7.70% N 11.89% O 9.05%

Isolation: still known only as an artificial compound

Synthesis: Troxler, *Helvetica Chimica Acta* 40: 1706, 1957; Sandoz Ltd., U.S. pat. 3,218,324, 1965

Chemistry: crystals, mp 194–196°; hydrogen maleate (*Sansert, Deseril*); dimaleate, dec. above 165,° sol. in methanol, sparingly sol. in water

Pharmacology: psychoptic above 7.5 mg oral, threshold dose (=25 mcg LSD) 4.3 mg (Abramson, *Use of LSD in Psychotherapy*, Bobbs Merrill, 1967)

Legal Status: controlled, prescription drug

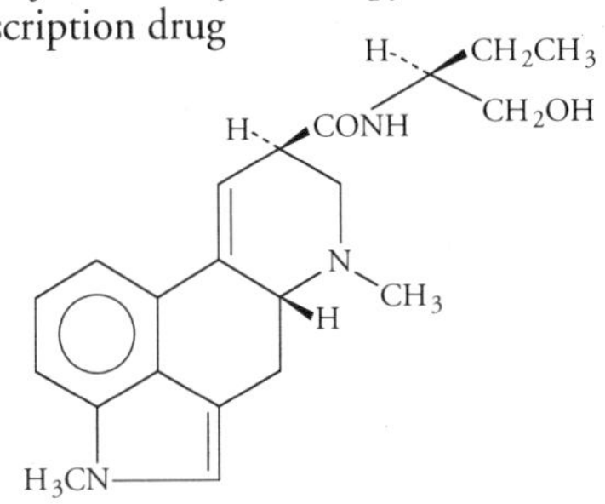

32. METHYSTICIN [*Merck Index* 11: 6056; 12: 6218]; **H_2-METHYSTICIN**

Synonyms: 6-[2-(1,3-benzodioxol-5-yl)ethenyl]-5,6-dihydro-4-methoxy-2*H*-pyran-2-one; kavahin; kavatin; kavakin; kawakin; kanakin

Physical: $C_{15}H_{14}O_5$ molecular weight 274.27; C 65.69% H 5.14% O 29.17%

Isolation: Cuzent, *Comptes Rendus Hebd. des Séances de l'Académie des Sciences* 52: 205, 1861; Gobley, *J. Pharm. Chem.* 37: 19, 1860 (*Piper methysticum*)

Synthesis: Klohs, *Journal of Organic Chemistry* 24: 1829, 1959

Chemistry: crystals from methanol, mp 132–134,° sol. in alcohol, benzene, chloroform, ether, acetone, practically insol. in water; **32A. DIHYDROMETHYSTICIN** [$C_{15}H_{16}O_5$ molecular weight 276.28; C 65.21% H 5.84% O 28.96%], prisms from methanol, mp 118°

Pharmacology: muscle relaxant (Meyer, *Ethnopharmacologic Search for Psychoactive Drugs*, U.S. Gov't. Print. Office, 1967); human anti-convulsant (Pfeiffer, *ibid.*); DIHYDROMETHYSTICIN human anti-convulsant (Pfeiffer *ibid.*)

Legal Status: not controlled

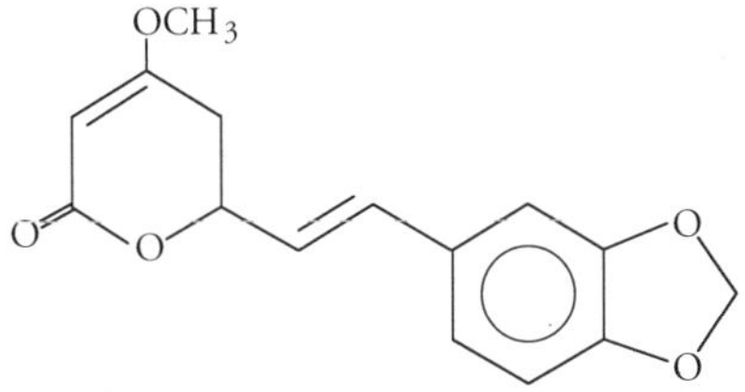

33. MUSCAZONE [*Merck Index* 11: 6220; 12: 6390]

Synonyms: α-amino-2,3-dihydro-2-oxo-5-oxazoleacetic acid; α-amino-2-oxo-4-oxazoline-5-acetic acid; Muscazon

Physical: $C_5H_6N_2O_4$ molecular weight 158.11; C 37.98% H 3.82% N 17.72% O 40.48%

Isolation: Eugster, *Tetrahedron Letters* 1813, 1965 (*Amanita muscaria*); Ott, unpublished (*Amanita pantherina*)

Synthesis: Göth, *Helvetica Chimica Acta* 50: 137, 1967; Chilton, unpublished (light-catalyzed rearrangement of ibotenic acid)

Chemistry: crystals, dec. above 190,° sol. in water

Pharmacology: human activity unknown but has weak activity in neurochemical tests (Lanthorn, Searle Co., unpublished communication, Oct. 1986)

Legal Status: not controlled

COO⁻ NH 3⁺ HN O O

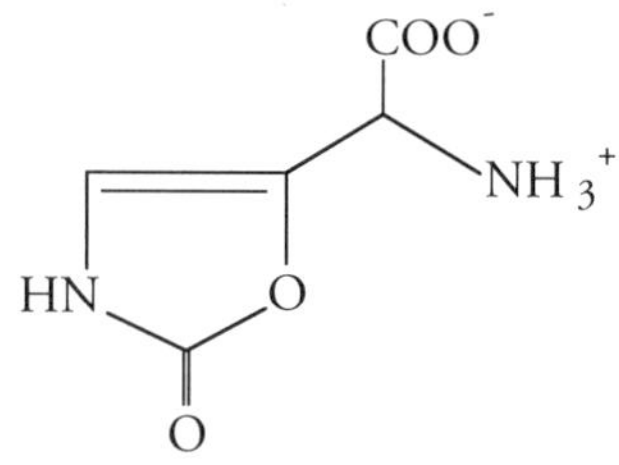

34. MUSCIMOL [*Merck Index* 11: 6221; 12: 6391]

Synonyms: 5-(aminomethyl)-3-[2*H*]-isoxazolone; 3-hydroxy-5-aminomethyl-isoxazole; Agarin; pantherine; muscimole

Physical: $C_4H_6N_2O_2$ molecular weight 114.10; C 42.11% H 5.30% N 24.55% O 28.04%

Isolation: Onda, *Chemical and Pharmacological Bulletin Japan* 12: 751, 1964 (*Amanita pantherina*); Bowden, *Tetrahedron Letters* 727, 1965; Eugster, *Helvetica Chimica Acta* 48: 910, 1965 (*Amanita muscaria*)

Synthesis: Gagneux, *Tet. Lett.* 2077, 1965; Welch, *Synth. Comm.* 12: 1089, 1982; Ott, *Physiological Chemistry & Physics* 7: 381, 1975 (from ibotenic acid)

Chemistry: crystals from methanol/water, mp 174–175° (dec), very sol. in water; star-shaped crystals from water, mp 155–156°

Pharmacology: 15 mg psychoptic (Waser, *Ethnopharm. Search Psychoactive Drugs*, U.S. Government Print. Office, 1967); 20 mg visionary (Ott, unpublished)

Legal Status: not controlled

NH 2 O O N H

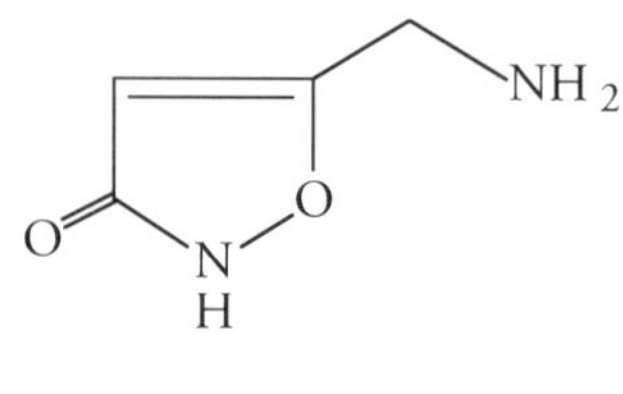

35. MYRISTICIN [*Merck Index* 11: 6247; 12: 6417; see *PIHKAL* No. 157]

Synonyms: 4-methoxy-6-(2-propenyl)-1,3-benzodioxole; 5-allyl-1-methoxy-2,3-(methylenedioxy)benzene

Physical: $C_{11}H_{12}O_3$ molecular weight 192.21; C 68.74% H 6.29% O 24.97%

Isolation: Power, *Journal of the Chemical Society* 91: 2037, 1907; Shulgin, *Nature* 197: 379, 1963 (*Myristica fragrans*)

Synthesis: Trikojus, *Nature* 14: 1016, 1939; Wulf, *J. Chromatography* 161: 271, 1978

Chemistry: colorless oil, bp 173,° sol. in ether, benzene

Pharmacology: psychotropic at 400 mg dose (Shulgin, *Nature* 210: 380, 1966; Shulgin, Truitt, *Ethnopharmacologic Search for Psychoactive Drugs*, U.S. Government Printing Office, 1967)

Legal Status: not controlled

CH_3O CH_2 O O

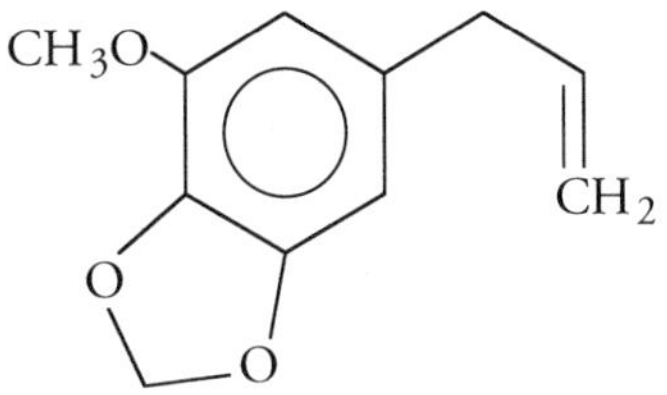

36. NICOTINE [*Merck Index* 11: 6434; 12: 6611]

Synonyms: 3-(1-methyl-2-pyrrolidinyl)pyridine; 1-methyl-2-(3-pyridyl)pyrrolidine; Nikotin; *Nicorette*; *Nicoderm*

Physical: $C_{10}H_{14}N_2$ molecular weight 162.23; C 74.03% H 8.70% N 17.27%

Isolation: Gattermann, *Laboratory Methods of Organic Chemistry*, New York, 1937

Synthesis: Pinner, *Berichte der Deutschen Chemischen Gesellschaft* 26: 294, 1893

Chemistry: oily liquid, bp 247,° sol. in alcohol, chloroform, ether, petroleum ether; tartrate dihydrate crystals, mp 90,° highly sol. in water, alcohol

Pharmacology: Gosselin, *Clin. Toxicology Commer. Prods.*, Williams & Wilkins, 1976; Wilbert, *Tobacco & Shamanism in S. America*, Yale Univ. Press, 1987

Legal Status: not controlled

N N CH_3

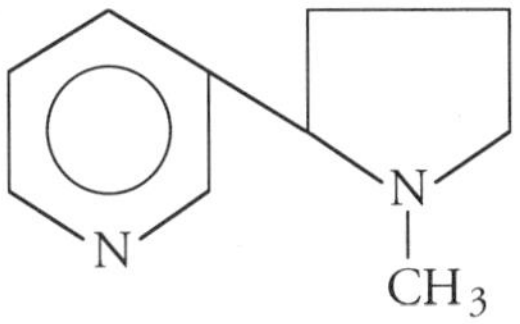

37. NORBAEOCYSTINE

Synonyms: 3-aminoethyl-1*H*-indol-4-ol dihydrogen phosphate ester; 4-phosphoryloxytryptamine; *bis*-desmethylpsilocybine; Norbaeocystin; 4-OP-T

Physical: $C_{10}H_{13}N_2O_4P$ molecular weight 256.20; C 46.88% H 5.11% N 10.93% O 24.98% P 12.09%

Isolation: Leung, *J. of Pharmaceutical Sciences* 57: 1667, 1968 (*Psilocybe baeocystis*)

Synthesis: Troxler, *Helvetica Chimica Acta* 42: 2073, 1959; Brenneisen, *Archiv der Pharmazie* 321: 487, 1988 (baeocystine)

Chemistry: crystals from methanol, mp 188–192,° sol. in water, methanol

Pharmacology: unknown, but likely dephosphorylates *in vivo* to 4-hydroxytryptamine, probable entheogen (Cerletti, *Advances in Pharmacology* 6B: 233, 1968)

Legal Status: not scheduled but potentially controlled as an analogue of psilocybine

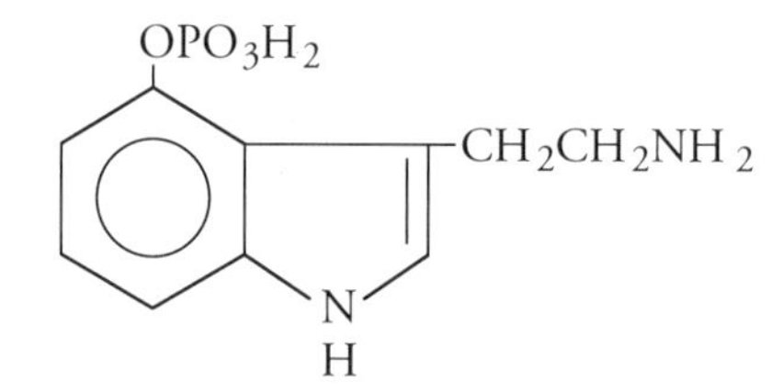

38. PSILOCINE [*Merck Index* 11: 7941; 12: 8110]

Synonyms: 3-[2-(dimethylamino)ethyl]-1*H*-indol-4-ol; psilocin; 4-hydroxy-*N,N*-dimethyltryptamine; psilocyn (legal error); Psilocin; CX-59; 4-OH-DMT

Physical: $C_{12}H_{16}N_2O$ molecular weight 204.27; C 70.56% H 7.89% N 13.71% O 7.83%

Isolation: Hofmann, *Experientia* 14: 107, 1958 (*Psilocybe mexicana*); Leung, *Journal of Pharmaceutical Sciences* 51: 393, 1962 (det. in *Psilocybe baeocystis*)

Synthesis: Hofmann, *Helvetica Chimica Acta* 42: 1557, 1959; Sandoz Ltd., German pat. 1,087,321, 1960

Chemistry: plates from methanol, mp 173–176,° slightly sol. in water, sol. in methanol, ethanol, chloroform

Pharmacology: psychoptic above 6 mg, 2–4 mg threshold (=25 mcg LSD) dose (Abramson, *Use of LSD in Psychotherapy*, Bobbs Merrill, 1967)

Legal Status: controlled, Schedule I

OH
CH2CH2N(CH3)2
N
H

39. PSILOCYBINE [*Merck Index* 11: 7942; 12: 8111]

Synonyms: 3-[2-(dimethylamino)ethyl]-1*H*-indol-4-ol dihydrogen phosphate ester; *O*-phosphoryl-4-hydroxy-*N,N*-dimethyltryptamine; *Indocybin*; CY-39; Psilocybin; 4-OP-DMT

Physical: $C_{12}H_{17}N_2O_4P$ molecular weight 284.25; C 50.71% H 6.03% N 9.86% O 22.51% P 10.90%

Isolation: Hofmann, *Experientia* 14: 107, 1958 (*Psilocybe mexicana*); Hatfield, *Lloydia* 41: 140, 1978 (*Gymnopilus validipes*)

Synthesis: Hofmann, *Helvetica Chimica Acta* 42: 1557, 1959; Sandoz Ltd., German pat. 1,087,321, 1960

Chemistry: crystals from boiling water, mp 220–228,° from boiling methanol, mp 185–195,° sol. in boiling water, methanol; insol. in benzene, chloroform

Pharmacology: psychoptic above 10 mg (Delay, *C.R. Acad. Sci.* 247: 1235, 1958); threshold 3.4 mg (Abramson, *Use of LSD in Psychother.*, Bobbs Merrill, 1967)

Legal Status: controlled, Schedule I

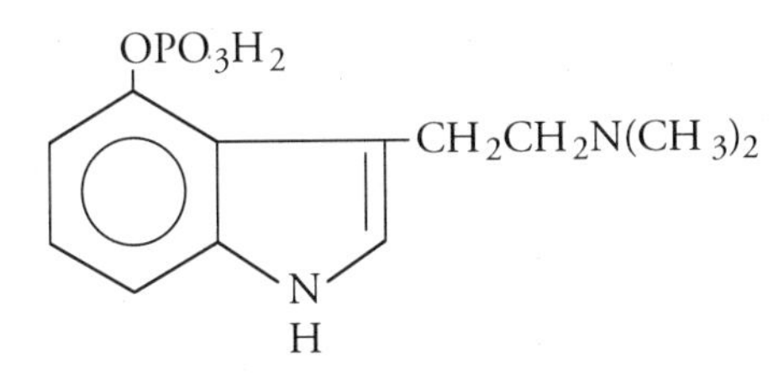

40. SAFROLE [*Merck Index* 11: 8287; 12: 8468; see *PIHKAL* No. 157]

Synonyms: 5-(2-propenyl)-1,3-benzodioxole; allylcatechol methylene ether; Safrol

Physical: $C_{10}H_{10}O_2$ molecular weight 162.19; C 74.06% H 6.21% O 19.73%

Isolation: Power, *Journal of the Chemical Society* 91: 2037, 1907; Bejnarowicz, *Journal of Pharmaceutical Sciences* 53: 988, 1963 (*Myristica fragrans*)

Synthesis: none reported

Chemistry: slightly yellow oil, bp 232–234,° sol. in alcohol, ether, chloroform; insol. in water

Pharmacology: presumed psychotropic constituent of nutmeg (Shulgin, *Ethnopharm. Search for Psychoactive Drugs*, U.S. Government Printing Office, 1967)

Legal Status: not controlled; carcinogen (IARC Monographs 10: 231, 1976)

41. SALVINORIN A; SALVINORIN B

Synonyms: divinorin A

Physical: $C_{23}H_{28}O_8$ molecular weight 432.47; C 63.88% H 6.53% O 29.6%

Isolation: Ortega, *Journal of the Chemical Society* I: 2505, 1982; Valdés, *Journal of Organic Chemistry* 49: 4716, 1984 (*Salvia divinorum*)

Synthesis: none reported; configuration: Koreeda, *Chemical Letters* 2015, 1990

Chemistry: colorless, orthorhombic crystals from methanol, mp 238–240°; 242–244° from ethanol; **41A. SALVINORIN B** [divinorin B; $C_{21}H_{26}O_7$ molecular weight 390.23; C 64.58% H 6.71% O 28.70%] cryst. from methanol, mp 213–216°; stereochem. Koreeda, *Chemical Letters* 2015, 1990

Pharmacology: psychoptic above 200 mcg vaporized (Siebert, *J. Ethnopharm.* 43: 53, 1994); 100 mcg sublingual human threshold (Ott, *Curare* 18: 103, 1995); SALVINORIN B inactive in mice; human pharmacology unknown

Legal Status: not controlled

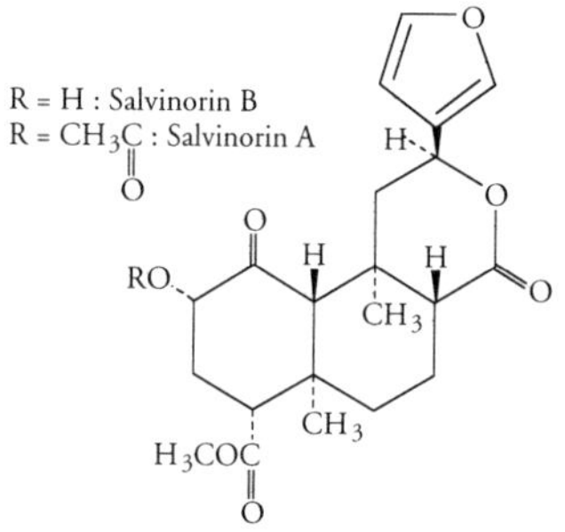

R = H : Salvinorin B
R = $CH_3C(=O)$: Salvinorin A

42. SCOPOLAMINE [*Merck Index* 11: 8361; 12: 8550]

Synonyms: [7(*S*)-(1α,2β,4β,5α,7β)]-α-(hydroxymethyl)benzeneacetic acid 9-methyl-3-oxa-9-azatricyclo-[3.3.1.0^{2,4}]non-7-yl ester; hyoscine; *Scopoderm TTS*; *Transderm-V*; Scopolamin; Hyoscin; hyoscine

Physical: $C_{17}H_{21}NO_4$ molecular wt. 303.36; C 67.31% H 6.98% N 4.62% O 21.10%

Isolation: Ladenburg, *Liebig's Annalen der Chemie* 206: 274, 1881 (*Datura, Scopolia* spp.); Chemnitius, *Journal der Praktische Chemie* 120: 221, 1928

Synthesis: Fodor, *Chemistry & Industry* 764, 1956; Dobo, *J. Chem. Soc.* 3461, 1959

Chemistry: viscous liquid, monohydrate crystals, mp 59,° sol. in water, alcohol, ether, chloroform, acetone; HBr trihydrate, mp 195,° sol. in water, alcohol

Pharmacology: deliriant (Heimann, *Die Scopolaminwirkung*, S. Karger, 1952)

Legal Status: controlled, prescription drug

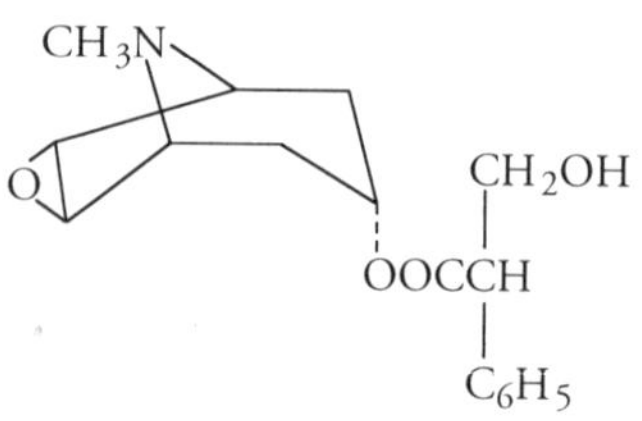

43. SCOPOLETIN [*Merck Index* 11: 8363; 12: 8552]

Synonyms: 7-hydroxy-6-methoxy-2*H*-1-benzopyran-2-one; 7-hydroxy-6-methoxy coumarin; chrysatropic acid; gelseminic acid; scopoletine

Physical: $C_{10}H_8O_4$ molecular weight 192.17; C 62.50% H 4.20% O 33.30%

Isolation: Eykman, *Ber. Deut. Chem. Gesell.* 17III: 442, 1884; Schultes, *Botany & Chemistry of Hallucinogens*, C.C. Thomas, 1980 (*Brunfelsia grandiflora*)

Synthesis: Crosby, *Journal of Organic Chemistry* 26: 1215, 1961

Chemistry: needles or prisms from acetic acid or chloroform, mp 204,° sol. in hot alcohol, hot acetic acid, chloroform, slightly sol. in water, alcohol

Pharmacology: psychopharmacological activity in mice (Schultes, *Botany & Chemistry of Hallucinogens*, C.C. Thomas, 1980); human pharmacology unknown

Legal Status: not controlled

CH_3O HO O O

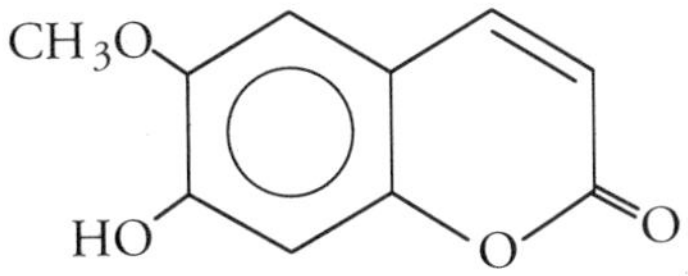

44. TABERNANTHINE [*Merck Index* 11: 9000; 12: 9195]

Synonyms: 13-methoxy-ibogamine; Tabernanthin

Physical: $C_{20}H_{26}N_2O$ molecular weight 310.44; C 77.38% H 8.44% N 9.02% O 5.15%

Isolation: Delourme-Houdé, *Annales Pharmaceutiques Françaises* 4: 30, 1946 (*Tabernanthe iboga*); Dickel, *Journal of the American Chemical Society* 80: 123, 1958 (*Tabernaemontana*, *Stemmadenia* spp.)

Synthesis: Bartlett, *Journal of the American Chemical Society* 80: 126, 1958 (structure)

Chemistry: needles from ethanol, mp 213.5–215,° sol. in alcohol, benzene, ether, chloroform, pract. insol. in water; HCL, mp 210,° sol. in water

Pharmacology: CNS stimulant (Zetler, *Arzneimittel-Forschung* 14: 1277, 1964); effect like ibogaine (Zetler, *N. Schmied. Archiv der Pharmazie* 260: 26, 1968)

Legal Status: not controlled

N CH_3O N H CH_2CH_3

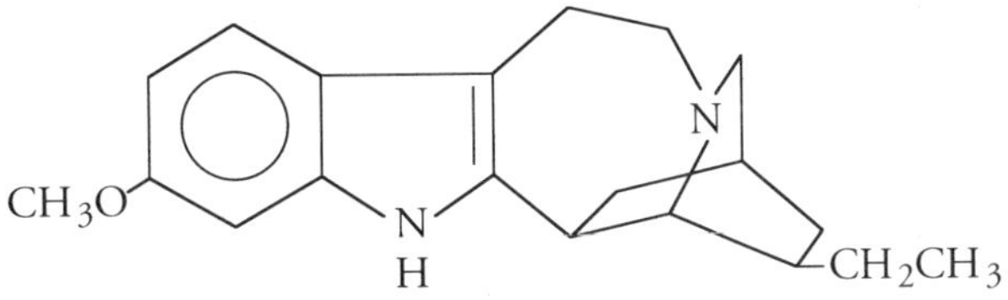

45. TETRAHYDROCANNABINOLS [*Merck Index* 11: 9142; 12: 9349]

Synonyms: tetrahydro-6,6,9-trimethyl-3-pentyl-6*H*-dibenzo[*b,d*]pyran-1-ol; THC; *Marinol*; dronabinol

Physical: $C_{21}H_{30}O_2$ molecular weight 314.47; C 80.21% H 9.62% O 10.18%

Isolation: Gaoni, *J. Am. Chem. Soc.* 86: 1646, 1964 (Δ^1-3,4-*trans*-THC); Hively, *J. Am. Chemical Soc.* 88: 1832, 1966 (Δ^6-3,4-*trans*-THC) (*Cannabis* spp.)

Synthesis: Mechoulam, *Journal of the American Chemical Society* 89: 4552, 1967, both (–)-Δ^1-3,4-*trans*-THC and (–)-Δ^6-3,4-*trans*-THC

Chemistry: Δ^1-3,4-*trans*-THC and Δ^6-3,4-*trans*-THC oils, bp 200,° sol. in oils

Pharmacology: Δ^1-THC psychoactive 3–5 mg (Mechoulam, *Fortschritte in der Chemie von Organischen Naturstoffe* 25: 175, 1967); Δ^6-THC above 0.25 mg/kg (Mechoulam, *Marijuana*, Academic Press, New York, 1973)

Legal Status: controlled, Schedule I

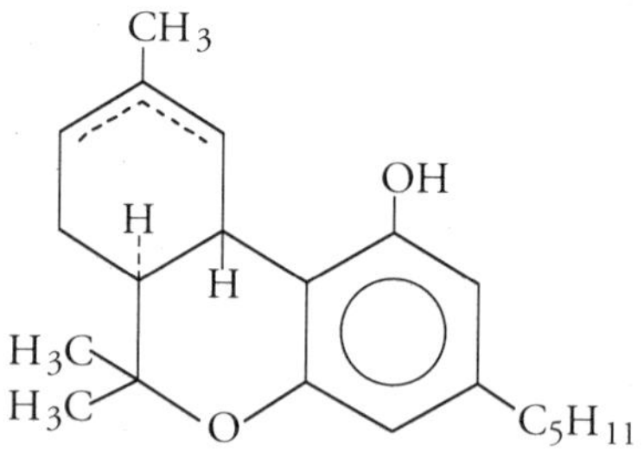

46. THUJONES [*Merck Index* 11: 9326; 12: 9533]

Synonyms: 4-methyl-1-(1-methylethyl)bicyclo[3.1.0]-hexan-3-one; 3-thujanone; absinthol; absynthol; salvanol; tanacetone; salviol; 3-sabinone

Physical: $C_{10}H_{16}O$ molecular weight 152.24; C 78.90% H 10.59% O 10.51%

Isolation: Gildemeister, *The Volatile Oils*, Pharmaceutical Review Publications, Milwaukee, 1900 (*Artemisia absinthium*)

Synthesis: Kutney, *Bioorg. Chem.* 7: 289, 1978; Kutney, *Can. J. Chem.* 57: 3145, 1979

Chemistry: colorless liquid, α-thujone bp 83.8–84.1°; β-thujone bp 85.7–86.2,° pract. insol. in water, sol. in alcohol, ether, chloroform, acetone

Pharmacology: Albert-Puleo, *Econ. Bot.* 32: 65, 1978; Del Castillo, *Nature* 253: 365, 1975

Legal Status: controlled as food additive

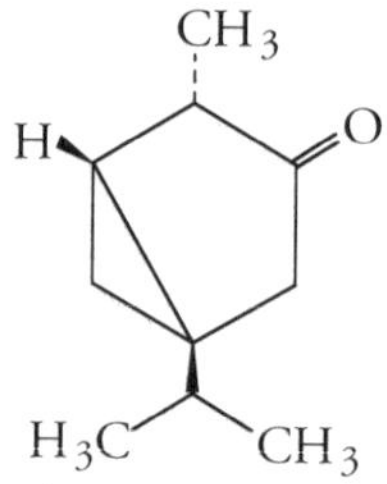

47. TMA-2 [*PIHKAL* No. 158]; **TMA** [*PIHKAL* No. 157]

Synonyms: 2,4,5-trimethoxy-phenylisopropylamine; 2,4,5-trimethoxyamphetamine

Physical: $C_{12}H_{19}NO_3$ molecular wt. 225.29; C 63.98% H 8.50% N 6.22% O 21.30%

Isolation: still only known as an artificial compound

Synthesis: Shulgin, *Nature* 189: 1011, 1961; Shulgin, *PIHKAL*, Transform, 1991

Chemistry: hydrochloride, white crystals, mp 188.5–189.5°; **47A. TMA** [3,4,5-trimethoxyamphetamine; EA-1319; $C_{12}H_{19}NO_3$ molecular wt. 225.29; C 63.98% H 8.50% N 6.22% O 21.30%] hydrochloride, white crystals, mp 195–211°

Pharmacology: TMA-2 psychoptic at 20–40 mg orally (Shulgin, *Nature* 189: 1011, 1961; Shulgin, *PIHKAL*, Transform Press, 1991); TMA psychoptic at 100–250 mg orally (Shulgin, *PIHKAL*, Transform Press, Berkeley, 1991)

Legal Status: TMA-2 controlled indirectly as an isomer of (Schedule I) TMA

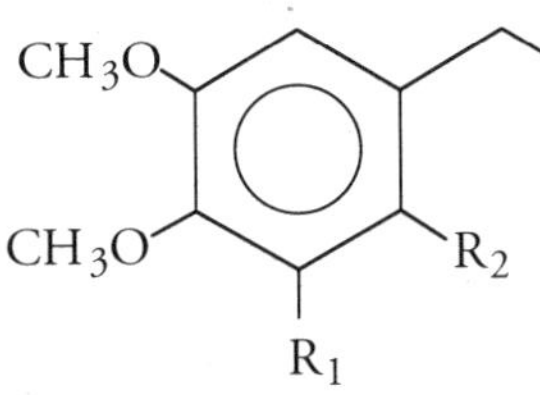

R_1 = H, R_2 = OCH_3 : TMA-2
R_1 = OCH_3, R_2 = H : TMA

48. TRICHOLOMIC ACID

Synonyms: L-*erythro*-α-amino-3-oxo-5-isoxazolidine acetic acid; dihydro-ibotenic acid; Dihydroibotensäure; Tricholomisäure

Physical: $C_5H_8N_2O_4$ molecular wt. 160.13; C 37.50% H 5.04% N 17.49% O 39.97%

Isolation: Takemoto, *Yakugaku Zasshi* 84: 1183, 1964 (*Tricholoma muscarium*); Takeda Ltd., Japanese pat. 69 16,354, 1969 (*Tricholomopsis rutilans*)

Synthesis: Kamiya, *Chemical and Pharmacological Bulletin Japan* 14: 1307, 1966; of racemate: Iwasaki, *Chem. and Pharm. Bulletin Japan* 13: 753, 1965

Chemistry: prisms from methanol/water, mp 207° (dec), sol. in water; synthetic racemate mp 195–198° (dec)

Pharmacology: insecticidal (Takemoto, *Yakugaku Zasshi* 33: 252, 1961); neurotoxic activity like ibotenic acid (Shinozaki, *Brain Research* 24: 368, 1970)

Legal Status: not controlled

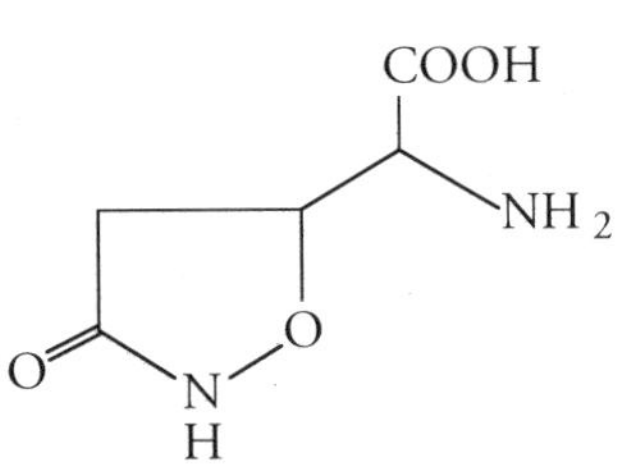

49. VOACANGINE [*Merck Index* 11: 9944; 12: 10168, Voacamine]

Synonyms: 12-methoxyibogamine-18-carboxylic acid methyl ester; carbomethoxy-ibogaine; Voacangin

Physical: $C_{22}H_{28}N_2O_3$ molecular wt. 368.48; C 71.71% H 7.66% N 7.60% O 13.03%

Isolation: Janot, *Compt. Rend. Acad. Sci.* 240: 1719, 1955 (*Voacanga* spp.); Gorman, *J. American Chemical Society* 82: 1142, 1960; (*Tabernaemontana* spp.)

Synthesis: Bartlett, *J. American Chemical Society* 80: 126, 1958 (structure); Winkler, *Die Naturwißenschaften* 48: 694, 1961 (acid degradation of voacamine)

Chemistry: prismatic needles from ethanol, mp 136–137,° sol. in acetone, chloroform, slightly sol. in ethanol, methanol

Pharmacology: CNS stimulant (Zetler, *Arzneimittel-Forschung* 14: 1277, 1964); effect like ibogaine (Zetler, *N. Schmied. Archiv der Pharmazie* 260: 26, 1968)

Legal Status: not controlled

CH3O N N H CH2CH3 COOCH3

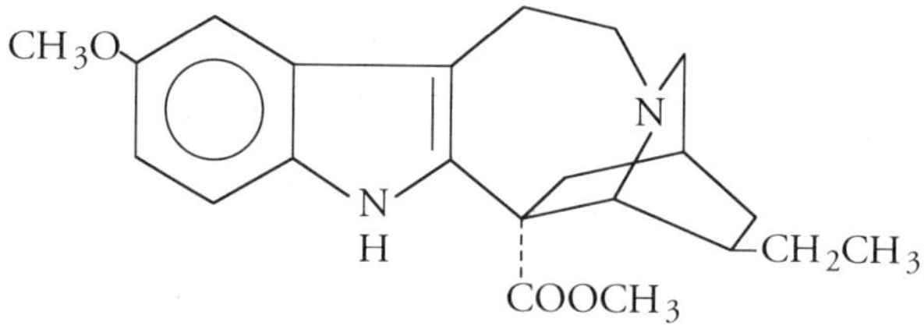

50. YANGONIN [*Merck Index* 11: 10001; 12: 10226]

Synonyms: 4-methoxy-6-[2-(4-methoxyphenyl)ethenyl]-2*H*-pyran-2-one

Physical: $C_{15}H_{14}O_4$ molecular weight 258.27; C 69.76% H 5.46% O 24.78%

Isolation: Shibata, *Bulletin of the Chemical Society Japan* 45: 930, 1972 (*Ranunculus quelpaertensis*); Winzhermer, *Naunyn Schmiedeberg's Archiv der Pharmazie* 246: 338, 1908 (*Piper methysticum*)

Synthesis: Harris, *Journal of Organic Chemistry* 33: 2399, 1968; Bacardit, *Journal of Heterocyclic Chemistry* 19: 157, 1982

Chemistry: crystals from methanol, mp 155–157,° sol. in hot ethanol, acetic acid, ethyl acetate, acetone; pract. insol. in water

Pharmacology: muscle relaxant (Meyer, *Ethnopharmacologic Search for Psychoactive Drugs*, U.S. Government Printing Office, 1967)

Legal Status: not controlled

OCH3 O O OCH3

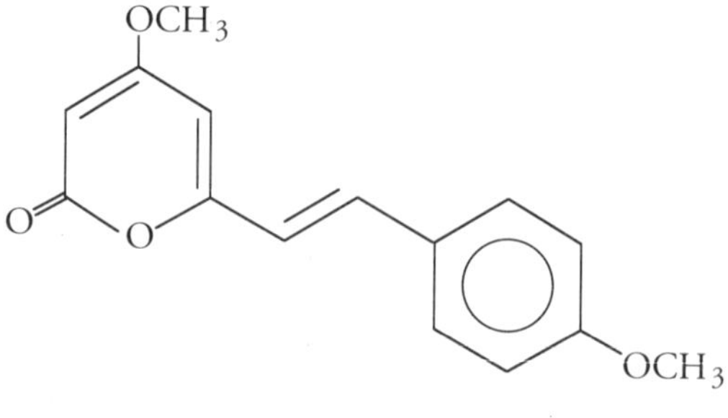

APPENDIX D
Entheopædia: Botanical Index

APPENDIX E
Entheography: Suggested General Reading

CHAPTER ONE: MESCALINE, *PÉYOTL*, *SAN PEDRO*, ARTIFICIAL PHENETHYLAMINES

ANDERSON, E.F. 1980. *Peyote: The Divine Cactus*. Univ. of Arizona Press, Tucson, AZ.

BENÍTEZ, F. 1975. *In the Magic Land of Peyote.* University of Texas Press, Austin, TX. Original *En la Tierra Mágica del Peyote*. Ediciones Era, México City, 1968.

FLATTERY, D.S. and J.M. PIERCE 1965. *Peyote.* Berkeley Press, Berkeley, CA.

JORALEMON, D. and D. SHARON 1993. *Sorcery and Shamanism: Curanderos and Clients in Northern Peru.* University of Utah Press, Salt Lake City, UT.

KLÜVER, H. 1966. *Mescal [sic] and Mechanisms of Hallucination.* University of Chicago Press, Chicago, IL. Originally published in 1928 as *Mescal [sic], the "Divine Plant" and its Psychological Effects*. Paul Kegan, London, England.

HOROWITZ, M. and C. PALMER (Eds.) 1977. *Aldous Huxley. Moksha: Writings on Psychedelics and the Visionary Experience.* Stonehill Publishing Co., New York.

LA BARRE, W. 1975. *The Peyote Cult.* Fourth Edition. Archon Books, Hamden, CT. Fifth edition in 1989, University of Oklahoma Press, Norman, OK.

MOUNT, G. (Ed.) 1987. *The Peyote Book: A Study of Native Medicine.* Sweetlight Books, Arcata, CA. Second edition in 1988.

MYERHOFF, B.G. 1974. *The Peyote Hunt: The Sacred Journey of the Huichol Indians.* Cornell University Press, Ithaca, NY.

ROUHIER, A. 1927. *La Plante qui fait les Yeux Émerveillés—Le Peyotl (Echinocactus Williamsii Lem.).* Gaston Doin et Cie, Paris, France. Préface by É. Perrot.

SCHAEFER, S.B. and P.T. FURST (Eds.) 1996. *People of the Peyote.* University of New Mexico Press, Albuquerque, NM.

SHULGIN, A.T. and A. SHULGIN 1991. *PIHKAL: A Chemical Love Story.* Transform Press, Berkeley, CA. Foreword by David E. Nichols.

STEWART, O.C. 1987. *Peyote Religion: A History.* University of Oklahoma Press, Norman, OK.

CHAPTER TWO: LSD, *OLOLIUHQUI*, *KYKEON*: THE ERGOLINE COMPLEX

BARGER, G. 1931. *Ergot and Ergotism.* Gurney and Jackson, London, England.

BAUER, V.H. 1973. *Das Antonius-Feuer in Kunst und Medizin.* Sandoz AG, Basel, Switzerland. Vorwort by Albert Hofmann.

BOVÉ, F.J. 1970. *The Story of Ergot: For Physicians, Pharmacists, Nurses, Biochemists, Biologists and Others Interested in the Life Sciences.* S. Karger, Basel, Switzerland.

GELPKE, R. (Translation by J. Ott) 1981. "On travels in the universe of the soul: Reports on self-experiments with Delysid (LSD) and psilocybin (CY)" *Journal of Psychoactive Drugs* 13(1): 81–89. First published in *Antaios* 3(5): 393–411, 1962.

HOFMANN, A. 1963. "The active principles of the seeds of *Rivea corymbosa* and *Ipomoea violacea*" *Botanical Museum Leaflets* Harvard University 20(6): 194–212. Reprinted in *The Psychedelic Review* 1(3): 302–316, 1964.

HOFMANN, A. 1964. *Die Mutterkornalkaloide.* F. Enke Verlag, Stuttgart, Germany.

HOFMANN, A. (Translation by J. Ott) 1980. *LSD: My Problem Child.* McGraw-Hill, New York. Paperback in 1983, J.P. Tarcher, Los Angeles, CA. Foreword by Jonathan Ott. Originally published in German, 1979. *LSD–Mein Sorgenkind.* Klett-Cotta, Stuttgart, Germany. French, Spanish, Japanese, other translations exist.

JÜNGER, E. 1970. *Annäherungen: Drogen und Rausch.* E. Klett Verlag, Stuttgart, Germany.

RÄTSCH, C. (Ed.) 1993. *50 Jahre LSD–Erfahrung: Eine Jubiläumsschrift.* Nachtschatten Verlag/MedienXperimente, Solothurn, Switzerland and Lörhbach, Germany.

SHELLEY, W.S. 1994. *The Elixir: An Alchemical Study of the Ergot Mushrooms.* Cross-Cultural Publications, Inc., Notre Dame, IN.

WASSON, R.G. 1963. "Notes on the present status of *ololiuhqui* and the other hallucinogens of Mexico" *Botanical Museum Leaflets* Harvard University 20(6): 161–193. Reprinted in *The Psychedelic Review* 1(3): 275–301, 1963, and in Weil, G.M. *et al.* (Eds.) 1965. *The Psychedelic Reader.* University Books, New York. pp. 163–189.

WASSON, R.G. *et al.* 1978. *The Road to Eleusis: Unveiling the Secret of the Mysteries.* Ethno-mycological Studies No. 4. Harcourt Brace Jovanovich, New York.

CHAPTER THREE: DMT, *COHOBA*, *EPÉNA*: SHORT-ACTING TRYPTAMINES

DE SMET, P.A.G.M. 1985. *Ritual Enemas and Snuffs in the Americas* [*Latin American*

Studies 33]. Centrum voor Studie en Documentatie van Latijns Amerika, Amsterdam, the Netherlands.

EFRON, D.H. *et al.* (Eds.) 1967. *Ethnopharmacologic Search for Psychoactive Drugs.* (Public Health Service Publication No. 1645) U.S. Government Printing Office, Washington, D.C. pp. 233–382. Reprinted in 1979 by Raven Press, New York.

FURST, P.T. 1976. *Hallucinogens and Culture.* Chandler & Sharp, Novato, CA. Translated into Spanish, 1980. Fondo de Cultura Económica, México City.

HARNER, M.J. (Ed.) 1973. *Hallucinogens and Shamanism.* Oxford University Press, Cambridge, England.

REICHEL-DOLMATOFF, G. 1975. *The Shaman and the Jaguar: A Study of Narcotic* [*sic*] *Drugs Among the Indians of Colombia.* Temple Univ. Press, Philadelphia, PA.

SCHULTES, R.E. 1954. "A new narcotic [*sic*] snuff from the northwest Amazon" *Botanical Museum Leaflets* Harvard University 16(9): 241–260.

SCHULTES, R.E. 1977. "De plantis toxicariis e mundo novo tropicale commentationes XVII: *Virola* as an oral hallucinogen among the Boras of Peru" *Botanical Museum Leaflets* Harvard University 25(9): 259–272.

SCHULTES, R.E. and A. HOFMANN 1979. *Plants of the Gods: Origins of Hallucinogenic Use.* McGraw-Hill, New York. Reprinted in 1992 as *Plants of the Gods: Their Sacred, Healing and Hallucinogenic Powers.* Healing Arts Press, Rochester, VT.

SCHULTES, R.E. and A. HOFMANN 1980. *The Botany and Chemistry of Hallucinogens.* Revised and Enlarged Second Edition. C.C. Thomas, Springfield, IL. Originally published in 1973. Foreword by Heinrich Klüver.

SCHULTES, R.E. and R.F. RAFFAUF 1992. *Vine of the Soul: Medicine Men, their Plants and Rituals in the Colombian Amazon.* Synergetic Press, Oracle, AZ.

TORRES, C.M. 1987. *The Iconography of South American Snuff Trays* [*Etnologiska Studier* 37]. Göteborgs Etnografiska Museet, Göteborg, Sweden.

WASSON, V.P. and R.G. WASSON 1957. *Mushrooms Russia and History.* Two volumes. Pantheon Books, New York.

CHAPTER FOUR: *BETA*-CARBOLINES AND *AYAHUASCA* POTIONS

EFRON, D.H. *et al.* (Eds.) 1967. *Ethnopharmacologic Search for Psychoactive Drugs.* (Public Health Service Publication No. 1645) U.S. Government Printing Office, Washington, D.C. pp. 385–402. Reprinted in 1979 by Raven Press, New York.

GATES, B. 1982. "Banisteriopsis, Diplopterys (Malpighiaceae)" *Flora Neotropica.* (Monograph No. 30). The New York Botanical Garden, Bronx, NY.

INSTITUTO INDIGENISTA INTERAMERICANO 1986. "Chamanismo y uso de plantas del género *Banisteriopsis* en la hoya amazónica" Proceedings of a conference held 7–11 July 1985, Bogotá, Colombia. *América Indígena* 46(1): 1–256.

LUNA, L.E. 1986. *Vegetalismo: Shamanism among the Mestizo Population of the Peruvian Amazon* [*Stockholm Studies in Comparative Religion* 27]. Almqvist & Wiksell International, Stockholm, Sweden.

LUNA, L.E. and P. AMARINGO 1991. *Ayahuasca Visions: The Religious Iconography of a Peruvian Shaman.* North Atlantic Books, Berkeley, CA.

MACRAE, E. 1992. *Guiado Pela Lua: Xamanismo e Uso Ritual da Ayahuasca no Culto do Santo Daime.* Editora Brasiliense, São Paulo, Brasil.

NARANJO, P. 1983. *Ayahuasca: Etnomedicina y Mitología.* Ediciones Libri Mundi, Quito, Ecuador. Originally published in 1970.

OTT, J. 1994. *Ayahuasca Analogues: Pangæan Entheogens.* Natural Products Co., Kennewick, WA.

REICHEL-DOLMATOFF, G. 1975. *The Shaman and the Jaguar: A Study of Narcotic* [*sic*] *Drugs Among the Indians of Colombia.* Temple Univ. Press, Philadelphia, PA.

SCHULTES, R.E. 1957. "The identity of the malpighiaceous narcotics [*sic*] of South America" *Botanical Museum Leaflets* Harvard University 18(1): 1–56.

SCHULTES, R.E. and A. HOFMANN 1979. *Plants of the Gods: Origins of Hallucinogenic Use.* McGraw-Hill, New York. Reprinted in 1992 as *Plants of the Gods: Their Sacred, Healing and Hallucinogenic Powers.* Healing Arts Press, Rochester, VT.

SCHULTES, R.E. and R.F. RAFFAUF 1992. *Vine of the Soul: Medicine Men, their Plants and Rituals in the Colombian Amazon.* Synergetic Press, Oracle, AZ.

CHAPTER FIVE: PSILOCYBINE/PSILOCINE/BAEOCYSTINE: THE *TEONANÁCATL* COMPLEX

FESTI, F. 1985. *Funghi Allucinogeni: Aspetti Psicofisiologici e Storici.* Musei Civici di Rovereto, Rovereto, Italy. Presentazione by Pietro G. Nonis.

GARTZ, J. 1996. *Magic Mushrooms around the World: A Scientific Journey Across Cultures & Time.* Luna Info Services, Fullerton, CA. Translation of: *Narrenschwämme: Psychotrope Pilze in Europa* [1992]. Foreword by Christian Rätsch.

HEIM, R. and R.G. WASSON 1958[9]. *Les Champignons Hallucinogènes du Mexique. Études Ethnologiques, Taxinomiques, Biologiques, Physiologiques et Chimiques.* Archives du Muséum National d'Histoire Naturelle, Paris, France.

OTT, J. 1985. *The Cacahuatl Eater: Ruminations of an Unabashed Chocolate Addict.* Natural Products Co., Vashon, WA.

OTT, J. and J. BIGWOOD (Eds.) 1978. *Teonanácatl: Hallucinogenic Mushrooms of North*

America. Madrona Publishers, Seattle, WA. See the next entry for Spanish edition.
OTT, J. *et al.* 1985. *Teonanácatl: Hongos Alucinógenos de Europa y América del Norte.* Editorial Swan, San Lorenzo de El Escorial, Spain.
RIEDLINGER, T.J. (Ed.) 1990. *The Sacred Mushroom Seeker: Essays for R. Gordon Wasson.* Ethnomycological Studies No. 11. Dioscorides Press, Portland, OR.
STAMETS, P. 1996. *Psilocybin [sic] Mushrooms of the World: An Identification Guide.* Ten Speed Press, Berkeley, CA. Foreword by Andrew Weil.
WASSON, R.G. 1980. *The Wondrous Mushroom: Mycolatry in Mesoamerica.* Ethnomycological Studies No. 7. McGraw-Hill, New York.
WASSON, R.G.*et al.* 1974. *María Sabina and her Mazatec Mushroom Velada.* Ethnomycological Studies No. 3. Harcourt Brace Jovanovich, New York.
WASSON, R.G. *et al.* 1986. *Persephone's Quest: Entheogens and the Origins of Religion.* Ethnomycological Studies No. 10. Yale University Press, New Haven, CT.
WASSON, V.P. and R.G. WASSON 1957. *Mushrooms Russia and History.* Two volumes. Pantheon Books, New York.

CHAPTER SIX: IBOTENIC ACID/MUSCIMOL: THE PRIMORDIAL *PANGK* AND *AMRTA*

BAUER, W. *et al.* (Eds.) 1991. *Der Fliegenpilz: Ein Kulturhistorisches Museum.* (Museum der Museen, Schriftenreihe des Karl Ernst Osthaus-Museums, Band 6) Wienand Verlag, Köln, Germany.
EUGSTER, C.H. 1967. *Über den Fliegenpilzen.* Kommißionsverlag Leemann, Zürich, Switzerland.
FERICGLA, J.M. 1985. *El Bolet i la Gènesi de les Cultures. Gnoms i Follets: Àmbits Culturals Forjats per l'*Amanita muscaria. Editorial Alta Fulla, Barcelona, Catalunya.
HEINRICH, C. 1995. *Strange Fruit: Alchemy, Religion and Magical Foods. A Speculative History*. Bloomsbury, London, England.
KEEWAYDINOQUAY (K.M. Peschel) 1979. "The legend of Miskwedo" *Journal of Psychedelic Drugs* 11(1-2): 29–31.
LOWY, B. 1974. "*Amanita muscaria* and the thunderbolt legend in Guatemala and Mexico" *Mycologia* 66: 188–191.
OTT, J. 1976. "Psycho-mycological studies of *Amanita*—From ancient sacrament to modern phobia" *Journal of Psychedelic Drugs* 8(1): 27–35.
OTT, J. 1979. *Hallucinogenic Plants of North America.* Second Edition Revised. Wingbow Press, Berkeley, CA. First published in 1976. Foreword by R.E. Schultes.
WASSON, R.G. 1968. *Soma: Divine Mushroom of Immortality.* Ethno-mycological Stu-

dies No. 1. Mouton, the Hague; and Harcourt Brace Jovanovich, New York.
WASSON, R.G. 1972. *Soma and the Fly-Agaric: Mr. Wasson's Rejoinder to Professor Brough.* Ethno-mycological Studies No. 2. Botanical Museum of Harvard University, Cambridge, MA.
WASSON, R.G. 1979. "Traditional use in North America of *Amanita muscaria* for divinatory purposes" *Journal of Psychedelic Drugs* 11(1-2): 25–28.
WASSON, R.G. *et al.* 1986. *Persephone's Quest: Entheogens and the Origins of Religion.* Ethnomycological Studies No. 10. Yale University Press, New Haven, CT.

APPENDIX A-I: ASARONES AND *ACORUS CALAMUS*

HOFFER, A. and H. OSMOND 1967. *The Hallucinogens.* Academic Press, New York.
KELLER, K. and E. STAHL 1982. "Kalmus: Inhaltßtoffe und β-Asarongehalt bei verschiedenen Herkünften" *Deutscher Apotheker Zeitung* 122: 2463–2466.
MOERMAN, D.E. 1986. *Medicinal Plants of Native America.* Two volumes. Univ. of Michigan Museum of Anthropology (Technical Reports #19), Ann Arbor, MI.
MORGAN, G.R. 1980. "The ethnobotany of sweet flag among North American Indians" *Botanical Museum Leaflets* Harvard University 28(3): 235–246.
SCHULTES, R.E. and A. HOFMANN 1980. *The Botany and Chemistry of Hallucinogens.* C.C. Thomas, Springfield, IL. Originally published in 1973.

APPENDIX A-II: ATROPINE, HYOSCYAMINE, SCOPOLAMINE: THE VISIONARY TROPANES

DE VRIES, H. 1991. "Über die sogenannten Hexensalben" *Integration: Zeitschrift für Geistbewegende Pflanzen und Kultur* 1: 30–42.
HANSEN, H.A. 1978. *The Witch's Garden.* Unity Press-Michael Kesend, Santa Cruz, CA. Originally published in 1976 as *Heksens Urtegård.* Laurens Bogtrykkeri, Tønder, Denmark.
HAWKES, J.G. *et al.* (Eds.) 1992. *Solanaceae III: Taxonomy, Chemistry, Evolution.* Royal Botanic Gardens, Kew, England.
HEISER, C.B. 1987. *The Fascinating World of the Nightshades: Tobacco, Mandrake, Potato, Tomato, Pepper, Eggplant, Etc.* Dover Publications, New York. First published in 1969.
SCHULTES, R.E. and A. HOFMANN 1980. *The Botany and Chemistry of Hallucinogens.* C.C. Thomas, Springfield, IL. Originally published in 1973.

APPENDIX A-III: IBOGAINE, TABERNANTHINE, VOACANGINE: FROM *EBOKA* TO *SANANHO*

BISSET, N.G. 1989. "Tabernanthe: Uses, phytochemistry, and pharmacology" *Wageningen Agricultural University Papers* 89(4): 19–26.

FERNANDEZ, J.W. 1972. "Tabernanthe iboga: Narcotic ecstasis and the work of the ancestors" In: Furst, P.T. (Ed.) *Flesh of the Gods: The Ritual Use of Hallucinogens.* Praeger, New York. pp. 237–260.

FERNANDEZ, J.W. 1982. *Bwiti: An Ethnography of the Religious Imagination of Africa.* Princeton University Press, Princeton, NJ.

SAMORINI, G. 1993. "Adam, Eve and Iboga" *Integration: Zeitschrift für Geistbewegende Pflanzen und Kultur* 4: 3–10.

VAN BEEK, T.A. *et al.* 1984. "*Tabernaemontana* L. (Apocynaceae): A review of its taxonomy, phytochemistry, ethnobotany and pharmacology" *Journal of Ethnopharmacology* 10(1): 1–156.

APPENDIX A-IV: NICOTINE, TOBACCOS AND *PITURI*

GOODMAN, J. 1993. *Tobacco in History: The Cultures of Dependence.* Routledge, Inc., New York.

HEISER, C.B. 1987. *The Fascinating World of the Nightshades: Tobacco, Mandrake, Potato, Tomato, Pepper, Eggplant, Etc.* Dover Publications, New York. First published in 1969.

LARSON, P. *et al.* 1961. *Tobacco: Experimental and Clinical Studies. A Comprehensive Account of the World Literature.* Williams & Wilkins, Baltimore, MD.

WATSON, P. 1983. *The Precious Foliage: A Study of the Aboriginal Psycho-Active Drug* Pituri. University of Sydney Press, Sydney, Australia.

WILBERT, J. 1987. *Tobacco and Shamanism in South America.* Yale University Press, New Haven, CT.

APPENDIX A-V: *KAVA*-PYRONES AND PSYCHOACTIVE *PIPER* SPECIES

COX, P.A. and S.A. BANACK (Eds.) 1991. *Islands, Plants, and Polynesians: An Introduction to Polynesian Ethnobotany.* Dioscorides Press, Portland, OR. pp. 169–201.

COX, P.A. and L. O'ROURKE 1987. "Kava (*Piper methysticum*, Piperaceae)" *Economic Botany* 41(3): 452–454.

EFRON, D.H. *et al.* (Eds.) 1967. *Ethnopharmacologic Search for Psychoactive Drugs.*

(Public Health Service Publication No. 1645) U.S. Government Printing Office, Washington, D.C. pp. 105–181. Reprinted in 1979 by Raven Press, New York.
LEBOT, V. and J. LÉVESQUE 1989. "The origin and distribution of Kava (Piper methysticum Forst. f., Piperaceae): A phytochemical approach" *Allertonia* 5(2): 223–278.
LEBOT, V. *et al.* 1992. *Kava: The Pacific Drug.* Yale University Press, New Haven, CT.
LEWIN, L. 1924. *Phantastica: Die Betäubenden und Erregenden Genußmittel. Für Ärzte und Nichtärzte.* G. Stilke, Berlin, Germany. English translations in 1931, 1965.

APPENDIX A-VI: SALVINORIN A AND *SKA PASTORA*

HOFMANN, A. 1990. "Ride through the Sierra Mazateca in search of the magic plant 'Ska María Pastora'" In: Riedlinger, T.J. (Ed.) *The Sacred Mushroom Seeker: Essays for R. Gordon Wasson.* Dioscorides Press, Portland, OR. pp. 115–127.
OTT, J. 1995. "Ethnopharmacognosy and human pharmacology of *Salvia divinorum* and salvinorin A" *Curare: Zeitschrift für Ethnomedizin* 18(1): 103–129.
SIEBERT, D.J. 1994. "*Salvia divinorum* and salvinorin A: New pharmacologic findings" *Journal of Ethnopharmacology* 43(1): 53–56.
VALDÉS III, L.J. *et al.* 1987. "Studies of *Salvia divinorum* (Lamiaceae), an hallucinogenic mint from the Sierra Mazateca in Oaxaca, Central Mexico" *Economic Botany* 41(2): 283–291.
WASSON, R.G. 1962. "A new Mexican psychotropic drug from the mint family" *Botanical Museum Leaflets* Harvard University 20(3): 77–84. Reprint in Feb. 1971.

APPENDIX A-VII: TETRAHYDROCANNABINOLS AND *CANNABIS* SPECIES

GRINSPOON, L. and J.B. BAKALAR 1993. *Marihuana [sic], the Forbidden Medicine.* Yale University Press, New Haven, CT.
LUDLOW, F.H. 1857. *The Hasheesh Eater: Being Passages from the Life of a Pythagorean.* Harper & Bros., New York. Facsimile printed in 1975 by Level Press, San Francisco. Introduction, chronology, bibliography and appendix "Bio-Critical Commentary" by Michael Horowitz; 11 illustrations by Sätty.
MECHOULAM, R. (Ed.) 1973. *Marijuana: Chemistry Pharmacology Metabolism and Clinical Effects.* Academic Press, New York.
MOREAU, J.-J. 1845. *Du Hachisch et de l'Aliénation Mentale: Études Psychologiques.* Fortin, Masson et CIE, Paris, France. Facsimile printed in 1970 by Esquirol, Paris, France.
RUBIN, V. (Ed.) 1975. *Cannabis and Culture.* Mouton & Co., the Hague, Netherlands.

APPENDIX A-VIII: THUJONES AND VISIONARY *ARTEMISIA* SPECIES

ALBERT–PULEO, M. 1978. "Mythobotany, pharmacology and chemistry of thujone-containing plants and derivatives" *Economic Botany* 32(1): 65–74.

CONRAD III, B. 1988. *Absinthe: History in a Bottle.* Chronicle Books, San Francisco, CA.

DEL CASTILLO, J. *et al.* 1975. "Marijuana, absinthe and the central nervous system" *Nature* 253: 365–366.

PENDELL, D.A. 1995. *Pharmako / Poeia: Plant Powers, Poisons, and Herbcraft.* Mercury House, San Francisco, CA. Foreword by Gary Snyder. First of a brace of books; companion volume *Pharmako / Gnosis* due in 1997.

VOGT, D.L. 1981. "Absinthium: A nineteenth-century drug of abuse [*sic*]" *Journal of Ethnopharmacology* 4(3): 337–342.

MISCELLANEOUS RECENT ENTHEOGRAPHY

LANGDON, E.J.M. and G. BAER (Eds.) 1992. *Portals of Power: Shamanism in South America.* University of New Mexico Press, Albuquerque, NM.

LIGGENSTORFER, R. and C. RÄTSCH (Eds.) 1996. *María Sabina: Botin der Heiligen Pilze. Vom Traditionellen Schamanentum zur Weltweiten Pilzkultur.* Nachtschatten Verlag and MedienXperimente; Solothurn, Switzerland and Löhrbach, Germany.

METZNER, R. 1994. *The Well of Remembrance: Rediscovering the Earth Wisdom Myths of Northern Europe.* Shambhala, Boston, MA. Foreword by Marija Gimbutas.

OCAÑA, E. 1993. *El Dioniso Moderno y la Farmacia Utópica.* Editorial Anagrama, Barcelona, Catalunya, Spain. Also: "Meta-química" Δαιμων 8: 155–166, 1994.

OHI, K. and M.F. TORRES (Eds.) 1994. *Piedras–Hongo.* Museo de Tabaco y Sal, Tokyo, Japan. Spanish/Japanese text with numerous mushroom-stone illustrations.

OTT, J. 1995. *The Age of Entheogens & The Angels' Dictionary.* Natural Products Co., Kennewick, WA.

SAMORINI, G. 1995. *Gli Allucinogeni nel Mito: Racconti sull'Origine delle Piante Psicoattive.* Nautilus, Torino, Italy.

SCHIVELBUSCH, W. (Translation by D. Jacobson) 1992. *Tastes of Paradise: A Social History of Spices, Stimulants, and Intoxicants.* Pantheon Books, New York. Originally published in German, 1980; Spanish translation in 1995, Editorial Anagrama.

SCHULTES, R.E. and S. VON REIS (Eds.) 1995. *Ethnobotany: Evolution of a Discipline.* Dioscorides Press, Portland, OR. Foreword by Noel D. Vietmeyer.

STRAUSBAUGH, J. and D. BLAISE (Eds.) 1991. *The Drug User. Documents: 1840–1960.* Blast Books, New York. Foreword by William S. Burroughs.

BIBLIOGRAPHY

Aaronson, B. and **H. Osmond** (Eds.) 1970. *Psychedelics: The Uses and Implications of Hallucinogenic Drugs.* Doubleday/Anchor, Garden City, NJ. Published the following year by The Hogarth Press, London, England.

Aaronson, S. 1988. "*Paspalum* spp. and *Claviceps paspali* in ancient and modern India" *Journal of Ethnopharmacology* 24(2,3): 345–348.

Abaul, J. *et al.* 1989. "Contributions to a study of American Tabernaemontanae. VI. Alkaloids of *Tabernaemontana citrifolia*" *Journal of Natural Products* 52(6): 1279–1283.

Abbas, J.A. *et al.* 1992. "Herbal plants in the traditional medicine of Bahrain" *Economic Botany* 46(2): 158–163.

Abbott, I.A. and **C. Shimazu** 1985. "The geographic origin of the plants most commonly used for medicine by Hawaiians" *Journal of Ethnopharmacology* 14(2,3): 213–222.

Abe, M. *et al.* 1955. "Researches on ergot fungus. Part 25. Production of alkaloids by ergot fungus parasitic on *Elymus mollis* TRIN. (Elymus-type ergot fungus)" *Journal of the Agricultural Society of Japan* 29: 364–369.

Abel, J.J. and **D.I. Macht** 1911. "Two crystalline pharmacological agents obtained from the tropical toad, *Bufo agua*" *Journal of Pharmacology and Experimental Therapeutics* 3: 319.

Aberdeen, J.E.C. and **W. Jones** 1958. "A hallucinogenic toadstool" *The Australian Journal of Science* 21: 149.

Aberle, D.F. 1966. *The Peyote Religion Among the Navaho.* Aldine, Chicago, IL.

Abramov, M.M. 1957. "The isolation of lagochilin" *Journal of Applied Chemistry of USSR* 30: 691–692.

Abramson, H.A. (Ed.) 1956. *Neuropharmacology.* Josiah Macy, Jr. Foundation, New York. 2nd conference, 25–27 May, 1955.

Abramson, H.A. 1958. "Lysergic acid diethylamide (LSD-25) antagonists II. Development of tolerance in man to LSD-25 by prior administration of MLD-41 (1-methyl-*d*-lysergic acid diethylamide)" *Archives of Neurology and Psychiatry* 79: 201–207.

Abramson, H.A. (Ed.) 1960. *The Use of LSD in Psychiatry.* Josiah Macy, Jr. Foundation, New York.

Abramson, H.A. and **A. Rolo** 1967. "Comparison of LSD with methysergide and psilocybin on test subjects" In: Abramson, H.A. (Ed.) *The Use of LSD in Psychotherapy and Alcoholism.* Bobbs Merrill, New York. pp. 53–73.

Abramson, H.A. *et al.* 1960. "Production of cross-tolerance to psychosis-producing [*sic*] doses of lysergic acid diethylamide and psilocybin" *Journal of Psychology* 49: 151–154.

Abulafatih, H.A. 1987. "Medicinal plants in southwest Saudi Arabia" *Economic Botany* 41(3): 354–356.

Abu-Zarga, M.H. 1986. "Three new simple indole alkaloids from *Limonia acidissima*" *Journal of Natural Products* 49(5): 901–904.

Adams, K.R. 1990. "Prehistoric reedgrass (*Phragmites*) 'cigarettes' with tobacco (*Nicotiana*) contents: A case study from Red Bluff cliff dwelling in Arizona" *Journal of Ethnobiology* 10(2): 123–139.

Adamson, S. (Ed.) 1985. *Through the Gateway of the Heart: Accounts of Experiences with MDMA and Other Empathogenic Substances.* Four Tree Publications, San Francisco, CA. Foreword, R. Metzner, pp. 1–6.

Adamson, S. and **R. Metzner** 1988. "The nature of the MDMA experience and its role in healing, psychotherapy, and spiritual practice" *ReVision: The Journal of Consciousness and Change* 10(4): 59–72.

Adler, H.F. *et al.* 1950. "Effect of various drugs on psychomotor performance at ground level and simulated altitudes of 18,000 feet in a low pressure chamber" *Journal of Aviation Medicine* 21: 221–236.

Adler, P.A. 1985. *Wheeling and Dealing: An Ethnography of an Upper-Level Drug Dealing and Smuggling Community.* Columbia University Press, New York.

Adovasio, J.M. and **G.F. Fry** 1976. "Prehistoric psychotropic drug use in northern Mexico and trans-Pecos Texas" *Economic Botany* 30(1): 94–96.

Aghajanian, G.K. *et al.* 1970. "LSD and mescaline: Comparison of effects on single units in the mid-brain raphe" In: Efron, D.H. (Ed.) *Psychotomimetic* [*sic*] *Drugs.* Raven Press, New York. pp. 165–176. Oral discussion [W. Dement, E. Domino, G. Lehrer, D.X. Freedman, B.R. Holmstedt, S.H. Snyder and L. Stein].

Agurell, S. 1969A. "Identification of alkaloid intermediates by gas chromatography-mass spectrometry. I. Potential mescaline precursors in *Trichocereus* species" *Lloydia* 32(1): 40–45.

Agurell, S. 1969B. "Cactaceae alkaloids. I." *Lloydia* 32(2): 206–216.

Agurell, S. *et al.* 1968A. "Identification of two new β-carboline alkaloids in South American hallucinogenic plants" *Biochemical Pharmacology* 17: 2487–2488.

Agurell, S. *et al.* 1968B. "Alkaloidal content of *Banisteriopsis rusbyana*" *American Journal of Pharmacy* 140(5): 148–151.

Agurell, S. *et al.* 1969. "Alkaloids in certain species of *Virola* and other South American plants of ethnopharmacologic interest" *Acta Chemica Scandinavica* 23(3): 903–916.

Agurell, S. *et al.* 1971. "Cactaceae alkaloids. X. Alkaloids of *Trichocereus* species and some other cacti" *Lloydia* 34(2): 183–187.

Ahmad, A. *et al.* 1992. "Study of the in vitro antimicrobial activity of harmine, harmaline and their derivatives" *Journal of Ethnopharmacology* 35(3): 289–294.

Ahmed, A.A. and **N.A.M. Saleh** 1987. "Peganetin, a new branched acetylated tetraglycoside of acacetin from *Peganum harmala*" *Journal of Natural Products* 50 (2): 256–258.

Akendengué, B. 1992. "Medicinal plants used by the Fang traditional healers in Equatorial Guinea" *Journal of Ethnopharmacology* 37(2): 165–173.

Alam, M.K. 1992. "Medicinal ethnobotany of the Marama tribe of Bangladesh" *Economic Botany* 46(3): 330–333.

Alarcón, R. 1990. Personal communications, Jatun Sacha Reserve, Ecuador.

Albaugh, B.J. and **P.O. Anderson** 1974. "Peyote in the treatment of alcoholism among American Indians" *American Journal of Psychiatry* 131: 1247–1251.

Albert-Puleo, M. 1978. "Mythobotany, pharmacology and chemistry of thujone-containing plants and derivatives" *Economic Botany* 32(1): 65–74.

Albert-Puleo, M. 1979. "The obstetrical use in ancient and early modern times of *Convolvulus scammonia* or Scammony: Another non-fungal source of ergot alkaloids?" *Journal of Ethnopharmacology* 1(2): 193–195.

Albert-Puleo, M. 1980. "Fennel and anise as estrogenic agents" *Journal of Ethnopharmacology* 2(4): 337–344.

Alcorn, J.B. 1984. *Huastec Mayan Ethnobotany*. University of Texas Press, Austin, TX.

Al-Deen, I.H.S. *et al.* 1987. "Toxicologic and histopathologic studies of *Pleurotus ostreatus* mushroom in mice" *Journal of Ethnopharmacology* 21(3): 297–305.

Aldhous, P. 1992. "Swiss drug giants seek antidote to activists" *Science* 256: 608–609.

Aldrich, M.R. 1977. "Tantric Cannabis use in India" *Journal of Psychedelic Drugs* 9 (3): 227–233.

Aldunate, C. *et al.* 1983. "Ethnobotany of pre-altiplanic community in the Andes of northern Chile" *Economic Botany* 37(1): 120–135.

Alexander, B. 1990. "Snow job" *Reason*. December issue. pp. 29–34.

Alhadeff, B.W. 1962. "Les effets psychotomimétiques [*sic*] du Délyside (LSD 25) et de l'Indocybine (psilocybine) dans l'exploration clinique de la personalité" *Médicine et Hygiène* 20(548): 392–393.

Allegro, J. 1970. *The Sacred Mushroom and the Cross.* Hodder & Stoughton, London, England. Originally serialized in *The News of the World.* Translated into French in 1971, *Le Champignon Sacré et la Croix.* A. Michel, Paris, France. Translated by P. Marginter into German, 1970. *Der Geheimkult des Heiligen Pilzes: Rauschgift als Ursprung Unserer Religionen.* Fritz Molden Verlag, Vienna, Austria; München, Germany and Zürich, Switzerland.

Allen, J.W. 1988. "A private inquiry into the circumstances surrounding the 1972 death of John Gomilla, Jr., who died after allegedly consuming ten hallucinogenic mushrooms while residing in Hawaii" *Journal of Psychoactive Drugs* 20(4): 451–453.

Allen, J.W. 1991. "Commercial activities related to psychoactive fungi in Thailand" *Boston Mycological Club Bulletin* 46(1): 11–14.

Allen, J.W. 1992A. *Spring Time Magic. A History of Entheogenic Mushrooms: Past and Present Applications with Special Attention Given to* Panaeolus *Species.* In prep.

Allen, J.W. 1992B. Personal communications, Maui, HI.

Allen, J.W. and M.D. Merlin 1989. "*Copelandia* and other psychoactive fungi in Hawai'i" *Hawaiian Botanical Society Newsletter* 28(2): 27–30.

Allen, J.W. and M.D. Merlin 1991. "Observations regarding the suspected psychoactive properties of *Panaeolina foenisecii* Maire" In: Rätsch, C. (Ed.) *Yearbook for Ethnomedicine and the Study of Consciousness* 1: 99–115. VWB, Berlin, Germany.

Allen, J.W. and M.D. Merlin 1992A. "Psychoactive mushroom use in Koh Samui and Koh Pha-Ngan, Thailand" *Journal of Ethnopharmacology* 35(3): 205–228.

Allen, J.W. and M.D. Merlin 1992B. "Psychoactive mushrooms in Thailand: Some aspects of their relationship to human use, law and art" *Integration: Zeitschrift für Geistbewegende Pflanzen und Kultur* 2&3: 98–108.

Allen, J.W. *et al.* 1991. "An ethnomycological review of psychoactive agarics in Australia and New Zealand" *Journal of Psychoactive Drugs* 23(1): 39–69.

Allen, J.W. *et al.* 1992. "Index to the botanical identification and chemical analysis of the known species of the hallucinogenic fungi" *Integration: Zeitschrift für Geistbewegende Pflanzen und Kultur* 2&3: 91–97.

Allen, R.F. and **B. Holmstedt** 1980. "The simple β-carboline alkaloids" *Phytochemistry* 19: 1573–1582.

Alles, G.A. 1959. "Some relations between chemical structure and physiological action of mescaline and related compounds" In: Abramson, H.A. (Ed.) *Neuropharmacology.* Josiah Macy, Jr. Foundation, New York. pp. 181–268. Fourth conference, 1957.

Alvear, S.L.H. 1971. *Chamanismo en el Reino de Quito.* Instituto Ecuatoriano de Ciencias Naturales, Quito, Ecuador, #75.

AlYahya, M. and **W.C. Evans** 1975. "Alkaloids of the F_1 hybrid of *Datura stramonium* x *Datura discolor*" *Journal of Pharmacy and Pharmacology* 27: 87.

Amato, I. 1992. "From 'hunter magic,' a pharmacopeia?" *Science* 258: 1306.

Ames, B.N. *et al.* 1987. "Ranking possible carcinogenic hazards" *Science* 236: 271–280.

Amigos de las Artes de México 1991. *México: Esplendores de Treinta Siglos.* The Metropolitan Museum of Art, New York. Introduction by Octavio Paz.

Amirati, J.F. *et al.* 1989. "Hallucinogens" In: *Poisonous Mushrooms of the Northern United States and Canada.* University of Minnesota Press, Minneapolis, MN.

Ammon, H.P.T. and **A.B. Müller** 1985. "Forskolin: From an Ayurvedic remedy to a modern agent" *Planta Medica* 51: 473–477.

Amor-Prats, D. and **J.B. Harborne** 1993. "New sources of ergoline alkaloids within the genus *Ipomoea*" *Biochemical Systematics and Ecology* 21(4): 455–462.

Andary, C. *et al.* 1978A. "Mise en évidence et dosage fluorodensitométrique des dérivés 5-hydroxyindoliques. Application au dosage de la sérotonine, de la bufotenine et du 5-hydroxytryptophane chez *Amanita citrina* Fr. ex Schaeff." *Travaux du Société Pharmacologique de Montpellier* 38: 247–256.

Andary, C. *et al.* 1978B. "Dérivés 5-hydroxyindoliques chez les amanites. Étude chimique et pharmacologique" *Collection du Médecine Légal et de Toxicologie Medical* 106: 43–54.

Anderson, E.F. 1969. "The biogeography, ecology and taxonomy of *Lophophora* (Cactaceae)" *Brittonia* 21(4): 299–310.

Anderson, E.F. 1980. *Peyote: The Divine Cactus.* University of Arizona Press, Tucson, AZ. Revised edition in 1996.

Anderson, E.F. 1986A. "Ethnobotany of Hill Tribes of northern Thailand. I. Medicinal plants of Akha" *Economic Botany* 40(1): 38–53.

Anderson, E.F. 1986B. "Ethnobotany of Hill Tribes of northern Thailand. II. Lahu medicinal plants" *Economic Botany* 40(4): 442–450.

Anderson, E.F. 1995. "The 'peyote gardens' of south Texas: A conservation crisis?" *Cactus & Succulent Journal* 67(2): 67–73.

Anderson, L.C. 1974. "A study of systematic wood anatomy in Cannabis" *Botanical Museum Leaflets* Harvard University 24(2): 29–36.

Anderson, L.C. 1980. "Leaf variation among Cannabis species from a controlled garden" *Botanical Museum Leaflets* Harvard University 28(1): 61–69.

Anderson, W.H. 1988. "Tetrodotoxin and the zombi phenomenon" *Journal of Ethnopharmacology* 23(1): 121–126. See rebuttal: Davis 1989.

Andoh, A. 1986. *The Science and Romance of Selected Herbs used in Medicine and Religious Ceremony.* North Scale Inst., SF, CA.

Andrews, G. and **S. Vinkenoog** (Eds.) 1967. *The Book of Grass.* Grove Press, New York.

Andritzky, W. 1988. *Schamanismus und Rituelles Heilen im Alten Peru.* Two volumes. Verlag Clemens Zerling, Berlin, Germany.

Andritzky, W. 1989. "Sociopsychotherapeutic functions of ayahuasca healing in Amazonia" *Journal of Psychoactive Drugs* 21(1): 77–89.

Annas, G.J. and **M.A. Grodin** (Eds.) 1992. *The Nazi Doctors and the Nuremberg Code.* Oxford University Press, New York and London, England.

Anon. 1855. "Journal of a voyage up the Amazon and Río Negro by Richard Spruce, San Carlos del Río Negro, June 27, 1853" *Hooker Journal of Botany and Kew Garden Miscellany.* Numbers 6 & 7.

Anon. 1914. "Verfahren zur Darstellung von Alkyloxyaryl-, Dialkyloxyaryl- und Alkylendioxyarylaminopropanen bzw. deren am Stickstoff monoalkylierten Derivaten" (German Patent 274,350, 16 May 1914) to E. Merck, Darmstadt, Germany.

Anon. 1975. "Teonanacatl: Mushroom of the gods" *High Times.* Spring issue. pp. 34 *et seq.*

Anon. 1986. Obituary of María Sabina. *South: The Third World Magazine.* January issue. p. 5.

Anon. 1987. *Alcohol and Health. Sixth Special Report to the U.S. Congress.* Department of Health & Human Services, National Institute on Drug Abuse, Rockville, MD.

Anon. 1990. *What You Should Know About AIDS.* U.S. Public Health Service, Centers for Disease Control, Washington, D.C.

Anon. 1991. "Some further steps in the new paradign [*sic*] agenda: A naturalized *ayahuasca* complex in N. America" Unpublished manuscript.

Anon. 1992A. "La DEA ya no puede actuar aquí" *La Jornada.* 16 June issue. pp. 1,10.

Anon. 1992B. "Un brebaje, fórmula del éxito chino en las Olimpiadas de Barcelona" *La Jornada.* 24 August issue. p. 30.

Anon. 1992C. "Oh, Wilbur" *Discover.* December issue.

Antonil (Pseudonym for Anthony Henman) 1978. *Mama Coca.* Hassle Free Press, London, England. Spanish translation, Oveja Negra, Bogotá, Colombia, 1981. Original signed, numbered edition of 350, Practical Paradise Publications, Suffolk, England, 1978. Excerpt "Mama Coca" *Journal of Psychedelic Drugs* 10(2): 99–104, 1978.

Applegate, R.B. 1975. "The Datura cult among the Chumash" *Journal of California Anthropology* 2(1): 7–17.

Arbain, D. *et al.* 1989. "Survey of some West Sumatran plants for alkaloids" *Economic Botany* 43(1): 73–78.

Arcamone, F. *et al.* 1960. "Production of lysergic acid derivatives by a strain of *Claviceps paspali* Stevens and Hall in submerged culture" *Nature* 187: 238–239.

Arenas, P. 1987. "Medicine and magic among the Maka Indians of the Paraguayan Chaco" *Journal of Ethnopharmacology* 21(3): 279–295.

Arévalo Valera, G. 1986. "El *ayahuasca* y el curandero Shipibo-Conibo del Ucayali (Perú)" *América Indígena* 46(1): 147–161.

Arnason, T. *et al.* 1980. "Maya medicinal plants of San José Succotz, Belize" *Journal of Ethnopharmacology* 2(4): 345–364.

Arnold, O.H. and **G. Hofmann** 1957. "Zur Psychopathologie [*sic*] des Dimethyl-tryptamin" *Wiener Zeitschrift für Nervenheilkunde* 13: 438–445.

Arriola, G. 1957. *Gordo.* Syndicated comic.

Arslanian, R.L. *et al.* 1986. "3-Methoxy-5-hydroxyflavonols from *Tillandsia purpurea*" *Journal of Natural Products* 49(6): 1177–1178.

Artaud, A. (Translation by H. Weaver) 1976. *The Peyote Dance.* Farrar Straus and Giroux, New York. Original 1971 *Les Tarahumaras, Tome IX, Oeuvres Complètes d'Antonin Artaud.* Éditions Gallimard, Paris, France.

Arthur, H.R. *et al.* 1967. "N_b-Methylated tryptamines and other constituents of *Acacia confusa* Merr. of Hong Kong" *Austra-*

lian Journal of Chemistry 20: 811–813.

Aschenbrandt, T. 1883. "Die physiologische Wirkung und die Bedeutung des Cocains" *Deutscher Medizinischer Wochenschrift.* 12 December issue.

Atta-Ur-Rahman *et al.* 1988. "Alkaloids from *Trachelospermum jasminoides*" *Planta Medica* 54(4): 364.

Audette, R.C.S. *et al.* 1969. "Phytochemical investigation of Manitoba plants II. A gas-liquid chromatographic screening technique for the identification of the alkaloids of *Phalaris* species" *Journal of Chromatography* 43: 295–302.

Audette, R.C.S. *et al.* 1970. "Phytochemical investigation of Manitoba plants. I. A new indole alkaloid and associated alkaloids from *Phalaris arundinacea*" *Canadian Journal of Chemistry* 48: 149–155.

Auert, V.G. *et al.* 1980. "Halluzinogene Wirkung zweier Hutpilze der Gattung *Psilocybe* aus der Tschechoslowakei" *Zeitschrift für Ärztliche Fortbildung* 74: 833–835.

Austin, D.F. 1991. "*Ipomoea littoralis* (Convolvulaceae)—Taxonomy, distribution, and ethnobotany" *Economic Botany* 45(2): 251–256.

Austin, D.F. and **G.R. Bourne** 1992. "Notes on Guyana's medical ethnobotany" *Economic Botany* 46(3): 293–298.

Awasthi, A.K. 1991. "Ethnobotanical studies of the Negrito Islanders of Andaman Islands, India—The Great Andamanese" *Economic Botany* 45(2): 274–280.

Ayres, W.A. *et al.* 1981. "The bogus drug: Three methyl and alpha methyl fentanyl sold as 'China White'" *Journal of Psychoactive Drugs* 13(1): 91–93.

Azéma, R.C. 1987. "Un nouveau champignon hallucinogène: *Cortinarius infractus* Pers. ex Fr." *Bulletin de la Société Mycologique de France* 103: 13–15.

Badham, E.R. 1984. "Ethnobotany of psilocybin [*sic*] mushrooms, especially *Psilocybe cubensis*" *Journal of Ethnopharmacology* 10(2): 249–254.

Baer, G. 1969. "Eine Ayahuasca-Sitzung unter den Piro (Ost-Perú)" *Bulletin de la Société Suisse des Americanistes* 33: 5–8.

Baer, G. and **W.W. Snell** 1974. "An ayahuasca ceremony among the Matsigenka (Eastern Peru)" *Zeitschrift für Ethnologie* 99(1&2): 64–80.

Bahre, C.J. and **D.E. Bradbury** 1980. "Manufacture of mescal in Sonora, Mexico" *Economic Botany* 34(4): 391–400.

Bailey, C. and **A. Danin** 1981. "Bedouin plant utilization in Sinai and the Negev" *Economic Botany* 35(2): 145–162.

Bailey, H.W. 1972. "A half-century of Indo-Iranian studies" *Journal of the Royal Asiatic Society* 2: 99–110.

Bailey, H.W. 1974. "The range of the colour *ZAR*– in Khotan Saka texts" *Mémorial: Jean de Menasce* 185: 369–374. Fondation Culturelle Iranienne, Louvain, France.

Bailin, J.E. 1975. "Las convolvuláceas psicotrópicas: Sus usos aborígenes, efectos clínicos y análisis recientes" *Cuadernos Científicos CEMEF* 4: 93–134.

Balasubrahmanyam, V.R. and **A.K.S. Rawat** 1990. "Betelvine (*Piper betle*, Piperaceae)" *Economic Botany* 44(4): 540–543.

Balestrieri, A. 1957. "Cross tolerance between LSD-25 and mescaline" In: Garattini, S. and V. Ghetti (Eds.) *Psychotropic Drugs.* Elsevier Publishing Company, Amsterdam, Netherlands. pp. 581–582.

Banack, S.A. 1991. "Plants and Polynesian voyaging" In: Cox, P.A. and S.A. Banack (Eds.) *Islands, Plants and Polynesians: An Introduction to Polynesian Ethnobotany.* Dioscorides Press, Portland, OR. pp. 25–39.

Banack, S.A. and **P.A. Cox** 1987. "Ethnobotany of ocean-going canoes in Lau, Fiji" *Economic Botany* 41(2): 148–162.

Bandoni, A.L. *et al.* 1976. "Survey of Argentinian medicinal plants—Folklore and phytochemistry—Screening II" *Economic Botany* 30(2): 161–185.

Banerjee, P.K. and **S. Ghosal** 1969. "Simple indole bases of *Desmodium gangeticum* (Leguminosae)" *Australian Journal of Chemistry* 22: 275–277.

Banerjee, S.L. and **S.P. Bhatnagar** 1974. "Indole bases of some seeds of *Ipomoea* species" *The Indian Journal of Pharmacy* 36(2): 44–46.

Barata, L.E.S. *et al.* 1978. "Neolignans of *Virola surinamensis*" *Phytochemistry* 17: 783–786.

Barber, P. 1988. *Vampires, Burial and Death.* Yale University Press, New Haven, CT.

Barclay, A.S. 1959. "New considerations in an old genus: *Datura*" *Botanical Museum Leaflets* Harvard University 18(6): 245–272.

Barger, G. 1931. *Ergot and Ergotism.* Gurney and Jackson, London, England.

Barik, B.R. *et al.* 1992. "Premnazole, an isoxazole alkaloid of *Premna integrifolia* and *Gmelina arborea* with anti-inflammatory activity" *Fitoterapia* 63(4): 295–299.

Barinaga, M. 1990A. "Amino acids: How much excitement is too much?" *Science* 247: 20–22.

Barinaga, M. 1990B. "MSG: A 20-year old debate continues" *Science* 247: 21.

Barinaga, M. 1992. "Pot, heroin unlock new areas for neuroscience" *Science* 258: 1882–1884.

Barlow, R.B. and **I. Khan** 1959. "Actions of some analogues of tryptamine on the isolated rat uterus and on the isolated rat fundus strip preparations" *British Journal of Pharmacology and Chemotherapeutics* 14: 99–107.

Barnard, M. 1963. "The god in the flowerpot" *American Scholar* 32: 578–586. Reprint, 1963 *The Psychedelic Review* 1(2): 244.

Barnard, M. 1966. *The Mythmakers.* Ohio University Press, Athens, OH.

Barnes, D.M. 1988A. "New data intensify the agony over Ecstasy" *Science* 239: 864–866.

Barnes, D.M. 1988B. "Ecstasy returned to Schedule I" *Science* 240: 24.

Barnes, D.M. 1988C. "Drugs: Running the numbers" *Science* 240: 1729–1731.

Barrau, J. 1957. "À propos du *Piper methysticum*" *Journal d'Agriculture Tropical et de Botanique Appliquée* 4: 270–273.

Barrau, J. 1962. "Observations et travaux récents sur les végétaux hallucinogènes de la Nouvelle-Guinée" *Journal d'Agriculture Tropicale et de Botanique Appliquée* 9: 245–249.

Barrigar, R.H. 1964. "The regulation of psychedelic drugs" *The Psychedelic Review* 1(4): 394–441.

Barriga Villalba, A.M. 1925A. "Un nuevo alcaloide" *Boletín de la Sociedad Colombiana de Ciencias Naturales* 14(79): 31–36.

Barriga Villalba, A.M. 1925B. "Yagéin: Ein neues Alkaloid" *Journal of the Society of Chemistry and Industry* 44: 205–207.

Barrows, D.P. 1967. *Ethno-Botany of the Coahuilla Indians of Southern California.* Malki Museum Press, Banning, CA.

Batchily, F. *et al.* 1986. "Alkaloids from the seeds of *Sarcopharyngia crassa* (Benth.) Boiteau and Allorge" *Annales Pharmaceutiques Françaises* 44(6): 449–454.

Bates, R.C. 1964. "Psychedelics and the law: A prelude in question marks" *The Psychedelic Review* 1(4): 379–392.

Baudelaire, C. 1860. *Les Paradis Artificiels.* Poulet-Malassis, Paris, France. English by E. Fox, 1971. *Artificial Paradise: On Hashish and Wine as a Means of Expanding Individuality.* Herder & Herder, New York. Spanish by M. Armiño, 1983. *Los Paraísos Artificiales: Opio y Hachís.* Ediciones Akal, Fuenlabrada, Madrid, Spain.

Bauer, G. 1992. "Wabernde Wellen, dröhnende Glocken" *Integration: Zeitschrift für Geistbewegende Pflanzen und Kultur* 2&3: 130–132.

Bauer, V.H. 1973. *Das Antonius-Feuer in Kunst*

und Medizin. Sandoz AG, Basel, Switzerland. Foreword by Albert Hofmann, p. 5.

Bauer, W. 1991A. "Das Tabu um den Fliegenpilz—Einige Thesen und Anmerkungen" In: Bauer, W. *et al.* (Eds.) *Der Fliegenpilz: Ein Kulturhistorisches Museum.* (Museum der Museen, Schriftenreihe des Karl Ernst Osthaus-Museums, Bd. 6) Wienand–Verlag, Köln, Germany. pp. 21–42.

Bauer, W. 1991B. "Die Gestalten des Fliegenpilzes und ihre symbolischen Bezüge" In: Bauer, W. *et al.* (Eds.) *Der Fliegenpilz: Ein Kulturhistorisches Museum.* (Museum der Museen, Schriftenreihe des Karl Ernst Osthaus-Museums, Bd. 6) Wienand–Verlag, Köln, Germany. pp. 195–199.

Bauer, W. 1992. "Der Fliegenpilz in Zaubermärchen, Märchenbildern, Sagen, Liedern und Gedichten" *Integration: Zeitschrift für Geistbewegende Pflanzen und Kultur* 2&3: 39–54.

Bauer, W. *et al.* (Eds.) 1991. *Der Fliegenpilz: Ein Kulturhistorisches Museum.* (Museum der Museen, Schriftenreihe des Karl Ernst Osthaus-Museums, Bd. 6) Wienand–Verlag, Köln, Germany.

Bauereiß, E. 1995. *Heimische Pflanzen der Götter: Ein Handbuch für Hexen und Zauberer.* Raymond Martin Verlag, Nürnberg.

Baum, R.M. 1985. "New variety of street drugs poses growing problems" *Chemical and Engineering News.* Sept. 9 issue. pp. 7–16.

Baxter, C. and **M. Slaytor** 1972. "Biosynthesis and turnover of *N,N*-dimethyltryptamine and 5-methoxy-*N,N*-dimethyltryptamine in *Phalaris tuberosa*" *Phytochemistry* 11: 2767–2773.

Baxter, R.M. *et al.* 1960. "Separation of hypnotic potentiating principles from the essential oil of *Acorus calamus* Linn. of Indian origin by gas-liquid chromatography" *Nature* 185: 466–467.

Beaujard, P. 1988. "Plantes et médecine traditionnelle dans le sud-est de Madagascar" *Journal of Ethnopharmacology* 23 (2,3): 165–265.

Becker Popescu, C. 1985. "Tarnishing a spitting image: The health hazards of smokeless tobacco" *ACSH News and Views* (American Council on Science and Health) 6(1): 3–4.

Beckmann, R.L. Jr. and **J.M. Stucky** 1981. "Extrafloral nectaries and plant guarding in Ipomoea pandurata (L.) G.F.W. Mey (Convolvulaceae)" *American Journal of Botany* 68(1): 72–79.

Beer, A.G. 1939A. "Beiträge zur Pharmakologie des extrapyramidalen Systems. I. Mitteilung: Die Wirkung des Harmins bei Katzen mit intaktem Nervensystem" *Archiv für Experimentelle Pathologie und Pharmakologie* 193: 377–392.

Beer, A.G. 1939B. "Beiträge zur Pharmakologie des extrapyramidalen Systems. II. Mitteilung: Die Wirkung des Harmins bei Katzen ohne Neocortex" *Archiv für Experimentelle Pathologie und Pharmakologie* 193: 393–407.

Beers, D. 1991. "Just say whoa!" *Mother Jones.* July/August issue. pp. 36 *et seq.*

Bellakhdar, J. *et al.* 1991. "Repertory of standard herbal drugs in the Moroccan pharmacopoea [*sic*]" *Journal of Ethnopharmacology* 35(2): 123–143.

Bellier, I. 1986. "Los cantos Mai Huna del yajé (Amazonia peruana)" *América Indígena* 46(1): 129–145.

Beloz, A. 1992. "Brine shrimp bioassay screening of two medicinal plants used by the Warao: *Solanum straminifolium* and *Virola surinamensis*" *Journal of Ethnopharmacology* 37(3): 225–227.

Benabud, A. 1957. "Psycho-pathological aspects of the Cannabis situation in Morocco" *Bulletin on Narcotics* 9(4): 1–16.

Bender, L. 1970. "Children's reactions to psychotomimetic [*sic*] drugs" In: Efron, D.H. (Ed.) *Psychotomimetic* [*sic*] *Drugs.*

Raven Press, New York. pp. 265–273.

Bender, L. and **D.V.S. Sankar** 1968. "Chromosome damage not found in leukocytes of children treated with LSD-25" *Science* 159. Letter to the editor, 10 January issue.

Benedict, R.G. *et al.* 1962A. "Occurence [*sic*] of psilocybin and psilocin in certain *Conocybe* and *Psilocybe* species" *Lloydia* 25(3): 156–159.

Benedict, R.G. *et al.* 1962B. "Occurrence of psilocin in *Psilocybe baeocystis*" *Journal of Pharmaceutical Sciences* 51: 393–394.

Benedict, R.G. *et al.* 1966. "Chemotaxonomic significance of isoxazole derivatives in *Amanita* species" *Lloydia* 29(4): 333–342.

Benedict, R.G. *et al.* 1967. "Blueing in *Conocybe*, *Psilocybe*, and a *Stropharia* species and the detection of psilocybin" *Lloydia* 30(2): 150–157.

Benington, F. *et al.* 1965. "5-Methoxy-*N,N*-dimethyltryptamine, a possible endogenous psychotoxin [*sic*]" *Journal of Medical Sciences* 2: 397–403.

Benítez, F. 1964. *Los Hongos Alucinantes.* Ediciones Era, México City.

Benítez, F. 1973. *Historia de un Chamán Cora*. Ediciones Era, México City.

Benítez, F. 1975. *In the Magic Land of Peyote.* University of Texas Press, Austin, TX. Introduction by P.T. Furst. Translation of *En la Tierra Mágica del Peyote.* Ediciones Era, México City, 1968.

Benjamin, W. 1972. *Über Haschisch*. Suhrkamp Verlag, Frankfurt, Germany. Translated into Spanish by J. Aguirre, 1974. *Haschisch.* Taurus Ediciones, Madrid, Spain.

Benn, G. (Translation by R. Metzner) 1963. "Provoked life: An essay on the anthropology of the ego" *The Psychedelic Review* 1: 47–54. Original 1949. "Provoziertes Leben" In: *Ausdruckswelt, Essays und Aphorismen.* Limes Verlag, Wiesbaden, Germany. Reprinted in *The Psychedelic Reader.*

Bennett, B.C. and **R. Alarcón** 1994. "*Osteophloeum platyspermum* and *Virola duckei* (Myristicaceae): Newly-reported as hallucinogens from Amazonian Ecuador" *Economic Botany* 48(2): 152–158.

Bennett, C. *et al.* 1995. *Green Gold the Tree of Life. Marijuana in Magic & Religion.* Access, Frazier Park, CA. Forew. J. Herer.

Benzi, M. 1972. *Les Derniers Adorateurs du Peyotl: Croyances, Coutumes et Mythes des Indiens Huichol*. Gallimard, Paris, France.

Beretz, A. *et al.* 1985. "Polyindolinic alkaloids from *Psychotria forsteriana.* Potent inhibitors of the aggregation of human platelets" *Planta Medica* 51: 300–303.

Bergman, R.L. 1971. "Navajo peyote use: Its apparent safety" *American Journal of Psychiatry* 128: 695–699.

Beringer, K. 1927. *Der Meskalinrausch: Seine Geschichte und Erscheinungsweise.* Springer–Verlag, Berlin, Germany. Reprint 1969.

Beringer, K. 1928. "Über ein neues, auf das extra-pyramidal-motorische System wirkendes Alkaloid (Banisterin)" *Der Nervenärzt* 1: 265–275.

Beringer, K. and **K. Wilmanns** 1929. "Zur Harmin-Banisterin-Frage" *Deutscher Medizinischer Wochenschrift* 55: 2081–2086.

Berlet, C. 1981. "War on drugs: The strategy of Lyndon La Rouche" *High Times.* May issue. pp. 49 *et seq.*

Bernauer, K. 1964. "Notiz über die Isolierung von Harmin und (+)-1,2,3,4-Tetrahydro-harmin aus einer indianischen Schnupfdroge" *Helvetica Chimica Acta* 47(4): 1075–1077.

Bernheimer, A.W. and **L.S. Avigad** 1979. "A cytolytic protein from the edible mushroom *Pleurotus ostreatus*" *Biochimica et Biophysiologica Acta* 585: 451–461.

Berrin, K. (Ed.) 1988. *Feathered Serpent and Flowering Trees: Reconstruction of the Murals of Teotihuacan*. The Fine Arts Museum of San Francisco, San Francisco, CA.

Bert, M. *et al.* 1988. "Non-amphetamine

central stimulation by alkaloids from the ibogane and vobasine series" *Planta Medica* 54: 191–192.

Bert, M. *et al.* 1989. "Alkaloids of *Pagiantha cerifera*" *Fitoterapia* 60(2): 141–146.

Besl, H. 1993. "*Galerina steglichii* spec. nov., ein halluzinogener Häubling" *Zeitschrift für Mykologie* 59(2): 215–218.

Beug, M.W. and **J. Bigwood** 1982. "Psilocybin and psilocin levels in twenty species from seven genera of wild mushrooms in the Pacific Northwest, U.S.A." *Journal of Ethnopharmacology* 5(3): 271–285.

Beutler, J.A. and **A.H. Der Marderosian** 1978. "Chemotaxonomy of *Cannabis* I. Cross-breeding between *Cannabis sativa* and *C. ruderalis*, with analysis of cannabinoid content" *Economic Botany* 32(4): 387–394.

Beutler, J.A. and **A.H. Der Marderosian** 1981. "Chemical variation in *Amanita*" *Journal of Natural Products* 44(4): 422–431.

Bhattacharya, S.K. *et al.* 1971. "Investigations on the hallucinogenic activity of indole alkylamines isolated from *Mucuna pruriens* DC" *Indian Journal of Physiology and Applied Sciences* 25(2): 53–56.

Bhattacharya, S.K. *et al.* 1975. "Psychopharmacological investigations of the 4-methoxyindole alkaloids of *Alstonia venenata*" *Planta Medica* 27: 164–170.

Bhattacharyya, A. 1991. "Ethnobotanical observations in the Ladakh region of northern Jammu and Kashmir state, India" *Economic Botany* 45(3): 305–308.

Bhattarai, N.K. 1992. "Medical ethnobotany in the Karnali Zone, Nepal" *Economic Botany* 46(3): 257–61.

Bhide, N.K. and **R.A. Aimen** 1959. "Pharmacology of a tranquillizing principle in *Paspalum scrobiculatum* grain" *Nature* 183: 1735–1736.

Bhide, S.V. *et al.* 1991. "Chemopreventive efficacy of betel leaf extract against benzo[*a*]pyrene-induced forestomach tumors in mice" *Journal of Ethnopharmacology* 34(2,3): 207–213.

Bhide, V.P. *et al.* 1987. *Fungi of Maharashtra.* Government Press, New Delhi, India.

Bianchi, A. 1991. "Psicofisiologia dei rituali allucinatori dello sciamanesimo nord-peruviano" *Annali dei Musei Civici di Rovereto* 6: 147–152.

Bibra, E.F. von 1855. *Die Narkotischen Genußmittel und der Mensch.* Verlag von Wilhelm Schmid, Nürnberg, Germany. English translation, 1995. *Plant Intoxicants.* Healing Arts Press, Rochester, VT. "Technical notes" by Jonathan Ott, pp. 223–261.

Bieberman, L. 1968. *Phanerothyme: A Western Approach to the Religious Use of Psychochemicals.* Psychedelic Information Center, Cambridge, MA.

Bigwood, J. 1977. "STP and MDA: The love drug and other psychedelic [*sic*] amphetamines" *Head.* December issue. pp. 54 *et seq.*

Bigwood, J. 1978. Personal communication.

Bigwood, J. 1987. Personal communication.

Bigwood, J. and **J. Ott** 1977. "DMT" *Head.* November issue. p. 56 *et seq.*

Bigwood, J. *et al.* 1979. "Entheogenic effects of ergonovine" *Journal of Psychedelic Drugs* 11(1-2): 147–149. See: Ott & Neely 1980.

Bigwood, J. and **M.W. Beug** 1982. "Variation of psilocybin and psilocin levels with repeated flushes (harvests) of mature sporocarps of *Psilocybe cubensis* (Earle) Singer" *Journal of Ethnopharmacology* 5(3): 287–291.

Biocca, E.F. *et al.* 1964. "Sulla sostanze allucinogene impiegata in Amazonia. Nota I. Osservazioni sul paricá dei Tukâno e Tariâna del bacino del Río Uaupés" *Annali di Chimica* 54: 1175–1178.

Bisset, N.G. 1979. "Arrow poisons in China. Part I." *Journal of Ethnopharmacology* 1 (4): 325–384.

Bisset, N.G. 1992A. "War and hunting poisons of the New World. Part I. Notes on the early history of curare" *Journal of Ethnopharmacology* 36(1): 1–26.

Bisset, N.G. 1992B. "Uses, chemistry and pharmacology of *Malouetia* (Apocynaceae, subf. Apocynoideae)" *Journal of Ethnopharmacology* 36(1): 43–50.

Blackburn, T. 1976. "A query regarding the possible hallucinogenic effects of ant ingestion in South-Central California" *Journal of California Anthropology* 3(2): 78–81.

Blackmun, W. 1990. Dissenting opinion in U.S. Supreme Court case. *The United States Law Week* 58 LW 4443–4446.

Blair, T.S. 1921. "Habit indulgence [*sic*] in certain cactaceous plants among the Indians" *Journal of the American Medical Association* 76: 1033–1034.

Blanchette, R.A. *et al.* 1992. "Nineteenth century shaman grave guardians are carved *Fomitopsis officinalis* sporophores" *Mycologia* 84(1): 119–124.

Blanco, M.L. 1993. "Jonathan Ott: 'La heroína es menos tóxica que el alcohol'" *Cambio 16* 1108: 84–86. *Cambio16 América* pp. 42–44.

Blaschko, H. and **W.G. Levine** 1960. "A comparative study of hydroxyindole oxidases" *Biochemical Pharmacology* 3: 168–169.

Blewett, D. 1970. "The psychedelics [*sic*] and group therapy" In: Aaronson, B. and H. Osmond (Eds.) *Psychedelics: The Uses and Implications of Hallucinogenic Drugs.* Doubleday/Anchor, Garden City, NJ. pp. 342–357.

Block, S.S. *et al.* 1955. "The *Amanita* toxins in mushrooms" *Journal of Agricultural and Food Chemistry* 3: 584.

Blosser, B. 1991. Personal communications.

Blosser, B. 1992. "The return of the *peyoteros*" *Whole Earth Review.* Summer issue. 75: 44–46. Also published in 1992 in *Plant Wise* [Botanical Dimensions] 5: 4–5.

Blum, R. and **Associates** 1964. *Utopiates: The Use and Users of LSD 25.* Atherton Press, New York. Foreword by N. Sanford, pp. XI–XVI. Reprinted in 1965 by Tavistock Publications, Ltd., London, England.

Blumenthal, M. 1992. "Government stops legitimate medical use of marijuana" *HerbalGram* 26: 44.

Bluth, B.J. 1981. "Soviet space stress" *Science 81.* September issue. pp. 30–35.

Blyth, R.H. 1973. "Mushrooms in Japanese verse" *The Transactions of the Asiatic Society of Japan* Third Series 11: 1–14.

Bocek, B.R. 1984. "Ethnobotany of Costanoan Indians, California, based on collections of John P. Harrington" *Economic Botany* 38(2): 240–255.

Bocks, S.M. 1967. "Fungal metabolism–IV. The oxidation of psilocin by *p*-diphenol oxidase (laccase)" *Phytochemistry* 6: 1629–1631.

Bodendorf, K. and **H. Kümmer** 1962. "Über die Alkaloide in *Latua venenosa*" *Pharmazeutische Zentralhalle* 101: 620–622.

Bodner, C.C. and **R.B. Gereau** 1988. "A contribution to Bontoc ethnobotany" *Economic Botany* 42(3): 307–369.

Bohinc, P. *et al.* 1977. "Xanthine alkaloids in *Ilex ambigua* leaves" *Farmacevtski Vestnik* 28: 89–96.

Boire, R.G. 1994. "Criminalizing nature & knowledge: Toads, cacti, mushrooms and the domain of the human brain" *The Entheogen Law Reporter* 2: 7–9.

Boire, R.G. 1995. *Sacred Mushrooms & the Law.* Spectral Mindustries, Davis, CA.

Boldó i Climent, J. (Ed.) 1986. *La Coca Andina: Visión Indígena de una Planta Satanizada.* Instituto Indigenista Interamericano, Coyoacán, México.

Bonhour, A. *et al.* 1967. "Estudios psicofarmacológicos con bufotenina" *Revista de Psiquiatría y Psicología Médica* 8: 123–143.

Boom, B.M. 1987. *Ethnobotany of the Chácobo Indians, Beni, Bolivia.* (Advances in Economic Botany, Vol. 4) New York Botanical Garden, Bronx, NY. pp. 1–68.

Boom, B.M. and **S. Moestl** 1990. "Ethnobotanical notes of José M. Cruxent from the Franco-Venezuelan expedition to the headwaters of the Orinoco River, 1951–1952" *Economic Botany* 44(3): 416–419.

Booth, W.B. 1988A. "Voodoo science" *Science* 240: 274–276. See rebuttal: Davis 1988B; also: Anderson 1988; Davis 1989.

Booth, W.B. 1988B. "An underground drug for AIDS" *Science* 241: 1279–1281.

Böszörményi, Z. and **G. Brunecker** 1957. "Dimethyltryptamine (DMT) experiments with psychotics" In: Garattini, S. and V. Ghetti (Eds.) *Psychotropic Drugs*. Elsevier, Amsterdam, Netherlands. pp. 580–581.

Böszörményi, Z. and **S.I. Szára** 1958. "Dimethyltryptamine experiments with psychotics" *Journal of Mental Science* 104: 445–453.

Böszörményi, Z. *et al.* 1959. "Observations on the psychotogenic [*sic*] effect of N-N diethyltryptamine, a new tryptamine derivative" *Journal of Mental Science* 105: 171–181.

Bourdy, G. and **A. Walter** 1992. "Maternity and medicinal plants in Vanuatu I. The cycle of reproduction" *Journal of Ethnopharmacology* 37(3): 179–196.

Bourdy, G. *et al.* 1992. "Traditional remedies used in the Western Pacific for the treatment of ciguatera poisoning" *Journal of Ethnopharmacology* 36(2): 163–174.

Bourget, S. 1990. "Caracoles sagrados en la iconografía moche" *Boletín del Instituto Francés de Estudios Andinos* 19(2): 45–58.

Bourgetau, S. 1992. "Colombie: La guerre des herbicides" *Interdépendances* 9: 24–25.

Bourke, J.G. 1936. *Scatalogic* [*sic*] *Rites of All Nations*. American Anthropological Assoc., Washington, D.C. Original published in 1891, Loudermilk, Washington, D.C.

Bové, F.J. 1970. *The Story of Ergot: For Physicians, Pharmacists, Nurses, Biochemists, Biologists and Others Interested in the Life Sciences*. S. Karger, Basel, Switzerland; New York. Foreword by H. Buess, pp. IX–X.

Bowden, K. and **A.D. Drysdale** 1965. "A novel constituent of *Amanita muscaria*" *Tetrahedron Letters* 1965: 727–728.

Bowden, K. *et al.* 1965. "Constituents of *Amanita muscaria*" *Nature* 206: 1359–1360.

Boyd, D. 1974. *Rolling Thunder*. Dell Publishing Co., New York. Intro. D. Brown.

Boyer, L.B. *et al.* 1973. "Shamanism and peyote use among the Apaches of the Mescalero Indian reservation" In: Harner, M.J. (Ed.) *Hallucinogens and Shamanism*. Oxford University Press, London, England. pp. 53–66.

Brack, A. *et al.* 1961. "Tryptophan als biogenetische Vorstufe des Psilocybins" *Archiv der Pharmazie* 294(4): 230–234.

Brack, A. *et al.* 1962. "Mikrobiologische Hydroxylierung an Mutterkornalkaloiden vom Clavin-Typus mit dem mexikanischen Rauschpilz *Psilocybe semperviva* Heim et Cailleux" *Helvetica Chimica Acta* 45(1): 276–281.

Brackelaire, V. 1992. "La coca dévoreuse de forêts et de sols" *Interdépendances* 9: 20–21.

Braden, W. 1967. *The Private Sea: LSD & the Search for God*. Quadrangle Books, Chicago, IL. Paperback, Bantam Books 1968.

Braden, W. 1970. "LSD and the press" In: Aaronson, B. and H. Osmond (Eds.) *Psychedelics: The Uses and Implications of Hallucinogenic Drugs*. Doubleday/Anchor, Garden City, NJ. pp. 400–418.

Bradley, D. 1993. "Frog venom cocktail yields a one-handed painkiller" *Science* 261: 1117.

Brady, L.R. and **V.E. Tyler** 1959. "A chromatographic examination of the alkaloidal fraction of *Amanita pantherina*" *Journal of the American Pharmaceutical Association* 48: 417–419.

Braun, V. *et al.* 1980A. "Centrally-active *N*-substituted analogs of 3,4-methylenedioxyphenylisopropylamine (3,4-methylenedioxyamphetamine)" *Journal of Phar-*

maceutical Sciences 69(2): 192–195.

Braun, V. *et al.* 1980B. "Prüfung auf zentrale Aktivität und Analgesie von *N*-substituierten Analogen des Amphetamin-Derivates 3,4-Methylendioxyphenylisopropylamin" *Arzneimittel-Forschung* 30(5): 825–830.

Brecher, E.M. 1972. *Licit and Illicit Drugs: Report on Narcotics, Stimulants, Depressants, Inhalants, Hallucinogens, and Marijuana.* Little, Brown & Co., Vernon, NY.

Brekhman, I.I. and **Y.A. Sam** 1967. "Ethnopharmacological investigation of some psychoactive drugs used by Siberian and far-eastern minor nationalities of U.S.S.R." In: Efron, D.H. *et al.* (Eds.) *Ethnopharmacologic Search for Psychoactive Drugs.* (PHS Publication No. 1645) U.S. Government Printing Office, Washington, D.C. p. 415.

Bresinsky, A. and **H. Besl** 1990. *A Colour Atlas of Poisonous Fungi.* Wolfe Publishing Co., London, England.

Brewer-Carias, C. and **J.A. Steyermark** 1976. "Hallucinogenic snuff drugs of the Yanomamo Caburiwe–Teri in the Cauaburi River, Brazil" *Economic Botany* 30(1): 57–66.

Briggs, J.R. 1887. "Muscale buttons—Physiological action—Personal experiences" *Medical Register* 1: 276–277; also *Druggist's Bulletin* 1(5): 78.

Bristol, M.L. 1966A. "The psychotropic *Banisteriopsis* among the Sibundoy of Colombia" *Botanical Museum Leaflets* Harvard University 21(5): 113–140.

Bristol, M.L. 1966B. "Notes on the species of tree Daturas" *Botanical Museum Leaflets* Harvard University 21(8): 229–248.

Bristol, M.L. 1969. "Tree Datura drugs of the Colombian Sibundoy" *Botanical Museum Leaflets* Harvard University 22(5): 165–227.

Bristol, M.L. *et al.* 1969. "The alkaloids of the genus *Datura*, section *Brugmansia*. Part VI. Tree *Datura* drugs (*Datura candida* cvs) of the Colombian Sibundoy" *Lloydia* 32: 123–130. See: Bristol 1969.

Britton, E.B. 1984. "A pointer to a new hallucinogen of insect origin" *Journal of Ethnopharmacology* 12(3): 331–333.

Brooker, S.G. *et al.* 1981. *New Zealand Medicinal Plants.* Heinemann, Auckland, NZ.

Brough, J. 1971. "Soma and *Amanita muscaria*" *Bulletin of the School of Oriental and African Studies* 34(2): 331–362.

Browman, D.L. and **R.A. Schwarz** (Eds.) 1979. *Spirits, Shamans and Stars: Perspectives from South America.* Mouton and Co., the Hague, the Netherlands.

Brown, N.A. *et al.* 1979. *Science* 206: 573.

Brown, J.K. and **M.H. Malone** (Eds.) 1973A. "Status of drug quality in the street-drug market" *Pacific Information Service on Street Drugs* 3(1): 1–7.

Brown, J.K. and **M.H. Malone** (Eds.) 1973B. "The chemical composition of illicit drugs in Munich" *Pacific Information Service on Street Drugs* 3(2): 9–16.

Brown, R.W. 1968. *The Psychedelic Guide to Preparation of the Eucharist.* Linga Sharira Incense Co., Austin, TX.

Browner, C.H. 1985. "Plants used for reproductive health in Oaxaca, Mexico" *Economic Botany* 39(4): 482–504.

Bruhn, J.G. and **C. Bruhn** 1973. "Alkaloids and ethnobotany of Mexican peyote cacti and related species" *Economic Botany* 27(2): 241–251.

Bruhn, J.G. and **B. Holmstedt** 1974. "Early peyote research: An interdisciplinary study" *Economic Botany* 28(4): 353–390.

Bruhn, J.G. and **J.-E. Lindgren** 1976. "Cactaceae alkaloids XXIII. Alkaloids of *Pachycereus pecten-aboriginum* and *Cereus jamacaru*" *Lloydia* 39(2): 175–177.

Bruhn, J.G. and **J. Lundström** 1976. "Alkaloids of *Carnegiea gigantea*. Arizonine, a new tetrahydroisoquinoline alkaloid" *Lloydia* 39(2): 197–203.

Bruhn, J.G. *et al.* 1970. "Biosynthesis of tetrahydroisoquinoline alkaloids in *Carnegiea gigantea* Br. & R." *Acta Chemica Scandinavica* 24: 3775–3777.

Bruhn, J.G. *et al.* 1978. "Peyote alkaloids: Identification in a prehistoric specimen of *Lophophora* from Coahuila, Mexico" *Science* 199: 1437–1438.

Bruneton, J. *et al.* 1976. "Alcaloïdes du *Daturicarpa elliptica* Stapf" *Plantes Médicinales et Phytothérapie* 10: 20–23.

Brunner, T.F. 1977. "Marijuana in ancient Greece and Rome? The literary evidence" *Journal of Psychedelic Drugs* 9(3): 221–225.

Brunton, R. 1989. *The Abandoned Narcotic. Kava and Cultural Instability in Melanesia.* Cambridge University Press, Cambridge, England.

Brüzzi A. da S., A. 1962. *A Civilização Indígena do Uaupés.* Linográfica Editôra Ldta., São Paulo, Brasil.

Buck, R.W. 1963. "Toxicity of *Amanita muscaria*" *Journal of the American Medical Association* 185(8): 663–664.

Buck, R.W. 1967. "Psychedelic [*sic*] effect of *Pholiota spectabilis*" *The New England Journal of Medicine* 276(7): 391–392.

Buckholtz, N.S. and **W.O. Boggan** 1977. "Monoamine oxidase inhibition in brain and liver produced by β-carbolines: Structure-activity relationships and substrate specificity" *Biochemical Pharmacology* 26: 1991–1996.

Buckley, J.P. *et al.* 1967. "Pharmacology of kava" In: Efron, D.H. *et al.* (Eds.) *Ethnopharmacologic Search for Psychoactive Drugs.* (Public Health Service Publication No. 1645) U.S. Government Printing Office, Washington, D.C. pp. 141–151.

Budavari, S. *et al.* (Ed.) 1989. *The Merck Index: An Encyclopedia of Chemicals, Drugs, and Biologicals.* Eleventh edition. Merck & Co., Rahway, NJ. 12th edition, 1996.

Burchard, R.E. 1975. "Coca chewing: A new perspective" In: Rubin, V. (Ed.) *Cannabis and Culture.* Mouton and Co., the Hague, the Netherlands. Spanish by E. Mayer and C. Cristóbal, 1986. "Una nueva perspectiva sobre la masticación de la coca" In: Boldó i Climent, J. (Ed.) *La Coca Andina: Visión Indígena de una Planta Satanizada.* Instituto Indigenista Interamericano, Coyoacán, México. pp. 65–103.

Burchard, R. 1979. "Coca, nutrition and health: Recent research in Bolivia" Paper presented at a symposium "Erythroxylon—New Historical and Scientific Aspects," 3–5 December 1979, Quito, Ecuador. Proceedings published in 1981, minus this paper, in *Journal of Ethnopharmacology* 3(2&3): 105–376.

Burk, W.R. 1983. "Puffball usages among North American Indians" *Journal of Ethnobiology* 3(1): 55–62.

Burroughs, W.S. 1953. *Junkie: Confessions of an Unredeemed Drug Addict.* Lee 1953.

Burroughs, W.S. 1959. *The Naked Lunch.* Olympia Press, Paris.

Burroughs, W.S. 1961. *The Soft Machine.* Grove Press, New York.

Burroughs, W.S. 1962. *The Ticket that Exploded.* Grove Press, New York.

Burroughs, W.S. 1963. *Dead Fingers Talk.* Calder & Boyars Ltd., London, England.

Burroughs, W.S. 1964. *Nova Express.* Grove Press, New York.

Burroughs, W.S. 1966. *Exterminator!* The Viking Press, New York.

Burroughs, W.S. and **A. Ginsberg** 1963. *The Yage Letters.* City Lights Books, San Francisco, CA. Translated into Spanish, 1977. *Cartas del Yagé.* Producciones Editoriales, Barcelona, Catalunya, Spain.

Butler, E.G. *et al.* 1981. "*Petunia violacea*: hallucinogen or not?" *Journal of Ethnopharmacology* 4(1): 111–114.

Bye, R.A. 1975. "Plantas psicotrópicas de los tarahumaras" *Cuadernos Científicos CEMEF* 4: 49–72. See: Bye 1979A.

Bye, R.A. 1979A. "Hallucinogenic plants of the Tarahumara" *Journal of Ethnopharmacology* 1(1): 23–48. See: Bye 1975.

Bye, R.A. 1979B. "An 1878 ethnobotanical collection from San Luis Potosí: Dr. Edward Palmer's first major Mexican collection" *Economic Botany* 33(2): 135–162.

Bye, R.A. 1986A. "Medicinal plants of the Sierra Madre: Comparative study of the Tarahumara and Mexican market plants" *Economic Botany* 40(1): 103–124.

Bye, R.A. 1986B. "Voucher specimens in ethnobiological studies and publications" *Journal of Ethnobiology* 6(1): 1–8.

Bye, R.A. and **E. Linares** 1986. "Ethnobotanical notes from the valley of San Luis, Colorado" *Journal of Ethnobiology* 6(2): 289–306.

Bye, R.A. and **E. Linares** 1990. "Mexican market plants of the 16th century. I. Plants recorded in *Historia Natural de Nueva España*" *Journal of Ethnobiology* 10(2): 151–168.

Bye, S.N. and **M.F. Dutton** 1991. "The inappropriate use of traditional medicines in South Africa" *Journal of Ethnopharmacology* 34(2,3): 253–259.

Byrne, G. 1988. "Nicotine likened to cocaine, heroin" *Science* 240: 1143.

Cabieses, F. 1986. Personal communication to R.L. Arslanian cited in: Arslanian, R. L. *et al.* 1986. "3-Methoxy-5-hydroxy-flavonols from *Tillandsia purpurea*" *Journal of Natural Products* 49(6): 1177–1178.

Cáceres, A. 1984. *In Xóchitl in Cuícatl: Hallucinogens and Music in Mesoamerican Amerindian Thought*. Thesis, University of Indiana, Bloomington, IN.

Cagliari, G.E. 1897. "Mushroom poisoning" *Medical Records* 52: 298.

Calderón, E. *et al.* 1982. *Eduardo el Curandero: The Words of a Peruvian Healer.* North Atlantic Books and Society for the Study of Native Arts and Sciences, Richmond, CA. Preface by Douglas Sharon, pp. 6–15.

Calella, P. de 1935. "Los indios Sionas del Putumayo" *Boletín de Estudios Históricos* 73-74: 49–52.

Calella, P. de 1944A. "Datos mitológicos de los Huitotos de La Chorrera" *Amazonia Colombiana Americanista* 2(4-8): 33–37.

Calella, P. de 1944B. "Breves notas mitológicas de los Huitotos de Santa Clara" *Amazonia Colombiana Americanista* 2(4-8): 38–40.

Callaway, J.C. 1992. Personal communications, San Luis Potosí, México.

Callaway, J.C., Jr. 1994. "Pinoline and other tryptamine derivatives: Formation and functions" *Kuopion Yliopiston Julkaisuja A. Farmaseuttiset Tieteet* 15: 1–63.

Callieri, B. and **M. Ravetta** 1957. "The action of Pervitin on the syndrome induced by LAE-32 in schizophrenics" In: Garattini, S. and V. Ghetti (Eds.) *Psychotropic Drugs*. Elsevier Publishing Co., Amsterdam, the Netherlands. pp. 583–584.

Calvin, W.H. 1991. *How the Shaman Stole the Moon: In Search of Ancient Prophet-Scientists from Stonehenge to the Grand Canyon*. Bantam Books, New York.

Camazine, S. 1983. "Mushroom chemical defense: Food aversion learning induced by hallucinogenic toxin [*sic*], muscimol" *Journal of Chemical Ecology* 9(11): 1473–1481.

Camazine, S. and **R.A. Bye** 1980. "A study of the medicinal ethnobotany of the Zuni Indians of New Mexico" *Journal of Ethnopharmacology* 2(4): 365–388.

Camilla, G. 1995. "Le erbe del diavolo I. Aspetti antropologici" *Altrove* 2: 105–115.

Campbell, J. (with B. Moyers and B.S. Flowers, Ed.) 1988. *The Power of Myth.* Doubleday, New York.

Campbell, T.N. 1958. "Origin of the mescal bean [*sic*] cult" *American Anthropologist* 60: 156–160.

Campbell, T.N. 1965. *The Rock Paintings of*

the Chumash. University of California Press, Berkeley, CA.

Camporesi, P. (Translation by D. Gentilcore) 1989. *Bread of Dreams: Food and Fantasy in Early Modern Europe.* University of Chicago Press, Chicago, IL. Preface by Roy Porter, pp. 1–16. Originally published in 1980 as *Il Pane Salvaggio.* Il Mulino, Bologna, Italy.

Caporael, L.R. 1976. "Ergotism: The satan loosed in Salem?" *Science* 192: 21–26.

Cardinale, G.J. *et al.* 1987. "Morphine and codeine are endogenous components of human cerebrospinal fluid" *Life Sciences* 40(3): 301–306.

Carlini, E.A. *et al.* 1983. "Psychopharmacological effects of the essential oil fraction and of the hydrolate obtained from the seeds of *Licaria puchury-major*" *Journal of Ethnopharmacology* 8(2): 225–236.

Carlson, G.G. and **V.H. Jones** 1940. "Some notes on uses of plants by the Comanche Indians" *Papers of the Michigan Academy of Sciences, Arts and Letters* 25: 517–542.

Carlsson, A. *et al.* 1963. "Basische Derivate des 4,5,6–Trimethoxyindols und des 3,4,5-Trimethoxyphenols" *Helvetica Chimica Acta* 46: 1231–1235.

Carneiro, R.L. 1964. "The Amahuaca and the spirit world" *Ethnology* 3: 6–11.

Carneiro, R.L. 1970. "Hunting and hunting magic among the Amahuaca" *Ethnology* 9: 331–341.

Carneiro, R.L. 1980. "Chimera of the Upper Amazon" In: De Mille, R. (Ed.) *The Don Juan Papers: Further Castaneda Controversies.* Ross-Erikson Publishers, Santa Barbara, CA. pp. 94–98.

Carstairs, G.M. 1954. "Daru and bhang: Cultural factors in the choice of intoxicant" *Quarterly Journal of Studies on Alcohol* 15(2): 220–237. Reprinted in 1965 in *Psychedelic Review* 6: 67–83.

Carter, M. 1976. "Will the legal Liberty Cap cause Home Office hallucinations?" *New Scientist.* 16 September issue. p. 59.

Caso, A. 1942. "El paraíso terrenal en Teotihuacán" *Cuadernos Americanos* 1: 127–136.

Caso, A. 1963. "Representaciones de hongos en los códices" *Estudios de Cultura Náhuatl* 4: 27–38.

Cassady, J.M. *et al.* 1971. "The isolation of 6-methoxyharmalan and 6-methoxy-harman from *Virola cuspidata*" *Lloydia* 34(1): 161–162.

Castaneda, C. 1968. *The Teachings of Don Juan: A Yaqui [sic] Way of Knowledge.* University of California Press, Los Angeles, CA.

Castaneda, C. 1971. *A Separate Reality: Further Conservations with Don Juan.* Simon & Schuster, New York.

Castaneda, C. 1972. *Journey to Ixtlan: The Lessons of Don Juan.* Simon & Schuster, New York.

Castaneda, C. 1974. *Tales of Power.* Simon & Schuster, New York.

Castaneda, C. 1987. *The Power of Silence: Further Lessons of Don Juan.* Simon & Schuster, New York.

Castorena, J.L. *et al.* 1987. "A fatal poisoning from *Nicotiana glauca*" *Journal of Toxicology* 25(5): 429–435.

Catalfomo, P. and **C.H. Eugster** 1970. "*Amanita muscaria*: Present understanding of its chemistry" *Bulletin on Narcotics* 22(4): 33.

Catalfomo, P. and **V.E. Tyler** 1961. "Investigation of the free amino acids and *Amanita* toxins in *Amanita* species" *Journal of Pharmaceutical Sciences* 50: 689–692.

Cavé, A. *et al.* 1984. "Alkaloids from Annonaceae; LV. Chemistry and pharmacology of *Cymbopetalum brasiliense*" *Planta Medica* 50: 517–519.

Cawte, J. 1985. "Psychoactive substances of the South Seas: Betel, kava and pituri" *Australia and New Zealand Journal of Psychiatry* 19(1): 83–87.

Cerletti, A. 1959. "Pharmacology of psilocybin" *Neuro-Psychopharmacology.* Vol. 1. Elsevier, Amsterdam, Netherlands. pp. 291–294.

Cerletti, A. 1965. "Decision regarding LSD-25 and other hallucinogenic substances" Press release, Basel, Switzerland, 23 August. Document in files of "Tina and Gordon Wasson Ethnomycological Collection" Harvard Botanical Museum.

Cerletti, A. *et al.* 1968. "Pharmacological studies on the structure-activity relationship of hydroxyindole alkylamines" *Advances in Pharmacology* 6B: 233–246.

Chagnon, N.A. 1968. *Yanomamö: The Fierce People.* Holt, Rinehart and Winston, New York. Second edition 1977. Fourth edition in 1992. *Yanomamö: The Last Days of Eden.* Harcourt, Brace Jovanovich, New York.

Chagnon, N.A. *et al.* 1971. "Yanomamö hallucinogens: Anthropological, botanical, and chemical findings" *Current Anthropology* 12(1): 72–74.

Chakraborty, R. and **K.K. Kidd** 1991. "The utility of DNA typing in forensic work" *Science* 254: 1735–1739. See also: rebuttal by Lewontin & Hartl 1991; editorial by Koshland 1992; news item by Roberts 1991; and letters to editor by Wills *et al.* 1992.

Chamberlin, R.V. 1911. "The ethno-botany of the Gosiute Indians of Utah" *Memoirs of the American Anthropological Association* 2(5): 331–405.

Chandler, R.F. *et al.* 1979. "Herbal remedies of the Maritime Indians" *Journal of Ethnopharmacology* 1(1): 49–68.

Chango, A. *et al.* 1984. *Yachaj Sami Yachachina.* Colección Mundo Shuar, Quito, Ecuador. Preliminary comment by Norman E. Whitten, Jr., pp. 4–5.

Chao, J.-M. and **A.H. Der Marderosian** 1973A. "Ergoline alkaloidal constituents of Hawaiian baby wood rose, *Argyreia nervosa* (Burm. f.) Bojer" *Journal of Pharmaceutical Sciences* 62(4): 588–591.

Chao, J.-M. and **A.H. Der Marderosian** 1973B. "Identification of ergoline alkaloids in the genus *Argyreia* and related genera and their chemotaxonomic implications in the Convolvulaceae" *Phytochemistry* 12: 2435–2440.

Chauhan, A.K. *et al.* 1988. "A review of medicinal plants showing anticonvulsant activity" *Journal of Ethnopharmacology* 22(1): 11–23.

Chaumeil, J.P. 1982. "Représentation du monde d'un chamane Yagua" *L'Éthnographie* 87-88: 49–84.

Chayet, N.L. 1967. "Social and legal aspects of LSD usage" In: DeBold, R.C. and R.C. Leaf (Eds.) *LSD, Man and Society.* Wesleyan University Press, Middletown, CT. pp. 92–124.

Chein, I. *et al.* 1964. *The Road to H: Narcotics, Delinquency, and Social Policy.* Basic Books, New York. Reprinted by Tavistock Publications, London, England.

Chen, A.L. and **K.K. Chen** 1939. "Harmin: The alkaloid of *caapi*" *Quarterly Journal of Pharmacy and Pharmacology* 12: 30–38.

Chen, K.K. and **H. Jensen** 1929. "A pharmacognostic study of *Ch'an Su*, the dried venom of the Chinese toad" *Journal of the American Pharmaceutical Association* 23: 244–251.

Cherniak, L. 1979. *The Great Books of Hashish.* Volume 1, Book 1. And/Or Press, Berkeley, CA. Introduction by Michael R. Aldrich, pp. XIX–XXIII.

Chestnut, V.K. 1902. "Plants used by the Indians of Mendocino County, California" *United States National Herbarium Contributions* 7: 295–408.

Chew, W.-L. 1972. "The genus *Piper* (Piperaceae) in New Guinea, Solomon Islands and Australia" *Journal of the Arnold Arboretum* 53: 1–25.

Chilton, W.S. 1975. "The course of an intentional poisoning" *McIlvainea* 2: 17-18.

Chilton, W.S. 1978. "Chemistry and mode of action of mushroom toxins" In: Rumack, B.H. and E. Salzman (Eds.) *Mushroom Poisoning: Diagnosis and Treatment.* CRC Press, W. Palm Beach, FL. pp. 87–124.

Chilton, W.S. 1979. Personal communications, Seattle, WA.

Chilton, W.S. and **J. Ott** 1976. "Toxic metabolites of *Amanita pantherina*, *A. cothurnata*, *A. muscaria* and other *Amanita* species" *Lloydia* 39(2&3): 150–157.

Chilton, W.S. *et al.* 1974. "Stizolobic and stizolobinic acids in *Amanita pantherina*" *Phytochemistry* 13: 1179–1181.

Chilton, W.S. *et al.* 1979. "Psilocin, bufotenine and serotonin: Historical and biosynthetic observations" *Journal of Psychedelic Drugs* 11(1-2): 61–69.

Chin, W.Y. and **H. Keng** 1992. *An Illustrated Dictionary of Chinese Medicinal Herbs.* CRCS Publications, Sebastopol, CA. Foreword by Richard Keng Mun Eu, p. 5.

Ching, P. 1991. "Spinning tales of the 'nightmare weke'" *Ka Wai Ola O Oha* 8(7): 18.

Cho, A.K. 1990. "Ice: A new dosage form of an old drug" *Science* 249: 631–634.

Chowdhury, B.K. and **P. Bhattacharya** 1985. "A further quinazoline alkaloid from *Adhatoda vasica*" *Phytochemistry* 24(12): 3080–3082.

Christian, S. *et al.* 1976. "Evidence for dimethyltryptamine (DMT) as a naturally-occurring transmitter in mammalian brain" *Alabama Journal of Medical Sciences* 13: 162–165.

Christian, S. *et al.* 1977. "The *in vitro* identification of dimethyltryptamine (DMT) in mammalian brain and its characterization as a possible endogenous neuroregulatory agent" *Biochemical Medicine* 18: 164–183.

Christiansen, A. *et al.* 1962. "Changes in spider webs brought about by mescaline, psilocybin and an increase in body weight" *Journal of Pharmacology* 136: 31–37.

Christiansen, A.L. and **K.E. Rasmussen** 1982. "Analysis of the indole alkaloids in Norwegian *Psilocybe semilanceata* using high-performance liquid chromatography and mass spectrometry" *Journal of Chromatography* 244: 357–364.

Christiansen, A.L. *et al.* 1981. "The content of psilocybin in Norwegian Psilocybe semilanceata" *Planta Medica* 42: 229–235.

Christiansen, A.L. *et al.* 1984. "Detection of psilocybin and psilocin in Norwegian species of *Pluteus* and *Conocybe*" *Planta Medica* 50: 341–343.

Cimino, G. and **S. De Stefano** 1978. "Chemistry of Mediterranean Gorgonians: Simple indole derivatives from *Paramuricea chamaeleon*" *Comptes Rendus Biochemie Physiologie Série C* 61: 361–362.

Clark, A.J. 1921. "Flying ointments" In: Murray, M.A. 1921. *The Witch-Cult in Western Europe: A Study in Anthropology.* Clarendon Press, Oxford, England. pp. 279–280.

Clark, J. 1970. "Psilocybin: The use of psilocybin in a prison setting" In: Aaronson, B. and H. Osmond (Eds.) *Psychedelics: The Uses and Implications of Hallucinogenic Drugs.* Doubleday/Anchor, Garden City, NJ. pp. 40–44.

Clark, W.H. 1969. *Chemical Ecstasy: Psychedelic Drugs and Religion.* Sheed & Ward, New York. Translated into German, 1971. *Chemische Ekstase: Drogen und Religion.* Salzburg, Austria.

Clark, W.H. 1970. "The psychedelics and religion" In: Aaronson, B. and H. Osmond (Eds.) *Psychedelics: The Uses and Implications of Hallucinogenic Drugs.* Doubleday/Anchor, Garden City, NJ. pp. 182–195.

Clarke, L. 1992. "Technocultures" Review of Ross, A. 1991. *Strange Weather: Culture, Science, and Technology. Science* 256: 1036.

Clarren, S.K. and **D.W. Smith** 1978. *New*

England Journal of Medicine 298: 1063.

Clinch, P.G. and **J.C. Turner** 1968. "Estimation of tutin and hyenanchin in honey. 2. The toxicity of honey samples from test hives during the period 1962–1967" *New Zealand Journal of Science* 11: 346–351.

Coblentz, M. 1991. Personal communications, Xalapa, Veracruz, México.

Cochran, K.W. and **E.H. Lucas** 1959. "Chemoprophylaxis of poliomyelitis in mice through the administration of plant extracts" *Antibiotics Annual* 1958–1959: 104–109.

Cohen, M.M. *et al.* 1967. "In vivo and in vitro chromosomal damage induced by LSD-25" *New England Journal of Medicine* 227: 1043.

Cohen, S.I. 1964. *The Beyond Within: The LSD Story.* Atheneum, New York. Foreword by Gardner Murphy, pp. VII–IX. Later reprinted in 1970 as *Drugs of Hallucination.* Paladin, St. Albans, England.

Cohen, S.I. and **J.R. Goldsmith** 1971. "Epidemiology" In: Epstein, S.S. (Ed.) *Drugs of Abuse* [*sic*]: *Their Genetic and other Chronic Nonpsychiatric Hazards.* MIT Press, Cambridge, MA. pp. 27–44.

Cohn, B. and **S. Reiss** 1992. "Noriega: How the feds got their man" *Newsweek.* 20 April (Latin American) issue. p. 24.

Cohn, N. 1975. *Europe's Inner Demons: An Enquiry Inspired by the Great Witch-Hunt.* The New American Library, New York.

Coker, W.C. and **J.N. Couch** 1928. *The Gasteromycetes of the Eastern United States and Canada.* The University of North Carolina Press, Chapel Hill, NC.

Colton, T. *et al.* 1968. "The tolerance of coffee drinkers to caffeine" *Clinical Pharmacology and Therapeutics* 9(1): 31–39.

Conrad III, B. 1988. *Absinthe: History in a Bottle.* Chronicle Books, San Francisco, CA.

Cook, W.B. and **W.E. Kealand** 1962. "Isolation and partial characterization of a glucoside from *Rivea corymbosa* (L.) Hall. f." *Journal of Organic Chemistry* 27: 1061.

Cooke, M.C. 1860. *The Seven Sisters of Sleep. Popular History of the Seven Prevailing Narcotics of the World.* Blackwell, London, England. Reprinted in facsimile in 1989 (Volume V, Bioactive Plants) by Quarterman Publications, Lincoln, MA. With a foreword by Richard Evans Schultes and Michael R. Aldrich, pp. VII–XI.

Cooper, R. (C. Render, Ed.)1977. *A Guide to British Psilocybin Mushrooms.* Red Shift Research Collective, London, England.

Corbett, L. *et al.* 1978. "Hallucinogenic N-methylated indolealkylamines in the cerebrospinal fluid of psychiatric and control populations" *British Journal of Psychiatry* 132: 139–144.

Córdova-Ríos, M. and **F.B. Lamb** 1971. *Wizard* [*sic*] *of the Upper Amazon.* Atheneum, New York. See Lamb 1974.

Cordy-Collins, A. 1977. "Chavín art: Its shamanic/hallucinogenic origins" In: Cordy-Collins, A. and J. Stearn (Eds.) *Precolumbian Art History: Selected Writings.* Peek Publications, San Diego, CA. pp. 353–362.

Cordy-Collins, A. 1980. "An artistic record of the Chavín hallucinatory experience" *The Masterkey* 54: 84–93.

Cordy-Collins, A. 1982. "Psychoactive painted Peruvian plants: The shamanism textile" *Journal of Ethnobiology* 2(2): 144–153.

Cornué, A. 1961. "Un cas d'intoxication par *Amanita gemmata*" *Revue de Mycologie* 26(3): 191.

Corothie, E. and **T. Nakano** 1969. "Constituents of the bark of *Virola sebifera*" *Planta Medica* 17(2): 184–188.

Costa, C. *et al.* 1992. "Indole alkaloids from the roots of an African plant *Securidaca longipedunculata.* I. Isolation by column chromatography and preliminary structural characterization by mass spectrometry" *Jour-*

nal of Heterocyclic Chemistry 29: 1641–7.
Costa, M. *et al.* 1989. "Screening in mice of some medicinal plants used for analgesic purposes in the State of São Paulo. Part II." *Journal of Ethnopharmacology* 27(1,2): 25–33.
Costantini, E.S. 1975. "El uso de alucinógenos de orígen vegetal por las tribus indígenas del Paraguay actual" *Cuadernos Científicos CEMEF* 4: 35–48.
Coto, T. de 1983. *Vocabvlario de la Lengua Cakchiquel... Ediciones René Acuña*. Instituto de Investigaciones Filológicas, UNAM, México City.
Coulter, J.N. 1894. "Preliminary revision of the North American species of *Cactus*, *Anahalonium* and *Lophophora*" *Contributions U.S. National Herbarium* 3: 91–132.
Cox, P.A. 1981. "Use of a hallucinogenic mushroom, *Copelandia cyanescens*, in Samoa" *Journal of Ethnopharmacology* 4(1): 115–116.
Cox, P.A. 1991. "Polynesian herbal medicine" In: Cox, P.A. and S.A. Banack (Eds.) *Islands, Plants, and Polynesians: An Introduction to Polynesian Ethnobotany*. Dioscorides Press, Portland, OR. pp. 147–168.
Cox, P.A. 1992. "Polynesian kava: Legend, custom and rhetoric" Paper presented at annual meeting of Society for Economic Botany, 9–13 August, Honolulu, HI, USA.
Cox, P.A. and **S.A. Banack** (Eds.) 1991. *Islands, Plants, and Polynesians: An Introduction to Polynesian Ethnobotany*. Dioscorides Press, Portland, OR.
Cox, P.A. and **L. O'Rourke** 1987. "Kava (*Piper methysticum*, Piperaceae)" *Economic Botany* 41(3): 452–454.
Cox, P.A. *et al.* 1989. "Pharmacological activity of the Samoan ethnopharmacopoeia" *Economic Botany* 43(4): 487–497.
Coyote Man and **Brother William** 1972. *Get the Buzzzon or A New World Immigrant's Guide to Dope, Herbs, Indians and Magic Meeting Places.* Brother William Press, Berkeley, CA. Excerpt: *Kyoi-Kuksu: A Journal of Backcountry Writing* 3: 7–9.
Crawford, A. 1982. "Lyndon La Rouche's goon squad" *Inquiry*. 15 February issue. pp. 8–10.
Crawford, M. 1988. "Testing urine for drugs" *Science* 241: 150–152.
Crosby, D.M. and **J.L. McLaughlin** 1973. "Cactus alkaloids. XIX. Crystallization of mescaline HCL and 3-methoxytyramine HCL from *Trichocereus pachanoi*" *Lloydia* 36(4): 416–418.
Cruz-Sánchez, G. 1948. "Informe sobre las aplicaciones de la Cimora en el norte del Perú" *Revista de la Farmacología y Medicina Experimental* 1(2): 253–258.
Cuatrecasas, J. 1965. "*Banisteriopsis caapi*, *B. inebrians*, *B. rusbyana*" *Journal d'Agriculture Tropicale et de Botanique Appliquée* 12: 424–429.
Cuéllar, A. 1981. *Tezcatzóncatl Escultórico—El "Chac-Mool"—(Dios Mesoamericano del Vino)*. Avangráfica, S.A., México City.
Culvenor, C.C.J. *et al.* 1964. "The occurrence of indolealkylamine alkaloids in *Phalaris tuberosa* L. and *P. arundinacea* L." *Australian Journal of Chemistry* 17: 1301–1304.
Culvenor, D. 1984. Personal communication to D.C. Hyndman 1984. *Economic Botany* 38(3): 287–303.
Cuthbertson, D.P. and **J.A.C. Knox** 1947. "The effects of analeptics on the fatigued subject" *Journal of Physiology* 106: 42–58.
Cuzent, M. 1861. "Composition chimique de la kavahine" *Comptes Rendus Hebdomadaires des Séances de l'Académie des Sciences* 52: 205–206.
Dagar, H.S. and **J.C. Dagar** 1991. "Plant folk medicine among the Nicobarese of Katchal Island, India" *Economic Botany* 45(1): 114–119.
Daly, J.W. and **C.W. Myers** 1973. "Toxicity of Panamanian poison frogs (*Dendrobates*): Some biological and chemical aspects" *Science* 156: 970.

Daly, J.W. and **B. Witcop** 1971. "Chemistry and pharmacology of frog venoms" In: Bucheri, W. *et al.* (Eds.) *Venomous Animals and their Venoms*. 2 Vols. Academic Press, New York. Vol. II, pp. 497–519.

Da Mota, C.N. 1987. *As Jurema Told Us: Kariri Shoko and Shoko Mode of Utilization of Medicinal Plants in the Context of Modern Northeastern Brazil*. Thesis, University of Texas, Austin, TX.

Dandekar, U.P. *et al.* 1992. "Analysis of a clinically important interaction between phenytoin and Shankhapushpi, an Ayurvedic preparation" *Journal of Ethnopharmacology* 35(3): 285–288.

Dannhardt, G. and **L. Steindl** 1985. "Alkaloids of *Lolium temulentum*: Isolation, identification and pharmacological activity" *Planta Medica* 51: 212–214.

Darias, V. *et al.* 1986. "Contribution to the ethnopharmacological study of the Canary Islands" *Journal of Ethnopharmacology* 15(2): 169–193.

Davis, E.W. 1983A. "Notes on ethnomycology of Boston's Chinatown" *Botanical Museum Leaflets* Harvard University 29(1): 59–65.

Davis, E.W. 1983B. "Sacred plants of the San Pedro cult" *Botanical Museum Leaflets* Harvard University 29(4): 367–386.

Davis, E.W. 1983C. "The ethnobiology of the Haitian zombi" *Journal of Ethnopharmacology* 9(1): 85–104.

Davis, E.W. 1983D. "Preparation of the Haitian zombi poison" *Botanical Museum Leaflets* Harvard University 29(2): 139–149.

Davis, E.W. 1985. *The Serpent and the Rainbow*. Warner Books, New York.

Davis, E.W. 1988A. *Passage of Darkness: The Ethnobiology of the Haitian Zombie*. University of North Carolina Press, Chapel Hill, NC. Foreword by R.F. Thompson; Preface by R.E. Schultes, pp. XI–XVIII.

Davis, E.W. 1988B. "Zombification" *Science* 240: 1715–1716. Rebuttal to Booth, W.B. 1988. "Voodoo science" *Science* 240: 274–276. See: Anderson, 1988; Davis 1989.

Davis, E.W. 1989. *Journal of Ethnopharmacology* 25(1): 119–122. Response to Anderson, W.H. 1988. "Tetrodotoxin and the zombi phenomenon" *Journal of Ethnopharmacology* 23(1): 121–126.

Davis, E.W. and **A.T. Weil** 1992. "Identity of a New World psychoactive toad" *Ancient Mesoamerica* 3: 51–59.

Davis, E.W. and **J.A. Yost** 1983A. "Novel hallucinogens from Ecuador" *Botanical Museum Leaflets* Harvard University 29(3): 291–295.

Davis, E.W. and **J.A. Yost** 1983B. "The ethnomedicine of the Waorani of Amazonian Ecuador" *Journal of Ethnopharmacology* 9(2,3): 273–297. Also "The ethnobotany of the Waorani of eastern Ecuador" *Botanical Museum Leaflets* Harvard University 29(3): 159–218.

Davis, J.M. and **R.F. Schlemmer** 1979. "The amphetamine psychosis" In: Caldwell, J. (Ed.) *Amphetamines and Related Stimulants: Chemical, Biological, Clinical, and Sociological Aspects*. CRC Press, Boca Raton, FL. pp. 161–173.

Dawson, P. 1975. *A Guide to the Major Psilocybin Mushroom of British Columbia (Psilocybe semilanceata)*. Self-published, Vancouver, B.C., Canada.

DEA 1989. *Annual Report of the National Narcotics Intelligence [sic] Consumers Committee*. Drug Enforcement Administration, Department of Justice, Washington, D.C.

De Avila, B.A. *et al.* 1980. "Notes on the ethnomycology of Hueyapan, Morelos, Mexico" *Journal of Ethnopharmacology* 2(4): 311–321.

De Borhegyi, S.F. 1961. "Miniature mushroom stones from Guatemala" *American Antiquity* 26(4): 498–504.

De Borhegyi, S.F. 1962. *The Enigmatic Mushroom Stones of Meso-America*. Middle

American Research Institute, Tulane University, New Orleans, LA.

De Borhegyi, S.F. 1963. "Pre-Columbian pottery mushrooms from Mesoamerica" *American Antiquity* 28(3): 328–338.

De Budowski, J. *et al.* 1974. "On the alkaloid composition of the snuff drug yopo from the upper Orinoco (Venezuela)" *Il Farmaco (Edizione Scientifica)* 29(8): 574–578.

De Carvalho, J.E. and **A.J. Lappa** 1990. "Pharmacology of Indian snuff obtained from Amazonian *Maquira sclerophylla*" *Journal of Ethnopharmacology* 30(1): 43–54.

De Feo, V. *et al.* 1992. "Traditional phytotherapy in the Peninsula Sorrentina, Campania, Southern Italy" *Journal of Ethnopharmacology* 36(2): 113–125.

De Korne, J.B. (Ed.) 1992. *The Entheogen Review.* 1(1). September. Newsletter.

De la Serna, J. 1953. *Tratado de las Idolatrías, Supersticiones, Dioses, Ritos, Hechicerías y Otras Costumbres Gentílicas de las Razas Aborígenes de México.* Ediciones Fuente Cultural, México City. Originally published in 1656. Some 75% of this text was taken from the first draft of Ruiz de Alarcón's 1629 [1953] *Tratado*; about 40% consists of direct quotations.

Delay, J. *et al.* 1958. "Effets psychophysiologiques de la psilocybine" *Comptes Rendus Hebdomadaires des Séances de l'Académie des Sciences* 247: 1235–1238.

Delay, J. *et al.* 1959A. "Premiers essais de la psilocybine en psychiatrie" *Neuro-Psychopharmacology* Volume 1. Elsevier, Amsterdam, the Netherlands. pp. 528–531.

Delay, J. *et al.* 1959B. "Action de la psilocybine sur le comportement des souris normales et des souris I.D.P.N. Comparaison avec les monoéthylamide (LAE) et diéthylamide (LSD 25) de l'acide lysergique" *Comptes Rendus de la Société de Biologie* 153: 244–248.

Del Castillo, J. *et al.* 1975. "Marijuana, absinthe and the central nervous system" *Nature* 253: 365–366.

Del Pozo, E.C. 1967. "Empiricism and magic in Aztec pharmacology" In: Efron, D.H. *et al.* (Eds.) *Ethnopharmacologic Search for Psychoactive Drugs.* (Public Health Service Publication No. 1645) U.S. Government Printing Office, Washington, D.C. pp. 59–76.

Del Pozo, E.C. 1975. "Las fuentes históricas de las drogas vegetales mexicanas" *Cuadernos Científicos CEMEF* 4: 3–16.

De Mille, R. 1976. *Castaneda's Journey: The Power and the Allegory.* Capra Press, Santa Barbara, CA.

De Mille, R. 1979. "The shaman of academe: Carlos Castaneda" *Horizon* 22(4): 64–70.

De Mille, R. (Ed.) 1980. *The Don Juan Papers: Further Castaneda Controversies.* Ross-Erikson, Santa Barbara, CA.

De Moraes, E.H.F. *et al.* 1990. "As bases nitrogenadas de *Mimosa scabrella* Bentham" *Química Nova* 13(4): 308–309.

Dennis, P.A. 1988. "Herbal medicine among the Miskito of eastern Nicaragua" *Economic Botany* 42(1): 16–28.

Department of Health and Human Services 1986. *Toward a National Plan to Combat Alcohol Abuse and Alcoholism: A Report to the United States Congress.* Washington, D.C.

De Rementeria, I. 1992. "Subventions agricoles contre environnement" *Interdépendances* 9: 22–23.

Der Marderosian, A.H. 1966. "Current status of hallucinogens in the Cactaceae" *American Journal of Pharmacy* 138: 204–212.

Der Marderosian, A.H. 1967. "Psychotomimetic indoles in the Convolvulaceae" *American Journal of Pharmacy* 139(1): 19–26.

Der Marderosian, A. and **L.E. Liberti** 1988. *Natural Product Medicine: A Scientific Guide to Foods Drugs Cosmetics.* George F. Stickley, Philadelphia, PA.

Der Marderosian, A.H. and **H.W. Youngken** 1966. "The distribution of indole alkaloids among certain species and varieties of *Ipomoea*, *Rivea* and *Convolvulus* (Convolvulaceae)" *Lloydia* 29(1): 35–42.

Der Marderosian, A.H. *et al.* 1964A. "Preliminary studies of the comparative morphology and certain indoles of *Ipomoea* seeds" *Economic Botany* 18(1): 67–76.

Der Marderosian, A.H. *et al.* 1964B. "A uterine stimulant effect of extracts of morning glory seeds" *The Psychedelic Review* 1(3): 317–323.

Der Marderosian, A.H. *et al.* 1968. "Native use and occurence [*sic*] of N,N-dimethyltryptamine in the leaves of *Banisteriopsis rusbyana*" *American Journal of Pharmacy* 140(5): 137–147.

Der Marderosian, A.H. *et al.* 1969. Personal communication to G.T. Prance cited in *Economic Botany* 24(1): 62–68.

Der Marderosian, A.H. *et al.* 1970. "The use and hallucinatory [*sic*] principles of a psychoactive beverage of the Cashinahua tribe (Amazon basin)" *Drug Dependence* 5: 7–14.

De Ropp, R.S. 1957. *Drugs and the Mind.* St. Martin's Press, New York. Foreword by Nathan S. Kline, pp. VI–X.

De Ropp, R.S. 1968. *The Master Game: Pathways to Higher Consciousness Beyond the Drug Experience.* A Seymour Lawrence Book, Delacorte Press, New York.

De Smet, P.A.G.M. 1983. "A multidisciplinary overview of intoxicating enema rituals in the western hemisphere" *Journal of Ethnopharmacology* 9(2,3): 129–166.

De Smet, P.A.G.M. 1985A. "A multidisciplinary overview of intoxicating snuff rituals in the western hemisphere" *Journal of Ethnopharmacology* 13(1): 3–49. Amended in 1985: "Corrigendum" *Journal of Ethnopharmacology* 13(2): 235.

De Smet, P.A.G.M. 1985B. *Ritual Enemas and Snuffs in the Americas.* CEDLA, Amsterdam, the Netherlands. *Latin American Studies* Vol. 33: 1–240; plus 43 plates.

De Smet, P.A.G.M. 1991. "Is there any danger in using traditional remedies?" *Journal of Ethnopharmacology* 32(1-3): 43–50.

De Smet, P.A.G.M. 1996. "Some ethnopharmacological notes on African hallucinogens" *Journal of Ethnopharmacology* 50(3): 141–146.

De Smet, P.A.G.M. and **N.M. Hellmuth** 1986. "A multidisciplinary approach to ritual enema scenes on ancient Maya pottery" *Journal of Ethnopharmacology* 16(2,3): 213–262.

De Smet, P.A.G.M. and **F.J. Lipp** 1987. "Supplementary data on ritual enemas and snuffs in the western hemisphere" *Journal of Ethnopharmacology* 19(3): 327–331.

De Smet, P.A.G.M. and **L. Rivier** 1985. "Intoxicating snuffs of the Venezuelan Piaroa Indians" *Journal of Psychoactive Drugs* 17 (2): 93–103.

De Smet, P.A.G.M. and **L. Rivier** 1987. "Intoxicating paricá seeds of the Brazilian Maué Indians" *Economic Botany* 41(1): 12–16.

De Solier, R. 1965. *Curandera: Les Champignons Hallucinogènes.* Jean-Jacques Pauvert, Montreuil, France.

Deulofeu, V. 1948. "The chemistry and constituents of toad venoms" *Progress in the Chemistry of Organic Natural Products* 5: 241–266.

Deulofeu, V. 1967. "Chemical components isolated from Banisteriopsis and related species" In: Efron, D.H. *et al.* (Eds.) *Ethnopharmacologic Search for Psychoactive Drugs.* (Public Health Service Publication No. 1645) U.S. Government Printing Office, Washington, D.C. pp. 393–402.

Deulofeu, V. and **E. Rúveda** 1971. "The basic constituents of toad venoms" In: *Venomous Vertebrates. Venomous Animals and their Venoms.* Volume 2. Academic Press, New York. pp. 475–495.

Devane, W.A. *et al.* 1992. "Isolation and

structure of a brain constituent that binds to the cannabinoid receptor" *Science* 258: 1946–1949. See: Barinaga 1992.

Devereux, P. 1992. "An apparently nutmeg-induced experience of magical flight" *Jahrbuch für Ethnomedizin und Bewußtseinsforschung* 1: 189–191.

De Vries, H. 1991A. "Über die sogenannten Hexensalben" *Integration: Zeitschrift für Geistbewegende Pflanzen und Kultur* 1: 30–42.

De Vries, H. 1991B. "Iconae plantarum inebriantium—1" *Integration: Zeitschrift für Geistbewegende Pflanzen und Kultur* 1: 71–77. Photo essay featuring black-and-white photographs of seven species.

De Vries, H. 1991C. "Die Namen des Fliegenpilzes: Eine kurze Übersicht–Mit einigen Anmerkungen" In: Bauer, W. *et al.* (Eds.) *Der Fliegenpilz: Ein Kulturhistorisches Museum.* (Museum der Museen, Schriftenreihe des Karl Ernst Osthaus-Museums, Bd. 6) Wienand, Köln, Germany. pp. 15–18.

De Wet, J.M.J. *et al.* 1983. "Diversity in Kodo millet, *Paspalum scrobiculatum*" *Economic Botany* 37(2): 159–163.

Díaz, A.M.P. and **O.R. Gottlieb** 1979. "Propiophenones from Piper marginatum" *Planta Medica* 35: 190–191.

Díaz, J.L. 1975. "Etnofarmacología de algunos psicotrópicos vegetales de México" *Cuadernos Científicos CEMEF* 4: 135–201.

Díaz, J.L. (Ed.) 1976. *Indice y Sinonimia de las Plantas Medicinales de México* (Monografías Científicas IMEPLAM I); *Usos de las Plantas Medicinales de México.* (Monografías Científicas IMEPLAM II) Instituto Mexicano para el Estudio de las Plantas Medicinales, México City.

Díaz, J.L. 1977. "Ethnopharmacology of sacred psychoactive plants used by the Indians of Mexico" *Annual Review of Pharmacology and Toxicology* 17: 647–675.

Díaz, J.L. 1979. "Ethnopharmacology and taxonomy of Mexican psychodysleptic plants" *Journal of Psychedelic Drugs* 11(1-2): 71–101. Paper presented at conference "Hallucinogens in Native American Shamanism and Modern Life," 28 September–1 October 1978, San Francisco, CA, USA.

Díaz, J.L. 1980. Personal communication, letter dated 18 September.

Dickman, S. 1991. "East Germany: Science in the disservice of the state" *Science* 254: 26–27.

Dieckhofer, K. *et al.* 1971. "*Datura stramonium* als Rauschmittel" *Der Nervenärzt* 42: 431–437.

Diószegi, V. (Ed.) 1963. *Glaubenswelt und Folklore der Sibirischen Völker.* Budapest, Hungary.

Diószegi, V. 1968. *Tracing Shamans in Siberia.* Oosterhaut, the Netherlands.

Dishotsky, N.I. *et al.* 1971. "LSD and genetic damage" *Science* 172: 431.

Djerassi, C. 1992. "Drugs from Third World plants: The future" *Science* 258: 203–204. Letter to the editor in response to Roberts 1992A; Roberts 1992B.

Dobkin, M. 1968. "*Trichocereus pachanoi*—A mescaline cactus used in folk healing in Peru" *Economic Botany* 22(2): 191–194.

Dobkin de Ríos, M. 1970A. "Banisteriopsis in witchcraft [*sic*] and healing activities in Iquitos, Peru" *Economic Botany* 24(3): 296–300.

Dobkin de Ríos, M. 1970B. "A note on the use of ayahuasca among urban mestizo populations in the Peruvian Amazon" *American Anthropologist* 72(6): 1419–1422.

Dobkin de Ríos, M. 1972. *Visionary Vine: Hallucinogenic Healing in the Peruvian Amazon.* Chandler Publishing Co., San Francisco, CA. Reprinted in 1984 by Waveland Press, Prospect Heights, IL. With a poem "Oh Amazonas Putrefacto" by R. Rumrrill, and translation "Oh, Putrefied Amazonas" by the author, pp. 2–5.

Dobkin de Ríos, M. 1973. "Curing with

ayahuasca in an urban slum" In: Harner, M.J. (Ed.) *Hallucinogens and Shamanism.* Oxford University Press, London, England. pp. 67–85.

Dobkin de Ríos, M. 1974. "The influence of psychotropic flora and fauna on Maya religion" *Current Anthropology* 15: 147–164.

Dobkin de Ríos, M. 1975. "Una teoría transcultural del uso de los alucinógenos de orígen vegetal" *Cuadernos Científicos CEMEF* 4: 17–34. Also published in 1977. *América Indígena* 37(2).

Dobkin de Ríos, M. 1977. "Plant hallucinogens and the religion of the Mochica—An ancient Peruvian people" *Economic Botany* 31(2): 189–203.

Dobkin de Ríos, M. 1984. *Hallucinogens: Cross-Cultural Perspectives.* University of New Mexico Press, Albuquerque, NM. Also 1979: *The Wilderness of Mind.* Sage Publications, Beverly Hills, CA. Paperback 1990, Prism Press, Dorset, England.

Dobkin de Ríos, M. 1986. "Enigma of drug-induced altered states of consciousness among the !Kung Bushmen of the Kalahari Desert" *Journal of Ethnopharmacology* 15(3): 297–304.

Dobkin de Ríos, M. 1992. *Amazon Healer: The Life and Times of an Urban Shaman.* Prism Press, Bridport, England, and Unity Press, Lindfield, Australia.

Dobkin de Ríos, M. and **M. Cárdenas** 1980. "Plant hallucinogens, shamanism and Nazca ceramics" *Journal of Ethnopharmacology* 2(3): 233–246.

Dobkin de Ríos, M. and **O. Ríos Reátegui** 1967. "Psychotherapy with *ayahuasca* (a harmine drink) in northern Peru" *Transcultural Psychiatric Research* 4.

Doetsch, P.W. *et al.* 1980. "Cactus alkaloids. XL. Identification of mescaline and other β-phenethylamines in *Pereskia*, *Pereskiopsis*, and *Islaya* by use of fluorescamine conjugates" *Journal of Chromatography* 189: 79.

Dollfuss, D. and **H. Schlumberger** 1842. "Matièrs colorantes du *Peganum harmala*" *Bulletin de la Société Industrielle de Mulhouse* 16: 547–552.

Doniger, W. 1990. "'Somatic' memories of R. Gordon Wasson" In: Riedlinger, T.J. (Ed.) *The Sacred Mushroom Seeker: Essays for R. Gordon Wasson.* Ethnomycological Studies No. 11. Dioscorides, Portland, OR. pp. 55–59.

Doniger O'Flaherty, W. 1968. "The post-Vedic history of the Soma plant" In: Wasson, R.G. *Soma: Divine Mushroom of Immortality.* Ethno-mycological Studies No. 1. Mouton & Co., the Hague, the Netherlands. pp. 95–147.

Doniger O'Flaherty, W. 1982. "Epilogue" *Journal of the American Oriental Society* 102(4): 591–603; also in *Botanical Museum Leaflets* Harvard University 29(3): 246–247, 1983; and in Wasson, R.G. *et al.* 1986. *Persephone's Quest: Entheogens and the Origins of Religion.* Ethnomycological Studies No. 10. Yale University Press, New Haven, CT. pp. 138–139.

Dos Santos, F.D.C.C. *et al.* 1974. "Intoxicação experimental do bovines pela 'faveira,' *Dimorphandra mollis* Benth." *Arquivos da Escola Superior de Veterinaria do Estado de Minas Gerais* 26: 319–330.

Douglas, B. 1917. "Mushroom poisoning" *Torreya* 17(10): 171–175; 17(12): 207–221.

Drake, B. (W.D.) 1970. *The Cultivator's Handbook of Marijuana.* The Agrarian Reform Co., Eugene, OR.

Dreisbach, R.H. and **C. Pfeiffer** 1943. "Caffeine withdrawal headache" *The Journal of Laboratory and Clinical Medicine* 28: 1212–1219.

Drewitz, G. 1983. "Eine halluzinogene Rißpilzart: Grünlichverfärbender Rißpilz (*Inocybe aeruginascens*)" *Mykolgisches Mitteilungsblatt* 26: 11–17.

Drury, N. 1989. *Vision Quest.* Prism Press, Bridport, Dorset, England.

Dubey, M.P. *et al.* 1981. "Pharmacological studies on coleonol, a hypotensive diterpene from *Coleus forskohlii*" *Journal of Ethnopharmacology* 3(1): 1–13.

Ducke, A. 1938. "Plantes nouvelles" *Archivos del Instituto de Biología Vegetal* 4(1): 3.

Ducke, A. 1957. "Capí caapi, cabi, cayahuasca e yagé" *Revista da Associação Brasileira de Farmácia* 38(12): 283–284.

Ducloux, E.H. 1930. *Revista de la Facultad de Ciencias Químicas* 6: 75.

Dudley, H.W. and **J.C. Moir** 1935. "The substance responsible for the traditional clinical effect of ergot" *British Medical Journal* 1: 520–523; also *Science* (London) 81: 559–560.

Dufva, E. *et al.* 1976. "*Duboisia myoporoides*: Native antidote against ciguatera poisoning" *Toxicon* 14: 55–64.

Duke, J.A. 1975. "Ethnobotanical observations on the Cuna Indians" *Economic Botany* 29(3): 278–293.

Duke, J.A. 1983. *Medicinal Plants of the Bible*. Trado-Medic Books, Owerri, New York and London, England.

Duke, J.A. 1985. *CRC Handbook of Medicinal Herbs*. CRC Press, Boca Raton, FL.

Duke, J.A. 1987. *Living Liqueurs*. (Volume IV, Bioactive Plants) Quarterman Publications, Lincoln, MA.

Duke, J.A. *et al.* 1975. "Nutritional value of coca" *Botanical Museum Leaflets* Harvard University 24(6): 113–119.

Dumbacher, J.P. *et al.* 1992. "Homobatrachotoxin in the genus *Pitohui*: Chemical defense in birds?" *Science* 258: 799–801. See also letter to the editor by J.I. Glendinning, 1993. "Pitohui: How toxic and to whom?" *Science* 259: 582; J.P. Dumbacher *et al.* 1993. *Science* 259: 582–583.

Duncan, A. 1810. "Observations on the preparation of soporific medicines from common garden lettuce" *Memoirs of the Caledonian Horticultural Society* 1: 160–165.

Dunlap, J. (Pseudonym for Adelle Davis) 1961. *Exploring Inner Space: Personal Experiences under LSD-25.* Harcourt, Brace and World, New York. Introduction by Robert S. Davidson, pp. 3–10. Excerpt published in 1962 "Exploring the soul with LSD" *Fate* 15(6): 25–31.

Dunn, A.T. 1988. Review of Castaneda 1987. *The Power of Silence*. *Shaman's Drum: A Journal of Experiential Shamanism* 12: 50–51.

Durán, D. (Á.M. Garibay, Ed.) 1967. *Historia de las Indias de Nueva España e Islas de la Tierra Firme*. Two volumes. Editorial Porrúa, México City. Introduction by Ángel M. Garibay K., pp. XI–XLVII (Tomo I); 7–10 (Tomo II). Original in 1581.

Du Toit, B.M. 1980. *Cannabis in Africa.* Balkema, Rotterdam, the Netherlands.

Duve, R.N. 1981. "Gas-liquid chromatographic determination of major constituents of *Piper methysticum*" *Analyst* 106: 160–165.

Duve, R.N. and **V. Prasad** 1983. "Changes in chemical composition of Yaqona (*Piper methysticum*) with time" *Fiji Agricultural Journal* 45: 45–60.

Dyson, F.J. 1992. "Dragon's teeth" Review of *The Los Alamos Primer. Science* 256: 388–389. My letter to the editor correcting Dyson's numerous misstatements of fact (*re*: LSD 'addiction') was rejected.

Ebin, D. (Ed.) 1961. *The Drug Experience: First-Person Accounts of Addicts, Writers, Scientists and Others.* The Orion Press, New York. Grove Press paperback 1965.

Edison, G.R. 1978. "The drug laws: Are they effective and safe?" *Journal of the American Medical Association* 239(24): 2578–2583.

Editors 1963. "The subjective after-effects of psychedelic experiences" *The Psychedelic Review* 1(1): 18–26. Reprinted in Weil, G.M. *et al.* (Eds.) 1965. *The Psychedelic Reader.* University Books, New York. pp. 13–21 [reprint 1996, Carol Publishing].

Efron, D.H. (Ed.) 1970. *Psychotomimetic [sic] Drugs*. (Workshop Series of Pharmacology Section, National Institute of Mental Health, No. 4) Raven Press, New York. Proceedings of a conference "Psychotomimetic [*sic*] Drugs," 25–26 January 1969, Irvine, CA. With appendix by Morris A. Lipton, pp. 345–348, 351.

Efron, D.H. *et al.* (Eds.) 1967. *Ethnopharmacologic Search for Psychoactive Drugs.* (Public Health Service Publication No. 1645) U.S. Government Printing Office, Washington, D.C. Reprinted in 1979 by Raven Press, New York.

Einhorn, I. 1970. "From data collection to pattern recognition: The sociology of the now" In: Aaronson, B. and H. Osmond (Eds.) *Psychedelics: The Uses and Implications of Hallucinogenic Drugs.* Doubleday/Anchor, Garden City, NJ. pp. 439–457.

Eisele, J.W. and **D.T. Reay** 1980. "Deaths related to coffee enemas" *Journal of the American Medical Association* 244(14): 1608–1609.

Eisner, B. (Pseudonym for B. Ehrlich) 1977. "LSD purity: Cleanliness is next to godheadliness" *High Times*. January issue. pp. 73 *et seq.*

Eisner, B. (Pseudonym for B. Ehrlich) 1989. *Ecstasy: The MDMA Story*. Ronin Publications Inc., Berkeley, CA. With foreword by S. Krippner; introduction by P. Stafford; bibliography by A.T. Shulgin.

Elferink, J.G.R. 1983. "The narcotic and hallucinogenic use of tobacco in pre-Columbian Central America" *Journal of Ethnopharmacology* 7(1): 111–122.

Elferink, J.G.R. 1988. "Some little-known hallucinogenic plants of the Aztecs" *Journal of Psychoactive Drugs* 20(4): 427–435.

Elger, F. 1928. "Über das Vorkommen von Harmin in einer südamerikanischen Liane (Yagé)" *Helvetica Chimica Acta* 11: 162–166.

Eliade, M. 1951. *Le Chamanisme et les Techniques Archaïques de l'Extase.* Paris, France. Translated into English, 1964. *Shamanism: Archaic Techniques of Ecstasy*. Pantheon Books, New York. Translated into Spanish by E. de Champourcin, 1976. *El Chamanismo y las Técnicas Arcáicas del Éxtasis.* Fondo de Cultura Económica, México City. Translated into German, 1975. *Schamanismus und Arkaische Ekstasetechnik*. Frankfurt, Germany.

Eliade, M. 1954. *Le Yoga: Immortalité et Liberté*. Paris, France. Translated into English, 1958. *Yoga: Immortality and Freedom.* Pantheon Books, New York.

Eliade, M. 1976. *Histoire des Croyances et des Idées Religieuses. I. De l'Age de la Pierre aux Mystères d'Eleusis.* Payot, Paris, France.

El Imam, Y.M.A. and **W.C. Evans** 1984. "Tropane alkaloids of species of *Anthocercis*, *Cyphanthera* and *Crenidium*" *Planta Medica* 50: 86–87.

El Imam, Y.M.A. and **W.C. Evans** 1990. "Alkaloids of a *Datura candida* cultivar, *D. aurea* and various hybrids" *Fitoterapia* 61(2): 148–152.

Elisabetsky, E. *et al.* 1992. "Traditional Amazonian nerve tonics as antidepressant agents: *Chaunochiton kappleri*: A case study" *Journal of Herbs, Spices & Medicinal Plants* 1(1/2): 125–162.

Elisabetsky, E. and **D.A. Posey** 1989. "Use of contraceptives and related plants by the Kayapó Indians (Brazil)" *Journal of Ethnopharmacology* 26(3): 299–316.

Elizondo, M.G. 1991. "Ethnobotany of the Southern Tepehuan of Durango, Mexico: 1. Edible mushrooms" *Journal of Ethnobiology* 11(2): 165–173.

Ellickson, P.L. and **R.M. Bell** 1990. "Drug prevention in junior high: A multi-site longitudinal test" *Science* 247: 1299–1305. See also: Ferrence 1990.

Ellis, H. 1897. "A note on the phenomena of

mescal [*sic*] intoxication." *The Lancet* 1: 1540–1542.

Ellis, H. 1898A. "Mescal [*sic*]: A new artificial paradise" *Contemporary Review* 73: 130–141. Reprinted in Ebin, D. (Ed.) 1961. *The Drug Experience: First-Person Accounts of Addicts, Writers, Scientists and Others.* The Orion Press, New York. pp. 225–236.

Ellis, H. 1898B. "Mescal [*sic*]: A new artificial paradise" *Smithsonian Institution Annual Report for 1898.* U.S. Government Printing Office, Washington, D.C. pp. 537–548.

Elmi, A.S. 1983. "The chewing of khat in Somalia" *Journal of Ethnopharmacology* 8(2): 163–176.

El-Moghazy, A.M. *et al.* 1982. *Egyptian Journal of Pharmaceutical Sciences* 23: 247.

Emboden, W.A. 1972A. "Ritual use of *Cannabis sativa* L.: A historical-ethnographic survey" In: Furst, P.T. (Ed.) *Flesh of the Gods: The Ritual Use of Hallucinogens.* Praeger, New York. pp. 214–236.

Emboden, W.A. 1972B. *Narcotic Plants.* The Macmillan Co., New York.

Emboden, W.A. 1974. "*Cannabis*—A polytypic genus" *Economic Botany* 28(3): 304–310.

Emboden, W.A. 1977. "Dionysus as a shaman and wine as a magical drug" *Journal of Psychedelic Drugs* 9(3): 187–192.

Emboden, W.A. 1978. "The sacred narcotic lily of the Nile: *Nymphaea caerulea*" *Economic Botany* 32(4): 395–407.

Emboden, W.A. 1979. *Narcotic Plants.* Second Edition Revised and Enlarged. Macmillan Publishing Co., New York.

Emboden, W.A. 1981A. "The genus *Cannabis* and the correct use of taxonomic categories" *Journal of Psychoactive Drugs* 13(1): 15–21.

Emboden, W.A. 1981B. "Transcultural use of water lilies in Maya and Egyptian civilizations" *Journal of Ethnopharmacology* 3(1): 39–83.

Emboden, W.A. 1982. "The mushroom and the water lily: Literary and pictorial evidence for *Nymphaea* as a ritual psychotogen [*sic*] in Mesoamerica" *Journal of Ethnopharmacology* 5(2): 139–148.

Emboden, W.A. 1983A. "The ethnobotany of the Dresden Codex with especial reference to the narcotic [*sic*] Nymphaea ampla" *Botanical Museum Leaflets* Harvard University 29(2): 87–132.

Emboden, W.A. 1983B. "Absinthe, absintheurs and absinthism" *Terra* 21(4).

Emmerich, A. 1965. *Sweat of the Sun and Tears of the Moon.* University of Washington Press, Seattle, WA.

Enos, L. 1970. *A Key to the American Psilocybin Mushroom.* Youniverse, Lemon Grove, CA. Revised editions in 1971; 1972.

Epling, C. and **C.D. Játiva-M.** 1962. "A new species of *Salvia* from Mexico" *Botanical Museum Leaflets* Harvard University 20(3): 75–76. This *Leaflet* was reprinted with Wasson 1962B in February 1971.

Erickson, H.T. *et al.* 1984. "Guaraná (*Paullinia cupana*) as a commercial crop in Brazilian Amazonia" *Economic Botany* 38(3): 273–286.

Erlich, J. 1992. "Brain gain: Drugs that boost intelligence" *Omni.* September issue. pp. 42 *et seq.*

Erspamer, V. *et al.* 1965. "5-Methoxy and 5-hydroxyindolealkylamines in the skin of *Bufo alvarius*" *Experientia* 21: 504.

Erspamer, V. *et al.* 1967. "5-Methoxy- and 5-hydroxyindoles in the skin of *Bufo alvarius*" *Biochemical Pharmacology* 16: 1149–1164.

Escalante, R. *et al.* 1973. *Datos Etnomicológicos de los Matlatzincas.* Instituto Nacional de Antropología e Historia, México City.

Escalante, R. and **A. López** 1971. *Hongos Sagrados de los Matlatzincas.* Museo Nacional de Antropología, México City.

Escohotado, A. 1989A. *Historia General de las Drogas.* Three volumes. Alianza Editorial, Madrid, Spain. Revised edition in 1992 with technical editing by J. Ott.

Escohotado, A. 1989B. "El espíritu como naturaleza: Entrevista con [Albert] Hofmann" *El Paseante* 13: 116–121. Reprinted in *El Nacional* 4 April 1990.

Escohotado, A. 1990. *El Libro de los Venenos: Guia de Drogas, las Lícitas y las Otras.* Mondadori, Madrid, Spain. Reprint 1992. *Para una Fenomenología de las Drogas.* Biblioteca Mondadori, Madrid, Spain.

Estrada, A. 1977. *Vida de María Sabina: La Sabia de los Hongos.* Siglo Veintiuno, México City. "Presentación" by R. Gordon Wasson, pp. 9–22. Editions in French by M. Bibard, 1979, *Autobiographie de María Sabina: La Sage aux Champignons Sacrés*, Éditions du Seuil, Paris, France; English by Henry Munn, 1981, *María Sabina: Her Life and Chants*, Ross-Erikson, Santa Barbara, CA; Portuguese, 1984, *A Vida de María Sabina, a Sabia dos Cogumelos*, Livraria Martins Fontes Editôra Ltda., São Paulo, Brasil; German, 1980, *María Sabina: Botin der Heiligen Pilze*, Trikont, München, Germany. See: Liggenstorfer & Rätsch 1996. Wasson introduction reprinted in *Head*, February 1978, p. 52 *et seq.*

Estrada Lugo, E.I.J. 1991. *El Códice Florentino: Su Información Etnobotánica.* Colegio de Posgraduados, Chapingo, México.

Eugster, C.H. 1956. "Über Muscarin aus Fliegenpilzen" *Helvetica Chimica Acta* 39(4): 1002–1022.

Eugster, C.H. 1959. "Brève revue d'ensemble sur la chimie de la muscarine" *Revue de Mycologie* 24(5): 369–385.

Eugster, C.H. 1967. "Isolation, structure and synthesis of central-active compounds from *Amanita muscaria* (L. ex Fr.) Hooker" In: Efron, D.H. *et al.* (Eds.) *Ethnopharmacologic Search for Psychoactive Drugs.* (Public Health Service Publication No. 1645) U.S. Government Printing Office, Washington, D.C. pp. 416–418.

Eugster, C.H. 1968. "Wirkstoffe aus dem Fliegenpilz" *Die Naturwißenschaften* 7: 305.

Eugster, C.H. 1969. "Chemie der Wirkstoffe aus dem Fliegenpilz (*Amanita muscaria*)" *Fortschritte der Chemie Organischer Naturstoffe* 27: 262.

Eugster, C.H. and **T. Takemoto** 1967. "Zur Nomenklatur der neuen Verbindungen aus *Amanita*-Arten" *Helvetica Chimica Acta* 50: 726.

Eugster, C.H. and **P.G. Waser** 1954. "Zur Kenntnis des Muscarins" *Experientia* 10: 298.

Eugster, C.H. *et al.* 1965. "Wirkstoffe aus *Amanita muscaria*: Ibotensäure und Muscazon" *Tetrahedron Letters* 1813–1815.

Evans, R.L. and **I.M. Berent** 1992. *Drug Legalization: For and Against.* (For and Against, Volume 1) Open Court, La Salle, IL.

Evans, W.C. 1979. "Tropane alkaloids in the Solanaceae" In: Hawkes, J.G. *et al.* (Eds.) *The Biology and Taxonomy of the Solanaceae.* (Linnean Society Symposium Series, Number 7) Academic Press, London, England. pp. 241–254.

Evans, W.C. 1989. *Trease and Evans' Pharmacognosy.* Thirteenth edition. Baillière Tindall, London, England and W.B. Saunders, Philadelphia, PA.

Evans, W.C. and **K.P.A. Ramsey** 1983. "Alkaloids of the Solanaceae tribe Anthocercidae" *Phytochemistry* 22(10): 2219–2225.

Evans, W.C. *et al.* 1965. "The alkaloids of the genus *Datura*, section Brugmansia. Part III. *Datura sanguinea* R. and P." *Planta Medica* 13: 353–358.

Evans, W.C. *et al.* 1972. "Alkaloids of *Solandra* species" *Phytochemistry* 2: 470–472.

Evarts, E.V. *et al.* 1955. "Some effects of lysergic acid diethylamide and bufotenine on electrical activity in the cat's visual system" *The American Journal of Physiology* 182: 594–598.

Evarts, E.V. *et al.* 1956. "Some effects of bufotenine and lysergic acid diethylamide on the monkey" *Archives of Neurology and Psychiatry* 75: 49–53.

Fabing, H.D. 1956. "On going berserk: A neurochemical inquiry" *Science Monthly* 83(5): 232–237.

Fabing, H.D. 1957. "Toads, mushrooms and schizophrenia" *Harper's Magazine* 214(1284): 50–55.

Fabing, H.D. and **J.R. Hawkins** 1956. "Intravenous bufotenine injection in the human being" *Science* 123: 886–887.

Facciola, S. 1990. *Cornucopia: A Source Book of Edible Plants.* Kampong Publications, Vista, CA. Preface by Noel Vietmeyer, p. III.

Fadiman, J. 1965. "*Genista canariensis*: A minor psychedelic [*sic*]" *Economic Botany* 19: 383–384. Reprinted in 1990 as: "Psychedelic [*sic*] properties of *Genista canariensis*" In: Tart, C.T. (Ed.) *Altered States of Consciousness.* Harper San Francisco, New York. pp. 432–438.

Faillace, L.A. *et al.* 1967. "Clinical evaluation of some hallucinogenic tryptamine derivatives" *The Journal of Nervous and Mental Disease* 145(4): 303–313.

Faillace, L.A. *et al.* 1970. "Hallucinogenic drugs in the treatment of alcoholism: A two-year follow-up" *Comprehensive Psychiatry* 11: 51–56.

Federal Aviation Regulations/Airman's Information Manual 1991. Aviation Supplies Academics, Renton, WA.

Feest, C.F. 1983. "New wines and beers of North America" *Journal of Ethnopharmacology* 9(2,3): 329–335.

Feinhandler, S.J. *et al.* 1979. "Pre-Columbian tobaccos in the Pacific" *Economic Botany* 33(2): 213–226.

Félice, P. de 1936. *Poisons Sacrés* [*sic*], *Ivresses Divines: Essai sur quelques Formes Inférieures* [*sic*] *de la Mystique.* A. Michel, Paris, France. Facsimile 1970, A. Michel, Paris. Italian edition, 1990. *Le Droghe degli Dei: Veleni Sacri, Estasi Divine.* ECIG, Genova.

Fellows, L. 1984. Personal communcation.

Ferckel, S. 1954. "'Hexensalben' und ihre Wirkung" *Kosmos, Handweiser für Naturfreunde* 50: 414–415.

Fericgla, J.M. 1985. *El Bolet i la Gènesi de les Cultures. Gnoms i Follets: Àmbits Culturals Forjats per l'*Amanita muscaria. Editorial Alta Fulla, Barcelona, Spain. Text in Catalán; Apèndix "Mites i al·lucinacions" by C. Esteva i Fabregat, pp. 185–215. Spanish translation 1994. Los Libros de la Liebre de Marzo, Barcelona, Spain.

Fericgla, J.M. 1992. "*Amanita muscaria* usage in Catalunya" *Integration: Zeitschrift für Geistbewegende Pflanzen und Kultur* 2&3: 63–65.

Fericgla, J.M. 1994A. *Els Jívaros: Caçadors de Somnis.* La Campana, Barcelona, Catalunya. Spanish edition 1994. Integral, Barcelona.

Fericgla, J.M. (Ed.) 1994B. *Plantas, Chamanismo y Estados de Consciencia.* Los Libros de la Liebre de Marzo, Barcelona, Spain.

Fernandez, J.W. 1972. "*Tabernanthe iboga*: Narcotic ecstasis and the work of the ancestors" In: Furst, P.T. (Ed.) *Flesh of the Gods: The Ritual Use of Hallucinogens.* Praeger, New York. pp. 237–260.

Fernandez, J.W. 1982. *Bwiti: An Ethnography of the Religious Imagination of Africa.* Princeton University Press, Princeton, NJ.

Ferrence, R.G. 1990. "Drug abuse prevention programs" *Science* 250: 739–740. Letter to the editor and rebuttal in response to Ellickson & Bell 1990.

Ferrigni, N.R. *et al.* 1982. "Cactus alkaloids. XLVIII. $N,^{\alpha}N^{\alpha}$–Dimethylhistamine, a hypotensive component of *Echinocereus triglochidiatus*" *Journal of Ethnopharmacology* 5(3): 359–364.

Festi, F. 1985. *Funghi Allucinogeni: Aspetti Psicofisiologici e Storici.* (Book produced by the Società Museo Civico di Rovereto; LXXXVI Publicazione dei Musei Civici di Rovereto) Manfrini, Calliano, Trento, Italy.

Festi, F. 1995. "Le erbe del diavolo. 2. Botanica, chimica e farmacologia"; "Le erbe del diavolo 3. Note bibliografiche" *Altrove* 2: 116–133; 134–145.

Festi, F. and **G. Alliota** 1990. "Piante psicotrope spontanee o coltivate in Italia" *Annali dei Musei Civici di Rovereto* 5: 135–166.

Festi, F. and **A. Bianchi** 1991. "*Amanita muscaria*. Myco-pharmacological outline and personal experiences" *Psychedelic Monographs and Essays* 5: 209–250.

Festi, F. and **A. Bianchi** 1992. "*Amanita muscaria*" *Integration: Zeitschrift für Geistbewegende Pflanzen und Kultur* 2&3: 79–89.

Festi, F. and **G. Samorini** 1993. "Alcaloidi indolici psicoattivi nei generi *Phalaris* e *Arundo* (*Graminaceae*) [*sic*]: Una rassegna" *Annali dei Musei Civici di Rovereto* 9: 239–287.

Fischer Cárdenas, G. 1923. *Estudio Sobre el Principio Activo del Yagé.* Thesis, Universidad Nacional, Bogotá, Colombia.

Fischer, O. 1899. "Über Harmin und Harmalin. II." *Berichte der Deutschen Chemischen Gesellschaft* 32(2): 637–645.

Fischer, O. 1901. *Chemical Society Abstracts* 1: 405.

Fish, M.S. and **E.C. Horning** 1956. "Studies on hallucinogenic snuffs" *The Journal of Nervous and Mental Disease* 124: 33–37.

Fish, M.S. *et al.* 1955. "Piptadenia alkaloids. Indole bases of *P. peregrina* (L.) Benth. and related species" *Journal of the Amerierican Chemical Society* 77: 5892–5895.

Fisher, G. 1963. "Some comments concerning dosage levels of psychedelic compounds for psychotherapeutic experiences" *The Psychedelic Review* 1(2): 208–218. Reprinted in Weil, G.M. *et al.* (Eds.) 1965. *The Psychedelic Reader.* University Books, New York. pp. 149–159 [reprinted 1996].

Fitzgerald, J.S. and **A.A. Sioumis** 1965. "Alkaloids of the Australian Leguminosae V. The occurrence of methylated tryptamines in Acacia maidenii F. Muell." *Australian Journal of Chemistry* 18: 433–434.

Fiussello, N. and **J. Ceruti Scurti** 1972. "Idrossi-indol derivati in Basidiomiceti. II. Psilocibina, psilocina e 5-idrossi-indol derivati in carpofori di Panaeolus e generi affini" *Allionia* 18: 85–90.

Flattery, D.S. and **J.M. Pierce** 1965. *Peyote.* Berkeley Press, Berkeley, CA.

Flattery, D.S. and **M. Schwartz** 1989. *Haoma and Harmaline: The Botanical Identity of the Indo-Iranian Sacred Hallucinogen [sic] "Soma" and its Legacy in Religion, Language, and Middle Eastern Folklore.* (Near Eastern Studies Volume 21) University of California Press, Berkeley, CA.

Fletcher, R. 1896. "The witches' pharmacopoeia" *Bulletin of the Johns Hopkins Hospital* 7: 147–156.

Fleurentin, J. *et al.* 1983. "Cultural background of the medicinal plants of Yemen" *Journal of Ethnopharmacology* 7(2): 183–203.

Flores, F.A. and **W.H. Lewis** 1978. "Drinking the South American hallucinogenic ayahuasca" *Economic Botany* 32(2): 154–156.

Fo, R.B. *et al.* 1984. "The chemistry of Brazilian Myristicaceae" *Planta Medica* 50: 53–55.

Foote, J. 1992. "Gypsies of the New Age" *Newsweek.* 15 June (Latin American) issue. p. 33.

Forbes, R.J. 1948. *Short History of the Art of Distillation.* E.J. Brill, Leiden, the Netherlands.

Ford, C.S. 1967. "Ethnographical aspects of kava" In: Efron, D.H. *et al.* (Eds.) *Ethnopharmacologic Search for Psychoactive Drugs.* (Public Health Service Publication No. 1645) U.S. Government Printing Office, Washington, D.C. pp. 162–173.

Ford, W.W. 1923. "A new classification of mycetismus (mushroom poisoning)" *Transactions of the Association of American Physicians* 38: 225–229.

Forte, R. 1988. "A conversation with R. Gordon Wasson (1898–1986)" *ReVision: The*

Journal of Consciousness and Change 10(4): 13–30.
Foster, S. 1984. *Herbal Bounty: The Gentle Art of Herb Culture.* Gibbs M. Smith, Layton, VT. Preface by Shiu Ying Hu, pp. 9–10; foreword by Richard Evans Schultes, p. 11.
Foster, S. 1991. "Milk thistle: *Silybum marianum*" *American Botanical Council Botanical Series* No. 305: 1–8.
Foster, S. and **J.A. Duke** 1990. *A Field Guide to Medicinal Plants. Eastern and Central North America.* Houghton-Mifflin, Boston, MA.
Frahn, J.L. and **D.F. O'Keefe** 1971. "The occurrence of tetrahydro-β-carboline alkaloids in *Phalaris tuberosa* (Gramineae)" *Australian Journal of Chemistry* 24: 2189–2192.
Franch, J.A. 1982. "Religiosidad, alucinógenos y patrones artísticos taínos" *Boletín del Museo del Hombre Dominicano* 10(17): 103–117.
Frank, M. and **E. Rosenthal** 1974. *The Indoor Outdoor Highest Quality Marijuana Grower's Guide.* And/Or, Berkeley, CA.
Frankel, M. *et al.* 1992A. "The great coffee bust" *Newsweek.* 28 September (Latin American) issue. pp. 34–35.
Frankel, M. *et al.* 1992B. "Billows of smoke" *Newsweek.* 30 November (Latin American) issue. pp. 44–45.
Fraser, L. 1992. "Xochipilli: A context for ecstasy" *Whole Earth Review* 75: 38–43. Article about "Xochi Speaks" poster illustrated on *verso* of the magazine. See: Lord Nose! 1992, *Mondo 2000* No. 7.
Freedman, D.X. 1967. "Perspectives on the use and abuse of psychedelic drugs" In: Efron, D.H. *et al.* (Eds.) *Ethnopharmacologic Search for Psychoactive Drugs.* (Public Health Service Publication No. 1645) U.S. Government Printing Office, Washington, D.C. pp. 77–102.
French, N. 1990. "ASCII no questions, tell ye no spies" *Mondo 2000* 5: 22.
Friedberg, C. 1959. "Rapport sommaire sur une mission au Pérou" *Journal d'Agriculture Tropicale et de Botanique Appliquée* 6(8-9): 1.
Friedberg, C. 1960. "Utilisation d'un cactus à mescaline au nord du Pérou—(*Trichocereus Pachanoi*)" *Sixth International Congress of Anthropology and Ethnological Sciences* 2(2): 21–6.
Friedberg, C. 1965. "Des *Banisteriopsis* utilisés comme drogue en Amérique du Sud. Essai d'ètude critique" *Journal d'Agriculture Tropicale et de Botanique Appliquée* 12(9-12): 403–437; 550–594; 729–780.
Friedlander, I. 1975. *The Whirling Dervishes.* Collier Books, New York.
Fritz, H. *et al.* 1965. "The structure of muscazone" *Tetrahedron Letters* 25: 2075–2076.
Fritzsche, J. 1847. "Bestandtheile der Samen von *Peganum Harmala*" *Justus Liebig's Annalen der Chemie* 64: 360–364.
Fukamiya, N. and **K.-H. Lee** 1986. "Antitumor agents, 81. Justicidin A and diphyllin, two cytotoxic principles from *Justicia procumbens*" *Journal of Natural Products* 49(2): 348–350.
Fuller, J.G. 1968. *The Day of St. Anthony's Fire.* The Macmillan Company, New York.
Furst, P.T. 1971. "*Ariocarpus retusus*, the 'false peyote' of Huichol tradition" *Economic Botany* 25(2): 182–187.
Furst, P.T. 1972. "To find our life: Peyote among the Huichol Indians of Mexico" In: Furst, P.T. (Ed.) *Flesh of the Gods: The Ritual Use of Hallucinogens.* Praeger, New York. pp. 136–184. Reprinted in 1990 by Waveland Press, Prospect Heights, IL, with new introduction, pp. VII–XXVIII.
Furst, P.T. 1974A. "Morning Glory and mother goddess at Tepantitla, Teotihuacan: Iconography and analogy in pre-Columbian art" In: Hammond, N. (Ed.) *Mesoamerican Archaeology—New Approaches.* Duckworth, London, England. pp. 187–215.
Furst, P.T. 1974B. "Archaeological evidence

for snuffing in prehispanic Mexico" *Botanical Museum Leaflets* Harvard University 24(1): 1–27.

Furst, P.T. 1976. *Hallucinogens and Culture.* Chandler & Sharp, Novato, CA. Translated into Spanish by J. Agustín in 1980. *Los Alucinógenos y la Cultura.* Fondo de Cultura Económica, México City.

Furst, P.T. 1986. *Mushrooms: Psychedelic Fungi.* Chelsea House Publishers, New York. The Encyclopedia of Psychoactive Drugs. Spanish edition, 1995. *Hongos: Especies Alucinógenas.* Editorial Diana, México City.

Furst, P.T. 1989. "The life and death of the crazy kiéri: Natural and cultural history of a Huichol myth" *Journal of Latin American Folklore* 15(2): 155–177.

Furst, P.T. 1990. "'Vistas beyond the horizon of this life': Encounters [posthumous] with R. Gordon Wasson" In: Riedlinger, T.J. (Ed.) *The Sacred Mushroom Seeker: Essays for R. Gordon Wasson.* Ethnomycological Studies No. 11. Dioscorides Press, Portland, OR. pp. 67–81.

Furst, P.T. 1995. "The drunkard kiéri: New observations of an old problem in Huichol psychotropic ethnobotany" *Integration: Zeitschrift für Geistbewegende Pflanzen und Kultur* 5: 51–62.

Furst, P.T. and **M.D. Coe** 1977. "Ritual enemas" *Natural History* 86: 88–91. Reprinted in 1989. In: Lehmann, A.C. and J.E. Meyers (Eds.) *Magic, Witchcraft and Religion.* Mayfield, Mountain View, CA. pp. 127–131.

Furst, P.T. and **B. Myerhoff** 1972. "El mito como historia: El ciclo del peyote y la datura entre los Huicholes" In: Nahmad S., S. *et al.* (Eds.) *El Peyote y los Huicholes.* SEP Setenta, México City. pp. 55–108.

Gackenbach, J. and **J. Bosveld** 1990. *Control your Dreams.* Harper-Collins, New York.

Gage, T. 1946. *Nueva Relación que Contiene los Viajes de Tomás Gage en la Nueva España.* (Biblioteca "Goathemala," Volume XVIII) Sociedad de Geografía e Historia de Guatemala, Guatemala City, Guatemala.

Gagneux, A.R. *et al.* 1965A. "Synthesis of pantherine (agarin)" *Tetrahedron Letters* 25: 2077–2079.

Gagneux, A.R. *et al.* 1965B. "Synthesis of ibotenic acid" *Tetrahedron Letters* 25: 2081–2084.

Gaignault, J.C. and **J. Delourme-Houdé** 1977. "Les alcaloïdes de l'iboga (*Tabernanthe iboga* H. Bn.)" *Fitoterapia* 48: 243–265.

Gaines, B. 1963. "LSD: Hollywood's status-symbol drug" *Cosmopolitan.* November.

Gajdusek, D.C. 1967. "Recent observations on the use of kava in the New Hebrides" In: Efron, D.H. *et al.* (Eds.) *Ethnopharmacologic Search for Psychoactive Drugs.* (Public Health Service Publication No. 1645) U.S. Government Printing Office, Washington, D.C. pp. 119–125.

Galeffi, C. *et al.* 1983. "*N,N*-Dimethyl-5-methoxytryptamine, a component of a dart poison of the Yanoamá Indians" *Journal of Natural Products* 46(4): 586–587.

Gallagher, C.H. *et al.* 1964. "Toxicity of *Phalaris tuberosa* for sheep" *Nature* 204: 542–545.

Gallagher, R.T. *et al.* 1984. "Tremorigenic neurotoxins from perennial ryegrass causing ryegrass staggers disorder of livestock: Structure elucidation of lolitrem B" *Journal of the Chemical Society Chemical Communications* 1984: 614–616.

Gander, J.E. *et al.* 1976. "The occurrence of 2-methyl-1,2,3,4-tetrahydro-β-carboline and variation in alkaloids in *Phalaris arundinacea*" *Phytochemistry* 15: 737–738.

Gangwar, A.K. and **P.S. Ramakrishnan** 1990. "Ethnobiological notes on some tribes of Arunachal Pradesh, northeastern India" *Economic Botany* 44(1): 94–105.

Gans, D. and **R.U. Sirius** 1990. "Civilizing the electronic frontier: An interview with Mitch Kapor and John Barlow of the Electronic Frontier Foundation" *Mondo 2000* 3: 45–49.

Gaoni, Y. and **R. Mechoulam** 1964. "Isolation and partial synthesis of an active constituent of hashish" *Journal of the American Chemical Society* 86: 1646–1647.

Garbrecht, W.L. 1959. "Synthesis of amides of lysergic acid" *Journal of Organic Chemistry* 24: 368–372.

García Barriga, H. 1958. "El yagé, caapi o ayahuasca: Un alucinógeno amazónico" *Revista de la Universidad Nacional de Colombia* 23: 59–76.

García Barriga, H. 1975. *Flora Medicinal de Colombia*. Instituto de Ciencias Naturales, Universidad Nacional, Bogotá, Colombia.

Gardiner, M.R. *et al.* 1965. "*Ipomoea muelleri* intoxication of sheep in western Australia" *British Veterinary Journal* 121(6): 272–277.

Garibay, Á.M. (Ed.) 1964–1968. *Poesía Náhuatl*. Three volumes. Instituto de Investigaciones Históricas, Universidad Nacional Autónoma de México, México City.

Garner, L.F. and **J.D. Klinger** 1985. "Some visual effects caused by the beverage kava" *Journal of Ethnopharmacology* 13(3): 307–311.

Gartz, J. 1985A. "Vergleichende dünnschichtchromatographische Untersuchungen zweier Psilocybe- und einer halluzinogenen Inocybeart" *Pharmazie* 40(2): 134.

Gartz, J. 1985B. "Dünnschichtchromatographische Analyse der Inhaltßtoffe von Pilzen der Gattung Stropharia" *Pharmazie* 40(2): 134–135.

Gartz, J. 1985C. "Zur Isolierung des Baeocystins aus den Fruchtkörpern einer Psilocybeart" *Pharmazie* 40(4): 274.

Gartz, J. 1985D. "Zur Extraktion und Chromatographie des blauen Farbstoffes einer Psilocybeart" *Pharmazie* 40(4): 274–275.

Gartz, J. 1985E. "Zur radikalische Hydroxylierung von Indol" *Pharmazie* 40(5): 356.

Gartz, J. 1985F. "Zur Analytik der Inhaltßtoffe zweier Pilzarten der Gattung Conocybe" *Pharmazie* 40(5): 366.

Gartz, J. 1985G. "Zum Nachweis der Inhaltßtoffe einer Pilzart der Gattung Panaeolus" *Pharmazie* 40(7): 431.

Gartz, J. 1985H. "Zur Unterzuchung von Psilocybe semilanceata (Fr.) Kumm." *Pharmazie* 40(7): 506.

Gartz, J. 1985I. "Untersuchungen zur radikalischen Hydroxylierung von Tryptophan und Tryptamin" *Pharmazie* 40(11): 811.

Gartz, J. 1986A. "Untersuchungen zum Vorkommen des Muscarins in Inocybe aeruginascens Babos" *Zeitschrift für Mykologie* 52(2): 359–361.

Gartz, J. 1986B. "Quantitative Bestimmung der Indolderivate von *Psilocybe semilanceata* (Fr.) Kumm." *Biochemie und Physiologie der Pflanzen* 181: 117–124.

Gartz, J. 1986C. "Nachweis von Tryptaminderivaten in Pilzen der Gattungen *Gerronema*, *Hygrocybe*, *Psathyrella* und *Inocybe*" *Biochemie und Physiologie der Pflanzen* 181: 275–278.

Gartz, J. 1986D. "Psilocybin in Mycelkulturen von *Inocybe aeruginascens*" *Biochemie und Physiologie der Pflanzen* 181: 511–7.

Gartz, J. 1986E. "Ethnopharmakologie und Entdeckungsgeschichte der halluzinogenen Wirkstoffe von europäischen Pilzen der Gattung Psilocybe" *Zeitschrift für Ärztliche Fortbildung* 80: 803–805.

Gartz, J. 1987A. "Vorkommen von Psilocybin und Baeocystin in Fruchtkörpern von *Pluteus salicinus*" *Planta Medica* 53(3): 290–291.

Gartz, J. 1987B. "Variation der Alkaloidmengen in Fruchtkörpern von *Inocybe aeruginascens*" *Planta Medica* 53(6): 539–541.

Gartz, J. 1987C. "Variation der Indolalkaloide von Psilocybe cubensis durch unterschiedliche Kultivierungsbedingungen"

Beiträge zur Kenntnis der Pilze Mitteleuropas 3: 275–281.

Gartz, J. 1989A. "Occurrence of psilocybin, psilocin and baeocystin in Gymnopilus purpuratus" *Persoonia* 14(1): 19–22.

Gartz, J. 1989B. "Analyse der Indolderivate in Fruchtkörpern und Mycelien von *Panaeolus subalteatus* (Berk. & Br.) Sacc. [*sic*]" *Biochemie und Physiologie der Pflanzen* 184: 171–178.

Gartz, J. 1989C. "Biotransformation of tryptamine derivatives in mycelial cultures of *Psilocybe*" *Journal of Basic Microbiology* 29(6): 347–352.

Gartz, J. 1989D. "Analysis of aeruginascin in fruit bodies of the mushroom *Inocybe aeruginascens*" *International Journal of Crude Drug Research* 27(3): 141–144.

Gartz, J. 1989E. "Biotransformation of tryptamine in fruiting mycelia of *Psilocybe cubensis*" *Planta Medica* 55(3): 249–250.

Gartz, J. 1989F. "Bildung und Verteilung der Indolalkaloide in Fruchtkörpern, Mycelien und Sklerotien von Psilocybe cubensis" *Beiträge zur Kenntnis der Pilze Mitteleuropas* 5: 167–174.

Gartz, J. 1991. "Einfluß von Phosphat auf Fruktifikation und Sekundärmetabolismen der Myzelien von Psilocybe cubensis, Psilocybe semilanceata und Gymnopilus purpuratus" *Zeitschrift für Mykologie* 57 (1): 149–154.

Gartz, J. 1992A. Personal communications.

Gartz, J. 1992B. "Further investigations on psychoactive mushrooms of the genera *Psilocybe*, *Gymnopilus* and *Conocybe*" *Annali dei Musei Civici di Rovereto* 7: 265–274.

Gartz, J. 1993. *Narrenschwämme: Psychotrope Pilze in Europa–Herausforderung an Forschung und Wertsystem.* Editions Heuwinkel, Basel, Switzerland. Vorwort "Wer war der erste Narr?" by Christian Rätsch, pp. 9–10. English edition, 1996.

Gartz, J. 1994. "Cultivation and analysis of *Psilocybe* species and an investigation of *Galerina steglichii*" *Annali dei Musei Civici di Rovereto* 10: 297–306.

Gartz, J. and **J.W. Allen** 1993. "Entheogenic fungi in Southeast Asia: An ethnomycological report" In press.

Gartz, J. and **G. Drewitz** 1985. "Der erste Nachweis der Vorkommens von Psilocybin in Rißpilzen" *Zeitschrift für Mykologie* 51: 199–203.

Gartz, J. and **G. Drewitz** 1986. "Der Grünlichverfärbende Rißpilz—Eine Inocybeart mit halluzinogener Wirkung" *Zeitschrift für Ärztliche Fortbildung* 80: 551–553.

Gartz, J. and **G.K. Müller** 1989. "Analysis and cultivation of fruit bodies and mycelia of *Psilocybe bohemica*" *Biochemie und Physiologie der Pflanzen* 184(3-4): 337–341.

Gartz, J. and **G.K. Müller** 1990. "Versuche zur Kultur von Gymnopilus purpuratus, Purpurflämmling" *Mykologisches Mitteilungsblatt* 33(1): 29–30.

Gartz, J. *et al.* 1990. "Growth-promoting effect of a brassinosteroid in mycelial cultures of the fungus *Psilocybe cubensis*" *Die Naturwißenschaften* 77: 388–389.

Gartz, J. *et al.* 1994. "Ethnomycology, biochemistry, and cultivation of *Psilocybe samuiensis* Guzmán, Bandala and Allen, a new psychoactive fungus from Koh Samui, Thailand" *Journal of Ethnopharmacology* 43(2): 73–80.

Garza, M. de la 1990. *Sueño y Alucinación en el Mundo Náhuatl y Maya*. Universidad Nac. Autónoma de México, México City.

Gates, B. 1982. "A monograph of Banisteriopsis and Diplopterys, Malpighiaceae" *Flora Neotropica.* (Monograph No. 30) The New York Botanical Garden, Bronx, NY.

Gates, B. 1986. "La taxonomía de las *malpigiáceas* utilizadas en el brebaje del *ayahuasca*" *América Indígena* 46(1): 49–72.

Gatty, R. 1956. "Kava—Polynesian beverage shrub" *Economic Botany* 10(2): 241–249.

Gautier, T. (Translation by P. Kraft) 1961. "Phantasma" and "Kief" In: Ebin, D. (Ed.) *The Drug Experience: First-Person Accounts of Addicts, Writers, Scientists and Others.* The Orion Press, New York. pp. 6–15. Originally published in *Revue de Deux Mondes.* 1 February 1846.

Gebhart-Sayer, A. 1986. "Una terápia estética. Los diseños visionarios del ayahuasca entre los Shipibo-Conibo" *América Indígena* 46(1): 189–218.

Geerken, H. 1988. *Mappa.* Verlag Klaus Ramm, Spange, Germany.

Geerken, H. 1992. "Fliegen Pilze? Merkungen & Anmerkungen zum Schamanismus in Sibirien & Andechs" *Integration: Zeitschrift für Geistbewegende Pflanzen und Kultur* 2&3: 109–114. Original 1990. *Schreibheft, Zeitschrift für Literatur* 35.

Geiger, P.L. and **O. Hesse** 1833. "Über einige neue giftige organische Alkalien" *Annales Pharmaceutiques* 7: 269–280.

Gelfand, M. and **C. Harris** 1982. "Poisoning by *Amanita pantherina*. A description of two cases" *Central African Medical Journal* 28: 159–163.

Gelpke, R. 1966A. *Vom Rausch im Orient und Okzident.* E. Klett Verlag, Stuttgart, Germany. Paperback 1975. *Drogen und Seelenerweiterung.* Vorwort by Wendel Gelpke, pp. 11–12. Kindler Verlag, München, Germany. Original title reprint 1982. Klett-Cotta/Ullstein, Berlin, Germany.

Gelpke, R. 1966B. "Der Geheimbund von Alamut. Legende und Wirklichkeit" *Antaios* 8(3): 269–293.

Gelpke, R. (Translation by J. Ott) 1981. "On travels in the universe of the soul: Reports on self-experiments with Delysid (LSD) and psilocybin (CY)" *Journal of Psychoactive Drugs* 13(1): 81–89. Orig. "Von Fahrten in den Weltraum der Seele: Berichte über Selbstversuche mit Delysid (LSD) und Psilocyin (CY)" *Antaios* 3(5): 393–411, 1962.

Genest, K. 1965. "A direct densitometric method on thin-layer plates for the determination of lysergic acid amide, isolysergic acid amide and clavine alkaloids in morning glory seeds" *Journal of Chromatography* 19(3): 531–539.

Genest, K. and **M.R. Sahasrabudhe** 1966. "Alkaloids and lipids of *Ipomoea*, *Rivea* and *Convolvulus* and their application to chemotaxonomy" *Economic Botany* 20 (4): 416–428.

Gerber, P. 1975. *Die Peyote-Religion Nordamerikanischer Indianer.* Thesis, Universität Zürich, Zürich, Switzerland. Published in 1980. *Die Peyote Religion: Nordamerikanischer Indianer auf der Suche nach einer Identität.* Zürich, Switzerland.

Gerhardt, E. 1990. Personal communication to T. Stijve; Allen & Merlin 1992A.

Gershevitch, I. 1974. "An Iranianist's view of the Soma controversy" *Mémorial: Jean de Menasce* 185: 45–75. Fondation Culturelle Iranienne, Louvain, France.

Gershon, S. and **W.J. Lang** 1962. "A psychopharmacological study of some indole alkaloids" *Archives Internationales de Pharmacodynamie et de Thérapie* 135(1-2): 31–56.

Gessner, P.K. 1970. "Pharmacological studies of 5-methoxy-N,N-dimethyltryptamine, LSD and other hallucinogens" In: Efron, D.H. (Ed.) *Psychotomimetic* [*sic*] *Drugs.* Raven, New York. pp. 105–122.

Gessner, P.K. and **I.H. Page** 1962. "Behavioral efects of 5-methoxy-*N:N*-dimethyltryptamine, other tryptamines, and LSD" *American Journal of Physiology* 203: 167–172.

Gessner, P.K. *et al.* 1960. "The relationship between the metabolic rate and pharmacological actions of serotonin, bufotenine and psilocybin" *Journal of Pharmacology* 130: 126–133.

Gessner, P.K. *et al.* 1968. "Structure-activity relationships among 5-methoxy-N:N-dimethyltryptamine, 4-hydroxy-N:N-dimethyltryptamine (psilocin) and other substituted tryptamines" *Life Sciences* 7: 267–277.

Getahun, A. and **A.D. Krikorian** 1973. "Chat: Coffee's rival from Harar, Ethiopia. I. Botany, cultivation and use" *Economic Botany* 27(4): 353–377. Part II: Krikorian and Getahun 1973.

Ghosal, S. 1972. "Occurrence of psychodelic substances in some Indian medicinal plants" *Planta Medica* 21: 200–209.

Ghosal, S. and **U.K. Mazumder** 1971. "Malpighiaceae: Alkaloids of the leaves of *Banistereopsis* [*sic*] *argentea*" *Phytochemistry* 10: 2840–2841.

Ghosal, S. *et al.* 1969. "*Arundo donax* L. (*Graminae*) [*sic*]. Phytochemical and pharmacological evaluation" *Journal of Medicinal Chemistry* 12: 480–483.

Ghosal, S. *et al.* 1971. "Chemical and pharmacological evaluation of *Banistereopsis* [*sic*] *argentea* Spring ex Juss" *Journal of Pharmaceutical Sciences* 60(8): 1209–1212.

Ghosal, S. *et al.* 1972. In: Mothes, K. (Ed.) *4th Biochemistry and Physiology of Alkaloids International Symposium.* Akademie Verlag, Berlin, Germany. pp. 107–111.

Ghouled, F.C. 1972. *Field Guide to the Psilocybin Mushroom—Species Common to North America.* Guidance Publications, New Orleans, LA.

Giacomoni, L. 1985. "Des Mystères d'Eleusis au Feu de Saint Antoine: La fabuleuse histoire de l'érgotisme" *Bulletin de l'AEMBA* 17: 1–52.

Giacomoni, L. 1987. "Un nouveau champignon hallucinogène [*sic*] *Cortinarius infractus* (Pers.: Fr.) Fr." *Documents Mycologiques* 17(68): 15–16.

Giarman, N.J. 1967. "The pharmacology of LSD" In: DeBold, R.C. and R.C. Leaf (Eds.) *LSD, Man and Society.* Wesleyan Univ. Press, Middletown, CT. pp. 143–158.

Gibbons, A. 1992. "Plants of the apes" *Science* 255: 921.

Giesbrecht, A.M. 1960. "Sobre a ocorrência de bufotenina em semente de *Piptadenia falcata* Benth." *Anais da Associação Brasileira de Química* 19: 117–119.

Gilberti, F. and **L. Gregoretti** 1960. "Contributo alla studio psicofarmacologico delle depressioni e dell'ansia: Nota II. Ricerche con l'impiego della L.A.E. 32 e della psilocibina" *Le Sindromi Depressive.* Symposium volume, Rapallo, Italy.

Gilberti, G.C. 1983. "Herbal folk medicine in northwest Argentina: Compositae" *Journal of Ethnopharmacology* 7(3): 321–341.

Gilliland, K. and **D. Andress** 1981. "Ad lib caffeine consumption, symptoms of caffeinism, and academic performance" *American Journal of Psychiatry* 138(4): 512–514.

Gilmore, M.R. 1919. "Uses of plants by the Indians of the Missouri River region" *Thirty-third Annual Report of the Bureau of American Ethnology to the Smithsonian Institution.* U.S. Government Printing Office, Washington, D.C. Reprinted in 1977. University of Nebraska Press, Lincoln, NB.

Gilmour, L.P. and **R.D. O'Brien** 1967. "Psilocybin: Reaction with a fraction of rat brain" *Science* 155: 207–208.

Gils, C. van and **P.A. Cox** 1994. "Ethnobotany of nutmeg in the Spice Islands" *Journal of Ethnopharmacology* 42(2): 117–124.

Gimbutas, M. 1958. *Ancient Symbolism in Lithuanian Folk Art.* (Memoirs of the American Folklore Society, No. 49) American Folklore Society, Philadelphia, PA.

Gimbutas, M. 1974. *The Gods and Goddesses of Old Europe, 7000 to 3500 B.C.: Myths, Legends and Cult Images.* University of California Press, Berkeley, CA.

Girón, L.M. *et al.* 1991. "Ethnobotanical survey of the medicinal flora used by the Caribs of Guatemala" *Journal of Ethnopharmacology* 34(2,3): 173–187.

Gitte, S. *et al.* 1983. "Contributo alla conoscenza della micoflora psicotropa del territorio Bresciano" *Natura Bresciana* 20: 125–130.

Glassman, A.H. *et al.* 1984. "Cigarette craving, smoking withdrawal, and clonidine" *Science* 226: 864–866.

Gnirss, F. 1959. "Untersuchungen mit Psilocybin, einem Phantastikum aus dem mexikanischen Rauschpilz *Psilocybe mexicana*" *Schweizer Archiv der Neurologie und Psychiatrie* 84: 346–348.

Göbel, H. 1838. "Über die Gewinnung von einer rothen Farbstoffes aus den Samen der Pflanze *Peganum Harmala*" *Dinglers Polytechnisches Journal* 1938: 373–376.

Göbel, H. 1841. *Justus Liebig's Annalen der Chemie* 38: 363.

Gobley, M. 1860. "Recherches chimiques sur la racine de kava" *Journal de Pharmacie et de Chimie* 37: 19–23.

Gold, L.S. *et al.* 1992. "Rodent carcinogens: Setting priorities" *Science* 258: 261–265.

Goldman, I. 1963. *The Cubeo: Indians of the Northwest Amazon.* (Illinois Studies in Anthropology No. 2) University of Illinois Press, Urbana, IL.

Goldstein, A. and **S. Kaizer** 1969. "Psychotropic effects of caffeine in [wo]man. III. A questionnaire survey of coffee drinking and its effects on a group of housewives" *Clinical Pharmacology and Therapeutics* 10: 477–488.

Goldstein, A. and **H. Kalant** 1990. "Drug policy: Striking the right balance" *Science* 249: 1513–1521. See also: Hollister *et al.* 1991. Copyright © 1990, AAAS. Paid permission granted. See: Nadelmann 1989.

Goldstein, A. *et al.* 1969. "Psychotropic effects of caffeine in man. IV. Quantitative and qualitative differences associated with habituation to coffee" *Clinical Pharmacology and Therapeutics* 10: 489–497.

Golowin, S. 1973. *Die Magie der Verbotenen Märchen: Von Hexendrogen und Feenkräutern.* Merlin Verlag, Hamburg, Germany.

Golowin, S. 1991. "Psychedelische Volkskunde" In: Bauer, W. *et al.* (Eds.) *Der Fliegenpilz: Ein Kulturhistorisches Museum.* (Museum der Museen, Schriftenreihe des Karl Ernst Osthaus-Museums, Band 6) Wienand-Verlag, Köln, Germany. pp. 43–65.

Gonçalves de Lima, O. 1946. "Observações sôbre o 'vinho da Jurema' utilizado pelos índios Pancarú de Tacaratú (Pernambuco)" *Arquivos do Instituto de Pesquisas Agronómicas* 4: 45–80.

Gonçalves de Lima, O. 1956. *El Maguey y el Pulque en los Códices Mexicanos.* Fondo de Cultura Económica, México City.

González, J.G. *et al.* 1982. "Chuchuhuasha—A drug used in the Amazonian and Andean areas. A chemical study of *Maytenus* leaves" *Journal of Ethnopharmacology* 5(1): 73–77.

Good, R. *et al.* 1965. "Isolierung und Charakterisierung von Prämuscimol (=Ibotensäure) und Muscazon aus *Amanita muscaria*" *Helvetica Chimica Acta* 48: 927–930.

Goodman, S.M. and **J.J. Hobbs** 1988. "The ethnobotany of the Egyptian desert: A comparison of common plant usage between two culturally distinct Bedouin groups" *Journal of Ethnopharmacology* 23(1): 73–89.

Goodman, T. 1957. "Quest for the sacred" *Fate* 10(10): 30–43.

Goodspeed, T. 1954. *The Genus Nicotiana: Origins, Relationships, and Evolution of the Species in the Light of Their Distribution, Morphology, and Cytogenetics.* Chronica Botanica, Waltham, MA.

Gorman, P. 1992. "Peyote justice in New Mexico" *High Times.* July issue.

Gorman, P. 1993. "Sciamanesimo tra i Matses" *Altrove* 1: 47–63.

Göth, H. *et al.* 1967. "2(^{3}H)-Oxazolone durch Photoumlagerung von 3-Hydroxyisoxazolen. Synthese von Muscazon" *Helvetica Chimica Acta* 50: 137–142.

Gottlieb, O.R. 1979. "Chemical studies on medicinal Myristicaceae from Amazonia" *Journal of Ethnopharmacology* 1(4): 309–323.

Gotu, M. *et al.* 1958. "Studies on useful components of natural sources. XVII. Studies on uterus contracting ingredients in plants. (2). On uterus contracting ingredients in *Lespedeza bicolor* Turcz. var. *japonica* Nakai" *Yakugaku Zasshi* 78(5): 464–467.

Gracie and **Zarkov** 1985A. "DMT: How and why to get off" *Notes from the Underground* 3: 1–6.

Gracie and **Zarkov** 1985B. "Three β-carboline containing plants as potentiators of synthetic DMT and other indole psychedelics" *Notes from the Underground* 7: 1–8.

Gracie and **Zarkov** 1986. "An Indo-European plant teacher" *Notes from the Underground* 10: 1–5.

Grattan, F.J.H. 1948. *An Introduction to Samoan Customs.* Samoa Publishing Co., Apia, Western Samoa.

Graves, R. 1957. "Mushrooms, food of the gods" *Atlantic Monthly* 200(2): 73–77.

Graves, R. 1962. "A journey to paradise: Of toadstools and toxins, and a vivid tour of the Heaven (and Hell) that lies within us all" *Holiday* 32(2): 36–37; 100–111. French translation 1962, "Je suis alle au paradis" *Planète.* Nov.-Dec. issue. pp. 54–63.

Greden, J.F. 1974. "Anxiety or caffeinism. A diagnostic dilemma" *American Journal of Psychiatry* 131(10): 1089–1092.

Green, R.C. 1959. "Nutmeg poisoning" *Journal of the American Medical Association* 171: 1342–1344.

Greene, M.T. 1992. *Natural Knowledge in Preclassical Antiquity.* Johns Hopkins University Press, Baltimore, MD.

Griffith, J.D. *et al.* 1970. "Psychosis induced by the administration of *d*-amphetamine to human volunteers" In: Efron, D.H. (Ed.) *Psychotomimetic [sic] Drugs.* Raven Press, New York. pp. 287–298.

Griffith, W.J. 1976. "Agronomic evaluation of *Datura candida*—A new source of hyoscine" *Economic Botany* 30(4): 361–369.

Grina, J.A. *et al.* 1982. "Constituents of *Zanthoxylum*. Part 7. Old and new alkaloids from *Zanthoxylum arborescens*" *Journal of Organic Chemistry* 47(13): 2648–2651.

Grinspoon, L. 1977. *Marihuana [sic] Reconsidered.* Second edition revised. Harvard University Press, Cambridge, MA.

Grinspoon, L. and **J.B. Bakalar** 1976. *Cocaine: A Drug and its Social Evolution.* Basic Books, New York.

Grinspoon, L. and **J.B. Bakalar** 1979. *Psychedelic Drugs Reconsidered.* Basic Books, New York. Reprinted in 1981 with "Annotated Bibliography," pp. 313–374.

Grinspoon, L. and **J.B. Bakalar** 1993. *Marihuana, [sic] the Forbidden Medicine.* Yale University Press, New Haven, CT.

Grob, C. 1995. "Psychiatric research with hallucinogens: What have we learned?" *Jahrbuch für Ethnomedizin und Bewußtseinsforschung* 3: 91–112.

Grob, C. and **M. Dobkin de Ríos** 1992. "Adolescent drug use in cross-cultural perspective" *The Journal of Drug Issues* 22(1): 121–138.

Grof, S. 1973. "Theoretical and empirical basis of transpersonal psychology and psychotherapy: Observations from LSD research" *Journal of Transpersonal Psychology* 5: 15.

Grof, S. 1975. *Realms of the Human Unconscious: Observations from LSD Research.* The Viking Press (An Esalen Book), New York. German translation, 1988. *Topographie des Unbewußten: LSD im Dienst der Tiefenpsychologischen Forschung.* Klett-Cotta, Stuttgart, Germany. Portuguese 1987. *Além Do Cérebro.* São Paulo, Brasil.

Grof, S. 1980. *LSD Psychotherapy.* Hunter House, Alameda, CA. Reprint in 1994.

Grof, S. and **J. Halifax** 1977. *The Human*

Encounter with Death. E.P. Dutton, New York. Foreword by Elisabeth Kübler-Ross, pp. VI–VIII. Translated into German, 1980. *Die Begegnung mit dem Tod.* Klett-Cotta, Stuttgart, Germany.

Grof, S. *et al.* 1973. "DPT as an adjunct in psychotherapy of alcoholics" *International Pharmacopsychiatry* 8: 104–115.

Gröger, D. 1963. "Über das Vorkommen von Ergolinderivaten in *Ipomoea*-Arten" *Flora* 153(2): 373–382.

Gröger, D. *et al.* 1963. "Zur Biogenese von Ergolin-Derivaten in *Ipomoea rubro-caerulea* Hook" *Zeitschrift für Naturforschung* 18B(12): 1123–1124.

Grotjahn, D.B. 1983. "Synthesis and characterization of 5-*H*-1,3-dioxolo[4,5-*f*]-indoleethylamines" *Journal of Heterocyclic Chemistry* 20: 1031–1036.

Guerra, F. and **H. Olivera** 1954. *Las Plantas Fantásticas de México.* Imprenta el Diario Español, México City.

Guggisberg, H. 1954. *Mutterkorn. Vom Gift zum Heilstoff.* S. Karger, Basel, Switzerland.

Gunn, J.A. 1937. "The harmine group of alkaloids" In: Hübner, W. and J. Schüller (Eds.) *Handbuch der Experimentellen Pharmakologie.* Vol. 5. Springer Verlag, Berlin, Germany. pp. 184–196.

Gunther, E. 1981. *Ethnobotany of Western Washington: The Knowledge and Use of Indigenous Plants by Native Americans.* University of Washington Press, Seattle, WA.

Gupta, M.P. *et al.* 1979. "The occurrence of tryptamine and *N*-methyltryptamine in *Mimosa somnians*" *Journal of Natural Products* 42(2): 234–236.

Gupta, M.P. *et al.* 1985. "Safrole, the main component of the essential oil from *Piper auritum*" *Journal of Natural Products* 48 (2): 330–343.

Gutiérrez-Noriega, C. and **G. Cruz-Sánchez** 1947. "Alteraciones mentales producidas por la *Opuntia cylindrica*" *Revista Neuro-Psiquiátrica* 10: 422–468.

Guttmann, E. 1936. "Artificial psychoses [*sic*] produced by mescaline" *Journal of Mental Science* 82: 1–19.

Guttmann, E. and **W.S. Maclay** 1936. "Mescaline and depersonalization, therapeutic experiments" *Journal of Neurology and Psychopathology* 16: 193–212.

Guzmán, G. 1958. "El habitat de *Psilocybe muliercula* Singer & Smith (=*Ps. wassonii* Heim), agaricáceo alucinógeno mexicano" *Revista de la Sociedad Mexicana de Historia Natural* 19(1-4): 215–229.

Guzmán, G. 1976. Personal communications, México City.

Guzmán, G. 1983. *The Genus Psilocybe: A Systematic Revision of the Known Species Including the History, Distribution and Chemistry of the Hallucinogenic Species. Beihefte zur Nova Hedwigia Heft 74.* J. Cramer, Vaduz, Germany.

Guzmán, G. 1990. "Wasson and the development of mycology in Mexico" In: Riedlinger, T.J. (Ed.) *The Sacred Mushroom Seeker: Essays for R. Gordon Wasson.* Ethnomycological Studies No. 11. Dioscorides Press, Portland, OR. pp. 83–110.

Guzmán, G. 1992. "The sacred mushroom in Mesoamerica" In: Miyanishi, T. (Ed.) *The Ancient Maya and Hallucinogens.* Wakayama University, Wakayama, Japan. pp. 75–95.

Guzmán, G. 1995. "Supplement to the monograph of the genus *Psilocybe*" *Bibliotheca Mycologica* 159: 91–141.

Guzmán, G. and **J. Ott** 1976. "Description and chemical analysis of a new species of hallucinogenic *Psilocybe* from the Pacific Northwest" *Mycologia* 68(6): 1261–1267.

Guzmán, G. and **S.H. Pollock** 1978. "A new bluing species of *Psilocybe* from Florida" *Mycotaxon* 7: 373–376.

Guzmán, G. *et al.* 1976. "Psychotropic mycoflora of Washington, Idaho, Oregon,

California and British Columbia" *Mycologia* 68(6): 1267–1272.

Guzmán, G. *et al.* 1988. "Nuevos registros de los hongos alucinógenos del género *Psilocybe* en México y análisis de la distribución de las especies conocidas" *Revista Mexicana de Micología* 4: 255–265.

Guzmán, G. *et al.* 1991. "A new species of *Psilocybe* of section *Zapotecorum* from New Zealand" *Mycological Research* 95(4): 507–508.

Guzmán, G. *et al.* 1993. "A new bluing *Psilocybe* from Thailand" *Mycotaxon* 46: 155–160.

Haard, R. and **K. Haard** 1975. *Poisonous and Hallucinogenic Mushrooms.* Cloudburst Press, Seattle, WA. Second edition, 1977.

Hajicek-Dobberstein, S. 1995. "Soma siddhas and alchemical enlightenment: Psychedelic mushrooms in Buddhist tradition" *Journal of Ethnopharmacology* 48(2): 99–118.

Halifax, J. 1979. *Shamanic Voices: A Survey of Visionary Narratives.* E.P. Dutton, New York. Translated into German, 1979. *Die Andere Wirklichkeit der Schamanen.* Bern, Switzerland. Spanish translation, 1995. *Las Voces del Chamán.* Editorial Diana, México.

Halifax, J. 1982. *Shaman: The Wounded Healer.* (The Illustrated Library of Sacred Imagination; J. Purce, Ed.) Crossroad, New York. Translated into German, 1983. *Schamanen.* Frankfurt, Germany.

Hall, R. *et al.* 1977. "Angel's trumpet psychosis: A central nervous system anticholinergic syndrome" *American Journal of Psychiatry* 134: 312–314.

Haller, A. and **E. Heckel** 1901. "Sur l'ibogaïne, principe actif d'une plante du genre *Tabernaemontana* originaire du Congo" *Comptes Rendus Hebdomadaires des Séances de l'Académie des Sciences* 133: 850–853.

Halpern, L. 1930A. "Der Wirkungsmechanismus des Harmins und der Pathophysiologie der Parkinsonehen Krankheit" *Deutscher Medizinischer Wochenschrift* 56: 651–655.

Halpern, L. 1930B. "Über die Harminwirkung im Selbstversuch" *Deutscher Medizinischer Wochenschrift* 56: 1252–1254.

Halstead, B. 1978. *Poisonous and Venomous Marine Animals of the World.* Darwin Press, Princeton, NJ.

Hamel, P.B. and **M.U. Chiltoskey** 1975. *Cherokee Plants.* Herald Publishing Co., Sylva, NC.

Hamilton, D.P. 1990. "Still flying blind in the war on drugs" *Science* 250: 28.

Hamilton, D.P. 1992. "Clean needles puncture ADAMHA plan" *Science* 256: 1383.

Handovsky, H. 1920. "Ein Alkaloid in Gifte von *Bufo vulgaris*" *Archiv für Experimentelle Pathologie und Pharmakologie* 86: 138–158.

Haney, A. and **B.B. Kutscheid** 1973. "Quantitative variation in the chemical constituents of marihuana [*sic*] from stands of naturalized *Cannabis sativa* in east-central Illinois" *Economic Botany* 27(2): 193–203.

Hänsel, R. 1968. "Characterization and physiological activity of some kava constituents" *Pacific Science* 22: 369–373.

Hänsel, R. *et al.* 1966. "Fungistatische Wirkung der Kavadroge und ihrer Inhaltßtoffe" *Planta Medica* 14(1): 1–9.

Hansen, H.A. (Translation by M. Cross) 1978. *The Witch's Garden.* Unity Press-Michael Kesend, Santa Cruz, CA. Foreword to the English edition by Richard Evans Schultes, pp. IX–XII. Originally published as *Heksens Urtegård.* Laurens Bogtrykkeri, Tønder, Denmark, 1976.

Harlan, J.R. 1986. "Lettuce and the sycamore: Sex and romance in ancient Egypt" *Economic Botany* 40(1): 4–15.

Harner, M. 1972. *The Jívaro:* [*sic*] *People of the Sacred Waterfalls.* University of California Press, Berkeley, CA.

Harner, M.J. (Ed.) 1973A. *Hallucinogens and Shamanism.* Oxford University Press, London, England. Translated into Spanish, 1976. *Alucinógenos y Chamanismo.* Punto Omega Guardarama, Madrid, Spain.

Harner, M.J. 1973B. "The sound of rushing water" In: Harner, M.J. (Ed.) *Hallucinogens and Shamanism.* Oxford University Press, London, England. pp. 15–27. Originally published in *Natural History* 77(6): 28–33 *et seq.*

Harner, M.J. 1973C. "The role of hallucinogenic plants in European witchcraft" In: Harner, M.J. (Ed.) *Hallucinogens and Shamanism.* Oxford University Press, London, England. pp. 125–150.

Harner, M.J. 1973D. "Common themes in South American Indian *yagé* experiences" In: Harner, M.J. (Ed.) *Hallucinogens and Shamanism.* Oxford University Press, London, England. pp. 155–175.

Harris, B. 1976. *Growing Wild Mushrooms: A Complete Guide to Cultivating Edible and Hallucinogenic Mushrooms.* Wingbow Press, Berkeley, CA. Second edition in 1978.

Harris, M. 1974. "Broomsticks and sabbats" In: *Cows, Pigs, Wars, and Witches: The Riddles of Culture.* Random House, New York. pp. 207–221.

Harris, W.F. and **D.W. Filmer** 1947. "A recent outbreak of honey poisoning. Part VI. Botanical investigations of pollen and nectar flora" *New Zealand Journal of Science and Technology* 29(3): 134–143.

Harrison McKenna, K. 1989. "Plant collecting in Thailand—January 1989" *Whole Earth Review* 64: 32–33.

Harsh, M.I. and **T.N. Nag** 1984. "Anti-microbial principles from in vitro tissue culture of *Peganum harmala*" *Journal of Natural Products* 47(2): 365–367.

Hart, J.A. 1976. *Montana—Native Plants and Early Peoples.* Montana Historical Society and Montana Bicentennial Administration, Helena, MT.

Hart, J.A. 1981. "The ethnobotany of the northern Cheyenne Indians of Montana" *Journal of Ethnopharmacology* 4(1): 1–55.

Hartwich, C. 1911. *Die Menschlichen Genußmittel: Ihre Herkunft, Verbreitung, Geschichte, Anwendung, Bestandteile und Wirkung.* Chr. Herm. Tauschnitz, Leipzig, Germany.

Hartzell, H. 1991. *The Yew Tree: A Thousand Whispers. Biography of a Species.* Hulogosi, Eugene, OR. Afterword by Jerry Rust, pp. 281–282.

Harvey, D.J. 1990. "Stability of cannabinoids in dried samples of Cannabis dated from around 1896–1905" *Journal of Ethnopharmacology* 28(1): 117–128.

Haseneier, M. (Pseudonym for Martin Hanslmeier) 1990. "Mykographie einer Wiese in der Hohen Rhön" *Eschenau Summer Press Publications* 29: 728–743.

Haseneier, M. (Pseudonym for Martin Hanslmeier) 1992. "Der Kahlkopf und das kollektive Unbewußte—Einige Anmerkungen zur archetypischen Dimension des Pilzes" *Integration: Zeitschrift für Geistbewegende Pflanzen und Kultur* 2&3: 5–38.

Hashimoto, Y. and **K. Kawanishi** 1975. "New organic bases from Amazonian *Banisteriopsis caapi*" *Phytochemistry* 14: 1633–1635.

Hashimoto, Y. and **K. Kawanishi** 1976. "New alkaloids from *Banisteriopsis caapi*" *Phytochemistry* 15: 1559–1560.

Hassan, I. 1967. "Some folk uses of *Peganum harmala* in India and Pakistan" *Economic Botany* 21(4): 384.

Hastorf, C.A. 1987. "Archaeological evidence of coca (*Erythroxylum coca*, Erythroxylaceae) in the Upper Mantaro Valley, Peru" *Economic Botany* 41(2): 292–301.

Hatfield, G.M. and **L.R. Brady** 1969. "Occurrence of bis-noryangonin in *Gymnopilus spectabilis*" *Journal of Pharmaceutical Sciences* 58(10): 1298–1299.

Hatfield, G.M. and **L.R. Brady** 1971. "Occurrence of bis-noryangonin and hispidin in *Gymnopilus* species" *Lloydia* 34(2): 260–263.

Hatfield, G.M. and **L.R. Brady** 1975. "Toxins of higher fungi" *Lloydia* 38(1): 36–55.

Hatfield, G.M. *et al.* 1977. "Proceedings—Isolation of psilocybin from the hallucinogenic mushroom *Gymnopilus validipes*" *Lloydia* 40: 619.

Hatfield, G.M. *et al.* 1978. "The occurrence of psilocybin in *Gymnopilus* species" *Lloydia* 41(2): 140–144.

Hayman, J. 1985. "Datura poisoning—The Angel's Trumpet" *Pathology* 17: 465–466.

Hayter, A. 1968. *Opium and the Romantic Imagination.* University of California Press, Berkeley, CA.

Hazlett, D.L. 1986. "Ethnobotanical observations from Cabecar and Guaymí settlements in Central America" *Economic Botany* 40(3): 339–352.

Hazslinszky, B. 1956. "Toxische Wirkung eines Honigs der Tollkirsche (*Atropa belladonna* L)" *Zeitschrift für Bienenforschung* 3(5): 93–96. There followed a note in 1957 under same title, 3(10): 240.

Hazum, E. *et al.* 1981. "Morphine in cow and human milk: Could dietary morphine constitute a ligand for specific morphine (μ) receptors?" *Science* 213: 1010–1012.

Heard, G. 1963. "Can this drug enlarge man's mind?" *The Psychedelic Review* 1 (1): 7–17. Reprinted in Weil, G.M. *et al.* (Eds.) 1965. *The Psychedelic Reader.* University Books, New York. pp. 1–11 [reprint 1996].

Hedberg, I. *et al.* 1982. "Inventory of plants used in traditional medicine in Tanzania. I. Plants of the families Acanthaceae—Cucurbitaceae" *Journal of Ethnopharmacology* 6(1): 29–60.

Heffter, A. 1896. "Ueber Cacteenalkaloïde. (II. Mittheilung.)" *Berichte der Deutschen Chemischen Gesellschaft* 29: 216–227.

Heffter, A. 1898. "Über Pellote. Beiträge zur chemischen und pharmakologischen Kenntnis der Cacteen. Zweite Mittheilung" *Archiv für Experimentelle Pathologie und Pharmakologie* 40: 385–429.

Heidel, A. 1946. *The Gilgamesh Epic and New Testament Parallels.* University of Chicago Press, Chicago, IL.

Heim, R. 1956A. "Les champignons divinatoires utilisés dan les rites des Indiens Mazatèques, recueillis au cours de leur premier voyage au Mexique, en 1953, par Mme. Valentina Pavlovna Wasson et M. R. Gordon Wasson" *Comptes Rendus Hebdomadaires des Séances de l'Académie des Sciences* 242: 965–968. Reprinted in 1957 in *Revue de Mycologie* 22(1): 58–62; and in Heim, R. 1957. *Notes Préliminaires sur les Agarics Hallucinogènes du Mexique* [has sold for $225]. Muséum National d'Histoire Naturelle, Paris, France. pp. 1–5.

Heim, R. 1956B. "Les champignons divinatoires recueillis par Mme. Valentina Pavlovna Wasson et M. R. Gordon Wasson au cours de leurs missions de 1954 et 1955 dans les pays mije, mazatèque, zapotèque et nahua du Mexique méridional et central" *Comptes Rendus Hebdomadaires des Séances de l'Académie des Sciences* 242: 1389–1395. Reprinted in 1957 in *Revue de Mycologie* 22(1): 62–70; and in Heim, R. 1957. *Notes Préliminaires sur les Agarics Hallucinogènes du Mexique* [worth $225]. Muséum National d'Histoire Naturelle, Paris, France. pp. 5–13.

Heim, R. 1957A. "Sur les *Psilocybes* hallucinatoires des Aztèques et sur le microendémisme des Agarics utilisés par les Indiens du Mexique à des fins divinatoires" *Comptes Rendus Hebdomadaires des Séances de l'Académie des Sciences* 245: 1761–1765. Reprinted in 1957 in *Revue de Mycologie* 22(3): 300–305; and in Heim, R. *et al.* 1958. *Nouvelles Observations sur les Agarics Hallucinogènes du Mexique.* Muséum National d'Histoire Naturelle, Paris. pp. 3–8.

Heim, R. 1957B. "A l'ergot de seigle, qui fit 'le mal des ardents,' devrons-nous la guérison des psychoses?" *Chronique Scientifique, Figaro Littéraire.* 28 September 1957. Reprinted in 1957 in *Revue de Mycologie* 22(2): 203–207; and in Heim, R. 1957. *Notes Préliminaires sur les Agarics Hallucinogènes du Mexique* [worth $225]. Muséum National d'Histoire Naturelle, Paris, France. pp. 42–46.

Heim, R. 1957C. "Les Agarics hallucinogènes du genre *Psilocybe* recueillis au cours de notre récente mission dans le Mexique méridional et central en compagnie de M. R. Gordon Wasson" *Comptes Rendus Hebdomadaires des Séances de l'Académie des Sciences* 244: 695–700. Reprinted in *Revue de Mycologie* 22(1): 70–76; and in Heim, R. 1957. *Notes Préliminaires sur les Agarics Hallucinogènes du Mexique* [worth $225]. Muséum National d'Histoire Naturelle, Paris, France. pp. 13–19.

Heim, R. 1957D. "Analyse de quelques expériences personelles produites par l'ingestion des Agarics hallucinogènes du Mexique" *Comptes Rendus Hebdomadaires des Séances de l'Académie des Sciences* 245: 597–603. Reprinted in 1957 in *Revue de Mycologie* 22(2): 189–197; and in Heim, R. 1957. *Notes Préliminaires sur les Agarics Hallucinogènes du Mexique* [worth $225]. Museúm National d'Histoire Naturelle, Paris, France. pp. 28–36.

Heim, R. 1958. "Diagnose latine du *Psilocybe Wassonii* Heim, espèce hallucinogène des Aztèques" *Revue de Mycologie* 23(1): 119–120. Reprinted in Heim, R. *et al.* 1958. *Nouvelles Observations sur les Agarics Hallucinogènes du Mexique.* Muséum National d'Histoire Naturelle, Paris. pp. 22–23.

Heim, R. 1961. "La psilocybine en psychiatrie et au-delà (à propos de la thèse de Mademoiselle Anne-Marie Quétin)" *Revue de Mycologie* 26(1): 42–60.

Heim, R. 1963. "Diagnoses latines des espèces de champignons, ou *nonda*, associés à la folie du *komugl taï* et du *ndaadl*" *Revue de Mycologie* 28(3-4): 277–283.

Heim, R. 1965. "Les champignons associés à la folie des Kuma. Étude descriptive et iconographie" *Cahiers du Pacifique* 7: 7–64.

Heim, R. 1966. "Le *Boletus flammeus*" *Cahiers du Pacifique* 9: 67–69.

Heim, R. 1973. "Une nouvelle contribution à la connaissance de la folie fongique des Papous" *Cahiers du Pacifique* 17: 31–39.

Heim, R. 1978. *Les Champignons Toxiques et Hallucinogènes.* Société Nouvelle des Éditions Boubée, Paris. Originally published in 1963.

Heim, R. and **R. Cailleux** 1957. "Culture pure et obtention semi-industrielle des Agarics hallucinogènes du Mexique" *Comptes Rendus Hebdomadaires des Séances de l'Académie des Sciences* 244: 3109–3114. Reprinted in 1957 in *Revue de Mycologie* 22(2): 183–189; and in Heim, R. 1957. *Notes Préliminaires sur les Agarics Hallucinogènes du Mexique* [worth $225]. Muséum National d'Histoire Naturelle, Paris, France. pp. 22–28.

Heim, R. and **R. Cailleux** 1959. "Nouvelle contribution à la connaissance des *Psilocybes* hallucinogènes du Mexique" *Comptes Rendus Hebdomadaires des Séances de l'Académie des Sciences* 249: 1842–1845. Reprinted in 1959 in *Revue de Mycologie* 24(5): 437–441; and in Heim, R. 1962. *Deuxième Supplément aus Observations sur les Agarics Hallucinogènes du Mexique.* Muséum National d'Histoire Naturelle, Paris, France.

Heim, R. and **A. Hofmann** 1958. "Isolement de la psilocybine à partir du *Stropharia cubensis* Earle et d'autres espèces de champignons hallucinogènes mexicains appartenant au genre *Psilocybe*" *Comptes Rendus Hebdomadaires des Séances de l'Ac-

adémie des Sciences 247: 557–561. Reprinted in 1958 in *Revue de Mycologie* 23(3): 347–351; and in Heim, R. *et al.* 1958. *Nouvelles Observations sur les Agarics Hallucinogènes du Mexique.* Muséum National d'Histoire Naturelle, Paris, France. pp. 24–28.

Heim, R. and **A. Hofmann** 1958[9]. "La psilocybine et la psilocine chez les *Psilocybes* et *Strophaires* hallucinogènes" In: Heim, R. and R.G. Wasson. *Les Champignons Hallucinogènes du Mexique. Études Ethnologiques, Taxinomiques, Biologiques, Physiologiques et Chimiques.* Archives du Muséum National d'Histoire Naturelle, Séries 7, Vol. vi, Paris, France. pp. 258–262.

Heim, R. and **P. Thévenard** 1967. "Expériences nouvelles d'ingestion des Psilocybes hallucinogènes" In: Heim, R. *et al.* 1967. *Nouvelles Investigations sur les Champignons Hallucinogènes.* Muséum National d'Histoire Naturelle, Paris, France. pp. 201–211.

Heim, R. and **R.G. Wasson** 1958[9]. *Les Champignons Hallucinogènes du Mexique. Études Ethnologiques, Taxinomiques, Biologiques, Physiologiques et Chimiques.* Archives du Muséum National d'Histoire Naturelle, Series 7, Vol. vi, Paris, France. Originally priced at $64, has sold for as much as $850 with Heim *et al.* 1967.

Heim, R. and **R.G. Wasson** 1962. "Une investigation sur les champignons sacrés des Mixtèques" *Comptes Rendus Hebdomadaires des Séances de l'Académie des Sciences* 254: 788–791.

Heim, R. and **R.G. Wasson** 1964. "Note préliminaire sur la folie fongique des Kuma" *Comptes Rendus Hebdomadaires des Séances de l'Académie des Sciences* 258: 1593–1598.

Heim, R. and **R.G. Wasson** 1965. "The 'mushroom madness' of the Kuma" *Botanical Museum Leaflets* Harvard University 21(1): 1–36.

Heim, R. and **R.G. Wasson** 1970. "Les Putka des Santals: Champignons doués d'une ame" *Cahiers du Pacifique* 14: 59–85.

Heim, R. *et al.* 1958. "Detérminisme de la formation des carpophores et des sclérotes dans la culture du *Psilocybe mexicana* Heim, Agaric hallucinogène du Mexique, et mise en évidence de la psilocybine et de la psilocine" *Comptes Rendus Hebdomadaires des Séances de l'Académie des Sciences* 246: 1346–1351. Reprinted in 1958 in *Revue de Mycologie* 23(1): 106–113; and in Heim, R. *et al.* 1958. *Nouvelles Observations sur les Agarics Hallucinogènes du Mexique.* Muséum National d'Histoire Naturelle, Paris, France. pp. 9–16.

Heim, R. *et al.* 1966. "Sur une intoxication collective à syndrome psilocybiene causée en France par un *Copelandia*" *Comptes Rendus Hebdomadaires des Séances de l'Académie des Sciences* 262: 519–523.

Heim, R. *et al.* 1967. *Nouvelles Investigations sur les Champignons Hallucinogènes.* Muséum National d'Histoire Naturelle, Paris, France. Has sold for $850 as a set with Heim & Wasson 1958[9].

Heimann, H. 1952. *Die Scopolaminwirkung.* S. Karger, Basel, Switzerland.

Heimann, H. 1961. "Ausdrucksphänomenologie der Modellpsychosen (Psilocybin)" *Psychiatria et Neurologia* (Basel) 141: 69–100.

Heimann, H. 1962. "Zur Behandlung therapieresistenter Neurosen mit Modellpsychosen (Psilocybin)" *Schweizer Archiv der Neurologie und Psychiatrie* 89: 214–220.

Heinrich, C. 1992. "*Amanita muscaria* and the penis of god, an extract of a work in progress" *Integration: Zeitschrift für Geistbewegende Pflanzen und Kultur* 2&3: 55–62.

Heinrich, C. 1995. *Strange Fruit: Alchemy, Religion, and Magical Foods. A Speculative History.* Bloomsbury, London, England. Appendix "The legend of Miskwedo" by Keewaydinoquay (1979), pp. 201–203.

Heinrich, M. *et al.* 1992. "Indigenous phytotherapy of gastrointestinal disorders in a lowland Mixe community (Oaxaca, Mexico): Ethnopharmacologic evaluation" *Journal of Ethnopharmacology* 36(1): 63–80.

Heiser, C.B., Jr. 1987. *The Fascinating World of the Nightshades: Tobacco, Mandrake, Potato, Tomato, Pepper, Eggplant, Etc.* Dover Publications, New York.

Heizer, R.F. 1944. "Mixtum Compositum: The use of narcotic [*sic*] mushrooms by primitive peoples" *Ciba Symposia* 5(11): 1713–1716.

Helfrich, P. and **A. Banner** 1960. "Hallucinatory mullet poisoning" *Journal of Tropical Medicine and Hygiene.* April issue. pp. 86–89.

Helmer, J. 1975. *Drugs and Minority Oppression.* The Seabury Press, New York.

Henderson, L.A. and **W.J. Glass** (Eds.) 1994. *LSD: Still With Us After All These Years.* Lexington Books, New York.

Henman, A.R. 1978. *Mama Coca.* See: Antonil 1978.

Henman, A.R. 1982. "Guaraná (*Paullinia cupana* var. *sorbilis*): Ecological and social perspectives on an economic plant of the central Amazon basin" *Journal of Ethnopharmacology* 6(3): 311–338.

Henman, A.R. 1986. "Uso del ayahuasca en un contexto autoritario. El caso de la *União do Vegetal* en Brasil" *América Indígena* 46(1): 219–234.

Henman, A.R. (Ed.) 1990. *The Anti-Prohibitionist Review.* No. 1, January 1990.

Hennings, P. 1888. "Eine giftige Kaktee, *Anhalonium lewinii* n. sp." *Gartenflora* 37: 410–412.

Henry, T.A. 1949. *The Alkaloids.* J. Churchill and A. Churchill, London, England.

Herald, G.W. 1958. "The truth about the 'Devil's drugs'" *Real.* February issue. pp. 16 *et seq.*

Herer, J. 1990. *The Emperor Wears No Clothes—Hemp and the Marijuana Conspiracy.* Hemp Publishing, Los Angeles, CA. French translation, 1993. *L'Empereur est Nu.* Les Éditions du Lézard, Paris, France.

Hernández, F. 1651. *Nova Plantarum, Animalium et Mineralium Mexicanorum Historia.* Deversini and Masotti, Rome, Italy. Spanish translation in 1959, *Historia Natural de la Nueva España.* Two volumes. Universidad Nacional Autónoma de México, México City. Original 1577.

Herrera, T. 1967. "Consideraciones sobre el efecto de los hongos alucinógenos mexicanos" *Neurología–Neurocirugía–Psiquiatría* 8(2): 101–123.

Herrick, J.W. 1977. *Iroquois Medical Botany.* Thesis, Univ. Microfilms, Ann Arbor, MI.

Hesse, O. 1901. "Über die Alkaloide der Mandragorawurzel" *Journal für Praktische Chemie* 64: 274–286.

Heyl, G. 1928. "Über das Alkaloid von *Carnegiea gigantea* (Engelm.) Britt. and Rose (*Cereus giganteus* Englem.)" *Archiv der Pharmazie* 266: 668–673.

Hill, W.W. 1938. "Navajo use of Jimsonweed" *New Mexico Anthropologist* 3(2): 19–21.

Hillig, K. 1993. Personal communication, letter dated 12 January.

Hindmarch, J. *et al.* 1979. "The effects of an ergot alkaloid derivative (Hydergine) on aspects of psychomotor performance, arousal, and cognitive processing ability" *The Journal of Clinical Pharmacology* 19: 726–732.

Hirschhorn, H.H. 1983. "Botanical remedies of the former Dutch East Indies (Indonesia). Part II. Dicotyledons up to and including Leguminosae" *Journal of Ethnopharmacology* 8(1): 65–96.

Hively, R.L. *et al.* 1966. "Isolation of *trans*-Δ^6-tetrahydrocannabinol from marijuana" *Journal of the American Chemical Society* 88: 1832–1833.

Hochstein, F.A. and **A.M. Paradies** 1957.

"Alkaloids of *Banisteria caapi* and *Prestonia amazonicum* [*sic*]" *Journal of the American Chemical Society* 79: 5735–5736.

Hoffecker, J.F. *et al.* 1993. "The colonization of Beringia and the peopling of the New World" *Science* 259: 46–53. My "Technical Comment" to *Science* in response, "Colonization of the New World: A spiritual barrier?" was summarily rejected.

Hoffer, A. 1970. "Treatment of alcoholics with psychedelic therapy" In: Aaronson, B. and H. Osmond (Eds.) *Psychedelics: The Uses and Implications of Hallucinogenic Drugs.* Doubleday/Anchor, Garden City, NJ. pp 357–366.

Hoffer, A. and **H. Osmond** 1967. *The Hallucinogens.* Academic Press, New York. With "Animal studies of hallucinogenic drugs" by T. Weckowicz. pp. 555–594.

Hoffmann, D. *et al.* 1986. "Carcinogenic agents in snuff" *Journal of the National Cancer Institute* 76(3): 435–437.

Hofmann, A. 1955. "Die Geschichte des LSD-25" *Triangel Sandoz Zeitschrift für Medizinische Wißenschaften* 2(3): 117–124.

Hofmann, A. 1960. "Die psychotropen Wirkstoffe der mexikanischen Zauberpilze" *Chimia* 14: 309–318.

Hofmann, A. 1961. "Die Wirkstoffe der mexikanischen Zauberdroge 'Ololiuqui'" *Planta Medica* 9(4): 354–367.

Hofmann, A. 1963A. "The active principles of the seeds of *Rivea corymbosa* and *Ipomoea violacea*" *Botanical Museum Leaflets* Harvard University 20(6): 194–212; also published in *The Psychedelic Review* 1(3): 302–316. Reprinted in 1966 as "The active principles of the seeds of *Rivea corymbosa* (L.) Hall. f. (*Ololiuqui*, *Badoh*) and *Ipomoea tricolor* Cav. (*Badoh* negro)" In: Jiménez Moreno, W. *et al.* (Eds.) *Summa Antropológica en Homenaje a Roberto J. Weitlaner.* Instituto Nacional de Antropología e Historia, INAH, México City.

Hofmann, A. 1963B. "Psychotomimetic [*sic*] substances" *Indian Journal of Pharmacology* 25: 245–256.

Hofmann, A. 1964. *Die Mutterkornalkaloide.* F. Enke Verlag, Stuttgart, Germany.

Hofmann, A. 1966. "Alcaloïdes indoliques isolés des plantes hallucinogènes et narcotiques [*sic*] du Mexique" *Colloques Internationaux du Centre National de la Recherche Scientifique* 144: 223–241.

Hofmann, A. 1967. "Psycho-aktive Stoffe aus Pflanzen" *Therapie Woche* 17: 1739–1746.

Hofmann, A. 1968. "Psychotomimetic [*sic*] agents" In: Burger, A. (Ed.) *Chemical Constituents and Pharmacological Action.* Dekker, New York. pp. 169–235.

Hofmann, A. 1970A. "Les hallucinogènes" *La Recherche* 1(3): 239–257.

Hofmann, A. 1970B. "The discovery of LSD and subsequent investigations on naturally occurring hallucinogens" In: Ayd, F. J. and B. Blackwell (Eds.) *Discoveries in Biological Psychiatry.* Lippincott, Philadelphia, PA. Chapter 7.

Hofmann, A. 1971. "Le teonanácatl et l'ololiuqui, deux anciennes drogues magiques du Mexique" *Bulletin des Stupéfiants* 23(1): 3–14. Also in English version, 1971. "Teonanacatl and ololiuqui: Two ancient magic drugs of Mexico" *Bulletin on Narcotics* 23(1): 3–14.

Hofmann, A. 1977. Personal communications, Port Townsend, WA.

Hofmann, A. 1978A. "A challenging question and my answer" In: Wasson, R.G. *et al.* *The Road to Eleusis: Unveiling the Secret of the Mysteries.* Ethno-mycological Studies No. 4. Harcourt Brace Jovanovich, New York. pp. 25–34. Translated into Spanish by F. Garrido, 1980. "Una pregunta inquietante, y mi respuesta" *El Camino a Eleusis: Una Solución al Enigma de los Misterios.* Fondo de Cultura Económica, México City. pp. 35–52.

Hofmann, A. 1978B. "History of the basic chemical investigations on the sacred mushrooms of Mexico" In: Ott, J. and J. Bigwood (Eds.) *Teonanácatl: Hallucinogenic Mushrooms of North America.* (Psycho-Mycological Studies No. 2) Madrona Publishers, Seattle, WA. pp. 47–61. Translated into Spanish by M.S. Antolín, 1985. "Historia de las investigaciones químicas básicas sobre los hongos sagrados de México" *Teonanácatl: Hongos Alucinógenos de Europa y América del Norte.* Editorial Swan, San Lorenzo de El Escorial, Spain. pp. 55–68.

Hofmann, A. (Translation by J. Ott) 1979A. "How LSD originated" *Journal of Psychedelic Drugs* 11(1-2): 53–60. Paper presented at conference "Hallucinogens in Native American Shamanism and Modern Life," 28 September–1 October 1978, San Francisco, CA, USA. Organized by Conference.

Hofmann, A. 1979B. "Planned research and chance discovery" *International Sandoz Gazette* 23: 3 *et seq.*

Hofmann, A. (Translation by J. Ott) 1980. *LSD: My Problem Child.* McGraw-Hill, New York. Translator's preface by J. Ott, pp. VII–VIII. Originally published as *LSD–Mein Sorgenkind.* Klett-Cotta, Stuttgart, Germany, 1979; translation reprinted as *LSD: My Problem Child—Reflections on Sacred Drugs, Mysticism, and Science.* J.P. Tarcher, Inc., Los Angeles, CA, 1983. Excerpt published in *High Times.* Translated into French by D. Aviat, 1989. *LSD: Mon Enfant Terrible.* Gris Banal, Montpellier, France. Translated into Spanish by R. Bein, 1980. *LSD: Cómo Descubrí el Ácido y qué Pasó Después en el Mundo.* Gedisa, Barcelona, Spain. Italian excerpt by R. Fedeli, 1992. *LSD i Miei Incontri con Huxley Leary Jünger Vogt.* Stampa Alternativa, Roma, Italy.

Hofmann, A. 1981. "Die kulturhistorische Bedeutung halluzinogener Drogen" In: Hein, W.-G. and G. Schramm (Eds.) *Die Vortrage des Internationalen Pharmaziehistorischen Kongreßes Basel 1979.* Wißenschaftliche Verlagsgesellschaft, Stuttgart, Germany. Reprinted in *Sphinx Magazin* No. 16. Spring 1982, pp. 12–13.

Hofmann, A. 1987. "Die heiligen Pilze in der Heilbehandlung der María Sabina" In: Dittrich, A. and C. Scharfetter (Eds.) *Ethnopsychotherapie: Psychotherapie Mittels Außergewöhnlicher Bewußtseinszustände in Westlichen und Indigenen Kulturen.* Stuttgart, Germany.

Hofmann, A. 1988. "The transmitter-receiver concept of reality" *ReVision: The Journal of Consciousness and Change* 10(4): 5–11.

Hofmann, A. (Translation by D. Hagenbach) 1989. *Insight Outlook.* Humanics New Age, Atlanta, GA. Foreword by R.G. Hall, pp. VII–XI. Originally published as *Einsichten Ausblicke.* Sphinx Verlag, Basel, Switzerland, 1986.

Hofmann, A. 1990. "Ride through the Sierra Mazateca in search of the magic plant 'Ska María Pastora'" In: Riedlinger, T.J (Ed.) *The Sacred Mushroom Seeker: Essays for R. Gordon Wasson.* Ethnomycological Studies No. 11. Dioscorides Press, Portland, OR. pp. 115–127.

Hofmann, A. 1991. Personal communications, correspondence.

Hofmann, A. (Translation by R. Fedeli) 1992. *LSD i Miei Incontri con Huxley Leary Jünger Vogt.* Stampa Alternativa, Roma, Italy. Excerpts from Hofmann 1980.

Hofmann, A. and **F. Troxler** 1959. "Identifizierung von Psilocybin" *Experientia* 15: 101–102.

Hofmann, A. and **H. Tscherter** 1960. "Isolierung von Lysergsäure-Alkaloiden aus der mexikanischen Zauberdroge Ololiuqui (*Rivea corymbosa* [L.] Hall. f.)" *Experientia* 16(9): 414.

Hofmann, A. *et al.* 1957. "Neue Alkaloide aus der saprophytischen Kultur des Mutterkornpilzes von *Pennisetum typhoideum* Rich." *Helvetica Chimica Acta* 40: 1358–1373.

Hofmann, A. *et al.* 1958. "Psilocybin, ein psychotroper Wirkstoff aus dem mexikanischen Rauschpilz *Psilocybe mexicana* Heim" *Experientia* 14(3): 107–109. Reprinted in 1958 in *Revue de Mycologie* 23(1): 114–118; and in Heim, R. *et al.* 1958. *Nouvelles Observations sur les Agarics Hallucinogènes du Mexique.* Muséum National d'Histoire Naturelle, Paris, France. pp. 17–21.

Hofmann, A. *et al.* 1959. "Psilocybin und Psilocin, zwei psychotrope Wirkstoffe aus mexikanischen Rauschpilzen" *Helvetica Chimica Acta* 42: 1557–1572.

Hofmann, A. *et al.* 1961. *Experientia* 17: 206.

Hofmann, A. *et al.* 1963. "Présence de la psilocybine dans une espèce européenne d'Agarics, le *Psilocybe semilanceata* Fries" *Comptes Rendus Hebdomadaires des Séances de l'Académie des Sciences* 257: 10–12. Reprinted, 1963 in *Revue de Mycologie* 27.

Hoge, W. 1977. "The other Cary Grant" *New York Times Magazine.* 3 July issue. pp. 14 *et seq.*

Høiland, K. 1978. "The genus Psilocybe in Norway" *Norwegian Journal of Botany* 25 (2): 111–122.

Holden, C. 1985. "ADAMHA funding pressed" *Science* 227: 147–149.

Holden, C. 1989A. "Street-wise crack research" *Science* 246: 1376–1381.

Holden, C. 1989B. "Flipping the main switch in the central reward system?" *Science* 246: 1378–1379.

Holden, C. 1990A. "Legal drugs: The view from Neuroscience" *Science* 247: 919.

Holden, C. 1990B. "Crimebusters vs. *Cyberpunk*" *Science* 249: 245.

Holden, C. 1990C. "Hairy problems for new drug testing method" *Science* 249: 1099–1100.

Hollingshead, M. 1974. *The Man Who Turned on the World.* Abelard-Schuman, New York.

Hollingworth, H.L. 1912. "The influence of caffeine on mental and motor efficiency" *Archives of Psychology* 3(22): 1–166.

Hollister, L.E. 1961. "Clinical, biochemical and psychological effects of psilocybin" *Archives Internationales de Pharmacodynamie et de Thérapie* 130(1-2): 42–52.

Hollister, L.E. *et al.* 1960. "Comparison of three psychotropic drugs (Psilocybin, JB-329 and IT-290) in volunteer subjects" *The Journal of Nervous and Mental Disease* 131: 428–434.

Hollister, L.E. *et al.* 1991. "Drug abuse policy" *Science* 252: 11–14. Three letters and rebuttal in response to: Goldstein, A. and H. Kalant. 1990. "Drug policy: Striking the right balance" *Science* 249: 1513–1521.

Holloway, P.S. and **G. Alexander** 1990. "Ethnobotany of Fort Yukon region, Alaska" *Economic Botany* 44(2): 214–225.

Holmes, L.D. 1967. "The function of kava in modern Samoan culture" In: Efron, D.H. *et al.* (Eds.) *Ethnopharmacologic Search for Psychoactive Drugs.* (Public Health Service Publication No. 1645) U.S. Government Printing Office, Washington, D.C. pp. 107–118.

Holmstedt, B. 1965. "Tryptamine derivatives in epéna: An intoxicating snuff used by some South American Indian tribes" *Archives Internationales de Pharmacodynamie et de Thérapie* 156(2): 285–305.

Holmstedt, B. 1967. "Historical survey" In: Efron, D.H. *et al.* (Eds.) *Ethnopharmacologic Search for Psychoactive Drugs.* (Public Health Service Publication No. 1645) U. S. Government Printing Office, Washington, D.C. pp. 3–32.

Holmstedt, B. 1978. Personal communications, San Francisco, CA and letters.

Holmstedt, B. and **G. Liljestrand** 1963. *Readings in Pharmacology.* The Macmillan Co., New York.

Holmstedt, B. and **J.-E. Lindgren** 1967. "Chemical constituents and pharmacology of South American snuffs" In: Efron, D.H. *et al.* (Eds.) *Ethnopharmacologic Search for Psychoactive Drugs.* (Public Health Service Publication No. 1645) U.S. Government Printing Office, Washington, D.C. pp. 339–373.

Holmstedt, B. *et al.* 1971. "Determination of cocaine in some South American species of *Erythroxylum* using mass fragmentography" *Phytochemistry* 16: 1753–1755.

Holmstedt, B. *et al.* 1978. "Cocaine in blood of coca chewers" *Botanical Museum Leaflets* Harvard University 26(5): 199–201.

Holmstedt, B. *et al.* 1980. "Indole alkaloids in Amazonian Myristicaceae: Field and laboratory research" *Botanical Museum Leaflets* Harvard University 28(3): 215–234.

Hoogshagen, S. 1959. "Notes on the sacred (narcotic) [*sic*] mushroom from Coatlán, Oaxaca, Mexico" *Oklahoma Anthropology Society Bulletin* 7: 71–74.

Hooper, D. and **H. Field** 1937. "Useful plants and drugs of Iran and Iraq" *Field Museum of Natural History, Botanical Series* 9: 69–241.

Horak, E. 1978. "Pluteus (Pluteaceae)" *Flore Illustrée des Champignons d'Afrique Centrale.* (Fascicule 6) Ministère de l'Agriculture—Jardin Botanique National de Belgique, Meise, Belgium.

Horgen, P.A. *et al.* 1976. "Occurrence of amatoxins in *Amanita ocreata*" *Lloydia* 39(5): 368–371.

Horita, A. 1963. "Some biochemical studies on psilocybin and psilocin" *Journal of Neuropsychiatry* 4: 270–273.

Horita, A. and **L.J. Weber** 1961A. "Dephosphorylation of psilocybin to psilocin by alkaline phosphatase" *Proceedings of the Society for Experimental Biology* 106(1): 32–34.

Horita, A. and **L.J. Weber** 1961B. "The enzymatic dephosphorylation and oxidation of psilocybin by mammalian tissue homogenates" *Biochemical Pharmacology* 7(1): 47–54.

Horita, A. and **L.J. Weber** 1962. "Dephosphorylation of psilocybin in the intact mouse" *Toxicology and Applied Pharmacology* 4: 730–737.

Hornemann, K.M.K. *et al.* 1973. "Cactus alkaloids XII. β-Phenethylamine alkaloids of the genus *Coryphantha*" *Journal of Pharmaceutical Sciences* 61: 41–45.

Horowitz, M. 1976. "Interview: Albert Hofmann" *High Times.* July issue. pp. 25 *et seq.*

Horowitz, M. 1979. *Phantastica: Rare and Important Psychoactive Drug Literature—1700 to the Present.* William and Victoria Dailey, Los Angeles, CA. An annotated catalogue of literature on psychotropic drugs, especially entheogens. Foreword by R. Gordon Wasson, unpaginated. See Wasson 1979B.

Horowitz, M. 1985. *Flashback Books—Catalogue One.* Flashback Books, Petaluma, CA. An annotated book catalogue.

Horowitz, M. 1991. "Just say know: Gordon Wasson and the Psychedelic Revolution" *Integration: Zeitschrift für Geistbewegende Pflanzen und Kultur* 1: 4–6.

Horowitz, M. 1992. *Flashback Books—Catalog 7.* Flashback Books, Petaluma, CA. An annotated book catalogue.

Horowitz, M. 1994. *Flashback Books—Catalog 8.* Flashback Books, Petaluma, CA. An annotated book catalogue.

Horowitz, M. and **C. Palmer** (Eds.) 1977. *Aldous Huxley. Moksha: Writings on Psychedelics and the Visionary Experience (1931–1963).* Stonehill, New York. Preface by

Albert Hofmann, pp. XIII–XV; introduction by Alexander T. Shulgin, pp. XVII–XIX. German in 1990, MedienXperimente.

Hosack, D. 1824. "Observations on ergot" In: Hosack, D. *Essays on Various Subjects of Medical Science.* J. Seymour, New York. Volume 2, pp. 295–301.

Hotson, J.W. 1934. "Mushroom poisoning at Seattle" *Mycologia* 26(2): 194–195.

Hough, W. 1904. "Kava drinking as practiced by the Papuans and Polynesians" *Smithsonian Institution Miscellaneous Collection* 47: 85–92.

Houghton, P.J. and **J. Manby** 1985. "Medicinal plants of the Mapuche" *Journal of Ethnopharmacology* 13(1): 89–103.

Howard, J.H. 1957. "The mescal bean cult of the central and southern plains: An ancestor of the peyote cult?" *American Anthropologist* 59: 75–87.

Hoyle, R.L. 1938. *Los Mochicas.* Casa Editora La Crónica y Variedades, Lima, Perú.

Hu, S.-Y. *et al.* 1980. *An Enumeration of the Chinese Materia Medica.* The Chinese University Press, Hong Kong, UK. Foreword by Richard Evans Schultes, pp. IX–X; preface by E. John Staba, p. XI.

Hugh-Jones, S. 1979. *The Palm and the Pleiades: Initiation and Cosmology in the Northwest Amazonia.* Cambridge University Press, Cambridge, England.

Hull, C.L. 1935. "The influence of caffeine and other factors on certain phenomena of rote learning" *Journal of General Psychology* 13: 249–274.

Humboldt, A. von and **A. Bonpland** (Translation and editing by T. Ross) 1852–1853. *Personal Narrative of Travels to the Equinoctial Regions of America.* Henry G. Bohn, London, England.

Husain, S. and **I. Khan** 1985. "An update on *Cannabis* research" *Bulletin on Narcotics* 37(4): 3–13.

Huxley, A. 1931A. "A treatise on drugs" *Chicago Herald and Examiner.* 10 October issue. Cited in Horowitz & Palmer 1977.

Huxley, A. 1931B. "Wanted, a new pleasure" In: Huxley, A. *Music at Night, and other Pleasures.* Chatto and Windus, London, England. pp. 248–257. Cited in Horowitz & Palmer 1977.

Huxley, A. 1932. *Brave New World.* Harper, New York.

Huxley, A. 1944. *The Perennial Philosophy.* Harper and Row Publishers, New York.

Huxley, A. 1954. *The Doors of Perception.* Harper, New York.

Huxley, A. 1956. *Heaven and Hell.* Chatto and Windus, London, England.

Huxley, A. 1962. *Island.* Harper, New York.

Huxley, A. (posthumous) 1967. "Culture and the individual" In: Andrews, G. and S. Vinkenoog (Eds.) *The Book of Grass.* Grove Press, New York. pp. 192–201.

Huxley, L.A. 1968. *This Timeless Moment: A Personal View of Aldous Huxley.* Farrar, Straus and Giroux, New York.

Huxtable, R.J. 1992. "The pharmacology of extinction" *Journal of Ethnopharmacology* 37(1): 1–11.

Huysmans, J.-K. 1976. *Grünewald.* Phaidon. Oxford, England and E.P. Dutton, New York.

Hyder, D. and **M. Oliver** 1983. "Style and chronology in Chumash rock art" *American Indian Rock Art* 10: 86–101.

Hylin, J.W. and **D.P. Watson** 1965. "Ergoline alkaloids in tropical wood roses" *Science* 148: 499–500.

Hyndman, D.C. 1984. "Ethnobotany of Wopkaimin *Pandanus*: Significant Papua New Guinea plant resource" *Economic Botany* 38(3): 287–303.

Iacobucci, G.A. and **E.A. Rúveda** 1964. "Bases derived from tryptamine in Argentine *Piptadenia* species" *Phytochemistry* 3: 465–467.

Ibérico, C.C. 1941. "Ayahuasca" *Boletín del*

Museo de Historia Natural Javier Prado (Lima, Perú) 5: 313–321.
Ikan, R. *et al.* 1968. "The presence of agroclavine in *Cuscuta monogyna* seeds" *Israeli Journal of Chemistry* 6(1): 65–67.
Ikeda, K. 1908. *Journal of the Tokyo Chemical Society* 30: 820.
Imai, S. 1932. "On *Stropharia caerulescens*, a new species of poisonous toadstool" *Transactions of the Sapporo Natural History Society* 12(3): 148–151.
Imazeki, R. 1973. "Japanese mushroom names" *The Transactions of the Asiatic Society of Japan* Third Series 11: 26–80.
Imazeki, R. and **R.G. Wasson** 1973. "Kinpu, mushroom books of the Toku-Gawa period" *The Transactions of the Asiatic Society of Japan* Third Series 11: 1–12.
Ingalls, D.H.H. 1971. "Not hashish, hops, *Datura*, *Ephedra*, *Sarcostemma* or rhubarb: Soma" *The New York Times Book Review.* 5 September issue. p. 15. Also: "Remarks on Mr. Wasson's *Soma*" *Journal of the American Oriental Society* 91(2): 188–191. Reviews of Wasson 1968. *Soma: Divine Mushroom of Immortality.* The latter paper preceded by Wasson, R.G. 1971. "The Soma of the *Rig Veda*: What was it?" *Journal of the American Oriental Society* 91(2): 169–187. See: Wasson 1971.
Irving, D. 1978. *Guide to Growing Marijuana in the British Isles and Other Cool Climates.* Hassle Free Press, London, England.
Isbell, H.S. 1959. "Comparison of the reactions induced by psilocybin and LSD-25 in man" *Psychopharmacologia* 1(1): 29–38.
Isbell, H.S. and **C.W. Gorodetzky** 1966. "Effect of alkaloids of ololiuqui in man" *Psychopharmacologia* 8: 331–339.
Isbell, H.S. *et al.* 1961. "Cross tolerance between LSD and psilocybin" *Psychopharmacologia* 2: 147–159.
Jackson, B. and **A. Reed** 1969. "Catnip and the alteration of consciousness" *Journal of the American Medical Association* 207: 1349–1350. Editors switched catnip and marijuana captions, prompting suspicion the authors confused catnip and marijuana in their study. See: Tyler 1987.
Jackson, B.P. and **M.I. Berry** 1979. "Mandragora: Taxonomy and chemistry of the European species" In: Hawkes, J.G. *et al.* (Eds.) *The Biology and Taxonomy of the Solanaceae.* (Linnean Society Symposium Series, Number 7) Academic Press, London, England. pp. 505–512.
Jacob, J.N. and **D.E. Nichols** 1982. "Isomeric cyclopropyl ring-methylated homologues of *trans*-2-(2,5-dimethoxy-4-methylphenyl)cyclopropylamine, an hallucinogenic analogue" *Journal of Medicinal Chemistry* 25: 526–530.
Jacob III, P. and **A.T. Shulgin** 1994. "Structure-activity relationships of the classic hallucinogens and their analogs" In: Lin, G.C. and R.A. Glennon (Eds.) *Hallucinogens: An Update.* (NIDA Research Monograph 146) National Institute on Drug Abuse, Rockville, MD. pp. 74–91.
Jacobs, W.A. and **L.C. Craig** 1934A. "The degradation of ergotinine with alkali: Lysergic acid" *Journal of Biological Chemistry* 104: 547–551.
Jacobs, W.A. and **L.C. Craig** 1934B. "On lysergic acid" *Journal of Biological Chemistry* 106: 393–399.
Jacobsen, T. and **C.C. Richardson** 1971. "Mr. Allegro among the mushrooms" *Union Seminary Quarterly Review* 26(3): 1. Reviews of Allegro 1970.
Jacques, J.H. 1970. *The Mushroom and the Bride: A Believer's Examination and Refutation of J.M. Allegro's Book:* The Sacred Mushroom and the Cross. Citadel Press, Derby, England. See: Allegro 1970.
Jain, S.K. and **S.K. Borthakur** 1980. "Ethnobotany of the Mikirs of India" *Economic Botany* 34(3): 264–272.

James, J. 1964. "Shouted from the housetops: A peyote awakening" *The Psychedelic Review* 1(4): 459–483.

James, W. 1902. *The Varieties of Religious Experience.* Longman, Green & Co., London, England. Various reprints exist.

Janesko, J.L. and **T.A. Dal Cason** 1987. "Seizure of a clandestine laboratory: The *N*-Alkyl MDA analogs" Paper from 39th annual meeting of the American Academy of Forensic Sciences, San Diego, CA, USA, 16–21 February 1987.

Janiger, O. 1959. "The use of hallucinogenic agents in psychiatry" *California Clinicians* 55: 251–259.

Janiger, O. and **M. Dobkin de Ríos** 1976. "Nicotiana an hallucinogen?" *Economic Botany* 30(2): 149–151; 30(3): 295–297.

Janot, M.-M. and **R. Goutarel** 1955. "Alcaloïdes des Voacanga: Voacamine et vobtusine" *Comptes Rendus Hebdomadaires des Séances de l'Académie des Sciences* 240: 1719–1720.

Jansen, K.L.R. and **C.J. Prast** 1988a. "Ethnopharmacology of Kratom and the *Mitragyna* alkaloids" *Journal of Ethnopharmacology* 23(1): 115–119.

Jansen, K.L.R. and **C.J. Prast** 1988b. "Psychoactive properties of mitragynine (kratom)" *Journal of Psychoactive Drugs* 20(4): 455–457.

Janzen, D. 1973. "Community structure of secondary compounds in plants" *Pure and Applied Chemistry* 34: 529–538.

Jarvik, M.E. 1990. "The drug dilemma: Manipulating the demand" *Science* 250: 387–392. Article inspired by Nadelmann 1989. See also Goldstein & Kalant 1990.

Jenett-Siems, K. *et al.* 1994. "Ergobalansine/ergobalansinine, a proline-free peptide-type alkaloid of the fungal genus *Balansia*, is a constituent of *Ipomoea piurensis*" *Journal of Natural Products* 57(9): 1304–1306.

Jirawongse, V. *et al.* 1977. "The distribution of indole alkaloids in certain genera of Convolvulaceae growing in Thailand" *Journal of the National Research Council Thailand* 9(1): 17–24.

Johannes, A. 1975. "Medicinal plants of the Nekematigi of the eastern highlands of New Guinea" *Economic Botany* 29(3): 268–277.

John, A. 1935. "Maßenvergiftungen mit dem Pantherpilz (*Amanita pantherina* DC.) in Plauen im Vogtland" *Zeitschrift für Pilzkunde* 14: 9–11; 43–49.

Johnson, C. and **C.P. Johnson** 1861. *British Poisonous Plants.* John Van Voorst, London, England. This book, famous for its illustrations, is widely known under the name of the illustrator, Sowerby.

Johnson, C.E. 1957. "Mystical force of the nightshade" *International Journal of Neuropsychiatry* 3: 268–275.

Johnson, D. 1953. *The Hallucinogenic Drugs.* C. Johnson, London, England.

Johnson, J.B. 1939a. "The elements of Mazatec witchcraft" *Göteborgs Etnografiska Museum Etnologiska Studier* 9: 119–149.

Johnson, J.B. 1939b. "Some notes on the Mazatec" *Revista Mexicana de Antropología* 3(2): 142–156.

Johnson, T.F. 1972. "*Datura fastuosa*: Its use in Tsonga girl's initiation" *Economic Botany* 26(4): 340–351.

Johnson Gottesfeld, L.M. and **B. Anderson** 1988. "Gitksan traditional medicine: Herbs and healing" *Journal of Ethnobiology* 8(1): 13–33.

Johnston, J.F. 1857. *The Chemistry of Common Life.* Two volumes, Ninth Edition. D. Appleton & Co., New York. Originally published in Edinburgh, Scotland, 1853–1855.

Johnston, L.D. *et al.* 1981. "Marijuana decriminalization: The impact on youth 1975–1980" *Monitoring the Future.* (Occasional Paper 13) University of Michigan Institute for Social Research, Ann Arbor, MI.

Johnston, P.R. and **P.K. Buchanan** 1995. "The genus *Psilocybe* (Agaricales) in New Zealand" *New Zealand Journal of Botany* 33: 379–388.

Johri, R.K. and **U. Zutshi** 1992. "An Ayurvedic formulation 'Trikatu' and its constituents" *Journal of Ethnopharmacology* 37(2): 85–91.

Jokiranta, J. *et al.* 1984. "Psilocybin in Finnish *Psilocybe semilanceata*" *Planta Medica* 50: 277–278.

Jolly, F. 1896. "Über Pellotin als Schlafmittel" *Deutscher Medizinischer Wochenschrift* 22: 375.

Joly, L.G. 1981. "Feeding and trapping fish with *Piper auritum*" *Economic Botany* 35(4): 383–390.

Joly, L.G. *et al.* 1987. "Ethnobotanical inventory of medicinal plants used by the Guaymi in western Panama. Part I" *Journal of Ethnopharmacology* 20(2): 145–171.

Jones, R. 1963. "'Up' on psilocybin" *The Harvard Review* 1(4): 38–43.

Joralemon, D. and **D. Sharon** 1993. *Sorcery and Shamanism: Curanderos and Clients in Northern Peru.* University of Utah Press, Salt Lake City, UT.

Joseph, H. *et al.* 1989. "Justicidin B, a cytotoxic principle from *Justicia pectoralis*" *Journal of Natural Products* 51(3): 599–600.

Joseph, R. 1973. "The economic significance of *Cannabis sativa* in the Moroccan Rif" *Economic Botany* 27(2): 235–240.

Joshi, A.R. and **J.M. Edington** 1990. "The use of medicinal plants by two village communities in the Central Development Region of Nepal" *Economic Botany* 44(1): 71–83.

Jössang, P. and **D. Molho** 1967. "Dihydrokavain has sedative properties like dihydromethysticin" *Journal of Chromatography* 31: 375.

Jössang, P. and **D. Molho** 1970. "Étude des constituants des feuilles de *Piper methysticum* Forst." *Bulletin de Muséum National d'Histoire Naturelle* 42: 440–447.

Joyal, E. 1987. "Ethnobotanical field notes from Ecuador: Camp, Pricto, Jørgensen and Giler" *Economic Botany* 41(2): 163–189.

Joyce, C.R.B. and **S.H. Curry** 1970. *The Botany and Chemistry of Cannabis.* J. & A. Churchill, London, England.

Jude, S. 1991. "Are you as smart as your drugs?" *Mondo 2000* 5: 38–41.

Jünger, E. 1970. *Annäherungen: Drogen und Rausch.* E. Klett Verlag, Stuttgart, Germany. Spanish translation in 1996.

Kalberer, F. *et al.* 1962. "The fate of psilocin in the rat" *Biochemical Pharmacology* 11(1): 261–269.

Kamel, S.H. *et al.* 1970. "Chemical studies on the Egyptian plant, *Peganum harmala*" *United Arab Republic Journal of Veterinary Science* 7: 61–68.

Kamen-Kaye, D. 1971. "Chimó: An unusual form of tobacco in Venezuela" *Botanical Museum Leaflets* Harvard University 23(1): 1–59.

Kamen-Kaye, D. 1975. "Chimó—Why not? A primitive form of tobacco still in use in Venezuela" *Economic Botany* 29(1): 47–68.

Kan-Fan, C. *et al.* 1970. "Alcaloïdes de *Vepris ampody* (Rutacées)" *Phytochemistry* 9: 1283–1291.

Kaplan, H.R. and **M.H. Malone** 1966. "A pharmacologic study of nesodine, cryogenine and other alkaloids of *Heimia salicifolia*" *Lloydia* 29: 348–359.

Kaplan, R.H. 1975. "The sacred mushroom in Scandinavia" *Man* 10(1): 72–79.

Kapoor, L.D. 1995. *Opium Poppy: Botany, Chemistry, and Pharmacology.* Food Products Press, Binghamton, NY.

Kast, E.C. 1963. "The analgesic action of lysergic acid compared with dihydromorphinone and meperidine" *Bulletin on Drug Addiction and Narcotics* 27: 3517.

Kast, E.C. 1966. "An understanding of pain"

Medical Times 94: 1501–1513.

Kast, E.C. 1970. "A concept of death" In: Aaronson, B. and H. Osmond (Eds.) *Psychedelics: The Uses and Implications of Hallucinogenic Drugs.* Doubleday/Anchor, Garden City, NJ. pp. 366–381.

Kast, E.C. and **V.J. Collins** 1964. "A study of lysergic acid diethylamide as an analgesic agent" *Anæsthesia and Analgesia Current Research* 43: 285–291.

Katz, I. 1949. *Contribution à l'Étude de l'Ivraie Enivrante (Lolium temulentum L.).* Thésis, École Polytechnique Fédérale, Zürich, Switzerland.

Kawanishi, K. *et al.* 1982. "Shihunine and dihydroshihunine from *Banisteriopsis caapi*" *Journal of Natural Products* 45(6): 637–639.

Kazin, A. (Ed.) 1946. *The Portable Blake.* The Viking Press, New York.

Keeler, K.H. 1977. "The extrafloral nectaries of Ipomoea carnea (Convolvulaceae)" *American Journal of Botany* 64(10): 1182–1188.

Keeler, K.H. 1980. "The extrafloral nectaries of Ipomoea leptophylla (Convolvulaceae)" *American Journal of Botany* 67(2): 216–222.

Keeler, K.H. and **R.B. Kaul** 1979. "Morphology and distribution of petiolar nectaries in Ipomoea (Convolvulaceae)" *American Journal of Botany* 66(8): 946–952.

Keewaydinoquay (K.M. Peschel) 1978. *Puhpohwee for the People: A Narrative Account of Some Uses of Fungi Among the Ahnishinaubeg.* Ethnomycological Studies No. 5. Botanical Museum of Harvard University, Cambridge, MA. Includes "Presenting Keewaydinoquay" by R.G. Wasson, p. v.

Keewaydinoquay (K.M. Peschel) 1979. "The legend of Miskwedo" *Journal of Psychedelic Drugs* 11(1-2): 29–31. Paper presented at "Hallucinogens in Native American Shamanism and Modern Life," 28 September–1 October 1978, San Francisco, CA, USA. See: Heinrich 1995; Wasson *et al.* 1980A.

Keewaydinoquay (K.M. Peschel) *et al.* 1990. "The people of Miniss Kitigan who were and are honor the spirit of Waussung-Naabe who was and is" In: Riedlinger, T.J. (Ed.) *The Sacred Mushroom Seeker: Essays for R. Gordon Wasson.* Ethnomycological Studies No. 11. Dioscorides Press, Portland, OR. pp. 141–145.

Keil, R. 1991. "Bob Martinez: A Czar is born" *Mother Jones.* July/August. pp. 42–43.

Keller, F. and **M.W. Klohs** 1963. "A review of the chemistry and pharmacology of the constituents of *Piper methysticum*" *Lloydia* 26: 1–15.

Keller, K. and **E. Stahl** 1982. "Kalmus: Inhaltßtoffe und β-Asarongehalt bei verschiedenen Herkünften" *Deutscher Apotheker Zeitung* 122: 2463–2466.

Keller, W.J. 1975. "Alkaloids from *Sophora secundiflora*" *Phytochemistry* 14: 2305–2306.

Keller, W.J. *et al.* 1976. "Isolation of lupinine and Δ^5-dehydrolupanine from *Sophora secundiflora*" *Lloydia* 39: 472.

Kennedy, A.B. 1982. "*Ecce Bufo*: The toad in nature and in Olmec iconography" *Current Anthropology* 23(3): 273–290.

Kennedy, J.G. 1987. *The Flower of Paradise: The Institutionalized Use of the Drug Qat in North Yemen.* Dordrecht, Netherlands.

Kensinger, K.M. 1973. "*Banisteriopsis* usage among the Peruvian Cashinahua" In: Harner, M.J. (Ed.) *Hallucinogens and Shamanism.* Oxford University Press, London, England. pp. 9–14.

Kern, J.R. and **J.H. Cardellina II** 1983. "Native American medicinal plants. Anemonin from the horse stimulant *Clematis hirsutissima*" *Journal of Ethnopharmacology* 8(1): 121–123.

Kettenes-van den Bosch, J.J. and **C.A. Salemink** 1980. "Biological activity of the tetrahydrocannabinols" *Journal of Ethnopharmacology* 2(3): 197–231.

Keys, J.D. 1976. *Chinese Herbs: Their Bot-*

any, Chemistry and Pharmacology. Charles E. Tuttle Co., Rutland, VT. Foreword by Ilza Veith, pp. 9–10.

Kharasch, M.S. and **R.R. Legault** 1935. "Ergotocin" *Science* (London): 81: 388–389; also "The new active principle of ergot" *Science* (London) 81: 614–615.

Khashimov, H.N. *et al.* 1971. "The dynamics of the accumulation of alkaloids in *Peganum harmala*" *Chemistry of Natural Compounds* 3: 364–365.

Khashimov, K. *et al.* 1971. "O dynamyke nakopleni alkaloidov v *Peganum harmala*" *Khimija Prirodnykh Soedinenij* 7: 382.

Khattack, S.G. *et al.* 1985. "Antipyretic studies on some indigenous Pakistani medicinal plants" *Journal of Ethnopharmacology* 14(1): 45–51.

Khuong-Huu, F. *et al.* 1972. "Alchornéine, isoalchornéine, et alchornéinone, produits isolés de l'*Alchornea floribunda* Muell. Arg." *Tetrahedron* 28: 5207–5220.

Kiesewetter, K. 1892. *Geschichte des Neueren Occultismus.* Leipzig, Germany.

Kindscher, K. 1992. *Medicinal Wild Plants of the Prairie: An Ethnobotanical Guide.* University Press of Kansas, Lawrence, KS.

King, S.R. 1991. "Among the Secoya" *The Nature Conservancy Magazine.* January/February issue, pp. 6–15.

King, S.R. 1992. "Conservation and tropical medicinal plant research" *HerbalGram* 27: 28–35.

Kinross-Wright, V.J. 1959. "Research on ololiuqui: The Aztec drug" In: Bradley, P.B. *et al.* (Eds.) *Neuro-Psychopharmacology.* Elsevier, Amsterdam, the Netherlands, pp. 453–456.

Kirch, P.V. 1978. "Indigenous agriculture on Uvea (Western Polynesia)" *Economic Botany* 32(2): 157–181.

Kirimura, J. *et al.* 1969. "The contribution of peptides and amino acids to the taste of foodstuffs" *Journal of Agricultural and Food Chemistry* 17(4): 689–695.

Kirsch, M.M. 1986. *Designer Drugs.* CompCare Publications, Minneapolis, MN.

Kishida, Y. *et al.* 1966. "Studies on acetylenic compounds. XLIII. Synthesis of ibotenic acid" *Chemical and Pharmacological Bulletin Japan* 14: 92–94.

Klapp, E. 1991. "Die Masken des Fliegenpilzes" In: Bauer, W. *et al.* (Eds.) *Der Fliegenpilz: Ein Kulturhistorisches Museum.* (Museum der Museen, Schriftenreihe des Karl Ernst Osthaus-Museums, Bd. 6) Wienand-Verlag, Köln, Germany. pp. 66–120.

Kleps, A. 1977. *Millbrook.* Bench, Oakland, CA.

Klerman, G.L. 1972. "Psychotropic hedonism vs pharmacological Calvinism" *Hastings Center Report* 2(4): 1–3.

Kline, N.S. 1967. "Introduction: The psychology, philosophy, morality and legislative control of drug usage" In: Efron, D.H. *et al.* (Eds.) *Ethnopharmacologic Search for Psychoactive Drugs.* (Public Health Service Publication No. 1645) U.S. Government Printing Office, Washington, D.C. pp. XVII–XIX.

Kline, T.B. *et al.* 1982. "Structure-activity relationships in potentially hallucinogenic *N,N*-dialkyltryptamines substituted in the benzene moiety" *Journal of Medicinal Chemistry* 25: 908–913.

Klohs, M.W. 1967. "Chemistry of kava" In: Efron, D.H. *et al.* (Eds.) *Ethnopharmacologic Search for Psychoactive Drugs.* (Public Health Service Publication No. 1645) U.S. Government Printing Office, Washington, D.C. pp. 126–132.

Klüver, H. 1928. *Mescal* [*sic*], *the "Divine Plant" and its Psychological Effects.* Paul Kegan, London, England. Introduction by Macdonald Critchley.

Klüver, H. 1966. *Mescal* [*sic*] *and Mechanisms of Hallucination.* University of Chicago Press, Chicago, IL. Revised and expanded edition of Klüver 1928.

Knab, T. 1974. "Narcotic use of toad toxins in southern Veracruz" Unpublished ms.

Knab, T. 1976–1978. "Minor Mexican pharmacogens [*sic*]: Context and effects" Unpublished manuscript.

Knab, T. 1977. "Notes concerning use of *Solandra* among the Huichol" *Economic Botany* 31(1): 80–86.

Knauer, A. and **W.J.M.A. Maloney** 1913. "A preliminary note on the psychic action of mescaline with special reference to the mechanism of visual hallucinations" *The Journal of Nervous and Mental Disease* 40: 425–438.

Knauth, L.G. 1962. "Historia de los indios de la Nueva España" *Estudios de Cultura Náhuatl* 3: 262.

Kneebone, L.R. 1960. "Methods for the production of certain hallucinogenic agarics" *Developments in Industrial Microbiology* 1: 109.

Knox, J.R. and **J. Slobbe** 1975. "Indole alkaloids from *Ervatamia orientalis*. 1. Isolation of alkaloids and structural identification of two dimers" *Australian Journal of Chemistry* 28: 1813.

Koch-Grünberg, T. 1909. *Zwei Jahre unter den Indianern. Reisen in Nordwest-Brasilien 1903/1905.* Two volumes. Ernst Wasmuth, Berlin, Germany. Volume 2 published in 1910.

Koch-Grünberg, T. 1923. *Von Roraima zum Orinoco.* Strecker und Schröder, Stuttgart, Germany. Volume 3, p. 324.

Kohn, E.O. 1992. "Some observations on the use of medicinal plants from primary and secondary growth by the Runa of eastern lowland Ecuador" *Journal of Ethnobiology* 12(1): 141–152.

Koike, Y. *et al.* 1981. "Isolation of psilocybin from *Psilocybe argentipes* and its determination in specimens of some mushrooms" *Journal of Natural Products* 44(3): 362–365.

Konda, Y. *et al.* 1985. "Structure elucidation of pantherine, a flycidal alkaloid from *Amanita pantherina*" *Chemical and Pharmacological Bulletin Japan* 33(3): 1083–1087.

König-Bersin, P. *et al.* 1970. "Monoamines in the brain under the influence of muscimol and ibotenic acid, two psychoactive principles of *Amanita muscaria*" *Psychopharmacologia* 18: 1–10.

Kornfeld, E.C. *et al.* 1954. "The total synthesis of lysergic acid and ergonovine" *Journal of the American Chemical Society* 76: 5256–5257.

Kornfeld, E.C. *et al.* 1956. "The total synthesis of lysergic acid" *Journal of the American Chemical Society* 78: 3087–3114.

Koshland, D.E. 1989. "The war? program? experiment? on drugs" *Science* 245: 1309. Copyright © 1989, AAAS. Paid permission granted to quote.

Koshland, D.E. 1992. "DNA fingerprinting and eyewitness testimony" *Science* 256: 593. Editorial comment on Chakraborty & Kidd 1991; Lewontin & Hartl 1991. See also: Roberts 1991; Wills *et al.* 1992.

Krajick, K. 1992. "Vision quest" *Newsweek.* 15 June (Latin American) issue. pp. 44–45. With sidebar "Can't Lick 'Em? Then Smoke 'Em" p. 45.

Kramrisch, S. 1972. Review of Wasson 1968. *Soma: Divine Mushroom of Immortality. Artibus Asiae* 34(2/3): 263–267.

Kramrisch, S. 1975. "The Mahavira Vessel and the plant Putika" *Journal of the American Oriental Society* 95(2): 222–235; reprinted in Wasson, R.G. *et al.* 1986. *Persephone's Quest: Entheogens and the Origins of Religion.* Ethnomycological Studies No. 10. Yale University Press, New Haven, CT. pp. 95–116.

Kramrisch, S. *et al.* 1986. *Persephone's Quest: Entheogens and the Origins of Religion.* See: Wasson *et al.* 1986.

Krause, K. 1926. "Über den giftigen Honig des pontischen Kleinasien" *Die Naturwißenschaften* 44: 976–978.

Kreig, M. 1964. *Green Medicine: The Search for Plants that Heal...* Rand McNally & Co., Chicago, IL.

Kreig, M. 1967. *Black Market Medicine.* Prentice-Hall, Englewood Cliffs, NJ. "FDA Documentation" by George P. Larrick, then-FDA Commissioner, pp. IX–X.

Kreisel, H. and **U. Lindequist** 1988. "*Gymnopilus purpuratus*, ein psilocybin-haltiger Pilz adventiv im Bezirk Rostock" *Zeitschrift für Mykologie* 54: 73–76.

Kretszchmar, R. 1970. "Kavain als Psychopharmakon" *Münchner Medizinischer Wochenschrift* 112: 154–158.

Krieglsteiner, G.J. 1984. "Studien zum *Psilocybe cyanescens*-Komplex in Europa" *Beiträge zur Kenntnis der Pilzes Mitteleuropas* 1: 61.

Krikorian, A.D. and **A. Getahun** 1973. "Chat: Coffee's rival from Harar, Ethiopia. II. Chemical composition" *Economic Botany* 27(4): 378–389. Part I: Getahun & Krikorian 1973.

Krötenstuhl, S. 1992. "Eine Reise im Herbst" *Integration: Zeitschrift für Geistbewegende Pflanzen und Kultur* 2&3: 129–130.

Kruger, T.L. *et al.* 1977. "Identification of alkaloids in crude extracts by mass-analyzed ion kinetic energy spectrometry" *Journal of Organic Chemistry* 42: 4161–4162.

Kubler, G. 1967. *The Iconography of the Art of Teotihuacan.* (Studies in Pre-Columbian Art and Archaeology Number Four) Dumbarton Oaks, Washington, D.C.

Kuiper, F.B.J. 1970. Review of Wasson 1968. *Soma: Divine Mushroom of Immortality. Indo-Iranian Journal* 12(4): 279–285. Followed by Wasson, R.G. 1970. "Soma: Comments inspired by Professor Kuiper's review" *Indo-Iranian Journal* 12(4): 286–298. See: Wasson 1970B.

Kusel, H. 1965. "Ayahuasca drinkers among the Chama Indians of Northeast Peru" *Psychedelic Review* 6: 58–66.

Kutler, S.I. 1982. *The American Inquisition: Justice and Injustice in the Cold War.* Hill and Wang, New York.

Kutlu, H. and **H. Amal** 1967. "Türkiyede yetisen *Peganum harmala* L. üzerinde kimyasal arastirmalar" *Istanbul Üniversitesi Eczacilik Fakültesi Mecmuasi* 3: 133–147.

Kvambe, V. and **J. Edenberg** 1979. "Sopp med hallusinogen effekt" *Tidsskr. Nor. Lægeforen* 29: 1453–1454.

Kwitny, J. 1987. *The Crimes of Patriots: A True Tale of Dope, Dirty Money and the CIA.* Norton and Co., New York. With critical afterword by Adml. E. Yates (ret.).

La Barre, W. 1938A. *The Peyote Cult.* (Yale University Publications in Anthropology No. 13) Yale University Press, New Haven, CT. Fifth edition in 1989, University of Oklahoma Press, Norman, OK. Translated into Spanish by C. Millet, 1980. *El Culto del Peyote.* Premia Editora, México City.

La Barre, W. 1938B. "Native American beers" *American Anthropologist* 40: 234.

La Barre, W. 1957. "Mescalism and peyotism" *American Anthropologist* 59: 708–711.

La Barre, W. 1960. "Twenty years of peyote studies" *Current Anthropology* 1: 45–60. Reprinted in 1975, appendix to fourth edition of *The Peyote Cult* (La Barre 1938A).

La Barre, W. 1970. *The Ghost Dance: The Origins of Religion.* Doubleday, Garden City, NJ.

La Barre, W. 1972. "Hallucinogens and the shamanic origins of religion" In: Furst, P.T. (Ed.) *Flesh of the Gods: The Ritual Use of Hallucinogens.* Praeger, New York. pp. 261–278.

La Barre, W. 1975. Notes and Addenda to *The Peyote Cult.* Fourth Edition Enlarged. Archon Books, Hamden, CT. Contains "Twenty years of peyote studies"; "The last five years of peyote studies" from 1969 edition and "Peyote studies, 1963–1973." Also "Preface to the 1969 edition."

La Barre, W. 1979A. "Shamanic origins of religion and medicine" *Journal of Psychedelic Drugs* 11(1-2): 7–11. Paper presented at conference "Hallucinogens in Native American Shamanism and Modern Life," 28 September–1 October 1978, San Francisco, CA, USA.

La Barre, W. 1979B. "Peyotl and mescaline" *Journal of Psychedelic Drugs* 11(1-2): 33–39. Paper presented at conference "Hallucinogens in Native American Shamanism and Modern Life," 28 September–1 October 1978, San Francisco, CA, USA.

La Barre, W. 1980A. "Anthropological perspectives on hallucination, hallucinogens and the shamanic origins of religion" In: La Barre, W. *Culture in Context: Selected Writings of Weston La Barre.* Duke University Press, Durham, NC. pp. 37–92.

La Barre, W. 1980B. "History and ethnography of *Cannabis*" In: La Barre, W. *Culture in Context: Selected Writings of Weston La Barre.* Duke University Press, Durham, NC. pp. 93–107.

La Barre, W. 1980C. "Soma: The three-and-one-half millennia mystery" In: La Barre, W. *Culture in Context: Selected Writings of Weston La Barre.* Duke University Press, Durham, NC pp. 108–115. Review of Wasson 1968. *Soma: Divine Mushroom of Immortality.* Originally published in *American Anthropologist* 72: 368–373, 1970.

La Barre, W. 1988. Review of Wasson *et al.* 1986. *Persephone's Quest: Entheogens and the Origins of Religion. Journal of Ethnobiology* 8(2): 221–222.

La Barre, W. *et al.* 1951. "Statement on peyote" *Science* 114: 582–583.

LaBerge, S. and **H. Rheingold** 1990. *Exploring the World of Lucid Dreaming.* Random House, New York.

Labra, V.B. 1991. *El Venado Azul.* Editorial Diana, México City.

Labrousse, A. *et al.* 1992. "En la prensa" *Observatoire Géopolitique des Drogues* 11: 2.

Lagarde, P.A. de 1866. *Gesammelte Abhandlungen.* Leipzig, Germany.

Lai, A. *et al.* 1973. "Phytochemical investigations of *Virola peruviana*, a new hallucinogenic plant" *Journal of Pharmaceutical Sciences* 62: 1561–1563.

Lajoux, J. 1963. *The Rock Paintings of Tassili.* World Publishing Co., Cleveland, OH.

Lal, S.D. and **B.K. Yadav** 1983. "Folk medicines of Kurukshetra District (Haryana), India" *Economic Botany* 37(3): 299–305.

L'Allemant, C. 1626. Letter from Québec to his brother in France. 1 August 1626. See: Wasson, R.G. 1979. "Traditional use in North America of *Amanita muscaria* for divinatory purposes" *Journal of Psychedelic Drugs* 11(1-2): 25–28.

Lamb, F.B. 1974. *Wizard of the Upper Amazon: The Story of Manuel Córdova-Ríos.* Houghton-Mifflin, Boston, MA. With an introduction by A.T. Weil, pp. V–XII. Paperback reprint of Córdova-Ríos, M. and F.B. Lamb 1971. *Wizard of the Upper Amazon.* Atheneum, New York. Later re-released under paperback title by North Atlantic Books and Society for the Study of Native Arts and Sciences, Berkeley, CA. Excerpt published in 1974. "Witch Doctor [*sic*] of the Upper Amazon" *Fate.*

Lamb, F.B. 1981A. "Comment on Bock's review of *The Don Juan Papers*" *American Anthropologist* 88(3): 641.

Lamb, F.B. 1981B. "*Wizard of the Upper Amazon* as Ethnography" *Current Anthropology* 22(5): 577–580.

Lamb, F.B. 1985. *Río Tigre and Beyond: The Amazon Jungle Medicine of Manuel Córdova.* North Atlantic Books, Society for the Study of Native Arts and Sciences, Berkeley, CA. Preface by W. Johnson, pp. I–XVI.

Lame Deer, J.(F.) and **R. Erdoes** 1972. *Lame Deer: Seeker of Visions*. Washington Square Press, New York.

Langdon, E.J. 1986. "Las clasificaciones del yajé dentro del grupo Siona. Etnobotánica, etnoquímica e historia" *América Indígena* 46(1): 101–116.

Lange, W.R. 1987. "Ciguatera toxicity" *American Family Physician* 35(4): 177–182.

Larris, S. 1980. *Forbyde Hallucinogener? Forbyd Naturen at Gro!* Fourth edition. Forlaget Indkøbstryk, Nimtofte, Denmark.

Larsen, S. 1976. *The Shaman's Doorway: Opening the Mythic Imagination to Contemporary Consciousness.* Harper & Row, New York. Reprint 1988, Station Hill Press, Barrytown, NY; Foreword J. Halifax, p. V–VI.

Larson, P. *et al.* 1961. *Tobacco: Experimental and Clinical Studies: A Compehensive Account of the World Literature.* Williams & Wilkins, Baltimore, MD.

Lascano, C. *et al.* 1967. "Estudio fitoquímico de la especie psicotomimética [*sic*] *Ipomoea carnea*" *Ciencias Naturales* 9: 3.

Latimer, D. and **J. Goldberg** 1981. *Flowers in the Blood: The Story of Opium.* Franklin Watts, New York. Introduction by W.S. Burroughs, pp. 1–4.

Latorre, D.L. and **F.A. Latorre** 1977. "Plants used by the Mexican Kickapoo Indians" *Economic Botany* 31(3): 340–357.

Latta, R.P. and **B.J. Eaton** 1975. "Seasonal fluctuations in cannabinoid content of Kansas marihuana [*sic*]" *Economic Botany* 29(2): 153–163.

Lazos Chavero, E. and **M.E. Álvarez-Buylla Roces** 1988. "Ethnobotany in a tropical-humid region: The home gardens of Balzapote, Veracruz, Mexico" *Journal of Ethnobiology* 8(1): 45–79.

Leary, J.D. 1970. "Alkaloids of the seeds of *Datura sanguinea*" *Lloydia* 33(3): 264–266.

Leary, T. 1964. "The religious experience: Its production and interpretation" *The Psychedelic Review* 1(3): 324–346. Reprinted in Weil, G.M. *et al.* (Eds.) *The Psychedelic Reader.* University Books, New York. pp. 191–213.

Leary, T. 1966A. "Playboy interview: Timothy Leary" *Playboy* 13(9): 93 *et seq.*

Leary, T. 1966B. "The experiential typewriter" *Psychedelic Review* 7: 70–85.

Leary, T. 1966C. "Programmed communication during experiences with DMT (dimethyl-tryptamine)" *Psychedelic Review* 8: 83–95.

Leary, T. 1968. *High Priest.* The World Publishing Co., New York.

Leary, T. and **R. Alpert** 1963. "The politics of consciousness expansion" *The Harvard Review* 1(4): 33–37.

Leary, T. *et al.* 1964. *The Psychedelic Experience: A Manual Based on the Tibetan Book of the Dead.* University Books, New York.

Leboeuf, M. *et al.* 1977. "Alcaloïdes et triterpènes du *Testulea gabonensis* Pellegr." *Plantes Médicinales et Phytothérapie* 11: 230–235.

Lebot, V. 1991. "Kava (*Piper methysticum* Forst. f.): The Polynesian dispersal of an Oceanian plant" In: Cox, P.A. and S.A. Banack (Eds.) *Islands, Plants and Polynesians: An Introduction to Polynesian Ethnobotany.* Dioscorides Press, Portland, OR. pp. 169–201.

Lebot, V. and **J. Lévesque** 1989. "The origin and distribution of kava (*Piper methysticum* Forst. f.): A phytochemical approach" *Allertonia* 5(2): 223–280.

Lebot, V. *et al.* 1986. "Le kava des ancêtres est-il l'ancêtre du kava?" *Journal of the Vanuatu Natural Science Society, Alaika* 23: 1–10.

Lebot, V. *et al.* 1992. *Kava: The Pacific Drug.* Yale University Press, New Haven, CT.

Lee, M.A. and **B. Shlain** 1985. *Acid Dreams: LSD, the CIA and the Sixties Rebellion.* Grove Press, New York. Reprint 1992, introduction by A. Codrescu, pp. xiii–xv.

Lee, W. (Pseudonym for William Burroughs) 1953. *Junkie: Confessions of an Unredeemed Drug Addict.* Ace Books, New York. Originally published as a 35¢ paperback, back-to-back with the 1941 *Narcotic Agent* by M. Helbrant, with a lurid cover drawing of a rape scene.

Legler, G. and **R. Tschesche** 1963. "Die Isolierung von N-Methyltryptamin, 5-Methoxy-N-methyltryptamin und 5-Methoxy-N,N-dimethyltryptamin aus der Rinde von Piptadenia peregrina Benth." *Die Naturwißenschaften* 50: 94–95.

Lehane, B. 1977. *The Power of Plants.* McGraw-Hill, New York.

Lehmann, H.E. and **J. Csank** 1957. "Differential screening of phrenotropic agents in man" *Journal of Clinical Psychopathology* 18: 222–235.

Lema, W.J. *et al.* 1986. "Prostaglandin synthetase inhibition by alkaloids of *Heimia salicifolia*" *Journal of Ethnopharmacology* 15(2): 161–167.

Lenson, D. 1995. *On Drugs.* University of Minnesota Press, Minneapolis, MN.

Leonhardt, W. 1992. "Über Rauschzustände bei Pantherpilzvergiftungen" *Integration: Zeitschrift für Geistbewegende Pflanzen und Kultur* 2&3: 119–128. First published in 1949. *Der Nervenärzt* 20(4): 181–188.

León Portilla, M. 1961. *Los Antiguos Mexicanos.* Fondo de Cultura Económica, México City.

Leuner, H. and **G. Baer** 1965. "Two new short-acting hallucinogens of the psilocybin group" In: Bente, D. and P.B. Bradley (Eds.) *Neuro-Psychopharmacology.* Elsevier, Amsterdam, the Netherlands. pp. 471–474.

Leuner, H. and **H. Holfeld** 1962. "Ergebnisse und Probleme der Psychotherapie mit Hilfe von LSD-25 und verwandten Substanzen" *Psychiatria et Neurologia* 143: 379–391.

Leuner, H. and **M. Schlichting** (Translation by J. Baker) 1989. "A report on the symposium 'On the current state of research in the area of psychoactive substances'" In: Rätsch, C. (Ed.) *Gateway to Inner Space: Sacred Plants, Mysticism and Psychotherapy—A Festschrift in Honor of Albert Hofmann.* Prism Press, Bridport, England. pp. 213–240.

Leung, A.Y. 1967. *Investigations on Psilocybin and its Analogues in Certain Fungi.* Thesis, University of Michigan, Ann Arbor, MI.

Leung, A.Y. and **A.G. Paul** 1968. "Baeocystin and norbaeocystin: New analogs of psilocybin from *Psilocybe baeocystis*" *Journal of Pharmaceutical Sciences* 57: 1667–1671.

Leung, A.Y. and **A.G. Paul** 1969. "Relation of carbon and nitrogen nutrition of *Psilocybe baeocystis* to the production of psilocybin and its analogs" *Lloydia* 32(1): 66–71.

Leung, A.Y. *et al.* 1965. "Production of psilocybin in *Psilocybe baeocystis* saprophytic culture" *Journal of Pharmaceutical Sciences* 54(11): 1576–1579.

Leverant, R. 1986. "MDMA reconsidered" *Journal of Psychoactive Drugs* 18(4): 373–379.

Levin, L. *et al.* 1992. "Cigarettes and addiction" *Science* 256: 427. Three letters to the editor in response to: Schelling, T.C. 1992. "Addictive drugs: The cigarette experience" *Science* 255: 430–433.

Levine, W.G. 1967. "Formation of blue oxidation product from psilocybin" *Nature* 215: 1292–1293.

Levy, S. 1991. "Search and destroy: What happened when the Secret Service visited Steve Jackson Games" *Macworld.* March issue. pp 51. *et seq.* See also: Ortega 1993.

Levy, S. 1992. "Fighting the code war" *Macworld.* August issue. pp. 57–62.

Lewin, L. 1886. *Über Piper Methysticum*

(Kawa). A. Hirschwald, Berlin, Germany.

Lewin, L. 1888. "XXVII. Ueber Anhalonium Lewinii." *Archiv für Experimentelle Pathologie und Pharmakologie* 24: 401–411.

Lewin, L. 1924. *Phantastica—Die Betäubenden und Erregenden Genußmittel. Für Ärzte und Nichtärzte.* Georg Stilke Verlag, Berlin, Germany. First translated into English in 1931, Rutledge and Kegan Paul, London, England. Translation reprinted in 1964 as *Phantastica: Narcotic and Stimulating Drugs. Their Use and Abuse...* E.P. Dutton, New York. Foreword by B. Holmstedt. French translationn in 1928.

Lewin, L. 1928. "Untersuchung über *Banisteria caapi* Spr. (ein südamerikanisches Rauschmittel)" *Archiv für Experimentelle Pathologie und Pharmakologie* 129: 133–149.

Lewin, L. 1929. *Banisteria caapi, Ein Neues Rauschgift und Heilmittel.* Georg Stilke Verlag, Berlin, Germany. Facsimile 1986, EXpress Edition, Berlin; Einleitung von C. Rätsch, "Die Erforschung des 'Telepathins'" pp. VII–X.

Lewis, B. 1955. "Atropine in mushrooms—Therapeutic implications" *South African Medical Journal* 29: 262.

Lewis, W.H. and **M.P.F. Elvin-Lewis** 1977. *Medical Botany: Plants Affecting Man's Health.* John Wiley & Sons, New York.

Lewis, W.H. and **M.P.F. Elvin-Lewis** 1990. "Obstetrical use of the parasitic fungus *Balansia cyperi* by the Amazonian Jívaro [*sic*] women" *Economic Botany* 44(1): 131–133.

Lewis, W.H. *et al.* 1991. "Ritualistic use of the holly *Ilex guayusa* by Amazonian Jívaro [*sic*] Indians" *Journal of Ethnopharmacology* 33(1,2): 25–30.

Lewontin, R.C. and **D.L. Hartl** 1991. "Population genetics in forensic DNA typing" *Science* 254: 1745–1750. Rebuttal to Chakraborty & Kidd 1991; see also: Koshland 1992; Roberts 1991; Wills *et al.* 1992.

Lhote, H. 1959. *The Search for the Tassili Frescoes.* E.P. Dutton, New York.

Li, H.-L. 1974A. "The origin and use of *Cannabis* in eastern Asia: Linguistic-cultural implications" *Economic Botany* 28(2): 293–301.

Li, H.-L. 1974B. "An archaeological and historical account of Cannabis in China" *Economic Botany* 28(4): 437–448.

Li, H.-L. 1978. "Hallucinogenic plants in Chinese herbals" *Journal of Psychedelic Drugs* 10(1): 17–26. Originally published in 1977 in *Botanical Museum Leaflets* Harvard University 25(6): 161–181.

Liggenstorfer, R. and **C. Rätsch** (Eds.) 1996. *María Sabina: Botin der Heiligen Pilze. Vom Traditionellen Schamanentum zur Weltweiten Pilzkultur.* Nachtschatten Verlag, Solothurn, Switzerland. Translation, with *addenda*, of Estrada 1977.

Lin, G.C. and R.A. Glennon (Eds.) 1994. *Hallucinogens: An Update.* (NIDA Research Monograph 146) National Institute on Drug Abuse, Rockville, MD.

Lincoff, G. and **D.H. Mitchel** 1977. *Toxic and Hallucinogenic Mushroom Poisoning—A Handbook for Physicians and Mushroom Hunters.* Van Nostrand Reinhold, New York. Foreword A.H. Smith, pp. V–VI.

Ling, T.M. and **J. Buckman** 1963. *Lysergic Acid (LSD 25) and Ritalin in the Treatment of Neurosis.* Lambarde Press, London, England.

Ling, T.M. and **J. Buckman** 1964. "The treatment of frigidity with LSD and Ritalin" *The Psychedelic Review* 1(4): 450–458.

Linzer, J. 1970. "Some anthropological aspects of yagé" In: Aaronson, B.S. and H. Osmond (Eds.) *Psychedelics: The Uses and Implications of Hallucinogenic Drugs.* Doubleday/Anchor, Garden City, NJ. pp. 108–115.

Liounis, A. 1992. "Silk for cocaine" *Omni*. 14(9).

Lipp, F.J. 1990. "Mixe concepts and uses of

entheogenic mushrooms" In: Riedlinger, T.J. (Ed.) *The Sacred Mushroom Seeker: Essays for R. Gordon Wasson.* Ethnomycological Studies No. 11. Dioscorides Press, Portland, OR. pp. 151–159.

Lipp. F.J. 1991. *The Mixe of Oaxaca: Religion, Ritual and Healing*. University of Texas Press, Austin, TX. Foreword by M. S. Edmondson, pp. IX–XI.

Litten, W. 1975. "The most poisonous mushroom" *Scientific American*. March issue. p. 91 *et seq*. Cover story.

Litzinger, W.J. 1981. "Ceramic evidence for prehistoric *Datura* use in North America" *Journal of Ethnopharmacology* 4(1): 57–74.

Liu, K.C. *et al.* 1977. "Studies on the constituents of the cortex radicus of *Acacia confusa*" *Hua Hsueh Hsueh Pao* 1977(1): 15–16.

Liwszyc, G.E. *et al.* 1992. "Daime—A ritual herbal potion" *Journal of Ethnopharmacology* 36(1): 91–92.

Lloyd, H.A. *et al.* 1985. "Brunfelsamidine: A novel convulsant from the medicinal plant *Brunfelsia grandiflora*" *Science* 227: 634–636.

Lockwood, T.E. 1973A. *A Taxonomic Revision of Brugmansia (Solanaceae).* Thesis, Harvard University, Cambridge, MA.

Lockwood, T.E. 1973B. "Generic recognition of Brugmansia" *Botanical Museum Leaflets* Harvard University 23(6): 273–284.

Lockwood, T.E. 1979. "The ethnobotany of *Brugmansia*" *Journal of Ethnopharmacology* 1(2): 147–164.

Lonitzer, A. (Lonicerus) 1582. *Kräuterbuch.* Frankfurt-am-Main, Germany.

López Austin, A. 1967. "Terminos del Nahuallatolli" *Historia Mexicana* 17(1): 1–36.

LordNose! (Pseudonym for M. Franklin) 1992. *A Guide to the Psychedelics*. Privately printed, San Francisco, CA. Booklet with bibliography to accompany "XochiSpeaks" poster/photograph of the ancient Mexican statue of Xochipilli surmounted by space-filling molecular models of a dozen psychoactive substances. See also: Fraser 1992; back cover of *Whole Earth Review* 75, 1992; and *Mondo 2000* No. 7, 1992.

Louria, D.B. 1967. "The abuse of LSD" and "First Discussion" In: DeBold, R.C. and R.C. Leaf (Eds.) *LSD, Man and Society.* Wesleyan University Press, Middletown, CT. pp. 36–49; 50–59.

Lowie, R.H. 1946. "The indians of eastern Brazil. Eastern Brazil: An introduction" In: Steward, J.H. (Ed.) *Handbook of South American Indians.* (Bureau of American Ethnology Bulletin No. 143) U.S. Government Printing Office, Washington, D.C. pp. 381–397.

Lowy, B. 1971. "New records of mushroom stones from Guatemala" *Mycologia* 63(5): 983–993.

Lowy, B. 1972. "Mushroom symbolism in Mayan codices" *Mycologia* 64(4): 816–821.

Lowy, B. 1974. "*Amanita muscaria* and the thunderbolt legend in Guatemala and Mexico" *Mycologia* 66: 188–191.

Lowy, B. 1975. "Notes on mushrooms and religion" *Revista/Review Interamericana* 5(1): 110–117.

Lowy, B. 1977. "Hallucinogenic mushrooms in Guatemala" *Journal of Psychedelic Drugs* 9(2): 123–125.

Lowy, B. 1980. "Ethnomycological inferences from mushroom stones, Maya codices, and Tzutuhil legend" *Revista/Review Interamericana* 10(1): 94–103.

Lowy, B. 1987. "Caapi revisted—In Christianity" *Economic Botany* 41(3): 450–452.

Lozoya, X. 1990. *Los Señores de las Plantas: Herbolaria y Medicina en Mesoamérica.* Pangea Editores, México City. Also: *Estudios de Cultura Náhuatl* 17: 193–206, 1983.

Ludlow, F.H. 1857. *The Hasheesh Eater: Be-*

ing Passages from the Life of a Pythagorean. Harper & Bros., New York. Reprinted in 185x, 1860 and in facsimile; limited edition of 300 copies of last signed by Sätty, some of which illustrations later reappeared in *The Archaic Revival* (McKenna 1991), Level Press, San Francisco, 1975. Introduction by Michael Horowitz, pp. 6–8. German translation in 1980. *Das Haschisch Eßer.* Sphinx Verlag, Basel, Switzerland.

Ludwig, A.M. and **J. Levine** 1966. "The clinical effects of psychedelic agents" *Clinical Medicine* 73: 21–24.

Luk, K.-C. *et al.* 1983. "Isolation and identification of 'diazepam-like' compounds from bovine urine" *Journal of Natural Products* 46(6): 852–861.

Lumholtz, C. 1894. "Tarahumari dances and plant-worship" *Scribners Magazine* 16: 438–456. October issue.

Lumholtz, C. 1902. *Unknown Mexico.* Scribner, New York.

Luna, L.E. 1984A. "The healing practices of a Peruvian shaman" *Journal of Ethnopharmacology* 11(2): 123–133.

Luna, L.E. 1984B. "The concept of plants as teachers among four mestizo shamans of Iquitos, northeastern Peru" *Journal of Ethnopharmacology* 11(2): 135–156.

Luna, L.E. 1986A. "Bibliografía sobre el ayahuasca" *América Indígena* 46(1): 235–245.

Luna, L.E. 1986B. "Apéndices" *América Indígena* 46(1): 247–251.

Luna, L.E. 1986C. *Vegetalismo: Shamanism among the Mestizo Population of the Peruvian Amazon.* (Acta Universitatis Stockholmensis, Stockholm Studies in Comparative Religion No. 27) Almqvist and Wiksell International, Stockholm, Sweden.

Luna, L.E. 1991. "Plant spirits in ayahuasca visions by Peruvian painter, Pablo Amaringo. An iconographic analysis" *Integration: Zeitschrift für Geistbewegende Pflanzen und Kultur* 1: 18–29.

Luna, L.E. 1992. Personal communications, San Luis Potosí, SLP, México.

Luna, L.E. 1993. Personal communications, Madrid and Huelva, Spain.

Luna, L.E. and **P. Amaringo** 1991. *Ayahuasca Visions: The Religious Iconography of a Peruvian Shaman.* North Atlantic Books, Berkeley, CA.

Lund, U. 1979. "Estimation of muscimol and ibotenic acid in *Amanita muscaria* using high-performance liquid chromatography" *Arch. Pharm. Chem. Sci.* 7: 115–118.

Lundström, J. 1971. "Biosynthetic studies on mescaline and related cactus alkaloids" *Acta Pharmaceutica Suecica* 8: 275–302.

Luz, P. 1995. Personal communications, Salvador, Bahia, Brasil.

Ma, W.W. *et al.* 1986. "Cactus alkaloids, LXI. Identification of mescaline and related compounds in eight additional species using TLC and MS/MS" *Journal of Natural Products* 49(4): 735–737.

McAllester, D.P. 1949. *Peyote Music.* Viking Fund (Anthropology No. 13), New York.

McCawley, E.L. *et al.* 1962. "Convulsions from *Psilocybe* mushroom poisoning" *Proceedings of the Western Pharmacology Society* 5: 27–33.

McCleary, J.A. *et al.* 1960. "Antibiotic activity of an extract of peyote (*Lophophora williamsii* [Lemaire] Coulter)" *Economic Botany* 14(2): 247–249.

McCoy, A.W. 1972. *The Politics of Heroin in Southeast Asia.* Harper & Row, New York. Reprinted in 1991. *The Politics of Heroin: CIA Complicity in the Global Drug Trade.* Lawrence Hill Books, New York.

McCoy, A.W. and **A.A. Block** (Eds.) 1992. *War on Drugs: Studies in the Failure of U.S. Narcotics Policy.* Westview Press, Oxford, England.

McCullough, R.A. 1971. "A read BAD fishing trip" *Fate* 24(10): 53–57.

McDonald, A. 1978. "The present status of Soma: The effects of California *Amanita muscaria* on normal human volunteers" In: Rumack, B.H. and E. Salzman (Eds.) *Mushroom Poisoning: Diagnosis and Treatment.* CRC Press, West Palm Beach, FL. pp. 215–223.

McDonald, A. 1980. "Mushrooms and madness: Hallucinogenic mushrooms and some psychopharmacological implications" *Canadian Journal of Psychiatry* 25(7): 586–594.

MacDonald, H.R. *et al.* 1967. "Circulatory effects of heroin in patients with myocardial infarction" *The Lancet* 1: 1070–1074.

MacDougall, T. 1960. "Ipomea [*sic*] tricolor a hallucenogenic [*sic*] plant of the Zapotecs." *Boletín del Centro de Investigaciones Antropológicas de México* 6: 6–8.

MacDougall, T. 1968. "A composite with psychotropic properties" *Garden Journal* 18: 105.

McFarland, R.A. 1953. *Human Factors in Air Transportation.* McGraw-Hill, New York.

McFarland, R.A. *et al.* 1944. *Aviation Medicine* 15: 381.

MacFoy, C.A. and **A.M. Sama** 1983. "Medicinal plants in Pujehun District, Sierra Leone" *Journal of Ethnopharmacology* 8(2): 215–223.

McGlothlin, W.H. 1965. "Hallucinogenic drugs: A perspective with special reference to peyote and Cannabis" *Psychedelic Review* 6: 16–57.

McIsaac, W.M. and **V. Estévez** 1966. "Structure-action relationship of β-carbolines as monoamine oxidase inhibitors" *Biochemical Pharmacology* 15: 1625–1627.

McKenna, D.J. 1992. Personal communications, San Luis Potosí, SLP, México.

McKenna, D.J. and **T.K. McKenna** 1975. *The Invisible Landscape: Mind, Hallucinogens, and the I Ching.* Seabury Press, New York. Reprint in 1994, Harper San Francisco.

McKenna, D.J. and **S.J. Peroutka** 1990. "Neurochemistry and neurotoxicity of 3,4-methylenedioxyamphetamine (MDMA, 'Ecstasy')" *Journal of Neurochemistry* 54(1): 14–22.

McKenna, D.J. and **J.M. Saavedra** 1987. "Autoradiography of LSD and 2,5-dimethoxyphenylisopropylamine psychotomimetics demonstrates regional, specific cross-displacement in the rat brain" *European Journal of Pharmacology* 142: 313–315.

McKenna, D.J. and **G.H.N. Towers** 1981. "Ultra-violet mediated cytotoxic activity of β-carboline alkaloids" *Phytochemistry* 20(5): 1001–1004.

McKenna, D.J. and **G.H.N. Towers** 1984. "Biochemistry and pharmacology of tryptamines and beta-carbolines: A mini-review" *Journal of Psychoactive Drugs* 16(4): 347–358.

McKenna, D.J. and **G.H.N. Towers** 1985. "On the comparative ethnopharmacology of malpighiaceous and myristicaceous hallucinogens" *Journal of Psychoactive Drugs* 17(1): 35–39.

McKenna, D.J. *et al.* 1984A. "Monoamine oxidase inhibitors in South American hallucinogenic plants: Tryptamine and β-carboline constituents of *ayahuasca*" *Journal of Ethnopharmacology* 10(2): 195–223.

McKenna, D.J. *et al.* 1984B. "Monoamine oxidase inhibitors in South American hallucinogenic plants Part 2: Constituents of orally-active myristicaceous hallucinogens" *Journal of Ethnopharmacology* 12(2): 179–211.

McKenna, D.J. *et al.* 1986. "Ingredientes biodinámicos en las plantas que se mezclan al ayahuasca. Una farmacopea tradicional no investigada" *América Indígena* 46(1): 73–99. English version published in *Rituales y Fiestas de las Américas*. Ediciones Uniandes, Bogotá, Colombia. pp. 301–316. Reprinted in Schultes, R.E. and

S. von Reis (Eds.) 1995. *Ethnobotany: Evolution of a Discipline.* Dioscorides Press, Portland, OR. pp. 349–361.

McKenna, D.J. *et al.* 1989. "Common receptors for hallucinogens in rat brain: A comparative autoradiographic study using [125I]LSD and [125I]DOI, a new psychotomimetic [*sic*] radioligand" *Brain Research* 476: 45–56.

McKenna, D.J. *et al.* 1990. "Differential interactions of indolealkylamines with hydroxytryptamine receptor subtypes" *Neuropharmacology* 29: 193–198.

McKenna, D.J. *et al.* 1991. "3,4-Methylenedioxyamphetamine (MDA) analogues exhibit differential effects on synaptosomal release of ^{3}H-dopamine and ^{3}H-5-hydroxytryptamine" *Pharmacology Biochemistry and Behavior* 38: 505–512.

McKenna, T.K. 1988. "Hallucinogenic mushrooms and evolution" *ReVision: The Journal of Consciousness and Change* 10(4): 51–57.

McKenna, T.K. 1989A. "Plan/Plant/Planet" *Whole Earth Review* 64: 4–11.

McKenna, T.K. 1989B. "Among Ayahuasquera" In: Rätsch, C. (Ed.) *Gateway to Inner Space: Sacred Plants, Mysticism and Psychotherapy—A Festschrift in Honor of Albert Hofmann.* Prism Press, Dorset, England. pp. 179–211.

McKenna, T.K. 1990. "Wasson's literary precursors" In: Riedlinger, T.J. (Ed.) *The Sacred Mushroom Seeker: Essays for R. Gordon Wasson.* Ethnomycological Studies No. 11. Dioscorides Press, Portland, OR. pp. 165–175.

McKenna, T.K. 1991. *The Archaic Revival: Speculations on Psychedelic Mushrooms, the Amazon, Virtual Reality, UFOs, Evolution, Shamanism, the Rebirth of the Goddess and the End of History.* Harper San Francisco, New York. Foreword by Tom Robbins, pp. XII–XIV.

McKenna, T.K. 1992. *Food of the Gods: The Search for the Original Tree of Knowledge. A Radical History of Plants, Drugs, and Human Evolution.* Bantam Books, New York.

McKenna, T.K. 1993. Personal communications, Catemaco, Veracruz, México.

McLaughlin, J.L. 1973. "Peyote: An introduction" *Lloydia* 36(1): 1–8.

McLaughlin, J.L. 1979. Personal communication to R.A. Bye in: Bye, R.A. 1979. "Hallucinogenic plants of the Tarahumara" *Journal of Ethnopharmacology* 1(1): 23–48.

McManamy, M.C. and **P.G. Schube** 1936. "Caffeine intoxication: Report of a case the symptoms of which amounted to a psychosis" *New England Journal of Medicine* 215(14): 616–620.

McManus, G.B. and **H. Seidler** 1992. "Ice man: Victim of prehistoric schnapps?" *Science* 258: 1867–1868.

McMeekin, D. 1992. "Representations on pre-Columbian spindle whorls of the floral and fruit structure of economic plants" *Economic Botany* 46(2): 171–180.

MacRae, E. 1992. *Guiado Pela Lua: Xamanismo e Uso Ritual da Ayahuasca no Culto do Santo Daime.* Brasiliense, São Paulo, Brasil.

MacRae, W.D. 1984. *Ethnobiological and Chemical Investigations on Selected Amazonian Plants.* Thesis, University of British Columbia, Vancouver, B.C., Canada. *Dissertation Abstracts* 45(12): 3704–B.

MacRae, W.D. and **G.H.N. Towers** 1984A. "An ethnopharmacological examination of *Virola elongata* bark: A South American arrow poison" *Journal of Ethnopharmacology* 12(1): 75–92.

MacRae, W.D. and **G.H.N. Towers** 1984B. "*Justicia pectoralis*: A study of the basis for its use as a hallucinogenic snuff ingredient" *Journal of Ethnopharmacology* 12(1): 93–111.

MacRae, W.D. *et al.* 1988. "Studies on the pharmacological activity of Amazonian

Euphorbiaceae" *Journal of Ethnopharmacology* 22(2): 143–172.

Malamus, M. and **M. Marselos** 1992. "The tradition of medicinal plants in Zagori, Epirus (northeastern Greece)" *Journal of Ethnopharmacology* 37(3): 197–203.

Malone, M.H. and **A. Rother** 1994. "*Heimia salicifolia*: A phytochemical and phytopharmacologic review" *Journal of Ethnopharmacology* 42(3): 135–159.

Manandhar, N.P. 1991. "Medicinal plant lore of Tamang tribe of Kabhrepalanchoc district, Nepal" *Economic Botany* 45(1): 58–71.

Mandel, M. 1992. "Eine sonderbare Begegnung" *Integration: Zeitschrift für Geistbewegende Pflanzen und Kultur* 2&3: 132–133.

Mann, J. 1992. *Murder, Magic, and Medicine.* Oxford University Press, Oxford, England.

Manske, R.H.F. 1931. "A synthesis of the methyltryptamines and some derivatives" *Canadian Journal of Research* 5: 592–600.

Manske, R.H.F. *et al.* 1927. "Harmine and harmaline. Part IX. A synthesis of harmaline" *Journal of the Chemical Society (Organic)* 1927: 1–15.

Mantle, P.G. and **E.S. Waight** 1969. "Occurrence of psilocybin in the sporophores of Psilocybe semilanceata" *Transactions of the British Mycological Society* 53(2): 302–304.

Marcano, V. *et al.* 1994. "Occurrence of psilocybin and psilocin in *Psilocybe pseudobullacea* (Petch) Pegler from the Venezuelan Andes" *Journal of Ethnopharmacology* 43 (2): 157–159.

Marczynski, T. 1959. "Some pharmacological properties of a recently-isolated alkaloid, 5-methoxy-*N*-methyltryptamine" *Bull. Acad. Pol. Sci.* 7: 151–154.

Marczynski, T. and **J. Vetulani** 1960. "Further investigations on the pharmacological properties of 5-methoxy-*N*-methyltryptamine" *Dissertationes Pharmaceuticae* 12: 67–84.

Marglin, F.A. 1985. *The Wives of the God-King: The Rituals of the Devadasis of Puri.* Oxford University Press, Oxford, England.

Margot, P. and **R. Watling** 1981. "Studies in Australian agarics and boletes. 2. Further studies in *Psilocybe*" *Transactions of the British Mycological Society* 76(3): 485–489.

Mariani, A. 1890. *Coca and its Therapeutic Application.* J.N. Jaros, New York.

Mariani Ramírez, C. 1965. *Temas de Hipnosis.* Editorial Andrés Bello, Santiago, Chile.

Marks, J. 1979. *The Search for the "Manchurian Candidate"—The CIA and Mind Control.* Times Books, New York.

Marles, R.J. *et al.* 1988. "A contribution to the ethnopharmacology of the lowland Quichua people of Amazonian Ecuador" *Revista de la Academia Colombiana de Ciencias Exactas, Físicas y Naturales* 16(63): 111–120.

Marnell, T. (Ed.) 1993. *Drug Identification Bible.* Drug Identification Bible, Denver, CO. Second edition in 1995.

Marrazzi, A.S. 1967. "Electropharmacological and behavioral actions of kava" In: Efron, D.H. *et al.* (Eds.) *Ethnopharmacologic Search for Psychoactive Drugs.* (Public Health Service Publication No. 1645) U.S. Government Printing Office, Washington, D.C. pp. 152–154.

Marriott, A. and **C.K. Rachlin** 1971. *Peyote.* T.Y. Crowell, New York. Paperback 1972.

Marshall, E. 1988A. "Flying blind in the war on drugs" *Science* 240: 1605–1607.

Marshall, E. 1988B. "A war on drugs with real troops?" *Science* 241: 13–15.

Marshall, E. 1988C. "Drug wars: Legalization gets a hearing" *Science* 241: 1157–1159.

Marshall, E. 1988D. "The drug of champions" *Science* 242: 183–184.

Marshall, E. 1989. "The Drug Czar: No Walter Wallflower" *Science* 243: 1287.

Marshall, J. 1991. *Drug Wars: Corruption, Counterinsurgency and Covert Operations in the Third World.* Cohan & Cohen Publishers, Forestville, CA.

Marshman, J. and **R.J. Gibbins** 1970. "A note on the composition of illicit drugs" *Ontario Medical Review.* Sept. pp. 1–3.

Marten, G.C. 1973A. "Alkaloids in reed canarygrass" In: Matches, A.G. (Ed.) *Anti-Quality Components of Forages.* Crop Sciences Society of America, Madison, WI. pp. 15–31.

Marten, G.C. 1973B. "Alkaloids and palatability of *Phalaris arundinacea* L. grown in diverse environments" *Agronomy Journal* 65: 199–201.

Martin, R.T. 1970. "The role of coca in the history, religion and medicine of South American Indians" *Economic Botany* 24 (4): 422–438. Reprinted in 1975 in Andrews, G. and D. Solomon (Eds.) *The Coca Leaf and Cocaine Papers.* Harcourt Brace Jovanovich, New York. pp. 20–37.

Martínez V., J.C. and **L.E. Cuca S.** 1987. "Flavonoids of *Virola calophylloidea*" *Journal of Natural Products* 50(6): 1045–1047.

Marx, J.L. 1985. "'Anxiety peptide' found in brain" *Science* 227: 934.

Marx, J.L. 1990. "Marijuana receptor gene cloned" *Science* 249: 624–626.

Mash, D.C. *et al.* 1995. "Identification of a primary metabolite of ibogaine that targets serotonin transporters and elevates serotonin" *Life Sciences* 57(3): PL45–PL50.

Maslow, A.H. 1962. *Toward a Psychology of Being.* Litton Publishing, Inc., New York.

Mason, A.P. and **A.J. MacBay** 1985. "Cannabis: Pharmacology and interpretation of effects" *Journal of Forensic Science* 30(3): 615–631.

Masters, R.E.L. and **J. Houston** 1966. *The Varieties of Psychedelic Experience.* Holt, Rinehart & Winston, New York.

Masters, R.E.L. and **J. Houston** 1970. "Toward an individual psychedelic psychotherapy" In: Aaronson, B. and H. Osmond (Eds.) *Psychedelics: The Uses and Implications of Hallucinogenic Drugs.* Doubleday/Anchor, Garden City, NJ. pp. 323–342.

Mata, R. and **J.L. McLaughlin** 1976. "Cactus alkaloids. XXX. N-Methylated tyramines from *Trichocereus spachianus, T. candicans,* and *Epostoa huanucensis*" *Lloydia* 39(6): 461–463.

Matossian, M.K. 1982. "Ergot and the Salem witchcraft affair" *American Scientist.* July-August issue. 70: 185–192.

Matossian, M.K. 1989. *Poisons of the Past: Molds, Epidemics and History.* Yale University Press, New Haven, CT.

Matossian, M.K. 1992. "The crucible of Salem: Witchcraft, ergo, ergotism" *MD.* November issue. pp. 85–96. W.B. Ober "Ergotism and the afflicted girls" p. 92.

Matsuda, I. 1960. "Hallucination caused by *Psilocybe venenata* (Imai) et Hongo" *Transactions of the Mycological Society of Japan* 2(4): 16–17.

Matsumoto, T. *et al.* 1969. "Isolierung von 4-hydroxypyrrolidon-2- und einigen weiteren Verbindungen aus *Amanita muscaria*" *Helvetica Chimica Acta* 52: 716.

Matthiessen, P. 1967. *At Play in the Fields of the Lord.* Signet Books, New York. 1965 novel filmed in 1992 by Hector Babenco.

Mayagoitia, L. *et al.* 1986. "Psychopharmacologic analysis of an alleged oneirogenic plant, *Calea zacatechichi*" *Journal of Ethnopharmacology* 18(3): 229–243.

Mayer, K.H. 1975. "Die heiligen Pilze Mexikos" *Ethnologia Americana* 11(5): 594–596 (Teil 1); 11(6): 603–608 (Teil 2).

Mayer, K.H. 1977A. *The Mushroom Stones of Mesoamerica.* Acoma Books, Ramona, CA. *Archiv für Völkerkunde* 29: 37–73, 1975.

Mayer, K.H. 1977B. "*Salvia divinorum*: Ein Halluzinogen der Mazateken von Oaxaca, Mexiko" *Ethnologia Americana* 14(2): 776–779.

Mechoulam, R. 1973. "Cannabinoid chemistry" In: Mechoulam, R. (Ed.) *Marijuana: Chemistry, Pharmacology, Metabolism and Clinical Effects.* Academic Press, New York. pp. 1–99.

Meckes-Lozoya, M. *et al.* 1990. "N,N-Dimethyltryptamine alkaloid in *Mimosa-tenuiflora* bark (tepescohuite)" *Archivos de Investigación Médica* 21(2): 175–177.

Mehra, K.L. 1979. "Ethnobotany of the Old World Solanaceae" In: Hawkes, J.G. *et al.* (Eds.) *The Biology and Taxonomy of the Solanaceae.* (Linnean Society Symposium Series, Number 7) Academic Press, London, England. pp. 161–170.

Mellen III, C. 1963. "Reflections of a peyote eater" *The Harvard Review* 1(4): 63–67.

Menser, G.P. 1977. *Hallucinogenic and Poisonous Mushroom Field Guide.* And/Or Press, Berkeley, CA.

Merlin, M.D. and **J.W. Allen** 1993. "Species identification and chemical analysis of psychoactive fungi in the Hawaiian Islands" *Journal of Ethnopharmacology* 40(1): 21–40.

Merrill, W.L. 1977. *An Investigation of Ethnographic and Archaeological Specimens of Mescalbeans* (Sophora secundiflora) *in American Museums.* (Technical Reports No. 6) Museum of Anthropology, University of Michigan, Ann Arbor, MI.

Merrill, W.L. and **C.F. Feest** 1975. "An exchange of botanical information in the early contact situation: Wisakon of the southeastern Algonquians" *Economic Botany* 29(2): 171–184.

Metzner, R. 1963. "The pharmacology of psychedelic drugs I: Chemical and biochemical aspects" *The Psychedelic Review* I: 69–115.

Metzner, R. 1967. "Subjective effects of anticholinergic hallucinogens" *Psychedelic Review* 10.

Metzner, R. 1968. *The Ecstatic Adventure.* The Macmillan Co., New York. Foreword by A. Watts, pp. XI–XIII.

Metzner, R. 1970. "Mushrooms and the mind" In: Aaronson, B. and H. Osmond (Eds.) *Psychedelics: The Uses and Implications of Hallucinogenic Drugs.* Doubleday/ Anchor, Garden City, NJ. pp. 90–107.

Metzner, R. (Ed.) 1988. "Psychedelics revisited" *ReVision: The Journal of Consciousness and Change* 10(4): 1–72.

Metzner, R. 1994. *The Well of Remembrance: Rediscovering the Earth Wisdom Myths of Northern Europe.* Shambhala, Boston, MA. Foreword, Marija Gimbutas, pp. XI–XII; appendix "The Mead of Inspiration and Magical Plants of the Ancient Germans," by Christian Rätsch, pp. 279–295.

Metzner, R. *et al.* 1965. "The relation of expectation and mood to psilocybin reactions: A questionnaire study" *Psychedelic Review* 5: 3–39.

Meyer, B.N. *et al.* 1980. "β-Phenethylamines from the cactus genus *Opuntia*" *Phytochemistry* 19: 719.

Meyer, H.J. 1967. "Pharmacology of kava" In: Efron, D.H. *et al.* (Eds.) *Ethnopharmacologic Search for Psychoactive Drugs.* (Public Health Service Publication No. 1645) U.S. Government Printing Office, Washington, D.C. pp. 133–140.

Michael, H.N. (Ed.) 1963. *Studies in Siberian Shamanism.* Toronto, Canada.

Michaux, H. 1956. *Misérable Miracle. La Mescaline.* Éditions du Rocher, Monaco. English translation by L. Varèse, 1963. *Miserable Miracle (Mescaline).* City Lights Books, San Francisco, CA.

Michaux, H. 1957. *L'Infini Turbulent.* Mercure de France, Paris, France. Translated into English, 1975. *Infinite Turbulence.* Calder and Boyars, London, England.

Michaux, H. 1960. "La psilocybine (expériences et autocritique)" *Revue de Mycologie* 25(1): 52–68. Also published in *Lettres Nouveau* 7(35): 1–16; and in *Connaissance par les Gouffres.* Éditions Gallimard, Paris, France 1961. The last translated into English by H. Chevalier, 1963. *Light Through Darkness.* The Orion Press, New York.

Michaux, H. (Translation by P. Gregory from Michaux 1957) 1965. "Experiment five" *Psychedelic Review* 6: 84–97. Translation first published in *New World Writing*. New American Library, New York.

Middleton, D.J. 1992. "A chemotaxonomic survey of flavonoids and simple phenols in the leaves of *Gaultheria* L. and related genera (Ericaceae)" *Botanical Journal of the Linnean Society* 110(4): 313–324.

Mikuriya, T. 1970. "Marijuana in Morocco" In: Aaronson, B. and H. Osmond (Eds.) *Psychedelics: Uses and Implications of Hallucinogenic Drugs*. Doubleday/Anchor, Garden City, NJ. pp. 115–128.

Mikuriya, T. 1971. "*Cannibus* [*sic*] as a treatment for alcoholism" *Psychedelic Review* 11: 71–73.

Mikuriya, T. (Ed.) 1973. *Marijuana: Medical Papers, 1839–1972*. Medi-Comp Press, Oakland, CA.

Miller, J. and **R. Koral** (Eds.) 1995. *White Rabbit: A Psychedelic Reader*. Chronicle Books, San Francisco, CA.

Miller, J.S. 1993. Personal communications, Catemaco, Veracruz, México.

Miller, O.K. Jr. 1972. *Mushrooms of North America*. E.P. Dutton, New York.

Miller, R.W. 1980. "A brief survey of *Taxus* alkaloids and other taxane derivatives" *Journal of Natural Products* 34(4): 425–437.

Miller, W.S. 1966. "El tonalmatl mixe y los hongos sagrados" In: Jiménez Moreno, W. *et al.* (Eds.) *Summa Antropológica en Homenaje a Roberto J. Weitlaner*. Instituto Nacional de Antropología e Historia, México City.

Millet, Y. *et al.* 1980. "Étude de la toxicité d'huiles essentielles végétales du commerce: Essence d'hysope et du sauge" *Médecine Légale* 23(1): 9–20.

Ministry of Welfare, Health and Cultural Affairs 1985. *Policy on Drug Users*. Rijswijk, the Netherlands.

Mitchell, S.W. 1896. "Remarks on the effects of Anhelonium [*sic*] Lewinii (the mescal [*sic*] button)." *The British Medical Journal* 2: 1625–1629.

Mitsuhashi, H. 1976. "Medicinal plants of the Ainu" *Economic Botany* 30(3): 209–217.

Mochtar, S.G. and **H. Geerken** 1979. "Die Halluzinogene Muscarin [*sic*] und Ibotensäure im mittleren Hindukusch" *Afghanistan Journal* 6(2): 62–65.

Moerman, D.E. 1986. *Medicinal Plants of Native America*. (Research Reports in Ethnobotany, Contribution 2; Technical Reports No. 19) University of Michigan Museum of Anthropology, Ann Arbor, MI. Foreword by R.I. Ford, pp. VII–VIII.

Monardes, N. 1990. *Herbolaria de Indias*. "Presentación" and commentaries by X. Lozoya. Redacta, México City. Original 1569. *Primera, Segunda y Tercera Partes de la Historia Medicinal de las Cosas que se Traen de Nuestras Indias Occidentales*. Sevilla, Spain. English by J. Frampton, 1574. *Joyfull Newes Out of the Newe Founde Worlde*. Constable & Co., London, England. English reprinted in 1925 by A.A. Knopf, New York.

Montagne, M. and **D.D. Vogt** 1982. "Absinthe: Behind the green mask" *The International Journal of the Addictions* 17(6): 1015–1029.

Montgomery, R. 1989. "Ethnobotanical research field kit" *Whole Earth Review* 64: 30–31.

Montgomery, R. 1990. Personal communications, Occidental, CA.

Montgomery, R. 1991. "Botanical Preservation Corps meets Ecuadorian shaman woman" *Whole Earth Review* 71: 80–82.

Mooney, J. 1896. "The Mescal plant [*sic*] and ceremony" *Therapeutic Gazette*, 3rd Serial 20: 7–11.

Moore, M. 1979. *Medicinal Plants of the Mountain West*. Museum of New Mexico Press, Santa Fe, NM. Foreword by D. Copperfield, p. 5.

Moore, M. and **H.S. Altounian** 1978. *Jour-*

neys into the Bright World. Para Research, Inc., Rockport, ME.

Morales, E. 1989. *Cocaine: White Gold Rush in Peru.* Univ. of Arizona Press, Tucson, AZ.

Morán, A. *et al.* 1989A. "Pharmacological screening and antimicrobial activity of the essential oil of *Artemisia caerulescens* subsp. *gallica*" *Journal of Ethnopharmacology* 26(2): 197–203.

Morán, A. *et al.* 1989B. "Analgesic, antipyretic and antiinflammatory activity of the essential oil of *Artemisia caerulescens* subsp. *gallica*" *Journal of Ethnopharmacology* 27(3): 307–317.

Moreau, J.-J. 1845. *Du Hachisch et de l'Aliénation Mentale: Études Psychologiques.* Fortin, Masson et Cie, Paris, France. Facsimile 1970, Collection "Esquirol," Paris, France. Préface by H. Ey, unpaginated.

Morgan, G.R. 1976. *Man, Plant, and Religion: Peyote Trade on the Mustang Plains of Texas.* Thesis, University of Colorado.

Morgan, G.R. 1980. "The ethnobotany of sweet flag among North American Indians" *Botanical Museum Leaflets* Harvard University 28(3): 235–246.

Morgan, G.R. 1983A. "The biogeography of peyote in south Texas" *Botanical Museum Leaflets* Harvard University 29(2): 73–86.

Morgan, G.R. 1983B. "Hispano-Indian trade of an Indian ceremonial plant, peyote (*Lophophora williamsii*), on the Mustang Plains of Texas" *Journal of Ethnopharmacology* 9(2,3): 319–321.

Morgan, W.T.W. 1981. "Ethnobotany of the Turkana: Use of plants by a pastoral people and their livestock in Kenya" *Economic Botany* 35(1): 96–130.

Morgenthaler, J. 1990. "Smart drug update" *Mondo 2000* 5: 36–37.

Morgenthaler, J. and **W. Dean** 1991. *Smart Drugs and Nutrients.* B&J, Santa Cruz, CA.

Morland, J. *et al.* 1985. "Cannabinoids in blood and urine after passive inhalation of Cannabis smoke" *Journal of Forensic Science* 30(4): 997–1002.

Mors, W.B. and **O. Ribeiro** 1957. "Occurrence of scopoletin in the genus *Brunfelsia*" *Journal of Organic Chemistry* 22: 978–979.

Mors, W.B. and **P. Zaltzman** 1954. "Sôbre o alcaloide da *Banisteria caapi* Spruce e do *Cabi paraensis* Ducke" *Boletím do Instituto de Química Agrícola* 34: 17–27.

Mortimer, W.G. 1901. *Peru. History of Coca: "The Divine Plant" of the Incas.* J.H. Vail & Co., New York. Facsimile, 1974, And/Or Press, San Francisco, CA. Preface by M. Horowitz, pp. VI–VII. French translation by H.-B. Gausseron, 1904. *Histoire de la Coca: La Plante Divine des Incas.* A. Maloine, Paris. Abridged French edition, 1992. *De la Coca à la Cocaine.* Utz, Paris. Préface by T.H. Saigne and J. Bouriland.

Morton, C.V. 1931. "Notes on *yagé*, a drug-plant of southeastern Colombia" *Journal of the Washington Academy of Sciences* 21: 485–488.

Morton, J.F. 1977. *Major Medicinal Plants: Botany, Culture and Uses.* C.C. Thomas, Springfield, IL. Foreword by Maynard W. Quimby, pp. V–IX.

Moser, M. and **E. Horak** 1968. "*Psilocybe serbica* sp. nov., eine neue Psilocybin und Psilocin bildenden Art aus Serbien" *Zeitschrift für Pilzkunde* 34: 137–144.

Moskalenko, S.A. 1987. "Slavic ethnomedicine in the Soviet Far East. Part 1. Herbal remedies among Russians/Ukrainians in the Sukhodal Valley, Primorye" *Journal of Ethnopharmacology* 21(3): 231–251.

Most, A. 1984. *Bufo alvarius: The Psychedelic [sic] Toad of the Sonoran Desert.* Venom Press, Denton, TX.

Motley, T.J. 1992. "The ethnobotany of sweet flag, *Acorus calamus* (Araceae)" Paper presented at meeting of Society for Economic Botany, 9–13 August, Honolulu, HI.

Motolinía, F. de (Pseudonym for Toribio de Benavente; E. O'Gorman, Ed.) 1971. *Memoriales o Libro de las Cosas de la Nueva España*. Universidad Nacional Autónoma de México, México City. Originally published in 1541.

Motte, E. 1982. *Les Plantes Chez les Pygmées Aka et les Monzobo de la Lobaye (Centrafrique).* Centre National de la Recherche Scientifique, Paris, France.

Mount, G. (Ed.) 1987. *The Peyote Book: A Study of Native Medicine.* Sweetlight Books, Arcata, CA. Second edition, 1988.

Mountain Girl (Pseudonym for Carolyn Adams García) 1977. *The Primo Plant: Growing Sinsemilla*. Wingbow Press, Berkeley, CA.

Mulamba, T. *et al.* 1981. "Alcaloïdes de *Tabernanthe pubescens*" *Journal of Natural Products* 44(2): 184–189.

Müller, G.F.R. and **C.H. Eugster** 1965. "Muscimol, ein pharmakodynamisch wirksamer Stoff aus *Amanita muscaria*" *Helvetica Chimica Acta* 48: 910–916.

Müller, G.K. and **J. Gartz** 1986. "Psilocybe cyanescens—Eine weitere halluzinogene Kahlkopf-Art in der DDR" *Mykologisches Mitteilungsblatt* 29(2): 33–35.

Mulvena, D.P. and **M. Slaytor** 1982. "Separation of tryptophan derivatives in *Phalaris aquatica* by thin-layer chromatography" *Journal of Chromatography* 245: 155–157.

Munn, H. 1973. "The mushrooms of language" In: Harner, M.J. (Ed.) *Hallucinogens and Shamanism.* Oxford University Press, London, England. pp. 86–122.

Muñóz Camargo, D. 1892. *Historia de Tlaxcala*. Oficina Tipográfica de la Secretaría de Fomento, México City.

Murrill, W.A. 1916. "A very dangerous [*sic*] mushroom" *Mycologia* 8(1): 186–187.

Musès, C. (Translation by J. Baker) 1989. "The sacred plants of ancient Egypt" In: Rätsch, C. (Ed.) *Gateway to Inner Space: Sacred Plants, Mysticism and Psychotherapy—A Festschrift in Honor of Albert Hofmann.* Prism Press, Bridport, England. pp. 143–159.

Musto, D.F. 1973. *The American Disease: Origins of Narcotic Control.* Yale University Press, New Haven, CT. Reprinted in 1988 by Oxford University Press, New York.

Myerhoff, B.G. 1970. "The deer-maize-peyote symbol complex among the Huichol Indians of Mexico" *Anthropological Quarterly* 43(2): 64–78.

Myerhoff, B.G. 1974. *Peyote Hunt: The Sacred Journey of the Huichol Indians.* Cornell University Press, Ithaca, NY. Foreword by Victor Turner, pp. 7–10. Translation 1980. *Der Peyote Kult*. München, Germany.

Myers, C.W. *et al.* 1978. "A dangerously toxic new frog (*Phyllobates*) used by Emberá Indians of Western Colombia, with discussion of blowgun fabrication and dart poisoning" *Bulletin of the Museum of Natural History* 161: 307–366.

Mylonas, G.E. 1961. *Eleusis and the Eleusinian Mysteries.* Princeton University Press, Princeton, NJ.

Nabhan, G.P. 1989. *Enduring Seeds: Native American Agriculture and Wild Plant Conservation.* North Point Press, San Francisco, CA. Foreword by Walter Berry, pp. IX–X.

Nadelmann, E.A. 1988. "Isn't it time to legalize drugs?" *The Boston Sunday Globe.* 20 October issue. p. A25.

Nadelmann, E.A. 1989. "Drug prohibition in the United States: Costs, consequences, and alternatives" *Science* 245: 939–947. Copyright © 1989, AAAS. Paid permission granted. See also: Vance, M.A. *et al.* 1989.

Nadelmann, E.A. 1992. "Thinking seriously about alternatives to drug prohibition" *Daedalus* 121(3): 85–132.

Nahas, G.G. (Ed.) 1976. *Marihuana:* [*sic*] *Chemistry, Biochemistry and Cell Effects.* Springer Verlag, New York.

Naranjo, C. 1967. "Psychotropic properties of the harmala alkaloids" In: Efron, D.H. *et al.* (Eds.) *Ethnopharmacologic Search for Psychoactive Drugs.* (Public Health Service Publication No. 1645) U.S. Government Printing Office, Washington, D.C. pp. 385–391.

Naranjo, C. 1973A. *The Healing Journey: New Approaches to Consciousness.* Pantheon Books, New York. Preface by Stanislaus Grof, pp. IX–XIII.

Naranjo, C. 1973B. "Psychological aspects of the *yagé* [*sic*] experience in an experimental setting" In: Harner, M.J. (Ed.) *Hallucinogens and Shamanism.* Oxford University Press, London, England. pp. 176–190.

Naranjo, C. 1987. "*Ayahuasca* imagery and the therapeutic property of the harmala alkaloids" *Journal of Mental Imagery* 11(2): 131–136.

Naranjo, C. 1990. "A posthumous 'encounter' with R. Gordon Wasson" In: Riedlinger, T.J. (Ed.) *The Sacred Mushroom Seeker: Essays for R. Gordon Wasson.* Ethnomycological Studies No. 11. Dioscorides Press, Portland, OR. pp. 177–181.

Naranjo, P. 1969. "Etnofarmacología de las plantas psicotrópicas de América" *Terápia* 24: 5–63.

Naranjo, P. 1970. *Ayahuasca: Religión y Medicina.* Editorial Universitaria, Quito, Ecuador.

Naranjo, P. 1975. "Drogas psiquedélicas [*sic*] en medicina mágica" *Cuadernos Científicos CEMEF* 4: 73–92.

Naranjo, P. 1979. "Hallucinogenic plant use and related indigenous belief systems in the Ecuadorian Amazon" *Journal of Ethnopharmacology* 1(2): 121–145.

Naranjo, P. 1983. *Ayahuasca: Etnomedicina y Mitología.* Ediciones Libri Mundi, Quito, Ecuador. Revised edition of Naranjo 1970.

Naranjo, P. 1986. "El *ayahuasca* en la arqueología ecuatoriana" *América Indígena* 46(1): 117–127.

Naranjo, P. and **E. Naranjo** 1961. "Estudio farmacodinámico de una planta psicotomimética [*sic*]: *Coriaria thymifolia* (shanshi)" *Archivos de Criminología Neuro-Psiquiátrica y Disciplinas Conexas* (Quito) 9: 600–616.

Naranjo, P. *et al.* 1964. "Estudio de una especie psicotomimética [*sic*]: *Ipomoea carnea*" *Archivos de Criminología Neuro-Psiquiátrica y Disciplinas Conexas* (Quito) 14: 4.

Nath, D. *et al.* 1992. "Commonly used Indian abortifacient plants with special reference to their teratologic effects in rats" *Journal of Ethnopharmacology* 36(2): 147–154.

National Commission on Marihuana [*sic*] and Drug Abuse 1972. *Marihuana* [*sic*]: *A Signal of Misunderstanding.* The New American Library, New York. Foreword by ex-Pennsylvania governor & Commission Chairman, Raymond P. Shafer, pp. V–VI.

Navchoo, I.A. and **G.M. Buth** 1990. "Ethnobotany of Ladakh, India: Beverages, narcotics, foods" *Economic Botany* 44(3): 318–321.

Navet, E. 1988. "Des Ojibway et l'Amanite Tue-Mouche (*Amanita muscaria*): Pour une ethnomycologie des Indiens d'Amérique du Nord" *Journal de la Société des Americanistes* 76: 163–180. Translated into German, 1993. "Die Ojibway und der Fliegenpilz: Für eine Ethnomykologie der Indianer von Nordamerika" *Integration: Zeitschrift für Geistbewegende Pflanzen und Kultur* 4: 15–51.

Neal, J.M. *et al.* 1972. "Peyote alkaloids: Identification in the Mexican cactus *Pelecyphora aselliformis* Ehrenberg" *Science* 176: 1131–1133.

Negbi, M. 1992. "A sweetmeat plant, a perfume plant and their weedy relatives: A chapter in the history of *Cyperus esculentus* L. and *C. rotundus* L." *Economic Botany* 46(1): 64–71.

Neogi, B. *et al.* 1989. "Ethnobotany of some weeds of Khasi and Garo Hills, Meghalaya, northeastern India" *Economic Botany* 43(4): 471–479.

Newland, C. (Pseudonym for Thelma Moss) 1962. *My Self and I.* Coward-McCann, New York. Foreword by Harold Greenwald, pp. 7–9; introduction by R.A. Sandison, pp. 11–16.

Nguyen, X.D. and **T.L. Do** 1991. "Selection of traditional medicines for study" *Journal of Ethnopharmacology* 32(1-3): 57–70.

Nichols, D.E. *et al.* 1982. "Effects of certain hallucinogenic amphetamine analogues on the release of [^{3}H]serotonin from rat brain synaptosomes" *Journal of Medicinal Chemistry* 25: 530–535.

Nieto, M. *et al.* 1982. *Anales de la Associación de Química de Argentina* 70: 295–299.

Nir, I. *et al.* 1974. "Behavioural effect of intraventricular application of methoxyindolealkylamines in the rat" *Psychopharmacologia* 39: 323–327.

Nordal, A. 1980. "Khat: Pharmacognostical aspects" *Bulletin on Narcotics* 32(3): 51–64.

Nordbø, K. 1979. "Sopp som rusmiddel" *Tidsskr. Nor. Lægeforen* 29: 1476–1477.

Norland, R.H. 1976. *What's in a Mushroom.* Pear Tree Publications, Ashland, OR.

Norquist, D.G. and **J.L. McLaughlin** 1970. "Cactus alkaloids VIII. Isolation of *N*-methyl-3,4-dimethoxy-β-phenethylamine from *Ariocarpus fissuratus* var. *fissuratus*" *Journal of Pharmaceutical Sciences* 59: 1840.

Novák, M. *et al.* 1984. "Biological activity of the alkaloids of *Erythroxylum coca* and *Erythroxylum novogranatense*" *Journal of Ethnopharmacology* 10(3): 261–274.

Ocaña, E. 1993. *El Dioniso Moderno y la Farmacia Utópica.* Editorial Anagrama, Barcelona, Spain; see Δαιμων 8: 155–166, 1994.

O'Connell, F.D. and **E.V. Lynn** 1953. "The alkaloid of *Banisteriopsis inebrians* Morton" *Journal of the American Pharmaceutical Association* 42: 753–754.

O'Connell, J.F. *et al.* 1983. "Traditional and modern plant use among the Alyamara of Central Australia" *Economic Botany* 37(1): 80–109.

Oga, S. *et al.* 1984. "Pharmacological trials of crude extracts of *Passiflora alata*" *Planta Medica* 50: 303–306.

Ohenoja, E. *et al.* 1987. "The occurrence of psilocybin and psilocin in Finnish fungi" *Journal of Natural Products* 50(4): 741–744.

Ohi, K. and **M.F. Torres** 1994. *Piedras-Hongo.* Museo de Tabaco y Sal, Tokyo, Japan.

Ola'h, G.M. 1968. "Étude chimiotaxinomique sur les *Panaeolus*. Recherches sur la présence des corps indoliques psychotropes dans ces champignons" *Comptes Rendus Hebdomadaires des Séances de l'Académie des Sciences* 267: 1369–1372.

Ola'h, G.M. 1970. "Le genre Panaeolus: Essai taxinomique et physiologique" *Revue de Mycologie: Mémoire hors-série No. 10.* Muséum National d'Histoire Naturelle, Paris, France. Préface R. Heim, pp. V–VII.

Ola'h, G.M. and **R. Heim** 1967. "Une nouvelle espèce nord-américaine de Psilocybe hallucinogène: *Psilocybe quebecensis* G. Ola'h et R. Heim" *Comptes Rendus Hebdomadaires des Séances de l'Académie des Sciences* 264: 1601–1604.

Oliver-Bever, B. 1983. "Medicinal plants in tropical West Africa. II. Plants acting on the nervous system" *Journal of Ethnopharmacology* 7(1): 1–93.

Olney, J.W. *et al.* 1991. "NMDA antagonist neurotoxicity: Mechanism and prevention" *Science* 254: 1515–1518.

Oram, R.N. and **J.D. Williams** 1967. "Variation in concentration and composition of toxic alkaloids among strains of *Phalaris tuberosa* L." *Nature* 213: 946–947.

Ortega, A. *et al.* 1982. "Salvinorin, a new *trans*-neoclerodane diterpene from *Salvia divinorum* (Labiatae)" *Journal of the Chemical Society Perkins Transactions* I: 2505–2508. See: Valdés III *et al.* 1984.

Ortega, B. 1993. "Secret Service held guilty of violating computer privacy" *The Wall Street Journal*. 16 March issue. p. A10. See also: Gans & Sirius 1990; Levy 1991.

Ortíz de Montellano, B.R. 1975. "Empirical Aztec medicine" *Science* 188: 215–220.

Ortíz de Montellano, B.R. 1981. "Entheogens: The interaction of biology and culture" *Reviews in Anthropology* 8: 339–363.

Ortíz de Montellano, B.R. 1990. *Aztec Medicine, Health, and Nutrition*. Rutgers University Press, Brunswick, NJ.

Ortíz de Montellano, B.R. and **C.H. Browner** 1985. "Chemical bases for medicinal plant use in Oaxaca, Mexico" *Journal of Ethnopharmacology* 13(1): 57–88.

Osmond, H. 1955. "Ololiuqui: The ancient Aztec narcotic [*sic*]. Remarks on the effects of *Rivea corymbosa* (ololiuqui)" *Journal of Mental Science* 101: 526–537.

Osmond, H. 1961. "Peyote night" *Tomorrow* 9(2): 105–125.

Osmond, H. 1970. "Peyote night" In: Aaronson, B. and H. Osmond (Eds.) *Psychedelics: The Uses and Implications of Hallucinogenic Drugs*. Doubleday/Anchor, Garden City, NJ. pp. 67–86. Reprint of 1961 *Tomorrow* article.

Oss, O.T. and **O.N. Oeric** with **I.T. Obscure** and **Kat** (Pseudonyms for J. Bigwood, K. Harrison McKenna, D.J. McKenna and T.K. McKenna) 1976. *Psilocybin: Magic Mushroom Grower's Guide: A Handbook for Psilocybin Enthusiasts*. And/Or Press, Berkeley, CA. Second edition in 1986, Lux Natura, Berkeley, CA. Translated into German, 1981. *Psilocybin: Ein Handbuch für die Pilzzucht*. Volksverlag, Linden, Germany.

Ostolaza, C.N. *et al.* 1985. "*Neoraimondia arequipensis* var. *roseiflora* (Werd. & Backeb.) Rauh." *Cactus and Succulent Journal* 57: 60–64.

Ott, J. 1975A. "Notes on recreational use of hallucinogenic mushrooms" *Boletín de la Sociedad Mexicana de Micología* 9: 131–135.

Ott, J. 1975B. "*Amanita muscaria*: Usos y química" *Cuadernos Científicos CEMEF* 4: 203–221.

Ott, J. 1976A. "Psycho-mycological studies of *Amanita*—From ancient sacrament to modern phobia" *Journal of Psychedelic Drugs* 8(1): 27–35.

Ott, J. 1976B. *Hallucinogenic Plants of North America*. (Psycho-Mycological Studies Number One) Wingbow Press, Berkeley, CA. Introduction by Richard Evans Schultes, p. IX. Drawings by M.J. Eloheimo.

Ott, J. 1977A. "The magic mushrooms" *The Weekly* (Seattle) 2(26): 10–13, 28.

Ott, J. 1977B. "*Amanita muscaria*: Mushroom of the gods" *Head*. March/April issue. pp. 55 *et seq.*

Ott, J. 1978A. *Mr. Jonathan Ott's Rejoinder to Dr. Alexander H. Smith*. Ethnomycological Studies No. 6. Botanical Museum of Harvard University, Cambridge, MA. "Introducing Mr. Ott" by R. G. Wasson, p. 1. Rebuttal to A.H. Smith 1977. See also Singer 1982; Wasson 1982A.

Ott, J. 1978B. "Exordium: A Brief history of hallucinogenic mushrooms" In: Ott, J. and J. Bigwood (Eds.) *Teonanácatl: Hallucinogenic Mushrooms of North America*. (Psycho-Mycological Studies No. 2) Madrona Publishers, Seattle, WA. pp. 5–22. Translated into Spanish by M.S. Antolín, 1985. "Exordium: Breve historia de los hongos alucinógenos" *Teonanácatl: Hongos Alucinógenos de Europa y América del Norte*. Editorial Swan, San Lorenzo de El Escorial, Spain. pp. 19–38.

Ott, J. 1978C. "Recreational use of hallucinogenic mushrooms in the United States" In: Rumack, B.H. and E. Salzman (Eds.) *Mushroom Poisoning: Diagnosis and Treatment*. CRC Press, West Palm Beach, FL. pp. 231–243.

Ott, J. (Ed.) 1979A. *Journal of Psychedelic Drugs* 11(1-2): 1–149; Proceedings of "Hallucinogens in Native American Shamanism and Modern Life," 28 September–1 October 1978, San Francisco, CA, USA.

Ott, J. 1979B. *Hallucinogenic Plants of North America.* (Psycho-Mycological Studies Number One, Revised Edition) Wingbow Press, Berkeley, CA. Introduction by Richard Evans Schultes, p. IX.

Ott, J. 1980. "Isolation yield of ibotenic acid from *Amanita pantherina*" Manuscript.

Ott, J. 1985. *The Cacahuatl Eater: Ruminations of an Unabashed Chocolate Addict.* Natural Products Co., Vashon, WA.

Ott, J. 1990. "A twentieth century Darwin" In: Riedlinger, T.J. (Ed.) *The Sacred Mushroom Seeker: Essays for R. Gordon Wasson.* Ethnomycological Studies No. 11. Dioscorides Press, Portland, OR. pp. 183–191.

Ott, J. 1992A. "Problemas técnicas con la prohibición de drogas" Conference "Economía Agrícola de las Regiones Productoras de Drogas," March 1992, Valencia, Spain.

Ott, J. 1992B. "*Ayahuasca*: Ethnobotany, phytochemistry and human pharmacology" Conference "Plantas, Chamanismo y Estados de Conciencia," 16–20 November 1992, San Luis Potosí, SLP, México.

Ott, J. 1992C. "Le peyotl rapproche les Amérindiens des dieux..." *Interdépendances* 10: 23–24.

Ott, J. 1993[5]. "*Ayahuasca*: Ethnobotany, phytochemistry and human pharmacology" *Integration: Zeitschrift für Geistbewegende Pflanzen und Kultur* 5: 72–97.

Ott, J. 1994A. *Ayahuasca Analogues: Pangæan Entheogens.* Natural Products Co., Kennewick, WA. German translation by B.M. Schuldes, 1995. *Ayahuasca Analoge.* MedienXperimente, Löhrbach, Germany.

Ott, J. 1994B. "La historia de la planta del 'soma' después de R. Gordon Wasson" In: Fericgla, J.M. (Ed.) *Plantas, Chamanismo y Estados de Consciencia.* Los Libros de la Liebre de Marzo, Barcelona, Spain. pp. 117–150.

Ott, J. 1995A. "Ethnopharmacognosy and human pharmacology of *Salvia divinorum* and salvinorin A" *Curare* 18(1): 103–129.

Ott, J. 1995B. *The Age of Entheogens & The Angels' Dictionary.* Natural Products Co., Kennewick, WA. Illustrated by T. Girvin.

Ott, J. 1996A. "Entheogens II: On entheology and entheobotany" *Journal of Psychoactive Drugs* 28(2): 205–209. Reprint of "Entheogens," pp. 208–209; Ruck *et al.* 1979.

Ott, J. 1996B. "Pharmahuasca: On phenethylamines and potentiation" *MAPS Bulletin* VI(3): 32–35.

Ott, J. and **J. Bigwood** (Eds.) 1978. *Teonanácatl: Hallucinogenic Mushrooms of North America.* (Psycho-Mycological Studies No. 2) Madrona Publishers, Seattle, WA.

Ott, J. and **J. Bigwood** (Eds.) (Translation by M.S. Antolín) 1985. *Teonanácatl: Hongos Alucinógenos de Europa y América del Norte.* Editorial Swan, San Lorenzo de El Escorial, Spain. Revised by J. Ott and D. Belmonte.

Ott, J. and **G. Guzmán** 1976. "Detection of psilocybin in species of *Psilocybe*, *Panaeolus* and *Psathyrella*" *Lloydia* 39(4): 258–260.

Ott, J. and **P. Neely** 1980. "Entheogenic (hallucinogenic) effects of methyl-ergonovine" *Journal of Psychedelic Drugs* 12(2): 165–166.

Ott, J. and **S.H. Pollock** 1976A. Interview of R. Gordon Wasson. *High Times.* No. 14, October issue. pp. 23 *et seq.*

Ott, J. and **S.H. Pollock** 1976B. "Mushroom hunting in Oregon V. The psychomycological perspective" *Journal of Psychedelic Drugs* 8(1): 81–82. Letter criticising letters by A.T. Weil; see Weil 1977A.

Ott, J. and **R.G. Wasson** 1983. "Carved 'disembodied eyes' of Teotihuacan" *Botanical Museum Leaflets* Harvard University 29 (4): 387–400. Reprinted in Wasson *et al.* 1986. *Persephone's Quest: Entheogens and* *the Origins of Religion*. Ethnomycological Studies No. 10. Yale University Press, New Haven, CT. pp. 141–148.

Ott, J. *et al.* 1975A. "Fate of muscimol in the mouse" *Physiological Chemistry and Physics* 7: 381–384.

Ott, J. *et al.* 1975B. "Nuevos datos sobre los supuestos Licoperdáceos psicotrópicos y dos casos de intoxicación provocados por hongos del género *Scleroderma* en México" *Boletín de la Sociedad Mexicana de Micología* 9: 67–76.

Overfield, T. *et al.* 1980. "Eskimo use of *Artemisia tilesii* (Compositae)" *Economic Botany* 34(2): 97–100.

Pachter, I.J. and **A.F. Hopkinson** 1960. "Note on the alkaloids of *Methysticodendron amesianum*" *Journal of the American Pharmaceutical Association* 49: 621–622.

Pachter, I.J. *et al.* 1959. "Indole alkaloids of *Acer saccharinum* (the silver maple), *Dictyoloma incanescens*, *Piptadenia colubrina*, and *Mimosa hostilis*" *Journal of Organic Chemistry* 24: 1285–1287.

Packer, H.L. 1968. *The Limits of the Criminal Sanction*. Stanford University Press, Menlo Park, CA.

Packer, J.G. and **G.S. Ringius** 1984. "The distribution status of Acorus (Araceae) in Canada" *Canadian Journal of Botany* 62: 2248–2252.

Padoch, C. and **W. De Jong** 1991. "The house gardens of Santa Rosa: Diversity and variability in an Amazonian agricultural system" *Economic Botany* 45(2): 166–175.

Pagani, S. (Pseudonym for G. Samorini) 1993. *Funghetti*. Nautilus, Torino, Italy.

Pagan Perdomo, D. 1978. *Nuevas Pictografías en la Isla de Santo Domingo: Las Cuevas de Borbon*. Museo del Hombre Dominicano, Santo Domingo, Dominican Republic.

Pahnke, W.N. 1970. "Drugs and mysticism" In: Aaronson, B. and H. Osmond (Eds.) *Psychedelics: The Uses and Implications of Hallucinogenic Drugs*. Doubleday/Anchor, Garden City, NJ. pp. 145–165. Originally published in 1966, *The International Journal of Parapsychology* 8(2): 295–313.

Pahnke, W.N. 1971. "The psychedelic mystical experience in the human encounter with death" *Psychedelic Review* 11: 4–13. Followed by two letters to the editor by H.K. Beecher and G.D. Kaufman *Psychedelic Review* 11: 15–20. First printed in *Harvard Theological Review* 62: 1–21.

Pahnke, W.N. and **W.A. Richards** 1990. "Implications of LSD and experimental mysticism" In: Tart, C.T. (Ed.) *Altered States of Consciousness: A Book of Readings*. Revised edition, Harper San Francisco, New York. pp. 481–515. Original 1966, *Journal of Religion and Health* 5: 175–208.

Pahnke, W.N. *et al.* 1970A. "Psychedelic therapy (utilizing LSD) with cancer patients" *Journal of Psychedelic Drugs* 3(1): 63–75.

Pahnke, W.N. *et al.* 1970B. "The experimental use of psychedelic (LSD) psychotherapy" *Journal of the American Medical Association* 212: 1856–1863.

Painter, J. *et al.* 1971. "Nutmeg poisoning—A case report" *Clinical Toxicology* 4: 1–4.

Pal, D.C. and **S.K. Jain** 1989. "Notes on Lodha medicine in Midnapur District, West Bengal, India" *Economic Botany* 43 (4): 464–470.

Palmer, C. and **M. Horowitz** (Eds.) 1982. *Shaman Woman, Mainline Lady: Women's Writings on the Drug Experience*. William Morrow and Co., New York.

Palmer-Jones, T. 1965. "Poisonous honey overseas and in New Zealand" *New Zealand Medical Journal* 64: 631–637.

Palmer-Jones, T. and **E.P. White** 1949. "A recent outbreak of honey poisoning Part VII. Observations on the toxicity and toxin of the tutu (*Coriaria Arborea* Lindsay)" *New Zealand Journal of Science and Technology* 31: 246–256.

Panayotopoulos, D.J. and **D.D. Chisold** 1970. "Hallucinogenic effects of nutmeg" *British Medical Journal* 754.

Pardanani, J.H. *et al.* 1977. "Cactus alkaloids. XXXVI. Mescaline and related compounds from *Trichocereus peruvianus*" *Lloydia* 40(6): 585–590.

Pardanani, J.H. *et al.* 1978. "Cactus alkaloids. XXXVII. Mescaline and related compounds from *Opuntia spinosior*" *Lloydia* 41(3): 286–288.

Paris, M. *et al.* 1975. "The constituents of *Cannabis sativa* pollen" *Economic Botany* 29(3): 245–253.

Paris, R. and **R. Goutarel** 1958. "Les Alchornea Africains. Présence de yohimbine chez l'*Alchornea floribunda* (Euphorbiacées)" *Annales Pharmaceutiques Françaises* 16: 15–20.

Passie, T. 1995. "Psilocybin in der modernen Psychotherapie" *Curare* 18(1): 131–152.

Pasztory, E. 1974. *The Iconography of the Teotihuacan Tlaloc.* (Studies in Pre-Columbian Art and Archaeology Number Fifteen) Dumbarton Oaks, Washington, D.C.

Patiño, V.M. 1968. "Guayusa, a neglected stimulant from the eastern Andean foothills" *Economic Botany* 22(3): 310–316.

Paton, W.D.M. and **R.G. Pertwee** 1973A. "The pharmacology of Cannabis in animals" In: Mechoulam, R. (Ed.) *Marijuana: Chemistry, Pharmacology, Metabolism and Clinical Effects.* Academic Press, New York. pp. 191–285.

Paton, W.D.M. and **R.G. Pertwee** 1973B. "The actions of Cannabis in man" In: Mechoulam, R. (Ed.) *Marijuana: Chemistry, Pharmacology, Metabolism and Clinical Effects.* Academic Press, New York. pp. 287–333.

Paton, W.D.M. *et al.* 1973. "Clinical aspects of Cannabis action" In: Mechoulam, R. (Ed.) *Marijuana: Chemistry, Pharmacology, Metabolism and Clinical Effects.* Academic Press, New York. pp. 335–365.

Patouillard, N. 1907. "Champignons nouveaux du Tonkin" *Bulletin de Mycologie de France* 23: 69–79.

Paul, M.A. 1966. "Two cases of alerted [*sic*] consciousness with amnesia apparently telepathically induced" *Psychedelic Review* 8: 4–8.

Payne, R.B. 1963. "Nutmeg intoxication" *New England Journal of Medicine* 269: 36–39.

Paz, O. 1967. *Corriente Alterna.* Siglo Veintiuno Editores, México City. Translated into English, 1973. *Alternating Current.* Viking Press, New York.

Peele, S.L. 1985. "Camotillos created by the mushroom *Psilocybe tampanensis* may be useful in psychotherapy and treatment of asthma" *The Mushroom Culture, Journal of Mushroom Cultivation* 6: 3–4.

Peigen, X. and **H. Liyi** 1983. "Ethnopharmacologic investigations on tropane-containing drugs in Chinese Solanaceous plants" *Journal of Ethnopharmacology* 8(1): 1–18.

Pelt, J.-M. *et al.* 1967. "Sur la constitution alcaloïdique de quelques Solanacées d'Afghanistan. I. Constitution des feuilles et valeur des espéces examinées (Datura et Jusquiames)" *Annales Pharmaceutiques Françaises* 25(1): 59–68.

Pendell, D.A. 1992. Personal communications, San Luis Potosí, SLP, México.

Pendell, D.A. 1995. *Pharmako/Poeia: Plant Powers, Poisons, and Herbcraft.* Mercury House, San Francisco, CA. Foreword by Gary Snyder, pp. XIII–XIV.

Pennes, H.H. and **P.H. Hoch** 1957. "Psychotomimetics [*sic*], clinical and theoretical considerations: Harmine, WIN-2299 and nalline" *American Journal of Psychiatry* 113: 887–892.

Peretz, D.I. *et al.* 1955. "A new hallucinogen: 3,4,5-Trimethoxyphenyl-β-aminopropane. With notes on the stroboscopic phenomenon" *Journal of Mental Science* 101: 317–329.

Pérezamador, M.C. and **J. Herrán** 1960. "Turbicoryn: A new glucoside obtained from the seeds of a sacred plant" *Tetrahedron Letters* 1960: 30.

Perkin, W.H. and **R. Robinson** 1919A. "Harmine and harmaline. Part III." *Journal of the Chemical Society (Organic)* 115: 933–967.

Perkin, W.H. and **R. Robinson** 1919B. "Harmine and harmaline. Part IV." *Journal of the Chemical Society (Organic)* 115: 967–972.

Perrot, E. and **Raymond-Hamet** 1927A. "Le yagé, plante sensorielle des indiens de la région amazonienne de l'Equateur et de la Colombie" *Comptes Rendus Hebdomadaires des Séances de l'Académie des Sciences* 184: 1266–1268.

Perrot, E. and **Raymond-Hamet** 1927B. "Yagé, ayahuasca, caapi et leur alcaloïde, télépatheine ou yagéine" *Bulletin des Sciences Pharmacologiques* 34: 337–347; 417–426; 500–514. Also in *Trav. Lab. Mat. Méd. Pharm. Galén.* 18(2): 1.

Perry, L.M. 1980. *Medicinal Plants of East and Southeast Asia.* MIT Press, Cambridge, MA.

Perry, P. 1990. *On the Bus: The Complete Guide to the Legendary Trip of Ken Kesey, the Merry Pranksters and the Birth of the Counterculture.* Plexus, London, England. Forewords by Hunter S. Thompson and Jerry García, "Flashbacks" by Ken Babbs, editing by M. Schwartz and N. Ortenberg.

Peterson, N. 1979. "Aboriginal uses of Australian Solanaceae" In: Hawkes, J.G. *et al.* (Eds.) *The Biology and Taxonomy of the Solanaceae.* Academic Press, London, England. pp. 171–189.

Petroski, R.J. *et al.* 1989. "Isolation, semisynthesis and NMR studies of loline alkaloids" *Journal of Natural Products* 52(6): 810–817.

Peuckert, W.-E. 1960. "Hexensalben" *Medizinischer Monatßpiegel* 8: 169–174.

Pfaff, R.C. *et al.* 1994. "Lysergamides revisited" In: Lin, G.C. and R.A. Glennon (Eds.) *Hallucinogens: An Update.* (NIDA Research Monograph 146) National Institute on Drug Abuse, Rockville, MD. pp. 52–73.

Pfeiffer, C.C. *et al.* 1967. "Effect of kava in normal subjects and patients" In: Efron, D.H. *et al.* (Eds.) *Ethnopharmacologic Search for Psychoactive Drugs.* (Public Health Service Publication No. 1645) U.S. Government Printing Office, Washington, D.C. pp. 155–161.

PharmChem Laboratories 1973. Personal communications from B. Ratcliffe and data from *The PharmChem Newsletter.*

Phokas, G.F. 1959. *Contribution to the Definition of the Drastic Components of Mandrake Root.* Thesis, Univ. of Athens, Greece.

Picker, J. and **R.W. Rickards** 1970. "The occurrence of the psychotomimetic [*sic*] agent psilocybin in an Australian agaric, *Psilocybe subaeruginosa*" *Australian Journal of Chemistry* 23: 853–855.

Pierce, P.A. and **S.J. Peroutka** 1988. "Ring-substituted amphetamine interactions with neurotransmitter receptor binding sites in human cortex" *Neuroscience Letters* 95(1-2): 208–212.

Pike, E.V. 1960. "Mazatec sexual impurity [*sic*] and Bible reading" *Practical Anthropology* 7(2): 49–53.

Pike, E.V. and **F. Cowan** 1959. "Mushroom ritual versus Christianity" *Practical Anthropology* 6(4): 145–150.

Pinkley, H.V. 1969. "Plant admixtures to *ayahuasca*, the South American hallucinogenic drink" *Lloydia* 32(3): 305–314.

Pinkson, T. (Translation by J. Baker) 1989. "Purification, death and rebirth: The clinical use of entheogens within a shamanic context" In: Rätsch, C. (Ed.) *Gateway to Inner Space: Sacred Plants, Mysticism and Psychotherapy—A Festschrift in Honor of Albert Hofmann.* Prism Press, Bridport, Dorset, England. pp. 91–118.

Pitre, S. and **S.K. Srivastava** 1987. "Two new anthraquinones from the seeds of *Peganum harmala*" *Planta Medica* 53: 106–107.
Pletscher, A. and **D. Ladewig** (Eds.) 1994. *50 Years of LSD: Current Status and Perspectives of Hallucinogens*. Parthenon, New York.
Pletscher, A. *et al.* 1959. "Über pharmakologische Beeinflußung des Zentralnervensystems durch kurzwirkende Monoaminoxidasehemmer aus der Gruppe der Harmala-Alkaloide" *Helvetica Physiologica et Pharmacologica Acta* 17: 202–214.
Plotkin, M.J. *et al.* 1980. "Psychotomimetic [*sic*] use of tobacco in Surinam and French Guiana" *Journal of Ethnopharmacology* 2(3): 295–297.
Plowman, T.C. 1973. "Four new Brunfelsias from northwestern South America" *Botanical Museum Leaflets* Harvard University 23(6): 245–272.
Plowman, T.C. 1974. "Two new Brazilian species of Brunfelsia" *Botanical Museum Leaflets* Harvard University 24(2): 37–48.
Plowman, T.C. 1977. "Brunfelsia in ethnomedicine" *Botanical Museum Leaflets* Harvard University 25(10): 289–320.
Plowman, T.C. 1979. "Botanical perspectives on coca" *Journal of Psychedelic Drugs* 11(1-2): 103–117. Conference "Hallucinogens in Native American Shamanism and Modern Life," 28 September–1 October 1978, San Francisco, CA, USA.
Plowman, T.C. 1980. "The genus *Brunfelsia*: A conspectus of the taxonomy and biogeography" In: Hawkes, J.G. *et al.* (Eds.) *The Botany and Taxonomy of the Solanaceae.* (Linnean Soc. Symposium Ser. No. 7) Linnean Soc., London, England. pp. 475–491.
Plowman, T.C. 1981. "Amazonian coca" *Journal of Ethnopharmacology* 3(2&3): 195–225.
Plowman, T.C. *et al.* 1971. "*Latua pubiflora*: Magic plant from southern Chile" *Botanical Museum Leaflets* Harvard University 23(2): 61–92.
Plowman, T.C. *et al.* 1990. "Significance of the fungus *Balansia cyperi* infecting medicinal species of *Cyperus* (Cyperaceae) from Amazonia" *Economic Botany* 44(4): 452–462.
Plugge, P.C. 1891. "Giftiger Honig von *Rhododendron ponticum*" *Archiv der Pharmazie* 229: 554–558.
Pöder, R. *et al.* 1992. "Mykologische Untersuchungen an dem Pilz-Beifunden der Gletschermumie vom Hauslabjoch" In: Spindler, K. (Ed.) *Bericht über das Internationale Symposium "Der Mann im Eis—Ein Fund aus der Steinzert Tirols."* Veröffentlichungen der Universität Innsbruck, Innsbruck, Austria. pp. 313–320.
Poisson, J. 1960. "Présence de mescaline dans une Cactacée péruvienne" *Annales Pharmaceutiques Françaises* 18: 764–765.
Poisson, J. 1965. "Note sur le 'Natem', boisson toxique péruvienne et ses alcaloïdes" *Annales Pharmaceutiques Françaises* 23(4): 241–244.
Polia, M. and **A. Bianchi** 1991. "Ethnological evidence and cultural patterns of use of *Trichocereus pachanoi* B.R. among Peruvian curanderos" *Integration: Zeitschrift für Geistbewegende Pflanzen und Kultur* 1: 65–70. Italian version published in 1991 by A. Bianchi and M. Polia. "Dati etnofarmacologici e modelli culturali dell'uso del *Trichocereus pachanoi* Britton & Rose tra i curanderos peruviani" *Annali dei Musei Civici di Rovereto* 6: 139–146.
Polia, M. and **A. Bianchi** 1992. "The plant teachers of northern Peruvian Andean healers: Ethnobotanical and ethnomedical data" Paper presented at conference "Plantas, Chamanismo y Estados de Conciencia," 16–20 November 1992, San Luis Potosí, SLP, México. *Integration: Zeitschrift für Geistbewegende Pflanzen und Kultur.*
Pollock, S.H. 1974. "A novel experience with *Panaeolus*: A case study from Hawaii" *Journal of Psychedelic Drugs* 6(1): 85–89.

Pollock, S.H. 1975A. "The psilocybin mushroom pandemic" *Journal of Psychedelic Drugs* 7(1): 73–84.

Pollock, S.H. 1975B. "The Alaskan Amanita quest" *Journal of Psychedelic Drugs* 7(4): 397–399.

Pollock, S.H. 1976. "Psilocybian mycetismus with special reference to *Panaeolus*" *Journal of Psychedelic Drugs* 8(1): 43–57.

Pollock, S.H. 1977. *Magic Mushroom Cultivation*. HMRF, San Antonio, TX.

Pollock, S.H. 1979. "Prima donna and the cosmic camote" *HiLife* 1(12): 12 *et seq.*

Ponglux, D. *et al.* (Eds.) 1987. *Medicinal Plants*. Victory Power Point Corp., Bangkok, Thailand. Preface K. Manunapichu.

Pongprayoon, U. *et al.* 1991. "Neutralization of toxic effects of different crude jellyfish venoms by an extract of *Ipomoea pes-caprae*" *Journal of Ethnopharmacology* 35(1): 65–69.

Pool, R. 1989. "Crime and chemical analysis" *Science* 243: 1554–1555.

Pope, H.G. 1969. "*Tabernanthe iboga*: An African narcotic [*sic*] plant of social importance" *Economic Botany* 23(2): 174–184.

Popelak, A. and **G. Lettenbauer** 1967. "The mesembrine alkaloids" In: Manske, R.H.F. and H.L. Holmes (Eds.) *The Alkaloids*. Academic, New York. Vol. 9, pp. 467–482.

Porter, D.M. 1962. "The taxonomic and economic uses of *Peganum harmala* (Zygophyllaceae)" Ms, Oakes Ames Lib., Bot. Mus. Harvard Univ., Cambridge, MA.

Porter, J.K. 1995. "Analysis of endophyte toxins: Fescue and other grasses toxic to livestock" *Journal of Animal Science* 73: 871–880.

Porter, J.K. *et al.* 1979. "Lysergic acid amide derivatives from *Balansia epichloë* and *Balansia claviceps* (Clavicipitaceae)" *Journal of Natural Products* 42(3): 309–314.

Porter, J.K. *et al.* 1981. "Ergot alkaloid identification in Clavicipitaceae systemic fungi of pasture grasses" *Journal of Agricultural and Food Chemistry* 29(3): 653–657.

Posey, D.A. 1990. "Intellectual property rights: What is the position of ethnobiology?" *Journal of Ethnobiology* 10(1): 93–98.

Potter, B.A. and **S. Orfali** 1990. *Drug Testing at Work: A Guide for Employers and Employees*. Ronin Publishing Co., Berkeley, CA.

Poupat, C. *et al.* 1976. "Plantes de Nouvelle-Calédonie. Partie 38. Alcaloïdes de *Acacia simplicifolia*" *Phytochemistry* 15: 2019–2020.

Pouzar, Z. 1953. "Poznámky kmykoflore studenho vrchu u Stribrné Skalice" *Ceska Mykologie* 7: 139–141.

Power, F.B. and **V.K. Chestnut** 1919. "*Ilex vomitoria* as a native source of caffeine" *Journal of the American Chemical Society* 41: 1307–1312.

Prance, G.T. 1970. "Notes on the use of plant hallucinogens in Amazonian Brazil" *Economic Botany* 24(1): 62–68.

Prance, G.T. and **A.E. Prance** 1970. "Hallucinations in Amazonia" *Garden Journal* 20: 102–107.

Prance, G.T. *et al.* 1977. "The ethnobotany of the Paumarí Indians" *Economic Botany* 31(2): 129–139.

Pratt, R.A. (Ed.) 1966. *Selections from the Tales of Canterbury and Short Poems by Geoffrey Chaucer*. Houghton-Mifflin, Boston, MA.

Prentiss, D.W. and **F.P. Morgan** 1895. "*Anhalonium Lewinii* (*mescal* [*sic*] *buttons*). A study of the drug, with especial reference to its physiological action upon man, with report of experiments." *Therapeutic Gazette* 19(9): 577–585.

Prescott, J. and **G. McCall** (Eds.) 1988. *Kava: Use and Abuse in Australia and the South Pacific*. (Monograph No. 5) National Drug and Alcohol Research Centre, University of New South Wales, Sydney, Australia.

Prescott, W.H. 1843. *The History of the Conquest of Mexico with a Preliminary View of the Ancient Mexican Civilization and the*

Life of the Conqueror Hernando Cortés. Two volumes. Harper & Bros., New York.

Puharich, A. 1959A. *The Sacred Mushroom: Key to the Door of Eternity.* Doubleday, NY.

Puharich, A. 1959B. "Mushroom icons" *Bulletin of the Mycological Society of San Francisco* 9(12): 8–10, 16.

Puharich, A. 1962. *Beyond Telepathy.* Doubleday, New York.

Pulling, N. 1990. "Toad licking puts man in hospital" *The Globe and Mail.* 30 July issue. pp. A1–A2.

Pummangura, S. *et al.* 1982. *Journal of Natural Products* 45: 224–225.

Purkinje, J.E. 1829. "Einige Beiträge zur physiologischen Pharmakologie" *Neue Breslauer Sammlungen aus dem Gebiete der Heilkunde* 1: 423–443.

Pushpangadan, P. and **C.K. Atal** 1986. "Ethnomedicinal and ethnobotanical investigations among some scheduled caste communities of Travancore, Kerala, India" *Journal of Ethnopharmacology* 16(2): 175–190.

Quimby, M.W. *et al.* 1973. "Mississippi-grown marihuana [*sic*]—*Cannabis sativa* cultivation and observed morphological variations" *Economic Botany* 27(1): 117–127.

Raffauf, R.F. and **T.M. Zennie** 1983. "The phytochemistry of *Quararibea funebris*" *Botanical Museum Leaflets* Harvard University 29(2): 151–157.

Raffauf, R.F. *et al.* 1984. *Journal of Organic Chemistry* 49: 2714.

Ramírez de Jara, M.C. and **C.E. Pinzón C.** 1986. "Los hijos del bejuco solar y la campana celeste. El yajé en la cultura popular urbana" *América Indígena* 46(1): 163–188.

Rao, G.S. 1970. "Identity of peyocactin, an antibiotic from peyote (*Lophophora williamsii*), and hordenine" *Journal of Pharmacy and Pharmacology* 22: 544–545.

Rao, R.R. 1981. "Ethnobotany of Meghalaya: Medicinal plants used by Khasi and Garo tribes" *Economic Botany* 35(1): 4–9.

Rasoanaivo, P. *et al.* 1992. "Medicinal plants used to treat malaria in Madagascar" *Journal of Ethnopharmacology* 37(2): 117–127.

Ratcliffe, B. 1973. "Psilocybin demand creates new drug deception" *The PharmChem Newsletter* 2(2): 1 *et seq.*

Rätsch, C. 1987. *Indianische Heilkräuter: Tradition und Anwendung.* Diederichs, Köln, Germany.

Rätsch, C. (Ed.; Translation by J. Baker) 1989. *Gateway to Inner Space: Sacred Plants, Mysticism and Psychotherapy—A Festschrift in Honor of Albert Hofmann.* Prism Press, Bridport, England.

Rätsch, C. 1991. "Bridges to the gods (Psychedelic rituals of knowledge)" *Annali dei Musei Civici di Rovereto* 6: 127–138. Condensed version; originally published in 1990. "Bridges to the gods: Psychedelics, religion and ethnography" *The Albert Hofmann Foundation Newsletter* 1(3).

Rätsch, C. (Translation by J. Baker) 1992. *The Dictionary of Sacred and Magical Plants.* Prism Press, Bridport, England. Original 1988. *Lexikon der Zauberpflanzen.* Akademische Verlagsanstatt, Graz, Austria.

Rätsch, C. (Ed.) 1993. *50 Jahre LSD-Erfahrung: Eine Jubiläumsschrift.* Nachtschatten Verlag/MedienXperimente, Solothurn, Switzerland and Löhrbach, Germany.

Rätsch, C. 1994[5]. "Die Alraune in der Antike" *Annali dei Musei Civici di Rovereto* 10: 249–296.

Rätsch, C. 1996. *Urbock: Bier Jenseits von Hopfen und Malz.* AT Verlag, Aarau, Switzerland.

Ravicz, R. 1960[1]. "La Mixteca en el estudio comparativo del hongo alucinante" *Anales del Instituto Nacional de Antropología e Historia* 13(42): 73–92.

Rayl, A.J.S. 1992. "LSD psychotherapy: A promising Swiss experiment proves more than a trip down memory lane" *Omni.* October issue. p. 12.

Raymond-Hamet 1941. "Sur les effets vasculaires de l'harmine, de l'harmaline et de la tétrahydroharmine" *Comptes Rendus Hebdomadaires des Séances de la Societé de Biologie et de ses Filiales* 135: 69–73.

Raymond-Hamet and **R. Goutarel** 1965. "L'*Alchornea floribunda* Mueller-Arg. Do it-il à la yohimbine ses effets excitants chez l'homme?" *Comptes Rendus Hebdomadaires des Séances de l'Académie des Sciences* 261: 3223–3224.

Reagan, A.B. 1928. "Plants used by the Bois Fort Chippewa (Ojibwa) Indians of Minnesota" *Wisconsin Archaeologist* 7(4): 230–248.

Reagan, A.B. 1929. "Plants used by the White Mountain Apache Indians of Arizona" *Wisconsin Archaeologist* 8: 143–161.

Reay, M. 1959. *The Kuma: Freedom and Conformity in the New Guinea Highlands.* Melbourne Univ. Press, Melbourne, Australia.

Reay, M. 1960. "'Mushroom madness' in the New Guinea Highlands" *Oceania* 31 (2): 137–139.

Recinos, A. (Ed.) 1947. *Popol Vuh: Antiguas Historias del Quiché.* Fondo de Cultura Económica, México City.

Reichel-Dolmatoff, G. 1944. "La cultura material de los Indios Guahibo" *Revista del Instituto Etnológico Nacional* 1(1): 437–506.

Reichel-Dolmatoff, G. 1960. "Notas etnográficas sobre los Indios del Chocó" *Revista Colombiana de Antropología* 11: 75–158.

Reichel-Dolmatoff, G. 1969 "El contexto cultural de un alucinógeno aborígen" *Revista de la Academia Colombiana de Ciencias Exactas, Físicas y Naturales* 13(51): 327–345.

Reichel-Dolmatoff, G. 1970. "Notes on the cultural extent of the use of yajé (*Banisteriopsis caapi*) among the Indians of the Vaupés, Colombia" *Economic Botany* 24 (1): 32–33.

Reichel-Dolmatoff, G. 1971. *Amazonian Cosmos: The Sexual and Religious Symbolism of the Tukano Indians.* University of Chicago Press, Chicago, IL. Original 1968.

Reichel-Dolmatoff, G. 1972. "The cultural context of an aboriginal hallucinogen: *Banisteriopsis caapi*" In: Furst, P.T. (Ed.) *Flesh of the Gods: The Ritual Use of Hallucinogens.* Praeger, New York. pp. 84–113.

Reichel-Dolmatoff, G. 1975. *The Shaman and the Jaguar: A Study of Narcotic Drugs among the Indians of Colombia.* Temple Univ. Press, Philadelphia, PA. Foreword R.E. Schultes, pp. XI–XIV. Spanish edition 1978. *El Chamán y el Jaguar: Estudio de las Drogas Narcóticas entre los Indios de Colombia.* Siglo Veintiuno, México City.

Reichel-Dolmatoff, G. 1978. *Beyond the Milky Way: Hallucinatory Imagery of the Tukano Indians. A Book on Lore.* (UCLA Latin American Studies Vol. 42) University of California Press, Los Angeles, CA.

Reinberg, P. 1921. "Contribution à l'étude des boissons toxiques des Indiens du nord-ouest de l'Amazone: l'Ayahuasca, le yajé, le huanto. Étude comparative toxico-physiologique d'une experience personelle" *Journal de la Société des Americanistes Paris* 13: 25–54; 197–216.

Reiner, R. and **C.H. Eugster** 1967. "Zur Kenntnis des Muscazons" *Helvetica Chimica Acta* 50: 128–136.

Reis Altschul, S. von 1964. "A taxonomic study of the genus Anadenanthera" *Contributions from the Gray Herbarium of Harvard University* 193: 3–65.

Reis Altschul, S. von 1967. "Vilca and its use" In: Efron, D.H. *et al.* (Eds.) *Ethnopharmacologic Search for Psychoactive Drugs.* (Public Health Service Publication No. 1645) U.S. Government Printing Office, Washington, D.C. pp. 307–314.

Reis Altschul, S. von 1972. *The Genus Anadenanthera in Amerindian Cultures.* Botanical Museum of Harvard University, Cambridge, MA.

Reis Altschul, S. von 1973. *Drugs and Foods*

from Little-Known Plants: Notes in Harvard University Herbaria. Harvard University Press, Cambridge, MA. Foreword by Richard Evans Schultes, pp. XI–XII.

Reis, S. von and **F.J. Lipp** 1982. *New Plant Sources for Drugs and Foods from the New York Botanical Garden Herbarium.* Harvard University Press, Cambridge, MA.

Reisfield, A.S. 1993. "The botany of *Salvia divinorum* (Labiatae)" *SIDA* 15(3): 349–366.

Reko, B.P. 1919. "De los nombres botánicos Aztecas" *El México Antiguo* 1(5): 113–157. Translated by Jonathan Ott, 1996. *On Aztec Botanical Names,* VWB, Berlin.

Reko, B.P. 1929. "Alcaloides y glucósidos en plantas mexicanas" *Memorial de la Sociedad Alzate* 49: 412.

Reko, B.P. 1934. "Das mexikanische Rauschgift Ololiuqui" *El México Antiguo* 3(3-4): 1–7. First psychonautic bioassay of drug.

Reko, B.P. 1945. *Mitobotánica Zapoteca.* Privately published, Tacubaya, México.

Reko, V.A. 1936. *Magische Gifte: Rausch- und Betäubungsmittel der Neuen Welt.* Ferdinand Enke Verlag, Stuttgart, Germany. Facsimile (2nd Ed.), EXpress, Berlin, 1986. Vorwort by Christian Rätsch, pp. I–II; "Allgemeine Bibliographie" pp. 207–214.

Rendon, P. and **J. Willy** 1985. "Isolation of bufotenine from seeds of *Piptadenia macrocarpa* Benth." *Revista Boliviana de Química* 5: 39–43.

Repke, D.B. 1992. Personal communications, San Carlos, CA.

Repke, D.B. 1993. Personal communications, correspondence.

Repke, D.B. and **W.J. Ferguson** 1982. "Psilocin analogs. III. Synthesis of 5-methoxy and 5-hydroxy-1,2,3,4-tetrahydro-9*H*-pyrido[3,4-*b*]indoles" *Journal of Heterocyclic Chemistry* 19: 845–848.

Repke, D.B. and **D.T. Leslie** 1977. "Baeocystin in *Psilocybe semilanceata*" *Journal of Pharmaceutical Sciences* 66(1): 113–114.

Repke, D.B. *et al.* 1973. "Alkaloids of *Acacia baileyana*" *Lloydia* 36(2): 211–213.

Repke, D.B. *et al.* 1977A. "Baeocystin in *Psilocybe, Conocybe* and *Panaeolus*" *Lloydia* 40(6): 566–578.

Repke, D.B. *et al.* 1977B. "Psilocin analogs. I. Synthesis of 3-[2-(dialkylamino)ethyl]- and 3-[2-(cycloalkylamino)ethyl]indol-4-ols" *Journal of Heterocyclic Chemistry* 14: 71–74.

Repke, D.B. *et al.* 1978. "GLC-Mass spectral analysis of fungal metabolites" *Journal of Pharmaceutical Sciences* 67(4): 485–487.

Repke, D.B. *et al.* 1981. "Psilocin analogs II. Synthesis of 3-[2-(dialkylamino)ethyl]-, 3-[2-(*N*-methyl-*N*-alkylamino)ethyl]-, and 3-[2-(cycloalkylamino)ethyl]indol-4-ols" *Journal of Heterocyclic Chemistry* 18: 175–179.

Repke, D.B. *et al.* 1985. "Psychotomimetic [*sic*] *N*-methyl-*N*-isopropyltryptamines. Effects of variation of aromatic oxygen substituents" *Journal of Medicinal Chemistry* 28: 892–896.

Reti, L. and **J.A. Castrillon** 1951. "Cactus alkaloids I. *Trichocereus terscheckii* (Parmentier) Britton & Rose" *Journal of the American Chemical Society* 73: 1767–1769.

Reyes G., L. 1970. "Una relación sobre los hongos alucinantes" *Tlalocan* 6(2): 140–145.

Rhead, J.C. *et al.* 1977. "Psychedelic drug (DPT)-assisted psychotherapy with alcoholics: A controlled study" *Journal of Psychedelic Drugs* 9(4): 287–300.

Rice, K.C. and **R.S. Wilson** 1976. "(−)-3-Isothujone, a small nonnitrogenous molecule with antinociceptive activity in mice" *Journal of Medicinal Chemistry* 19(8): 1054–1057.

Ricer, R.E. 1987. "Smokeless tobacco use: A dangerous nicotine habit" *Postgraduate Medicine* 81(4): 89–94.

Rich, M.A. *et al.* 1965. "Inhibition of human tumor cells by cordycepin" *Biochimica et*

Biophysiologica Acta 95: 194–204.

Richard, B. *et al.* 1983. "Alkaloids from *Voacanga schweinfurthii* var. *puberula*" *Journal of Natural Products* 46(2): 283–284.

Richards, W.A. 1975. *Counseling, Peak Experiences and the Human Encounter with Death. An Empirical Study of the Efficacy of DPT-Assisted Counseling in Enhancing the Quality of Life of Persons with Terminal Cancer and their Closest Family Members.* Thesis, Catholic University of America, Washington, D.C.

Richards, W.A. *et al.* 1977. "The peak experience variable in DPT-assisted psychotherapy with cancer patients" *Journal of Psychedelic Drugs* 9(1): 1–10.

Richards, W.A. *et al.* 1979. "DPT as an adjunct in brief psychotherapy with cancer" *Omega* 10: 9–26.

Richardson, A.B. 1990. "Recollections of R. Gordon Wasson's 'friend and photographer'" In: Riedlinger, T.J. (Ed.) *The Sacred Mushroom Seeker: Essays for R. Gordon Wasson.* Ethnomycological Studies No. 11. Dioscorides Press, Portland, OR. pp. 193–203.

Richardson, C.C. 1971. "Mr. Allegro among the mushrooms" *Union Seminary Quarterly Review* 26(3): 1. Review of Allegro 1970. See also: Jacobson & Richardson 1971; Jacques 1970.

Rickard, P.P. and **P.A. Cox** 1986. "Use of *Derris* as a fish poison in Guadalcanal, Solomon Islands" *Economic Botany* 40(4): 479–484.

Ricks, D.F. 1963. "Mushrooms and mystics: A caveat" *The Harvard Review* 1(4): 51–55.

Ricuarte, G. *et al.* 1985. "Hallucinogenic amphetamine selectively destroys brain serotonin nerve terminals" *Science* 229: 986–988.

Riedlinger, T.J. (Ed.) 1990. *The Sacred Mushroom Seeker: Essays for R. Gordon Wasson.* (Dudley, T.R., General Editor, Historical, Ethno- & Economic Botany Series, Volume 4) Ethnomycological Studies No. 11. Dioscorides Press, Portland, OR.

Riedlinger, T.J. 1990. "A latecomer's view of R. Gordon Wasson" In: Riedlinger, T.J. (Ed.) *The Sacred Mushroom Seeker: Essays for R. Gordon Wasson.* Ethnomycological Studies No. 11. Dioscorides Press, Portland, OR. pp. 205–220.

Riedlinger, T.J. 1993. "Wasson's alternative candidates for Soma" *Journal of Psychoactive Drugs* 25(2): 149–156.

Rinkel, M. *et al.* 1960. "Experimental psychiatry. V.—Psilocybin, a new psychotogenic [*sic*] drug" *New England Journal of Medicine* 262(6): 295–297.

Ríos, O. *et al.* 1965. "Estudios sobre la harmina y el ayahuasca" *Revista de Ciencias Psicológicas y Neurológicas* 1(2).

Ripinsky-Naxon, M. 1993. *The Nature of Shamanism: Substance and Function of a Religious Metaphor.* State University of New York Press, Albany, NY.

Ritchie, E. and **W.C. Taylor** 1967. "The galbulimima alkaloids" In: Manske, R.H.F. and H.L. Holmes (Eds.) *The Alkaloids.* Academic Press, New York. Vol. 9, pp. 529–543.

Rivera, A. *et al.* 1989. "*Brugmansia sanguinea* subsp. *vulcanicola*, a good source of scopolamine" *Fitoterapia* 60(6): 542–544.

Rivier, L. and **J.-E. Lindgren** 1972. "'Ayahuasca,' the South American hallucinogenic drink: An ethnobotanical and chemical investigation" *Economic Botany* 26(1): 101–129.

Rivier, L. and **P.-É Pilet** 1971. "Composés hallucinogènes indoliques naturels" *Année Biologique* 10(3-4): 129–149.

Robbers, J.E. *et al.* 1969. "Additional evidence supporting the occurrence of psilocybin in *Panaeolus foenisecii*" *Lloydia* 32 (3): 399–400.

Robbins, T. 1974. "The toadstool that conquered the universe" *Northwest Passage* pp. 5 *et seq. High Times* Dec. 1976, p. 91.

Roberts, L. 1991. "Fight erupts over DNA fingerprinting" *Science* 254: 1721–1723. See also: Chakraborty & Kidd 1991; Koshland 1992; Lewontin & Hartl 1991; Wills *et al.* 1992.

Roberts, L. 1992A. "Chemical prospecting: Hope for vanishing ecosystems?" *Science* 256: 1142–1143.

Roberts, L. 1992B. "The drug industry goes green" *Science* 256: 1143.

Roberts, T.B. 1990. "Cognitive science, religion and academic freedom *vs.* the drug prohibition ideology" Paper presented at "Drug Policy Conference," 31 October–4 November 1990, Washington, D.C.

Robertson, M.G. 1973. Personal communication in: Rubel, A.J. and J. Gettelfinger-Krejci 1976. "The use of hallucinogenic fungi for diagnostic purposes among some highland Chinantecs" *Economic Botany* 30(3): 235–248.

Robichaud, R.C. *et al.* 1964. "Pharmacodynamics of cryogenine, an alkaloid isolated from *Heimia salicifolia* Link and Otto. Part I." *Archives Internationales de Pharmacodynamie et de Thérapie* 150: 220–232.

Robichaud, R.C. *et al.* 1965. "Pharmacodynamics of cryogenine, an alkaloid isolated from *Heimia salicifolia* Link and Otto. Part II." *Archives Internationales de Pharmacodynamie et de Thérapie* 157: 43–52.

Robicsek, F. 1978. *The Smoking Gods: Tobacco in Maya Art, History and Religion*. University of Oklahoma Press, Norman, OK.

Rodríguez, E. *et al.* 1982. "The possible role of Amazonian psychoactive plants in the chemotherapy of parasitic worms—A hypothesis" *Journal of Ethnopharmacology* 6(3): 303–309.

Roffman, R.A. 1982. *Marijuana as Medicine*. Madrona Publishers, Seattle, WA. Foreword by Sidney Cohen, pp. IX–X.

Rogers, J.E. 1981. "Is there a doctor in orbit?" *Science 81*. September. pp. 80–81.

Rohr, M. *et al.* 1979. "New sesquiterpenoids of sweet flag oil (*Acorus calamus*)" *Phytochemistry* 18: 279–281.

Rold, J.F. 1986. "Mushroom madness: Psychedelic [*sic*] fungi and the risk of fatal poisoning" *Postgraduate Medicine* 79(5): 217–218.

Römer, S. 1992. "Amanita muscaria" *Integration: Zeitschrift für Geistbewegende Pflanzen und Kultur* 2&3: 133–134.

Romero, J.B. 1954. *The Botanical Lore of the California Indians.* Vantage Press, New York.

Roquet, S. and **P. Favreau** 1981. *Los Alucinógenos: De la Concepción Indígena a una Nueva* [*sic*] *Psicoterápia*. Ediciones Prisma, México City. Preface by Walter Houston Clark, pp. 9–12.

Roseman, B. 1963. *225,000 Indians Can't be Wrong.* Self-published, Joshua Tree, CA. Expanded and republished as: *The Peyote Story.* Wilshire Book Co., Hollywood, CA, 1966.

Roseman, B. 1966. *LSD: The Age of Mind.* Wilshire Book Co., Hollywood, CA. Originally published in 1963.

Rosenberg, D.E. *et al.* 1963. "Comparison of a placebo, N-dimethyltryptamine, and 6-hydroxy-N-dimethyltryptamine in man" *Psychopharmacologia* 4: 39–42.

Rosenberg, D.E. *et al.* 1964. "The effect of N,N-dimethyltryptamine in human subjects tolerant to lysergic acid diethylamide" *Psychopharmacologia* 5: 217–227.

Rosenbohm, A. 1991A. *Halluzinogene Drogen im Schamanismus: Mythos und Ritual im Kulturellen Vergleich*. (Marburger Studien zur Völkerkunde, Band 8; H. Nachtigall, Ed.) Dietrich Reimer Verlag, Berlin, Germany.

Rosenbohm, A. 1991B. "Der Fliegenpilz in Nordasien" In: Bauer, W. *et al.* (Eds.) *Der Fliegenpilz: Ein Kulturhistorisches Museum.* (Museum der Museen, Schriftenreihe des Karl Ernst Osthaus-Museums, Bd. 6)

Wienand, Köln, Germany. pp. 121–164.

Rosengarten, F. 1977. "An unusual spice from Oaxaca: The flowers of *Quararibea funebris*" *Botanical Museum Leaflets* Harvard University 25(7): 183–202.

Ross, A. 1991. *Strange Weather: Culture, Science, and Technology.* Verso Publishers, New York.

Roth, A. *et al.* 1985. "Preliminary study of the alkaloids of *Psychotria forsteriana*" *Planta Medica* 51: 289.

Rothlin, E. 1957. "Pharmacology of lysergic acid diethylamide and some of its related compounds" *Journal of Pharmacy and Pharmacology* 9: 569–587.

Rouhier, A. 1924. "Le *yagé*: Plante télépathique [*sic*]" *Paris Médical* 52: 341.

Rouhier, A. 1926. "Documents pour servir à l'étude du yagé" *Bulletin des Sciences Pharmacologiques* 33: 252–261.

Rouhier, A. 1927. *La Plante qui Fait les Yeux Émerveillés—Le Peyotl (Echinocactus Williamsii Lem.).* Gaston Doin et Cie, Paris, France. Préface by É. Perrot, pp. v–xii.

Rovelli, B. and **G.N. Vaughan** 1967. "Alkaloids of *Acacia* I. N_b,N_b-Dimethyltryptamine in *Acacia phlebophylla* F. Muell." *Australian Journal of Chemistry* 20: 1299–1300.

Rowan, D.D. *et al.* 1986. "Peramine, a novel insect feeding deterrent from ryegrass infected with the endophyte *Acremonium loliae*" *Journal of the Chemical Society Chemical Communications* 1986: 935–936.

Roys, R.L. 1931. *The Ethno-Botany of the Maya.* (The Department of Middle American Research, Publication No. 2) The Tulane University of Louisiana, New Orleans, LA.

Rubel, A.J. and **J. Gettelfinger-Krejci** 1976. "The use of hallucinogenic fungi for diagnostic purposes among some highland Chinantecs" *Economic Botany* 30(3): 235–248.

Rubin, V. (Ed.) 1975. *Cannabis and Culture.* Mouton and Co., the Hague, the Netherlands.

Ruck, C.A.P. 1981. "Mushrooms and philosophers" *Journal of Ethnopharmacology* 4(2): 179–205. Reprinted in Wasson, R.G. *et al.* 1986. *Persephone's Quest: Entheogens and the Origins of Religion.* Ethnomycological Studies No. 10. Yale University Press, New Haven, CT. pp. 151–177.

Ruck, C.A.P. 1982. "The wild and the cultivated: Wine in Euripides' Bacchae" *Journal of Ethnopharmacology* 5(3): 231–270. Reprinted in Wasson, R.G. *et al.* 1986. *Persephone's Quest: Entheogens and the Origins of Religion.* Ethnomycological Studies No. 10. Yale University Press, New Haven, CT. pp. 179–223.

Ruck, C.A.P. 1983. "The offerings from the Hyperboreans" *Journal of Ethnopharmacology* 8(2): 177–207. Reprinted in Wasson, R.G. *et al.* 1986. *Persephone's Quest: Entheogens and the Origins of Religion.* Ethnomycological Studies No. 10. Yale Univ. Press, New Haven, CT. pp. 225–256.

Ruck, C.A.P. and **D. Staples** 1994. *The World of Classical Myth: Gods and Goddesses; Heroines and Heroes.* Carolina Academic Press, Durham, NC.

Ruck, C.A.P. *et al.* 1979. "Entheogens" *Journal of Psychedelic Drugs* 11(1-2): 145–146. Translated by F. Garrido as apéndice "Enteógenos" in Wasson, R.G. *et al.* 1980. *El Camino a Eleusis: Una Solución al Enigma de los Misterios.* Fondo de Cultura Económica, México City. pp. 231–235. Also in *El Europeo* 42: 82–3, 1992. English original reprinted as appendix to Ott, J. 1996. "Entheogens II: On entheology and entheobotany" *Journal of Psychoactive Drugs* 28(2): 205–209.

Rudgley, R. 1994. *Essential Substances: A Cultural History of Intoxicants in Society.* Kodansha International, New York.

Ruiz de Alarcón, H. 1953. *Tratado de las Ido-*

latrías, Supersticiones, Dioses, Ritos, Hechicerías y Otras Costumbres Gentílicas de las Razas Aborígenes de México. Ediciones Fuente Cultural, México City. Limited edition of 400 copies edited by F. del Paso y Troncoso. Original in 1629; first modern edition in 1892. Translation by J.R. Andrews & R. Hassig, 1984. *Treatise on the Heathen Superstitions...* University of Oklahoma Press, Norman, OK.

Rusby, H.H. 1923. "The aboriginal uses of *caapi*" *Journal of the American Pharmaceutical Association* 12: 1123

Russo, E.B. 1992. "Headache treatments by native peoples of the Ecuadorian Amazon: A preliminary cross-disciplinary assessment" *Journal of Ethnopharmacology* 36(3): 193–206.

Saar, M. 1991A. "Ethnomycological data from Siberia and north-east Asia on the effect of *Amanita muscaria*" *Journal of Ethnopharmacology* 31(2): 157–173.

Saar, M. 1991B. "Fungi in Khanty folk medicine" *Journal of Ethnopharmacology* 31(2): 175–179.

Sacco, T. and **F. Chialva** 1988. "Chemical characteristics of the oil from *Artemisia absinthium* collected in Patagony (Argentina)" *Planta Medica* 54: 93.

Safford, W.E. 1910. "The sacred ear-flower of the Aztecs: Xochinacaztli" *Smithsonian Institution Annual Report for 1910*. Washington, D.C. pp. 427–430.

Safford, W.E. 1911. "The rediscovery of the Xochinacaztli of the Aztecs, with notes on Mexican Anonaceae [*sic*]" *Science* 33: 470–471.

Safford, W.E. 1915. "An Aztec narcotic [*sic*]" *Journal of Heredity* 6(7): 291–311.

Safford, W.E. 1916. "Identity of cohoba, the narcotic [*sic*] snuff of ancient Haiti" *Journal of the Washington Academy of Sciences* 6: 547–562.

Safford, W.E. 1921A. "*Datura*—an inviting genus for the study of heredity" *Journal of Heredity* 12: 178–190.

Safford, W.E. 1921B. "Synopsis of the genus *Datura*" *Journal of the Washington Academy of Sciences* 11(8): 173–189.

Safford, W.E. 1921C. "Peyote, the narcotic [*sic*] mescal button [*sic*] of the Indians" *Journal of the American Medical Association* 77(16): 1278–1279.

Safford, W.E. 1922. "Daturas of the Old World and New: An account of their narcotic [*sic*] properties and their use in oracular and initiatory ceremonies" *Smithsonian Institution Annual Report for 1920*. Washington, D.C. pp. 537–567.

Safina, L.K. *et al.* 1970. "Dinamika alkaloidov v garmale obyknovennoj—*Peganum harmala* L." *Trudy Instituta Botaniki Akademij Nauk Kazakskoj SSR* 28: 226–235.

Sahagún, B. de (Translation and editing by C.E. Dibble and A.J.O. Anderson) 1950–1969. *Florentine Codex: General History of the Things of New Spain by Fray Bernardino de Sahagún*. Twelve volumes. University of Utah Press, Salt Lake City, UT. This was Sahagún's raw data, completed in 1569, his Náhuatl text as dictated by 10–12 elderly, monolingual informants and then recorded by trilingual (Náhuatl, Spanish and Latin) scribes. See: Sahagún 1982 for his partial Spanish translation.

Sahagún, B. de 1982. *Historia General de las Cosas de Nueva España*. Editorial Porrúa, México City. This is a partial Spanish translation of the Náhuatl *Florentine Codex*. With a general proemium by Ángel M. Garibay K., pp. 1–14.

Sai-Halász, A. *et al.* 1958. "Dimethyltryptamin: Ein neues Psychoticum [*sic*]" *Psychiatria et Neurologia* (Basel) 135: 285–301.

Saint-Hilaire, A.F.C.P. de 1824. *Histoire du Plantes les plus Remarquables du Bresil et du Paraguay*. Republished in 1946 by A. Jenkins (Ed.) *Chronica Botanica* 10: 24–61.

Saito, K. and **A. Komamine** 1978. "Biosynthesis of stizolobic and stizolobinic acids" *Zeitschrift für Naturforschung* 33C: 793–795.

Saleminck, C. *et al.* 1963. "Über die basischen Inhaltßtoffe des Fliegenpilzes. XII. Mitteilung: Über die Anwesenheit von *l*-Hyoscyamin" *Planta Medica* 11: 139–144.

Salgueiro, E.E.G. 1964. *A Psicose* [*sic*] *Experimental pela Psilocibina: Estudo-Clinico-Labortorial em Voluntarios Humanos*. Inquerito, Lisboa, Portugal.

Samorini, G. 1989. "Etnomicologia nell'arte rupestre Sahariana (Periodo delle 'Teste Rotondo')" *B.C. Notizie: Notiziario del Centro Camuno di Studi Preistorici* 6(2): 18–22.

Samorini, G. 1990. "Sullo stato attuale della conoscenza dei basidiomiceti psicotropi Italiani" *Annali dei Musei Civici di Rovereto* 5: 167–184.

Samorini, G. 1992A. "The oldest representations of hallucinogenic mushrooms in the world (Sahara Desert, 9000–7000 B.P.)" *Integration: Zeitschrift für Geistbewegende Pflanzen und Kultur* 2&3: 69–78.

Samorini, G. 1992B. "Funghi allucinogeni Italiani" *Atti del 2° Convegno Nazionale sugli Avvelenamenti da Funghi. Annali dei Musei Civici di Rovereto* 8: 125–150.

Samorini, G. 1992C. "La religión Buiti y la planta psicoactiva *Tabernanthe iboga* (Africa Ecuatorial)" Paper presented at the conference "Plantas, Chamanismo y Estados de Conciencia," 16–20 November 1992, San Luis Potosí, SLP, México. *Integration: Zeitschrift für Geistbewegende Pflanzen und Kultur* 5: 105–114, 1995.

Samorini, G. 1992D. "Neurotossicologia delle Graminacee e di loro patogeni vegetali. Un'Introduzione" *Annali dei Musei Civici di Rovereto* 7: 253–264.

Samorini, G. 1993A. Personal communications, correspondence.

Samorini, G. 1993B. "Adam, Eve and iboga" *Integration: Zeitschrift für Geistbewegende Pflanzen und Kultur* 4: 3–10.

Samorini, G. 1995. *Gli Allucinogeni nel Mito: Racconti sull'Origine delle Piante Psicoattive*. Nautilus, Torino, Italy.

Samorini, G. and **F. Festi** 1989. "Le micotossicosi psicotrope volontarie in Europa: Osservazioni sui casi clinici" *Atti del 1° Convegno Nazionale sugli Avvelenamenti da Funghi. Annali dei Musei Civici di Rovereto* 4: 251–257.

San Antonio, J.P. 1971. "A laboratory method to obtain fruit from cased grain spawn of the cultivated mushoom [*sic*] *Agaricus bisporus*" *Mycologia* 63(1): 16–21.

Sandford, J. 1973. *In Search of the Magic Mushroom: A Journey through Mexico*. Potter, New York.

Sanford, J.H. 1972. "Japan's 'laughing mushrooms'" *Economic Botany* 26(2): 174–181.

Sankar, D.V.S. (Ed.) 1975. *LSD: A Total Study*. PJD Publications, Westbury, NY.

Santesson, C.G. 1937A. "Notiz über Piule, eine mexikanische Rauschdroge" *Göteborgs Etnografiska Museum Etnologiska Studier* 4: 1–11.

Santesson, C.G. 1937B. "Piule, eine mexikanische Rauschdroge" *Archiv der Pharmazie* 1937: 532–537.

Santesson, C.G. 1938. "Noch eine mexikanische 'Piule'-Droge. Semina Rhynchosiae phaseoloides DC" *Göteborgs Etnografiska Museum Etnologiska Studier* 6: 179–183.

Santesson, C.G. 1939. "Einige mexikanische Rauschdrogen" *Arkiv för Botanik* 29A(12): 1–9.

Sargent, T. *et al.* 1975. "*In vivo* human pharmacodynamics of the psychodysleptic [*sic*] 4-Br-2,5-dimethoxyphenylisopropylamine labelled with ^{82}Br or ^{77}Br" *Neuropharmacology* 14: 165–174.

Sato, P.T. *et al.* 1973. "Cactus alkaloids XVI. Isolation and identification of alkaloids in *Coryphantha ramillosa*" *Journal of Pharmaceutical Sciences* 62: 411–414.

Satory, E. *et al.* 1961. "Die Wirkung von Diäthyltryptamin auf die Monoaminoxidase-Aktivität" *Acta Physiologica Acad. Sci. Hungary* 18: 83.

Saüer, H. and **R. Hänsel** 1967. "Kawa-lactone und Flavonoide aus einer endemischen Piper-Art Neu Guineas" *Planta Medica* 15: 443–458.

Saunders, N. 1993. *E for Ecstasy*. Privately-printed, London, England. Bibliography by Alexander T. Shulgin, pp. 223–302.

Saupe, S.G. 1981. "Occurrence of psilocybin/psilocin in *Pluteus salicinus* (Pluteaceae)" *Mycologia* 73(4): 781–784.

Savage, C. *et al.* 1990. "*Ipomoea purpurea*: A naturally-occurring psychedelic" In: Tart, C.T. (Ed.) *Altered States of Consciousness: A Book of Readings*. Revised, Harper San Francisco, New York. pp. 529–531.

Savona, G. *et al.* 1978. "Salviarin, a new diterpenoid from *Salvia splendens*" *Journal of the Chemical Society, Perkins Transactions* I: 643–646.

Savona, G. *et al.* 1979. "Splendidin, a new *trans*-clerodane from *Salvia splendens*" *Journal of the Chemical Society, Perkins Transactions* I: 533–534.

Schaefer, S.B. 1992A. Personal communications, McAllen, TX.

Schaefer, S.B. 1992B[5]. "The crossing of souls: Peyote, perception and meaning among the Huichol Indians of Mexico" Presented at the conference "Plantas, Chamanismo y Estados de Concienca," 16–20 November, San Luis Potosí, SLP, México. *Integration: Zeitschrift für Geistbewegende Pflanzen und Kultur* 5: 34–50, 1995.

Schaefer, S.B. 1993. "The loom as a sacred power object in Huichol culture" In: Anderson, R. and K.L. Field (Eds.) *Art in Small Scale Societies: Contemporary Readings*. Prentice-Hall, New York. pp. 118–130.

Schele, L. and **D. Freidel** 1990. *A Forest of Kings: The Untold Story of the Ancient Maya*. William Morrow & Co., New York.

Schele, L. and **M.E. Miller** 1986. *The Blood of Kings: Dynasty and Ritual in Maya Art.* George Braziller, Inc., New York. Foreword by Emily J. Sano, pp. IX–XII; preface by Michael D. Coe, pp. 1–4.

Schelling, T.C. 1992. "Addictive drugs: The cigarette experience" *Science* 255: 430–433. See also: Levin *et al.* 1992.

Schenk, G. 1954. *Das Buch der Gifte*. Safari Verlag, Berlin, Germany.

Schivelbusch, W. (Translation by D. Jacobson) 1992. *Tastes of Paradise: A Social History of Spices, Stimulants, and Intoxicants*. Pantheon Books, New York. Original 1980.

Schleiffer, H. (Ed.) 1974. *Sacred Narcotic* [*sic*] *Plants of the New World Indians.* Hafner Press, New York.

Schleiffer, H. (Ed.) 1979. *Narcotic* [*sic*] *Plants of the Old World: An Anthology of Texts from Ancient Times to the Present.* Lubrecht & Cramer, Monticello, NY. Introduction by Richard Evans Schultes, pp. 1–3.

Schmeda-Hirschmann, G. 1993. "Magic and medicinal pants of the Ayoreos of the Chaco Boreal (Paraguay)" *Journal of Ethnopharmacology* 39(2): 105–111.

Schmeda-Hirschmann, G. and **E. Bordas** 1990. "Paraguayan medicinal Compositae" *Journal of Ethnopharmacology* 28(2): 163–171.

Schmeda-Hirschmann, G. and **A.R. De Arias** 1990. "A survey of medicinal plants of Minas Gerais, Brazil" *Journal of Ethnopharmacology* 29(2): 159–172.

Schmidt, C.J. 1987. "Neurotoxicity of the psychedelic [*sic*] amphetamine methylenedioxy-methamphetamine" *Journal of Pharmacology and Experimental Therapeutics* 240: 1.

Schmiedeberg, O. and **R. Koppe** 1869. *Das Muscarin: Das Giftige Alkaloid des Fliegenpilzes (Agaricus Muscarius L.). Seine Darstellung, Chemischen Eigenschaften,*

Physiologischen Wirkungen, Toxicologische Bedeutung und Sein Verhältnis zur Pilzvergiftung im Allgemeinen. Verlag von F. C.W. Vogel, Leipzig, Germany.

Schonle, R. 1925. "Peyote, the giver of visions" *American Anthropologist* 27: 53–75.

Schroeder, R.F. and **G. Guzmán** 1981. "A new psychotropic fungus in Nepal" *Mycotaxon* 13(2): 346–348.

Schultes, R.E. 1937A. "Peyote and plants used in the peyote ceremony" *Botanical Museum Leaflets* Harvard University 4(8): 129–152. Reprinted in January 1973.

Schultes, R.E. 1937B. "Peyote (*Lophophora williamsii*) and plants confused with it" *Botanical Museum Leaflets* Harvard University 5(5): 61–88. Reprint March 1976.

Schultes, R.E. 1938. "The appeal of peyote (*Lophophora williamsii*) as a medicine" *American Anthropologist* 40: 698–715.

Schultes, R.E. 1939. "Plantae Mexicanae II. The identification of teonanacatl, a narcotic [*sic*] Basidiomycete of the Aztecs" *Botanical Museum Leaflets* Harvard University 7(3): 37–54.

Schultes, R.E. 1940. "Teonanacatl: The narcotic [*sic*] mushroom of the Aztecs" *American Anthropologist* 42: 429–443.

Schultes, R.E. 1941. *A Contribution to Our Knowledge of Rivea corymbosa, the Narcotic [sic] Ololiuqui of the Aztecs.* Harvard Botanical Museum, Cambridge, MA.

Schultes, R.E. 1942. "Plantae Colombianae II. Yoco: A stimulant of southern Colombia" *Botanical Museum Leaflets* Harvard University 10(10): 301–324. Reprint August 1971.

Schultes, R.E. 1945. "El uso del tabaco entre los Huitotos" *Agricultura Tropical* 1(9): 19–22.

Schultes, R.E. 1954A. "Plantae Austro-Americanae IX. Plantarum novarum vel notabilium notae diversae" *Botanical Museum Leaflets* Harvard University 16(8): 179–228. Includes 16 plates.

Schultes, R.E. 1954B. "A new narcotic [*sic*] snuff from the northwest Amazon" *Botanical Museum Leaflets* Harvard University 16(9): 241–260. Reprint Oct. 1970.

Schultes, R.E. 1955. "A new narcotic [*sic*] genus from the Amazon slope of the Colombian Andes" *Botanical Museum Leaflets* Harvard University 17(1): 1–11. Reprinted in November 1970.

Schultes, R.E. 1957A. "The identity of the malpighiaceous narcotics [*sic*] of South America" *Botanical Museum Leaflets* Harvard University 18(1): 1–56. Reprint May 1968.

Schultes, R.E. 1957B. "The genus *Quararibea* in Mexico and the use of its flowers as a spice for chocolate" *Botanical Museum Leaflets* Harvard University 17(9): 247–264. Reprinted in February 1975.

Schultes, R.E. 1960. "A reputedly toxic *Malouetia* from the Amazon" *Botanical Museum Leaflets* Harvard University 19(5): 123–124. Reprinted in May 1974.

Schultes, R.E. 1961. "Botany attacks the hallucinogens" *Texas Journal of Pharmacy* 2: 141–185. Revised version in 1963, "Botanical Sources of The New World Narcotics [*sic*]" *The Psychedelic Review* 1(2): 145–166. Reprinted in Weil G.M. *et al.* (Eds.) 1965. *The Psychedelic Reader.* University Books, New York. pp. 89–110. Originally part of the "Third Lecture Series," University of Texas College of Pharmacy, 1960.

Schultes, R.E. 1962. "The role of the ethnobotanist in the search for new medicinal plants" *Lloydia* 25(2): 257–266.

Schultes, R.E. 1963. "Hallucinogenic plants of the New World" *The Harvard Review* 1(4): 18–32.

Schultes, R.E. 1964. "The correct names for two Mexican narcotics" *Taxon* 13: 65–66.

Schultes, R.E. 1965. "Ein halbes Jahrhundert Ethnobotanik amerikanischer Halluzinogene" *Planta Medica* 13: 126–157.

Schultes, R.E. 1966. "The search for new natural hallucinogens" *Lloydia* 29(2): 293–308.

Schultes, R.E. 1967. "The botanical origins of South American snuffs" In: Efron, D. H. *et al.* (Eds.) *Ethnopharmacologic Search for Psychoactive Drugs.* (Public Health Service Publication No. 1645) U.S. Government Printing Office, Washington, D.C. pp. 291–306. Also: "The place of ethnobotany in the ethnopharmacologic search for psychotomimetic drugs" *ibid.* pp. 33–57.

Schultes, R.E. 1968. "Some impacts of Spruce's explorations on modern phytochemical research" *Rhodora* 70: 313–339.

Schultes, R.E. 1969A. "De plantis toxicariis e mundo novo tropicale commentationes IV" *Botanical Museum Leaflets* Harvard University 22(4): 133–164.

Schultes, R.E. 1969B. "De plantis toxicariis e mundo novo tropicale commentationes V. *Virola* as an orally administered hallucinogen" *Botanical Museum Leaflets* Harvard University 22(6): 229–240.

Schultes, R.E. 1970A. "The botanical and chemical distribution of hallucinogens" *Annual Review of Plant Physiology* 21: 571–594.

Schultes, R.E. 1970B. "The New World Indians and their hallucinogenic plants" *Bulletin of the Morris Arboretum* 21: 3–14.

Schultes, R.E. 1970C. "The plant kingdom and hallucinogens" *Bulletin on Narcotics* 21(3): 3–16; 21(4): 15–27; 22(1): 25–53.

Schultes, R.E. 1972A. "An overview of hallucinogens in the Western Hemisphere" In: Furst, P.T. (Ed.) *Flesh of the Gods: The Ritual Use of Hallucinogens.* Praeger, New York. pp. 3–54.

Schultes, R.E. 1972B. "De plantis toxicariis e mundo novo tropicale commentationes XI. The ethnotoxicological significance of additives to New World hallucinogens" *Plant Sciences Bulletin* 18: 34–41.

Schultes, R.E. 1972C. "De plantis toxicariis e mundo novo tropicale commentationes X. New data on the malpighiaceous narcotics [*sic*] of South America" *Botanical Museum Leaflets* Harvard University 23(3): 137–147.

Schultes, R.E. 1972D. "*Ilex guayusa* from 500 A.D. to the present" *Göteborgs Etnografiska Museum Etnologiska Studier* 32: 115–138.

Schultes, R.E. 1972E. "The utilization of hallucinogens in primitive societies—use misuse or abuse?" In: Keup, W. (Ed.) *Drug Abuse* [*sic*]*: Current Concepts and Research.* C.C. Thomas, Springfield, IL. pp. 17–26.

Schultes, R.E. 1972F. "*Quararibea funebris*: A curious spice for chocolate drinks" *The Bulletin* (The Horticultural Society of New York) 3(4): 1 *et seq.*

Schultes, R.E. 1975. "De plantis toxicariis e mundo novo tropicale commentationes XIII. Notes on poisonous or medicinal malpighiaceous species of the Amazon" *Botanical Museum Leaflets* Harvard University 24(6): 121–131. Schultes and Swain 1976 was also designated No. XIII.

Schultes, R.E. 1976. *Hallucinogenic Plants* (A Golden Guide). Golden Press, New York. French translation by J. Lepage, *Atlas des Plantes Hallucinogènes du Monde: Un Précis de Chimie et de Botanique.* Éditions de l'Aurore, Montréal, Québec, Canada, 1978. Pirated Spanish translation by S.C. Estrada, *Plantas Alucinógenas.* La Prensa Médica Mexicana, México City, 1982.

Schultes, R.E. 1977A. "A new hallucinogen from Andean Colombia: *Iochroma fuchsioides*" *Journal of Psychedelic Drugs* 9(1): 45–49.

Schultes, R.E. 1977B. "Mexico and Colombia: Two major centres of aboriginal use of hallucinogens" *Journal of Psychedelic Drugs* 9(2): 173–176.

Schultes, R.E. 1977C. "De plantis toxicariis e mundo novo tropicale commentationes XV. Desfontainia: A new Andean hallucinogen" *Botanical Museum Leaflets* Harvard University 25(3): 99–104.

Schultes, R.E. 1978. "Evolution of the identification of the sacred hallucinogenic mushrooms of Mexico" In: Ott, J. and J. Bigwood (Eds.) *Teonanácatl: Hallucinogenic Mushrooms of North America.* (Psycho-Mycological Studies No. 2) Madrona Publishers, Seattle, WA. pp. 27–43. Translated into Spanish by M.S. Antolín, 1985. "Proceso de identificación de los sagrados hongos alucinógenos de México" *Teonanácatl: Hongos Alucinógenos de Europa y América del Norte.* Editorial Swan, San Lorenzo de El Escorial, Spain. pp. 41–53.

Schultes, R.E. 1979A. "De plantis toxicariis e mundo novo tropicale commentationes. XIX. Biodynamic apocynaceous plants of the northwest Amazon" *Journal of Ethnopharmacology* 1(2): 165–192.

Schultes, R.E. 1979B. "Evolution of the identification of the myristicaceous hallucinogens of South America" *Journal of Ethnopharmacology* 1(3): 211–239.

Schultes, R.E. 1979C. "Hallucinogenic plants: Their earliest botanical descriptions" *Journal of Psychedelic Drugs* 11(1-2): 13–24. Paper presented at conference "Hallucinogens in Native American Shamanism and Modern Life," 28 September–1 October 1978, San Francisco, CA, USA.

Schultes, R.E. 1979D. "Evolution of the identification of the major South American narcotic [*sic*] plants" *Journal of Psychedelic Drugs* 11(1-2): 119–134. Paper presented at conference "Hallucinogens in Native American Shamanism and Modern Life," 28 September–1 October 1978, San Francisco, CA, USA.

Schultes, R.E. 1979E. "Solanaceous hallucinogens and their role in the development of the New World cultures" In: Hawkes, J.G. *et al.* (Eds.) *The Biology and Taxonomy of the Solanaceae.* (Linnean Society Symposium Series, Number 7) Academic Press, London, England. pp. 137–160.

Schultes, R.E. 1979F. "Discovery of an ancient guayusa plantation in Colombia" *Botanical Museum Leaflets* Harvard University 27(5-6): 143–153.

Schultes, R.E. 1980. "De plantis toxicariis e mundo novo tropicale commentationes XXIX. A suspected new Amazonian hallucinogen" *Botanical Museum Leaflets* Harvard University 28(3): 271–275.

Schultes, R.E. 1981. "Coca in the northwest Amazon" *Journal of Ethnopharmacology* 3(2&3): 173–194. Published in 1980 in *Botanical Museum Leaflets* Harvard University 28(1): 47–60. Paper presented at conference "Erythroxylon—New Historical and Scientific Aspects," 3–5 December 1979, Quito, Ecuador.

Schultes, R.E. 1983A. "De plantis toxicariis e mundo novo tropicale commentationes XXXII. Notes, primarily of field tests and native nomenclature, on biodynamic plants of the northwest Amazon" *Botanical Museum Leaflets* Harvard University 29(3): 251–272.

Schultes, R.E. 1983B. "De plantis toxicariis e mundo novo tropicale commentationes XXXIII. Ethnobotanical, floristic and nomenclatural notes on plants of the northwest Amazon" *Botanical Museum Leaflets* Harvard University 29(4): 343–365.

Schultes, R.E. 1983C. "Richard Spruce: An early ethnobotanist and explorer of the northwest Amazon and northern Andes" *Journal of Ethnobiology* 3(2): 139–147.

Schultes, R.E. 1984. "Fifteen years of study of psychoactive snuffs of South America: 1967–1982—A review" *Journal of Ethnopharmacology* 11(1): 17–32.

Schultes, R.E. 1985A. "De plantis toxicariis e mundo novo tropicale commentationes XXXV. Miscellaneous notes on biodynamic plants of the northwest Amazon" *Journal of Ethnopharmacology* 14(2,3): 125–158.

Schultes, R.E. 1985B. "De plantis toxicariis e mundo novo tropicale commentationes XXXVI. A novel method of utilizing the hallucinogenic Banisteriopsis" *Botanical Museum Leaflets* Harvard University 30(3): 61–63. Both this paper and Schultes 1990 were designated number XXXVI in Schultes' "De plantis toxicariis..." series.

Schultes, R.E. 1985C. "De plantis toxicariis e mundo novo tropicale commentationes XXXIV: Biodynamic rubiaceous plants of the northwest Amazon" *Journal of Ethnopharmacology* 14(2,3): 105–124.

Schultes, R.E. 1986A. "Recognition of variability in wild plants by Indians of the northwest Amazon: An enigma" *Journal of Ethnobiology* 6(2): 229–238.

Schultes, R.E. 1986B. "El desarrollo histórico de la identificación de las malpigiáceas empleadas como alucinógenos" *América Indígena* 46(1): 9–47.

Schultes, R.E. 1987A. "The strange activity of *Malouetia tamaquarina* (Apocynaceae), a toxic Amazonian plant" *Economic Botany* 41(2): 324–325.

Schultes, R.E. 1987B. "A caffeine drink prepared from bark" *Economic Botany* 41(4): 526–527.

Schultes, R.E. 1988. *Where the Gods Reign: Plants and Peoples of the Colombian Amazon*. Synergetic Press, Oracle, AZ. Preface by Mark J. Plotkin, pp. 1–3.

Schultes, R.E. 1990. "De plantis toxicariis e mundo novo tropicale commentationes XXXVI. *Justicia* (Acanthaceae) as a source of an hallucinogenic snuff" *Economic Botany* 44(1): 61–70. This paper and Schultes 1985B were designated number XXXVI in Schultes' "De plantis toxicariis..." series.

Schultes, R.E. 1992. Personal communications, correspondence.

Schultes, R.E. and **M.R. Aldrich** 1990. "Foreword" to facsimile edition of Cooke, M.C. *The Seven Sisters of Sleep. Popular History of the Seven Prevailing Narcotics of the World.* Quarterman Publications, Lincoln, MA. pp. VII–XI.

Schultes, R.E. and **A. Bright** 1977. "A native drawing of an hallucinogenic plant from Colombia" *Botanical Museum Leaflets* Harvard University 25(6): 151–159.

Schultes, R.E. and **A. Bright** 1979. "Ancient gold pectorals from Colombia: Mushroom effigies?" *Botanical Museum Leaflets* Harvard University 27(5-6): 113–141.

Schultes, R.E. and **N.R. Farnsworth** 1980. "Ethnomedical, botanical and phytochemical aspects of natural hallucinogens" *Botanical Museum Leaflets* Harvard University 28(2): 123–214.

Schultes, R.E. and **A. Hofmann** 1979. *Plants of the Gods: Origins of Hallucinogenic Use.* McGraw-Hill, New York. Reprinted in 1992. *Plants of the Gods: Their Sacred, Healing and Hallucinogenic Powers.* Healing Arts Press, Rochester, VT. Translated into Spanish in 1982. *Las Plantas de los Dioses: Orígenes del Uso de los Alucinógenos.* Fondo de Cultura Económica, México City. Translated into German, 1980. *Pflanzen der Götter.* AT Verlag, Aarau, Switzerland. Translated into French, 1993. *Les Plantes des Dieux: Les Plantes Hallucinogènes, Botanique et Ethnologie.* Les Éditions du Lézard, Paris, France. Préface by J.-P. Galland, p. 7.

Schultes, R.E. and **A. Hofmann** 1980. *The Botany and Chemistry of Hallucinogens.* Revised and enlarged second edition. C. C. Thomas, Springfield, IL. Foreword by H. Klüver, pp. VII–XV. Original in 1973. Monograph, The Bannerstone Division of American Lectures in Living Chemistry; foreword by editor I.N. Kugelmass, pp. V–VI.

Schultes, R.E. and **B. Holmstedt** 1968. "De plantis toxicariis e mundo novo tropicale commentationes II. The vegetal ingredients of the myristicaceous snuffs of the northwest Amazon" *Rhodora* 70: 113–160.

Schultes, R.E. and **R.F. Raffauf** 1960. "Prestonia: An Amazon narcotic [*sic*] or not?" *Botanical Museum Leaflets* Harvard University 19(5): 109–122. Reprint May 1974.

Schultes, R.E. and **R.F. Raffauf** 1990. *The Healing Forest: Medicinal and Toxic Plants of the Northwest Amazonia.* (Dudley, T.R., General Ed.; Historical, Ethno- & Economic Botany Series, Volume 2) Dioscorides Press, Portland, OR. Foreword by H.R.H. Philip, Duke of Edinburgh, p. 7.

Schultes, R.E. and **R.F. Raffauf** 1992. *Vine of the Soul: Medicine Men, their Plants and Rituals in the Colombian Amazon.* Synergetic Press, Oracle, AZ. Foreword by Ghillean T. Prance, pp. 1–3; epilogue by Michael J. Balick, pp. 274–275. Spanish translation 1994, Univ. de los Andes, Bogotá.

Schultes, R.E. and **T. Swain** 1976. "De plantis toxicariis e mondo novo tropicale commentationes XIII. Further notes on Virola as an orally administered hallucinogen" *Journal of Psychedelic Drugs* 8(4): 317–324. Schultes 1975 also called No. XIII.

Schultes, R.E. *et al.* 1969. "De plantis toxicariis e mundo novo tropicale commentationes III. Phytochemical examination of Spruce's original collection of Banisteriopsis caapi" *Botanical Museum Leaflets* Harvard University 22(4): 121–132.

Schultes, R.E. *et al.* 1974. "Cannabis: An example of taxonomic neglect" *Botanical Museum Leaflets* Harvard University 23(9): 337–367.

Schultes, R.E. *et al.* 1977A. "De plantis toxicariis e mundo novo tropicale commentationes XVII. *Virola* as an oral hallucinogen among the Boras of Peru" *Botanical Museum Leaflets* Harvard University 25(9): 259–272.

Schultes, R.E. *et al.* 1977B. "De plantis toxicariis e mundo novo tropicale commentationes XVIII. Phytochemical examination of Spruce's ethnobotanical collection of *Anadenanthera peregrina*." *Botanical Museum Leaflets* Harvard University 25(10): 273–287.

Schulz, B. 1959. "*Lagochilus inebrians* Sge., eine intereßante neue Arzneipflanze" *Deutscher Apotheker Zeitung* 99: 1111.

Schulze, R.G. 1976. "Nutmeg as an hallucinogen" *New England Journal of Medicine* 295(3): 174.

Schutzenberger, M.P. 1867. *Traité des Matièrs Colorantes.* 2 volumes. Paris, France.

Schwartz, H.T. 1972. *Windigo and Other Tales of Ojibway.* McClelland and Steward, Toronto, Ontario, Canada.

Schwartz, R.H. *et al.* 1987. "Urinary cannabinoids in monitoring abstinence in a drug abuse treatment program" *Archives of Pathology and Laboratory Medicine* 111(8): 708–711.

Schwarz, H.F. 1948. "Stingless Bees (Meliponidae) of the Western Hemisphere" *Bulletin of the American Museum of Natural History* 90: 1–536.

Scott, P.D. and **J. Marshall** 1991. *Cocaine Politics: Drugs, Armies, and the CIA in Central America.* University of California Press, Berkeley, CA.

Seaforth, C.E. 1991. *Natural Products in Caribbean Folk Medicine.* The University of the West Indies, St. Augustine, Trinidad, West Indies. Second revised edition.

Seashore, R.H. and **A.C. Ivy** 1953. "Effects of analeptic drugs in relieving fatigue" *Psychology Monographs* 67(15): 1–16.

Seidler, H. *et al.* 1992. "Some anthropological aspects of the prehistoric Tyrolean ice man" *Science* 258: 455–457.

Seitz, G.J. 1967. "Epéna, the intoxicating snuff powder of the Waika Indians and the Tucano medicine man, Agostino" In: Efron, D.H. *et al.* (Eds.) *Ethnopharmacologic Search for Psychoactive Drugs.* (Public Health Service Publication No. 1645) U.S. Government Printing Office, Washington, D.C. pp. 315–338.

Semerdzieva, M. and **F. Nerud** 1973. "Halluzinogene Pilze in der Tschechoslowakei" *Ceska Mykologie* 27: 42–47.

Semerdzieva, M. and **M. Wurst** 1986. "Psychotrope Inhaltßtoffe zweier *Psilocybe* Arten (Kahlköpfe) aus der CSSR" *Mykologisches Mitteilungsblatt* 29: 65.

Semerdzieva, M. *et al.* 1986. "Psilocybin in Fruchtkörpern von *Inocybe aeruginascens*" *Planta Medica* 52: 83–85.

Sen, S. *et al.* 1989. "Betel cytotoxicity" *Journal of Ethnopharmacology* 26(3): 217–247.

Sengupta, S. and **A.B. Ray** 1987. "The chemistry of *Piper* species: A review" *Fitoterapia* 58: 147–166.

Seymour, R. and **D.E. Smith** 1987. *The Physician's Guide to Psychoactive Drugs.* The Haworth Press, New York.

Shafer, J. 1984. "The war on drugs is over. The government has lost" *Inquiry.* February issue. pp. 14–20.

Shafer, J. 1985. "Designer drugs" *Science 85.* March issue. pp. 60–67.

Shah, N.C. 1982. "Herbal folk medicine of northern India" *Journal of Ethnopharmacology* 6(3): 293–301.

Shamma, A. al- and **A.-M. Abdul-Ghany** 1977. "A comparative study of the alkaloidal contents of *Peganum harmala* L." *Bulletin of the Biology Research Center, Baghdad* (Iraq) 8: 10–16.

Shannon, P.V.R. and **W.M. Leyshon** 1971. "The structure and synthesis of the tetrahydro-β-carboline alkaloids from *Phalaris arundinacea*: Some new tetrahydro-β-carbolines" *Journal of the Chemical Society* 1971: 2837–2839.

Shapira, Z. *et al.* 1989. "Abortifacient potential for the epigeal parts of *Peganum harmala*" *Journal of Ethnopharmacology* 27(3): 319–325.

Sharma, G.K. 1977. "Ethnobotany and its significance for *Cannabis* studies in the Himalayas" *Journal of Psychedelic Drugs* 9(4): 337–339.

Sharma, J.D. *et al.* 1961. "Pharmacodynamical effects of asarone and β-asarone" *Nature* 192: 1299–1300.

Sharon, D. 1972. "The San Pedro cactus in Peruvian folk healing" In: Furst, P.T. (Ed.) *Flesh of the Gods: The Ritual Use of Hallucinogens.* Praeger, New York. pp. 114–135.

Sharon, D. 1978. *Wizard of the Four Winds: A Shaman's Story.* The Free Press, New York. Translated into Spanish by D. Huerta, 1980. *El Chamán de los Cuatro Vientos.* Siglo Veintiuno Editores, México City.

Sharon, D. and **C.B. Donnan** 1977. "The magic cactus: Ethnoarchaeological continuity in Peru" *Archaeology* 30(6): 374–381.

Shawcross, W.E. 1981. "'Funny mushrooms'—Natural fungal hallucinogens" Unpublished manuscript, Cambridge, MA.

Shawcross, W.E. 1982. "A history of hemp fiber in American cordage" Unpublished manuscript, Cambridge, MA.

Shawcross, W.E. 1983. "Recreational use of ergoline alkaloids from *Argyreia nervosa*" *Journal of Psychoactive Drugs* 15(4): 251–259.

Shellard, E.J. 1983. "Mitragyna: A note on the alkaloids of African species" *Journal of Ethnopharmacology* 8(3): 345–347.

Shellard, E.J. 1989. "Ethnopharmacology of kratom and the *Mitragyna* alkaloids" *Journal of Ethnopharmacology* 25(1): 123–124.

Shelley, W.S. 1994. *The Elixir: An Alchemical Study of the Ergot Mushrooms.* Cross-Cultural Publications, Notre Dame, IN.

Shemluck, M.J. 1979. "The flowers of Ilex guayusa" *Botanical Museum Leaflets* Harvard University 27(5-6): 155–160.

Shemluck, M.J. 1990. Thesis, Northeastern University, Boston, MA.

Shemluck, M.J. 1991. *Journal of Natural Products* 54: 1601–1606.

Shen, W.W. and **T.C. D'Souza** 1979. "Cola-induced psychotic organic brain syndrome" *Rocky Mountain Medical Journal* 76: 312–313.

Sheng-ji, P. 1985. "Preliminary study of the ethnobotany of Xishuang Banna, People's Republic [*sic*] of China" *Journal of Ethnopharmacology* 13(2): 121–137.

Sherry, C.J. *et al.* 1982. "The pharmacological effects of a ligroin extract of nutmeg (*Myristica fragrans*)" *Journal of Ethnopharmacology* 6(1): 61–66.

Shick, J.F.E. and **D.E. Smith** 1972. "The illicit use of the psychotomimetic [*sic*] amphetamines with special reference to STP (DOM) toxicity" *Journal of Psychedelic Drugs* 5(2): 131–138.

Shinozaki, H. and **S. Konishi** 1970. "Actions of several anthelmintics and insecticides on rat cortical neurones" *Brain Research* 24: 368–371.

Shrestha, T. *et al.* 1992. "The Moraceae-based dart poisons of South America. Cardiac glycosides of *Maquira* and *Naucleopsis* species" *Journal of Ethnopharmacology* 37(2): 129–143.

Shulgin, A.T. 1963A. "Composition of the myristicin fraction from oil of nutmeg" *Nature* 197: 379.

Shulgin, A.T. 1963B. "Psychotomimetic [*sic*] agents related to mescaline" *Experientia* 19: 127–128.

Shulgin, A.T. 1963C. "Concerning the pharmacology of nutmeg" *Mind* 1: 299.

Shulgin, A.T. 1964A. "3-Methoxy-4,5-methylenedioxy amphetamine, a new psychotomimetic agent" *Nature* 201: 1120–1121.

Shulgin, A.T. 1964B. "Psychotomimetic [*sic*] amphetamines: Methoxy-3,4-dialkoxyamphetamines" *Experientia* 20: 366–367.

Shulgin, A.T. 1966. "Possible implication of myristicin as a psychotropic substance" *Nature* 210: 380–384.

Shulgin, A.T. 1970. "Chemistry and structure-activity relationships of the psychotomimetics [*sic*]" In: Efron, D.H. (Ed.) *Psychotomimetic* [*sic*] *Drugs.* Raven Press, New York. pp. 21–41.

Shulgin, A.T. 1971. "Chemistry and sources" In: Epstein, S.S. (Ed.) *Drugs of Abuse* [*sic*]*: Their Genetic and other Chronic Nonpsychiatric Hazards.* The MIT Press, Cambridge, MA. pp. 3–26.

Shulgin, A.T. 1973. "Mescaline: The chemistry and pharmacology of its analogs" *Lloydia* 36(1): 46–58.

Shulgin, A.T. 1976A. "Psychotomimetic [*sic*] agents" In: Gordon, M. (Ed.) *Psychopharmacological Agents.* Academic Press, New York. Volume 4, pp. 59–146.

Shulgin, A.T. 1976B. "Profiles of psychedelic drugs. 1. DMT" *Journal of Psychedelic Drugs* 8(2): 167–168.

Shulgin, A.T. 1976C. "Profiles of psychedelic drugs. 2. TMA-2" *Journal of Psychedelic Drugs* 8(2): 169.

Shulgin, A.T. 1976D. "Profiles of psychedelic drugs. 3. MDMA" *Journal of Psychedelic Drugs* 8(4): 331.

Shulgin, A.T. 1977A. Personal communications, Berkeley, CA.

Shulgin, A.T. 1977B. "Profiles of psychedelic drugs. 6. α,O-DMS" *Journal of Psychedelic Drugs* 11(3): 247.

Shulgin, A.T. 1979A. "Profiles of psychedelic drugs. 7. Mescaline" *Journal of Psychedelic Drugs* 11(4): 355.

Shulgin, A.T. 1979B. "Chemistry of phenethylamines related to mescaline" *Journal of Psychedelic Drugs* 11(1-2): 41–52. "Hallucinogens in Native American Shamanism and Modern Life," 28 September–1 October 1978, San Francisco, CA, USA.

Shulgin, A.T. 1980A. "Profiles of psychedelic drugs. 8. Psilocybin" *Journal of Psychedelic Drugs* 12(1): 79.

Shulgin, A.T. 1980B. "Profiles of psychedelic drugs. 9. LSD" *Journal of Psychedelic Drugs* 12(2): 173–174.

Shulgin, A.T. 1981. "Profiles of psychedelic drugs. 10. DOB" *Journal of Psychoactive Drugs* 13(1): 99.

Shulgin, A.T. 1982. "Chemistry of psychotomimetics [*sic*]" In: Hofmeister, F. and G. Stilke (Eds.) *Psychotropic Agents* Vol. 55/III. Springer, Berlin, Germany. pp. 3–29.

Shulgin, A.T. 1986. "The background and chemistry of MDMA" *Journal of Psychoactive Drugs* 18(3): 291.

Shulgin, A.T. 1991. "Confessions of a psychedelic alchemist" *Whole Earth Review* 72: 22–27.

Shulgin, A.T. 1992. Personal communications, San Luis Potosí, SLP, México.

Shulgin, A.T. and **D.C. Dyer** 1975. "Psychotomimetic [*sic*] phenylisopropylamines. 5. 4-Alkyl-2,5-dimethoxyphenylisopropylamines" *Journal of Medicinal Chemistry* 18: 1201–1204.

Shulgin, A.T. and **H.O. Kerlinger** 1964. "Isolation of methoxyeugenol and trans-isoelemicin from oil of nutmeg" *Die Naturwißenschaften* 51: 360–361.

Shulgin, A.T. and **D.E. Nichols** 1978. "Characterization of three new psychotomimetics [*sic*]" In: Stillman, R.C. and R.E. Willette (Eds.) *The Psychopharmacology of Hallucinogens.* Pergamon Press, New York.

Shulgin, A.T. and **T. Sargent** 1967. "Psychotropic phenylisopropylamines derived from apiole and dillapiole" *Nature* 215: 1494–1495.

Shulgin, A.T. and **A. Shulgin** 1991. *PIHKAL: A Chemical Love Story.* Transform Press, Berkeley, CA. Foreword by David E. Nichols, pp. IX–X.

Shulgin, A.T. and **A. Shulgin** 1996. *TIHKAL.* Transform Press, Berkeley, CA.

Shulgin, A.T. *et al.* 1961. "The psychotomimetic [*sic*] properties of 3,4,5-trimethoxyamphetamine" *Nature* 189: 1011–1012.

Shulgin, A.T. *et al.* 1967. "The chemistry and psychopharmacology of nutmeg and of several related phenylisopropylamines" In: Efron, D.H. *et al.* (Eds.) *Ethnopharmacologic Search for Psychoactive Drugs.* (Public Health Service Publication No. 1645) U.S. Government Printing Office, Washington, D.C. pp. 202–214.

Shulgin, A.T. *et al.* 1969. "Structure-activity relationship of one-ring psychotomimetics [*sic*]" *Nature* 221: 537–542. Followed by *erratum* 221: 786, 1969.

Shulgin, A.T. *et al.* 1971. "4-Bromo-2,5-dimethoxyphenylisopropylamine, a new centrally active amphetamine analog" *Pharmacology* 5: 103–107.

Siebert, D.J. 1994. "*Salvia divinorum* and salvinorin A: New pharmacologic findings" *Journal of Ethnopharmacology* 43(1): 53–56.

Siegel, R.K. 1977. "Hallucinations" *Scientific American* 237(4): 132–140.

Siegel, R.K. 1989. *Intoxication: Life in Pursuit of Artificial* [*sic*] *Paradise.* Simon & Schuster, London, England.

Siegel, R.K. 1992. *Fire in the Brain: Clinical Tales of Hallucination.* Dutton, New York.

Siegel, R.K. and **M.E. Jarvik** 1975. "Drug-induced hallucinations in animals and man" In: Siegel, R.K. and L.J. West (Eds.) *Hallucinations—Behavior, Experience and Theory.* John Wiley & Sons, New York.

Siegel, R.K. and **L.J. West** (Eds.) 1975. *Hallucinations—Behavior, Experience and Theory.* John Wiley and Sons, New York.

Siegel, R.K. *et al.* 1974. "An observational study of hallucinogen-induced behavior in unrestrained *Macaca mulatta*" *Psychopharmacologia* 40: 211–223.

Siegel, R.K. *et al.* 1977. "On the use of *Tagetes lucida* and *Nicotiana rustica* as a Huichol smoking mixture: The Aztec 'Yahutli' with suggestive hallucinogenic effects" *Economic Botany* 31(1): 16–23.

Sigstedt, S. 1990. "Bear medicine: Self-medication by animals" Abstract of 13th Annual Conference, Society of Ethnobiology. *Journal of Ethnobiology* 10(2): 257.

Silver, W. 1971. "Insomnia, tachycardia and cola drink" *Pediatrics* 47: 635.

Silverstone, T. and **B. Wells** 1979. "Clinical psychopharmacology of amphetamine and related compounds" In: Caldwell, J. (Ed.) *Amphetamines and Related Stimulants: Chemical, Biological, Clinical, and Sociological Aspects.* CRC Press, Boca Raton, FL. pp. 147–159.

Silverwood-Cope, P. 1980. Personal communication to R.E. Schultes, cited in Schultes, R.E. and A. Hofmann 1980. *The Botany and Chemistry of Hallucinogens.* C.C. Thomas, Springfield, IL.

Sinclair, A. 1957. *Field and Clinical Survey of the Mental Health of the Indigenes of the Territory of Papua New Guinea.* W.S. Nicholas, Port Moresby, New Guinea.

Singer, R. 1949(51). "The Agaricales in modern taxonomy" *Lilloa* 22: 1–832.

Singer, R. 1957. "Sacred mushrooms inspire medical research" *Chicago Natural History Museum Bulletin.* December 1957. p. 7.

Singer, R. 1958A. "Mycological investigations on teonanácatl, the Mexican hallucinogenic mushroom. Part I. The history of teonanácatl, field work and culture work" *Mycologia* 50(2): 239–261. Published "out-of-order with financial assistance."

Singer, R. 1958B. "Pilze, die Zerebralmyzetismen verursachen" *Schweizerische Zeitschrift für Pilzkunde* 36(6): 81–89.

Singer, R. 1959. "Hongos alucinógenos" *Boletín de la Academia Nacional de Ciencias* (Argentina) 41: 31–46.

Singer, R. 1973. "Diagnoses fungorum novorum Agaricaium" *Sydowia* 7: 1–106.

Singer, R. 1978. "Hallucinogenic mushrooms" In: Rumack, B.H. and E. Salzman (Eds.) *Mushroom Poisoning: Diagnosis and Treatment.* CRC Press, West Palm Beach, FL. pp. 201–214.

Singer, R. 1982. *A Correction* [*sic*]. Ethnomycological Studies No. 8. Botanical Museum of Harvard University, Cambridge, MA. Reply to Ott 1978A. See also: rebuttal: Wasson 1982A; A.H. Smith 1977.

Singer, R. and **A.H. Smith** 1958A. "New species of *Psilocybe*" *Mycologia* 50(1): 141–142.

Singer, R. and **A.H. Smith** 1958B. "Mycological investigations on teonanácatl, the Mexican hallucinogenic mushroom. Part II. Taxonomic monograph of *Psilocybe*, section *Caerulescentes*" *Mycologia* 50(2): 262–303.

Singer, R. *et al.* 1958A. "A new species of *Psathyrella*" *Lloydia* 21(1): 26–28.

Singer, R. *et al.* 1958B. "Observations on agarics causing cerebral mycetisms" *Mycopathologia et Mycologia Applicata* 9(4): 261–284. Introduction by R. Singer, pp. 261–262; and 4 parts: I. "An unusual effect from a species of Mexican mushrooms *Psilocybe cubensis*" by S.I. Stein, pp. 263–267; II. "The influence of temperature of [*sic*] mycelial growth of *Psilocybe*, *Panaeolus*, and *Copelandia*" by R.W. Ames, pp. 268–274; III. "A *Russula* provoking hysteria in New Guinea" by R. Singer, pp. 275–279; and IV. "About the identity of the weed *Panaeolus* or poisonous *Panaeolus*" by R. Singer & A.H. Smith, pp. 280–284.

Singh, M.P. *et al.* 1979. "Medicinal plants of Nepal—Retrospects and prospects" *Economic Botany* 33(2): 185–198.

Singh, Y.N. 1983. "Effects of kava on neuromuscular transmission and muscle contractility" *Journal of Ethnopharmacology* 7(3): 267–276.

Singh, Y.N. 1992. "Kava: An overview" *Journal of Ethnopharmacology* 37(1): 13–45.

Singh, Y.N. *et al.* 1984. "Folk medicine in Tonga. A study of the use of herbal medicines for obstetrical and gynaecological conditions and disorders" *Journal of Ethnopharmacology* 12(3): 305–329.

Sirakawa, K. *et al.* 1966. "Synthesis of ibotenic acid and 3-deoxyibotenic acid" *Chemical and Pharmacological Bulletin Japan* 14: 89–91.

Sirius, R.U. and **G. Gleason** 1990. "Do G-

men dream of electric sheep?" *Mondo 2000* 3: 40–43.
Siskind, J. 1973. "Visions and cures among the Sharanahua" In: Harner, M.J. (Ed.) *Hallucinogens and Shamanism.* Oxford University Press, London, England. pp. 28–39.
Sitaram, N. *et al.* 1978. "Human serial learning: Enhancement with arecholine [*sic*] and choline and impairment with scopolamine" *Science* 201: 274–276.
Skerrett, P.J. 1990. "Substance P causes pain—But also heals" *Science* 249: 625.
Skolnick, J.H. 1968. "Coercion to virtue: The enforcement of morals" *South California Law Review* 41: 588–641.
Skolnick, P. *et al.* 1982. "β-Carbolines and benzodiazepine receptors: Structure-activity relationships and pharmacologic activity" *Progress in Clinical and Biological Research* 90: 122.
Sledge, W.A. and **R.E. Schultes** 1988. "Richard Spruce: A multi-talented botanist" *Journal of Ethnobiology* 8(1): 7–12.
Slotkin, J.S. 1952. "Menomini peyotism" *Transactions of the American Philosophical Society* 42(3): 565–700.
Slotkin, J.S. 1956. *The Peyote Religion: A Study in Indian-White Relations.* Free Press, Glencoe, IL.
Slotkin, T.A. *et al.* 1970. "Blood levels and urinary excretion of harmine and its metabolites in man and rats" *The Journal of Pharmacology and Experimental Therapeutics* 173(1): 26–30.
Small, E. 1975A. "American law and the species problem in *Cannabis*: Science and semantics" *Bulletin on Narcotics* 27(3): 1–20.
Small, E. 1975B. "On toadstool soup and legal species of marihuana [*sic*]" *Plant Sciences Bulletin.* September issue. pp. 34–39.
Small, E. 1975C. "Morphological variation of achenes of *Cannabis*" *Canadian Journal of Botany* 53: 978–987.
Small, E. 1976. "The forensic taxonomic debate on *Cannabis*: Semantic hokum" *Journal of Forensic Science* 21: 239–251.
Small, E. and **A. Cronquist** 1976. "A practical and natural [*sic*, political] taxonomy for *Cannabis*" *Taxon* 25: 405–435.
Small, E. *et al.* 1975. "The evolution of cannabinoid phenotypes in *Cannabis*" *Economic Botany* 29(3): 219–232.
Small, L.F. and **R.E. Lutz** 1932. *Chemistry of the Opium Alkaloids.* (Supplement No. 103 to the Public Health Reports) U.S. Government Printing Office, Washington, D.C. Foreword by Heinrich Wieland, p. III.
Small, L.F. *et al.* 1938. *Studies on Drug Addiction. With Special Reference to Chemical Structures of Opium Derivatives and Allied Synthetic Substances and their Physiological Action.* (Supplement No. 138 to the Public Health Reports) U.S. Government Printing Office, Washington, D.C. Introduction by Wm. Charles White, p. III–VI.
Smith, A.H. 1977. "Some comments on hallucinogenic agarics and the hallucinations of those who study them" *Mycologia* 69(6): 1196–1200. See also: Ott 1978A; Singer 1982; Wasson 1982A.
Smith, G.M. and **H.K. Beecher** 1959. "Amphetamine sulfate and athletic performance. I. Objective effects" *Journal of the American Medical Association* 170: 542.
Smith, G.W. 1973. "Arctic pharmacognosia" *Arctic* 26: 324–333.
Smith, H.I. 1929. "Materia Medica of the Bella Coola and neighbouring tribes" *National Museum of Canada Bulletin* 56: 47–68.
Smith, H.H. 1923. "Ethnobotany of the Menomini Indians" *Bulletin of the Public Museum of Milwaukee* 4: 1–174.
Smith, H.H. 1933. "Ethnobotany of the forest Potawatomi Indians" *Bulletin of the Public Museum of Milwaukee* 7: 1–230.
Smith, M.V. (Pseudonym for Michael Starks)

1976. *Psychedelic Chemistry*. Fourth edition, corrected and expanded. Rip Off Press, San Francisco, CA.

Smith, R.M. 1979. "Pipermethystin, a novel pyridone alkaloid from *Piper methysticum* (cultivated in the South Pacific as a drug plant and beverage plant)" *Tetrahedron* 5: 437–439.

Smith, R.M. 1983. "Kava lactones in *Piper methysticum* from Fiji" *Phytochemistry* 22: 1055–1056.

Smith, R.M. *et al.* 1984. "High-performance liquid chromatography of kava lactones from *Piper methysticum*" *Journal of Chromatography* 283: 303–308.

Smith, S. and **G.M. Timmis** 1932. "The alkaloids of ergot. Part III. Ergine, a new base obtained by the degradation of ergotoxine and ergotinine" *Journal of the Chemical Society* 1932: 763–766.

Smith, T.A. 1977. "Tryptamine and related compounds in plants" *Phytochemistry* 16: 171–175. Review article.

Snyder, S.H. and **S. Matthysse** 1975. *Opiate Receptor Mechanisms.* MIT Press, Cambridge, MA.

Snyder, S.H. *et al.* 1968. "DOM (STP); a new hallucinogenic drug, and DOET: Effects in normal subjects" *American Journal of Psychiatry* 125: 357–364.

Snyder, S.H. *et al.* 1970. "DOET (2,5-dimethoxy-4-ethylamphetamine) and DOM (STP) (2,5-dimethoxy-4-methylamphetamine), new psychotropic agents: Their effects in man" In: Efron, D.H. (Ed.) *Psychotomimetic* [*sic*] *Drugs.* Raven Press, New York. pp. 247–264.

Solms, H. 1956A. "Relationships between chemical structure and psychoses with the use of psychotoxic [*sic*] substances" *Journal of Clinical and Experimental Psychopathology. Quarterly Review of Psychiatry and Neurology* 17: 429–433.

Solms, H. 1956B. "Chemische Struktur und Psychose [*sic*] bei Lysergsäure-Derivaten" *Praxis* 45: 746.

Solomon, D. (Ed.) 1964. *LSD: The Consciousness-Expanding Drug.* G.P. Putnam's Sons, New York. Introduction by Timothy Leary.

Soukup, J. 1970. *Vocabulario de los Nombres Vulgares de la Flora Peruana y Catálogo de los Géneros*. Editorial Salesiana, Lima, Perú.

Southcott, R.V. 1974. "Notes on some poisonings and other clinical effects following ingestion of Australian fungi" *South Australian Clinics* 6(5): 441–478.

Spalding, R.J. 1991. "Black-market biotechnology: Athletes abuse [*sic*] EPO and hGH" *Biotechnology* 9: 1050–1053.

Spanos. N.P. 1983. "Ergotism and the Salem witch panic: A critical analysis and an alternative conceptualization" *Journal of the History of the Behavioral Sciences* 19: 358–369.

Spanos, N.P. and **J. Gottlieb** 1976. "Ergotism and the Salem witch trials" *Science* 194: 1390–1394. See: Caporael 1976.

Sparkman, P.S. 1908. *The Culture of the Luiseño Indians.* (University of California Publications, Volume 8, No. 4) University of California Press, Los Angeles, CA.

Späth, E. 1919. "Über die Anhalonium-Alkaloide. I. Anhalin und Mezcalin" *Monatshefte für Chemie und Verwandte Teile Anderer Wißenschaften* 40: 129–154.

Späth, E. and **E. Lederer** 1930A. "Synthese der Harmala-Alkaloide: Harmalin, Harmin und Harman" *Berichte der Deutschen Chemischen Gesellschaft* 63: 120–125.

Späth, E. and **E. Lederer** 1930B. "Synthesen von 4-Carbolinen" *Berichte der Deutschen Chemischen Gesellschaft* 63: 2102–2111.

Speck, F.G. 1941. "A list of plant curatives from the Houma Indians of Louisiana" *Primitive* [*sic*] *Man* 14: 49–75.

Speck, F.G. *et al.* 1942. "Rappahannock herbals: Folklore and science of cures" *Pro-*

ceedings of the Delaware County Institute of Science 10: 7–55.

Speeter, M.E. and **W.C. Anthony** 1954. "The action of oxalyl chloride on indoles: A new approach to tryptamines" *Journal of the American Chemical Society* 76: 6208–6210.

Speroni, E. and **A. Minghetti** 1988. "Neuropharmacological activity of extracts from *Passiflora incarnata*" *Planta Medica* 54: 488–491.

Spruce, R. 1873. "On some remarkable narcotics [*sic*] of the Amazon Valley and Orinoco, Ocean highways" *Geographical Magazine* 1(55): 184–193.

Spruce, R. (A.R. Wallace, Ed.) 1908. *Notes of a Botanist on the Amazon and Andes.* Two volumes. Macmillan, London, England. Reprinted in 1970 by Johnson Reprint, New York. Translated into Spanish, 1938. *Notas de un Botánico sobre el Amazonas y los Andes.* Imprenta de la Universidad Central, Quito, Ecuador.

Srivastava, J.G. 1966. "The Soma plant" *Quarterly Journal of Crude Drug Research* 6(1): 811.

Staba, E.J. and **P. Laursen** 1966. "Morning glory tissue cultures: Growth and examination for indole alkaloids" *Journal of Pharmaceutical Sciences* 55(10): 1099–1101.

Stafford, P. 1970. "Yage in the Valley of Fire" In: Aaronson, B.S. and H. Osmond (Eds.) *Psychedelics: The Uses and Implications of Hallucinogenic Drugs.* Doubleday/Anchor, Garden City, NJ. pp. 58–65.

Stafford, P. (J. Bigwood, Technical Ed.) 1983. *Psychedelics Encyclopedia.* Revised Edition. J.P. Tarcher, Inc., Los Angeles, CA. With foreword by Andrew Weil, pp. x–xi. Translated into German, 1980. *Enzyklopädie der Psychedelischen Drogen.* Volksverlag, Linden, Germany.

Stahl, E. *et al.* 1978. "Rauschgiftpilze mit LSD" *Archiv für Kriminologie* 162: 23–33.

Stamets, P. 1978. *Psilocybe Mushrooms and their Allies.* Homestead Book Co., Seattle, WA. Foreword by G. Guzmán, pp. 11–12.

Stamets, P. 1993. *Growing Gourmet and Medicinal Mushrooms.* Mycomedia, Olympia, WA.

Stamets, P. 1996. *Psilocybin* [*sic*] *Mushrooms of the World: An Identification Guide.* Ten Speed Press, Berkeley, CA. Forw. A. Weil.

Stamets, P. and **J.S. Chilton** 1983. *The Mushroom Cultivator—A Practical Guide to Growing Mushrooms at Home.* Agarikon Press, Olympia, WA. Foreword by Andrew Weil, pp. XIII–XIV.

Stamets, P. *et al.* 1980. "A new species and a new variety of *Psilocybe* from North America" *Mycotaxon* 11: 476–484.

Stark, H.J. *et al.* 1973. "Toxicological and cultural studies in the genus *Amanita*" *ASB Bulletin* 20: 84.

Starks, M. 1977. *Marijuana Potency.* And/Or Press, Berkeley, CA.

Staub, H. 1962. "Über die chemischen Bestandteile der Mandragorawurzel. 2. Die Alkaloide" *Helvetica Chimica Acta* 45: 2297–2305.

Stauffacher, D. von *et al.* 1965. "Isolierung von Ergosin und Ergosinin neben Agroclavin aus den Samen von *Ipomoea argyrophylla* Vatke (Convolvulaceae)" *Helvetica Chimica Acta* 48(6): 1379–1380.

Stearns, J. 1808. "An account of the *pulvis parturiens*, a remedy for quickening childbirth" *Med. Phil. News.* pp. 308–309.

Steedman, E.V. 1928. "The ethnobotany of the Thompson Indians" *Forty-fifth Annual Report of the Bureau of American Ethnology to the Smithsonian Institution.* U.S. Government Printing Office, Washington, D.C. pp. 441–522.

Steglich, W. *et al.* 1984. "Indolalkaloide aus dem Blätterpilz *Cortinarius infractus* (Agaricales)" *Tetrahedron Letters* 25(22): 2341–2344.

Stein, S.I. 1959. "Clinical observations on the effects of *Panaeolus venenosus* versus *Psilocybe caerulescens* mushrooms" *Mycologia* 51(1): 49–50.

Stein, S.I. 1960. Some biochemical and physiological correlations developed from clinical observations with various toxic mushrooms and medicinal products" *Developments in Industrial Microbiology* 1: 111–119.

Stein, S.I. *et al.* 1959. "Observations on psychoneurophysiologically significant mushrooms" *Mycopathologia et Mycologia Applicata* 11: 205.

Steinmetz, E.F. 1960. Piper methysticum (*Kava*)—*Famous Drug Plant of the South Seas Islands*. Privately printed, Amsterdam, the Netherlands.

Sterling, B. 1992. *The Hacker Crackdown: Law and Disorder on the Electronic Frontier.* Bantam Books, New York.

Stermitz, F.R. *et al.* 1983. "New and old phenanthrene derivatives from *Oncidium cebolleta*, a peyote replacement plant" *Journal of Natural Products* 46(3): 417–423.

Sterne, L. 1761. *The Life and Opinions of Tristram Shandy, Gent.* London, England. Various modern editions exist, such as the 1935 limited edition of The Heritage Press, New York, with illustrations by T. M. Cleland (who bequeathed his house to R. Gordon Wasson in a sort of tontine—when he retired from banking in 1962, Wasson lived and worked in what had once been Tom Cleland's studio).

Stevens, J. 1987. *Storming Heaven: LSD and the American Dream.* Atlantic Monthly Press, New York.

Stevens, J. and **R. Gee** 1977. *How to Identify and Grow Psilocybin Mushrooms.* Sun Magic Publishing, Seattle, WA.

Stevenson, M.C. 1915. "Ethnobotany of the Zuni Indians" *Thirtieth Annual Report of the Bureau of American Ethnology to the Smithsonian Institution.* U.S. Government Printing Office, Washington, D.C. pp. 35–102.

Stewart, O.C. 1987. *Peyote Religion: A History.* Univ. Oklahoma Press, Norman, OK.

Stijve, T. 1979. "Bufotenine concentrations in carpophores of Amanita citrina (Schaeff.) S.F. Gray" *Mitt. Geb. Lebensmittel. Hyg.* 70: 246–253.

Stijve, T. 1987. "Vorkommen von Serotonin, Psilocybin und Harnstoff in Panaeoloideae" *Beiträge zur Kenntnis der Pilze Mitteleuropas* 3: 229–234.

Stijve, T. 1992. "Psilocin, psilocybin, serotonin and urea in *Panaeolus cyanescens* from various origins" *Persoonia* 15(1): 117–121.

Stijve, T. and **J. Bonnard** 1986. "Psilocybine et urée dans le genre *Pluteus*" *Mycologia Helvetica* 2(1): 123–130.

Stijve, T. and **B. Bourqui** 1991. "Arsenic in edible mushrooms" *Deutsche Lebensmittel-Rundschau* 87(10): 307–310.

Stijve, T. and **A.A.R. De Meijer** 1993. "Macromycetes from the state of Paraná, Brazil. 4. The psychoactive species" *Arquivos do Biología y Tecnología* 36(2): 313–329.

Stijve, T. and **T.W. Kuyper** 1985. "Occurrence of psilocybin in various higher fungi from several European countries" *Planta Medica* 51: 385–387.

Stijve, T. and **T.W. Kuyper** 1988. "Absence of psilocybin in species of fungi previously reported to contain psilocybin and related tryptamine derivatives" *Persoonia* 13(4): 463–465.

Stijve, T. and **M. Poretti** 1990. "Radio-cesium levels in wild-growing mushrooms from various locations" *Mushroom the Journal*. Summer issue. pp. 5–9.

Stijve, T. *et al.* 1984. "Occurrence of 5-hydroxylated indole derivatives in Panaeolina foenisecii (Fries) Kuehner from various origins" *Zeitschrift für Mykologie* 50(2): 361–366.

Stijve, T. *et al.* 1985. "Occurrence of psilocybin and baeocystin in the genus Inocybe (Fr.) Fr." *Persoonia* 12(4): 469–473.

Stijve, T. *et al.* 1986. "Agaritine, a *p*-hydroxymethylphenylhydrazine derivative in cultivated mushrooms (*Agaricus bisporus*) and in some of its wild-growing relatives" *Deutsche Lebensmittel-Rundschau* 82(8): 243–248.

Stijve, T. *et al.* 1990. "Arsenic accumulation in some higher fungi" *Persoonia* 14(2): 161–166.

Stillman, J.M. 1922. *The Story of Alchemy and Early Chemistry*. Dover, New York.

Stillner, V. *et al.* 1978. "Caffeine-induced delirium during prolonged competitiveness" *American Journal of Psychiatry* 135: 855–856.

Stolaroff, M.J. 1994. *Thanatos to Eros: Thirty-five Years of Psychedelic Exploration.* VWB, Berlin, Germany. "Forword" [*sic*] by A.T. and A. Shulgin, pp. 7–8.

Stoll, A. 1965. "The ergot alkaloids" In: Manske, R.H.F. and H.L. Holmes (Eds.) *The Alkaloids*. Academic Press, New York. Volume 18, pp. 726–779.

Stoll, A. and **E. Burckhardt** 1935. "L'ergobasine, un nouvel alcaloïde de l'ergot de seigle, soluble dans l'eau" *Bulletin des Sciences Pharmacologiques* 37: 257–266.

Stoll, A. and **A. Hofmann** 1943. "Partialsynthese von Alkaloiden vom Typus des Ergobasins" *Helvetica Chimica Acta* 26: 944–965.

Stoll, A. *et al.* 1949. "Über die Isomerie von Lysergsäure und Isolysergsäure" *Helvetica Chimica Acta* 32: 506–521.

Stoll, A. *et al.* 1955. "Eine neue Synthese von Bufotenin und verwandten Oxytryptaminen" *Helvetica Chimica Acta* 38: 1452–1472.

Stoll, W.A. 1947. "Lysergsäure-diäthylamid, ein Phantasticum aus der Mutterkorngruppe" *Schweizer Archiv für Neurologie und Psychiatrie* 60: 279.

Stone, B.C. 1984. "*Pandanus* from Ok Tedi Region, Papua New Guinea, collected by Debra Donoghue" *Economic Botany* 38(3): 304–313.

Stone, R. 1991. "Radio astronomers seek a clear line to the stars" *Science* 251: 1316.

Stone, R. 1992. "Make that... 1002 uses for fungi" *Science* 257: 1049.

Storl, W.-D. 1996. *Heilkräuter und Zauberpflanzen zwischen Haustür und Gartentor.* AT Verlag, Aarau, Switzerland.

Stowe, B. 1959. "Occurrence and metabolism of simple indoles in plants" *Fortschritt der Chemie des Organischen Naturstoffe* 17: 248–297.

Strassman, R.J. 1991. "Human hallucinogenic drug research in the United States: A present-day case history and review of the process" *Journal of Psychoactive Drugs* 23(1): 29–38.

Strassman, R.J. and **C.R. Qualls** 1994. "Dose-response study of N,N-dimethylytryptamine in humans I. Neuroendocrine, autonomic, and cardiovascular effects" *Archives of General Psychiatry* 51: 85–97.

Strassman, R.J. *et al.* 1994. "Dose-response study of N,N-dimethylytryptamine in humans II. Subjective effects and preliminary results of a new rating scale" *Archives of General Psychiatry* 51: 98–108.

Strath, R. 1903. "Materia Medica, pharmacy and therapeutics of the Cree Indians of the Hudson Bay Territory" *The St. Paul Medical Journal* 5: 735–746.

Strausbaugh, J. and **D. Blaise** (Eds.) 1991. *The Drug User. Documents: 1840–1960.* Blast Books, New York. Foreword by W. S. Burroughs, pp. IX–XV.

Stresser-Péan, G. 1990. "Travels with R. Gordon Wasson in Mexico: 1956–1962" In: Riedlinger, T.J. (Ed.) *The Sacred Mushroom Seeker: Essays for R. Gordon Wasson.* Ethnomycological Studies No. 11. Dioscorides Press, Portland, OR. pp. 231–237.

Stromberg, V.L. 1954. "The isolation of bufotenine from *Piptadenia peregrina*" *Journal of the American Chemical Society* 76: 1707.

Stuntz, D. *et al.* 1972. *Mushroom Poisoning in the Pacific Northwest.* Puget Sound Mycological Society, Seattle, WA.

Subbaratnam, A.V. and **W.B. Cook** 1963. "Subsidiary constituents from *Amanita muscaria*" *Journal of Medicinal Chemistry* 6: 448–449. [CIA undercover work.]

Sun, M. 1988. "Herbicide refused for coca spraying" *Science* 240: 1401.

Superweed, M.J. 1970. *Drug Manufacturing for Fun and Profit (D.M.T. Guide).* Flash Books, San Francisco, CA.

Szára, S.I. 1956. "Dimethyltryptamin: Its metabolism in man; the relation of its psychotic [*sic*] effect to the serotonin metabolism" *Experientia* 15(6): 441–442.

Szára, S.I. 1957. "The comparison of the psychotic [*sic*] effect of tryptamine derivatives with the effects of mescaline and LSD-25 in self-experiments" In: Garattini, S. and V. Ghetti (Eds.) *Psychotropic Drugs.* Elsevier, New York. pp. 460–467.

Szára, S.I. 1961. "Hallucinogenic effects and metabolism of tryptamine derivatives in man" *Federation Proceedings* 20: 885–888.

Szára, S.I. 1962. "Metabolism and behavioral action of psychotropic tryptamine homologues" *International Journal of Neuropharmacology* 1: 111–117.

Szára, S.I. 1970. "DMT (N,N-dimethyltryptamine) and homologues: Clinical and pharmacological considerations" In: Efron, D.H. (Ed.) *Psychotomimetic* [*sic*] *Drugs.* Raven, New York. pp. 275–286.

Szára, S.I. and **J. Axelrod** 1959. "Hydroxylation and *N*-demethylation of *N,N*-dimethyltryptamine" *Experientia* 15: 216–217.

Szára, S.I. and **E. Hearst** 1962. "The 6-hydroxylation of tryptamine derivatives: A way of producing psychoactive metabolites" *Annals of the New York Academy of Sciences* 96: 134–141.

Szára, S.I. and **L.H. Rockland** 1961. "Psychological effects and metabolism of *N,N*-dimethyltryptamine, an hallucinogenic drug" *Proceeding of the Third World Congress of Psychiatry* 1: 670.

Szára, S.I. *et al.* 1966. "Psychological effects and metabolism of N,N-diethyltryptamine in man" *Archives of General Psychiatry* 15: 320–329.

Szára, S.I. *et al.* 1967. "Discussion on the psychoactive action of various tryptamine derivatives" In: Efron, D.H. *et al.* (Eds.) *Ethnopharmacologic Search for Psychoactive Drugs.* (Public Health Service Publication No. 1645) U.S. Government Printing Office, Washington, D.C. pp. 374–382.

Szasz, T. 1961. *The Myth of Mental Illness: Foundations of a Theory of Personal Conduct.* Hoeber-Harper, New York.

Szasz, T. 1970. *The Manufacture of Madness: A Comparative Study of the Inquisition and the Mental Health Movement.* Harper & Row, New York.

Szasz, T. 1974. *Ceremonial Chemistry: The Ritual Persecution of Drugs, Addicts and Pushers.* Doubleday/Anchor, New York. Spanish edition, 1975. *Droga y Ritual.* Fondo de Cultura Económica, México City.

Szasz, T. 1992. *Our Right to Drugs: The Case for a Free Market.* Greenwood Press, New York. Spanish edition, 1993. *Nuestro Derecho a las Drogas.* Anagrama, Barcelona.

Szendrei, K. 1980. "The chemistry of khat" *Bulletin on Narcotics* 32(3): 5–35.

Taber, W.A. and **R.A. Heacock** 1962. "Location of ergot alkaloids and fungi in the seed of *Rivea corymbosa* (L.) Hall. f., 'Ololiuqui'" *Canadian Journal of Microbiology* 8: 137–143.

Taber, W.A. *et al.* 1963A. "Clavine and lysergic acid alkaloids in varieties of Morning Glory" *Phytochemistry* 2: 65–70.

Taber, W.A. *et al.* 1963B. "Ergot-type alkaloids in vegetative tissue of *Rivea corymbo-*

sa (L.) Hall. f." *Phytochemistry* 2: 99–101.

Taborsky, R.G. *et al.* 1966. "6-Hydroxylation: Effect on the psychotropic potency of tryptamines" *Science* 153: 1018–1020.

Taesotikul, T. *et al.* 1989. "Hippocratic screening of ethanolic extracts from two *Tabernaemontana* species" *Journal of Ethnopharmacology* 27(1,2): 99–106.

Takemoto, T. 1961. "On the insecticidal component of *Tricholoma muscarium*" *Yakugaku Kenkyu* 33: 252–254.

Takemoto, T. and **T. Nakajima** 1964. "Structure of tricholomic acid" *Yakugaku Zasshi* 84(12): 1230–1232.

Takemoto, T. *et al.* 1964A. "Studies on the constituents of indigenous fungi II: Isolation of flycidal constituent from *Amanita strobiliformis*" *Yakugaku Zasshi* 84(12): 1186–1188.

Takemoto, T. *et al.* 1964B. "Structure of ibotenic acid" *Yakugaku Zasshi* 84(12): 1232–1233.

Takemoto, T. *et al.* 1964C. "Isolation of a flycidal constituent 'Ibotenic Acid' from *Amanita muscaria* and *A. pantherina*" *Yakugaku Zasshi* 84(12): 1233–1234.

Talbot, G. and **L. Vining** 1963. "Pigments and other extractives from carpophores of *Amanita muscaria*" *Canadian Journal of Botany* 41: 639–647.

Tantaquidgeon, G. 1942. *A Study of Delaware Indian Medicine Practice and Folk Beliefs*. Pennsylvania Historical Commission, Harrisburg, PA.

Tart, C.T. (Ed.) 1969. *Altered States of Consciousness: A Book of Readings*. John Wiley & Sons, New York. Revised edition 1990, Harper San Francisco, New York.

Taussig, M. 1987. *Shamanism, Colonialism, and the Wild Man: A Study in Terror and Healing*. University of Chicago Press, Chicago, IL.

Taylor, B. 1961. "The visions of hasheesh" In: Ebin, D. (Ed.) *The Drug Experience: First-Person Accounts of Addicts, Writers, Scientists and Others*. The Orion Press, New York. pp. 43–52. Original in 1855. *The Land of the Saracen or Pictures of Palestine, Asia Minor, Sicily and Spain*.

Taylor, N. 1944. "Come and expel the green pain; use of peyotl and ololiuqui" *Science Monthly* 58: 177–184. Reprint: Taylor 1949.

Taylor, N. 1949. *Flight from Reality*. Duell, Sloan and Pierce, New York. Reprinted in 1966 as *Narcotics: Nature's Dangerous Gifts*. Dell Publishing Co., New York.

Tedlock, D. (Translator) 1985. *Popol Vuh: The Mayan Book of the Dawn of Life*. Simon & Schuster, New York. Spanish edition, 1993. *Popol Vuh: El Libro Maya del Albor de la Vida y las Glorias de Dioses y Reyes*. Editorial Diana, México City.

Telban, B. 1988. "The role of medicinal ethnobotany in ethnomedicine: A New Guinea example" *Journal of Ethnobiology* 8(2): 149–169.

Tena-Betancourt, E. *et al.* 1987. "Effect of an aqueous infusion of *Guatteria guameri* bark upon gallbladder calculi in the golden hamster" *Journal of Ethnopharmacology* 19(2): 221–226.

Tezozómoc, H.A. 1975. *Crónica Mexicáyotl*. Instituto de Investigaciones Históricas, Universidad Nacional Autónoma de México, México City. Original from 1598.

Theobald, W. *et al.* 1968. "Pharmakologische und experimentalpsychologische Untersuchungen mit 2 Inhaltßtoffen des Fliegenpilzes (*Amanita muscaria*)" *Arzneimittel-Forschung* 18(1): 311–315.

Thomas, D.W. and **K. Biemann** 1968. "The alkaloids of *Voacanga africana*" *Lloydia* 31(1): 1–8.

Thompson, A.C. *et al.* 1987. "Indolealkylamines of *Desmanthus illinoensis* and their growth inhibition activity" *Journal of Agricultural and Food Chemistry* 35(3): 361–365.

Thompson, C.J.S. 1968. *The Mystic Mandrake.* University Books, New York.

Thompson, J.E.S. 1970. *Maya History and Religion.* University of Oklahoma Press, Norman, OK.

Thompson, J.E.S. 1977. "Hallucinatory drugs and hobgobling in the Maya lowlands" *Tlalocan* 7.

Thompson, M.R. 1935. "The active constituents of ergot: A pharmacological and chemical study" *Journal of the American Pharmaceutical Association* 24: 24–38; 24: 185–196.

Thomson, D.F. 1961. "A narcotic [*sic*] from *Nicotiana ingulba*, used by the desert Binbidu" *Man* 61: 5–8.

Thorn, R.G. and **G.L. Barron** 1984. "Carnivorous mushrooms" *Science* 224: 76–78.

Thornton, G.R. *et al.* 1939. "The effects of benzedrine and caffeine upon performance in certain psychomotor tasks" *Journal of Abnormal Psychology* 34: 96–113.

Thresh, J.C. 1887. "Notes on Trebizonde honey" *The Pharmaceutical Journal and Transactions.* 12 November issue. pp. 397–400. Includes "Supplementary note" by E.M. Holmes, pp. 399–400.

Tibón, G. 1983. *La Ciudad de los Hongos Alucinantes.* Panorama Editorial, México City.

Timbrook, J. 1984. "Chumash ethnobotany: A preliminary report" *Journal of Ethnobiology* 4(2): 141–169.

Timbrook, J. 1987. "Virtuous herbs: Plants in Chumash medicine" *Journal of Ethnobiology* 7(2): 171–180.

Timbrook, J. 1990. "Ethnobotany of Chumash Indians, California, based on collections by John P. Harrington" *Economic Botany* 44(2): 236–253.

Titcomb, M. 1948. "Kava in Hawaii" *Journal of the Polynesian Society* 57: 105–201.

Tjio, J.H. *et al.* 1969. "LSD and chromosomes: A controlled experiment" *Journal of the American Medical Association* 210: 849.

Todd, J.S. 1969. "Thin-layer chromatography analysis of Mexican population of *Lophophora* (Cactaceae)" *Lloydia* 32(3): 395–398.

Torres, C.M. 1981. "Evidence for snuffing in the prehistoric stone sculpture of San Agustín, Colombia" *Journal of Psychoactive Drugs* 13(1): 53–60.

Torres, C.M. 1987A. "The iconography of the prehispanic snuff trays from San Pedro de Atacama, northern Chile" *Andean Past* 1: 191–245.

Torres, C.M. 1987B. "The iconography of South American snuff trays and related paraphernalia" *Göteborgs Etnografiska Museum Etnologiska Studier* 37: 1–134.

Torres, C.M. 1988. "El arte de los taíno" In: Torres, C.M. (Ed.) *Taíno: Los Descubridores de Colón.* Museo Chileno de Arte Precolombino, Santiago, Chile. pp. 9–22.

Torres, C.M. 1992. "Iconografía del uso de polvos alucinógenos en Sudamérica" Conference "Plantas, Chamanismo y Estados de Conciencia," 16–20 November 1992, San Luis Potosí, SLP, México. Translated into English, 1993. "Snuff trails of Atacama: Psychedelics and iconography in prehispanic San Pedro de Atacama" *Integration: Zeitschrift für Geistbewegende Pflanzen und Kultur* 4: 17–28.

Torres, C.M. 1996. "Polveri da fiuto allucinogene nel Cile precolombiano" *Altrove* 3: 29–39

Torres, C.M. *et al.* 1991. "Snuff powders from pre-hispanic San Pedro de Atacama: Chemical and contextual analysis" *Current Anthropology* 32(5): 640–649.

Toth, B. 1979. "Mushroom hydrazines: Occurrence, metabolism, carcinogenesis and environmental implications" In: Miller, E.C. *et al.* (Eds.) *Naturally Occurring Carcinogens-Mutagens and Modulators of Carcinogenesis.* University Park Press, Baltimore, MD. pp. 57–65.

Touw, M. 1981. "The religious and medicinal uses of *Cannabis* in China, India and Tibet" *Journal of Psychoactive Drugs* 13(1): 23–34.

Train, P. *et al.* 1941. *Medicinal Uses of Plants by the Indian Tribes of Nevada.* (Contributions to a Flora of Nevada, No. 33, United States Department of Agriculture) U.S. Government Printing Office, Washington, D.C. Reprinted in 1988 (Volume III, Bioactive Plants) by Quarterman Publications, Lincoln, MA.

Trebach, A.S. 1982. *The Heroin Solution.* Yale University Press, New Haven, CT.

Troike, R.C. 1962. "The origins of Plains mescalism" *American Anthropologist* 64: 946–963.

Troxler, F. *et al.* 1959. "Abwandlungsprodukte von Psilocybin und Psilocin" *Helvetica Chimica Acta* 42: 2073–2103.

Truitt, E.B. 1967. "The pharmacology of myristicin and nutmeg" In: Efron, D.H. *et al.* (Eds.) *Ethnopharmacologic Search for Psychoactive Drugs.* (Public Health Service Publication No. 1645) U.S. Government Printing Office, Washington, D.C. pp. 215–222. Followed by "Discussion," pp. 223–229.

Truitt, E.B. *et al.* 1961. "The pharmacology of myristicin. A contribution to the psychopharmacology of nutmeg" *Journal of Neuropsychiatry* 2: 205–210.

Truitt, E.B. *et al.* 1963. "Evidence of monoamine oxidase inhibition by myristicin and nutmeg" *Proceedings of the Society for Experimental Biology and Medicine* 112: 647–650.

Tsarong, T.J. 1991. "Tibetan psychopharmacology" *Integration: Zeitschrift für Geistbewegende Pflanzen und Kultur* 1: 43–60.

Tucker, A.O. and **S.S. Tucker** 1988. "Catnip and the catnip response" *Economic Botany* 42(2): 214–231.

Tucker, A.O. *et al.* 1980. "Botanical aspects of commercial sage" *Economic Botany* 34 (1): 16–19.

Tugrul, L. 1985. "Abuse of henbane by children in Turkey" *Bulletin on Narcotics* 37 (2&3): 75–78.

Turek, I.S. *et al.* 1974. "Methylenedioxyamphetamine (MDA): Subjective effects" *Journal of Psychedelic Drugs* 6(1): 7–14.

Turner, D.M. 1994. *The Essential Psychedelic Guide.* Panther Press, San Francisco, CA.

Turner, J.C. and **P.G. Clinch** 1968. "Estimation of tutin and hyenanchin in honey. I. A comparison of the thin-layer chromatography and intracerebral injection methods" *New Zealand Journal of Science* 11: 342–345.

Turner, N.J. and **A.F. Bell** 1973. "Ethnobotany of the southern Kwakiutl Indians of British Columbia" *Economic Botany* 27(3): 257–310.

Turner, N.J. and **A.F. Szczawinski** 1991. *Common Poisonous Plants and Mushrooms of North America.* Timber Press, Portland, OR.

Turner, N.J. *et al.* 1983. *Ethnobotany of the Nitinaht Indians of Vancouver Island.* (Occasional Papers of the Provincial Museum, No. 24) The British Columbia Provincial Museum, Victoria, B.C., Canada.

Turner, N.J. *et al.* 1990. *Thompson Ethnobotany: Knowledge and Usage of Plants by the Thompson Indians of British Columbia.* (Memoir No. 3) Royal British Columbia Museum, Victoria, B.C., Canada.

Turner, W.J. and **J.J. Heyman** 1960. "The presence of mescaline in *Opuntia cylindrica*" *Journal of Organic Chemistry* 25: 2250–2251.

Turner, W.J. and **S. Merlis** 1959. "Effect of some indolealkylamines on man" *Archives of Neurology and Psychiatry* 81: 121–129.

Turner, W.J. *et al.* 1955. "Concerning theories of indoles in schizophrenigenesis" *American Journal of Psychiatry* 112: 466–467.

Tyler, V.E. 1958A. "Pilzatropine, the ambiguous alkaloid" *American Journal of Pharmacy* 130(8): 264–269.

Tyler, V.E. 1958B. "Occurrence of serotonin in a hallucinogenic mushroom" *Science* 128: 718.

Tyler, V.E. 1961. "Indole drivatives in certain North American mushrooms" *Lloydia* 24(1): 71–74.

Tyler, V.E. 1966. "The physiological properties and chemical constituents of some habit-forming [*sic*] plants: Soma-Haoma, divine plant of the ancient Aryans" *Lloydia* 29(4): 284.

Tyler, V.E. 1979. "The case for Victor A. Reko—An unrecognized pioneer writer on new-world hallucinogens" *Journal of Natural Products* 42(5): 489–495.

Tyler, V.E. 1987. *The New Honest Herbal: A Sensible Guide to Herbs and Related Remedies.* G.F. Stickley, Philadelphia, PA. Original in 1982. Third edition in 1993. *The Honest Herbal: A Sensible Guide to the Use of Herbs and Related Remedies.* Food Products Press, Binghamton, NY.

Tyler, V.E. and **D. Gröger** 1964A. "Occurrence of 5-hydroxytryptamine and 5-hydroxytryptophan in *Panaeolus sphinctrinus*" *Journal of Pharmaceutical Sciences* 53: 462–463.

Tyler, V.E. and **D. Gröger** 1964B. "Investigation of the alkaloids of *Amanita* species II. *Amanita citrina* and *Amanita porphyria*" *Planta Medica* 12(4): 397–402.

Tyler, V.E. *et al.* 1966. "Occurrence of *Amanita* toxins in American collections of deadly *Amanitas*" *Journal of Pharmaceutical Sciences* 55(6): 590–593.

Tyler, V.E. *et al.* 1976. *Pharmacognosy.* Seventh Edition. Lea & Febiger, Philadelphia, PA.

Udenfriend, S. *et al.* 1958. "Studies with reversible inhibitors of monoamine oxidase: Harmaline and related compounds" *Biochemical Pharmacology* 1: 160–165.

Ueno, A. *et al.* 1978. "Studies on the constituents of *Desmodium caudatum* DC" *Chemical and Pharmacological Bulletin Japan* 26(8): 2411–2416.

Uhe, G. 1974. "Medicinal plants of Samoa" *Economic Botany* 28(1): 1–30.

Unger, S.E. and **R.G. Cooks** 1979. "Application of mass spectrometry/mass spectrometry (MS/MS) to the identification of natural products in *Psilocybe cyanescens*" *Analytical Letters* 12(B11): 1157–1167.

Unger, S.M. 1963. "Mescaline, LSD, psilocybin and personality change: A review" *Psychiatry* 26: 111–125.

Unger, S.M. 1964. "LSD and psychotherapy: A bibliography of the English-language literature" *The Psychedelic Review* 1(4): 442–449.

Uniyal, G.C. *et al.* 1985. "Volatile constituents of *Artemisia nilagirica*" *Planta Medica* 51: 457–458.

Urbina, M. 1897. *Catálogo de Plantas Mexicanas (Fanerógamas).* México City.

Urbina, M. 1903. "El peyote y el ololiuhqui" *Anales del Museo Nacional de México* 7: 25–48. *La Naturaleza* 1(4): 131–154, 1912.

Uscátegui M., N. 1959. "The present distribution of narcotics [*sic*] and stimulants amongst the Indian tribes of Colombia" *Botanical Museum Leaflets* Harvard University 18(6): 273–304. See: Uscátegui M. 1961 for a Spanish version of this paper.

Uscátegui M., N. 1961. "Distribución actual de las plantas narcóticas [*sic*] y estimulantes usadas por las tribus indígenas de Colombia" *Revista de la Academia Colombiana de Ciencias Exactas, Físicas y Naturales* 11(43): 215–228.

U.S. Sentencing Commission 1987. *Supplementary Report on the Initial Sentencing Guidelines and Policy Statements.* Washington, D.C.

Uyeno, E.T. 1969. "Alteration of a learned response of the squirrel monkey by hallu-

cinogens" *International Journal of Neuropharmacology* 8: 245–253.
Uyeno, E.T. 1971. "Relative potency of amphetamine derivatives and N,N-dimethyltryptamines" *Psychopharmacologia* 19: 381–387.
Valadez, S. 1986. "Guided tour spirituality: Cosmic way or cosmic rip-off?" *Shaman's Drum: A Journal of Experiential Shamanism.* Fall issue. pp. 4–6. Letter to editor.
Valdés III, L.J. 1983. *The Pharmacology of Salvia divinorum Epling and Játiva-M.* Thesis, Univ. of Michigan, Ann Arbor, MI.
Valdés III, L.J. 1986. "Loliolide from *Salvia divinorum*" *Journal of Natural Products* 49(1): 171.
Valdés III, L.J. 1995. "*Salvia divinorum* and the unique diterpene hallucinogen, salvinorin (divinorin) A" *Journal of Psychoactive Drugs* 26(3): 277–283.
Valdés III, L.J. *et al.* 1983. "Ethnopharmacology of *Ska María Pastora* (*Salvia divinorum*, Epling and Játiva-M.)" *Journal of Ethnopharmacology* 7(3): 287–312.
Valdés III, L.J. *et al.* 1984. "Divinorin A, a psychotropic terpenoid, and divinorin B from the hallucinogenic Mexican mint *Salvia divinorum*" *Journal of Organic Chemistry* 49(24): 4716–4720.
Valdés III, L.J. *et al.* 1987A. "Studies of *Salvia divinorum* (Lamiaceae), an hallucinogenic mint from the Sierra Mazateca in Oaxaca, central Mexico" *Economic Botany* 41(2): 283–291.
Valdés III, L.J. *et al.* 1987B. "*Coleus barbatus (C. forskohlii)* (Lamiaceae) and the potential new drug forskolin (coleonol)" *Economic Botany* 41(4): 474–483.
Van Beek, T.A. *et al.* 1984. "*Tabernaemontana* L. (Apocynaceae): A review of its taxonomy, phytochemistry, ethnobotany and pharmacology" *Journal of Ethnopharmacology* 10(1): 1–156.
Van Beek, T.A. *et al.* 1985. "Phytochemical investigation on *Tabernaemontana crassa*" *Journal of Ethnopharmacology* 14(2,3): 315–318.
Vance, M.A. *et al.* 1989. "Drug decriminalization" *Science* 246: 1102–1105. Seven letters to the editor in response to Nadelmann, E.A. 1989. "Drug prohibition in the United States: Costs, consequences, and alternatives" *Science* 245: 939–947.
Vanderveen, R.L. *et al.* 1974. "N-Methyltyramine from *Opuntia clavata*" *Phytochemistry* 13: 866–867.
Van Dyke, C. and **R. Byck** 1982. "Cocaine" *Scientific American* 246(3): 128–141.
Vázquez de Espinosa, A. 1948. *Compendio y Descripción de las Indias Occidentales.* (Smithsonian Misc. Collections, Vol. 108) Smithsonian Institution, Washington, D.C.
Veale, D.J.H. *et al.* 1992. "South African traditional herbal medicines used during pregnancy and childbirth" *Journal of Ethnopharmacology* 36(3): 185–191.
Velázquez Díaz, G. (Ed.) 1992. *Poxil Ta Vomoletik (Plantas Medicinales).* Bilingual Tzotzil/Spanish formulary. Instituto Mexicano de Seguro Social, IMSS, México City.
Veriditas (Pseudonym for R. Montgomery and H. Rheingold) 1989. "Botanical Peace Corps" *Whole Earth Review* 64: 26–29.
Verpoorte, R. *et al.* 1979. "Chemical constituents of Vietnamese toad venom collected from *Bufo melanostictus* Schneider" *Journal of Ethnopharmacology* 1(2): 197–202.
Verrill, A.E. 1914. "A recent case of mushroom intoxication" *Science* 40: 408.
Vestal, P.A. 1952. *Ethnobotany of the Ramah Navaho.* (Papers of the Peabody Museum of American Archæology and Ethnology, Volume 40, No. 4) Peabody Museum of Harvard University, Cambridge, MA.
Vestal, P.A. and **R.E. Schultes** 1939. *The Economic Botany of the Kiowa Indians as it Relates to the History of the Tribe.* Botanical Mus. Harvard Univ., Cambridge, MA.

Vickers, W.T. and **T.C. Plowman** 1984. "Useful plants of the Siona and Secoya Indians of eastern Ecuador" *Fieldiana* 15: 1–63.

Vijayanagar, H.M. *et al.* 1975. "Phytochemical investigation of Manibota [*sic*] plants. III. Identification of two β-carbolines from *Phalaris arundinacea*" *Lloydia* 38: 442–443.

Villavicencio, M. 1858. *Geografía de la República del Ecuador.* R. Craigshead, New York. Villavicencio was the first psychonaut to report the full effects of *ayahuasca*.

Villers, A. von and **F. von Thümen** 1893. *Die Pflanzen des Homöopathischen Arzneischatzes*. Verlag Wilhelm Baensch, Dresden, Germany.

Vogt, D.D. 1981. "Absinthium: A nineteenth-century drug of abuse [*sic*]" *Journal of Ethnopharmacology* 4(3): 337–342.

Vohora, S.B. *et al.* 1990. "Central nervous system studies on an ethanolic extract of *Acorus calamus* rhizomes" *Journal of Ethnopharmacology* 28(1): 53–62.

Wagner, J. 1991A. "Das 'dawa' der *mamiwata* (Ein möglicherweise pharmakologischer Aspekt des westafrikanischen Glaubens an Waßergeister)" *Integration: Zeitschrift für Geistbewegende Pflanzen und Kultur* 1: 61–63.

Wagner, J. 1991B. "Eine Reise mit dem Fliegenpilzmann" In: Bauer, W. *et al.* (Eds.) *Der Fliegenpilz: Ein Kulturhistorisches Museum*. (Museum der Museen, Schriftenreihe des Karl Ernst Osthaus-Museums, Bd. 6) Wienand-Verlag, Köln, Germany. pp. 165–194. Herewith Wagner describes her three psychonautic bioassays with *Amanita muscaria*.

Wahba Khalil, S.K. and **Y.M. Elkheir** 1975. "Dimethyltryptamine from the leaves of certain *Acacia* species of northern Sudan" *Lloydia* 38(2): 176–177.

Waldrop, M.M. 1989. "NIDA aims to fight drugs with drugs" *Science* 245: 1443–1444.

Waldschmidt, E. 1992. "Der Fliegenpilz als Heilmittel" *Integration: Zeitschrift für Geistbewegende Pflanzen und Kultur* 2&3: 67–68.

Walters, M.B. 1965. "*Pholiota spectabilis*, a hallucinogenic fungus" *Mycologia* 57(6): 837–838.

Walton, J.W. 1970. "Muiname diagnostic use of narcotics [*sic*]" *Economic Botany* 24(2): 187–188.

Waser, P.G. 1961. "Chemistry and pharmacology of muscarine, muscarone and some related compounds" *Pharmacology Reviews* 13: 465–515.

Waser, P.G. 1965. "Psychische Veränderungen durch Methyl-ergobasin" *Medizinische Klinik* 60: 2004. Response to letter to the editor by a physician to a medical journal.

Waser, P.G. 1967. "The pharmacology of *Amanita muscaria*" In: Efron, D.H. *et al.* (Eds.) *Ethnopharmacologic Search for Psychoactive Drugs.* (Public Health Service Publication No. 1645) U.S. Government Printing Office, Washington, D.C. pp. 419–439.

Waser, P.G. 1971A. "Pharmakologie der Halluzinogene" *Praxis* 60: 1001–1005.

Waser, P.G. 1971B. "Pharmakologische Wirkungßpektrum von Halluzinogener" *Bulletin der Schweizer Akademie von Medizinishe Wißenschaft* 27: 39–57.

Waser, P.G. and **P. Bersin** 1970. "Turnover of monoamines in brain under the influence of muscimol and ibotenic acid, two psychoactive principles of *Amanita muscaria*" In: Efron, D.H. (Ed.) *Psychotomimetic* [*sic*] *Drugs.* Raven, NY. pp. 155–162.

Wassel, G.M. and **N.M. Ammar** 1984. "Isolation of the alkaloid and evaluation of the diuretic activity of *Arundo donax*" *Fitoterapia* 15(6): 357–358.

Wassel, G.M. *et al.* 1985. "Alkaloids from the rhizomes of *Phragmites australis* (Cav.) Trin. ex Steud." *Scientia Pharmaceutica* 53(3): 169–170. *Chemical Abstracts* 104: 48723f.

Wassén, S.H. 1934A. "The frog-motive among the South American Indians" *Anthropos* 29: 319–370.

Wassén, S.H. 1934B. "The frog in Indian mythology and imaginative world" *Anthropos* 29: 613–658.

Wassén, S.H. 1964. "Some general viewpoints in the study of native drugs, especially from the West Indies and South America" *Ethnos* 1-2: 97–120.

Wassén, S.H. 1965. "The use of some specific kinds of South American Indian snuff and related paraphernalia" *Göteborgs Etnografiska Museum Etnologiska Studier* 28: 1–116. Includes original of Seitz 1967.

Wassén, S.H. 1967. "Anthropological survey of the use of South American snuffs" In: Efron, D.H. *et al.* (Eds.) *Ethnopharmacologic Search for Psychoactive Drugs.* (Public Health Service Publication No. 1645) U.S. Government Printing Office, Washington, D.C. pp. 233–289.

Wassén, S.H. 1972. "A medicine-man's implements and plants in a Tiahuanacoid tomb in highland Bolivia" *Göteborgs Etnografiska Museum Etnologiska Studier* 32: 7–114.

Wassén, S.H. 1979. "Was *espingo* (*ispincu*) of psychotropic and intoxicating importance for the shamans of Peru?" In: Browman, D.L. and R.A. Schwarz (Eds.) *Spirits, Shamans and Stars: Perspectives from South America.* Mouton and Co., the Hague, the Netherlands. pp. 55–62.

Wassén, S.H. and **B. Holmstedt** 1963. "The use of paricá, an ethnological and pharmacological review" *Ethnos* 28(1): 5–45.

Wasson, E.A. 1914. *Religion and Drink.* Burr Printing House, New York. Self-published by the father of R. Gordon Wasson, this seminal piece of American drug literature and libertarian thought was successful, and earned money required to send Gordon and elder brother Tom to Europe for their education (Gordon told me his father earned $20,000 from the sale of this book, a princely sum at the time!). I have in my library a copy of *Religion and Drink* extensively marked up in Edmund Atwill Wasson's hand, with a new introduction and many typewritten passages pasted over the original pages. This revision was for a planned second edition which never materialized, and it was presented to me as a gift by RGW.

Wasson, E.A. 1965. *That Gettysburg Address. Made by President Lincoln on the Battlefield of Gettysburg on November 19, 1863.* Privately-printed limited edition of 225 copies handmade by Giovanni Mardersteig at Officina Bodoni, Verona, Italy. Included also was a *Postscriptum* "A Memoir" by son R. Gordon Wasson. pp. 77–109 with 7 illustrations. The *Postscriptum* was reprinted in 1990, as: "Appendix I. Gordon Wasson's Account of his Childhood," in: Riedlinger, T.J. (Ed.) *The Sacred Mushroom Seeker: Essays for R. Gordon Wasson.* Ethnomycological Studies No. 11. Dioscorides Press, Portland, OR. pp. 239–256. The vignette of a Celtic cross at the end of the book was engraved by renowned artist Reynolds Stone, and appeared with much poorer quality reproduction at the end of the 1990 reprint.

Wasson, R.G. 1956. "Lightning-bolt and mushrooms: An essay in early cultural exploration" In: *For Roman Jakobson: Essays on the Occasion of his Sixtieth Birthday, Oct. 11, 1956.* Mouton and Co., the Hague, the Netherlands, pp. 605–612; reprinted with revisions in Wasson, R.G. *et al.* 1986. *Persephone's Quest: Entheogens and the Origins of Religion.* Ethnomycological Studies No. 10. Yale University Press, New Haven, CT, pp. 83–94. Reprinted with revisions in Dutch in 1960. *Antiquity and Survival* 3(1): 59–73.

Wasson, R.G. 1957. "Seeking the magic

mushroom" *Life* 13 May 1957, 42(19): 100 *et seq.* Also ran in the Spanish edition of *Life*, "En busca de los hongos mágicos" *Life en Español.* 3 June 1957 issue. There were six letters to the editors in the 4 June 1957 *Life* inspired by Wasson's article, p. 16. Reprinted in *The Drug User...* (*vide* Strausbaugh & Blaise 1991). pp. 70–79.

Wasson, R.G. 1958. "The divine mushroom: Primitive [*sic*] religion and hallucinatory agents" *Proceedings of the American Philosophical Society* 102(3): 221–223.

Wasson, R.G. 1959A. "The hallucinogenic mushrooms of Mexico: An adventure in ethnomycological exploration" *Transactions of the New York Academy of Sciences*, Series II 21(4): 325–339. Reprinted, *sans* bibliography, in 1961; Ebin, D. (Ed.) *The Drug Experience.* The Orion Press, New York. pp. 313–324. Originally given as a lecture before NYAS, 23 January 1959.

Wasson, R.G. 1959B. "Wild mushrooms: A world of wonder and adventure" *The Herbarist* 24: 13–28. With three reports of accidental inebriations—from Colorado, Fiji and Poland—the victims had written to Wasson after reading his *Life* article (1957). Signed reprint has sold for $195!

Wasson, R.G. 1961. "The hallucinogenic fungi of Mexico: An inquiry into the origins of the religious idea among primitive [*sic*] peoples" *Botanical Museum Leaflets* Harvard University 19(7): 137–162. This *Leaflet* reprinted in February 1973. Reprinted in *The Psychedelic Review* 1(1): 27–42, 1963; in Weil, G.M. *et al.* (Eds.) 1965. *The Psychedelic Reader.* University Books, New York, pp. 23–38; and in an abridged form in 1962 "Hallucinogenic fungi of Mexico" *International Journal of Parapsychology* 4(4): 41–58; and in 1963 "Mushroom rites of Mexico" *The Harvard Review* 1(4): 7–17. A revised version appeared in Ott, J. and J. Bigwood (Eds.) 1978. *Teonanácatl: Hallucinogenic Mushrooms of North America.* Madrona Publishers, Seattle, WA. pp. 65–84, which was translated into Spanish in 1985, as "Los hongos alucinógenos de México: Indagación sobre los orígenes de la idea religiosa entre los pueblos primitivos" pp. 69–87. Originally given on 30 August 1960 as the annual lecture of the Mycological Society of America in Stillwater, Oklahoma. The original, and English and Spanish versions of the 1978 revision were accompanied by an Appendix listing 24 species of Mexican entheogenic mushrooms, giving references to the first botanical and ethnological reports of each.

Wasson, R.G. 1962A. "The hallucinogenic mushrooms of Mexico and psilocybin: A bibliography" *Botanical Museum Leaflets* Harvard University 20(2): 25–73. Compiled with the assistance of S. Pau. A second printing was made, with corrections and *Addenda*, 1963. *ibid.* 20(2A): 25–73C.

Wasson, R.G. 1962B. "A new Mexican psychotropic drug from the mint family" *Botanical Museum Leaflets* Harvard University 20(3): 77–84. This *Leaflet*, reprinted in February 1971, has sold for $25.

Wasson, R.G. 1963. "Notes on the present status of *ololiuhqui* and the other hallucinogens of Mexico" *Botanical Museum Leaflets* Harvard University 20(6): 161–193. This *Leaflet* was reprinted in October 1975. Reprinted in *The Psychedelic Review* 1(3): 275–301, 1964; and in Weil, G.M. *et al.* (Eds.) 1965. *The Psychedelic Reader.* University Books, New York. pp. 163–189. Reprinted in 1966 as "*Ololiuhqui* and the other hallucinogens of Mexico" In: Jiménez Moreno, W. *et al.* (Eds.) *Summa Antropológica en Homenaje a Roberto J. Weitlaner.* Instituto Nacional de Antropología e Historia [INAH], México City. pp. 329–348. Accompanied by Hofmann 1963A.

Wasson, R.G. 1965. "Rite of the magic mushroom" In: *The Drug Takers*. Time-Life Books, New York. A modified version with some additional photographs of Wasson's seminal 1957 *Life* article. See: Wasson, R.G. 1957.

Wasson, R.G. 1967A. "Fly agaric and man" In: Efron, D.H. *et al.* (Eds.) *Ethnopharmacologic Search for Psychoactive Drugs.* (Public Health Service Publication No. 1645) U.S. Government Printing Office, Washington, D.C. pp. 405–414.

Wasson, R.G. 1967B. "Soma: The divine mushroom of immortality" *Discovery* 3(1): 41–48.

Wasson, R.G. 1968. *Soma: Divine Mushroom of Immortality.* Ethno-mycological Studies No. 1. Mouton and Co., the Hague, the Netherlands; Harcourt Brace Jovanovich, New York. Includes "The post-Vedic history of the Soma plant" by W. Doniger O'Flaherty, pp. 95–147. Limited half-leather bound and boxed edition of 680 copies. With 40 illustrations including 3 maps, 1 chart, 2 watercolors and 18 color plates, tipped-in. A 1970 trade hardcover and trade paperback facsimile editions followed, replete with the photographs ('though not tipped-in, as in the original), but lacking the two Pochoir prints of watercolors by Charles Poluzzi (a lithograph of one of these was used on the dust jacket of the U.S.$15.00 trade hardcover edition and on the obverse of the $7.50 trade paperback edition). There were three printings of the trade paperback edition. The limited edition originally cost U.S.$200/720 Dutch guilders and has since sold for as much as U.S.$2250 [the paperback for up to $70!].

Wasson, R.G. 1970A. "Soma of the Aryans: An ancient hallucinogen?" *Bulletin on Narcotics* 22(3): 25–30. Later reprinted in 1971. *Journal of Psychedelic Drugs* 3(2): 40–46. Published in French in 1971 "Le *Soma* des Aryens: Un ancien hallucinogène?" *Bulletin des Stupefíants* 22(3).

Wasson, R.G. 1970B. "*Soma*: Comments inspired by Professor Kuiper's review" *Indo-Iranian Journal* 12(4): 286–298. Followed review of *Soma: Divine Mushroom of Immortality* by Kuiper, F.B.J. 1970. *Indo-Iranian Journal* 12(4): 279–285. See: Kuiper 1970.

Wasson, R.G. 1971. "The Soma of the Rig Veda: What was it?" *Journal of the American Oriental Society* 91(2): 169–187. Followed by Ingalls, D.H.H. 1971. "Remarks on Mr. Wasson's *Soma*" *Journal of the American Oriental Society* 91(2): 188–191. Both papers were reprinted together in 1971. *R. Gordon Wasson on Soma, and Daniel H.H. Ingalls' Response.* Essay of the American Oriental Society, No. 7. Translated into Spanish in 1976 in the México City journal *Plural*, January-February issue. See: Ingalls 1971.

Wasson, R.G. 1972A. Review of Castaneda 1971. *A Separate Reality. Economic Botany* 26(1): 98–99. See also reviews of *The Teachings of Don Juan* [Castaneda 1968] *Economic Botany* 23(2): 197, 1969; *Journey to Ixtlan* [Castaneda 1972] *Economic Botany* 27(2): 151–152, 1973; and *Tales of Power* [Castaneda 1974] *Economic Botany* 28(3): 245–246, 1974. All four reviews were published in 1977 as an article "Wasson reviews Castaneda" in *Head.* November issue. pp. 53 *et seq.* The *Head* reprint was preceded by an unsigned introduction by Jonathan Ott, p. 53.

Wasson, R.G. 1972B. *Soma and the Fly-Agaric: Mr. Wasson's Rejoinder to Professor Brough.* Ethno-mycological Studies No. 2. Botanical Museum of Harvard University, Cambridge, MA. Foreword by Richard Evans Schultes, pp. 7–8. Limited U.S.$3.00 paperbound edition of 1000 copies [now worth $50]; Stamperia Valdonega, Verona, Italy. See: Brough 1971.

Wasson, R.G. 1972C. "The death of Claudius or mushrooms for murderers" *Botanical Museum Leaflets* Harvard University 23(3): 101–128. A revised version of Chapter IV. "Mushrooms for Murderers" from *Mushrooms Russia and History*. pp. 47–64. See: Wasson & Wasson 1957A.

Wasson, R.G. 1972D. "The divine mushroom of immortality" In: Furst, P.T. (Ed.) *Flesh of the Gods: The Ritual Use of Hallucinogens.* Praeger, New York. pp. 185–200.

Wasson, R.G. 1972E. "What was the Soma of the Aryans?" In: Furst, P.T. (Ed.) *Flesh of the Gods: The Ritual Use of Hallucinogens.* Praeger, New York. pp. 201–213.

Wasson, R.G. 1973A. "Mushrooms and Japanese culture" *The Transactions of the Asiatic Society of Japan* Third Series 11: 5–25.

Wasson, R.G. 1973B. "The role of 'flowers' in Nahuatl culture: A suggested interpretation" *Botanical Museum Leaflets* Harvard University 23(8): 305–324. Reprinted in 1974 in *Journal of Psychedelic Drugs* 6: 351–360, and with revisions in 1980, "Xochipilli, 'Prince of Flowers': A new interpretation." *The Wondrous Mushroom: Mycolatry in Mesoamerica*. Ethnomycological Studies No. 7. McGraw-Hill, New York. pp. 57–78.

Wasson, R.G. 1977. Personal communications, Danbury, CT.

Wasson, R.G. 1978. "SOMA brought up-to-date" *Botanical Museum Leaflets* Harvard University 26(6): 211–223; also in 1979 in *Journal of the American Oriental Society* 99(1): 100–105. Has sold for $90.

Wasson, R.G. 1979A. "Traditional use in North America of *Amanita muscaria* for divinatory purposes" *Journal of Psychedelic Drugs* 11(1-2): 25–28. Written version of a paper given at conference "Hallucinogens in Native American Shamanism and Modern Life," 28 September–1 October 1978, San Francisco, CA (under the editorship of Jonathan Ott; see Chapter 5, Note 11). Later reprinted as "Supporting evidence" in Wasson *et al.* 1980A.

Wasson, R.G. 1979B. "Foreword" Introduction to a book catalogue, *Phantastica.* William and Victoria Dailey, Los Angeles, CA, unpaginated. See: Horowitz 1979.

Wasson, R.G. 1980. *The Wondrous Mushroom: Mycolatry in Mesoamerica*. Ethnomycological Studies No. 7. McGraw-Hill, New York. Limited half-leather bound and boxed edition of 501 signed copies, followed by a paperbound trade edition. Lavishly illustrated with 139 plates, including two maps and 54 color plates. The cover features a lovely design of "disembodied eye-drops" by Margaret Seeler after Tepantitla murals. Original list price was U.S.$525, but the book sold for a pre-publication price of $400 and has recently been selling for up to $675. Translated into Spanish by F. Garrido, 1983. *El Hongo Maravilloso: Teonanácatl. Micolatría en Mesoamérica.* Fondo de Cultura Económica, México City.

Wasson, R.G. 1982A. *R. Gordon Wasson's Rejoinder to Dr. Rolf Singer.* Ethnomycological Studies No. 9. Botanical Museum of Harvard University, Cambridge, MA. Reply to Singer 1982, inspired by Ott 1976B; Ott 1978A.

Wasson, R.G. 1982B. "The last meal of the Buddha" *Journal of the American Oriental Society* 102(4): 591–603; also in *Botanical Museum Leaflets* Harvard University 29 (3): 219–249, 1983; and in Wasson, R.G. *et al.* 1986. *Persephone's Quest: Entheogens and the Origins of Religion.* Ethnomycological Studies No. 10. Yale University Press, New Haven, CT. pp. 117–139. With "Memorandum by Walpola Rahula of the early sources for the meaning of *sukaramaddava*" and "Epilogue" by W. Doniger (see Doniger O'Flaherty 1982).

Wasson, R.G. 1985. "In pursuit of mushrooms" *Discovery* 18(2): 9–15.

Wasson, R.G. 1986. "Persephone's Quest" In: Wasson, R.G. *et al.* 1986. *Persephone's Quest: Entheogens and the Origins of Religion.* Ethnomycological Studies No. 10. Yale University Press, New Haven, CT. pp. 17–81.

Wasson, R.G. 1995. "Ethnomycology: Discoveries about *Amanita muscaria* point to fresh perspectives" In: Schultes, R.E. and S. von Reis (Eds.) *Ethnobotany: Evolution of a Discipline.* Dioscorides Press, Portland, OR. pp. 385–390.

Wasson, R.G. *et al.* 1974. *María Sabina and her Mazatec Mushroom Velada.* Ethnomycological Studies No. 3. Harcourt Brace Jovanovich, New York. Limited half-leather bound and boxed edition (29 illustrations, including 10 color photographs tipped-in, 2 maps, 1 chart) of 250 numbered copies accompanied by 4 phonograph records, followed by a boxed clothbound trade edition accompanied by 4 cassette tapes. With photographs by Allan B. Richardson, pp. 211–225; "The Mazatec language" by George M. Cowan, pp. 229–249; and "Musicological notes on the Mazatec mushroom *velada*" by Willard Rhodes, pp. 253–267. A "Musical score to accompany the text and records" by Willard Rhodes was printed in a separate paperbound booklet of 79 pages, boxed with the records. Cover cloth design from a Mazatec *huipil* woven on a backstrap loom in Ayautla, México. The 175 copies of the *de luxe* edition offered for sale were priced at U.S.$250 and have since sold for $950; the trade hardcover edition came out at $82.50 and has since sold for $125. This unique snapshot of a ceremony characteristic of archaic religion stands unequalled in this era of rampant interest in shamanism, and was considered by Wasson to be far and away his most significant and important work.

Wasson, R.G. *et al.* 1978. *The Road to Eleusis: Unveiling the Secret of the Mysteries.* Ethnomycological Studies No. 4. Harcourt Brace Jovanovich, New York. With 16 illustrations, including 1 map and 9 color plates. Clothbound edition of 1500 copies from Stamperia Valdonega at U.S.$12.95 [and has since sold for as much as $1000] followed by a $4.95 trade paperback edition. German translation by A. Linder, 1984. *Der Weg nach Eleusis: Das Geheimnis der Mysterien.* Insel Verlag, Frankfurt, Germany. Italian translation, 1996, Urra, Milano. See also: Wasson *et al.* 1980B.

Wasson, R.G. *et al.* 1980A. Unpublished manuscripts: "The Miskwedo of the Ahnishinaubeg" by Keewaydinoquay; "Supporting Evidence" by R.G. Wasson; "A Mushroom Ceremony" by R.H. Kaplan. The three printed and bound copies of this rarest piece of Wassoniana are locked up in the Houghton Rare Book Library at Harvard University until the year 2020 (Schultes 1992). Since Wasson sent me copies of these three manuscripts for the book during its writing, these were available for examination. The three printed books contain a reproduction of a hand-painted scroll made by Keewaydinoquay, the original of which Wasson showed me, detailing the Ahnishinaubeg folk stories regarding *Amanita muscaria*, and the book features a series of Ahnishinaubeg tales in which the sacred mushroom also figures. Wasson's introductory chapter, "Supporting Evidence" is substantially similar to the paper he published in *Journal of Psychedelic Drugs* (Wasson 1979A), being the lecture he gave at a 1978 conference in

San Francisco, in which Keewaydinoquay M. Peschel and Reid H. Kaplan also participated, previewing this book.

Wasson, R.G. *et al.* (Translation by F. Garrido) 1980B. *El Camino a Eleusis: Una Solución al Enigma de los Misterios*. Fondo de Cultura Económica, México City. Clothbound edition of 5000 copies. With Appendix "Enteógenos," translation of: Ruck, C.A.P. *et al.* 1979. "Entheogens" *Journal of Psychedelic Drugs* 11(1-2): 145–146. See: Ott 1996A; Ruck *et al.* 1979; Wasson *et al.* 1978. Paperbacks in 1985, 1995.

Wasson, R.G. (S. Kramrisch) *et al.* 1986. *Persephone's Quest: Entheogens and the Origins of Religion*. Ethnomycological Studies No. 10. Yale University Press, New Haven, CT. Limited half-leather bound and boxed edition (with 27 illustrations including 10 color plates tipped-in) of 300 lettered and numbered copies followed by a clothbound trade hardcover edition. The *de luxe* edition has sold for U.S.$400 and the trade edition at $30.00; there have been two paperback editions, $14.95. This book was the last work of R. Gordon Wasson, and unfortunately appeared in print shortly after his death on the night of 23 December 1986. The title page of the *de luxe* edition lists the 4 coauthors in alphabetical order, starting with Stella Kramrisch. The trade edition lists R.G. Wasson's name first on the title page. Since this was clearly Wasson's book, financed and published by him, it is referred to throughout this book as Wasson *et al.* 1986. Translated into Spanish by O. Álvarez, 1992. *La Búsqueda de Perséfone: Enteógenos y los Orígenes de la Religión*. Fondo de Cultura Económica, México City. This anthology includes a revised version of Wasson 1956; as well as reprints of the following articles: Doniger O'Flaherty 1982; Kramrisch 1975; Ott and Wasson 1983; Ruck 1981; Ruck 1982; Ruck 1983; and Wasson 1982B.

Wasson, V.P. 1957. "I ate the sacred mushrooms" *This Week Magazine* 19 May 1957. pp. 8 *et seq.* Reprinted in 1982 in Palmer, C. and M. Horowitz (Eds.) *Shaman Woman, Mainline Lady: Women's Writings on the Drug Experience.* William Morrow and Co., New York. pp. 182–186. German translation in Rippchen, R. (Ed.) 1993. *ZauberPilze*. Nachtschatten Verlag/MedienXperimente, Solothurn, Switzerland and Lörbach, Germany. pp. 127–130.

Wasson, V.P. and **R.G. Wasson** 1957A. *Mushrooms Russia and History.* Two volumes. Pantheon Books, New York. Limited clothbound and boxed edition of 512 copies, and there also exists a brace (pair) of "mutilated and defective" copies. A beautiful book graced by 110 illustrations, with 82 plates, including 26 watercolors by Jean-Henri Fabre executed in color by D. Jacomet of Paris, and four additional color plates, including watercolors of entheogenic mushrooms by M. Bory and of "accessories to the mushroom rite" by co-author V.P. Wasson. Also includes a chart, "'Mushroom Stones' of Middle America" by S.F. De Borhegyi. Originally priced at U.S.$125, the price was doubled to $250 shortly after publication, and the book has since commanded as much as $6500.

Wasson, V.P. and **R.G. Wasson** 1957B. *Mushroom Ceremony of the Mazatec Indians of Mexico.* Vinyl L.P. record with transcription and translation in an accompanying booklet of a mushroom curing ceremony recorded on 21 July 1956. Folkway Records, New York. Translation and commentary by E.V. Pike and S.C. Gudschinsky with excerpts from *Mushrooms Russia and History.* Still available at U.S.$12.95. A new translation was presented in Munn's

1981 translation of Estrada 1977, pp. 105–125.
Wasson, V.P. and **R.G. Wasson** 1958. "The hallucinogenic mushrooms" *The Garden Journal*. January-February. pp. 1–6.
Watson, P.L. 1983. *The Precious Foliage: A Study of the Aboriginal Psycho-Active Drug* Pituri. University of Sydney Press, Sydney, Australia.
Watson, P.L. *et al.* 1983. "The ethnopharmacology of pituri" *Journal of Ethnopharmacology* 8(3): 303–311.
Watt, J.M. and **M.G. Breyer-Brandwijk** 1962. *The Medicinal and Poisonous Plants of Southern and Eastern Africa*. E. & S. Livingstone, Edinburgh, Scotland and London, England.
Watts, A.W. 1962. *The Joyous Cosmology: Adventures in the Chemistry of Consciousness.* Pantheon Books, New York. Foreword by T. Leary and R. Alpert, pp. IX–XV. German edition, 1972. *Kosmologie der Freude*. Melzer, Darmstadt, Germany,
Watts, A.W. 1963. "The individual as man/world" *The Psychedelic Review* 1(1): 55–65. Reprinted in Weil, G.M. *et al.* (Eds.) 1965. *The Psychedelic Reader*. University Books, New York. pp. 47–57.
Watts, A.W. 1970. "Psychedelics and religious experience" In: Aaronson, B. and H. Osmond (Eds.) *Psychedelics: The Uses and Implications of Hallucinogenic Drugs.* Doubleday/Anchor, Garden City, NJ. pp. 131–145. Originally published in 1968. *California Law Review* 56(1): 74–85.
Webb, L.J. 1949. *Australian Phytochemical Survey*. Part 1. (Bulletin No. 241) CSIRO, Melbourne, Australia.
Weber, J.M. 1976. "Microchemical investigations of medicinal plants. XIV. Identification of alkaloids in the leaves of *Ipomoea violacea* using preparative thin layer chromatography and solid probe mass spectrometry" *Mikrochimica Acta* (Wien) 1(2-3): 227–242.
Weber, J.M. and **T.S. Ma** 1976. "Microchemical investigations of medicinal plants. XIII. Separation of the alkaloids in the leaves of *Ipomoea violacea* using thin layer chromatography" *Mikrochimica Acta* (Wien) 1(2-3): 217–225.
Weeks, R.A. *et al.* 1979. "A new psilocybian species of *Copelandia*" *Journal of Natural Products* 42(5): 469–474.
Weidmann, H. and **A. Cerletti** 1959. "Zur pharmacodynamischen Differenzierung der 4-Oxyindolderivate Psilocybin und Psilocin im Vergleich mit 5-Oxyindolkörpern (Serotonin, Bufotenin)" *Helvetica Physiologica Acta* 17: C46–C48.
Weidmann, H. *et al.* 1958. "Zur Pharmakologie von Psilocybin, einem Wirkstoff aus *Psilocybe mexicana* Heim" *Experientia* 14: 378–379.
Weil, A.T. (Ed.) 1963A. "Drugs and the mind" *The Harvard Review* 1(4): 3–82.
Weil, A.T. 1963B. "The strange case of the Harvard drug scandal" *Look* 27(22): 46 *et seq*. While an undergraduate at Harvard, Weil reported on the Leary-Alpert group.
Weil, A.T. 1965. "Nutmeg as a narcotic [*sic*]" *Economic Botany* 19(2): 194–217.
Weil, A.T. 1967. "Nutmeg as a psychoactive drug" In: Efron, D.H. *et al.* (Eds.) *Ethnopharmacologic Search for Psychoactive Drugs.* (Public Health Service Publication No. 1645) U.S. Government Printing Office, Washington, D.C. pp. 188–201. Reprinted in *Journal of Psychedelic Drugs* 3(2): 72–80, 1971.
Weil, A.T. 1969. "Nutmeg and other psychoactive groceries" In: Gunckel, J.E. (Ed.) *Current Topics in Plant Science*. Academic Press, New York. pp. 355–366.
Weil, A.T. 1972. *The Natural Mind—A New Way of Looking at Drugs and the Higher Consciousness*. Houghton-Mifflin, Boston, MA. Revised edition in 1986. *The Natural Mind—An Investigation of Drugs*

and the Higher Consciousness. Houghton-Mifflin, Boston, MA. German translation, 1974. *Das Erweiterte Bewußtsein.* Stuttgart, Germany. Translated into Portuguese, 1975. *Drogas e Estados Superiores da Consciência.* Ground, São Paulo, Brasil.

Weil, A.T. 1974. "Introduction" In: Lamb, F.B. *Wizard of the Upper Amazon: The Story of Manuel Córdova-Ríos.* Houghton-Mifflin, Boston, MA, pp. V–XII. See Lamb 1974.

Weil, A.T. 1976. "The love drug" *Journal of Psychedelic Drugs* 8(4): 335–337.

Weil, A.T. 1977A. "The use of psychoactive mushrooms in the Pacific Northwest: An ethnopharmacologic[al] report" *Botanical Museum Leaflets* Harvard University 25(5): 131–149.

Weil, A.T. 1977B. "Some notes on *Datura*" *Journal of Psychedelic Drugs* 9(2): 165–169.

Weil, A.T. 1979. "*Yagé*: The vine that speaks" *High Times.* August issue.

Weil, A.T. 1980. "In the land of *yagé*" In: Weil, A.T. *The Marriage of the Sun and Moon: A Quest for Unity in Consciousness.* Houghton-Mifflin, Boston, MA. pp. 99–131. Originally published in *Journal of Altered States of Consciousness* 1(2).

Weil, A.T. 1990. *Natural Health, Natural Medicine: A Comprehensive Manual for Wellness and Self-Care.* Houghton-Mifflin, Boston, MA.

Weil, A.T. and **E.W. Davis** 1994. "*Bufo alvarius*: A potent hallucinogen of animal origin" *Journal of Ethnopharmacology* 41(1,2): 1–8. See: Davis & Weil 1992.

Weil, A.T. and **W. Rosen** 1983. *Chocolate to Morphine: Understanding Mind-Active Drugs.* Houghton-Mifflin, Boston, MA. Revised edition in 1993. *From Chocolate to Morphine: Everything you Need to Know about Mind-Altering Drugs.* Houghton-Mifflin, Boston, MA.

Weil, A.T. *et al.* 1968. "Clinical and psychological effects of marihuana [*sic*] in man" *Science* 162: 1234–1242. See: Weil 1972.

Weiss, B. and **V.G. Laties** 1962. "Enhancement of human performance by caffeine and the amphetamines" *Pharmacological Reviews* 14: 1–36.

Weiss, G. 1960. "Hallucinogenic and narcotic-like [*sic*] effects of powdered myristica (nutmeg)" *Psychiatric Quarterly* 34: 346–356.

Weiss, G. 1973. "Shamanism and priesthood in the light of the Campa *ayahuasca* ceremony" In: Harner, M.J. (Ed.) *Hallucinogens and Shamanism.* Oxford University Press, London, England. pp. 40–47.

Weiss, R.F. (Translation by A.R. Meuss) 1988. *Herbal Medicine.* AB Arcanum, Göteborg, Sweden. Original *Lehrbuch der Phytotherapie.* Sixth Edition. Hippokrates Verlag, Stuttgart, Germany.

Weitlaner, R.J. 1952. "Curaciones mazatecas" *Anales del Instituto Nacional de Antropología e Historia* 4: 279–285.

Weitlaner Johnson, I. 1990. "Remembrances of things past" In: Riedlinger, T.J. (Ed.) *The Sacred Mushroom Seeker: Essays for R. Gordon Wasson.* Ethnomycological Studies No. 11. Dioscorides Press, Portland, OR. pp. 135–140.

West, L.G. and **J.L. McLaughlin** 1973. "Cactus alkaloids. XVIII. Phenolic β-phenethylamines from *Mammillaria elongata*" *Lloydia* 36(3): 346–348.

Wheeler, J.W. *et al.* 1981. "Anabaseine: Venom alkaloid of *Aphaenogaster* ants" *Science* 211: 1051–1052.

Whistler, W.A. 1985. "Traditional and herbal medicine in the Cook Islands" *Journal of Ethnopharmacology* 13(3): 239–280.

Whistler, W.A. 1991. "Herbal medicine in the kingdom of Tonga" *Journal of Ethnopharmacology* 31(3): 339–372.

Whistler, W.A. 1992. *Polynesian Herbal Medicine.* National Tropical Botanical Garden, Lawai, HI.

White, B.C. *et al.* 1980. "Anxiety and muscle tension as consequences of caffeine withdrawal" *Science* 209: 1547–1548.

White, O.E. 1922. "Botanical exploration in Bolivia" *Brooklyn Botanical Garden Record* 11(3): 93–105.

White, P.C. 1979. "Analysis of extracts from *Psilocybe semilanceata* mushrooms by high-pressure liquid chromatography" *Journal of Chromatography* 169: 453–456.

Whiting, A. 1939. *Ethnobotany of the Hopi.* (Museum of Northern Arizona Bulletin No. 15) Northern Arizona Society of Science and Art, Flagstaff, AZ. Foreword by Harold S. Colton, p. v.

Whitten, N.E. 1976. *Sacha Runa: Ethnicity and Adaptation of Ecuadorian Jungle Quichua.* University of Illinois Press, Chicago and Urbana, IL.

Whitten, N.E. 1985. *Sicuanga Runa: The Other Side of Development in Amazonian Ecuador.* University of Illinois Press, Chicago and Urbana, IL.

Wieland, T. and **W. Motzel** 1953. "Über das Vorkommen von Bufotenin in gelben Knollenblätterpilz" *Justus Liebig's Annalen der Chemie* 581: 10–16.

Wilbert, J. 1972. "Tobacco and shamanistic ecstasy among the Warao Indians of Venezuela" In: Furst, P.T. (Ed.) *Flesh of the Gods: The Ritual Use of Hallucinogens.* Praeger, New York. pp. 55–83.

Wilbert, J. 1975. "Magico-Religious use of tobacco among South American Indians" In: Rubin, V. (Ed.) *Cannabis and Culture.* Mouton and Co., the Hague, the Netherlands. pp. 439–461.

Wilbert, J. 1983. "Warao ethnopathology of exotic epidemic disease" *Journal of Ethnopharmacology* 8(3): 357–361.

Wilbert, J. 1987. *Tobacco and Shamanism in South America.* (Schultes, R.E. and R.F. Raffauf, Editors, Psychoactive Plants of the World) Yale Univ. Press, New Haven, CT.

Wilbert, J. 1991. "Does pharmacology corroborate the nicotine therapy and practices of South American shamanism?" *Journal of Ethnopharmacology* 32(1-3): 179–186.

Wildmann, J. *et al.* 1987. "Diazepam and *N*-desmethyldiazepam are found in rat brain and adrenal and may be of plant origin" *Journal of Neural Transmission* 70(3-4): 383–398.

Wilkins, B. *et al.* 1962. "Clinical observations of simultaneous hallucinogen administration in identical twins" *American Journal of Psychiatry* 118: 815–818.

Wilkinson, R.E. *et al.* 1986. "Ergot alkaloid contents of *Ipomoea lacunosa, I. hederacea, I. trichocarpa,* and *I. purpurea* seed" *Canadian Journal of Plant Science* 66: 339–343.

Wilkinson, S. 1958. "5-Methoxy-N-methyltryptamine: A new indole alkaloid from *Phalaris arundinacea*" *Journal of the Chemical Society* 1958 II: 2079–2081.

Willaman, J.J. 1961. *Alkaloid-Bearing Plants and their Contained Alkaloids.* (United States Department of Agriculture Technical Bulletin No. 1234) U.S. Government Printing Office, Washington, D.C.

Williams, E.Y. and **F. West** 1968. "The use of nutmeg as a psychotropic drug. Report of two cases" *Journal of the American Medical Association* 60: 289–329.

Williams, H. 1989. *Sacred Elephant.* Harmony Books, New York.

Williams, L. 1931. "The death vine: Ayahuasca" *Field Museum News* 2(8): 3.

Williams, M. *et al.* 1971. "Characterization of alkaloids in palatable and unpalatable clones of *Phalaris arundinacea* L." *Crop Science* 11: 213–217.

Williamson, R.W. 1939. *Essays in Polynesian Ethnology.* Cambridge U. Press, England.

Wills, C. *et al.* 1992. "Forensic DNA typing" Five letters to the editor and two rebuttals in response to: Chakraborty, R. & K.K. Kidd 1991. "The utility of DNA typing in forensic work" *Science* 254: 1735–1739; and Lewontin, R.C. and D.L. Hartl 1991. "Population genetics in forensic DNA typing" *Science* 254: 1745–1750. See also: Koshland 1992 and Roberts 1991.

Witt, P. 1960. "'Tangled web' helps drug testing" *Medical News* 6(16): 2.

Wolbach, A.B. *et al.* 1962A. "Cross tolerance between mescaline and LSD-25 with a comparison of the mescaline and LSD reactions" *Psychopharmacologia* 3: 1–14.

Wolbach, A.B. *et al.* 1962B. "Comparison of psilocin with psilocybin, mescalin and LSD-25" *Psychopharmacologia* 3: 219–223.

Wolf, F.A. 1991. *The Eagle's Quest: A Physicist's Search for Truth in the Heart of the Shamanic World*. Simon & Schuster, New York. Spanish edition 1993, Los Libros de la Liebre de Marzo, Barcelona, Spain.

Wolfe, T. 1969. *The Electric Kool-Aid Acid Test.* Bantam Books, New York.

Wolfes, O. and **K. Rumpf** 1928. "Über die Gewinnung von Harmin aus einer südamerikanischen Liane" *Archiv der Pharmazie und Berichte der Deutschen Pharmazeutischen Gesellschaft* 266(3): 188–189.

Wong, W. 1976. "Some folk medicinal plants from Trinidad" *Economic Botany* 30(2): 103–142.

Wood, H.B. *et al.* 1954. "Andromedotoxin: A potent hypotensive agent from Rhododendron maximum" *Journal of the American Chemical Society* 76: 5689–5692.

Woodson, R.E. *et al.* (Eds.) 1957. *Rauwolfia: Botany, Pharmacognosy, Chemistry and Pharmacology*. Little, Brown and Co., New York.

Wurst, M. *et al.* 1984. "Analysis of psychotropic compounds of fungi of the genus *Psilocybe* by reversed-phase high-performance liquid chromatography" *Journal of Chromatography* 286: 229–235.

Wyman, L.C. and **S.K. Harris** 1951. *The Ethnobotany of the Kayenta Navaho*. The University of New Mexico Press, Albuquerque, NM.

X, M. with **A. Haley** 1964. *The Autobiography of Malcolm X.* Grove Press, New York. Made into 1992 film by Spike Lee.

Xia, B. and **I.A. Abbott** 1987. "Edible seaweeds of China and their place in the Chinese diet" *Economic Botany* 41(3): 341–353.

Yamada, H. *et al.* 1984. *Carbohydrate Research* 125: 107.

Yamatodani, S. and **I. Yamamoto** 1969. "Tricholomic acid production by Agaricales" (Japanese Patent 69 16,354, 19 July 1969). See: *Chemical Abstracts* 71: 234.

Yamatodani, S. and **I. Yamamoto** 1983. "Peptide-type ergot alkaloids produced by *Hypomyces aurantius*" *Journal of the Agricultural Chemical Society of Japan* 57(5): 453–456.

Yamaura, Y. and **I.-M. Chang** 1988. "Effects of aqueous extract of a poisonous mushroom, *Amanita pantherina* on mice and assay of toxic isoxazole derivatives by high performance liquid chromatography" *Korean Journal of Toxicology* 4(2): 85–94.

Yensen, R. and **D. Dryer** 1995. "Thirty years of psychedelic research: The Spring Grove experiment and its sequels" In: Schlichting, M. and H. Leuner (Eds.) *Worlds of Consciousness.* (Vol. 5) VWB, Berlin, Germany. pp. 141–176.

Yocum, R.R. and **D.M. Simons** 1977. "Amatoxins and phallotoxins in *Amanita* species of the northeastern United States" *Lloydia* 40(2): 178–190.

Yokoyama, K. 1973. "Poisoning by a hallucinogenic mushroom, *Psilocybe subcaerulipes* Hongo" *Transactions of the Mycological Society of Japan* 14: 317–320.

Yokoyama, K. 1976. "A new hallucinogenic mushroom, *Psilocybe argentipes* K. Yokoyama sp. nov. from Japan" *Transactions of the Mycological Society of Japan* 17: 349–354.

Young, J.H. 1961. *The Toadstool Millionaires.* Princeton University Press, Princeton, NJ.

Young, R.L. *et al.* 1966. "Analysis of kava pyrones in extracts of *Piper methysticum*" *Phytochemistry* 5: 795–798.

Younger, S.M. 1992. "The fifth dimension" *Eating Well: The Magazine of Food and Health.* 2(10): 69.

Younos, C. *et al.* 1987. "Repertory of drugs and medicinal plants used in traditional medicine of Afghanistan" *Journal of Ethnopharmacology* 20(3): 245–290.

Yu, C.-J. 1959. "Laughing mushroom" *The Continent Magazine* (Taipei) 19(8): 1–4. Chinese article cited in Wasson 1962A.

Yui, T. and **Y. Takeo** 1958. "Neuropharmacological studies on a new series of ergot alkaloids" *Japanese Journal of Pharmacology* 7: 157.

Zaehner, R.C. 1957. *Mysticism, Sacred and Profane: An Inquiry into Some Varieties of the Religious Experience.* Oxford University Press, London, England.

Zaehner, R.C. 1972. *Zen, Drugs and Mysticism.* Vintage Press, New York.

Zafar, M.M. *et al.* 1990. "Screening of *Artemisia absinthium* for antimalarial effects on *Plasmodium berghei* in mice: A preliminary report" *Journal of Ethnopharmacology* 30(2): 223–226.

Zamora-Martínez, M.C. and **C. Nieto de Pascual Pola** 1992. "Medicinal plants used in some rural populations of Oaxaca, Puebla and Veracruz, Mexico" *Journal of Ethnopharmacology* 35(3): 229–257.

Zardini, E.M. 1977. "The identification of an Argentinian narcotic [*sic*]" *Botanical Museum Leaflets* Harvard University 25 (3): 105–107.

Zelger, J.L. *et al.* 1980. "Behavioural effects of cathinone, an amine obtained from *Catha edulis* Forsk.: Comparisons with amphetamine, norpseudoephedrine, apomorphine and nomifensine" *Bulletin on Narcotics* 32(3): 67–81.

Zennie, T.M. *et al.* 1986. "Funebral, a new pyrrole lactone alkaloid of *Quararibea funebris*" *Journal of Natural Products* 49(4): 695–698.

Zerda Bayón, R. 1915. *Informe Sobre mi Excursión Científica en las Regiones Colombianas del Caquetá.* Bogotá, Colombia.

Zerries, O. 1960. "Medizinmannwesen und Geistglaube der Waiká-Indianer des oberen Orinoco" *Ethnologica, N.F.* 2: 485–507.

Zethelius, M. and **M. Balick** 1982. "Modern medicine and shamanistic ritual: A case of positive synergistic response" *Journal of Ethnopharmacology* 5(2): 181–185.

Zetler, G. *et al.* 1968. *Naunyn Schmiedeberg's Archiv für Pharmakologie* 220: 26.

Zigmond, M.L. 1981. *Kawaiisu Ethnobotany.* University of Utah Press, Salt Lake City, UT.

Zinberg, N.E. 1963. "Narcotics in the U.S.: A brief history" *The Harvard Review* 1(4): 56–62. See: Weil 1963a.

Zinberg, N.E. 1974. *"High" States: A Beginning Study.* Drug Abuse Council, Washington, D.C.

Zinberg, N.E. 1977. *Alternate States of Consciousness.* The Free Press, New York.

Zinberg, N.E. 1979. "On Cannabis and health" *Journal of Psychedelic Drugs* 11(1-2): 135–144. Conference "Hallucinogens in Native American Shamanism and Modern Life," 28 September–1 October 1978, San Francisco, CA, USA.

Zinberg, N.E. 1984. *Drug, Set, and Setting: The Basis for Controlled Intoxicant* [*sic*] *Use.* Yale University Press, New Haven, CT.

Zulueta Rodríguez, R. 1988. *Cuantificación del Safrol en el Aceite Esencial Extraido de* Piper auritum *(Piperaceae) en el Estado de Veracruz para su Aprovechamiento Industrial.* Master's Degree thesis, INIREB, Xalapa, Veracruz, México.

Zutshi, V. *et al.* 1980. "Absorption and distribution of vasicine, a modern uterotonic" *Planta Medica* 40: 373–377.

GENERAL INDEX

ACKNOWLEDGEMENTS

It is my great pleasure to acknowledge gratefully the generous assistance of Dr. Albert Hofmann of Burg, Switzerland, for kindly reviewing my manuscript and offering to write a foreword. I am likewise beholden to Prof. Alexander Shulgin of the University of California at Berkeley for reviewing the Proemium and the first chapter; to Dr. David B. Repke of Syntex Research in Palo Alto, California for reviewing the third and fifth chapters; to Dr. Dennis J. McKenna, consultant, Minneapolis, Minnesota, for reviewing the fourth chapter, and to Prof. Wm. Scott Chilton of North Carolina State University in Raleigh for going over the sixth chapter. I sincerely thank all these prominent experts for lending their time and expertise to this endeavor—the author of a multi-disciplinary work must needs depend on the advice and generosity of specialists to help ensure currentness and accuracy.

I am beholden to Dr. Robert Montgomery, founder of the Botanical Preservation Corps, for reviewing the manuscript and making comments based on his extensive knowledge of the ethnobotany and horticulture of entheogenic plants. Rob also aided my research by giving me access to his extensive files and library, and was instrumental in helping me organize the publication and distribution of this book.

I wish to express my deep appreciation to Dr. Jeremy Bigwood of El Salvador and to Dr. Ronald M. Cook of SIRIS Laboratories for much valuable advice and research assistance. Their diverse perspectives abundantly enriched mine. Fruitful discussions with Dr. Antonio Escohotado of the Universidad Nacional de Educación a Distancia of Madrid, Spain, were of considerable value to me in formulating my legal and political arguments in the Proemium. Other specialists who kindly shared information and insights with me are: Dr. Antonio Bianchi of Verona, Italy; Dr. Bret Blosser of Tulane University; Dr. Michael Bock of Australia; Dr. James C. Callaway of University of Kuopio, Finland; Dr. Herman de Vries of Eschenau, Germany; Dr. Mark S. Donnell of Barstow, California; Dr. Josep Mª. Fericgla of the Universitat de Barcelona, Catalunya; Dr. Peter T. Furst of the University of Pennsylvania; Dr. Jochen Gartz of Leipzig, Germany; Dr. Karl Hillig of Indiana University; Dr. Michael Horowitz of Petaluma, CA; Dr. Luis Eduardo Luna of the Universidade do Florianópolis, Brasil; Dr. Terence McKenna of Occidental, CA; Dr. Edward MacRae of São Paulo, Brasil; Dr. Ethan A. Marcano of Victoria, Canada; Dr. Jonathon S. Miller of the Centro de Investigación de Bosques Tropicales in Quito, Ecuador; Dr. Dale A. Pendell of Santa Cruz, CA; Dr. Mario Polia of Rome, Italy; Dr. Giorgio Samorini of Bologna, Italy; Dr. Stacy B. Schaefer of the University of Texas Pan-American; Dr. Tjakko Stijve of Nestec Ltd., Vevey, Switzerland; and Dr. C. Manuel Torres of Florida International University.

I am in debt to my ex-wife, Djahel Vinaver, for assistance with [at times] tedious library work and for her emotional support; and to Berta Ramírez of East Los Angeles, CA, for bibliographic assistance—her entheogen library supplemented mine in many respects.

In addition to his excellent graphic design work, Pablo Moya Rossi of México City helped to familiarize me with the nuances of 'desktop publishing' and the use of the relevant software for Apple Macintosh™ computers. I am grateful to Martín Vinaver of San Andrés Tlanelhuayocan, Veracruz for the drawings from the Mixtec *Codex Vindobonensis.* I am beholden to Drs. Douglas G. Sharon and Christopher B. Donnan, from whose 1977 paper the design of the Chavín *San Pedro* stele was drawn, also by Martín. I again thank Dr. Luis Eduardo Luna, for the photograph of Pablo Amaringo's *Pregnant by an Anaconda,* which appears in detail on the cover [and complete on the back-cover]; and Dr. Jeremy Bigwood for the superb photograph of the *Delysid*® ampules, which appears on the spine.

By subscribing in advance to a limited, signed, boxed first edition of *Pharmacotheon,* the following individuals contributed to financing the production of this book: Reinaldo Acevedo, Alaska, Lawrence Alexander, Leroy Anderson, Charles Andrew, C. Aras, Edward Atkins, John Baker [two], Ian Barrett, Robert J. Bassara, Jonathan Bentley, Antonio Bianchi, Mark Bishop, David Blackman, Barry Blacktop, Scott Bloomfield, Bret Blosser, Carmen Blue, John Blumer-Buell, Michael R. Bonnifield, Blane Bourgeois, Eli U. Brandt, Morgan Brent, Sam Brines, Warren Brownell, J. Alfred Bryan, Michael Buchele, Peter and Mimi Buckley, J.C. Callaway [Anita Hemmilä], Gilberto Camilla, Richard Carey [two], Phillip Cartier, Charles Chadwick, David Chapman, Carlos D'Arbel Chávez, Bryon Church, Mark Cirlin, Michael Coblentz, Richard A. Cohn [two], Walter Collins, David Copeland, Michael Cottingham, J.F. Coughlan, Anne Courtney, John Cover, Alasdair Coyne, Nicholas Cozzi, David Cronk, Michael Crouch, Michael Cuddy, Earl Davis, James B. DeKorne, G. Eric Demitoff, Seth Deutsch, Herman de Vries [two], Samuel Dilleshaw, Richard E. Doblin, Thomas Duda, Michael A. Dudock, Robert Ellingham, Haines Ely, Sims Ely, *The Fane of the Psilocybe Mushroom Assoc.*, John Farr, Jacob Felton [two], Leo D. Figgs [three], Jim Fish, Rudi Fliers, Robert Paul Forte, Scott Fowler, John Fox, David A. Foxton, Randy Fuller, Peter T. Furst, Carolyn Garcia [two], Richard Geggie, Jim Gelz, S. Gill, George Greer, Alex Grey, Walter J. Haberer III, Kim Hanna, Greg Hansen, James Hardin, Sue Ann Harkey, Ted Harrington, Kathleen Harrison, Gary Hart, John Hayes, Richard Heimanson, Ryan S. Hellmers, Karl Hillig, Jeffrey L. Hirschtick, Alan Hofmann, Lon Holmberg, Al Holter, Michael Horowitz, Greg White Hunt, Otto J. Hunt, Richard Hyman, Joseph Jenkins, Shepherd M. Jenks, Jr., David S. Johnson, Brad Jones, Philip Jones, Sasha Karlik, Robert J. Kelley, Jim King, Douglas Kline, Gerry Knight, Matt Knoke, Mike Knoke, Nan Koehler, John A. Koury III, Mark Krakowski, Steven Krolik, James N. Larson, M. David Leonard, Joan Lessin, William Lewis, Richard Liebmann, Marko Lindberg, Alex Lindsay, Ray Litlas, LordNose!, Christopher and Catherine Lord–Van Voorst, Richard Lucinio, David Lukoff, Luis Eduardo Luna, John Lund, Brian McBee, Harry J. McBride, Joel McCleary, Gary Mack, Randy Mack, Dennis J. McKenna, Anthony Marcano, Ethan A. Marcano, Richard Marchese [two], Steven Marshank, Al Mateczun, Robert S. Means, Mark D. Merlin, Thomas Metzinger [two], Ralph Metzner, Mark Myer, Jai Michael, Royce Milam, Jonathon S. Miller, Robin Minkler, Rob Montgomery, Charles Moore, Michael Moore, Dave Morris, Jacob Rose Moth, James Musser, J. August Muth, Jonathan B. Myers, Keith and Jeannette Navia, Andrew Niedzwiecki, James R. Norris, Allana Noury, R. Michael O'Bannon [two], David O'Callaghan, David Orr, Laurence Ostrow, David Ousley, Curt S. Palmer, Ken Panter, Thomas Parker, John Pearson, Alan Pence [Marty Burton], Dale A. Pendell, Glenn Perry, Dan Plas, David Platt, Kenneth Powell, *Psychedelic Monographs and Essays*, Magic Rabbit, David Racette, James A. Ransom, Felix Reuben, Tom Roberts, Mark Robertson, Darren Rock, Brian Rogers, Steve Rooke, Scott Ross, Coquelicot Rudiak-Gilland, David St. Thomas, Joseph G. Salter, Giorgio Samorini, Donald T. Santo, Peter Sartor, Alfred Savinelli [two], Robert Schafer, Richard Evans Schultes, Doug Schwartz, Gary Semerjian, Kenneth Shaw, William Shay, James Shields, Michael Shields, Steven Silberfein, John Sisson, Michael Smith, Scott and Kelly Spear, Noah Spurrier, Bradford Stanbeck [two], T. Starr, William S. Statler, Michael Stefenson, Lorin Stoll, Allen Stovall, A. Jane Straight, Rick J. Strassman, Reid Stuart, Jana Sullivan, Emily Swetland, Pete Swetland, T. Thacker, Richard Thieltges [two], Greg Toole,

Constantino Manuel and Donna Torres, Steven A. Van Heiden, Djahel Vinaver, Bob Wallace, Marc S. Walter [two], R. Kent Warren, Greg Wenneson, Ganga White, M. Whitney, Matthew Wilson, Linda Witt, James B. Work, Rosanna Workman, James Wrinkle, and Susan Irving Yates. I also thank the 16 anonymous subscribers, the many last-minute subscribers applying during the final production, and pseudonymous B.N.S., Clifford, DMT-13, Sherpa and Speed Well Dream Sleep.

Finally, I express my sincere thanks to Dr. Richard Evans Schultes of Harvard University for his continuing advice, support and inspiration. The fact that more than 80 of his articles and books are cited in the bibliography bears witness to the pioneering role he has played, and continues to play, in this field. It is literally true that one cannot take one's first steps in the study of any aspect of entheogenic plant science, without first becoming familiar with Prof. Schultes' contributions on the subject. The bibliography is also replete with numerous invaluable contributions by Prof. Schultes' many students, including the late Drs. Timothy C. Plowman and Thomas E. Lockwood. But beyond that, Prof. Schultes has made other, equally important contributions to the field of botany as a whole, and was rightfully awarded the Gold Medal of the Linnean Society of London in 1992, the highest scientific award in the field of botany. Even more important than these scientific achievements, however, has been Schultes' tireless work in the field of plant and habitat conservation, which has also led to awards, such as the 1984 Gold Medal for Conservation of the World Wide Fund for Nature and the 1987 John and Alice Tyler Ecology-Energy Prize. Thanks to the work of Schultes and others, the government of Colombia gave title to 6 million hectares of tropical forest to its traditional custodians, the Indians who continue to live there, thus bringing to 20 million hectares the amount of federally-protected land in Colombia. Schultes' prominent role in conservation in Colombia was recongized by the government, when it named a portion of a wilderness reserve after him. In Schultes' work and life is exemplified the connection I have drawn in this book between the insights we can obtain from entheogenic plants and the healing of our planet and conservation of its biotic resources. I hope the world will be blessed for many more years with Prof. Schultes' wisdom!

Dedico esta edición a mi seductiva Thorny Queen... musa más hermosa jamás inspiró el aliento vital; sirena más sensual jamás lo suspiró dulcemente a la noche.

Jonathan Ott, F.L.S.
Vashon Island—Xalapa—Seattle
Xalapa—Madrid—Salta
Summer 1991—Summer 1996

TECHNICAL NOTE

This book was written on a Toshiba T1000™ laptop computer with 1.28 MB [megabytes] of memory, MS-DOS™ version 2.11 in ROM, and a solitary 3.5 inch 720 KB [kilobyte] floppy-disk drive. Software employed was *Microsoft Works*™ version 2.0, using text-editing and database modules. In all 26 files were made, totaling 2.3 MB of data, and I used a Toshiba P321SL™ 24-pin dot-matrix printer for proofing. I later replaced my antiquated Toshiba with a faster and more modern Apple Macintosh PowerBook 5300™ computer with a 100 MHz 603e PowerPC microprocessor served by 24 MB of RAM, a Mirror Portrait™ full-page monitor, MacAlly MK105™ keyboard, 1.4 MB floppy and 500 MB Quantum™ hard disk drives (with PLI Infinity 105 Turbo S™ Syquest™ and Fujitsu 230 MB MO optical cartridge drives for backup) running the Apple Macintosh Disk Operating System version 7.5.2. For proofing I acquired a 300 dpi NEC Silentwriter II Model 95™ *PostScript*™ Level 2 laser printer with 4 MB of memory serving a 16.7 MHz 68000 microprocessor. Text files were transferred to the Macintosh hard drive using Insignia *AccessPC*™ version 2.01 and formatted for 1240 dpi output directly to film using *Microsoft Word*™ version 4.0, Adobe *Page Maker*™ version 6.0, and Adobe *Type Manager*™ version 3.0. Text type is 11 pt Adobe Garamond with 13 pt leading; with Garamond *Italics* and **Semibold** for highlighting and Apple Symbol font for Greek [α,β,Δ,μ] characters, with Adobe Garamond Expert fonts for numbers and ligatures. Titles are set in 16 pt Garamond Semibold with 20 pt leading; headings in 12 pt Garamond Semibold with 13 pt leading. Notes, Indices, Bibliography and epigrams are set in 10 pt Garamond with 11 pt leading. Chemical structures were drawn using *Chem Draw*™ version 2.1.3. For library work and while traveling, I also use an Apple Newton MessagePad 110™ 'Portable Digital Assistant' (PDA) with 4 MB of ROM and 3 MB of RAM, running Palm Computing's Graffiti™ version 1.01 for text entry, and Starcore Newton Utilities™ version 1.0.

Thanks to the many technological advances in 'desktop publishing,' it was possible for me to write, edit, typeset, print and proofread page proofs for this book in a rural, provincial part of México lacking even basic city services! Other than graphic design (on which I had input) and technical editing kindly provided by six leading experts in the field, I was able personally and single-handedly to execute the transformation of a complicated manuscript into a beautiful book. Thanks to cooperative financing of the first edition by subscribers (sale of 300 boxed subscribers' editions at $50 met 55% of $27,000 production costs for the first press run of 5000), it was possible to retain absolute editorial control despite my politically unpopular and risky stance against drug prohibition... now this is what I call freedom of the press!

NOTE ON COVER ILLUSTRATION

Pregnant by an Anaconda, by Pablo Amaringo [1989 tempera painting; photographed by Luis Eduardo Luna]; included by Luna and Amaringo in their superb and innovative treatise on the art of ethnobotany, *Ayahuasca Visions*. We have here clearly demarcated two worlds of experience: the Amazonian forest by night and the visionary realm of Sacha Runa. Like the Chinese *yin/yang* symbol, in each realm is imbued the essence of the other. The boas of *ayahuasca* vision at once define the boundary and symbolize the Portal between worlds; as the *yachaj* is suspended before the *ayahuasca* vessel on the back of his boa familiar. The serpentine phantasmagoria of the visionary realm is dominated by the universal archetype of the Tree of Life... as well as the universal chemical liana of life on this planet—the double-helix of DNA. The magical phlegm, azure essence of *logos*, the magical song or *icaro* of the *yachaj* made manifest, flows forth... like the serpents of creation from the woman's womb; like the spermatozoa, human serpents of fecundity rising. Beneath the arboreal spirits of the jungle, in the center of the chiaroscuro of the night forest... there hovers the disembodied eye of vision... or five eyes; a fifth-dimensional hyperchakra epoptically projected into space, as Gordon Wasson also envisioned it, beyond María Sabina's mushroomic portal:

> Elsewhere I once wrote that the bemushroomed person is poised in space, a disembodied eye, invisible, incorporeal, seeing but not seen. In truth, he is the five senses disembodied, all of them keyed to the height of sensitivity and awareness, all of them blending into one another most strangely, until the person, utterly passive, becomes a pure receptor, infinitely delicate, of sensations.

NOTE ON SPINE ILLUSTRATION

Ampules of *Delysid*® containing 100 mcg [Sandoz LSD-tartrate, distributed during the 1950s as an investigational new drug]. Courtesy of Albert Hofmann, photograph by Jeremy Bigwood.

NOTES ON ILLUSTRATIONS IN THE TEXT

TITLE PAGE: Mexican deity holding pair of *teonanácatl* mushrooms, from Mixtec *Codex Vindobonensis*, *circa* 1500 A.D. Drawing: Martín Vinaver, México, April 1993.

PAGE 79: Chavín human/jaguar deity with *San Pedro* cactus; stele from Chavín de

Huántar, Perú, *circa* 1300 B.C. Drawing by Martín Vinaver, México, April 1993.

PAGE 117: Mictlantecuhtli or other Mexican chthonic deity with pair of *teonanácatl* mushrooms, participating in a mushroom *agape*, from Mixtec *Codex Vindobonensis*, *circa* 1500 A.D. Drawn by Martín Vinaver, México, April 1993.

PAGE 321: Mexican deity participating in a mushroom *velada* and holding a pair of *teonanácatl* mushrooms, from Mixtec *Codex Vindobonensis*, *circa* 1500 A.D. Drawn by Martín Vinaver, México, April 1993.

PAGE 359: Mexican deity presiding over a mushroom *agape* from Mixtec *Codex Vindobonensis*, *circa* 1500 A.D. Drawn by Martín Vinaver, México, April 1993.

PAGE 429: Piltzintecuhtli, manifestation of Xochipilli, Mexican lord of entheogens, holding pair of *teonanácatl* mushrooms, from Mixtec *Codex Vindobonensis*, *circa* 1500 A.D. Drawn by Martín Vinaver, San Andrés Tlanelhuayocan, Veracruz, April 1993.

PAGE 640: Mexican goddess representing the spirit of *teonanácatl* mushrooms incarnate, from Mixtec *Codex Vindobonensis*, *circa* 1500 A.D. The mushrooms issuing from her head mirror a motif found in the Mexican *Lienzo de Zacatepec*, in first millennium B.C. petroglyphs from Siberia and in more ancient petroglyphs from Tassili, Algeria (Chapter 6, Note 2). Drawn by Martín Vinaver, México, April 1993.

BIOGRAPHICAL NOTE

JONATHAN OTT is founder of a chemical manufacturing firm producing neurotoxins for biomedical research. His books include *Hallucinogenic Plants of North America* [two American editions], *Teonanácatl: Hallucinogenic Mushrooms of North America* [American, Spanish editions], *The Cacahuatl Eater: Ruminations of an Unabashed Chocolate Addict*, *Ayahuasca Analogues: Pangæan Entheogens* [American, German editions] and *The Age of Entheogens & The Angels' Dictionary*. He has published numerous scientific papers, contributed to anthologies, was co-author of R. Gordon Wasson's book *Persephone's Quest: Entheogens and the Origins of Religion* and translator of Albert Hofmann's *LSD: My Problem Child*. He is Fellow of the Linnean Society; member of the American Association for the Advancement of Science, Society for Economic Botany and Society of Ethnobiology. He manages a botanical garden in México, teaches seminars on ethnobotany and plant conservation for the Botanical Preservation Corps and conducts entheobotanical field and laboratory research. He serves the editorial boards of bilingual journals *Integration: Journal for Mind-Moving Plants and Culture* and *Yearbook for Ethnomedicine and the Study of Consciousness*.

This second edition of *Pharmacotheon*
consists of 5000 copies, printed by Braun–Brumfield
on white 60 pound book recycled, acid-free paper,
with sewn-and-glued bindings for permanence.
A limited edition of 166 copies were Smythe-sewn,
casebound, signed and numbered by the author.
Printing was finished in December of 1996.